Encyclopedia
of Network
Blueprints

Encyclopedia
of Network
Blueprints

Ed Taylor

McGraw-Hill

New York   San Francisco   Washington, D.C.
Auckland   Bogotá   Caracas   Lisbon   London
Madrid   Mexico City   Milan   Montreal   New Delhi
San Juan   Singapore   Sydney   Tokyo   Toronto

Library of Congress Cataloging-in-Publication Data

Taylor, Ed.
    Encyclopedia of network blueprints / Ed Taylor.
        p.   cm.
    Includes index.
    ISBN 0-07-063406-8
    1. Computer networks.   I. Title.
TK5105.5.T3913   1998
004.6—dc21   98-24388
                                    CIP

McGraw-Hill

A Division of The McGraw-Hill Companies

1 2 3 4 5 6 7 8 9 0   DOC/DOC   9 0 3 2 1 0 9 8

ISBN 0-07-063406-8

*The sponsoring editor for this book was Steve Elliot and the production supervisor
was Pamela Pelton. It was set in Melior by Patricia Wallenburg.*

Printed and bound by R. R. Donnelly and Sons Company.

McGraw-Hill books are available at special quantity discounts to use as premiums and
sales promotions, or for use in corporate training programs. For more information,
please write to the Director of Special Sales, McGraw-Hill, 11 West 19th Street,
New York, NY 10011. Or contact your local bookstore.

 This book is printed on recycled, acid-free paper containing
a minimum of 50% recycled, de-inked fiber.

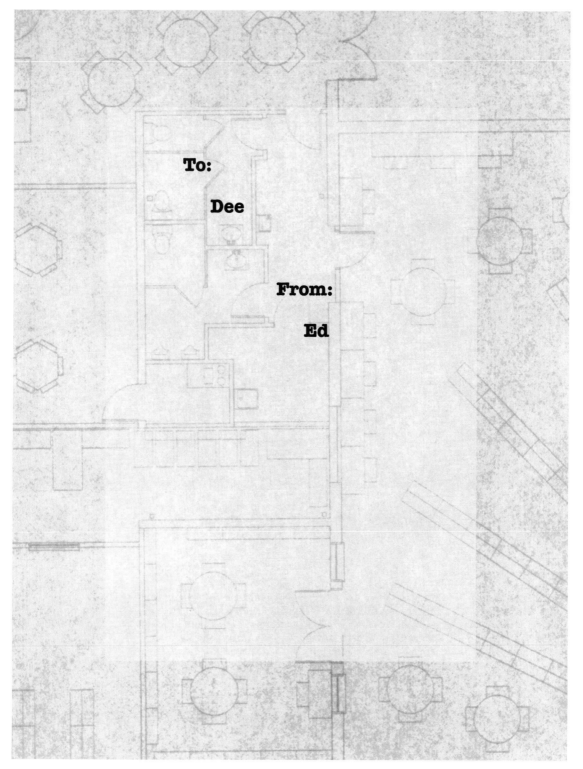

To:

Dee

From:

Ed

Preface

The purpose of this book is to provide the reader with helpful information on topics presented in the following pages. In most cases, I am presenting principles, technology, and products that implement certain technology. Use this book as a reference and guideline in your endeavors. The "how-to" of technology is learned by individuals on an individual basis; hopefully this is a tool to help you along that way.

Quotation of Ed Taylor from a presentation given in 1996:

"For the first time in the history of man, the human race has technology available to it in such quantity heretofore unseen. The lurking question: Is it possible to transfer the wealth of knowledge among the technical community from the current generation to the one following it, so an adequate understanding of this technology is understood and hence that technology maintained? It remains to be seen if this can be done."

Acknowledgments

MJH
IBM
Creative Labs
3ComUSRobotics
Great Lake Cabinets
Thomas & Betts
Liebert
Pass & Seymour
Belden
WaveTek
Tektronix
Hewlett Packard
McAfee
Altec Lansing
Wagner Edstrom
Microsoft
Adaptec Corporation
BAY Networks

General Cable
Sony Corporation
JetEye
Belkin
Oraycom
/SMS Dataproducts
Information World, Inc.
DHL
SAIA
Consolidated Freightways
Airborne
Emery Airfreight
Federal Express
United Parcel Service
 (UPS)
Roadway
United States Post Office

Table
of Contents

Chapter 1

Chapter 2

Chapter 3

Chapter 4
Electrical Consideration and Power Conditioning 87

Chapter 5

Chapter 6

Chapter 7

Chapter 8

Chapter 9

Chapter 11

Chapter 13
ATM Technology and Blueprints 905

Chapter 14

Frame Relay Technology and Blueprints 933

Data Communication Reference Information

Most popular networks can be categorized into a blueprint. For example, houses can be categorized regardless of the city in which they may be built. A three-bedroom, two-bath, two-car garage house is the same in any city. They may be shaped differently, arranged in various permutations, but the fundamentals are the same. Such a house will have plumbing fixtures for two bathrooms—no more, no less. The same is true with networks; they have fundamentals that are common in any city, in any country. Before discussing specific network blueprints, it is helpful to have reference information available or understood.

Signal Characteristics

Communication between entities is achieved through signals of some sort. This is true with humans or machines. Humans normally use speech, whereas networks, computers, and internetworking devices use electrical or optic signals. These signals have many characteristics and the signal type (electrical or optic) determines, to a degree, the characteristics of that signal.

This section explores signals and characteristics related to them. The details presented are a body of reference for information needed to work at fundamental layers within a network.

Signal Types

A signal can be defined or characterized many ways; we understand the difference between analog and digital as in the following definitions:

ANALOG

An analog signal can be described by what it is *not*. It is neither on or off, positive or negative, or some other diametrically opposed position. An example would be a dimmer switch used in electrical lighting; its function is to vary light intensity without full intensity or the light being off (unless the latter two states of intensity are desired).

DIGITAL

A digital signal is best defined as being in either an on or an off state, with no in-between point. In data communications a digital signal is a binary 1 or 0.

Signaling Methods

Two signaling methods exist: baseband and broadband. Baseband signaling uses digital signal techniques for transmission and broadband signaling uses analog signal techniques for transmission. Baseband signaling generally has a limited bandwidth whereas broadband signaling has a large bandwidth potential.

Signaling Characteristics

Signals, either analog or digital, are based on fundamental trigono-metric functions. Understanding some fundamental principles yields the benefit of being able to evaluate wave forms.

A baseline for evaluating waveforms is rooted in the Cartesian coordinate system. This system of measurement is mathematically unique for defining or locating a point on a line or plane, or in space. Fundamental to this coordinate system are numbered lines that inter-sect at right angles. See Figure 1.1.

FIGURE 1.1
Cartesian
Coordinate
System

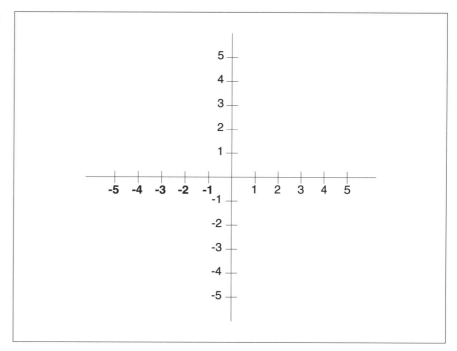

This coordinate system along with other aspects of trigonometry are used in signaling. Here the focus is on certain characteristics of signals.

Signals in computers, networking, or data communications can be categorized as being analog or digital. This coordinate system and other tools make it possible to explain signals.

Analog and Digital Commonalities

Both analog and digital signals have commonalities. Each can be evaluated by amplitude, frequency, and phase.

Amplitude

The amplitude of a signal refers to its height in respect to a baseline. Height may be a positive or negative voltage. The baseline is a zero voltage reference point. This amplitude value is proportional to the movement of the curve about the X axis of the coordinate system.

Frequency

Frequency is the number of cycles a wave makes per second. Specifically, frequency is measured in Hertz (Hz), which is also known as a unit of frequency. A cycle is a complete signal revolution from zero to the maximum positive voltage past zero to the maximum negative voltage then back to zero. In the coordinate system this is a complete revolution from 0 degrees to 360 degrees. Figure 1.2 is an example of signal characteristics, particularly one cycle.

FIGURE 1.2
Signal
Characteristics

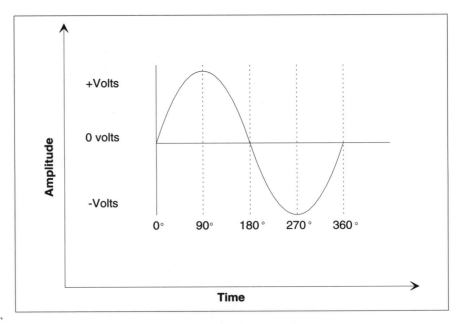

Figure 1.2 shows one cycle and the signal in respect to time and amplitude as well as its frequency.

Phase

Phase is normally measured in degrees that represent the location of a waveform. Another way of thinking about phase is that phase is a relative time of a signal with respect to another signal. A change of phase without the change of frequency or amplitude results in a scenario depicted by Figure 1.3.

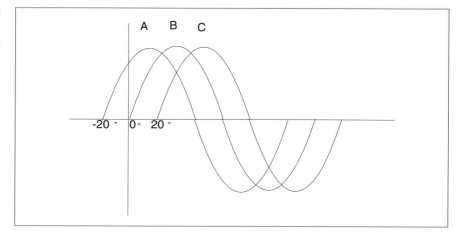

In Figure 1.3 three waveforms are present: A, B, and C. In this example waveform A has a 20-degree phase angle or leads waveform B by 20 degrees. Determination of the leading waveform is derived by visually ascertaining which waveform crosses the X axis first; in this case it is waveform A. Waveform C on the other hand is lagging behind waveform A by 20 degrees.

Figure 1.4 is an example of two signal waveforms (better known as sine waves) that have the same frequency but are out of phase with respect to the other.

In general, signals transmitted over a medium are subject to varying frequencies. Phase can be thought of as the distance of a waveform from its beginning point (zero degrees). This is particularly important when examining transmission characteristics of encoded signals. Encoded signaling characteristics will be examined in more detail; however the significance of this information becomes real when different measuring scopes are used to troubleshoot a line with varying frequencies.

Period

A period is best described as the length of a cycle. It is defined as the time required by the signal transmission of a wavelength.

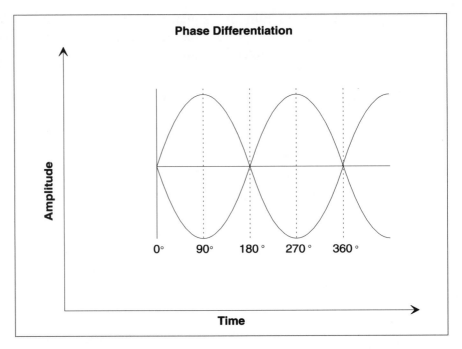

FIGURE 1.4
Phase
Differentiation

Waveforms

Waveforms come in many forms, including the sine wave and the square wave.

Sine Wave

A sine wave can be defined as a periodic wave. Characteristically, this is a wave's amplitude based upon the sine of its linear quantity of phase or time. See Figure 1.5.

Square Wave

A square wave is a wave with a square shape. It has the same characteristics as the sine wave. Consider Figure 1.6.

The square wave has similar characteristics to the sine wave except the *form* has a square appearance verses a *wave* appearance in the sine wave.

FIGURE 1.5
Example of a
Sine Wave

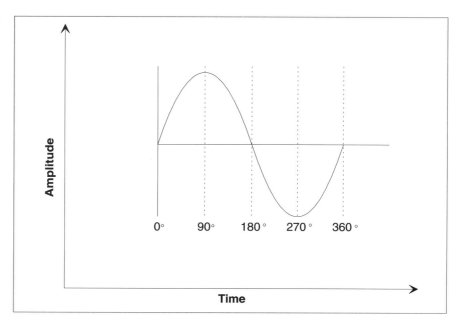

FIGURE 1.6
Example of a
Square Wave

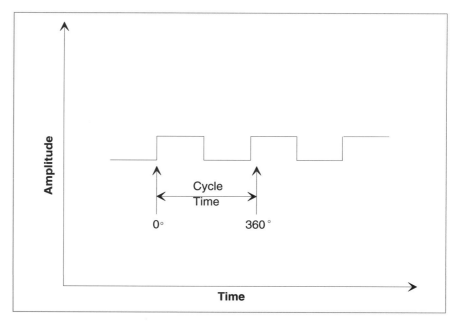

How to Use Data Representation

It is important to be able to perform manual conversions of data representations in any system, including computers and networks. Humans live in an analog world; however, it seems the majority of businesses in technologically advanced countries attempt to convert all business transactions and methods of maintaining information to binary form.

All things emanate from a point of singularity, but the reality of daily life leads to perceptions of gray. At the smallest particles of existence, binary reality exists. This becomes problematical when attempts are made to convert most aspects of life (which are analog to the native sense perception) into digital forms. The most fundamental aspect of computers and modern technology is the conversion from analog to digital. Invariably, this conversion involves tables used to correlate *something* to *something*. Consequently, if one understands conversion methods and ratios of correlation; then one has incredible power over that system because all else is built on this conversion and correlation.

Data representation can take different forms: binary, hexadecimal, decimal, and octal. Data representation can also be categorically explained.

Binary

Binary data representation uses ones and zeros to represent alphanumeric characters within computer systems. Another way of approaching binary representation is by way of ASCII, a method of data representation that uses 128 permutations of arrangements of ones and zeros.

This means that with a computer using an ASCII character set letters, numbers, control codes, and other keyboard symbols have a specific binary relationship. Consider the following examples which show the correlation between a letter or number in the ASCII character set and its binary equivalent.

LETTER OR NUMBER	BINARY VALUE
A	01000001
a	01100001
E	01000101
2	00110010
3	00110011
7	00110111
T	01010100
t	01110100
"	00100010
–	00101101

This example shows that each time a key is pressed on a keyboard the equivalent binary value is generated (a string of ones and zeros). This value is represented inside the computer as DC voltage.

For the most part, computers are digital; that is, either a 1 or 0. Hence, converting letters, numbers, or control codes to a numeric value is straightforward. When it comes to how computers work with data representation, consider that computers do not negotiate; they are binary. At the most fundamental place within computers, data representation is a method similar to being in an "off state" or an "on state".

A bit is a single digit; either one or zero. A byte is eight bits. Hence, in the previous example a single letter or number is represented by a combination of ones and zeros. The binary numbering system is based on powers of 2 and counted from right to left. The significance of this is that binary digits are determined by their positions in how they are noted. Consider:

POWERS OF TWO	VALUE
2x0	1
2x1	2
2x2	4
2x3	8
2x4	16
2x5	32
2x6	64
2x7	128
2x8	256
2x9	512
2x10	1024
2x11	2048
2x12	4096

Most people who have had some form of education would probably think I made a mistake showing that 2x0 is equivalent to 1! However, note what is being conveyed. I am explaining powers of two and the value that correlates to them. This is not multiplication. It helps not to try to superimpose previous knowledge onto something new; in this case tabula rasa is the best way to begin learning with computing.

With the previous example, one byte is 2x0 which is eight binary digits (either 1's or 0's, or some variation thereof). More examples are this correlates to keys one presses on a keyboard, or how letters/numbers are generated prior to representation in visual form.

LETTERS OR NUMBERS	BINARY VALUE
Ed	01000101 01100100
$	00100100

The two examples here: Ed and $ are shown with the corresponding binary value to the right. It is possible to convert binary numbers into shorthand. Popular methods of doing this are hexadecimal and octal.

Hexadecimal

Hex, as the term is used, refers to a numbering scheme that uses a base 16 for counting. It is a shorthand notation for expressing binary values of characters. Consider the following example:

HEXADECIMAL VALUE	DECIMAL VALUE
0	0
1	1
2	2
3	3
4	4
5	5
6	6
7	7
8	8
9	9
A	10
B	11
C	12
D	13
E	14
F	15

The following example correlates a character with a binary representation and hex expression of that value.

LETTER/NUMBER	BINARY	HEX VALUE
A	01000001	41
a	01100001	61
E	01000101	45
2	00110010	02
3	00110011	03
7	00110111	07
T	01010100	54
k	01101011	6B
m	01101101	6D
z	01111010	7A

As this example indicates it is easier to represent the letter z by hex value 7A than its binary representation.

Other methods of representation exists; Octal, uses base 8 for a numbering system, and decimal. Of these, binary and hex are prevalent and understanding this binary representation is helpful with other data communication concepts.

A final word about data representation. IBM uses EBCDIC as a prevalent method for representing data, alphanumeric, and control codes. EBCDIC uses an arrangement of 256 ones and zeros to make this possible. It should be noted that ASCII and EBCDIC are not one-for-one interchangeable.

Converting Binary to Hex

The ASCII character set includes representation of arrangements of 128 variations with ones and zeros to represent letters, numbers, and special characters used in many computers. As we have seen, a correlation can be made between a letter, its binary value, its hexadecimal value, and its decimal value.

Since the hexadecimal system is based on a power of sixteen, no letters higher in the alphabet than F are used. Therefore conversion of a binary value of 010101000 yields a hexadecimal value of A8. Another example could be a binary value of 10101010 which yields a hexadecimal value of AA.

Transmission Characteristics

The communication signals of networks, computers, and internet-working devices are electrical or optic. Their various characteristics are presented here.

Asynchronous Transmission

Asynchronous transmission is also called start/stop transmission and is characterized by character-oriented protocols. The reason for this is that data is transmitted synchronously and timed by the start and stop bits of the frame, primarily the start bit. Consider Figure 1.7.

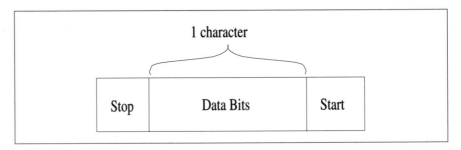

FIGURE 1.7
Example of an
Asynchronous
Frame

Figure 1.7 depicts a start bit, data bits, and a stop bit. In asynchronous transmission, the start bit notifies the receiving entity that data bits follow. Likewise, the stop bit signifies the end of data bits.

A problem with this method of communication exists if the last data bit and the stop bit are the same. If this occurs the receiving entity is confused. The problem is relatively unimportant because it is overcome with parity.

Parity is achieved by the originating entity counting the number of bits and appending the outgoing character as necessary to achieve an even or odd parity. The receiver on the other hand calculates for parity against 7 data bits and compares it to the parity bit received (the parity bit is the eighth bit transmitted). If the parity sent and computation on behalf of the receiver do not match an error has occurred.

Terms normally used with parity are odd and even; they reflect an accurate representation of the transmission. However, the terms MARK and SPACE are sometimes used as well. When they are they refer to parity as the bit setting of 1 and 0, respectively.

Ironically, asynchronous serial communication is a misnomer. In fact the start bit actually synchronizes the following bits, whereas synchronous serial communication is synchronized by byte. Both are synchronized: asynchronous synchronization is performed on bits while synchronous synchronization is typically performed at the byte level. The end result is theoretically that more overhead occurs with asynchronous communication than with synchronous communication.

Synchronous Transmission

Basic to synchronous transmission is the intent to reduce the overhead inherent in *asynchronous* transmission and to provide more efficient error detection and correction. Two categories of synchronous protocols are explained here.

Byte Oriented

An example of a byte-oriented protocol used in synchronous transmission is IBM's Binary Synchronous (BISYNC) Protocol. Introduced by IBM in 1967 it appears as in Figure 1.8.

FIGURE 1.8
Byte-Oriented
Protocol for
Synchronous
Transmission

S Y N	S T X	DATA	E T X	B C C

Figure 1.8 shows the beginning field as the synchronization (SYN) character. This precedes all data and a Synchronization (SYN) control character may even be inserted in the middle of a long message to ensure synchronization. The start of text (STX) character indicates that data immediately follows.

Data codes supported in BISYNC are ASCII, EBCDIC, and a six bit transparent code.

The end of text character (ETX) follows data. If a BISYNC transmission is lengthy and divided into segments, only the last segment will have a ETX indicator.

The block check character (BCC) can be either a longitudinal redundancy check (LRC) or a Cyclic Redundancy Check (CRC).

The byte-oriented protocol BISYNC is not as dominant today as it was in the 1970s. Its code dependence and transparency implementation are not flexible enough to support current needs.

Bit Oriented

Two examples of bit-oriented protocols transmitted synchronously are High Level Data Link Control (HDLC) and Synchronous Data Link Control (SDLC). Figure 1.9 is an example of an SDLC frame.

FIGURE 1.9
Bit-Oriented
Protocol Used
in SDLC

F l a g	Address	Control	Data	Frame Check Sequence	F l a g

The beginning and ending flag has a reserved value and is always 01111110 (7E).

The address field in the SDLC frame contains addresses.

The control field (CF) in the frame indicates the type of frame; that is, control, information, or supervisory.

The data field contains the data being transmitted.

The frame check sequence (FCS) is implemented for determining if errors in transmission have occurred.

The last field is the ending flag.

SDLC supports code transparency because it was designed into the protocol. The result of this architecture is good performance with low overhead.

Synchronization of these byte- and bit-oriented protocols is achieved by performing error checks upon larger blocks of data; the result is less overhead.

How to Interpret Bandwidth

Bandwidth is an interesting topic with many different aspects for discussion. For example, many think of a connection ability between given points A and B. This is an appropriate consideration for bandwidth. However before examining this line of discussion for bandwidth, a term called channel needs defining. A *channel* is the medium used for transmission—data, voice, or even multimedia. A channel can also be defined as a path along which data can be moved and over which analog or digital signals can pass.

Another way to examine bandwidth is to realize that it is the difference between the highest frequency and lowest frequency at which a signal can be sent simultaneously across the channel. Bandwidth directly reflects the data transfer rate of the channel. Obviously the higher the bandwidth the higher the data rate. This poses an interesting scenario.

If a given channel has a bandwidth value of X, that number, whatever it is, would seem fixed, but it is not. Consider implementing a compression algorithm for the data to be moved through the channel. Assume that algorithm operates on an 8-to-1 ratio. This could mean in most cases that the amount of data denoted as a quantity of one (1) going through a channel is actually eight (8) because of the compression algorithm.

In most instances today networks of all sorts employ algorithms to compress data so that more can move through a channel. Many different compression utilities are available, and some even come with systems in a pre-load package.

Understanding bandwidth encompasses more than knowing how much data can move through a channel. In some instances a bandwidth problem exists on either end of a given channel. Where fiber medium is the channel, either end will generally have a problem keeping up providing data to *feed* the channel or being capable of keeping up *receiving* the amount of data passing through the channel.

Still another twist on bandwidth is a focus on network devices. Some vendors provide network devices that operate as concentrators or hubs, then pass data to a processor. Figure 1.10 is an example of this idea.

This figure depicts multiple devices connected to hub and the hub connected to a processor. There is nothing inherently wrong with this configuration/implementation. When discussing bandwidth however, one must discuss the bandwidth ability of the hub's backplane. Bandwidth of the device channels to the hub is one matter; the capabilities of the backplane of this hub are entirely different. Not to discuss bandwidth of the hub's backplane and the link to the processor is to address only one side of the bandwidth equation.

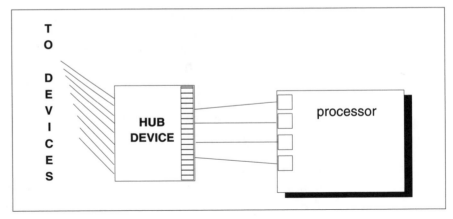

FIGURE 1.10
Interpreting
Various Aspects
of Bandwidth

How to Interpret Channel Capacity

Different types of channels exist. They can be described categorically as: voice, data, narrow-band, wide- or broadband, and a variety of other terms. Today a great variety of channels exists. There is growing migration to fiber channels; with encoding and compression techniques a channel can be exploited in ways not thought of just a few decades ago.

Generally, a channel is the "pipe" that moves data from point A to point B. The term itself is generic; however, IBM uses the term in a proprietary sense referring to their Byte, Block, and Selector channels. They also use the term to refer to ESCON (fiber) channels.

From a different perspective, some think of channels as referring to television, while still others use the term to refer to invisible channels such as microwave and radio frequency. Furthermore some online service providers now use the term channel to refer to accessible parts of their networks that can be easily identified such as weather or news.

Serial Transmission

Another transmission characteristic is how data is moved from one entity to another. Serial communication is bit-by-bit. An example of this is fiber-optic based data transfer. In this example photons are moved in serial fashion through the medium.

Figure 1.11 is an example of serial transmission of the letter T through a medium. This translates into a binary representation of 01010100.

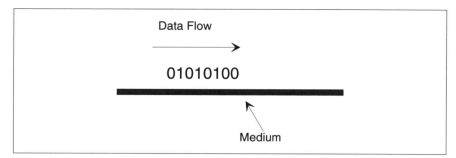

FIGURE 1.11
Serial
Transmission

Parallel Transmission

Parallel transmission is movement of data along a channel path in byte form. An example of this is IBM's parallel channels. The essence of parallel transmission is moving data in bytes rather than sequential bits. Figure 1.12 is an example of parallel data transfer.

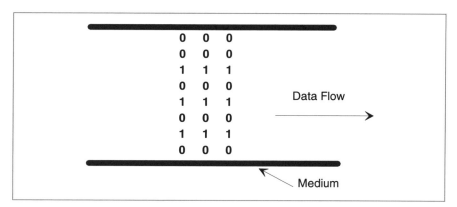

FIGURE 1.12
Parallel
Transmission

Simplex Transmission

Simplex transmission refers to the direction that data can move at any given instance. Simplex transmission is best exemplified by the analogy of a radio station broadcasting and multiple receivers detecting the signal. Direction of data flow is one way.

Half-Duplex Transmission

This direction of data flow means that data can flow in either of two directions, but only one direction at a time. An example of this is courteous communication between individuals. Normally, one speaks while another listens; then the reverse happens. This may not always be the case with humans, but it is with technology.

Full-Duplex Transmission

This direction of data flow is both directions at the same time. The implication here is that simultaneous data transfer can occur and be interpreted by both parties. Each entity can send and receive at the same time.

Modulation Techniques

When data is transmitted over a channel via a modem modulation is involved. Modulation is simply the conversion of digital signals into analog signals. Conversely, when this signal arrives at the destination the modem performs "reverse modulation"—*demodulation.*

Three modulation techniques are popular. Amplitude Modulation (AM) varies the amplitude of a signal without changing its frequency or phase. Frequency Modulation (FM) changes the frequency to reflect the fact that the change is binary state but maintains the amplitude. Phase Modulation (PM) varies the phase of the wave to reflect the binary value.

Amplitude Modulation

Amplitude modulation is the use of a single carrier frequency to convert the digital signals to analog. Figure 1.13 shows this.

FIGURE 1.13
Amplitude
Modulation

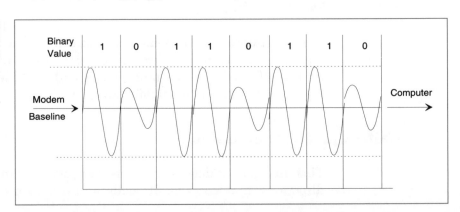

The high-wave amplitude indicates a binary one and a low-wave amplitude indicates a binary zero.

Frequency-Shift Key Modulation (FSK)

FSK uses a constant amplitude carrier signal along with two additional frequencies so a mark and space can be differentiated. Consider Figure 1.14.

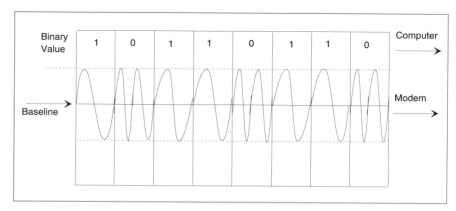

FIGURE 1.14
Frequency-shift
Key Modulation

This type of modulation technique is not prevalent among higher speed modems because of the simplicity of its nature. Higher speed baud rates require different modulation techniques.

Differential Phase-Shift Key Modulation

This modulation technique uses a phase angle comparison of an input signal to the prior di-bit. A di-bit concept is when each phase angle represents two bit values. Consider Figure 1.15.

Figure 1.15 shows the comparison of the wave pattern and its square wave interpretation. Actually, the modulation technique is a comparative-based modulation technique. Some medium speed modems use this technique.

Phase-Shift Key Modulation

In this method of modulation the phase of the signal is shifted at the baseline (transition point). Consider Figure 1.16.

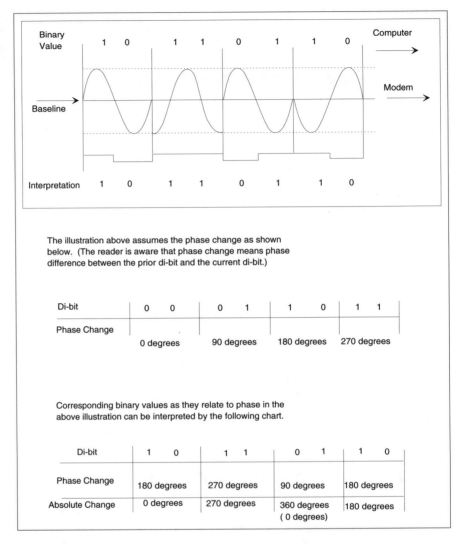

FIGURE 1.15
Differential
Phase-Shift Key
Modulation and
Assisting
Interpretation
Information

This type of modulation is comparative in nature, to a degree. It uses a phase shift relative to a fixed reference point. A modem using this type modulation has an oscillator inside to determine a signal phase angle as it enters the modem. (An oscillator is basically a component that generates an alternating signal, continuously. Its voltage, or current, is periodically relative to time.)

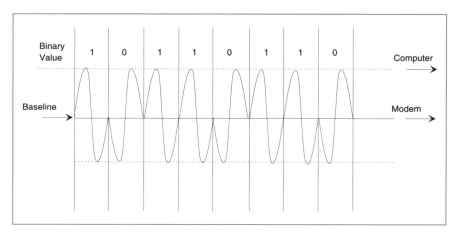

FIGURE 1.16
Phase-shift Key
Modulation

Encoding Techniques

The term encoding refers to how the signals are introduced onto the medium and how signals appear on the medium when examined. See Figure 1.17.

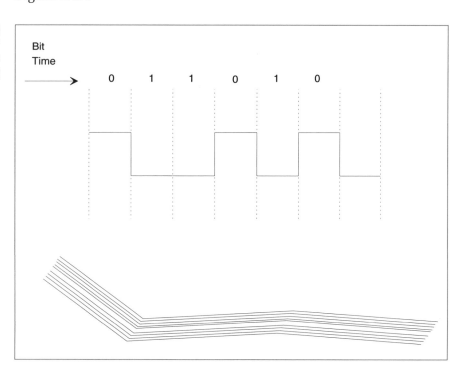

FIGURE 1.17
Non-Return to
Zero Encoding

Figure 1.17 is an example of "non-return to zero encoding," which uses each signal change to represent a bit.

Figure 1.18 represents a type of encoding known as "Manchester encoding" that changes the polarity each bit time.

FIGURE 1.18
Manchester
Encoding

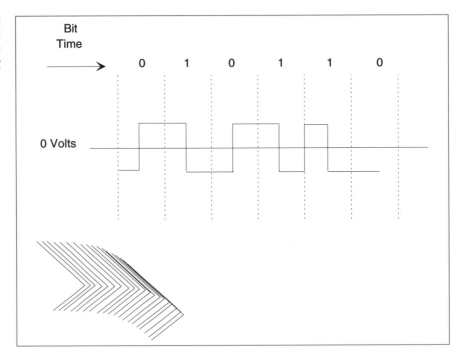

This method of encoding results in good clocking performance and is widespread in Local Area Network technology.

Other encoding schemes include Differential Manchester encoding, a form of Manchester encoding that uses the previous bit time as a base reference point for interpretation of the signal. "Return to zero" is another scheme that utilizes two signals to represent one bit change. It is similar to Manchester in that polarity is changed each bit time.

Popular Interface Standards

Interface standards include popular terms such as RS-232, V.35, T1, X.21. Entire books are devoted to explaining these and other interfaces.

Physical-layer interfaces have protocols to transfer data as do the higher layers within a network. A particular interface specification identifies the protocols of its operation. Some examples follow.

RS-232

RS-232-D is the follow-up to RS-232-C. The fundamental difference between the two is that RS-232-D is parallel with the V.24, V.28, and ISO 2110 specifications. The RS232 standard comes from the EIA. It specifies the pin-outs of a 25-pin cable used for serial communications. Although most of them are not used for typical modem installations for PCs, the 25 pins are nevertheless assigned.

V.35

This specification comes from the CCITT. It specifies modem operation of 48 Kbits/second but is typically implemented at 56 Kbits/sec.

T1

T1 interfaces have the capability to move data up to 1.54 Mbits/second. T1 lines are comprised of 24 channels, each using 8 bits per channel. One T1 line uses a twisted pair for 24 voice signals. The result is a ratio of 24 to 1.

X.21

This CCITT specification is flexible in that different signaling rates are supported. For example, a given DTE and DCE may differ with respect to adherence of their specification. X.21 calls for synchronous operations with public data networks. An example of this scenario is X.25 using X.21 as the interface.

Many other interfaces exist. To list them here would require the remainder of the book; but we need to be oriented about what happens at the physical layer.

Regardless of the vendor, interfaces exist to provide links between one system and another or a system and the medium. The interface standard used may be vendor-specific, but in most cases vendors adhere to guidelines the service providers offer.

A final note: interfaces do not have to be physical, in the sense that they are used to bridge cables or some tangible medium. For example, wireless networks require interfaces between network devices, transmitters, and receivers.

Multiplexing

The idea of multiplexing is maximum utilization of a channel. Multiplexing can be accomplished in a variety of ways; two of the most popular are explained here.

Frequency-Division Multiplexing (FDM)

FDM is the multiplexing of frequencies and can readily be used with analog transmission because frequencies are divided then multiplexed onto the medium. Consider Figure 1.19.

FIGURE 1.19
Frequency-
Division
Multiplexing

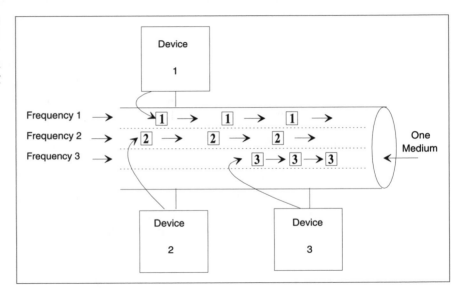

Figure 1.19 shows one medium and three devices connected to the medium. Each device transmits on a different frequency; in this hypothetical example the frequencies are 1, 2, and 3. These hypothetical frequencies could realistically be 10KHz-14KHz, 5KHz-9KHz, and 0Hz-4000KHz. The premise of an FDM multiplexer is that each device uses a range of frequencies and stays within that range. Bandwidth of the medium is utilized effectively to accommodate multiple users communicating with different frequencies.

Time-Division Multiplexing (TDM)

TDM involves multiplexing data via time. See Figure 1.20.

FIGURE 1.20
Time-Division
Multiplexing

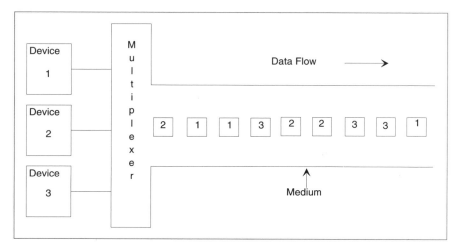

Time division multiplexing is the utilization of the medium by time-slicing devices attached to the multiplexer. Its premise of operation is that data transfer is based upon time. In Figure 1.20 three devices are attached to the multiplexer and the multiplexer itself multiplexes signals from devices 1, 2, and 3 to maximize the channel. Though not shown, on the receiving end of the data path is another multiplexer which de-multiplexes the data to its destination point.

Types of Multiplexers

A number of types of multiplexers exist. A network-based multiplexer may provide services for a variety of devices each utilizing different transfer speeds. T1 multiplexers operate at T1 speeds (1.54 Mbp/sec). Another type of T1 multiplexer is the fractional T1, which supports fractions of the T1 speeds incremented in 56K or 64 Kbp/sec. Normally, 1 to 23 circuits can be derived from a fractional T1.

Measuring Bandwidth

At the physical layer within a network numerous topics need consideration. A number of well-written books examine this level within a network. Information here is focused and concise. These topics provide sufficient reference information; at the end of the chapter references for additional information are provided.

Bit Rate

The bit rate is the number of bits transmitted per second, and is a term generally used with modems.

Baud Rate

The baud rate is a measurement of the number of times per second a change occurs in amplitude, frequency, or phase of a wave. One baud is a change in one of the aforementioned. To calculate the number of bits per second the following equation can be used.

Determine the number of bits that equal one baud. This information is usually ascertainable though documentation sources from modem suppliers, or it can be obtained by knowing the specifications for the modem. Next, multiply the number of bauds per second a modem can perform and that will equal the number of bits per second for that modem.

The equation can be rendered as: The number of bauds per second x 1 bit per baud (or the appropriate amount according to specifications) = the number of bits per second.

Types of Links

A network can be described by its upper-layer protocols that comprise the network or the bulk of the network. Another usage of the phrase could be in reference to the lower-layer protocols within the network, or to the prevalent one(s). Or the network could refer to the dominant media used throughout. Other definitions exist, but these are the dominant ones.

Two terms are used to explain various aspects of networks and sometimes the network itself. Most references to the term physical mean something tangible; aberrations will be discussed in later chapters.

The term logical does not necessarily imply sound reason; it may define a function.

In the case of this protocol (SNA) multiple transmission lines may exist. These are literally physical, tangible objects. Put together they can connect two devices. Transmission lines that form a transmission group may have data moving through a particular one for better throughput. Consider Figure 1.21.

FIGURE 1.21
Physical and Logical Characteristics

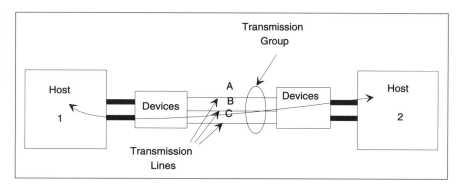

Figure 1.21 depicts two hosts, two devices, three physical lines (A, B, and C) connecting device 1 and device 2, and a circle around all three lines indicating that collectively they are considered a group; it shows data flow over link C.

Reference to these three lines can be thus: three physical lines exist between device 1 and device 2 and the logical path where data flows in this example is through line C. Theoretically data could pass over line A or line B. Since data could flow through either A, B, or C, reference to the selected path is considered logical. This may not necessarily be the *best* route for data flow but it is by definition, in this example, the *logical* path. Here it is not only logical, it is the physical path as well.

In most cases something referred to as logical in a network usually maps to something physical, though exceptions may occur. Though logical does not necessarily mean reasonable, or the best way for something to occur, it does refer to a characteristic or aspect of an occurrence—or the potential therefor.

Conversely, physical does not always mean physical in the sense of some thing tangible. In some uses of the term, *physical* refers to a function, service, or capability of a device. However, reality does set in, and if it is logical it must have basis in something physical, but because something is physical does not necessarily make it logical.

Practical Bandwidth Measurements

Many understand bandwidth as focusing upon the size of the *pipe* between one or more points. To understand bandwidth requires a total approach to networks and systems. For example, bandwidth analysis includes: examination of backplane throughput capabilities for devices throughout a network, consideration of computing device front-end drivers for *pipes* from one point to another, and actual application capabilities regarding user support. It also includes an operating system's analysis of user capacity, whether human or program. Total bandwidth analysis also includes other factors of networks and computing systems.

A total perspective for bandwidth consideration includes analysis of interface boards and buses used in fiber-based networks. It matters little if fiber links exist between any given points if a bottleneck for input/output exists in the interface cards that drive the fiber connections.

One rule of thumb to remember is that even if fiber connections are used extensively in a network, the maximum throughput capacity may be limited by the actual computing device or devices using these fiber links. In addition, it is best to remember that signal loss and degradation due to impairment also affects overall network speeds. Another way to examine this concept is to remember that the fastest part of any network is the slowest component.

Total component examination for bandwidth capacity is the most accurate way to determine the speeds at which bandwidth can be ascribed to any network. Evaluation of signal transmission is also important to understand bandwidth.

Signal Transmission

Signal transmission involves a number of topics, some of which are types of signals, how they are transmitted, the bandwidth used, and the way data are represented.

Signal distortion is no trivial matter. It occurs in most transmissions. For example, when lines originally designed for voice transmission are used for data transmission some distortion can occur. Distortion can be filtered out by the human ear when it occurs during a voice conversation between two or more parties speaking over a given medium. This happens frequently; we become used to the "noise" or distortion and unless it is extreme enough to cause difficulty interpreting another's words it is typically dismissed. This is not always possible when data are transmitted. Data are generally transmitted via machines with preprogrammed methods of dealing with distortion.

Delay is a type of distortion: the time it takes for a signal to arrive at its destination from its point of origin. Frequently, this type of delay is called *propagation delay*. It may seem trivial to discuss delay in light of how fast current technology can transmit and receive signals, but consider the following. If a signal is generated in Dallas and is routed through local switches then transmitted to a satellite and then received in Paris, a considerable time delay occurs. Granted the delay may be milliseconds or seconds, it is quite important. The significance of propagation delay is becoming increasingly important because of how technology is being implemented. Consider an example of how propagation delay can affect day-to-day operation. TCP/IP is the backbone protocol in the Internet. TCP/IP and certain devices encounter difficulty when delays occur in transmission of data packets from point A to point B. When significant delay is introduced to the transmission some devices cannot convey a data stream and reliable transmission fails. This is a significant topic for concern in many technical arenas.

Harmonic Distortion is an older reference to a type distortion. When a frequency is transmitted through a medium other harmonics can be measured as a result of the main tone in the medium; these are generally referred to as second and third harmonics.

Non-linear Distortion is a current way to evaluate what has been traditionally viewed as harmonic distortion. A non-linear distortion measurement is the value obtained from monitoring paired frequencies and the harmonics associated with them. The net effect of non-linear distortion is the introduction of other symbols of some measurable size that appear in low magnitude. This type of distortion is similar to harmonic distortion, but is different enough so that it can be compensated for, thus improving line quality.

Jitter is another type of distortion. It refers to the phenomena where a signal is moved around the center of an axis upon which it is being transmitted. This type of noise is a frequency-oriented noise or distortion. Jitter has been a common type of distortion with analog signals. In the world of digital signal transfer jitter causes problems with clocking an incoming signal on the receiving end of transmission.

Crosstalk is another form of distortion. It happens with analog signals when the lines carrying them are too close and there is literally cross-talk; a bleeding from one line onto the other. Technically, this is a form of induction that generally occurs between two wires or other types of equipment in close proximity.

Fading is another form of distortion: a signal becomes weaker and weaker. Generally, this is due to atmospheric conditions, especially in microwave and satellite transmission. Rain, snow, ice, and other atmospheric phenomena such as ozone and particulates create distortion of signals transmitted through space. Different times of the year, different seasons, affect some signals differently.

Other types of distortion exist. Many interferences happen when signal transmission occurs regardless of whether the signal is transmitted over a physical line, through space, or by other means. These types of distortion exemplify the difficulties encountered in signal transmission. Degradation of signals is a core topic to those entities who provide services to carry signals from place-to-place.

Summary

This chapter has provided background information to enable understanding of working with network blueprints.

Signal characteristics are common to all signals; they are a fundamental way to analyze operation in any network. Signal types and methods need to be understood to operate certain devices (both hardware and software) in network operation and maintenance.

Data representation is increasingly critical to working with network blueprints. When some networks were EBCDIC or ASCII in their native form it was not too important to understand the fundamentals of data representation conversion. Today integrated networks have increased the need to understand data representation; interpretation of information through analyzers and network test equipment requires a higher level of understanding network fundamentals.

Transmission characteristics of signals are important as well. They accompany all transmission methods used in networking blueprints today. Focusing upon understanding transmission characteristics enhances the comprehension of the overall interpretation of information obtained about networks.

Measuring bandwidth is a topic of conversation in all networks. The information presented in this chapter encourages focus on the overall approach to this topic. It should be used with the backdrop of understanding other topics in this and future chapters.

Modulation methods or techniques are equally important to understand for application of practical knowledge. Modulation effects the overall throughput of any network. The information here is applicable in almost all networks on the market today.

Much information is required to work with network blueprints. Networks today are not as simple as they were in the 1980s. One must be aware of diversity vendor equipment as well as the interaction of implementations in diverse geographic locations. This chapter has been the starting place for information provided in the rest of this book.

Network design has evolved in the past 20 years to emerge as an important aspect in the technological arena. When LANs began to take off in the early 1980s design and planning occurred mostly after the fact. Network design was rudimentary, involving little beyond what device would be located where. During the mid-to-late 1980s this began to change.

Because of rapid invention, creation, manufacturing, and growing consumer awareness and consumption, most technology was deployed without much planning. Certainly this is not true in every case or with large networks, but it does reflect the norm of operation for medium-to-small environments where technology was utilized. In the time frame from the early to mid 1990s, a shift began to occur in the technical community concerning the planning or design of networks.

By the mid 1990s sources of all types, including newspapers, employment agencies and consulting firms, had identified people with skill sets that reflected the title of Network Architect. Little consensus exists even today about what a Network Architect is able to do. Designing a network involves many different disciplines. In a sense, network design is as complex, or more so, as the work of an architect who designs buildings.

In this chapter, a variety of perspectives were presented regarding network architecture. The best place to begin is with the basics; in this case, that means addressing those ideas that need adjustment, removal, or deeper consideration.

CHAPTER 2

Blueprint Protocols

Designing a network involves many different components. From an operational perspective, a network is built around protocols, which can be divided into two categories; they are lower- and upper-layer. This chapter discusses the popular protocols currently used in blueprints.

Perspective

Protocols can be divided into layers based upon the OSI reference model, which has been widely used. Consider Figure 2.1

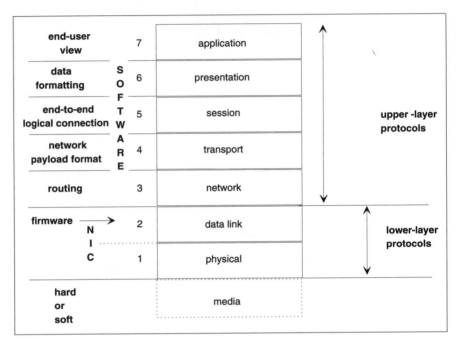

Notice the information presented in the figure. First, the model is divided into upper- and lower-layer protocols. The division comes at layer two in the network. All lower-layer protocols operate at layers one and two when their function is correlated to this model. This is an eight-layer model—one that illustrates the media. Technically, the ISO discusses media at layer one in the OSI model. However, I prefer a clearer explanation and therefore break out a layer beneath layer one. This layer, the media layer, includes all forms of media used to transport items from one location to another.

The media layer can be divided into two categories: hard and soft. Hard media includes: coaxial cable, fiber, twisted-pair cabling, and so forth. Soft media includes microwave, infrared, satellite, radio frequency, and other forms of transmission vehicles.

Notice also in Figure 2.1 that the NIC is found at layers one and two. It is the connection point between the media and the actual system used in the network. The physical layer part of the NIC defines interface standards such as RS-449, RS-232, and V.35. At layer two in the network firmware exist on network interface cards that contain the *lower-layer protocol*. For example, this is where Ethernet, ATM, Frame Relay, SDLC, FDDI, Token Ring, and other lower-layer protocols are found.

The network layer as shown in Figure 2.1 is where routing occurs. It is also where software begins to perform operations in a network. Notice in Figure 2.1 the word "software" is beside all layers from the network layer to the application layer.

The network layer is where routing tables are maintained. This is true in system host, routers, and other types of network devices. In TCP/IP networks, this is where IP and ICMP operate. The third layer also fits SNA networks for routing. In SNA, it is in the communications controller, also called a front-end processor, where much of the routing occurs. Software is loaded into this device and performs routing functions. The same holds true for routing in other networks as well.

The transport layer (layer four) as shown in the OSI model is that layer that *packages* the "payload" to be moved from one location to another. This "payload" is generated at the application layer from the user as well as from layers five and six.

Layer five is the session layer, where logical connections are made between two or more systems. In a sense one could consider this the point at which a logical pipe is created between two systems as a conduit for what is generated above this layer. Technically, logical connections can be, and are, made at lower layers in the network— particularly at the data-link layer.

Layer six is the presentation layer. This is where formatting of material generated at the application layer occurs. In data networks arrangement (formatting) of data is either ASCII or EBCDIC. Other formatting occurs at this layer as well.

Layer seven, the application layer, is what a user *sees* and interacts with. In most networks this is where we find interaction between "the system" itself and the material it carries.

Understanding all this information is helpful when examining lower- and upper-layer protocols. It is useful when working with network blueprints to realize where different software and hardware components fit and function. It is equally beneficial for those who troubleshoot networks, commonly to identify where symptoms of problems occur.

Lower-Layer Protocols

The lower-layer protocols provided in this chapter constitute the majority of protocols in use today and those increasingly coming into use.

Asynchronous Transfer Mode (ATM)

ATM is a cell-based protocol. It uses small packets (the cell is simply a small packet). To be precise about the concept of a cell versus a packet, a cell is a physical-layer component whereas a packet is a network-layer component, from the perspective of the OSI model. Figure 2.2 illustrates the conceptual view of ATM in a multiprotocol environment.

FIGURE 2.2
Conceptual View of ATM in a Mixed Protocol Environment

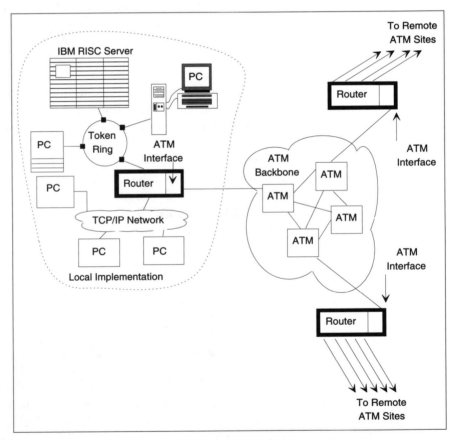

Notice the router with an ATM interface that enables the network to communicate with the ATM WAN, which in turn has ATM routers that enable connectivity with remote LANs and other WANs. Fundamentally, ATM is a broadband protocol and can use switched or nonswitched technology. Its beginnings are in broadband ISDN, particularly B-ISDN. ATM is a cell-based technology that has a cell structure of 53 bytes of which 48 are used for customer data. There is a 5-byte header of an ATM cell.

A particular advantage of ATM is that it can integrate data, voice, and video within the same application without concern for compatibility of the impact with communications in LANs or WANs. ATM is particularly suited to this task because it treats data as small-size packets and uses relatively simple protocols with low overhead. These two characteristics are basic requirements for a fast switching technology.

Enterprise System Connection (ESCON)

ESCON is IBM's fiber optic channel protocol. It is used with IBM's S/390 architecture as well as with other architectures. It can be implemented as point-to-point switched or nonswitched. Data are moved serially though fiber cable. Because photons are used to represent data, the length a cable can run is longer than with traditional copper stranded cable. For example, distances of 23 to 43 kilometers are supported for some devices. According to IBM, ESCON can accommodate up to 17 million bytes per second of data rate transfer. Figure 2.3 shows a conceptual view of an ESCON environment.

Notice in addition to ESCON connections some older parallel-channel technology is used as well. Parallel-channel technology is still capable of meeting many needs today and is supported widely throughout the world.

ESCON is the architectural follow-up to the channels IBM used with prior architectures. However, both are supported and it appears IBM will support both for some time to come. ESCON is radically different from parallel channels in two ways: first, ESCON cables are much lighter in weight than traditional copper stranded cable; second, ESCON moves data almost ten times faster than parallel channels do.

Ethernet

Originally, Ethernet was a Digital, Intel, and Xerox Corporation specification. Technically, it still is. However, the IEEE has an 802.3 specification compatible with Ethernet. Occasionally some conflicts emerge with different vendors who provide products that implement Ethernet technology, but for the most part coexistence is usual.

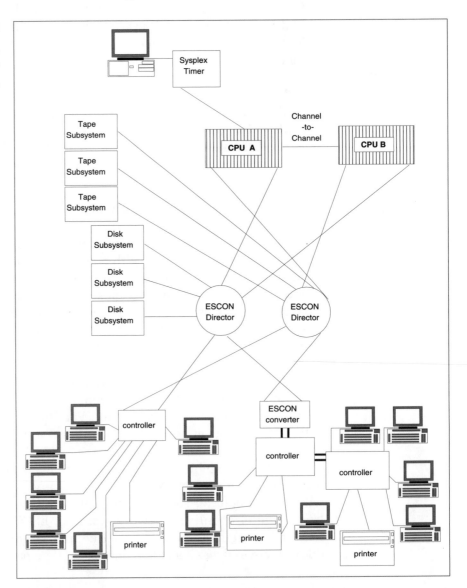

FIGURE 2.3
Conceptual View of an ESCON Environment

Ethernet is a data-link protocol that uses broadcast technology. It is typically implemented in bus topology, and may use twisted pairs, coaxial cabling, or fiber. Even in a hub implementation, the operational characteristics are the same. Consider Figure 2.4.

FIGURE 2.4
Conceptual View
of Ethernet

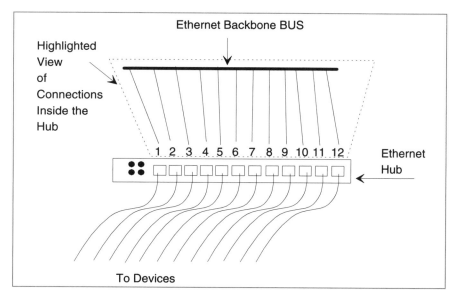

Figure 2.4 shows a network hub implementing Ethernet technology. Notice 12 ports exist where 12 devices are connected. Even though this illustration portrays a hub device, *inside* the actual communication is on a single bus using broadcast technology; this is the fundamental nature and characteristic of Ethernet

Ethernet is implemented on interface boards which may be used with personal, notebook, mid-range, or mainframe computers. Ethernet technology origins go back to the mid-1970s. It is an example of a de facto standard. Ethernet version 2.0 specifies data transfer speeds at 10 Mb/second. However, current Ethernet technology focuses on speeds of 100 Mb/second; this is also called Fast Ethernet. Gigabit Ethernet is now increasingly becoming a presence in the marketplace.

Gigabit Ethernet not only moves payloads quicker but also changes the actual frame when compared to regular Ethernet and Fast Ethernet. Gigabit Ethernet actually incorporates changes at the MAC layer, thus affecting fundamental operational characteristics.

Ethernet is a broadcast technology which is not connection-oriented at a data-link layer. Consequently, successful connectivity with Ethernet is inversely proportional to the number of devices attempting to participate in any given network segment.

Fiber Distributed Data Interface (FDDI)

FDDI is a dual-ring-based technology. As its name implies, it uses fiber media; however, copper-stranded media can be used and if they are it is called CDDI. FDDI data rate transfer is 100 Mb/second. Consider Figure 2.5.

FIGURE 2.5
FDDI
Implementation

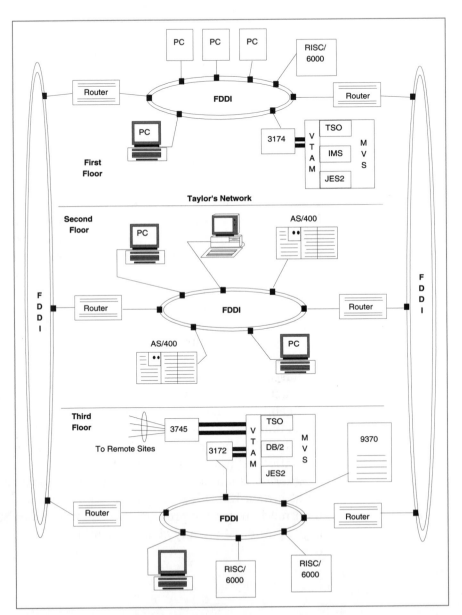

Figure 2.5 shows a multisegment FDDI network. Three floors of a facility are connected by two FDDI rings, both coupled via routers. This implementation provides a high degree of redundancy.

The FDDI standard was created by a committee that is part of the ANSI standards organization. FDDI is implemented by a number of vendors, including Digital Equipment Corporation.

FDDI is similar to Token Ring in its technology. The architectural structure uses the notion of a token and a station required to capture the token before it can transmit data onto the ring.

FDDI-II is an implementation of FDDI which operates isosynchronously and utilizes a 125-microsecond frame transfer on the ring. The primary difference in FDDI and FDDI-II is that the latter can accommodate voice and/or ISDN traffic.

Frame Relay

Frame relay is a lower-layer protocol technology. In reality it is implemented in public service providers. However, to operate with a frame relay network, interface connection points are required to couple the private sites to the public frame relay networks. See Figure 2.6

Operationally, frame relay is similar to X.25, but differs because routing decisions are made at the data-link layer within the network. Consider Figure 2.7 which illustrates a conceptual view of mapping that occurs in a frame-relay node.

Frame relay supports multiple speeds. In some instances 1.54 Mb/sec can be achieved. Frame relay can also support video and voice, in addition to data transfer.

Standards that frame relay supports include ANSI T1.602, T1S1/90-75, CCITT I.122, and Q.933. Frame relay is supported by a number of vendors, including IBM.

Parallel Channel

Parallel Channel is the term IBM used to rename their existing channels when ESCON was introduced. Two types of parallel channels exist: byte multiplexer and block multiplexer. They use channel protocols and bus and tag copper-stranded cable. Figure 2.8 shows a conceptual view of a channel subsystem.

FIGURE 2.6
Conceptual View
of Frame Relay

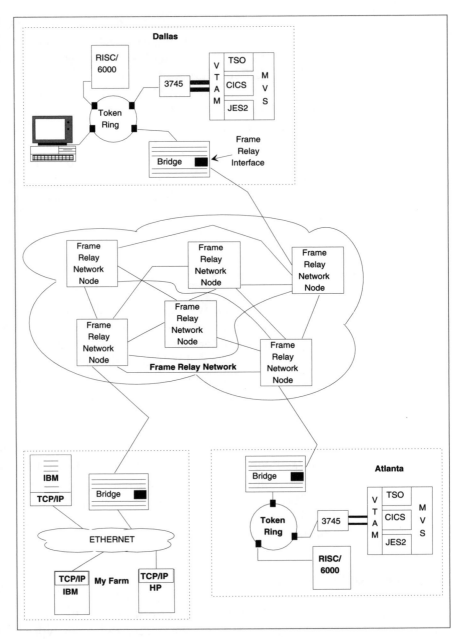

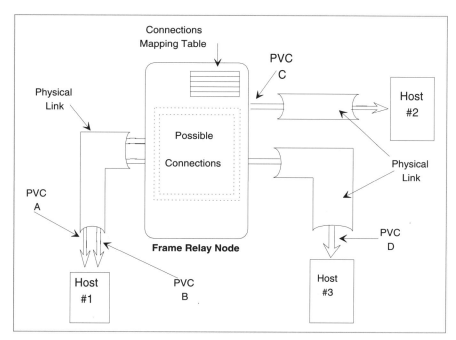

FIGURE 2.7
Enhanced View
of a Frame
Relay Node

FIGURE 2.7
Enhanced View
of a Frame
Relay Node

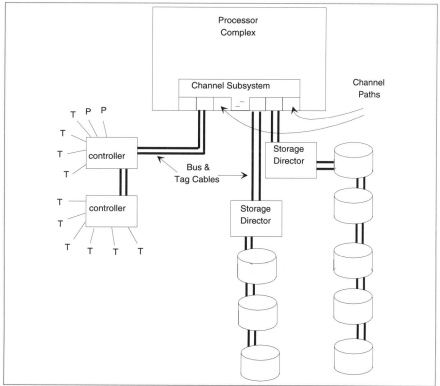

FIGURE 2.8
Conceptual View
of a Channel
Subsystem
Implemented

The nature of these channels and the cables used in conjunction with them restricts cable length to approximately 200 feet when units are daisy chained. In some instances these cables can be used for longer distances, but restrictions do apply. Channels operate as Figure 2.9 shows.

FIGURE 2.9
Parallel Data
Flow Through
a Channel

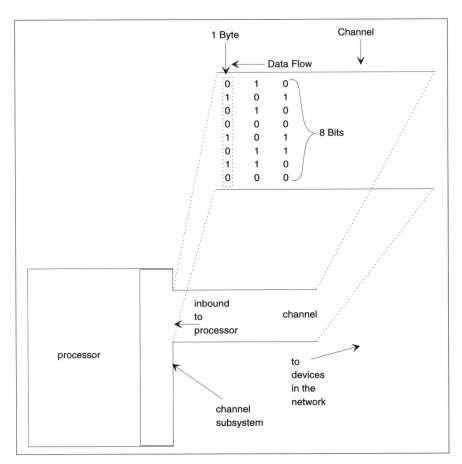

Parallel channels have different data rate transfer speed support depending upon how data is transferred. Typically, data rates are from 1 to 3.5 Mb/sec. These speeds may vary depending upon the device attached because some vendors offer devices which vary in channel speed supported.

Synchronous Data Link Control (SDLC)

SDLC is a bit-oriented protocol widely used in the industry. Figure 2.10 illustrates a conceptual view of its operation.

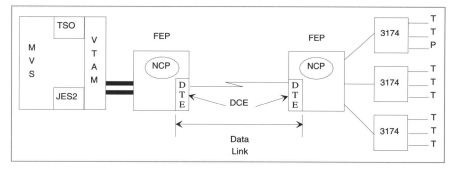

Notice that Figure 2.10 shows two communication controllers (also called front-end processors [FEPs]). The link between these two controllers uses SDLC for a communication protocol.

SDLC can be implemented with switched point-to-point, non-switched (dedicated) point-to-point, nonswitched multi-point, and loop configurations. SDLC frame structure is such that the control field supports multiple formats including unnumbered, supervisory, and information. Figure 2.11 provides a component view for an SDLC. It illustrates the actual data link, the medium, and the components that comprise the fundamentals of an SDLC implementation.

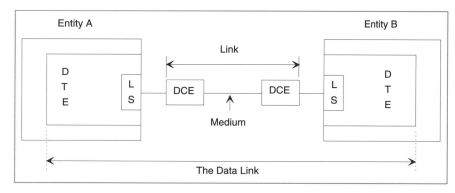

SDLC is implemented in many IBM installations. Other vendors supporting SDLC include: Hewlett-Packard, SUN Microsystems and Digital Equipment Corporation. Many vendors who offer network devices support SDLC because of its presence in the marketplace.

Token Ring

Token ring was originally an IBM product offering. The IEEE has an equivalent which will be discussed later in this chapter. Token ring

utilizes ring technology with a star implementation. Token ring operates at two speeds: 4Mb and 16Mb. This technology is connection-
oriented at a data-link layer. See Figure 2.12.

FIGURE 2.12
Conceptual View
of Token Ring

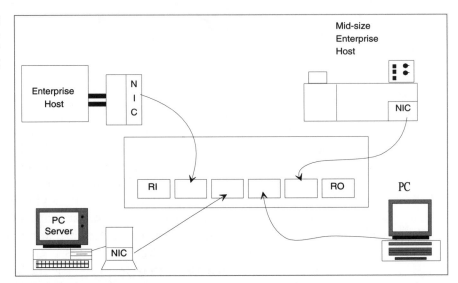

Token ring was announced in the mid 1980s by IBM and has since
grown to command a considerable market share. It is a fault-tolerant
technology because of the nature of its operation. Devices can be
inserted and taken off the ring without disturbing ring operations.

X.25

X.25 is a CCITT specification with considerable presence in the
worldwide marketplace. It is a packet switching technology: a packet
is created at the network layer and placed in a frame at the data-link
layer. Figure 2.13 illustrates basic X.25 operation.

   X.25 technology uses permanent virtual circuits. These are similar
to leased lines. It also uses a virtual-call concept: a node must request
a connection (place a call) to the destination node for communication
to take place. A fast-select call concept, also used by X.25, is an
extension to the data field used in the normal call issued by the node
desiring to make a connection. The extension means that up to 128
bytes of data can be used in the field rather than 16 in the normal
call.

FIGURE 2.13
Conceptual View
of X.25 Operation

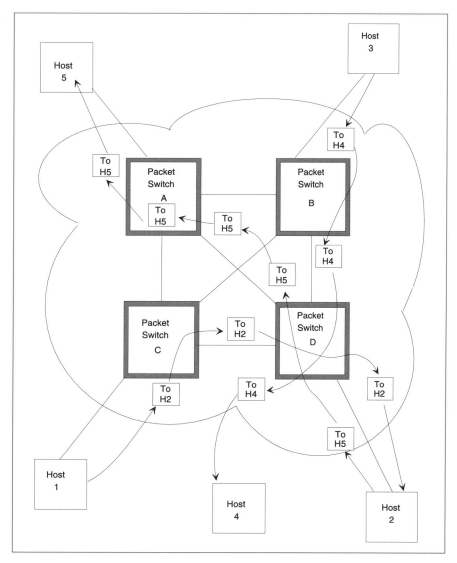

FIGURE 2.13
Conceptual View
of X.25 Operation

Packet switching technology has existed for more than two decades. These types of networks began to appear in the US about 1970. X.25 is a protocol used in many public network-oriented service providers.

IEEE 802 Protocols

The IEEE has a subcommittee devoted to a series of protocols called the 802.X series. A list of these protocols, the associated group name, and their function follows.

802.1

802.1 is the High Level Interface group. The focus of this group is concerned with network architecture. Additionally, the group focuses on internetworking heterogeneous networks and network management. This group also works with MAC bridges.

802.2

802.2 is the Logical Link Control (LLC) group. The focus of this group is upon the data-link layer in the OSI model. The data-link layer can be divided into two sublayers: the MAC and the LLC. Figure 2.14 illustrates this.

FIGURE 2.14
Data Link
Layer Sublayers

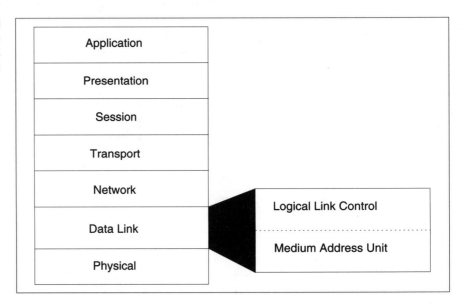

The MAC sublayer differs depending on the type of protocol and network implemented. The LLC is common among 802.3, 802.4, 802.5, and 802.6 networks, but is independent of MAC addressing and the actual medium. By dividing this layer into two sublayers a degree of independence can be achieved.

The LLC sublayer supports four types of service:

- Unacknowledged connectionless
- Connection mode
- Acknowledged connectionless
- All of the above.

Each MAC frame contains an LLC protocol data unit. Individual examination of these MAC frames follows.

802.3

This is carrier-sense multiple access with collision detection, also referred to as CSMA/CD. This frame is similar to Ethernet but different in one field. However, 802.3 will operate with Ethernet and uses the same basic technology.

802.4

This is called token bus. This type of implementation passes a token, but uses bus topology. Each station must capture the token in order to use it. This can easily be understood if we consider that a logical ring is formed on the bus.

802.5

This is a ring-oriented technology similar to IBM token ring. 802.5 is based upon ring technology and a hub implementation via a media access unit. It uses token passing technology, requiring each station to possess the token prior to transmission.

This technology is considered self-healing. Hosts can be put onto and removed from the ring at will without disturbing the ring. Ring speeds are either 4 or 16 MB/second.

802.6

This defines a metropolitan area network. For practical purposes this definition is superimposed on the ANSI X3T9.5 standard, which defines the FDDI. This specification defines a speed of 100 Mb/second, fiber channel, a 1300 nm signal, distributed clocking, and timed token rotation. The FDDI-II definition claims that up to 620 Mb/second are defined.

802.7

This group provides support to other working groups, particularly the broadband-oriented groups.

802.8

This group provides support for the optical-oriented technology groups.

802.9

This group is focused on integrated data and voice oriented networks.

802.10

This group focuses on LAN security. By definition it is related to all the LAN implementations.

Upper-Layer Protocols

Networks of all types use upper-layer protocols, for example, to fit into the system on which they operate, or in some cases the *remote* systems in which they operate. Regardless the level, protocols govern network operations. Without them networks might not be possible, and would certainly be less orderly.

Networks are generally the offerings of corporations. Some of these corporations are larger than others, some networks have their roots in government agencies and others in forums/organizations. Some protocols are de facto; this means in essence something was created, done, proven to work, then a "standard" of this protocol was documented explaining how the protocol works and what must be done to work with the protocol. The implication is that those who operate with such a protocol must follow the specifications recorded about the protocol.

Another type of protocol is known as de jure. In a de jure protocol *the plan* is created, then the protocol follows. Typically, the individuals who work with both types of protocols have different philosophical approaches to technology. These terms, de facto and de jure, are best understood when used in reference to developers of software and hardware.

Most networks can be described by their lower- and upper-layer protocols. Lower-layer protocols have been discussed, here the focus is on upper-layer protocols. Basic insights presented here provide a foundation. Even though network protocols can be categorically divided into layers, sometimes a clear division of function versus layer can be skewed.

Many are familiar with the OSI reference model. It can be used a yardstick to discuss other network protocols. When different protocols are evaluated in light of the OSI reference model, it is sometimes clear that not all network protocols fit all layers defined by the OSI model. A good example of this is the TCP/IP suite of protocols.

Systems Network Architecture (SNA)

SNA is IBM's networking solution for medium-to-large networks. Its origins go back to 1974 when it was introduced. It has been through many iterations since that time. It began as a layered-network architecture, and, until 1992 was IBM's primary networking solution.

FIGURE 2.15
SNA Layers

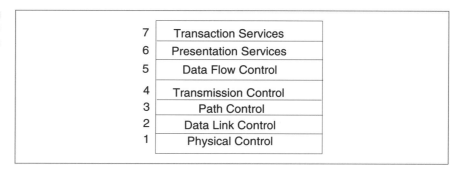

Figure 2.15 shows the SNA layers prior to the announcement in 1992 of a wider support including a variety of protocols not native to IBM.

In Spring 1992 IBM announced their Networking Blueprint. This announcement signaled a radical break from the past with regard to their approach to networking solutions. It embraced SNA, but also incorporated other protocols. Consider Figure 2.16.

This shows the complexity of SNA evolution. IBM now embraces a heterogeneous SNA. Figure 2.16 is the best representation of network protocol support in an SNA environment today. It clearly shows the transition support IBM now embraces for technology other than its native technology.

SNA is based on terms, concepts, hardware and software architecture. Until 1993, IBM produced its own dictionary of terms, defining them and explaining how they fit into the SNA environment. SNA is built upon concepts as well, though these concepts are for the most part abstract. Some SNA concepts are used in actual software and hardware definitions to make the network functional. IBM's hardware and software are the tangible components upon which SNA is built.

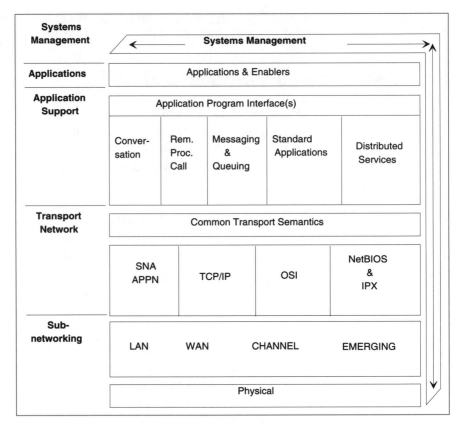

FIGURE 2.16
IBM Networking
Blueprint

To learn SNA is a challenge. To focus upon learning SNA concepts without understanding the terms is difficult at best. On the other hand, to memorize terms and not attempt to understand the abstract concepts is little more than memorization. The best way to learn SNA is from a topical perspective. In time as one learns topics (consisting of terms and concepts) a cumulative effect takes place and the whole picture begins to come into perspective.

Advanced Peer-to-Peer Architecture

APPN is another network solution offered by IBM. Its origins are in the 1983 time frame. As of this writing APPN is at version 2.

APPN is peer oriented whereas traditional SNA is hierarchical in nature. Simply put, APPN is designed for communication between two programs, without an intervening entity to aid in this communication. If an intervening entity is used, we have traditional SNA.

APPN is a proprietary networking technology. IBM has not allowed other vendors to implement it fully according to their architectural manuals. Figure 2.17 shows a conceptual view of APPN node structure.

Node Operator	Application Transaction Program
Node Operator Facility	
Control Point / Intermediate Session Routing	Logical Unit
Path Control	
Data Link Control	

Another characteristic of APPN is that some of its functions have been incorporated into SNA. Some of SNA's core components, namely the VTAM, began official support of some APPN functions with VTAM version 4.1. VTAM version 4.3 seems to point to more of an integration between SNA functionality and APPN.

We cannot predict what companies may or may not do, so it would be incorrect to conclude from this text that IBM is planning to merge SNA and APPN. The two are based on philosophical and functional differences and they have been positioned to meet different needs. IBM has simply incorporated some APPN functions into SNA. Other conclusions are mere speculation.

Open Systems Interconnection (OSI)

OSI is the culmination of the work of the ISO. Around 1977, the ISO chartered a committee to created a standard for networking. This standard became known as the OSI reference model. Consider Figure 2.18, that shows the model layers and components as defined by the ISO.

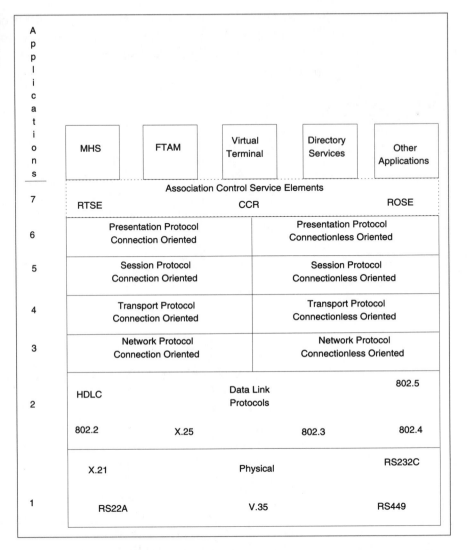

FIGURE 2.18
OSI Model and Components

This OSI model stated that at a minimum the seven layers identified should exist in a network. The committee defined what occurs at each layer, but did not define the layer that is the medium. Part of the rationale behind this was that different network protocols are capable of using different media types.

The ISO has come to embrace CCITT and other specifications it works with in its networking model. In a general sense the OSI model is an example of a de jure standard.

OSI products are implemented by vendors, because the ISO is an organization, not a company in the sense of production (at least at the time of this writing). Consequently, some companies are more involved than others in developing OSI compliant offerings.

Some parts of adopted OSI protocols including electronic mail and directory service protocols are used more than others.

Transmission Control Protocol/Internet Protocol (TCP/IP)

TCP/IP has its origins in time around 1975. It was the follow-up to the Arpanet, which was government related. In 1978 a public demonstration of TCP/IP was given and in 1983 the US government made a statement that if connection was to be made to what had become known as the Internet, it must be done with the TCP/IP protocol suite. Consider Figure 2.19.

FIGURE 2.19
Conceptual View
of TCP/IP

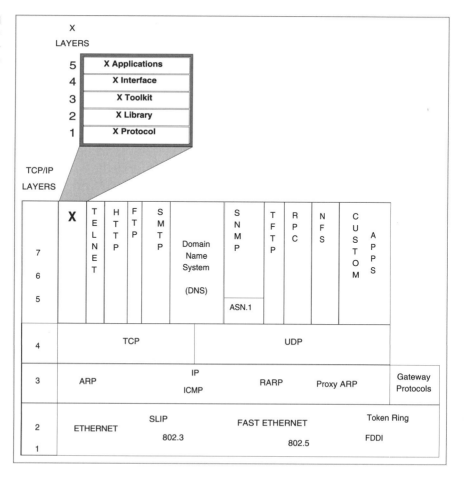

TCP/IP has been refined and been through many changes since 1975. It is unlike IBM's SNA in the sense that no particular corporation or entity charts its course and maintains proprietary aspects of it. TCP/IP is a prime example of a de facto network.

Even though TCP/IP has been funded by the US government at different times, its basic direction has come from citizens. TCP/IP is a protocol suite, a collection of protocols. The protocols have been the contributions and enhancements of individuals and corporations alike. Granted an overseeing body does provide guidance and maintain order, the protocols themselves that make TCP/IP what it is are not *owned* by any one body. This is commonly considered public domain.

As with OSI, TCP/IP is implemented by corporations who chose to make it available to prospective customers. If no other fuel had been added to the growth of TCP/IP, the mandate of the US government in 1983 was enough motivation to get many vendors interested to the point of making that protocol available to government and ancillary agencies.

TCP/IP is considered a client/server protocol. This terminology comes from the fact that two of the most popular applications in the TCP/IP protocol suite are client/server based. Clients initiate something; servers serve the requests of clients. In a sense, this concept is similar to the peer concept in APPN and peer capabilities in SNA.

TCP/IP is unique in one sense; it has as a part of the protocol specification a windowing system. Another interesting characteristic of TCP/IP, and the windowing system, is their hardware and software independence. This means TCP/IP can operate on practically any vendor equipment; exceptions exist, but for the most part this is the case. Another aspect of TCP/IP is that it does not have to be implemented in a full protocol suite; pieces of it can be implemented.

NetWare

The NetWare protocol is the product of the Novell Corporation. It began offering print and file services and has evolved into a full network protocol now at version four. NetWare has proliferated for multiple reasons. First, it operates on PCs and the Novell corporation has kept upgrading the product to be as robust as possible. Consider Figure 2.20.

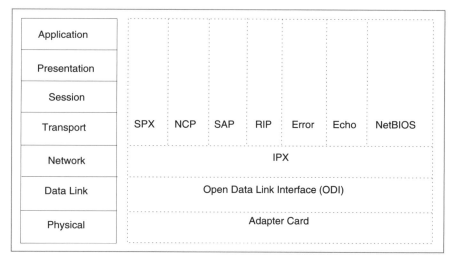

Second, Novell has ported NetWare to some UNIX operating platforms. This is significant because of the prevalence of UNIX throughout the marketplace. A third reason for NetWare's popularity is its user-friendliness. It operates as a peer environment which makes some parts of the installation easier to implement.

Another aspect of NetWare that keeps it in the circle of popularity is the protocol support it provides. For example, it supports FDDI, token ring, and Ethernet as data-link protocols. It also supports connectivity into IBM's AS/400 series. Additionally, Novell supports NetWare TCP/IP on a NetWare file server with services such as IP routing, tunneling, and SNMP.

Beyond this, NetWare supports IBM's RISC/6000 AIX operating system as well as OS/2. IBM included the NetWare functionality in the blueprint introduced in Spring 1992. Even in NetWare's early years it was broad in scope. NetWare version 2.01 had support for Digital Equipment's VAX operating system.

NetWare is different from the other protocols mentioned because its original design intent was different. However, today it has evolved into a competitive upper-layer network protocol.

It has grown in breadth to support large networks and a diverse mix of operating systems.

Digital Network Architecture

The Digital Equipment Corporation is completing the transition from the DNA phase IV method of networking to what their documentation calls, "DECnet/OSI for OpenVMS." This is Digital Equipment's implementation of OpenVMS that includes:

- Support for OSI communication specifications
- Digital Network Architecture (DNA) Phase V that is backward-compatible with Phase IV
- Standards provided by the CCITT
- Standards provided by the IEEE.

According to Digital Equipment documentation, this phase of their network offering supports more systems than did previous versions of DNA, provides distributed management, and maintains a multi-vendor network support environment.

Digital Equipment's DNA network architecture is not new. Consider Figure 2.21.

FIGURE 2.21
DECnet Layers

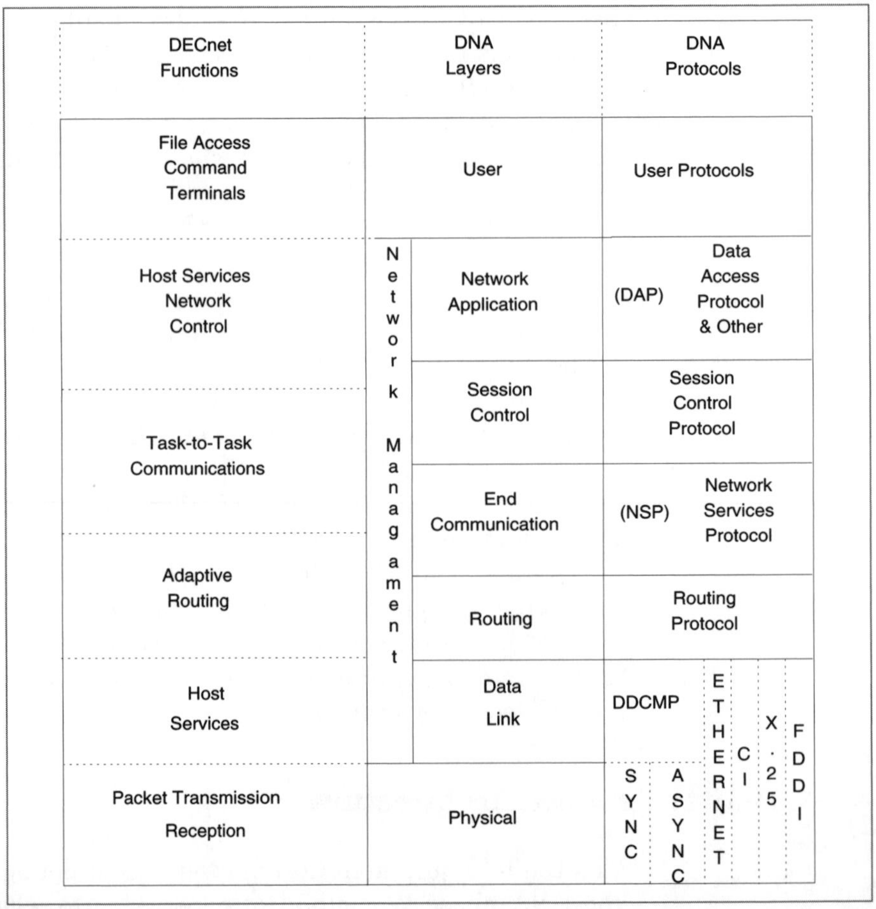

DECnet Functions	DNA Layers		DNA Protocols					
File Access Command Terminals	User		User Protocols					
Host Services Network Control	N e t w o r k	Network Application	(DAP)	Data Access Protocol & Other				
Task-to-Task Communications	M a n a g a m e n t	Session Control	Session Control Protocol					
		End Communication	(NSP)	Network Services Protocol				
Adaptive Routing		Routing	Routing Protocol					
Host Services		Data Link	DDCMP		E T H E R N E T	C I	X . 2 5	F D D I
Packet Transmission Reception		Physical	S Y N C	A S Y N C				

According to Digital Equipment documentation (DECnet/OSA for OpenVMS *Introduction and Planning* part number AA-PNHTB-TE), the first phase of DNA was introduced in 1976. Since then Digital has revised it and made enhancements to bring it to phase V. Some call DNA phase V, DECnet/OSI. But, whatever name may be attached, it is clear that the structure of Digital's network offering supports multiple protocols and is open to standards not previously available.

From a practical standpoint, Digital has managed to provide support for FTAM and CCR, Virtual Terminal support, and OSI application support through the VAX OSAK. Multiple transport layer protocols are supported, along with OSI network-layer-addressing support. At the data-link layer, Digital's DECnet/OSI for Open VMS supports: Ethernet, HDLC, FDDI, and X.25, among others. At the physical layer, the appropriate drivers are available to support a variety of interfaces. From a network management standpoint, DECnet/OSI for OpenVMS supports what Digital calls Enterprise Management Architecture (EMA).

The EMA defines a way to manage heterogeneous networking environments with distributed computing. This approach offers wide support for large enterprise environments.

Another feature of DECnet/OSI for OpenVMS is its scalar capabilities. It can meet the needs of small operations, or it can accommodate mission-critical data centers that require large amounts of processing power and versatility.

Windows NT

The physical architecture of NT is its separate components: workstation and server. Though they share characteristics, they operate independently.

The NT workstation is basically a standalone operating system. It does not require NT server to operate. It can function in different modes to support a variety of software applications. NT workstation does come with the networking component. It can easily be configured to operate in a networked environment.

NT server is software capable of supporting a variety of workstations in a networked environment. The architecture of NT is robust in design. Consider Figure 2.22.

Generally speaking, NT is capable of supporting a significant amount of resources. Some liken it to UNIX with a friendly interface. Windows NT architecture is considered modular because it contains multiple components.

FIGURE 2.22
Windows NT
Architecture

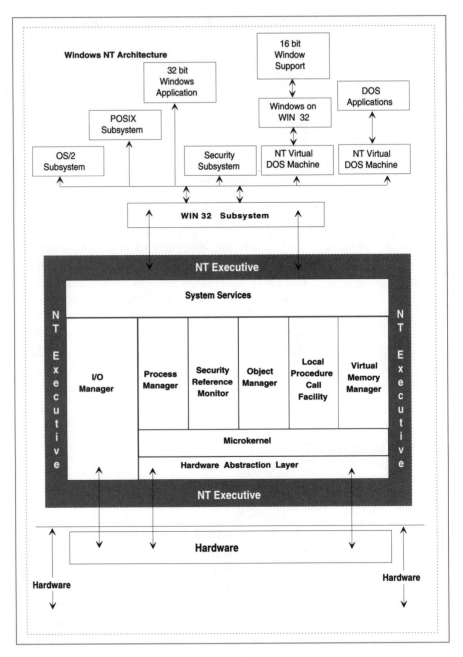

FIGURE 2.22
Windows NT
Architecture

Summary

Protocols are the operational nature of networks. Data, video, voice, and hybrid networks all use protocols. Most networks can be divided into upper- and lower-layer protocols. Layers one and two in networks are the functional backbone of a network. These two layers provide the infrastructure where upper-layer protocols operate and applications function to make communication possible between end users (programs or humans).

Lower-layer protocols can be found in all networks. Even if we argue that no lower-layer protocol exists, that in fact would be the protocol in use. Logic dictates that the absence of anything is the presence of something. Upper-layer protocols are more common in conversations among professionals. However, some lower-layer protocols have come to popularity because of much advertising.

The information presented in this chapter is intended to provide the reader with a highlighted view of each topic. It is not intended to be a substitute for other, more detailed information. It is however intended to lay some foundation required before further avenues are explored.

CHAPTER 3

How to Lay the Network Foundation

Well-designed networks begin with a "blank marker board." Few, if any, preconceived ideas dominate. Let the reader understand this: well-designed networks are not driven by CFOs, CIOs, CEOs, or anybody else with a potential ax to grind. A well-designed network has input from all aspects of an organization. One or a few people will have the ultimate design decisions, but the fact is that a network is an entity's lifeblood. If it is going to be used by engineering, product support, marketing, sales, manufacturing and others it should include knowledgeable, constructive input during the design phase. If this is not done, then a certain degree of pain will inevitably result. One final thought:

before an outside source is allowed come in and "tell you what you need," do your homework. There is nothing inherently wrong with having an outside source as a guide through the design and implementation aspects of the network; however, odds are that there are personnel inside your organization who know your business better than anybody on the outside ever will; exploit that talent. Blend the resources already available and with outside input/guidance.

Initial Planning

During the initial phase of network design the following questions should be asked and answered:

- Who
- What
- Where
- When
- Why
- How
- How Much
- How Long
- The Comprehensive Approach.

This may seem elementary but it is the elementary things with which people generally have the most difficulty. They may be overlooked because so many people take the fundamentals for granted. Let us examine these briefly and see the impact they have on network design.

Who

"Who" applies across the board. Who will plan, install, maintain, troubleshoot, and work with the network from every angle? It is important at least to pencil in a title for the person on whom the responsibility will fall. Who is going to be responsible for seeing the network from marker board to completion? Some person should be assigned this single task. That person may not understand all there is to know about the network, but at least there is a single point of contact. This person should not be the CFO. Finance departments are no more or less important than customer support; they simply serve a required purpose for the entity to operate effectively.

Who is going to be involved in the logical and physical design of the network? Who will be responsible for procurement of all the equipment? Who will be responsible for receiving the equipment? Who will be responsible for maintaining a vendor/resource contact list? Who is responsible for logistics if moving equipment from place-to-place within an entity is required?

This list of questions is a brief starting point. Your list may include many more "whos" and should cover all the bases; it may well be in a state of flux during the entire network design and implementation process. The "whos" should meet regularly to exchange information; things may work better if they do.

What

The "what" question applies to every feasible part of the network. What are the components to be used? What are the components to do? What are going to be the strategic plans if any particular piece of equipment does not arrive on time, arrives broken, and so forth? What is the plan to be designed? What are the phases of the network design? What are the phases of network implementation? What are the phases of network maintenance? What are the criteria for milestones of accomplishment in the installation phase of the network? What is the contingency plan? What is the requirement to support the number of users on the network? What is the purpose of the network? Again, the list may include many more "whats" than this, but these are basic considerations.

Where

Location is important. Most real estate agents will tell you the single most important thing about real estate is: "location, location, location." So it is with a network. Where is the network going to be installed? Where is each piece of equipment going to reside? Where are the users? Where is the place for storage once the equipment arrives but prior to installation? Where are all the people located who will participate in the network design and implementation, and in maintenance of the network? Where will all the equipment come from? Where will network management occur? As with the previous questions, so here: your list may well include additional "wheres."

When

Timing in anything is very important. Timing in network design, implementation, and maintenance is equally crucial. Here are some common timing questions that should be answered as soon as possible.

When is network design phase scheduled to begin? When will update meetings occur to brief concerned parties? When will the milestones for network implementation/installation be reached? When will each phase of network design commence? When will testing occur on each piece of equipment planned to be implemented? When is the scheduled time for completion? When will certain procedures be invoked if initial plans are not met?

This list of "whens" is a beginning point; expand upon it to embrace your needs and your network.

Why

Why is the network being built to begin with? Why are the people involved with it involved with it? Why are particular vendors selected; what criteria were used to select the vendors? Your list of "whys" could be much longer but should include these important questions.

How

This question gets primarily into logistics. For example, how is the equipment going to be received and stored until the installation phase commences? This may seem more of a question of where but it is not. How equipment is stored addresses topics such as temperature, humidity, security, and related topics. The "how" and "where" tend to overlap, but the "how" focuses more upon the step-by-step plan of action to get certain tasks complete.

Unfortunately, the "how" is not always planned for in advance and a shipping/receiving department is inundated with incoming equipment to the point where daily operations are paralyzed. Another twist on the question "how" focuses more on internal operations. For example, assume a company with multiple worldwide locations. A network is being built to connect multiple facilities; the question of "how" certain pieces of equipment will get from one location to another becomes important. In fact, this could be a "show-stopper" for some companies. It has happened that equipment is obtained, a network is being built, and equipment arrives in one location but is needed elsewhere. The ultimate question emerges: "How is this going to get there?" When this scenario arises problems usually ensue. Avert this and other problems by addressing this question as soon as possible.

How Much

Costs are important. Unfortunately, in many cases the costs are not weighed fairly and balanced in proportion. For example, executives, management at all levels, and even technical people can be "penny wise and pound foolish." Educated executives can say "less is more." Any reasonable human being knows this is not true in the broadest sense. This type of thinking has emerged from numerous roots, one of which is ignorance. The question for people who think less is more: "If you think less is more, then cut your pay in half and send it to me, or just take whatever you consider 'too much' and send it to me, then we'll see what you really think."

"How much" is a question that should be asked in at least a three-fold context. First, "how much" should be examined in light of the overall network with regard, among other things, to expected life span, products, services offered via the network, scope and capability of the network. Second, "how much" should be asked in light of what is being paid for given products and/or services compared to comparable products and/or services. Third, "how much" should be asked in regard to the estimated *payback* the network will provide.

Do not underestimate the financial part of your network. At the same time, do not expect to get something for nothing. Throwing money at a problem is not wise either. Somewhere along the way during the planning phase of the network, all parties involved should provide reasonable input and be prepared to discuss this in an open civil way for the betterment of the company at large.

How Long

This question of "how long" is broad. It encompasses aspects during the beginning of network design and the implementation phase, and also the length of expected life for the network and its services. "How long" can be directed to the group of people who will perform actual installation of equipment as well as to those who will bring the network into alpha and beta phases.

The question of "how long" should be applied to the entire network design and implementation plan. It should also be directed toward backup plans, in case of unforeseen difficulties that can arise. The flipside of the notion "how long" applies to a direct question of "survival;" "how long" can something survive in a worst-case scenario?

The "how long" question is general in nature and supposed to be a principle to use to get thoughts into order. Work exerted on the front end of network planning can help avert many possible problems later in the network implementation.

The Comprehensive Approach

The idea of a comprehensive approach is to provide a well-rounded understanding of the network. Included in this is everything from the purpose of the network to the method by which equipment will arrive at a facility. The notion of this approach includes understanding the "big" picture. Once this is in focus it is much easier to zero in on isolated segments and understand them in context.

Some networks have been implemented piecemeal. The result revealed over time is multiple headaches. It is far better to take the comprehensive view and design a network the best possible way from that perspective. One thing is sure, if this method is used many problems can be avoided at the beginning. A lot of the surprise is removed from the entire network implementation and use. The fundamental idea behind networks is to provide a vehicle to access data and to serve people. This thought alone tends to point one toward a comprehensive view of a network from the outset of planning.

Network Need Analysis

The best place to start with need analysis is to determine what the company/entity does. There should be fundamental tenets on which the company/entity is based; these should become the driving forces for a network. Other overall needs can also emerge. E-mail, file transfer, data services, and other needs may be reasons for a network. These comprehensive or overall needs may be dissected departmentally and reveal additional needs.

For example, say the entity being worked on has sales, customer service, shipping/receiving, and internal technical support departments. Each of these departments could have unique needs. All of them may need to exchange e-mail and certain files, but each department may have inter-departmental needs.

Consider the shipping department. Any given shipping/receiving department may be sizable. Numerous employees may be required to operate it adequately. It may include a large amount of floor space, hence numerous offices within the department. In such example, a departmental database may be needed to track incoming and outgoing packages. This information may not be needed by any other department except on an as-needed basis. Consequently, this example might justify a subnet, or a departmental network isolated from the rest of the entity.

On the other hand, the shipping/receiving department requires interaction with all the entity's staff. This means access to the corporate network is required. A two-fold need therefore exists. This example alone may dictate detailed planning and forethought adequately to meet the needs of an existing shipping/receiving department and anticipate its needs in the future.

This type of approach to your entity's size, structure, and requirements should play a large role in the design of your network. A well-designed network will include this level of thought in the preliminary stages of network design. This aspect of network planning is based more upon "needs" by department. It should be part of the overall planning process.

Additional considerations for network planning include evaluation of the following needs:

- Internal
- External
- Geographic.

Internal

Many times a network's primary purpose is to serve the needs inside a company. Understanding the internal structure of the operation is important. It may shed different light on network requirements other than departmental ones. This approach includes a through examination of an entity's internal needs and a detailed list of current technology in place, its use, and its anticipated use with addition of a network.

As mentioned previously, each company/entity, regardless of size, has internal needs. Multiple departments generally exist. This is not an all-inclusive list, but it is a place to begin. An examination of internal needs may reveal what departments exist today and those planned in the future.

Internal needs may be subtle, but take time to examine the inner workings of the company. If technology is involved, then engineering, support, and sales may all need access to varying depths of information about the product or services the company offers. What does this mean for a network? At a minimum it means people in these departments will need to be able to access, and most likely exchange, information. The information may include graphics, internal reports, external feedback from potential or existing customers, and possibly a databank of information.

Other internal information is most likely required for a given company to maintain some type order. For example, online calendars are handy. This information is considered generally public within the company and may well be needed by shipping/receiving. For example, if Ms. Hoover is on vacation and receives multiple packages, the receiving department could take advantage of an online calendar to know she is out of the office, and whether or not any special instructions exist regarding her absence.

Online calendars also help in scheduling meetings. Fewer conference rooms might be possible for a company if everyone in the company *knows* when a meeting is going to occur and what facility will be used to accommodate it. Parallel to this calendaring idea is the needs that may exist in the conference room which affect the network. For example, are telephone services or data network services needed in the conference room? If so, how will these services be provided? Will a cabling ability exist for those with portable computers to connect? What is the capacity of connections that can be made in the conference room at any given time? These and similar questions factor into the equation of network design. If these points are overlooked a crew may have to be hired to tear out part of wall to make something available that should have been available in the first place.

Many other *types* of information may need to be exchanged within a company. Regardless what they are, planning should be done as far into the future as possible when setting up the network design equation. Nobody can plan with 100% ability to be on target five to ten years ahead, but it is possible to plan for worst-case and best-case scenarios. Do this, and work with data communication gear will be less painful.

External

Needs external to the company will also affect the network. The way customers interact with the company is important. If there is a need for them to access certain information, to download files, or read certain information available to the public, then this should be factored into the network design equation.

Awareness of customer interaction with the company should include understanding of the number of customers (current and planned) who will need this interactive ability. Circumstances may well justify an entirely separate network to meet the needs of the customer base. If so, then how this network will or will not interact with the network being designed is important.

Geographic

Geographics is an important category of network planning. Consider Figure 3.1.

FIGURE 3.1
Locally Operated Network in Fort Worth, TX

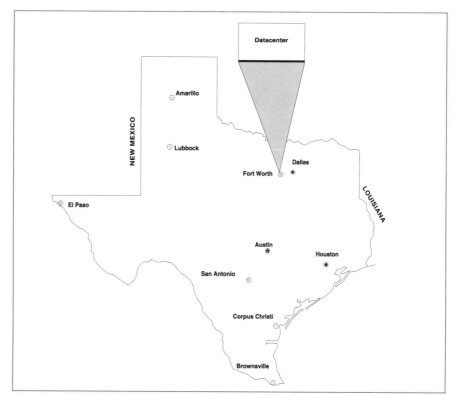

This illustration shows a single data center network location in one facility in Fort Worth, TX. This type of network is relatively straightforward in regard to network planning. Only one location exists, users of the network reside in the same physical plant as the network. Consider Figure 3.2.

FIGURE 3.2
San Francisco and
Atlanta Networks

Figure 3.2 shows an entity with facilities in San Francisco and Atlanta. This scenario requires that a network be more complex designed and installed because of different time zones, possibly different long distance service providers, and matters like personnel support after installation, logistics of equipment arrival, and coordination of installation. Other matters typically arise when a network is being installed in multiple locations where two or more time zones are involved.

Still another variation on geographic considerations is illustrated in Figure 3.3.

This illustration is next in the level of complexity for network planning and installation. It shows a multinational network and poses myriad considerations. For example, time zone differences are extreme and make communication a challenge. Each country represented has a different telephone network infrastructure. International laws apply to integration of all these networks. Even network components procured for implementation must be electrically compatible with the different electrical infrastructures. Adequate network management requires consideration from numerous angles. Matters such as bandwidth network availability, and other considerations are more complex because of the vast geographical distances between locations. These and other considerations should be taken into account when planning for this type of global network.

FIGURE 3.3
Multinational
Networks

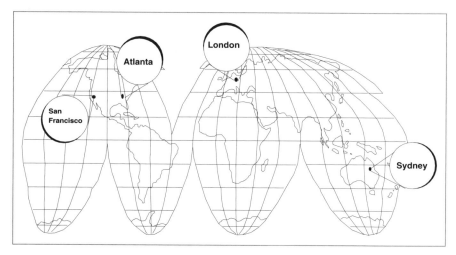

Physical Considerations

This section cannot be understated. This is probably the most important chapter in the entire book. When network design commences, it should first be done on paper. If a problem cannot be solved on the marker board (or paper) it cannot be fixed in reality. It is easier to work through painstaking areas on marker board than with experience.

Consider the physical part of network design. Before approaching to the technical part, we must address fundamentals.

Assume the needs of the company and customers have been addressed on paper. Ordering can begin. In this case assume the physical location is the place where the network will be built. The following should be a minimum checklist to use:

1. Is there enough free space so that when equipment begins to arrive it will not impede day-to-day operations?
2. Will any of the equipment arrive on pallets? If multiple pallets of equipment arrive, where will they be put initially to unload, and then where will they be stored until the equipment is used?
3. Are stairs used to access where the equipment is stored? If so, how many?
4. Can a forklift enter the location to unload and load equipment?

5. What is the estimated weight the floor can sustain per square foot?

6. How wide are the doors?

7. Are the hand-trucks used in loading/unloading capable of sustaining the weight of new equipment if it is shipped so hand-trucks are required?

8. Are elevators required to get to a location where the equipment will be stored? How accessible are they? Will using these elevators affect daily operations of your company or another company.

9. Will the location where the equipment is stored until implementation be secure?

10. Does the addition of the new equipment cause any code infringement with fire, police, or any other city, county, state, or federal government entity?

11. If any of the equipment is shipped on pallets or in large boxes, how do you plan to dispose of them?

12. Is any of the equipment sensitive to any environmental conditions in your location such as heat, cooling, humidity, etc.? Have you verified this with the vendor who manufactured the equipment?

13. Do you have a single point of contact with the company shipping equipment to you.

At a minimum these questions should have clear definable answers before the go-ahead is given to receive the first shipment of equipment. The particular location may require that additional questions be posed and answered. Think through the matter of physical location. It might even be helpful for someone who knows the physical plant well enough to go through this phase with you. Somebody should take responsibility for this task of physical premise evaluation/preparation; if this is not addressed prior to receipt of equipment, problems could arise.

Electrical Considerations

The importance of this section cannot be emphasized enough. It is imperative that the appropriate person know the electrical capability of the physical location. Once it is determined what equipment will be deployed, then ascertain the specifications for each piece of equipment. When the logical network illustration is created, this information will be critical.

There may be the idea that because there are plenty electrical outlets no additional sources will be needed. Here is where the problem begins. Most offices have multiple electrical outlets tied into one circuit breaker. A given room may have six outlets. Assume three are being used by a computer, light, and radio. To assume it would be possible to add a midsize photocopier to this room and plug it into an available wall outlet is at the least misguided. Even the addition of two laser printers could easily overload a single circuit breaker.

Network design and electrical considerations should begin with determining all pieces of equipment that require electricity. List all these pieces on paper. Next, obtain from the manufacturer the amount of watts, amps, and volts the devices will consume upon power-up and in idle state.

Once this information about all devices is available, next determine how power conditioning will be included in the equation. Forthcoming chapters explain the network designed and used as an example in this text. This network used Liebert power protection equipment. Once electrical information was obtained, details on the Liebert equipment were needed. Just because power protection equipment has multiple outlets on it does not mean each one can be filled and power protected. In the case of Liebert equipment, the specifications of the equipment were adhered to during the installation phase of the network. In order for power protection equipment to operate the way it was designed, one must use it the way the manufacturer designed it.

In the US, many offices have 20-amp circuit breakers for electrical outlets. Exceptions abound, but this is the general rule. Do not exceed 70 to 80% of the circuit breaker ability. If a given room has four outlets tied into one 20 amp breaker and none of these outlets is currently in use, then add equipment that will not exceed 15 amps. Why? Because it is safe. Odds are when you design your network, install equipment into this hypothetical office, and do not exceed 70 to 80% of a circuit breaker, someone will come along behind you in a few weeks or months and add a few additional items that will use the remaining percentage of the circuit ability.

If no planning goes into the electrical part of the location where the network will be installed there will be extra work. Do not assume a network can be superimposed onto an existing site without coping with the electrical factor.

Some companies have "computer" rooms where the bulk of computing/network equipment resides. These rooms are usually preplanned to handle computing/networking equipment. However, if there is no such room or designated area, then you must start from scratch. The best place to begin is to contact the facilities manager, who can put you in touch with electricians who can answer questions or assist in the planning phase.

The network designed, built and explained in later chapters has two laser printers. This is a good example because it is typical of many scenarios; it could even be typical of what you intend to implement. Both laser printers are IBM. Both have their power consumption stated explicitly on the appropriate plate as defined by national and international requirements. Additionally, both have power requirements stated clearly in the documentation shipped with the printers.

What if these two printers absorb 12.5 to 13.5 amps when powered-up simultaneously? Now assume some additional equipment to be added to this outlet. If this equipment were plugged into the place where the network printers are connected would these additions work without overloading a circuit breaker? This level of detail needs to be addressed and factored into the network design equation.

While plans were formulated for the network, Tektronix test instruments were used to obtain information on existing power supplied to the facility. Consider Figure 3.4.

FIGURE 3.4
Line Voltage
Information

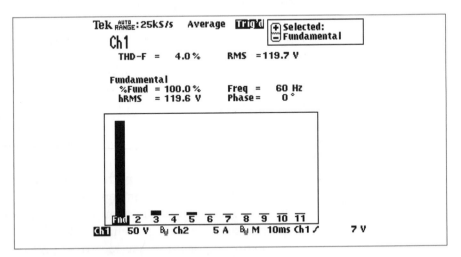

Figure 3.4 shows a line reading using channel one of the Tekronix THS720P scope. More information about this tool is presented later in this book. However, Figure 3.4 reveals a line voltage of 119.7 VAC. This is a *random* line voltage reading. It is a good practice to obtain and maintain preliminary readings prior to installation of any new

network equipment. As this figure indicates, the frequency is 60 cycles. The bar graph shows the harmonics from the fundamental through the eleventh.

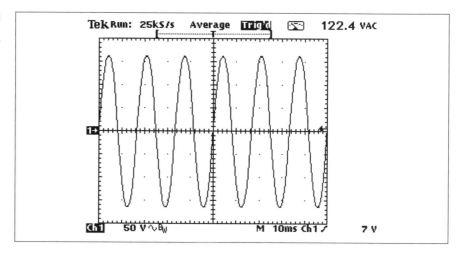

FIGURE 3.5
Sine Wave of
Line Voltage

Figure 3.5 shows a sine wave reading of the line voltage prior to any network equipment installation. Notice the voltage reading in the upper right corner of the graph indicates 122.4 VAC.

Figure 3.6 is another reading from the same line as the previous readings.

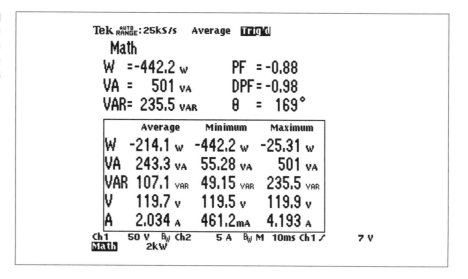

FIGURE 3.6
Math Calculations
of Voltage
and Current

This reading is a mathematical analysis of the AC signal. Later chapters have more discussions of the interpretation of readings like this. For the time being, realize this information is helpful in the preplanning stages of the network design implementation.

Figure 3.7 shows additional information obtained about the voltage supplying the facility where the network explained later in this book is installed.

FIGURE 3.7
Harmonic
Readings

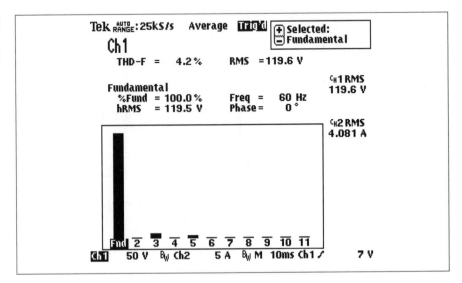

Figure 3.7 shows the harmonics from the fundamental through the eleventh. Consider Figure 3.8.

FIGURE 3.8
Harmonic
Readings from
2nd Through
22nd

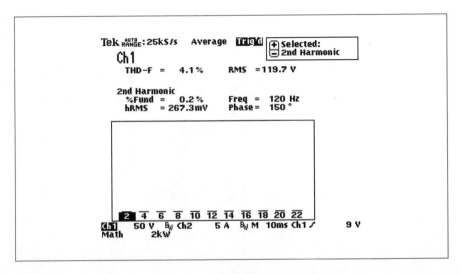

Figure 3.8 shows harmonic readings of even harmonics from the second through the twenty-second. Again, the important thing to understand here is that this level of information is obtainable by instruments like the Tektronix THS720P oscilloscope and digital multimeter.

Figure 3.9 shows a reading from the input of channel one and channel two. One displays the AC signal, the other shows the amperage draw on this particular line at this point in time.

FIGURE 3.9
Channel 1 and
Channel 2
Readings

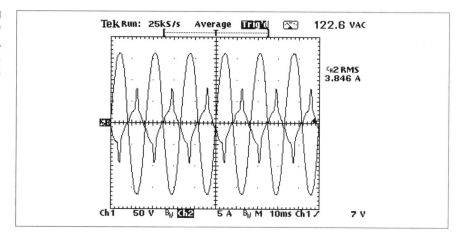

Another aspect of electrical consideration has to do with whether or not a raised floor will be used. In the network described later in this book specific electrical equipment was chosen and implemented to meet electrical needs.

Preliminary design regarding the electrical needs led me to explore the types of fixtures and fittings. Pass & Seymour Legrand (hereafter Pass & Seymour) fixtures were selected to meet these needs. Components examined at a wholesale supplier indicated Pass & Seymour had superior products. A partial list of Pass & Seymour equipment selected for use in the design of this network includes:

- Pin & Sleeve connectors
- Turnlock® R Plugs
- Turnlock® R Receptacles
- Turnlock® R Flanged Outlets
- Turnlock® R Connectors
- Specification Grade AC Switches
- Straight Blade Duplex Receptacles (Extra Heavy Duty).

A number of reasons were considered in selecting Pass & Seymour. First and foremost was the quality. Pass & Seymour has engineered their components to be of the highest quality.

Wherever electrical connections are made an electrical transfer is made. This means the connection is the weakest link in the electrical chain. Pass & Seymour has designed their Turnlock® receptacles to include:

- A single-piece, solid brass mounting strap
- One piece, high-grade brass contacts
- Impact-resistant nylon face and body
- A clear NEMA marking on the face.

The network I designed included a raised floor as well as power distribution from a single source, under the floor. To ensure safety, the Pass & Seymour Pin & Sleeve connectors were used as the connecting points for power distribution cables because they are water resistant, non-conducting, capable of sustaining large amounts of weight, and very durable. This level of preliminary design paid off. The result is a solid electrical infrastructure, suited to last for many years.

Heating, Ventilation & Air Conditioning (HVAC)

HVAC needs should be included in the design equation. The location will determine the degree this should be explored. If a data center will have large systems, storage silos, printers, and other devices, special HVAC construction may be required.

If rack cabinets with equipment are needed for your network, consider Figure 3.10.

Figure 3.10 shows Great Lake cabinets with air blowers in the bottom and nine fans in the fan tray, inside near the top. This level of airflow is required because of the temperatures reached in the cabinet.

Most equipment installed today has circulation requirements. It is a mistake to overlook this when designing a network. For example, the IBM Netfinity Server selected for in this network specifies how much space should be between it and other objects. The same is true for printers, monitors, and other devices.

One way of obtaining valid temperature readings is via a probe.

FIGURE 3.10
Cabinet Cooling
and Ventilation

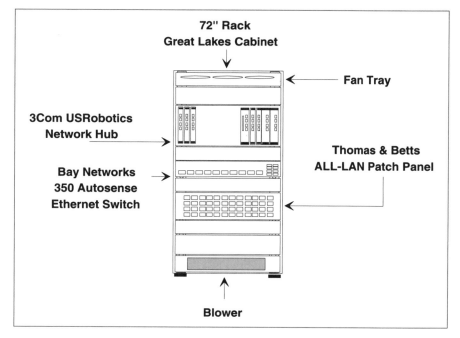

FIGURE 3.10
Cabinet Cooling
and Ventilation

Figure 3.11 shows a temperature of 74.0° F. Equipment for constant monitoring of temperature readings is vital for your facility.

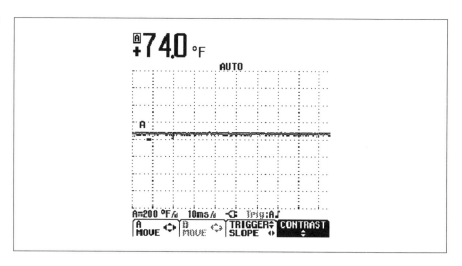

FIGURE 3.11
Datacenter Room
Temperature

HVAC requirements go beyond what is mentioned here. One person highly skilled in HVAC should participate in the network design project.

The Human Factor

Networks don't get built or maintained without people. Some time back there was a general personnel cutback in the data communication/telecommunication industry.

The idea that money is more important than people is unfortunate for many companies. There have been companies cash "rich" and brain poor when it came to technical people. Ironically, the past few years have dealt management of many companies a blow in this regard.

Networks are either planned for or they are not. In the planning of a network one must factor into the equation the human factor. If one does not, then the *defaults* of "life" will override and force a decision. It takes more than good people with technical skills to design a network. It also takes representatives from every aspect of a company which will use the network to participate in the planning of it. Not too long ago there was a move to get networks and data centers to operate in "lights out" mode...meaning as few of people as possible in operations. Some data centers went from "lights-out" operation to *everything-out* operation! The more advanced the networks and technology deployed the more brains it takes to keep them running.

Education is not optional, neither are people when it comes to network design and maintenance. If you are the one responsible for network design, please confer with the appropriate people and consider the skill sets required to keep the network operational. At least estimates of reality will be documented on paper; at most this phase of planning could get the right attention and make life easier for many as network implementation begins.

There should not be an army of people for the sake of having people. But there has yet to be any technology that created itself, maintained itself, and phased growth into itself. It is foolish to buy the best equipment available in the open market today and not pay to get reasonable technical skill, *and keep it*, to maintain the equipment; it does not matter what a *business plan* says about this.

Another aspect of the human factor is education. In the late 1980s Derek Bok, the dean of Harvard Law School was on the cover of *Time* magazine. The article quoted him as saying: "If you think education is expensive, try ignorance."

Go ahead and factor into the network equation continuing education across the board for all technical people who will be involved in the network.

Evolution

The network you are about to design, or are in the process of designing, will evolve. Sooner or later someone will make a suggestion that this or that be added to the network, and it probably will be. As the network evolves be sure to document additions and changes to the existing architectural layout.

More than likely as time goes by people will leave the company, for a variety of reasons, health-related, death, accident, promotion, transfer or otherwise. Try to plan for this as best you can. This is part of the evolution the network will experience.

Most networks tend to reflect the personalities of those who designed and worked with them, directly and indirectly. As the network changes, do not lose sight of the original design intent. This is critical. I have seen many arguments for this or against that in a network's operation that are squashed with the questions: "What was the original design intent of the network? Is it meeting that intent?" Some people feel about a network: "If it is not doing this or that *it is not right.*" These concerns can often be resolved when people realize their lack of forethought.

Recently I was in a location, with about a half dozen professionals designing a network. I came onto the scene a little late. Many aspects of the network had been penciled in on paper.

As I was being briefed about the network, its purpose, the size, and plan for implementation, I read through notes of what had been done so far. The network was large. It was fairly costly. As I examined the preliminary design I could not believe it. My facial expression prompted someone to ask: "What is the matter? Is there something that needs changing?"

I explained: "This network design is going to break. It is not a matter of *IF*, it is merely a matter of *WHEN*." One could have heard a pin drop. My point is: a group of people had made a preliminary design of a network around a single point of failure. This type of thinking was either intentional or those designers should be doing something other than designing networks.

During your design factor in evolution. Do not even think about designing a network that has a single point of failure. If that is the only way a design can be achieved, then design in redundancy—an alternative architecture (with real equipment) that will kick in *when* the first fails.

Technical Factors

During the penciling phase of network design, include a detailed examination of the following. Your actual checklist may vary, but these should be the minimum factors to look into; the impact of these areas on the network should be considered.

1. Telephone line abilities, or lack thereof
2. Heat considerations once all equipment is in place
3. Cooling considerations once all equipment is in place
4. Backup contingencies for electrical, telephone, and operations equipment
5. Electromaganetic field interference
6. Radio Frequency interference
7. Cable lengths (maximum for AC, DC, voice, and data)
8. Cable location
9. Service accessibility for all equipment
10. Hot site location for back up operational plans, architectural design plans, emergency procedures, etc.
11. Identified chain of command (technical people) to execute plans in case of emergency
12. Labelling of cables: data, voice, video, AV, DC, etc.
13. Checklist for testing *ALL* cables prior to use with anything—especially if they are new
14. Planing for ten worst-case technical scenarios with a detailed action plan ready to implement for any variation of need
15. Knowledge of security both physical and logical
16. Technical needs categorized into critical, urgent, and as-soon-as possible; most things are not urgent.

Your site may require a variation on this list, but the list has been used in many places with networks of all sizes.

Summary

This chapter has presented basic information for orientation in the preliminary stages of network design. The examples of my experience are real. The chapter should encourage you to begin thinking along the lines presented here.

Network design includes electrical considerations, cooling, heating, weight factors, height, width, storage, and knowing component functions. Subsequent chapters present additional information that goes hand-in-hand with this one. This book as a whole will provide the foundation you need to begin a solid network design.

CHAPTER 4

Electrical Consideration and Power Conditioning

The components that comprise networks require electrical Basic topics to be considered are electrical principles and facts, sample electrical readings and how to interpret them. Power conditioning will also be discussed.

If you are in an office environment consider that if all the electrical circuits are broken, you can't print, compute, or use anything that relies on electrical power. Battery driven or solar powered objects notwithstanding, without doubt the core of any business relies on electricity for daily operations. Electricity is taken for granted for the most part but it is not a source available worldwide. It is man-made in the way it is used in the business community, but technically it does exist in nature as a fundamental characteristic of the universe.

Electrical Terminology

If you are new to electricity, use caution at every turn when you work any electrical device, and particularly as you apply the topics presented here.

To understand and work with electricity understanding of terminology and concepts is required. Once some terms and concepts are grasped then application of knowledge can be realized. Consider the following list of important electrical terms.

Alternating Current (AC)	An electric current that is continually varying in value and reversing its direction of flow at regular intervals, usually in a sinusoidal manner. Each repetition from zero to a maximum in one direction and then to a maximum in the other direction and back to zero, is called a cycle.
AC Frequency	This is the speed at which an AC voltage or current wave form repeats itself. Frequency is measured in hertz.
Amperage	The amount of current in amperes.
Ampere	A practical unit of electrical current. Once ampere of current is 6.24×10^{18} electrons passing one point in one second. It equals 1C/s. This is the result of 1 Volt across a resistance of 1 ohm.
Apparent Power	This is the product of current and voltage and is expressed as kVA. It is the real power (kW) divided by the power factor (PF).
Atom	This is smallest particle into which an element can be divided and still retain the chemical properties of that element.

continued on next page

Balanced Current	This refers to a current flowing in the two conductors of a balanced line so that, at every point along the line, they are equal in magnitude and opposite in direction.
Balanced Line	This is a transmission line that consists of two conductors which are capable of being operated so that the voltages of the two conductors at any transverse plane are equal in magnitude and opposite in polarity with respect to the ground. The currents in the two conductors are then equal in magnitude and opposite in direction.
Balanced Voltages	This refers to voltages that are equal in magnitude and opposite in polarity with respect to ground. They are also called push-pull voltages.
Brownout	Normally this is a voltage reduction initiated by a utility to counter excessive demand on its electric power generation and distribution system.
Conductor	This is material that easily serves as a conduit for electric current because it offers little electrical resistance. Examples of conductors are: tin, metals, salt water, aluminum, copper, gold, nickel and platinum.
Current	In electricity, this refers to the flow of electrons, or the movement thereof, through a conductive material. The flow of electrons or holes is measured in amperes (A), or in fractions of an ampere such as milliamperes (mA), micro amperes (uA), nanoamperes (nA), or picoamperes (pA). Current can be induced by the application of an electric field through a conductor or by changing the electric field through a conductor or by changing the electric field across a capacitor (which is known as displacement current).
Direct Current (DC)	An electric current that flows in one direction.
Electric Field	The region around an electrically charged body in which other charged bodies are acted on by an attracting or repelling force.
Electricity	A fundamental quantity realized in nature that consists of electrons and protons either at rest or in motion. Electricity at rest has an electric field which possesses potential energy and can exert force. Electricity in motion has the characteristics of an electric and magnetic field that possesses potential energy and can exert force.

continued on next page

Electron	This is an elementary atomic particle that carries the smallest negative electric charge. It is highly mobile and orbits the nucleus of an atom.
Frequency	This is the number of complete cycles per unit of time for a periodic quantity such as alternating current, sound waves, or radio waves. A frequency of 1 cycle per second is 1 hertz. This is represented by the letter f.
Harmonic	A sinusoidal component of a periodic wave, with a frequency that is an integral multiple of the fundamental frequency. The frequency of the second harmonic is twice that of the fundamental frequency or first harmonic. This is also called harmonic component and harmonic frequency.
Harmonic Analysis	This is any method for identifying and evaluating the harmonics that make up a complex form of voltage, current, or some other varying quantity.
Hertz	This is the SI unit of frequency, equal to 1 cycle per second.
Impedance	This is the total opposition offered by a component or circuit to the flow of an alternating or varying current. It is represented by the letter Z. Impedance is expressed in ohms, and is the combination of resistance and reactance.
Inductance	This is the property of a circuit or circuit element that opposes a change in current flow. Inductance causes current changes to lag behind voltage changes. Inductance is measured in henrys, millihenrys, and microhenrys and is represented by the letter L.
kilo	One thousand.
kVA	One thousand voltamperes. This is a term for rating devices. The number is derived by multiplying the output in amperes by its rate operating voltage.
Linear	This is a term used to refer to a relationship in which one function is directly proportional to another function providing a straight sloped line when plotted on a graph.
Magnetic Field	This is any space or region in which a magnetic force is exerted on moving electric charges. This field can be produced by a current-carrying coil or conductor, by a permanent magnet, or by the earth itself.

continued on next page

Non-Linear	Anything with this characteristic is not directly proportional to its complement.
Non-Linear Element	This refers to an element in which an increase in applied voltage does not produce a proportional increase in current.
Non-Linear Load	This is a load for which the relationship between voltage and current is not a linear function. Examples of non-linear loads could be fluorescent lighting or UPS systems. These loads cause abnormal heating and voltage distortion.
Ohm	This is the SI unit of resistance and impedance. The electrical resistance between two points of a conductor is when a constant of potential difference of 1 Volt applied to these points produces in the conductor a current of 1 amp; the conductor is not the seat of any electromotive force.
Period	This is the time required for one complete cycle of a regularly repeated series of events.
Photon	This is a quantum of electromagnetic radiation equal to Planck's constant multiplied by the frequency in hertz. Electromagnetic radiation includes photons of light, X-rays, gamma rays, or radio rays.
Power	This is the time rate of doing work or the speed in which work is done and represented by the letter P. This is measured in watts.
Power Factor	The term power factor refers to the extent that the voltage zero differs from the current zero. In AC circuits inductances and capacitances cause a point where the voltage wave passes through zero to differ from the point where the current wave passes through zero. One complete cycle is 360°; consequently, the difference between zero points (for example voltage and current) can be expressed in an angle. The power factor is the cosine of the angle between zero points and is expressed as a decimal fraction (.8 or 80%). The power factor is the ratio of kW and kVA. The kW equals the kVA x the power factor.
Proton	This is an elementary particle that has a positive charge equal in magnitude to the negative charge of the electron. The atomic number of an element indicates the number of protons in the nucleus of each atom of that element. The rest mass of a

continued on next page

	proton is 1.67×10^{24}g. or 1836.13 times that of an electron.
Reactance	This is the opposition to the flow of alternating current by pure inductance or capacitance in a circuit expressed in ohms. It is the component of impedance that is not due to resistance.
Resistance	This is the opposition that a device or material offers to the flow of direct current, measured in ohms, kiloohms, or megaohms. In AC circuits, resistance is the real component of impedance.
Root-Mean-Squared (RMS)	This is the square root of the average of the squares of a series of related values. It is the effective value of an alternating current, corresponding to the DC value that will produce the same heating effect. The RMS value is computed as the square root of the average of the squares of the instantaneous amplitude for one complete cycle. For a sine wave the RMS value is 0.707 times the peak value. Unless otherwise specified, alternating quantities are assumed to be the RMS values. Another name for this is the effective value. In simpler terms this is the effective value of voltage, current, and power when they are expressed as such.
SAG	This is an AC power-line undervoltage condition that lasts more than 1/60 of a second. A condition lasting longer than this is referred to as a brownout.
Sinusoidal	This refers to the varying in proportion to the sine of an angle or time function. An ordinary alternating current is considered sinusoidal.
Spike	This is a short duration transient whose amplitude considerably exceeds the average amplitude of the associated pulse or signal.
Surge	This is a long duration overvoltage or overcurrent condition.
Time	This measures the duration of an event. The fundamental unit of time is the second.
Transient	This is a sudden very brief spike of high voltage on a power line caused by lightning, electrostatic discharge, or power-line switching.
Unbalanced Line	This refers to a transmission line that conducts voltage on its two conductors that are not equal with respect to the ground.

continued on next page

Volt	This is the SI unit of voltage or potential difference; the difference in electrical potential between two points of a conducting wire carrying a constant current of 1 amp when the power dissipated between these points is equal to 1 watt.
Voltampere	This is the unit of apparent power in an AC circuit that contains reactance. Apparent power is equal to the voltage in volts multiplied by the current in amperes, without considering phase.
Watt	The watt is the unit of electric power. It gives rise in one second to the energy of one joule. In an AC circuit, the true power is effective volts multiplied by effective amperes, then multiplied by the circuit power factor.
Wave	This is a propagated disturbance whose intensity at any point in the medium is a function of time, and the intensity at a given instant is a function of the position of the point. A wave can be electric, electromagnetic, acoustic, or mechanical.

Practical Information

The information provided in this and future chapters will help with network planning.

Wire

Many type of wire exist. The focus of this section is electrical wire, specifically, wire sizes and types. Understanding electrical wire is easy. The smaller the number the bigger the wire and hence, the more voltage and current it can accommodate. For example, many types of common table lamps have a 14 to 18 gauge wire.

Wire is generally referred to by the Average Wire Gauge (AWG) number. The smaller the number the larger the wire.

A 26 gauge wire is very small, smaller than wire in most telephone cords that connect a handset to the base. Much of the 10BASE-T wire is between 20 and 24 gauge in size. Some extension cords that can be purchased in discount stores are 14 to 18 gauge. These are considered *general purpose*.

Most houses are wired with 12 gauge wire; some use 10 gauge. A 12 gauge wire for an extension cord would be considered adequate for many shop-type purposes. Many outdoor-use extension cords are 12 gauge.

Ten gauge wire is fairly heavy duty. Going up in capability and down in numeric order are 8, 6, 4, 2, and 0 gauge. Wire sizes less than 10 become increasingly large and can carry significant voltage and current. Remember, voltage and current are two different things.

FIGURE 4.1
AM/FM Radio
Voltage and
Current Readings

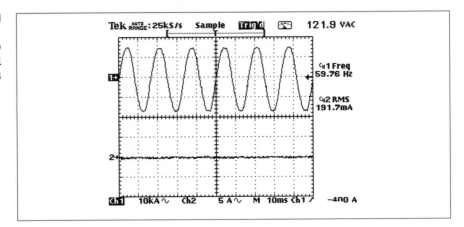

Figure 4.1 shows the voltage, frequency, and the amperage of an ordinary AM/FM radio/cassette deck. Technically, the voltage and frequency is what is available at the wall outlet. The amperage reading is what the radio is using to operate. Notice the amperage draw as indicated from channel 2 is 191.7 milliamps. This is not very much—this is simply a desktop radio. See Figure 4.2.

FIGURE 4.2
Microwave Oven
Voltage and
Current Readings

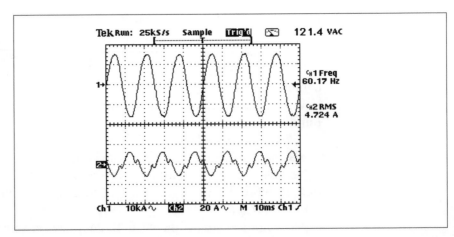

Figure 4.2 represents the readings from a microwave oven connected to a lab test outlet, as was a Tekronix THS720P power analyzer. Notice the voltage, frequency, and amperage readings. The microwave is drawing 4.724 amps as shown by channel 2, indicated on the lower portion of the figure. This illustration is the snapshot upon initial power-on of the microwave.

FIGURE 4.3
Microwave Oven
Voltage and
Current Readings

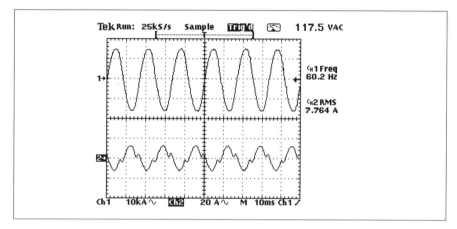

Figure 4.3 shows the reading of the microwave oven, and this time the current draw is 7.764 amps. This reading was taken with the microwave in operation, not just after initial power-on. The oven sustains a significant current draw.

These figures are important because they illustrate the difference in device current requirements. Remember, amperage is how much current a device uses. Refer to the alphabetical list for the definition of current.

The measure of current (the amperage draw) is *how much* electricity a given device uses. For example, the AM/FM radio obviously uses less electricity than the microwave. Technically the current draw is referred to in *amperage* or (*amps*). The more current or higher the amperage rating the more electrons are flowing through a wire. The more electrons flowing through a wire the hotter the wire gets. Consequently, the more amps required for a given device to function the smaller than the wire size required to deliver that number of amps.

Most wire sizes have an amperage rating. Ampacity is the word used to refer to the amount of amps a given wire can accommodate. Generally, the smaller the wire size the more amps the wire can accommodate. Different tables apply when measuring wire size and amp capacity. Whether or not the wire (also called conductor) is single or multiple, operating in free air, or otherwise factors into the capacity of the wire.

The following illustrates the current carrying capacity of 2 or 3 conductors. The measurement shown reflects the AWG in a neoprene jacket. Consider the following as a general reference.

2 or 3 Conductors	
AWG	**Current Capacity**
22	6
20	8
18	14
16	18
14	25
12	30
10	40
8	55
6	75
4	95
3	110
2	130
1	150
0	170
00	195
000	225
0000	260

One factor not presented in this chart is distance. The length of wire *always* factors into the equation of current draw. The longer the wire run, the larger the wire size needed to deliver X number of amps. Amperage is the movement of electrons. Anytime the length of something is extended, more resistance enters into the equation. Consider the following real-world example:

During the preparation for a Christmas show considerable electrical equipment was moved to a new location. Then someone realized the PA equipment needed multiple extension cords to reach an outlet. Three, 100-ft, 14 gauge extension cords were connected to each other. The voltage drop was too great at that distance to allow the PA system to work. The presentation began and about two minutes into the show the power amps went belly-up.

Equipment like computers, power amplifiers, and the like is very sensitive to voltage drops whether they are the result of a wire that is too long or some other reason. Just because there is access to an extension cord does not mean equipment will operate correctly. The previous chart of wire size and ampacity indicated a 20 gauge wire could accommodate 8 amps. This is not the case if the 20 gauge wire is 400 feet long.

Another factor that comes into play with the wire size and ampacity is the number of conductors. For example, some wire has one conductor, some two, some three, some four, and so forth.

Still another consideration is temperature. Different types of wire shielding work differently according to temperature. Consider the following information:

Material Type	Operating Temperature Range
Temperature Readings are in Celsius	
Cross-Linked Polyethylene	−55 to 150°
Hermetic	−60 to 125°
Hypalon	−30 to 105°
EPDM	−60 to 150°
Neoprene	−30 to 90°
PVC	−35 to 105°
Silicone Braided	−75 to 200°
Silicone Braidless	−75 to 200°
Teflon	−100 to 260°

To convert Celsius into Fahrenheit subtract 32 from the Celsius reading to get the Fahrenheit reading.

The information presented here is from one particular wire vendor; other wire vendors refer to wire by type as well and references may differ.

Wire used in houses and commercial buildings is typically Romex. This is a stiff outside jacket used to wrap the wire. Inside, each conductor is insulated and the earth ground is typically wrapped in a form of heavy gauge paper. In contrast, many ordinary extension cords are a type of SJ cable. This type of jacket is not as stiff as Romex. It is relatively flexible. Another type of jacket, SO and SO-w, are more pliable, like rubber. Most of them are oil- and water-resistant. This type of jacketing is used in many commercial-grade extension cords.

In summary, the important considerations to remember with wire are:

1. Wire size and length determine current capacity
2. Wire has a voltage rating
3. The smaller the wire number the larger the wire
4. The number of conductors affects the ampacity
5. The longer the cable length, the more resistance and voltage drop will occur.

Site Wiring

Houses, commercial buildings, and the majority of building facilities in modern cities today are already wired for electricity. Consider the explanation here as a highlighted overview a house (Figure 4.4).

FIGURE 4.4
Voltage and Cycle
Reading at
Breaker #1

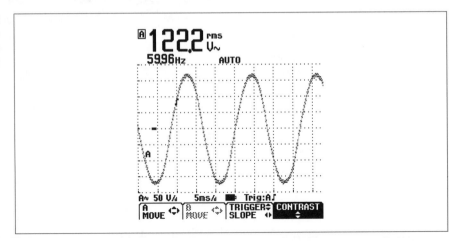

Figure 4.4 shows a voltage reading of 122.2 VAC. This reading was taken inside the load center where the wire connects to a breaker supplying the outlets in the dining room. It is a typical reading.

Figure 4.5 shows 244.3 volts and a 59.97 cycle reading. This voltage measurement was taken at the lines feeding the house load center.

Figure 4.6 shows a highlighted view of the load center, the garage, kitchen, dining room, hallway, porch, front door, and other noted items. Notice the load center is in the garage. Two AC outlets are in the dining room. A stove and refrigerator are in the kitchen. Notice the stove is wired to the load center it is 220 VAC. Notice the wire size indicated to the stove is larger than to the outlets. The wire size to the stove is a 4 gauge and that going to the outlets is a 12 gauge. The refrigerator is wired directly to the load center as well and is 120 VAC, and 6 gauge wire is used. The AC outlets are 120 VAC. Many of the outlets in the house are wired in parallel, meaning multiple outlets run from a single breaker. This is similar to conditions in the commercial world. In the commercial world more dedicated outlets exist, but the primary reason for this is to save money. Unless it is a custom building, most builders will install the outlets to standards in the industry and to electrical code. Notice in the illustration that the stove has a dedicated outlet, as do with the heater and air conditioning.

FIGURE 4.5
Input Voltage
Reading from
Electric Company

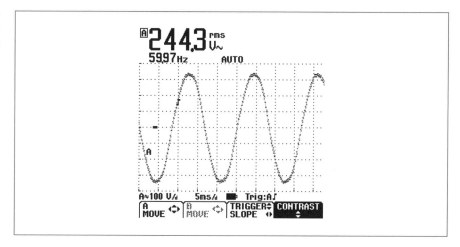

Figure 4.7 shows a detailed view of the load center. Notice three leads come in from the electric meter: two 120 VAC feeds and a neutral. The illustration shows the cable going to the dining room outlet, and the hot lead connects to a breaker, while the neutral and ground connect to the neutral bus bar as shown. Beneath the breakers shown in this figure two bus bars carry the voltage. Notice as well that a single main circuit breaker exists at the top of the load center. This breaker is the single *switch* used to turn on or off the feed to the entire house.

Most load centers are similar to this though they may differ if they work with much higher voltage.

FIGURE 4.6
Overview on
House Wiring

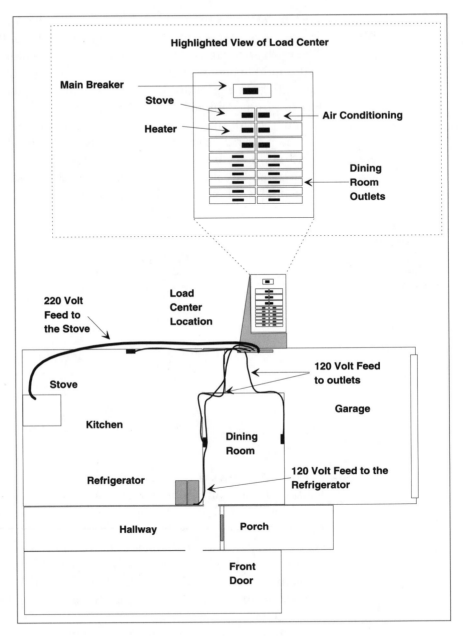

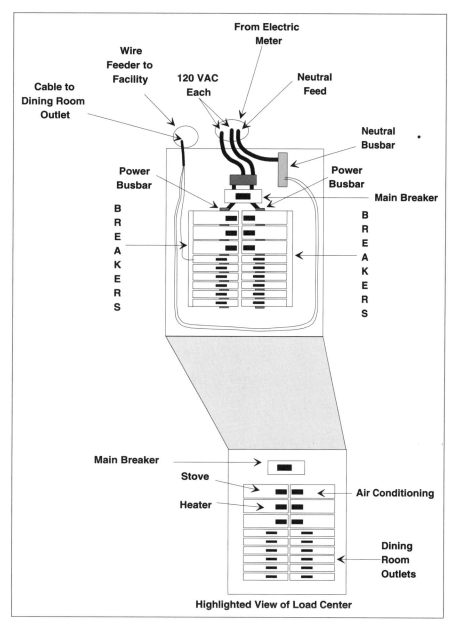

FIGURE 4.7
Detailed View
Inside Load
Center

Figure 4.8 shows the voltage reading at the top of the bus bar where the hot feeds come in from the electric meter: 243.7 volts. The cable size coming into the load center from the electric meter is 00.

This illustrates fundamental concepts that might not be familiar to a network- or computer-educated person. Be aware that electricity is serious business; if you are not educated in it always rely on someone who is. These illustrations show that not all outlets or even lighting for that matter have dedicated circuits. Furthermore, most of the wiring in the house is 12 gauge Romex wire. A 12 gauge wire is of significant size to use in a house, but considering the various loads that network equipment can generate, one might need a larger wire. Consider what happens if you plug two microwave ovens into the same circuit and it is only 20 amps. At 7.764 amps per microwave, as Figure 4.3 shows, you would be far beyond a 50% utilization of that breaker. Odds are that one more device on that breaker would overload it. Remember this when you begin working with laser or thermal printers. They tend to draw significant current, both at start-up and during the cycles of heating the drum.

This section should help create a healthier perspective of premises where the network needs to be installed.

FIGURE 4.8
Voltage Reading
From Electric
Meter

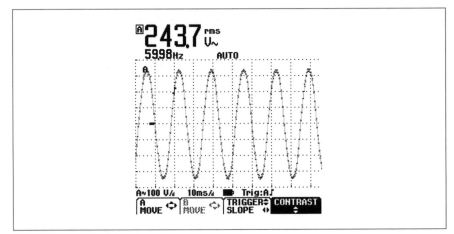

Harmonics

Harmonic evaluation reveals the quality of power. Depending upon the site, this could be significant, because the more sensitive the equipment the more susceptible it is to harmonic distortion. Remember the definition of harmonics: a sinusoidal component of a periodic wave, with a frequency that is an integral multiple of the fundamental frequency. The frequency of the second harmonic is twice that of the fundamental frequency or first harmonic. Remember also that harmonic analysis refers to any method used to identify and evaluate the harmonics (frequencies) that make up a complex form of voltage, current, or some other varying quantity.

Figure 4.9 shows channel one and two monitored on the Tekscope. This is a voltage harmonic reading from the fundamental harmonic to the eleventh. Notice the RMS harmonic is 117.9 while the RMS voltage is 118 VAC.

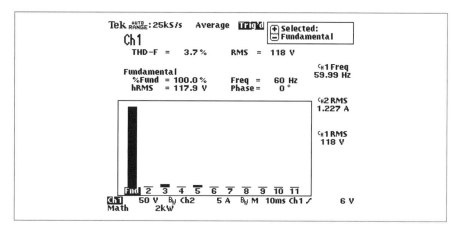

FIGURE 4.9
Voltage
Harmonics
of the Feed
to the Printer

Figure 4.10 shows the amperage harmonics while the network printer is at idle after a number of pages have been printed. The RMS amperage reading is 1.038 amps as channel two indicates, while the RMS harmonic amperage reading is 835.mA. Notice the scope has also calculated the RMS voltage from channel one and it reads 118.2 VAC.

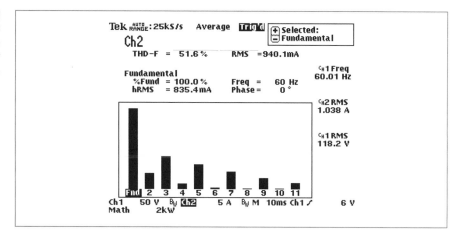

FIGURE 4.10
Amperage
Harmonics of
the Printer

Figure 4.11 shows the odd harmonics of the voltage reading from the fundamental harmonic to the twenty-first. This level of detail is quite helpful for those who need to analyze their power quality. Clean power is important, and ascertaining the harmonic values of various readings is important in the evaluation of the power.

FIGURE 4.11
Odd Harmonics

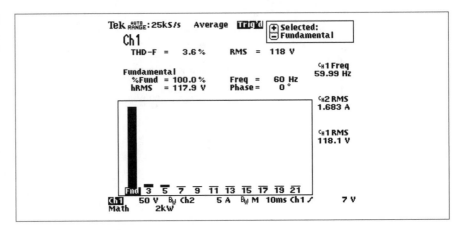

Ground Loops

Ground loops occur when multiple grounds exist, and a potential difference exists between them. It is possible to incur grounding from network cabling and through electrical wiring. These should not conflict.

Ground loops can eat away at bandwidth because they will inject distortion into a line. If the ground loop is significant enough it can cause power quality degradation. Be aware that the potential exists to pick up grounding in equipment wherever it may reside. It is best to check the grounding of telco wiring and network cabling, and to check for stray wires that could create such an environment.

Early familiarity with the electrical requirements of the project (what to consider and how to calculate these are discussed in the following section), is important as is knowledge of the wiring of the existing facility, estimates (if possible) of power quality, and information on the grounding of the facility within which the equipment will operate.

Calculating Power Requirements

Fundamental information is presented here, but contact a Liebert representative to assist you in determining exactly what your requirements are.

Equipment Category and List

It is a good idea to categorize. The categories worked from are:

- Printers
- Computers
- Peripherals
- Required 90% of the time
- Required 50% of the time
- Required less than 50% of the time
- Equipment in multiple locations
- Equipment in one location
- Number of hours able to lose work
- Amount of money you can afford to lose.

If you do not have an inventory list, start one. If you are starting in the middle of a network already established, then begin by inventorying the computers and monitors you have. How many printers are networked and how many are standalone. Is it feasible for all or some of them to use the same power source? List peripherals as well. It would be a very good idea to check the original vendor documentation and/or refer to the information on the equipment label and document the electrical and environmental requirements.

Then list the equipment required 50% and 90% of the time. If a PC is used all day everyday in your environment, then list it under the 90% column. On the other hand, if a system is used occasionally, list it appropriately.

It is also wise to list the equipment by the location where it will be installed. This is important because networks generally span multiple facilities and sometimes multiple locations. It may be necessary to purchase multiple types of equipment in order to get the coverage required.

Another important issue is to ask and answer the question; how much money can you afford to lose if equipment is *cooked* by way of a lightning hit. People have lost equipment because they did not prepare for this scenario.

Consider also the number of hours which could be lost in lack of productive work. If 25 people, all use computers, and you lose an entire day this equates to 25 person days.

Calculations

Liebert has a helpful tool for protection calculation. The equation here reflects their efforts. First determine whether there is one- or three-phase equipment. Most equipment has one phase. Be sure to obtain steady-state operating amperage. This is not the circuit breaker rating, surge current or inrush current. Use this number in the amperage portion of the equation. If you do not use steady-state current erroneous conclusions may result. In order to determine the amount of UPS coverage required use the following equation:

$$kVA = \frac{V \times A}{1000}$$

The number arrived at should be increased by 20–50%. The result is the approximate size required. Refer to the Liebert UPS kVA ratings. You would be better served by load balancing equipment through the use of three-phase UPS protection and then determining the UPS size based upon the largest load. This topic exceeds our scope here; contact Liebert and request assistance with three-phase power.

Types of Power Protection

Another topic for consideration is power protection. A discussion of the basic types of power protection and their purpose follows.

Surge Protectors

Surge protectors protect against surges. Spikes (sudden voltage increases) are typically inhibited with surge protection devices. This is probably the minimum level of protection you need. Even computers at home should have this level of protection.

Voltage Regulators

Voltage regulators have the ability to maintain a certain voltage and current level for the device drawing on the electrical source. A voltage regulator is a good device to use with printers, especially laser printers.

Uninterruptible Power Supplies (UPS)

A UPS is a device that is prepared to provide interim power. UPSs are not a solution to power outages; they are an interim solution to bridge the time between when power ceases and when it is restored. Large UPSs may be able to provide a considerable number of minutes or even hours of uptime. However, UPS use presupposes that power from the electric company will be restored or an alternative power supply will be provided from a source such as a generator.

Generators

Generators create or *generate* electricity. They are typically used as alternative power sources in case the main source of power fails. If big enough, a generator can keep generating electric power indefinitely—assuming the diesel or gasoline is available. Generators are typically reserved for use in large commercial settings.

Transfer Switch Gear

Transfer switch gear is used to change the source of electric power to a generator.

Parallel Switch Gear

Parallel switch gear is used in settings where multiple generators are used in parallel with each other. This is advanced technology. Generators, transfer switches, and paralleling UPSs are complex. These implementations are most always found in commercial settings. An example would be a hospital complex.

The UPS in My Network

Because of the amount of equipment in my network, I selected a 15 kVA UPS from Liebert.

Figure 4.12 shows the network equipment used and that the Liebert UPS is the power protection used to accommodate all the equipment in the network.

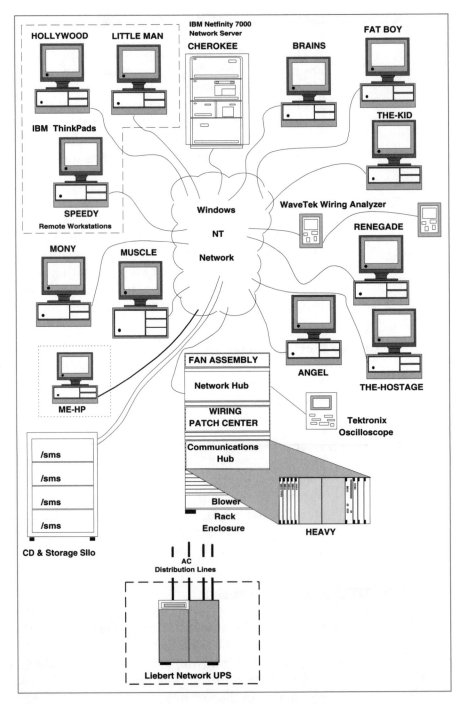

FIGURE 4.12
Liebert UPS for
the Network

Figure 4.13 shows the rear view of the UPS in my network. A great advantage of the UPS is the accessibility of the components.

FIGURE 4.13
Liebert UPS
Rear View

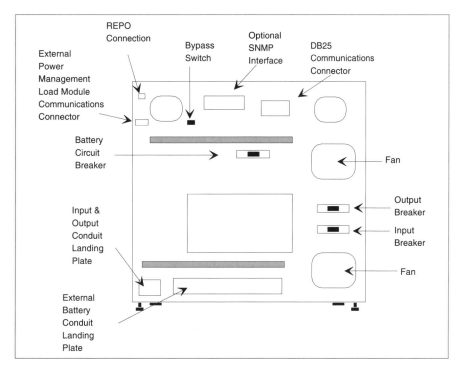

The 15 kVA UPS ordered arrived weighing over 800 pounds. With help, it took only an hour to get the UPS into the place prepared for it before the UPS arrived. I marked off the place for the UPS so that space would not be obstructed. This level of preplanning saved time.

It took approximately an additional hour to get the UPS unpacked and in its final spot. Placing an 800 pound UPS is a big job. Take the time to make this level of plans for yourself. If you do not, a sizable amount of weight arrives on the pallet and has nowhere to go.

Another function of the Liebert UPS used in my network is its participation in the network via the SNMP interface. The UPS arrived functional with existing SNMP protocol standards. It supports standard MIB definitions and interoperates well in the network. The SNMP interface is optional on the UPStation S UPSs from Liebert; this is advantageous for those purchasing UPSs because not all networks will use an SNMP management application.

The 15kVA Liebert UPS requires wiring into the load center of the facility in which it operates. Use a licensed electrician to assist in planning and during the installation of the UPS (or contact Liebert). Working with equipment like this is no trivial task, and the equipment should not be played with because it can kill you.

Figure 4.14 has three parts. It shows the AC load center that feeds AC to the facility where the network is located. Then it shows a highlighted view of the UPS wired into the load center. Finally, it shows a conceptual view of how some of the equipment is connected to the UPS.

This is the basic overview of how the UPS fits into the network. The fit is more complex than this because of all the equipment the UPS protects. Because the UPS is capable of protecting the entire network, approximately four output feeds (lines with outlets) were required to accommodate all components.

This discussion should promote understanding of the placement and purpose of the UPS. Your situation will vary, but this is a reference point for planning.

Liebert Information on the UPStations S UPS

The information here is the documentation of the Liebert UPStations S UPS. This specification defines the electrical and mechanical characteristics and requirements for a continuous-duty single-phase, solid-state, uninterruptible power supply system (UPS) which provides high-quality AC power for sensitive electronic equipment loads.

Standards

The UPS is designed in accordance with the applicable sections of the current revision of the following documents. Where a conflict arises between these documents and statements made herein, the statements in this specification govern.

ANSI C62.41-1980 (IEEE 587), Category A & B	National Electrical Code (NFPA 70)
ASME	NEMA PE-1
CSA 22.2, No. 107.1	OSHA
FCC Part 15, Sub Part J, Class A	UL Standard 1778

The UPS is UL listed to UL Standard 1778, and is CSA certified.

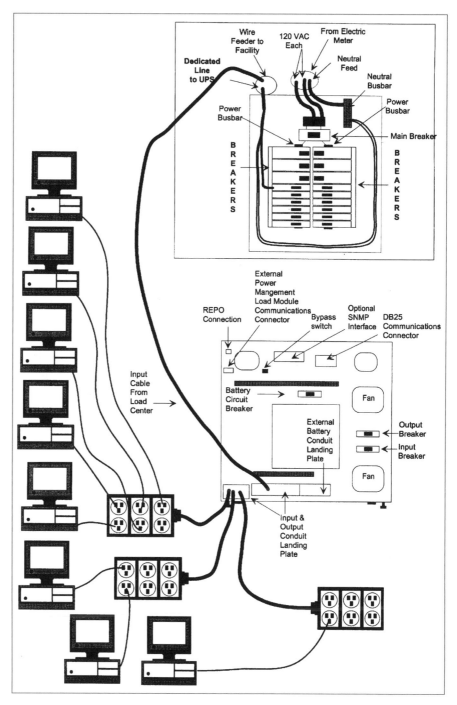

System Description (Modes of Operation)

The UPS is designed to operate as a true online system in the following modes:

- **Normal.** The critical AC load is continuously supplied by the UPS inverter. The input converter derives power from a utility AC source and supplies DC power to the inverter. The battery charger shall maintain a float-charge on the battery.
- **Back-up.** Upon failure of utility AC power, the critical AC load is supplied by the inverter, which obtains power from the battery. There is no interruption in power to the critical load upon failure or restoration of the utility AC source.
- **Recharge.** Upon restoration of utility AC power, after a utility AC power outage, the input converter automatically restarts and resumes supplying power to the inverter. Also the battery charger recharges the battery.
- **Automatic Restart.** Upon restoration of utility AC power, after a utility AC power outage and complete battery discharge, the UPS automatically restarts and resumes supplying power to the critical load. Also the battery charger automatically recharges the battery. This feature is enabled from the factory and is capable of being disabled by the user.
- **Bypass.** The factory-installed bypass (optional on 3.5–6.0 kVA UPS modules) provides an alternate path for power to the critical load that is capable of operating in the following manner:
    - **Automatic.** In the event of an internal failure or should the inverter overload capacity be exceeded, the UPS performs an automatic transfer of the critical AC load from the inverter to the bypass source.
    - **Manual.** Should the UPS need to be taken out of service for limited maintenance or repair, manual activation of the bypass causes an immediate transfer of the critical AC load from the inverter to the bypass source. The input converter, inverter, and battery charging operations are inhibited until the switch is moved back to the "UPS" position and the unit restarted.

System Performance Requirements

- **Upgradeability.** Select UPS systems are field upgradeable to higher power ratings as follows:
  3.5 kVA modules upgradeable to 4.5 kVA modules
  3.5 kVA modules upgradeable to 6.0 kVA modules
  4.5 kVA modules upgradeable to 6.0 kVA modules
  8.0 kVA modules upgradeable to 10.0 kVA modules
  8.0 kVA modules upgradeable to 12.0 kVA modules
  10.0 kVA modules upgradeable to 12.0 kVA modules
  15.0 kVA modules upgradeable to 18.0 kVA modules
- **Isolation.** Input to output isolation provided when operating in the UPS mode.
- **Remote Emergency Power Off.** The UPS provides provisions for remote emergency power off capability.

AC Input to UPS

- **Voltage Configuration.** 176 to 264 VAC, single-phase, 3-wire-plus-ground. 2-wire-plus-ground can be utilized for 3.5–6.0 kVA UPS modules without the optional bypass. The UPS modules (8–18 kVA only) are also capable of three-phase input to the rectifier. The UPS modules are capable of dual input to provide a separate power path for the bypass (optional on 8–18 kVA UPS modules only).
- **Frequency.** 45 to 65 Hz.
- **Input Current Distortion.** 5% THD maximum at full load. If three phase input is utilized (available on 8–18 kVA units), maximum THD does exceed 30%.
- **Input Power Factor.** 0.98 lagging minimum from 50% to 100% rated load
- **Inrush Current.** 150% of full load input current maximum for 3 cycles
- **Surge Protection.** Sustains input surges without damage per criteria listed in ANSI C62.41-1980 (IEEE 587), Category A and B.

AC Output, UPS Inverter

- **Voltage Configuration.** 208/120 VAC, single-phase, 3-wire-plus-ground; field programmable to 240/120 VAC, 230/115 VAC,

220/127 VAC, 220/110 VAC, 200/100 VAC. The UPS can also be ordered to supply line to neutral voltages of 240 VAC, 230 VAC, 220 VAC.

- **Voltage Regulation.** ±2% steady state
- **Frequency Regulation.** Field selectable 50 Hz or 60 Hz, ±0.01%
- **Frequency Slew Rate.** 1.0 Hertz per second maximum; field selectable from 0.3, 0.5, 1, 2, or 3 Hz per second from the LCD display
- **Bypass Frequency Synchronization Range.** ±1.0 Hertz; field selectable from ±0.1 Hz to ±5.0 Hz, in 0.1 Hz increments from the LCD display
- **Voltage Distortion.** 3% total harmonic distortion (THD) maximum into a 100% linear load, 5% THD maximum into a 100% non-linear load with crest factor ratio of 3:1
- **Load Power Factor Range.** 0.5 lagging to 0.5 leading
- **Output Power Rating.** Rated kVA at: 0.8 lagging power factor for 3.5 and 4.5 kVA models; 0.67–0.77 lagging power factor for 6.0 kVA models depending upon output voltage; 0.75 lagging power factor for 8.0 and 10.0 kVA models; 0.7 lagging power factor for 12.0, 15.0 and 18.0 kVA models.
- **Inverter Overload Capability.** 105% continuously, 125% for 10 minutes, 150% for 10 seconds, 250% for 12 cycles. For units with the bypass option installed, the load is transferred to bypass when any of the above conditions are exceeded.
- **Inverter Output Voltage Adjustment.** ±5% manual adjustment from the LCD by qualified service personnel
- **Voltage Transient Response.** ±5% maximum for any load step up to and including 100% of the UPS rating
- **Transient Recovery Time.** To within 1% of steady state output voltage within 50 milliseconds.

Batteries

- **Internal Battery.** The battery consists of sealed, valve-regulated, reduced-maintenance, lead acid cells. Flame retardant batteries can also be provided, which renders the UPS suitable for installation inside a computer room per requirements of UL Standard 1778.
- **Reserve Time.** (with ambient temperature between 20 and 30° C) The UPS contains an internal battery system to provide the following reserve time:
  3.5 kVA/ 2.8 kW—18 minutes at full load
  4.5 kVA/ 3.6 kW—12 minutes at full load

6.0 kVA/ 4.0 kW—11 minutes at full load
8.0 kVA/ 6.0 kW—17 minutes at full load
10.0 kVA/ 7.5 kW—11 minutes at full load
12.0 kVA/ 8.4 kW—10 minutes at full load
15.0 kVA/ 10.5 kW—14 minutes at full load
18.0 kVA/ 12.6 kW—10 minutes at full load.

The UPS contains provisions to interface with an external matching battery cabinet to extend reserve time capabilities.

- **Battery Recharge.** To prolong battery life, the UPS contains temperature-compensated battery charging. Recharge time is 10 times discharge time to 95% capacity (field selectable to 20 times discharge time to 95% capacity from the LCD display).

Environmental Conditions

- **Ambient Temperature**
  - **Operating.** UPS 0° C to +40° C; battery 20° C to 30° C for optimum performance
  - **Storage.** UPS −30° C to +70° C; battery 0° C to 32° C for maximum 6 months
- **Relative Humidity**
  - **Operating.** 0 to 95% non-condensing
  - **Storage.** 0 to 95% non-condensing
- **Altitude**
  - **Operating.** To 4,000 feet; derating or reduced operating temperature range required for higher altitudes
  - **Storage.** To 50,000 feet
- **Audible Noise.** Noise generated by the UPS during normal operation will not exceed 55 dBA measured at 1 meter from the surface of the UPS.
- **Electrostatic Discharge.** The UPS is able to withstand a minimum 15 kV without damage and does affect the critical load.

User Documentation

The specified UPS system is supplied with one user's manual. Manuals include installation drawings and instructions, a functional description of the equipment with block diagrams, safety precautions, illustrations, step-by-step operating procedures, and routine maintenance guidelines.

Warranty

The UPS manufacturer warrants the UPS against defects in materials and workmanship for one year. The warranty covers all parts for one year and onsite labor for 90 days. With the optional start-up provided by Customer Service and Support, the warranty covers all parts and onsite labor for one year. Extended warranty packages are also available.

Quality Assurance

- **Manufacturer Qualifications.** A minimum of 20 years' experience in the design, manufacture, and testing of solid-state UPS systems is required.
- **Factory Testing.** Before shipment, the manufacturer fully and completely tests the system to assure compliance with the specification. These tests include operational discharge and recharge tests on the internal battery to guarantee rated performance.

Product Fabrication

All materials and components making up the UPS are new, of current manufacture, and have not been in prior service except as required during factory testing. The UPS is constructed of replaceable sub-assemblies. All active electronic devices are solid-state.

Product Wiring

Wiring practices, materials, and coding are in accordance with the requirements of the National Electrical Code (NFPA 70) and other applicable codes and standards.

Product Cabinet

The UPS unit comprised of: input converter, battery charger, inverter, bypass, and battery consisting of the appropriate number of sealed battery cells, is housed in a single free-standing NEMA type 1 enclosure and meets the requirements of IP20. The UPS cabinet is cleaned, primed, and painted with the manufacturer's standard color. Casters and leveling feet are provided. UPS cabinet dimensions do exceed [select one: 9" wide, 27" deep, and 29" high (for 3.5–6.0 kVA units); 18" wide, 27" deep, and 29" high (for 8.0–12.0 kVA units); 27" wide, 27" deep, and 29" high (for 15.0–18.0 kVA units).

Product Cooling

The UPS is forced-air cooled by internally mounted, variable-speed fans to reduce audible noise.

Components

- **Input Converter (General).** Incoming AC power is converted to a regulated DC output by the input converter for supplying DC power to the inverter. The input converter provides input power factor and input current distortion correction. The input converter provides input to output isolation by means of a high frequency transformer.
- **AC Input Current Limit.** The input converter is provided with AC input current limiting whereby the maximum input current is limited to 125% of the full load input current rating.
- **Input Protection.** The UPS has built-in protection against undervoltage, overcurrent, and overvoltage conditions including low-energy surges, introduced on the primary AC source and the bypass source. The UPS can sustain input surges without damage per criteria listed in ANSI C62.41-1980 (IEEE 587). The UPS contains [select one: input fuses (3.5–6.0 kVA); or an input circuit breaker (8.0–18.0 kVA) sized to supply full-rated load and to recharge the battery at the same time.
- **Battery Recharge.** To prolong battery life, the UPS contains two battery recharge rates, and charging voltage is temperature-compensated. The "turbo" mode of recharge is capable of recharging the battery to 95% capacity within 10 times the discharge time of the battery. The "slow" mode of recharge is capable of recharging the battery to 95% capacity within 20 times the discharge time. The factory default is "turbo" mode and the microprocessor determines how often the faster recharge rate is employed to optimize battery life.
- **Charger Output Filter.** The battery charger has an output filter to minimize ripple current into the battery. Under no conditions does ripple current into the battery exceed 2% RMS.

- **Overvoltage Protection.** There is DC overvoltage protection so that if the DC voltage exceeds the pre-set limit, the UPS shuts down automatically and the critical load is transferred to bypass (if optional bypass is installed).
- **Inverter (General).** The UPS contains two independently controlled inverters and is a pulse-width-modulated (PWM) design capable of providing the specified AC output. The inverters convert DC power from the input converter output, or the battery, into precise regulated sine wave AC power for supporting the critical AC load.
- **Overload.** The inverter is capable of supplying current and voltage for overloads exceeding 100% and up to 150% of full-load current. A visual indicator and audible alarm indicate overload operation. For greater currents or longer time duration, the inverter has electronic current-limiting protection to prevent damage to components. The inverter is self-protecting against any magnitude of connected output overload. Inverter control logic senses and disconnects the inverter from the critical AC load without the requirement to clear protective fuses. For units supplied with the bypass option, the load is transferred to bypass when any of the above conditions are exceeded.
- **Inverter DC Protection.** The inverter is protected by the following DC shutdown levels:
  - DC Overvoltage Shutdown
  - DC Undervoltage Shutdown (End of Discharge)
  - DC Undervoltage Warning (Low Battery Reserve); this is factory set at 2 minutes and user adjustable from 1 to 99 minutes from the LCD display.
- **Inverter Output Voltage Adjustment.** The inverter employs a manual control to adjust the output voltage from ±5% of the nominal value from the LCD by qualified service personnel.
- **Output Frequency.** The output frequency of the inverter is controlled by an oscillator. The oscillator holds the inverter output frequency to ±0.01% for steady state and transient conditions. For units equipped with a bypass, the inverter tracks the bypass continuously providing the bypass source maintains a frequency within the user selected synchronization range. If the bypass source fails to remain within the selected range, the inverter reverts to the internal oscillator.
- **Output Protection.** The UPS inverter employs electronic current limiting and an output circuit breaker. The main output breaker is rated for a minimum 10kAIC.

- **Battery Over Discharge Protection.** To prevent battery damage from over discharging, the UPS control logic automatically raises the shutdown voltage set point as discharge time increases beyond 15 minutes.

Display and Controls

- **General.** The UPS is provided with a microprocessor-based unit status display and controls section designed for convenient and reliable user operation. The monitoring functions such as metering, status and alarms are displayed on a four-line by 16-character alphanumeric LCD display. Additional features of the LCD monitoring system include:
  - Menu-driven display with text format
  - Real time clock (time and date)
  - Alarm history with time and date stamp
  - Battery backed-up memory.
- **Metering.** The following parameter are displayed:
  - Input AC voltage line-to-line and line-to-neutral for each phase
  - Input AC current for each phase
  - Input frequency
  - Battery voltage
  - Battery charge/discharge current
  - Output AC voltage line-to-line and line-to-neutral for each phase
  - Output AC current for each phase
  - Output frequency
  - Percent of rated load being supplied by the UPS
  - Output kVA and kW for each phase
  - Battery time remaining during battery operation
  - Operating temperature of input converter, inverter, and internal battery.
- **Status Messages.** The following UPS status messages are displayed:
  - Normal operation
  - UPS on battery
  - System shutdown
  - Start up sequence aborted
  - Battery test enabled/disabled
  - System time set by operator
  - Load on bypass.

- **Alarm Messages.** The following alarm messages are displayed:
  - Input power out of tolerance
  - UPS output not synchronized to input
  - Output undervoltage
  - Input power single phased
  - Output overvoltage
  - Incorrect input frequency
  - Output overcurrent
  - Input in current limit charging batteries
  - Overcurrent detected in inverter
  - Charger failure
  - Control Error: software time-out
  - Battery charger problem
  - Control Error: internal test
  - Battery failed test
  - Critical power supply failure
  - Can't execute battery test: not recharged
  - External shutdown (remote EPO activated)
  - Can't execute battery test at this time
  - Fan failure
  - Low battery shutdown
  - Low battery warning (adjustable 1 to 99 minutes)
  - DC bus overvoltage
  - System shutdown due to overload
  - PFC fault
  - System shutdown impending due to over temperature
  - Inverter fault
  - Inverter failure
  - System shutdown: loss of control power
  - Over temperature shutdown
  - System output overloaded.

An audible alarm is provided and activated by any of the above alarm conditions.

On units equipped with the bypass option, the following additional alarms are displayed:

- Bypass frequency out of tolerance
- Bypass power out of tolerance
- Fault load transferred to bypass
- Load transferred to bypass due to overload
- Load transferred to bypass due to DC overvoltage

- Excessive retransfers attempted.

An audible alarm is provided and activated by any of the above alarm conditions.

- **Controls.** UPS start-up and shutdown operations are accomplished via the front LCD display panel. An advisory display and menu-driven user prompts are provided to guide the operator through system operation without the use of additional manuals. Push buttons are provided to display the status of the UPS and to test and reset visual and audible alarms. The UPS contains an output circuit breaker and a manual bypass switch (optional on 3.5–6.0 kVA) as additional user controls, that are located on the rear of the unit.

On-Line Battery Test

The UPS is provided with an on-line battery test feature. The test ensures the capability of the battery to supply power to the inverter while the load is supplied power in the normal mode. If the battery fails the test, the UPS displays a warning message and sounds an audible alarm. The battery test feature has the following user selectable options, accessible from the LCD display:

- DC bus voltage threshold (pass/fail value)
- Interval between tests (2 to 9 weeks)
- Duration of test (30 to 900 seconds; factory default is 30 seconds)
- Date and time of initial test
- Enable/disable test.

Remote Emergency Power Off (REPO)

REPO capabilities are provided. A connector is provided for connection of a normally open contact supplied by the user. A 50-foot cable with the mating connector and push-button are available as an option.

Bypass (Optional on 3.5–6.0 kVA UPS modules)

- **General.** A bypass circuit is provided as an integral part of the UPS. The bypass has an overload rating of 300% rated load for 10 cycles and 1000% for sub-cycle fault clearing. The bypass control logic contains an automatic transfer control circuit that senses the status of the inverter logic signals, and operating and alarm conditions. This control circuit provides a transfer of the load to the bypass source, without exceeding the transient limits specified herein, when an overload or malfunction occurs within the UPS.

- **Automatic Transfers.** The transfer control logic automatically activates the bypass, transferring the critical AC load to the bypass source, after the transfer logic senses one of the following conditions:
  - Inverter overload capacity exceeded
  - Critical AC load overvoltage or undervoltage
  - UPS fault condition.

  For inverter overload conditions, the transfer control logic inhibits an automatic transfer of the critical load to the bypass source if one of the following conditions exists:
  - Inverter/Bypass voltage difference exceeding preset limits (+10%, −15% of nominal)
  - Bypass frequency out of preset limits (±1.0 Hz, field selectable from ±0.1 Hz to ±5.0 Hz, in 0.1 Hz increments).

  For UPS fault or output over/under voltage conditions, the transfer control logic does inhibit automatic transfers of the critical load to the bypass source.
- **Automatic Retransfers.** Retransfer of the critical AC load from the bypass source to the inverter output is automatically initiated unless inhibited by manual control. The transfer control logic inhibits an automatic retransfer of the critical load to the inverter if one of the following conditions exists:
  - Bypass out-of-synchronization range with inverter output
  - Overload condition exists in excess of inverter full load rating
  - UPS fault condition is present.
- **Manual Transfer.** Manual operation of the bypass directly connects the critical load to the input AC power source, bypassing the input converter, battery charger, inverter, and battery.

Internal Battery

Sealed, valve-regulated, low maintenance, lead acid batteries are used as a stored-energy source for the specified UPS system. Flame retardant batteries are available for computer room applications. The battery is housed inside the UPS cabinet, and sized to support the inverter at rated load and power factor, in an ambient temperature between 20 and 30° C, for a minimum of 10 minutes reserve time. The expected life of the battery is 5 years or a minimum 250 complete discharge cycles. For extended battery reserve time, external matching battery cabinets are available as an option.

Output Load Modules

These are required on 3.5–6.0 kVA and may be used on the 8–12 kVA only with configurable distribution module. Output load modules (maximum of 4 on 3.5–12.0 kVA units. Maximum of 8 on 8.0–12.0 kVA units optional configurable distribution module) are provided for field addition to the UPS cabinet. Each load module includes user-specified receptacle(s), LED indicator lamp, and circuit breaker protection. The following load modules are provided:

Receptacle	Voltage (configuration)	Circuit Breaker
5-15R2	120 (L-N-G)	15A, 2 pole
L5-15R1	120 (L-N-G)	15A, 1 pole
6-15R1	208 or 240 (L-L-G)	15A, 2 pole
L6-15R1	208 or 240 (L-L-G)	15A, 2 pole
L5-15R2	120 (L-N-G)	15A, 2 pole
5-20R2	120 (L-N-G)	20A, 2 pole
L5-20R1	120 (L-N-G)	20A, 1 pole
L6-20R1	208 or 240 (L-L-G)	20A, 2 pole
L14-20R1	208/120 or 240/120 (L-L-N-G)	30A, 1 pole
L5-30R1	120 (L-N-G)	30A, 1 pole
L6-30R1	208 or 240 (L-L-G)	30A, 2 pole
L-14-30R1	208/120 or 240/120 (L-L-N-G)	30A, 2 pole
Hardwire (15A)	208/120 or 240/120 (L-L-N-G)	15A, 2 pole
Hardwire (20A)	208/120 or 240/120 (L-L-N-G)	20A, 2 pole
Hardwire (30A)	208/120 or 240/120 (L-L-N-G)	Not Required

UPS Accessories (Optional Components)

Communication interfaces are provided on field-installable, plug-in printed circuit boards. Installation is from the top of the UPS cabinet.

Two interface slots are provided to allow multiple communication capabilities.

RS-232 Interface Board

The RS-232 interface board facilitates communication interfaces for the following:

- RS-232 communication
- External Modem
- Computer/LAN interface
- AS/400 interface
- Customer-configured relay interface.

RS-232 Interface Port

The RS-232 interface port transmits UPS status for display at a remote terminal, computer, or external modem (all by others), via a DB25 connector. The remote display mimics the information provided on the LCD monitoring and control panel, including status of all UPS alarms, input voltage, output voltage, percentage load, and battery time remaining.

Auto-Dial

The UPS RS-232 interface port is capable of interfacing with an external modem to report alarm and status information to a remote location. The modem control system has the capability to store one telephone number. The UPS automatically dials the remote location in the event of the occurrence of any of the following alarms:

- User initiated UPS shutdown
- Battery SCR fault (short or open)
- PFC voltage high
- DC bus under voltage
- PFC voltage low
- On battery
- PFC shutdown due to over temperature
- Low battery
- PFC fault (hardware fault)
- Battery failed test
- Charger shutdown due to over temperature
- UPS fault
- Inverter shutdown due to over current

- Excessive retransfer attempts
- Inverter shutdown due to overload
- Control power supply failure
- Inverter shutdown due to under/over voltage
- ROM test failed
- Inverter shutdown due to over temperature
- RAM test failed
- Bypass shutdown due to overload (UPS shutdown)
- Time-out fault (self test at start-up).

Computer/LAN Interface Kits

Computer/LAN interface kits consist of a 10-foot communication cable and software. Two separate software kits are available to operate in the following manner:

- Computer/LAN shutdown software runs as a background task on the computer while monitoring the UPS. The software performs an unattended orderly shutdown of the computer operating system, when signaled by the UPS of a power failure or low battery condition.
- Power Surveillance software runs as a background task on the computer while monitoring the UPS. The Power Surveillance software incorporates the shutdown capabilities of Computer/LAN shutdown software (except DOS) and also provides UPS monitoring and control capabilities from a standalone computer.

IBM* AS/400* Interface Kits

A shielded cable compliant with NEMA Class 2 for plenum applications, with subminiature 9-pin D-type connector, is provided for connection to the IBM* AS/400* signal interface.

Contacts rated for 1.0 amp at 30 volts AC or DC are provided to indicate a change of status of each of the following conditions:

- On UPS
- On Battery
- Low Battery
- On Bypass.

---

* IBM and AS/400 are registered trademarks of International Business Machines Corporation.

An optional splitter cable is available to allow connection to either RS-232, Power Surveillance, or external modem communication and Computer/LAN shutdown software or AS/400 interface simultaneously.

Customer-Configured Relay Interface

An interface board is available that allows the customer to have UPS status/alarm conditions available for remote panel monitoring via relay contact closures. Programming is done via the LCD display.

Simple Network Management Protocol (SNMP) Interface Board

The SNMP interface board (agent) is provided to allow communication between the UPS and any Network Management System (NMS). The SNMP agent is installed in the UPS cabinet; external "proxy" agent configurations are not allowed. The SNMP interface is available in Ethernet or Token Ring TCP/IP message format to permit direct connection to the network. Ethernet connection is Unshielded Twisted Pair (UTP). Token Ring connection is Unshielded Twisted Pair (UTP) and Shielded Twisted Pair (STP). The SNMP agent includes software that contains the standard library of commands in the Management Information Base (MIB). An extended MIB is available to enable the user access to create custom UPS variable interface screens. SNMP Snap-in interfaces are available for major NOS platforms.

The SNMP connection allows multiple network managers to both monitor the status and control many operational features of the UPS. Monitoring data supplied by the UPS includes but is not limited to the input, output, and battery voltages and currents, battery condition, battery reserve time remaining, internal component temperatures, UPS loading, and UPS status and alarm indicators. UPS operational features include but are not limited to setting UPS operating parameters, turning the UPS off and on, and manually initiating battery tests.

Power Management Load Modules (Optional on 3.5–12.0 kVA Units)

Power management load modules (maximum of 4 on 3.5–12.0 kVA units, or maximum of 8 on 8.0–12.0 kVA units) are provided for field addition to the UPS cabinet. Power management load modules have the ability to individually control power through the output receptacles. The load modules listed are available as optional power management load modules with the exception of the hardwire modules. The output receptacles are capable of being turned on and off by either manual initiation or programmed time intervals. Power management load modules enable the user to:

- Extend battery run time, by selectively turning off loads at predetermined time intervals
- Conserve energy, by allowing the user to turn off "idle" equipment
- Reset or reboot loads, by remotely turning the load off then on enables the user to reboot "locked up" equipment
- Increase security, by remotely turning off loads to prohibit unauthorized personnel access
- Sequence load restarting, by selectively turning on loads at predetermined time intervals to minimize high inrush currents.

Power management programming is password-protected and can be accessed via the LCD display. The power management programming is user-specified, based upon four elements: load module identification, events, action, and delay. Load modules are numerically identified and capable of containing a user-defined alphanumeric label of up to 16 characters. An event is the triggering occurrence to cause the load module to take action. Events include but are not limited to: system power up, utility failure, utility restored, battery time remaining, time and date (day), and on bypass. Programmable actions include but are not limited to: output on (turns inverter on); output off (turn entire UPS off); turn on load (turns specified load module(s) on); and turn off load (turns specified load module(s) off). Each action has an associated delay, user-selected from 0 to 99 seconds or 0 to 99 minutes, prior to the execution of the action.

External Battery Cabinet

An external battery cabinet is provided for the UPS. It is used in parallel with the internal battery for extended power outage reserve time. It contains (1 or 2) strings of sealed, valve-regulated, low-maintenance, lead acid cells, housed in a separate cabinet that matches the UPS cabinet styling. Flame retardant batteries are available for computer room applications. Inter-cabinet wiring with mating connectors is supplied with the external battery cabinet (for 3.5–12.0 kVA only). The external battery cabinet contains two fuses per string, to provide individual string protection and isolation. The external battery cabinet increases power outage reserve time to (___) minutes at full load, when operating in an ambient temperature between 20 and 30° C.

Battery cabinets containing their own AC-DC chargers are available for applications requiring run times greater than 4 hours.

Dual Input (Optional on 8.0–18.0 kVA UPS Modules)

The UPS is provided with a separate input terminal block to provide the UPS with dual input capabilities. This separate feed is single-phase, 3-wire-plus-ground to match the UPS output configuration. The UPS inverter tracks the bypass source per parameters specified.

Field Quality Control

The following inspections and test procedures are performed by factory-trained field service personnel during the UPS start-up:

- Visual Inspection
  - Inspect equipment for signs of shipping or installation damage
  - Verify installation per drawings
  - Inspect cabinets for foreign objects
  - Verify neutral and ground conductors are properly sized and configured
  - Inspect battery cases
  - Inspect battery for proper polarity
  - Verify all printed circuit boards are configured properly
- Mechanical Inspection
  - Check all control wiring connections for tightness
  - Check all power wiring connections for tightness
  - Check all terminal screws, nuts, and/or spade lugs for tightness
- Electrical Inspection
  - Check all fuses for continuity
  - Confirm input voltage and phase rotation is correct
  - Verify control transformer connections are correct for voltages being used
  - Assure connection and voltage of the battery string(s).

Unit Start-up and Site Testing

Site testing is provided by the manufacturer's field service personnel if requested. Site testing consists of a complete test of the UPS system and the associated accessories supplied by the manufacturer. A partial battery discharge test is provided as part of the standard start-up procedure. The test results are documented, signed, and dated for future reference.

Manufacturer's Field Service

Service Personnel

The UPS manufacturer directly employs a nationwide service organization, consisting of factory-trained Customer Engineers dedicated to the start-up, maintenance, and repair of UPS and power equipment. The organization consists of factory-trained Customer Engineers working out of district offices in most major cities. An automated procedure is in place to insure that the manufacturer is dedicating the appropriate technical support resources to match escalating customer needs.

The manufacturer provides a fully automated national dispatch center to coordinate field service personnel schedules. One toll-free number reaches a qualified support person 24 hours/day, 7 days/week, 365 days/year. If emergency service is required, call-back response time from a local Customer Engineer is 20 minutes or less.

Replacement Parts Stocking

Parts are available through an extensive network to ensure around-the-clock parts availability throughout the country. Replacement spare parts are stocked by local Customer Engineers with backup available from district service offices and the manufacturing location. Customer Support Parts Coordinators are on call 24 hours a day, 7 days a week, 365 days a year for immediate parts availability.

UPS Maintenance Training

Maintenance training courses for customer employees are available by the UPS manufacturer. This training is in addition to the basic operator training conducted as a part of the system start-up.

The training course covers UPS theory, location of subassemblies, safety, battery considerations and UPS operational procedures. The course includes AC to DC conversion and DC to AC inversion techniques as well as control, metering, and feedback circuits to the Printed Circuit Board (PCB) level. Troubleshooting and fault isolation using alarm information and internal self-diagnostics are stressed.

Maintenance Contracts

A complete offering of preventive and full-service maintenance contracts for both the UPS system and battery system is available. An extended warranty and preventive maintenance package are available. Warranty and preventive maintenance service is performed by factory-trained Customer Engineers.

These guide specifications comply with the format outlined by the Construction Specifications Institute per CSI MP-2-1 and CSI MP-2-2. In correspondence, refer to Liebert document SL-24860 (R9/93).

Liebert Corporation Year 2000 Product Compliance Statement

Liebert Corporation certifies that all Liebert software and firmware accompanying Liebert manufactured Air Conditioning, Power Conditioning and Distribution (PCD), and Uninterruptible Power Supply (UPS) products **are Year 2000 compliant**. Attached is a list of products covered by this statement.

These Liebert products will function and operate as warranted in accordance with their performance specifications without regard for calendar year changes. Year 2000 compliant product design features consist of:

- Device functionality
- Date data century recognition
- Calculations that accommodate same century and multi-century formulas and data values
- Date data interface values that reflect the century.

Liebert product resident monitoring firmware does no sorting or processing by date; products only store and retrieve alarms. The date generator will work properly irrespective of calendar year changes, so alarm histories will remain intact and correct. Imbedded firmware in all microprocessor applications uses time increments and does not process dates. Therefore, all products will operate properly, and all alarm dates will be displayed on the customer display correctly.

Liebert product-monitoring front-end software (SiteScan® 2000W, SiteScan® SS2W, and Alert®, version 2.6) is presently not Year 2000 compliant. This software will be corrected to be Year 2000 compliant with the release of version 3.0. This version is scheduled for release in 1998, and will be available as an upgrade revision for all current SiteScan® systems. Liebert Access Control Security Systems are not Year 2000 compliant.

Product Compliance

Liebert is committed to providing its customers quality state-of-the-art products and timely solutions to current and future needs. The products below, when operated by Liebert imbedded firmware, Liebert controls, and/or Liebert software, are Year 2000 compliant:

ENVIRONMENTAL

Atlas PEC	Dealermate	Logicool®	Process Chiller
Challenger	Deluxe System 2	LS400	Quantum
Climate 3000	Deluxe System 3	Mini Air	Slimcool
CoolGuard	Deluxe System 4	Mini Tower	Small Systems Monitors
Condensers	Drycoolers	MiniMate	Spacemaster-SX
COP-SX	Industrial Cooling Series	MiniMate Plus	
CSU3000	Intelecool®	Modular 3000	
Datamate	Leak Detection System	Modular Plus	
Data Pad®	Little Glass House™	Modupac Chiller	

UPS & POWER PRODUCTS

Accupower®	Powersure™ Interactive	Series 4000	Sitenet® SNMP Manager
AL 300	PPD6300	Series 7200	TVSS/Surge Suppressor
AL 3300	Precision Power Center	Series 7200 1 + 1	Transformers
AP 70X	Resource	Series 7200 HE	UPStation® D
AP 200	Select	Series 7200 Single Phase	UPStation®G
AP 400	Series AP100 (1xx)	Series 7400	UPStation® G RT
AP 4300	Series AP300 (3xx)	Series 8000, 9000	UPStation®GX
Data Wave®	Series AP500 (5xx)	Static Transfer Switch	UPStation®GXT
MicroUPS™	Series AP600 (6xx)	SmartSwitch	UPStation®S
PowerMate™	Series 600T	Sitenet®Integrat or™	UPStation®S-3
Powersure™	Series AP700 (70x)	Sitenet® 1, and 2	

On-Site Access Control Software and Year 2000 Compliance

The OEM supplier states that the On-Site Access Control software is *not* Year 2000 compliant. This non-compliance includes Liebert On-Site/4, On-Site/10, On-Site/16, On-Site/64, and On-Site/128, the latest DOS version Liebert has been marketing. There are both external and internal causes of non-compliance:

External to On-Site Software

The On-Site software relies upon the system clock controlled by the BIOS of the host PC. Depending on the DOS version, when the year rolls over from 1999 to 2000, the system clock may fail to make the transition properly (for example, treating "00" as 1900 instead of 2000). If uncorrected, the On-Site software will receive incorrect timestamp information. If the date is manually corrected, the system clock should proceed to function properly.

Internal to On-Site Software

The On-Site software records dates using the two-digit format. This outdated strategy means that date comparison operations may not function properly. Functions that perform date comparisons include:

- **Transactions history reports.** These will not be able to span across the new millenium. Two separate reports—one for the 20th century dates, another for the 21st century dates—need to be performed. Note that transactions will continue to be logged with the timestamp as supplied by the system BIOS.
- **User access cards** have an optional "expiration date" feature, which relies on two-digit date comparisons. This feature can be disabled.
- The **overall access control system** should still accurately maintain its basic functionality, as the distributed IGMs (information gathering modules—door controllers for determining access) do not perform calculations involving dates.

On November 30, 1997 Liebert Corporation announced a decision to discontinue the sale of the On-Site Access Control product family of software and hardware components. This is in keeping with ongoing efforts to provide only products that directly tie into existing Environmental and UPS/Power market strategies. Liebert Corporation has evaluated a recommended supplier who can continue to support Access

Control products for customers. This supplier has demonstrated backward compatibility to the existing On-Site systems and full Year 2000 compliancy for software and hardware components. Contact a local Liebert Representative to obtain more information and product specifications. For more information, contact webmaster@liebertweb.com.

Summary

Electrical needs in a network are many times taken for granted. Understanding the terminology and instruments used to obtain information about the electrical environment is essential. This chapter presented terminology and basic information to use as a reference in beginning to consider the electrical needs for an environment. Use great caution when working with electricity; it is not to be played with.

The UPS used in my network is sufficient for my needs. I included this level of detail a reference in beginning a network design. Liebert is a recommended power source for all your needs.

CHAPTER 5

Network Components

This chapter presents the logical network design I created before obtaining any equipment. After the design is explained, sections in this and the following chapter discuss the components that comprise the network.

I began this network design the same way I have begun all others; literally at the drawing board. I use a marker board to work out ideas. This can take days, sometimes weeks to sift through the requirements, my thoughts, and variations on what equipment is needed and how it fits into the overall design scheme.

The network design explained in this chapter and those ahead, is based more on principle than a given piece of technology. The purpose of the network design here is to meet current needs and sustain growth. The original design intent of this network is to do what I want it to do now and be flexible enough to change and accommodate growth in the near future.

Before examining the components of the network, consider the logical network design as shown in Figure 5.1.

FIGURE 5.1
Logical Network
Design

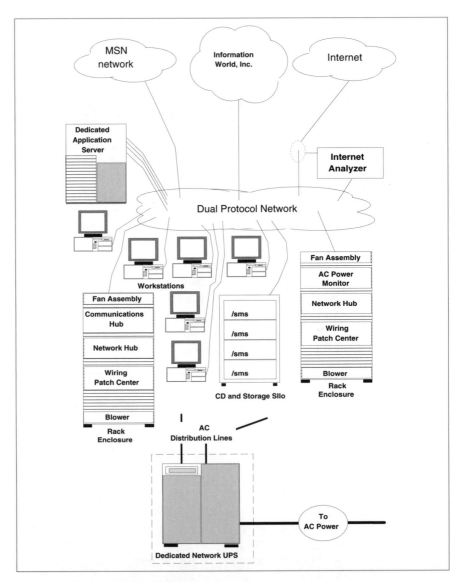

Notice the illustration shows numerous network components. Some are not shown in great detail, such as network interface cards, particular wiring, etc. However the figure does show the overall logical design of the network. Close inspection of the figure may tend to imply a single point of failure in a given place, but redundancies have been built into it.

This logical network design was driven by user requirements. The network enables users to exchange files, e-mail, and remote logons with systems such as servers, and even use network printing.

Component Overview

Before examining each component, this section provides a list of components that are part of the network explained in further detail in Chapters 6 and 7. The list includes a variety of components, the major components selected for use in this network, but is in no particular order.

Network Component List

- Rack enclosures (Great Lakes Cabinets)
- Network Hubs (BAY Networks)
- Network printer (IBM)
- Network storage silo (SMS Data Products Group)
- Oscilloscope (Tektronix)
- Cable tester (WaveTek LANPRO XL)
- Network server (IBM Netfinity 7000)
- Microsoft Windows 95
- Microsoft Windows NT
- Uninterruptable power supply (Liebert)
- 6 and 8 gauge wire (General Cable)
- Pass & Seymour plugs, outlets, pin and sleeve, and other electrical components
- Commercial desktop computers (IBM)
- Remote workstations (IBM ThinkPads)
- 3Com USRobotics enterprise network hub
- Multimedia devices (Creative Labs)
- Infrastructure components (Thomas & Betts)
- Ethernet adapters and SCSI interface boards (Adaptec)
- Network security and virus protection software (McAfee)
- Network tape drive (Sony)

- Electrical cable (Belden)
- Cables (serial, parallel, SCSI, gender changers, SCSI terminators, IEEE 1284 compliant printer cables, etc.) (Belkin)
- Jeteye infrared network interface

Rack Enclosures (Great Lakes Cabinets)

Network design includes a wide variety of equipment. The size and type network design you build will determine to some degree what components you will use. Most networks include rack mount equipment. The network I designed and built required multiple cabinets. See Figure 5.2.

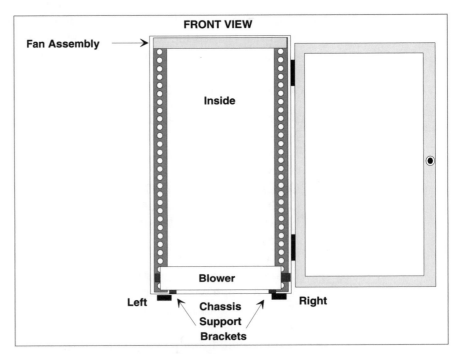

FIGURE 5.2
Great Lakes
Cabinet Front
View

I selected Great Lakes Cabinets because they have a unique characteristic: they are made of light-weight steel but are very durable. The significance of this cannot be overstated. When six or more rack cabinets are used to house network equipment the weight of these cabinets becomes an important factor.

Great Lakes Cabinets have the standard offerings of other cabinet makers: pullout shelves and stationary shelves. However, the unique selection of metal and design makes the shelves easy to work with but capable of handling heavy objects. Two Great Lakes Cabinets I used in this network design have IBM monitors and other equipment on a single shelf. This is significant because of the sheer weight of the equipment.

The Great Lakes cabinets used in this network were configured with the following:

- Removable side panels
- 6-Position power strip
- Dual packaged blowers
- Front and rear mounting adjustments
- Front and rear sliding mounting adjustments
- Fan trays with nine 75CFM fans
- Filler panels (3.50" and 1.5")
- Single-sided cable organizer
- Plexiglass doors
- Gray with highlighted black trim
- Vented steel rear door.

Another attractive aspect of these cabinets is the inside, side accessibility enabling reaching around installed components. They actually have more *inside* space between the side panel and the rack mount space. This makes maneuverability with mounted equipment easier. These cabinets also have a considerably larger opening in the bottom of the cabinet for air flow.

Network Hubs (Bay Networks)

Bay Networks has well designed internetworking equipment. The following information was obtained from Bay Networks and best describes the products used in this network.

"The BayStack 350T-HD is Bay Networks newest, high-density, low-cost Ethernet switch with 24 autosense 10BASE-T/100-BASE-TX ports. The 350T-HD facilitates high-density switched configurations in the wiring closet, for maximum price-per-port value, an important consideration for enterprise customers. As network performance requirements increase, any equipment upgrades from 10 Mbps to 100 Mbps will be autosensed and supported without administrative intervention.

The versatile switch can be used as a 10 Mbps segment switch, a 10+100 segment switch, a 10+100 Mbps desktop switch, a 100 Mbps segment switch or a 100 Mbps desktop switch. The BayStack 350T-HD has 24 auto-negotiating ports that operate in either 10BASE-T or 100BASE-TX mode. Any of the switched ports can be used for uplinks to network or data centers. Each port supports automatically adjusting, high-speed, full-duplex connections to servers or backbone switches, or half-duplex connections to legacy network interface cards (NICs) and hubs.

The BayStack 250 Series of autosense 10BASE-T/100BASE-TX hubs is a medium-density, stackable 10/100 Mbps Ethernet repeater system. With prices as low as $75 per port and featuring a multi-segment cascade with advanced management capabilities, the BayStack 250 Series 10/100 hubs deliver industry leading price/performance, feature-rich hubs that offer both SNMP- and built-in, web-based management. Three versions of the BayStack 250 10/100 hubs are available: BayStack 250, a 12-port model with built-in network management module (NMM) and an integrated 10/100 segment switch; and BayStack 251 and 252; 12 and 24 port manageable models that can be used within the stack or for stand-alone connectivity. Up to five units can be stacked for 112 managed ports.

The BayStack 200 Series 100BASE-TX Hubs are available in four versions: a 12-port model with built-in network management module (NMM); a 12-port model with built-in NMM and 100BASE-FX port; plus 12- and 24-port manageable models that can be used within the stack or for stand-alone connectivity where management is not required. BayStack 200 hubs are economical, easy-to-use, feature-rich hubs that deliver network flexibility and reliability with both SNMP and web-based management. Up to eight units can be stacked for 180 managed ports."

In this network two autosense switches are used. Consider Figure 5.3.

Notice that the Bay Network hubs provide the concentration point for the network backbone. These are Ethernet hubs, actually 10/100 Mbps autosense switches. These hubs are ideal to used in a mixed Ethernet network.

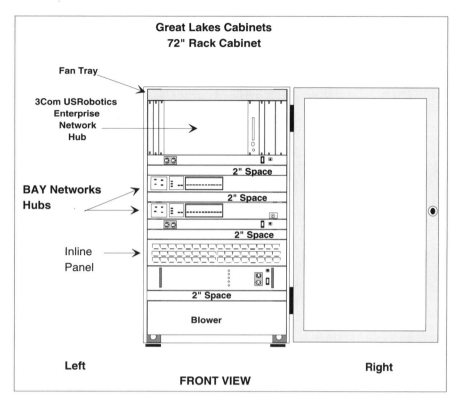

FIGURE 5.3
Bay Networks
Hubs

Network Printer (IBM)

Based upon performance, price, and maintenance cost the IBM network printer 17 is probably the best fit for networks of this scale and a little larger. The model 17 was determined to be the best fit. The following features/functions factored into that reasoning during the decision process. Before examining all features/functions of this printer, consider the first list of *standard* features/functions.

- 17 pages per minute
- 600 x 600 resolution
- Up to 5 addressable input trays
- 4MB RAM (optional to 66 MB)
- PCL5e standard language (postscript, IPDS, SCS optional)
- Auto language switching with options
- Auto I/O switching
- Standard parallel with two network interface slots.

The following options were added to the printer to make it capable of meeting the needs of all users on the network.

- 75 envelope feeder
- Ethernet interface
- Token ring interface
- 24 MB RAM
- Postscript language option level 2
- 500-sheet 2nd paper tray
- Duplex unit
- 10-bin secured mailbox unit

This printer arrived on a pallet weighing approximately 250 pounds (entire pallet weight). The printer itself is 40.9 pounds (18.6 Kilograms). With all options installed the dimensions are: 31" height, 25" front-to-back, and 17" wide and weight about 65 pounds. (These are my measurements made including space for rear cabling, etc. and are approximations.)

The printer was chosen because of its flexibility and power. Notice it supports IPDS and SCS character strings. This is valuable because if the network should need a system which uses either of these character strings for printing the printer itself is already capable of handling it.

Intelligent Printer Data Stream (IPDS) is used between an IBM host and a printer; generally this refers to an SNA environment. This data stream is used with an all-points addressable printer. IPDS can intermix text and graphics—both vector-and raster-based. An SCS character string is a protocol used with printers and certain terminals in the SNA environment. LU1 and LU6.2 can use this data stream. One unique aspect of this data stream is its lack of data flow control functions. The significance of the model 17 printer chosen for this network should not be overlooked. When the need arises for a host running MVS and VTAM the *current* printer can be used with it. This is another example of building success into the network.

Because the printer is on the network all network users can take advantage of it. An off-site user who desires to work on the network from a remote location, print something to someone, and have that document secure, can do so.

Figure 5.4 shows a remote user connecting via a switched line to the network. The "network" in this example is viewed as the equipment in the rack enclosure. It includes all devices participating in it. This example shows the remote user working with a file on the NT server, which then sends the file to the printer. The printer prints it and sends it to bin #3 where the owner of bin #3 must enter a code to receive the print.

Users onsite where the printer is installed have free access to it, with the exception of those who require secured access through the mailbox feature.

FIGURE 5.4
IBM Network
Printer

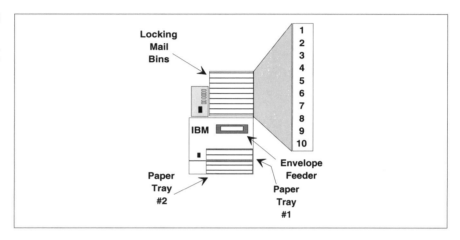

Author's Comment

The IBM model 17 printer arrived on a pallet as described previously. From time of delivery until the printer was operational one man day elapsed. I estimate about 2 hours for unpacking the printer and reading material IBM supplies. Assembling the various components (accessories) for the printer was easy. IBM designed the printer so that minimal tools are needed to install it. More than likely, you will require longer to configure it and integrate the network workstations and servers than actually to set up the printer.

IBM has a wealth of information that can assist in your network plans. You can reach IBM at: Internet:www.ibm.com; International Business Machines, Department M7FE, BLDG.003G, P. O. Box 190, Boulder, CO 80301.

Network Storage Silo (SMS Data Products Group)

The primary driving force behind the decision for SMS Data Products was ease-of-use.

Figure 5.5 shows the SMS network server with the following components:

- 28 Bay rack
- 25 CD-ROM drives
- 1 Barracuda hard disk drive
- 1 CD-ROM recorder
- 1 Jaz drive
- 1 AXIS storpoint module
- 1 NetWare connectivity module.

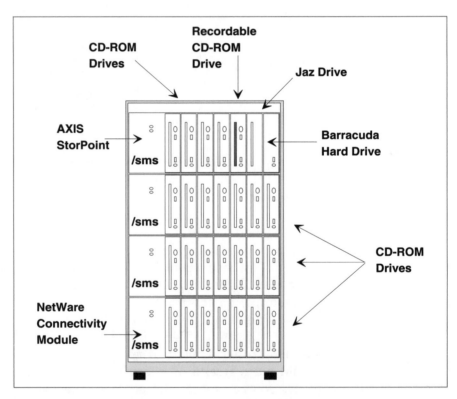

FIGURE 5.5
SMS Network
Storage Silo

Technically, the 28-bay tower from SMS can be configured any way you want it when it is ordered. For example, it could have three recordable CDs, four Barracuda hard drives, and multiple Jaz drives. Or, it could have 28 CD-ROM drives. The above configuration was selected because of the power behind this array for network implementation.

The simplicity in SMS products is one aspect that makes them powerful assets to a network.

SMS has other products, too many to mention here; below is the information provided by SMS Data Products Group.

Millennia Series S70028

The Millennia Series S70028 comes with 28 CD-ROM drive cells in a single frame using 4 Series 700 chassis that can be integrated with connectivity modules for Novell, Windows NT and the Web. The core of the Millennia Series is the Series 700 chassis: a robust, standards-based platform that can be preconfigured as an S70028.

Each 7-drive rack chassis can be separated into 4 individual towers and the following characteristics apply:

- Network direct connectivity modules for any network
- Scales up from 28 to 196 drives
- Swappable drives, LAN connectivity modules and power supplies
- Locking door
- 3-year advanced replacement warranty
- UL; FCC-B certified.

Standard SCSI

S70028S—A preconfigured SCSI server-attached workgroup enclosure consisting of four Series 700 chassis and 28 standard CD-ROM drive cells.

Network Direct for Novell

S70028NOV—A Novell network-direct 28 CD-ROM drive cell enclosure using four Series 700 towers with a Novell connectivity module. It comes complete with everything needed to install and access CD-ROMs on your network. Token ring version part number is S70028NOVTR.

Network Direct for Windows NT

S70028NT—A Windows NT network-direct 28 CD-ROM drive cell enclosure using four Series 700 towers with a Windows NT connectivity module. It comes complete with everything needed to install and access CD-ROMs on your network. Token ring version part number is S70028NTTR.

NETower for Windows NT

A NETower uses a built-in AXIS StorPoint connectivity module for Windows NT, WFW, Banyan Vines, UNIX, LAN Manager and OS/2 environments. It has the following features:

- Plugs directly into network node
- No software required
- Multiple CDs as one drive letter
- No dedicated file server necessary
- Token ring or Ethernet
- CD-ROM license metering
- No SCSI interface card to install
- Allows unlimited users
- SCSI 12X speed drives
- RJ45 and AUI connections
- Easy installation
- Easy sharing of CD-ROMS. The NETower allows several users to access CDs at the same time. No more changing discs and no need to search for discs around the office. Up to seven CD-ROM drives per NETower.
- Security and license. User access can be controlled by password. The number of users can also be restricted.
- Designed for mixed LAN Environment. Can be used simultaneously from Windows, OS/2, DOS, and UNIX.
- Location independent. Can be placed anywhere on the network, and does not need a file server.
- Quick to install and easy to use. Special drivers or software are not needed. Configuration and management is done via already existing application tools. 12X speed CD-ROM drives are supported through use of 32-bit RISC processor technology.
- Supported protocols. SMB, NetBIOS/NetBEUI, NFS, TCP, UDP, IP, RARP, BOOTP, SNMP, HTTP, FTP.
- Supported file systems. High Sierra (HSF), ISO 9660.

In addition, NETowers come with a one-year warranty, universal power supply and a powerful cooling fan. The FCC-B, UL and CUL listing labels indicate quality and safety.

SMS AXIS StorPoint Connectivity Module

This is a serverless solution for Windows NT & UNIX CD-ROM Networking. The AXIS StorPoint CD/T provides a flexible and cost-effective solution for sharing CD-ROM discs over networks, making all CDs easily accessible to all users at all times.

It attaches directly to the network without involving any file server or additional software. The AXIS StorPoint CD/T is a CD-ROM server that enables users to access and share CD-ROMs over the network. No more changing of discs or searching for them around the office. Place it where needed and connect up to seven CD-ROM drives and up to 56 discs to each unit.

The Axis StorPoint makes the SMS tower easy to use on any network. The CDs appear just like shared discs to all users. AXIS StorPoint CD/T can be used with NetWare, UNIX, Windows (including Windows NT and Windows 95), OS/2 and WWW/Intranet simultaneously. It is easily set up using platform independent Web-based management.

The Axis Storpoint is file server-independent. This approach allows peer-to-peer communication between the client and the CD-ROM server, which keeps the network traffic to a minimum, giving users direct, fast and familiar access to all CDs.

The server can also function as an Internet/intranet Web server. A built-in Web server makes it possible to access the CDs using any Web browser (e.g. Internet Explorer or Netscape Navigator). Put Web pages on a CD-ROM for a quick Web site).

The Axis StorPoint Technical Specifications include:

- **Network Systems.** Simultaneous operation in the following network environments: Novell: NetWare 3.11, 3.12 and 4.10; Windows 95, Windows NT, Windows for Workgroups; Microsoft LAN Manager 1.
- **File Systems and Protocols.** Simultaneous operation of the following file systems: NetWare: NCP over IPX; Windows, OS/2: SMB over NetBIOS and TCP/IP, SMB over NetBIOS and NetBEUI; UNIX: NFS over UDP/IP, TCP, ARP, RARP, B.
- **CD-ROM Standards.** ISO 9660, High Sierra (HSF), Multisession, ISO 9660 Rock Ridge.
- **Installation.** NetWare shows up as a NetWare file server. Mount with NetWare tools. All CDs can be mounted under one drive letter. Windows shows up as an NT server; mount in Explorer or File Manager.

- **Network Management.** SNMP MIB-II and private enterprise MIB. Platform-independent configuration and status monitoring via standard Web browser.
- **Software Updates.** Flash memory allows central and remote software updates over the network using FTP over TCP/IP.
- **Security.** The server unit can be user/group access-controlled by password and the number of users, specified in unit resident database, can be restricted. NetWare has encrypted passwords. Authorization is via file server, including NDS.
- **Performance.** Network throughput up to 900 kbytes/s.
- **Logical Connection.** Ethernet: IEEE802.2, IEEE802.3, SNAP, DIX and Ethernet II frame types simultaneously. Token ring: IEEE 802.2, IEEE802.3 (with early token release support for16 Mbps) frame types simultaneously.
- **Network Attachment.** Ethernet: 10baseT (twisted pair) and 10base2 (thin). Token ring: STP (Media Type 1/DB9) and UTP (Media Type 3/RJ45).
- **Hardware.** CPU: 32-bit RISC processor. Flash Memory: 2 Mbytes; RAM: 2 Mbytes, 32 Mbytes cache expansion.

RAID: The S700HDA

The S700HDA is the cornerstone of your future data storage architecture. It is a universal, standards-based storage platform for hard disk, CD-ROM, DVD and tape storage devices delivered on multiple and redundant SCSI and fiber channel data I/O paths.

High Availability

Beyond hot swap, the S700HDA provides automatic hot-spare failover. RAID levels 1, 0/1 and 5 can be configured on the fly. There is superior physical fault tolerance with active/inactive automatic failover power and cooling. Logical fault tolerance is further enhanced with real-time predictive failure sensing and reporting for each drive.

High Performance

Utilizing advanced Adaptec parity and calculating and caching technology, data are mobilized faster than native with OS and server manufacturer "RAID-like" solutions. For blazing speed, parity calculations are performed via a coprocessor accelerator on a separate, yet parallel data I/O path. SCSI channels support data transfer rates up to 40Mb/sec. FC-AL backplane options will support 100Mb/sec burst rates and beyond.

High Capacity

The S700HDA chassis meets the cooling and vibration isolation requirements of both current and future drive densities. The S700HDA is always available with the latest drive densities for the maximum storage capacity per array. As storage densities of drives double each year, the capacity of this subsystem will keep pace.

Low Cost

Utilizing the latest storage technologies, the S700HDA is not bound by the cost structures of legacy systems. The fresh and modular approach delivers advanced storage features at prices comparable to those of just the raw drives included with servers and legacy subsystems.

Storage Management

The S700HDA Array Management software is the command center for the network manager. Monitor and command the enterprise's storage subsystem from any workstation.

Reconfigure Arrays

Reconfiguration is a point and click away, simply highlight the drives from the graphical interface. Bar graphs instantly show data protection and performance trade-offs among the RAID levels you select. Multiple arrays, spares and banks of spares can be configured both within each chassis and across subsystems.

View Array and Device Information

On a single screen, physical and logical array configurations, individual channel and PCI host information are provided. Capacities, availability and predictive failure data are instantly displayed.

Monitor Array Activity

Color-coded messages and charts alert the system administrator to all array activity. Status indicators depict all active fault-tolerant and critical states. Real-time predictive failure sensing and analysis allows disks to be replaced before failure.

Features and Benefits

- Active hot spare
  - Enables fast rebuild of a failed disk
  - No user intervention required
- Active/Inactive power supplies and cooling fans
  - Improve data integrity
  - Improve data availability
  - Eliminate single point of failure
- Swappable and field-replaceable drives
  - Minimal downtime when replacing failed drives
  - Easily upgrade to the latest hard disk capacities
- RAID coprocessor
  - Offloads parity calculations and controlled tasks
  - Frees the CPU for other I/O tasks
- Racks mounts instantly
  - Standard 19" rack
  - Easy data management and expandability
- 3-Year advanced replacement warranty
  - Replacement products shipped overnight
- Scalable storage capacity
  - Expand on initial investment
  - Storage capacity grows with network requirements
- Unlimited, toll-free technical support
  - Fast response
  - Assurance of support for the life of the product
- Compatible with Windows NT and Novell
- FCC-B approved and UL listed.

Discport Pro XL

This is a high-performance CD-ROM networking solution that enables NetWare and Windows NT workgroups to share up to 14 CD-ROM devices simultaneously. The CD-ROM sharing solution should keep up wth the demands of the growing network. To find Windows NT and NetWare compatibility, increased speed and performance—look no further than DiscPort PRO, the CD-ROM networking solution for workgroups that offers speed and compatibility in one. With DiscPort PRO, you can access CD devices as easily as accessing an application on a file server.

DiscPort Pro and CD Sharing

DiscPort PRO is easy to install and requires no TSRs or client software on workstations. Attach DiscPort PRO anywhere on your Thin Ethernet or 10BASE-T network and install DiscView PRO management software. Attach up to 14 CD-ROM devices per DiscPort PRO and load your CD-ROM titles. DiscPort PRO supports 8X CD-ROM drives on your 10 Mbps Ethernet network and works with popular CD-ROM drives, towers and disc changers. As your network grows, it is easy to add more DiscPort PROs, and other Microtest workgroup products or Enterprise solutions. All Microtest CD-ROM Networking products work together seamlessly.

- One product, DiscPort PRO, supports both NetWare and Windows NT networks
- Easy to install, DiscPort PRO plugs into any network connection
- Includes two (2) SCSI ports, providing network users simultaneous access to as many as 14 CD-ROM devices per DiscPort PRO
- Lets you physically place CDs within workgroups, allowing local control of and access to CD-ROM libraries
- Includes DiscView PRO graphical user interface making DiscPort PRO easy to manage and use
- Supports multiple protocols including IPX/SPX and TCP/IP
- DiscPort PRO works seamlessly with additional DiscPort PROs or other Microtest Workgroup and Enterprise solutions.

One Device Supports NetWare and Windows NT Networks

Whether you're running NetWare, Windows NT or a combination, DiscPort PRO works with both operating systems. Administrators will find sharing CD-ROMs effortless with DiscView PRO software, Microtest's CD-ROM management interface. DiscView PRO includes SmartLaunch, the totally transparent user interface that allows users to access CD-ROM titles with point-and-click simplicity. DiscView PRO supports ISO 9660, HFS (Macintosh), CD-Bridge and Photo CDs on NetWare and ISO 9660 on Windows NT. DiscView PRO allows CD-ROM sharing using as little as 6K of RAM per CD, auto mounts and shares CDs instantly, and offers dynamic security and support for volume sets. CD-ROMs can appear as subdirectories under a single volume, so there is no need to map and unmap numerous drive letters.

DiscPort PRO comes complete with DiscView PRO, Windows-based software for easy CD-ROM installation, management and use. DiscView PRO:

- Allows your networked CD-ROMs to appear as subdirectories of a single drive letter—no need to map and unmap numerous DOS drive letters
- Integrates NetWare and NT security, caching, and usage statistics for your CD-ROMs
- Integrates with NetWare Directory Services (NDS) and NT Domains
- Instantly mounts and shares CD-ROM titles
- Provides cache control for managing serve resources
- Offers drag-and-drop CD-ROM management
- Offers dynamic security and dynamic volume sets for easy management.

DiscView PRO's SmartLaunch provides any user easy access to entire libraries of CD-ROMs. SmartLaunch:

- Automatically prepares and mounts your CD-ROMs—users can access titles with point-and-click simplicity
- CD format support includes ISO 9660 (NT), and ISO 9660, HFS (Macintosh), CD-I/Bridge and Photo CDs
- Allows easy access by DOS, Windows, Macintosh, UNIX, and OS/2 clients to CD-ROMs attached to DiscPort PRO
- Specifications
  - SCSI Port with two high density Mini-D connectors, one MiniD-to-SCSI 50 pin cable included and SCSI II protocol
- FileServer requirements
  - Novell NetWare 3.11 or higher with 8 MB of RAM or
  - Windows NT 3.51 (Intel-based) with 16 MB RAM
- Ethernet compatibility
  - Thin Ethernet RG-58 A/U BNC, and 10BASE-T twisted-pair RJ-45 connectors
  - IPX: 802.2, 802.3, Ethernet II, or SNAP frame types
  - TCP/IP: Ethernet II frame types
- Workstation requirements
  - Windows 3.1 or higher recommended
  - At least 4MB recommended for Windows users

- Macintosh users must run System 6.0.7 or higher
- Novell NetWare for Macintosh installed

Tektronix Oscilloscope

I selected a Tektronix model THS720P TekScope Isolated Channel Scope/DMM to use in this network. This device is one of the most (if not the most) powerful tools on the market today. It includes an oscilloscope and a digital multimeter. These are implemented as distinct and separate functions in the scope. In addition, the oscilloscope has two channels, which makes for powerful analysis.

The Tekscope is ideal for electric/power electronics applications. According to Tektronix:

It combines a full-featured 100 MHz bandwidth and 500 MS/s sample rate Digital Real-Time oscilloscope with a True RMS digital multimeter in a rugged, battery-operated instrument. Scope and meter modes can operate simultaneously and independently on the same or separate signals. The high-resolution, backlit display and pop-up menus make it easy for users to take full advantage of the instrument's many features. These include cursors, video trigger, voltage and resistance measurements, and storage of waveforms, data, and instrument setups. The THS720P includes features specifically for electric/power electronics measurements which allow testing and verifying correct operation of motors, checking transformer efficiency, verifying power-supply performance, and measuring the effect of neutral current. It also contains the powerful features of a modern oscilloscope that enable troubleshooting and verification of complicated electronic control circuits controlling the high-voltage power-electronics circuitry. The THS720P shares measurement features with the THS730A, THS720A, THS710A Scope/DMMs, which are ideal for electronic applications.

Consider the following characteristics and specifications as provided by Tektronix. The characteristics of the handheld battery operated oscilloscope/DMM Model THS720P include:

Oscilloscope Functions:

- Bandwidth—100 MHz
- Sample Rate (Each Channel)—500 MS/s

- Channels—Two
- Sensitivity—5 mV to 50 V/div (to 500 V/div with 10X probe)
- Position Range—±10 divisions
- DC Gain Accuracy —2% sample or average acquisition mode
- Vertical Resolution—8-Bits
- Record Length—2500 points
- Time/Division Range—5 ns to 50 s/div
- Horizontal Accuracy—±200 ppm over any ≥1 ms time interval
- Roll Mode— >/= 0.5 s/div
- Autorange—User-selectable
- Trigger Modes—Auto, normal
- Trigger Types—Edge, pulse, video, motor, external
- Video Trigger Formats and Field Rates—Odd field, even field, and line
- Motor Trigger—Triggers on 3- and 5-level pulse-width modulated power signal
- External Trigger Input—5 MHz TTL compatible
- Harmonics—Up to 31st (30hz-450hz)
- Waveform Processing—add, subtract, multiply, calculate watts = V x I
- Waveform Storage—10 waveforms
- Acquisition Modes—sample, envelope, average, peak detect
- Cursor Measurements—DELTAVolts, DELTATime, 1/DELTATime (Hz), Degree (phase).
- Cursor Types—Horizontal bars, vertical bars, paired (volts @ time)
- Display System—Interpolation: Sin(x)/x
- Mode—Vector, dot, vector accumulate, dot accumulate
- Format—YT and XY.

Automatic Measurements:

Period	Frequency
+Width	Rise Time
–Width	Fall Time
+Duty Cycle	+Overshoot
–Duty Cycle	–Overshoot
High	Max
Low	Min
Peak-to-Peak	Amplitude
Mean	RMS
Cycle Mean	Cycle RMS
Burst	Width

Power Measurements:

W	True power
VA	Apparent power
VAR	Reactive power
V	Volts (RMS, Peak)
A	Amps (RMS, Peak)
THD-F	Total harmonic distortion as a percentage of the fundamental
THD-R	Total harmonic distortion of the RMS of the input signal
PF	Power Factor
DPF	Displacement Power Factor
PHI	Phase difference between the voltage and current.

DMM Specifications:

- DC Voltage Ranges—400.0 mV to 880 V
- DC Volts Accuracy—±(0.5% of reading + 5 counts)
- True RMS AC Voltage Ranges—400.0 mV to 640 V
- Maximum Float Voltage—600 VRMS each channel (probe dependent).
- Resolution—4000 count, 3-3/4 digits
- AC Volts Accuracy—±(2% of reading + 5 counts)
- Resistance Ranges—400.0 Ohm to 40.00 MOhm
- Resistance Accuracy—±(0.5% of reading + 2 counts); 40 MOhm: ±(2% of reading + 5 counts)
- Diode Test Range—0 to 2 V
- Continuity Check—Audible tone when <Ohm50 Ohm
- Modes—Min, max, DELTAMax-Min, avg, hold
- Non-volatile Storage—10 DMM screenshots
- External Trigger Input—5 MHz TTL compatible
- Vertical Zoom Capability—2X, 5X, 10X
- dB Scale—Selectable, referenced from 1 mV to 10 V
- dBm Scale—Selectable, referenced from 50 Ohm to 600 Ohm.

General Specifications:

- Setups—10 front-panel setups
- Safety Certification—UL 3111-1 Listed, CSA Certified, complies with EN61010-1
- Power—NiCad rechargeable battery pack with AC adapter (both included)

- Battery Life—Approx. 2 hours from full charge
- Display—Backlit LCD
- Display Resolution—320 x 240.

Physical Characteristics:

Dimensions	mm	in
Width	177	6.95
Height	217	8.53
Depth	51	2
Weight	kg	lbs
Net	1.45	3.2

To provide examples of what the Tekscope can do, I took random readings with it.

Figure 5.6 shows the first sample reading. Notice to the upper right of the figure the scope reads 120.0 VAC. Just beneath that reading it shows channel one reading a frequency of 60.02 cycles. Channel one also shows the peak-to-peak reading of 326.2 volts. In addition, channel one shows an RMS voltage reading of 117.3.

FIGURE 5.6
Sample
Reading #1

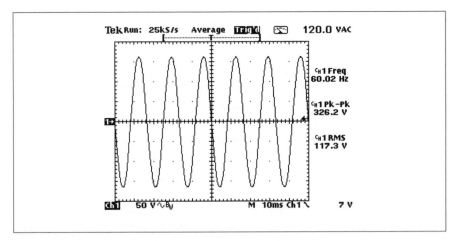

Figure 5.7 shows a voltage reading of 120.1 VAC. It also shows a frequency reading from channel one of 60 cycles. Channel one also shows a positive width of 8.357 milliseconds and a negative width of 8.31 milliseconds. Channel one readings also show the signal amplitude as 326.6 volts.

FIGURE 5.7
Sample
Reading #2

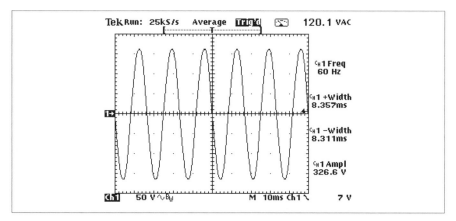

Figure 5.8 shows a voltage reading of 120.0 VAC. Channel one is configured to detect the mean reading and detects a -1.316 reading. Channel one also shows a cycle mean of -1.301. The cycle RMS is 117.3 volts, and the burst width reading is 83.34 milliseconds.

FIGURE 5.8
Sample
Reading #3

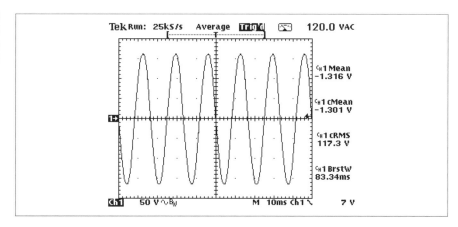

Figure 5.9 shows both channel one and channel two. Channel one is the voltage waveform, channel two shows the amperage waveform. The voltage reading is 120.0 VAC. The amperage draw is 1.977 amps RMS.

As these illustrations show, the Tekscope is a powerful tool for a wide variety of readings. During your network planning, you should determine what devices will be used to collect and maintain power information.

Tektronix has a wide offering of scopes and multi-meters. For more information contact them at: Tektronix, Inc., 26600 S. W. Parkway, P. O. Box 1000, Wilsonville, OR USA 97070-1000, 1-800-TEK-WIDE, www.tektronix.com.

FIGURE 5.9
Sample
Reading #4

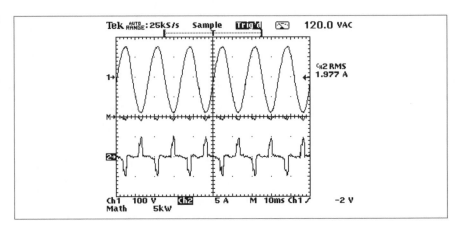

Network Cable Tester (WaveTek LANPro XL)

An integral part of installing and maintaining networks is having accurate information about the components used in the network. The planning phase revealed that the best instrument to use in this network was the Lantek Pro XL cable tester. Some of its features include:

- Autotest Time 25 seconds
- Dual NEXT
- Autotest Suites (reporting pass/fail for each)
  - Line Mapping
  - Length
  - DC Loop ohm
  - Attenuation
  - Dual NEXT
  - ACR
  - Average Impedance
  - Return Loss
  - Delay
- Cable Expert
- TDR (Impedance vs. Length)
- Average Noise (for EMI, RFI)
- Test Storage—500

- Graphical Display 160 X 160
- Flash EEPROM
- Cable Types supported—150*
- AutoSave/AutoPrint

Wavetek also has an instrument call the LanTEK Pro that can be used for cable testing. Its features include:

- Autotest Time 30 seconds
- Dual NEXT
- Autotest Suites (reporting pass/fail for each)
  - Line Mapping
  - Length
  - DC Loop ohm
  - Attenuation
  - Dual NEXT
  - ACR
  - Average Impedance
  - Return Loss
  - Delay
- Cable Expert
- TDR (Impedance vs. Length) (not included)
- Average Noise (for EMI, RFI) (not included)
- Test Storage—500
- Graphical Display 160 X 160
- Flash EEPROM
- Cable Types supported—150*
- AutoSave/AutoPrint.

The LANTEK PRO Series meets or exceeds all TIA requirements for Level II testing.

- Electrical Specifications
  - Line Map
  - 8-wire pin connectivity, cable destination and shield continuity.
- DC Resistance
  - Range 0–400 ohms autoranging
  - Accuracy: ± (1% + 2 ohms)
  - Resolution: 0.1 ohms

---

* Includes, but is not limited to UTP and STP for Category 3-5, ISO(Class B, C, and D), CATV and user-specified cabling. Specifications subject to change.

- Length
  - Range: 0–610 m (0–2000')
  - Accuracy: ± (3% + 3' + NVP uncertainty)
  - Resolution: 0.1m (0.33')
  - Propagation Rate: 0.5 0.99c +0.01
- Impedance
  - Range: 0–400 ohms
  - Accuracy: ± (3% + 1ms)
  - Resolution: 0.1m (0.33')
- Capacitance
  - Range: 0pF–100nF
  - Accuracy: ± (2% + 20pF)
  - Resolution: 1pF min.
- Average (wideband) Noise
  - Range: 0–1 VRMS
  - Bandwidth: 50Hz 30MHz
  - Resolution: 10mV
- Attenuation
  - Swept Frequency Range: 1 Mhz-102MHz
  - Frequency Steps: TIA TSB-67
  - Full Range: 0 to 70dB
  - Dynamic Range: 50dB @ 1MHz to 30dB @100MHz(log curve)
  - Accuracy: ± 1.0dB at channel or basic link
  - Resolution: 0.1dB
- Near End Crosstalk
  - Swept Frequency Range: 1MHz–102MHz
  - Frequency Steps: TIA TSB-67
  - Full Range: 70dB
  - Dynamic Range: 70dB @ 1MHz to 45dB @ 100MHz (log curve)
  - Residual NEXT: 55dB @ 100MHz
  - Accuracy: ± 1.6dB at basic link limit
  - Resolution: 0.1dB
- Delay
  - Range: 0–4000ms
  - Accuracy: ± (3% + 1ms)
  - Resolution: 0.1ns
- Average Impedance
  - Range: 0–400 ohms
  - Accuracy: ± (3% + 1 ohm)
  - Resolution: 1 ohm

- Return Loss
  - Swept Frequency Range: 1MHz–102MHz
  - Dynamic Range: 30dB
  - Accuracy: ± 0.1dB
  - Resolution: 0.1dB
- Environmental Specifications
  - Operating Temperature Range: 0–50°C
  - Temperature Coefficient: 0.1 x spec/°C
  - Storage Temperature Range: -20 to +70°C
  - Relative Humidity: 5–90%, noncondensing
- Mechanical Specifications
  - Display Handset
    Dimensions: 10" x 4.25" x 2.5" (250mm x 108 x 64mm)
    Weight: 1.75 lb (800g)
  - Remote Handset
    Dimensions: 10" x 4.25" x 2.5" (250mm x 108 x 64mm)
    Weight: 1.6 lb (728g)
  - Charging Bay
    Dimensions: 3.15" x 9.65" x 3.75" (80mm x 245mm x 95mm)
    Weight: 2.5 lb (1137g)
    Input Power: 110 volts ±10% or 240 volts + 10% 50 or 60 Hz
    Output Power: 9 VDC, 300MA
- Management
  - Display Handset: 8 hours typical
  - Remote Handset: 14 hours typical
  - Recharging Time: 3 hours or less

Network Server (IBM Netfinity 7000)

After other vendor's systems were evaluated, an IBM Netfinity 7000 was selected to use in this network. The system selected serves a critical role in the network explained in this text.

The Netfinity 7000 is available in tower (rack) and cabinet offerings. A cabinet system was chosen. Model TMO is the cabinet and THO refers to the rack. The most accurate information about the system comes from IBM.

Standard Features

Processor	This is a 200MHz Pentium Pro processor: 8651-RMO, 8651-RHO, 8651-TMO and 8651-THO models 200MHz standard with two dual processor complexes. One of the four ZIF sockets on the two processor complexes is populated, leaving room for up to three 200MHz Pentium Pro processors to be added via 387-pin ZIF sockets.
L2 Cache	8651-RHO and 8651-THO have 1MB of write back set associate cache integrated on each Pentium Pro processor. 8651-RMO and 8651-TMO have 512KB of write back set associate cache integrated on each Pentium Pro processor.
Memory	All models have 256MB ECC DIMMs (4 x 64MB),with 12 sockets available. A maximum system memory of 4GB can be achieved via 16 x 256MB DIMMs. All memory DIMMs are installed into one standard memory card with 16 sockets (2 banks of 8 sockets). Memory DIMMs are at parity with ECC implemented by the memory controller.
Memory Controller	ECC
Hard Drive	8651-RMO, 8651-RHO, 8651-TMO and 8651-THO models have Open bay. A maximum internal disk capacity of 54.6GB can be achieved via 6 x 9.1GB Wide Ultra SCSI hot-swap hard disk drives. 4.51GB Wide Ultra SCSI hot-swap hard disk drives are also supported.
SCSI Controller	All models have 2 x 7880 Wide Ultra SCSI PCI controllers. An IBM ServeRAID II Ultra SCSI Adapter is optional.
Architecture	PCI/EISA with I2O Ready dual PCI bus
Slots	There are 10 slots:
	Slot 1: full-size, 32-bit PCI
	Slot 2: full-size, 32-bit PCI
	Slot 3: full-size, 32-bit PCI
	Slot 4: full-size, 32-bit PCI
	Slot 5: full-size, 32-bit PCI
	Slot 6: full-size, 32-bit PCI;
	Slot 7: full-size, 32-bit EISA or 16-bit ISA
	Slot 8: full-size, 32-bit EISA or 16-bit ISA
	Slot 9: full-size, 32-bit EISA or 16-bit ISA

continued on next page

Slots (cont.)	Slot 10: full-size, 32-bit EISA or 16-bit ISA, Advanced System Management Adapter.
Bays	There are 18 bays. Twelve bays support hot-swap disks:
	Bank A: 6 x 3.5" bays, SL, access, hot-swap
	Bank B: 6 x 3.5" bays, SL, access, hot-swap.
	There are 6 device bays and 5 x 5.25" bays, HH, access, one bay used by CD-ROM drive; there is 1 x 3.5" bay, SL, access, 1.44MB diskette drive.
System Management	All models have one Advanced System Management Adapter
BIOS	512KB of EEPROM, Plug and Play BIOS support
Power Supply	All models have two standard 400 Watts, hot-swap power supplies. There is a hot-swap 400-Watt Redundant Power Supply Option, which backs up the two standard power supplies, and installs in a third power supply bay. All power supplies are PFA enabled.
Cooling	All models have three hot-swap fans. The three cooling fans provide redundancy. If one fan fails, the system will continue to operate safely for a period of time with only two fans.
Diskette Drive	3.5", 1.44 MB
CD-ROM	All models have front tray loading 8X IDE (1200KBps transfer rate and 120ms access time).
Keyboard	8651-TM0 and 8651-TH0 models have Basic 101-key. 8651-RM0 and 8651-RH0 models have optional keyboard
Mouse	8651-TM0 and 8651-TH0 models have an IBM Two-button Mouse, 400 dpi. On the 8651-RM0 and 8651-RH0 models the mouse is optional.
Graphics and Video Resolution	There is integrated RAMDAC with 262,144 color palette supporting SVGA with 512KB of DRAM; up to 1024 x 768 with 16 colors at 72Hz
Ports	There are two 9-pin serial ports, UART 16550A maximum 56KBps, one parallel port (ECP/EPP, IEEE 1284, 2MBps), keyboard, mouse, SVGA and two Wide Ultra SCSI PCI ports.
Security	The System Configuration Utility (SCU) is used to enable keyboard timer, disable keyboard and mouse inputs, enable power-on/reset administrator password and disable writing to diskette drive. A mechanical lock on the front door of the system limits access to

continued on next page

Security (cont.)	drive bays (tower models). Cover-intrusion switches on the top and the front covers provide cover-intrusion alarm warnings. An optional Netfinity Security Cover III can be installed to prevent unauthorized access to external cabling, adapter connectors and ports on the backplane (tower models).
Supported Operating Systems	Microsoft Windows NT 3.51/4.0 Workstation, Microsoft Windows NT 3.51/4.0 Server, Novell NetWare 3.12/4.1/4.11/4.1 SMP, IBM OS/2 Warp 3.0, IBM OS/2 Warp 3.0 with Win-OS/2, IBM OS/2 Warp Connect 3.0, IBM OS/2 SMP V2.11, IBM OS/2 Warp Server V4, IBM OS/2 Warp Server Advanced V4 (includes SMP enhancements), IBM OS/2 LAN Server 4.0 Entry, IBM OS/2 LAN Server 4.0 Advanced, SCO UNIXWare 2.x, SCO Open Server 5.0, SCO Open Desk-Top/Open Server 3.0 and SunSoft Solaris 2.5
Standard Software	IBM ServerGuide, IBM Netfinity Manager 5.1, QAPlus/PRO, IBM AntiVirus, APC PowerChute Plus and Lotus Domino 4.51 (single processor edition).
Support	There is IBM TechConnect and IBM Netfinity start-up support and an IBM HelpCenter.
Warranty	There is a three-year on-site limited warranty: IBM on-site repair, 8:00am to 5:00pm Monday through Friday, with eight-hour average response time.

Weight and Dimensions	Tower models (8651-TMO and 8651-THO):
	    Weight: 120 lbs
	    Height: 19.0", Width: 19.0"
	    Depth: 26"
	    Rack Model (8651-RMO and 8651-RHO):
	    Weight: 120 lbs
	    Height: 19.0"
	    Width: 16.5"
	    Depth: 24"

Legal Notices

1. MHz only measures internal clock speed, not application performance. Many factors affect application performance.
2. When referring to hard drive capacity, MB stands for million bytes and GB stands for billion bytes. Total user-accessible capacity may vary depending on operating environments.

3. For terms and conditions or copies of IBM's limited warranty, call 800-772-2227 in the US Limited warranty includes International Warranty Service in those countries where this statement of product is sold by IBM or IBM Business Partners (registration required).
4. Energy Star compliance: The EPA, as a matter of policy, does not endorse any particular company or its products.
5. Battery Life (and recharge times) will vary based on screen brightness, applications, features, power management, battery conditioning and other references. CD-ROM or hard disk drive usage may also have a significant impact on battery life.
6. Actual specifications may vary slightly depending on features and components.

Netfinity Manager

IBM Netfinity Manager gives total control over the entire Intel-based systems environment. It makes systems management easier by automating many processes. For example, you can monitor systems usage, log events and be alerted in the event of a problem. You have the tools to manage what you want, when you want, wherever you are.

- **Schedule asset management.** Set up routines to back up key systems, poll clients and servers for configuration information and more
- **Head off problems before they start** with Predictive Failure Analysis alerting and configuration information
- **Reduce time and distance** with remote access through IBM Netfinity Manager software and the Advanced System Management Adapter
- **Set up a remote help desk.** Take action to correct client and server systems problems remotely
- **Manage with remote control** over the World Wide Web. Connect to your servers and clients on any standard browser for total control
- **Link to TME10, SMS, OpenView and more.** Complete your total information technology management with integration with your system of choice
- **Manage your clusters** with ease from a single console with IBM Netfinity Cluster Management for Microsoft Cluster Server (when available)

- **Integrate** your multiplatform, multiprotocol systems management solution easily
- **Reduce total cost** of ownership by controlling many of the costs of operating your networked systems
- **Maintain high availability** and prevent problems with the IBM Advanced System Management Adapter's remote monitoring and control capabilities.

Netfinity Manager supports many of the industry's most popular PC operating systems like: Windows NT, Windows 95, Windows 3.1, Novell NetWare, OS/2, and network protocols such as: NetBIOS, IPX, SNA (LU6.2), TCP/IP and serial. Netfinity Manager also provides these functions over an Internet connection with a Web browser.

With Netfinity Manager as the foundation for IBM's System Management solution, you can help your business realize true, long-term success through comprehensive control.

Hardware and Software Information

The following charts of correlating information relates to the Netfinity:

Applications			
Product Type	**Manufacturer**	**Part Number**	**Product Description**
Backup	Seagate	BackupExecNT	Backup Exec for Windows NT Server 6.1
Backup	Seagate	BackupExecNW	Backup Exec for Netware Server 7.0
Backup	Cheyenne	OS2-SO17-PRO	Arcsolo for OS/2 (Version 1.7)
Backup	Cheyenne	ARCserveSCO-20A	ARCserve/Open for SCO V2.0A
Backup	Cheyenne	NT-AS60EE	ARCserve for Windows NT 6.0
Backup	Cheyenne	N3-AS60-EE	ARCserve 6.0 for NetWare
Backup	IBM	84H3129	ADSM for OS/2 2.1 Network Enabler

continued on next page

Applications (continued)

Product Type	Manufacturer	Part Number	Product Description
Backup	Seagate	ALEO-220SY	Sytos Autoloader v2.2 for OS/2
Backup	Seagate	PREO-220SY	Sytos Premium for OS/2 2.2
Communication	IBM	EagleCommSrv	IBM Communication Server
Database	IBM	41H2114	DB2/2 (OS/2) V2.1.1
Database	IBM	EagleDBSrv	Database Server
Database	Microsoft	SQL Server6.0	SQL Server (Back Office)
Database	Oracle	Oracle7NW	Oracle 7 Database (NW)
Database	Oracle	WrkGrpEntOS_2	Workgroup Enterprise OS/2
Firewall	Checkpoint	CPFireWall	Firewall
Groupware	IBM	EagleNotesSrv	Lotus Notes Server
Groupware	Lotus	Notes4.xNT	Notes 4.1 for Microsoft Windows NT
Groupware	Lotus	Notes4.xNW	Notes 4.1 for Novell NetWare
Groupware	Lotus	Notes4.xOS2	Notes 4.1 for IBM Warp Server
Groupware	Lotus	Domino4.5NT	Notes Domino Server 4.5 for Microsoft Windows NT
Groupware	Lotus	Domino4.5NW	Notes Domino Server 4.5 for Novell NetWare
Groupware	Lotus	Domino4.5OS	Notes Domino Server 4.5 for OS/2
High Avail.	Adaptec	Duralink	Duralink Redundant Network Link
Int. Server	IBM	EagleInetSrv	BM Internet Server
Int. Server	Netscape	Suitespot3.0	Suitespot Server 3.0

continued on next page

Applications (continued)

Product Type	Manufacturer	Part Number	Product Description
Net Mgmt	IBM	PCSServices	IBM Netfinity 4.x Services OS/2,NW,NT
Net Mgmt	IBM	PCSMgmt	IBM Netfinity 4.x Mgmt (OS/2,NW,NT)
Net Mgmt	Intel	LDM2NW	Intel LAN Desk Manager 2.5 NW & NT
Net Mgmt	Microsoft	SMS 1.1	Systems Management Server (Back Office)

Cables

Product Type	Manufacturer	Part Number	Product Description
SCSI	IBM	76H5400	IBM Third Channel Cable
SCSI	IBM	94G7421	Netfinity PCI SCSI Controller to Bulkhead
SCSI	IBM	01K8017	IBM .8mm to 68-pin SCSI Adapter
SCSI	IBM	70G9857	PC Server F/W to F/W External SCSI Cable
SCSI	IBM	70G9858	PC Server F/W to Fast External SCSI Cable

Clustering

Product Type	Manufacturer	Part Number	Product Description
Clustering	Microsoft	MCS1.0	MS Cluster Server 1.0
Clustering	IBM	94G7584	IBM Shared Disk Convenience Kit

continued on next page

Clustering (continued)			
Product Type	**Manufacturer**	**Part Number**	**Product Description**
Clustering	IBM	01k8018	IBM Netfinity Cluster Pack by Vinca
Clustering	IBM	94G6620	PC Server High Availability Solution for OS/2 Warp
Clustering	IBM	94G6621	PC Server High Availability Solution for Windows NT
Clustering	IBM	94G6622	PC Server High Availability Solution for NetWare

Controllers			
Product Type	**Manufacturer**	**Part Number**	**Product Description**
UltraSCSI	Adaptec	AHA-3940AUW	PCI Fast/Wide Ultra SCSI Adapter
SCSI-2/RAID	DPT	PM3334UW_3	SmartRAID IV SCSI Raid Adapter (3 Channel)
SSA/RAID	IBM	32H3811	IBM SSA RAID PCI Adapter
SSA/RAID	IBM	96H9835	IBM SSA RAID Cluster Adapter
UltraSCSI	Adaptec	AHA-2940UW	PCI Fast/Wide Ultra SCSI-2 Adapter
UltraSCSI	Adaptec	AHA-2940U	PCI Fast Ultra SCSI-2 Adapter
UltraSCSI	IBM	76H5401	IBM ServeRAID II 8Mb/Battery-Back-up Cache
UltraSCSI	IBM	76H3584	ServeRaid II Ultra SCSI Adapter
UltraSCSI	IBM	76H5407	PCI Ultra Wide SCSI Adapter

Ethernet LAN Adapters

Product Type	Manufacturer	Part Number	Product Description
Ethernet	IBM	13H9237	PCI Ethernet

Fast Ethernet LAN Adapters

Product Type	Manufacturer	Part Number	Product Description
Fast Ethernet	IBM	25H3501	10/100 ISA Ethernet
Fast Ethernet	Intel	PILA8465B	EtherExpress PRO/100 LAN
Fast Ethernet	Olicom	OC-2325	Fast Ethernet PCI/II 10/100
Fast Ethernet	3COM	3C905-TX	Fast EtherLink XL PCI
Fast Ethernet	Adaptec	ANA-6911_TX	Cogent 10/100 PCI Fast Ethernet
Fast Ethernet	Adaptec	ANA-6944A_TX	Cogent PCI Quartet 10/100 4-Port Ethernet
Fast Ethernet	IBM	86H2432	100/10 Etherjet PCI
Fast Ethernet	Intel	PILA8480	EtherExpress PRO/100 Server
Fast Ethernet	Olicom	OC-2326	Fast Ethernet PCI/II 10/100
Fast Ethernet	SMC	SMC9332BDT	EtherPower 10/100 32bit
Fast Ethernet	SMC	SMC9432TX	EtherPower II 10/100 32bit

High-speed Networking Products

Product Type	Manufacturer	Part Number	Product Description
ATM	3Com	3C975-F	ATMLink PCI-155 ATM
ATM	Fore	PCA-200EPC	ForeRunner PCA-200EPC PCI
ATM	Madge	32-01	Collage 155 ATM Adapter (Fiber)

continued on next page

High-speed Networking Products (continued)			
Product Type	Manufacturer	Part Number	Product Description
FDDI	Syskonnect	SK5541	PCI FDDI Adapter (SAS-MIC)
FDDI	Syskonnect	SK5544	PCI FDDI Adapter (DAS)
ATM	IBM	85H9035	Turboways 25 PCI ATM APE-Bridge Adapter

Networking Hardware: Routers, Switches and Hubs			
Product Type	Manufacturer	Part Number	Product Description
Ethernet	IBM	8224	8224 Ethernet Hub
Ethernet	IBM	8237	8237 Ethernet Hub
Token Ring	IBM	8238	8238 Token Ring 16 Port Hub
External	IBM	2210-14T	2210-T14 25 Mbit ATM Router
External	IBM	2210-12E	2210-E12 Router
External	IBM	2210-12T	2210-T12 Router
Router/Int	Sourcecom	Incarda_P	Incarda/P Server-based Router Adapter
ATM	IBM	42H0525	Turboways 25 ISA Adapter
Keyboard	IBM	76H0109	104-key Standard Keyboard (Raven Black)
Keyboard	IBM	13H6705	101-key Enhanced Keyboard with Trackpoint II (Blk)
Monitor	IBM	6540-0x0	G42P Monitor (14", 48KHertz)
Monitor	IBM	6540-02x	G42L Monitor (14", 48KHertz)
Monitor	IBM	6541-02x	G51L Monitor (15", 54KHertz)
Monitor	IBM	6542103	G40 Color Monitor 14"
			continued on next page

Networking Hardware: Routers, Switches and Hubs (continued)

Product Type	Manufacturer	Part Number	Product Description
Monitor	IBM	6543303	G50 Color Monitor 15"
Monitor	IBM	6553503	P50 Color Monitor 6553
Monitor	IBM	6544403	G70 Color Monitor 17"
Monitor	IBM	6554673	P70 Color Monitor 6554
Monitor	IBM	6553-5xx	P50 Color Monitor 6553
Mouse	IBM	13H6690	Enhanced Mouse (Pearl White)
Mouse	IBM	13H6714	Enhanced Mouse (Raven Black)
Monitor	IBM	6546-x0x	G52P Monitor (15", 69KHertz)
Monitor	IBM	6547-x1x	G72S Monitor (17", 69KHertz)
Monitor	IBM	6547-x0x	G72P Monitor (17", 69KHertz)
Monitor	IBM	6546-x1x	G52S Monitor (15", 69KHertz)
Printer	HP	C3155A#ABA	Laserjet 5P
Printer	IBM	4772001	4772 Universal Financial Printer
Rack	IBM	9306900	IBM Netfinity Rack
Upgrade Kit	IBM	94G7424	Tower to Rack Conversion Kit
Upgrade Kit	IBM	94G7425	Rack to Tower Conversion Kit

Storage Devices

Product Type	Manufacturer	Part Number	Product Description
Enclosure	IBM	7133-020	
		7133-020	SSA Storage Enclosure—Rack Mountable

continued on next page

Storage Devices (continued)

Product Type	Manufacturer	Part Number	Product Description
Enclosure	IBM	3519R01	3519—Rack Drawer Enclosure
Enclosure	IBM	7133-600	7133-600—SSA Storage Enclosure—Floor Standing
Enclosure	IBM	3517001	3517-001—SCSI Multi-Storage Enclosure
Enclosure	IBM	3517002	3517-002—SCSI Multi-storage Enclosure
Enclosure	IBM	3527001	3527—IBM SSA Entry Storage Subsystem
Enclosure	IBM	3518001	3518—PC Server Enterprise Expansion Enclosure
Enclosure	IBM	35201RU	IBM NetFinity EXP10 Rack Storage Enclosure
Enclosure	Symbios-Logic	DS-20E	Metastor RAID Storage Enclosure (Desktop)
Enclosure	Symbios-Logic	RM-20E	Metastor RAID Storage Enclosure (Rack)
HDD/HS	IBM	27H1062	4.51GB SL F/W SSA Hot-Swap HDD
HDD/HS	IBM	05J6413	2.25GB SSA Hot-Swap HDD II
HDD/HS	IBM	05J6414	4.51GB SSA Hot-Swap HDD II
HDD/HS	IBM	94G7429	4.51GB Wide Ultra SCSI Hot-Swap HDD
HDD/HS	IBM	94G7430	9.1GB Wide Ultra-SCSI Hot Swap HDD
HDD/HS	IBM	21H8734	9.1GB SL F/W SSA Hot-Swap HDD

continued on next page

Storage Devices (continued)

Product Type	Manufacturer	Part Number	Product Description
Repeater	IBM	94G7426	Netfinity SCA Back-plane Repeater Adapter Kit
Repeater	IBM	94G7585	IBM SCSI-2 F/W Enhanced Repeater Card
Tape Lib	Exabyte	EXB-220	EXB-220 Tape Library
Tape	IBM	76H0485	20/40GB 8MM Internal SCSI Tape Drive
Tape	IBM	01K1174	35/70GB External DLT Tape Drive
Tape Lib	IBM	3447106	DLT Tape Library (Rack—5U)
Tape	IBM	00K7900	35/70GB Internal DLT Tape Drive
Tape Lib	IBM	3449356	8MM Tape Library (Rack—15U)
Tape	Quantum	TH5AA-YF	DLT4000 40GB External SCSI-2 Tape Drive
Tape Lib	IBM	3449355	8MM Tape Library (Tower)
Tape Lib	IBM	3447105	DLT Tape Library (Desktop)

Token Ring LAN Adapters

Product Type	Manufacturer	Part Number	Product Description
Token Ring	IBM	04H8095	AutoLANStreamer PCI T/R
Token Ring	IBM	41H8900	PCI Token Ring Adapter
Token Ring	Madge	51-02	Smart 16/4 PCI Ring node
Token Ring	Olicom	OC-3137	Token Ring PCI/II 16/4 Adapter

System Upgrades			
Product Type	**Manufacturer**	**Part Number**	**Product Description**
DIMM	IBM	94G7384	64Mb FPM ECC DIMM (4-8Mx72) 60ns Memory Upgrade Kit
DIMM	IBM	94G7385	128Mb FPM ECC DIMM (4-16Mx72) 60ns Memory Upgrade Kit
DIMM	IBM	94G7386	256Mb FPM ECC DIMM (4-32Mx72) 60ns Memory Upgrade Kit
UPS	IBM	94G3135	APC Smart-UPS 1000
UPS	IBM	94G3136	APC Smart-UPS 1400
Security	IBM	94G7427	IBM Netfinity Security Cover III
Service	IBM	94G5570	Advanced Systems Management Adapter
Service	IBM	94G5571	Advanced Systems Management Power Unit
Service	IBM	94G7578	Advanced Systems Management Adapter
Hot-Plug	IBM	94G7150	400W Hot-Swap Redundant Power Supply
PP200MHz	IBM	94G6678	PC Server SMP 200MHz Upgrade
Card	IBM	94G7387	Netfinity 200MHz/1Mb Processor Card
PP200MHz	IBM	94G7147	Netfinity SMP 200MHz/1MB L2 Cache
UPS	IBM	94G6674	APC Smart-UPS 1400RMB (120V)

continued on next page

System Upgrades (continued)

Product Type	Manufacturer	Part Number	Product Description
UPS	IBM	94G6675	APC Smart-UPS 1400RMiB (230V)
UPS	IBM	94G6676	APC Smart-UPS 3000RMB (120V)
UPS	IBM	94G6677	APC Smart-UPS 3000RMiB (230V)

Wide-Area Networking

Product Type	Manufacturer	Part Number	Product Description
Modem/Bank	Digi	70001183	T1 Modem Bank (6-24 V.34 Modems)
Modem/Ext	Hayes	08-02349	Optima 28.8 V.34/V.FC modem
Modem/Ext	US Robotics	001224-0	Courier V.Everything with V.34
SDN/Ext	3COM	3C871	ISDN External Digital Modem
Asynch	Dig	70001169	C/X16 System PCI DB25
ISDN/LAN	Ascend	P25-1UBR	Pipeline 25 ISDN modem (Ethernet attach)
ISDN/Int	Digi	77000372	Datafire-U S1 Server ISDN Adapter
Multiprotocol	Digi	70001270	Sync/570i PCI (w/ V.35 cable)
Multiprotocol	IBM	85X2706	ARTIC Realtime Interface Coproc.
Multiprotocol	IBM	61G3862	ARTIC Multiport
Multiprotocol	IBM	06H3890	ARTIC Multiport 8-Port RS-232 w/1 MB
Multiprotocol	IBM	39H8058	ARTIC960/PCI
Multiprotocol	IBM	33F8791	ARTIC Multiport Model 2

continued on next page

Wide-Area Networking (continued)			
Product Type	**Manufacturer**	**Part Number**	**Product Description**
Multiprotocol	Software Group	570PCI-NH	Netcom Highway (570 PCI)
X.25	IBM	71G6460	ARTIC X.25 ISA Interface Coprocessor

Summary Information

Networks using a server, especially an application or file server, require the server be reliable, powerful, and expandable. The NetFinity 7000 used in this network is robust and expandable.

The most recent information about IBM's servers can be found at: www.ibm.com or by writing: International Business Machines, Armonk, NY 00000.

Microsoft Windows 95 and 98

Software used in this network includes Windows 95 and Windows 98 operating systems. Both work well with all the hardware and software integrated together. Windows 3.1 is also used in the network. Visit the Microsoft Web site for more information: www.microsoft.com.

Microsoft Windows NT

The network designed and explained in following chapters includes Windows NT operating systems. The following NT versions are used:

- Server Version 4.0
- Workstation Version 4.0
- Enterprise Edition
- Server Version 5.0
- Workstation Version 5.0.

Visit the Web site noted above to obtain more information.

Uninterruptable Power Supply-UPS (Liebert)

Early on it was determined that a significant-size UPS was needed to meet requirements. I have worked closely with Liebert equipment of all sizes in numerous data centers throughout the US and abroad. Liebert has been around for decades and will be around for decades to come. The company is established, has considerable market penetration, well-trained employees, tenured employees, well-built and furnished physical plants, and committed personnel at every level of the corporation. Liebert defines quality. Consider this first-hand evidence.

Large cooling systems Liebert offers are built in their facility. Liebert has certified welders on-site that build each frame by hand.

From the outset, devices built at Liebert are accompanied by a document which each employee stamps during the production process. Numerous checkpoints (quality control points) exist. If for any reason a product does meet a pre-set standard, that product is stopped and does not continue until the problem is resolved.

Another aspect of Liebert's quality is *how* they build products. Liebert starts with *raw* elements. They don't work with pre-fabricated material, except for one printed circuit board assembled in another location and included with one product at Liebert's facility. These printed circuit boards undergo tests to verify predefined standards.

Liebert's attention to detail is unmatched. The painting production process is monitored not only for quality but also for the control of paint substance so contamination does not leave the paint room. On their production floor no management exists. People work with each other to meet order requirements. This is the first team implementation I have ever seen that works well. Liebert's teams exploit the strength of each person. Change is driven by workers, not management.

Liebert uses technology where technology makes sense. They implement a computer-controlled metal cutter. This enables them to compute the greatest possible number of cuts from a given piece of metal and thereby reduces production costs.

This kind of knowledge of a company is important, significant money is to be invested in a device to serve network needs over a considerable period.

A Liebert UPStation S was selected to meet the needs of this network. This series of UPSes range from 3.5 to 18kVA in size. In this instance, I selected a 15kVA UPS. The capability of this system can meet the needs of all equipment in the network I built and explained in this book.

For further information contact Liebert at: www.liebert.com; Liebert Corporation, 1050 Dearborn Drive, P. O. Box 29186, Columbus, OH 43229, 614-841-5924; or Liebert Corporation, Globe Park, Marlow, Buckinghamshire SL7 1YG, United Kingdom, +44 1628 403200; or Liebert Corporation, 19/F Causeway Bay Plaza 1, 489 Hennessy Road, Causeway Bay, Hong Kong, 852-2-572-2201.

General Cable

Because the infrastructure in this network is extensive, considerable attention was paid to electrical requirements. The entire electrical infrastructure was designed and built. One aspect of that infrastructure included requirement for flexible electrical cable for extension cords.

General Cable 6-3 and 8-3 cable is used to meet electrical standards. The cable is flexible and easy to work with.

General Cable is distributed through Belden Cable. For more information, contact General Cable, #4 Tesseneer Drive, Highland Heights, KY 41076, 800-424-5666.

Electrical Components (Pass & Seymour Legrand)

Electrical components including plugs, receptacles, flange outlets, pin and sleeve connections, and connectors required for this network were chosen from Pass & Seymour products. Pass & Seymour has the highest-grade electrical components in the industry.

Each time an electrical connection is made resistance occurs. The more resistance there is, the more electrical loss occurs. The better the connection (where connections are made) the more *smoothly* electrical current can flow. In addition, the higher the quality of components used in electrical connections the safer the electrical infrastructure is.

Pass & Seymour products used in this network were:

- Commercial Grade Duplex Receptacles
- Boot Connectors
- L830 Receptacles
- L830 Connectors
- Pin and Sleeve Connectors.

For further information, contact Pass & Seymour Legrand, 50 Boyd Avenue, Syracuse, NY 13209, 800-776-4035.

Commercial Desktop Computers (IBM)

IBM personal computers, commercial desktop series PC350 and XL series are used in this network. Typical general specifications for the base system units (model 350s) used in this network include:

- 200 MHz Pentium MMX Processor
- 2.6 Gb Hard Disk (additional 3.0 GB hard drive)
- 16MB Non-parity EDO Memory (additional 48 Mb RAM)
- 3$\frac{1}{2}$" floppy disk drive.

Units in this network employ a PCI Busmaster controller and S.M.A.R.T. capabilities. These systems include: PCI-Enhanced IDE hard drives, Universal Serial Bus (USB) ports, infrared, and 64-bit PCI graphics, and wake on LAN capability.

Functionality of the USB makes peripheral connectivity easier. The hot-connect ability enables peripheral devices to be connected in seconds. Such devices can be added or removed without reconfiguring or rebooting. Each USB port permits up to 127 USB-capable devices.

Some of the PCs used in this network have the capability for Symmetrical Multi-Processing (SMP) when dual processors are used.

There is an L2 external CPU cache of 256KB and also pipeline burst L3 cache. The BIOS type is 256KB Flash, SurePath.

The systems can accommodate up to 192Mb RAM at a speed of 60ns deployed by 72-pin SIMMs. Their hard disk size average seek time is 12ms with a latency of approximately 5.8ms. They support RAID and hot-swappable drive bays.

The graphic capabilities of these systems employ an S3 Trio64 V+Graphics type chip set. The result is SVGA graphics and data width of 64-bit video RAM. Graphic resolution (with the standard video RAM) is: 1280 x 1024 in 16 colors. The maximum resolution (with a maximum video RAM) is: 1280 x 1024 with 65,536 colors. The graphics bus interface uses PCI architecture.

The systems have a 200 watt power supply type for either 110 or 220 volts with a universal manual switch. The heat and sound emissions are 48dB. The typical weight of each cabinet is 28 lbs, height is 6.3", width is 16.5", and depth is 17.6".

Systems used in this network include the following security features:

- Boot sequence control
- Boot without keyboard or mouse
- Cover key lock
- Diskette boot inhibit

- Diskette write protect (switch)
- Diskette I/O control
- Hard disk I/O control
- Parallel I/O control
- Power on password
- Secure fixed DASD
- Secure removable media
- Serial I/O control
- Setup utility password (administrator password)
- U-Bolt tie-down support.

The systems specifications used in this network also include the following product approvals and/or certifications according to IBM: BABT (UK); CE; CISPR-22 Class B; CSA C22.2 No. 950 (Canada); DEMKO (EN 60950); EIF (SETI) (EN 60950); Energy Saving Law (refer to N-B 1-9174-001); FCC Class B (US); IECEE CB Certificate and report to IEC-950 Second Edition; ISO 9241-3 Compliant; JATE; NEMKO (EN 60950); NS/G/1234/J/100003 (Telecommunications Safety only: no approval mark); OVE (EN 60950); Power Line Harmonics (refer to N-B 2-4700-017); SEMKO (EN 60950); TUV-GS (EN 60950); TUV-GS - ZH1/618; UL-1950 First Edition; VCCI Class 2 (Japan).

In addition, IBM's current warranty is a limited warranty period of type 3 (three-year) first on-site, second and third years carry-in; three years parts and labor.

The IBM desktop systems used in this network came with pre-installed software. Some of these systems were reconfigured to meet the needs of the network. Each system used in this network is covered by either a site license or has a dedicated piece of software and, has one user. In the case of servers, workstations, or other items, each manufacturer's legal guidelines were followed. These matters should be factored into network design. Using an unpaid for piece of software, unless it is clear that it is freeware, is stealing.

Model 658842U	Characteristics
266 MHz Pentium II 2.5GB Hard disk2	The IBM PC 300XL is designed with the latest technology to handle demanding business applications in a networked environment.

These are the high-end systems that deliver value and keep you ahead of the curve with the performance that power users demand.

The IBM PC 300XL series includes open bay models which can be custom configured via the Authorized Assembler Program (AAP).

Standard Features

- **Processors.** Pentium(R) II processors—233MHz, 266MHz or 300MHz with unified 512KB L2 Cache
- **Memory.** 32 MB non-parity EDO Memory (Expandable Memory to 384MB) 32MB, expandable to 384MB (3 DIMMs), EDO/60ns
- **Hard Drives.** 2.5GB or 4.2GB EIDE with S.M.A.R.T. or 4.3GB Wide Ultra SCSI with S.M.A.R.T. or open bay PCI bus master EIDE controller on planar; SCSI models include a SCSI-2 Fast and Wide PCI bus master adapter
- **Graphics and Video Resolution.** S3 Trio64V2; 64-bit; 2MB std./max. video DRAM; 256 colors @ 1280x1024
- **Network Features.** LAN-Client Control Manager supported, Wake on LAN, Plug-In and Go, Flash over LAN (BIOS/CMOS), Plug-and-Play, CID
- **Network Interface.** Integrated Intel EtherExpress 10/100Mbps Ethernet with Wake on LAN
- **CD-ROM.** Models available with 16X-8X (variable speed) CD-ROM (Variable read rate. Actual playback speed will vary and is often less than the maximum possible.)
- **Audio.** Models available with Crystal 4236B audio chip, 16-bit, support Sound Blaster Pro applications
- **Diskette Drive.** 3.5" 1.44MB standard
- **Slots.** 3 shared PCI/ISA, 2 ISA
- **Bays.** Three 3.5", two 5.25"
- **BIOS.** Flash ROM
- **Architecture.** PCI local bus, ISA data bus
- **Ports.** Serial (16550), enhanced parallel (ECP/EPP), two USB ports, SVGA video, EIDE controller, 10/100 Ethernet RJ-45, IrDA-2 compliant infrared, audio mic-in and line-out minijacks, keyboard, mouse
- **Keyboard/Mouse.** IBM Cameo 104-key (rubber dome) and enhanced mouse
- **Power Supply.** 200 watts
- **Security Features.** IBM AssetCare: serialization and laser etching of memory and processors, third-party registration available through Retainagoup Limited

- **IBM AntiVirus and ConfigSafe.** Vital Product Data (VPD) support, cover key lock, sliding front door lock, U-bolt anchor support, secure access openings, secure removable media, secure fixed DASD, diskette write protect, power-on password, configuration/administrator password, keyboard/mouse password, Wake on LAN password prompt, boot sequence control, diskette boot inhibit, boot without keyboard/mouse, mouse-disable, I/O controls
- **Software and Tools.** Windows 95 or Windows NT 4.0 preload available on models with a hard drive Lotus SmartSuite license, Microsoft NetMeeting (Windows 95 preload models only), LAN-Client Control Manager (downloadable via Internet), IBM Netfinity Manager software, Intel LANDesk Client Manager, Artisoft CoSession, QAPlus System Support CD (ready to configure) with additional software/drivers
- **Limited Warranty.** Three-year parts and one-year labor.

Legal Notices

1. MHz only measures internal clock speed, not application performance. Many factors affect application performance.
2. When referring to hard drive capacity, MB stands for million bytes and GB stands for billion bytes. Total user-accessible capacity may vary depending on operating environments.
3. For terms and conditions or copies of IBM's limited warranty, call 800-772-2227 in the US Limited warranty includes International Warranty Service in those countries where this statement of product is sold by IBM or IBM Business Partners (registration required).
4. Energy Star Compliance: The EPA, as a matter of policy, does not endorse any particular company or its products.
5. Battery life (and recharge times) will vary based on screen brightness, applications, features, power management, battery conditioning and other references. CD-ROM or hard disk drive usage may also have a significant impact on battery life.
6. Actual specifications may vary slightly depending on features and components.

For more information on IBM products contact www.IBM.com or write to International Business Machines, Armonk, New York.

Remote Workstations (IBM ThinkPads)

Multiple remote workstation were required to work with this network. The following are typical specifications for the IBM ThinkPads used.

ThinkPad 765D

166 MHz
Pentium with
MMX
technology1

13.3" TFT
1024x768
65,536 colors
3GB Hard
 Disk
RAM
 2/32MB
 Non-parity
 EDO Memory
 (Expandable
 to 104MB);
8X CD-ROM
 MPEG-1
Microsoft Windows 95

The latest power, connectivity and configuration flexibility to optimize effectiveness and maximize investment return. High performance features include: large 13.3" or 12.1" high-resolution displays with superb graphics, the latest Pentium processors with MMX technology, large hard drives, integrated infrared, and advanced multimedia.

Standard features:

Pointing device type: TrackPoint III
Standard diskette size: 3.5" 1.44MB
Optional diskette size: 3.5" 2.88MB

Diskette drive configuration:

External

Keyboard type standard:

Full size 84 key (tilt/palm rest space)
Keyboard type(s) selectable:

continued on next page

ThinkPad 765D (continued)	
Numeric Keypad:	Integrated
Product	CISPR-22 Class B; CSA C22.2 No. 950 (Canada);
approvals/	FCC Class B – Part 15; IEC-950; JATE; NOM
certifications 4:	(Mexico); SASO; UK-PTT; UL-1950; VCCI Class 2
	(Japan)
Warranty:	
Limited warranty	Three year (system battery: one year)
period and type 3:	Customer Carry-in Repair or provided by
	ThinkPad EasyServ (North America only)
Weight and dimensions:	
	Weight: 7.7 lbs
	Height: 2.2"
	Width: 11.7"
	Depth: 9.3"

Legal Notices

1. MHz only measures internal clock speed, not application performance. Many factors affect application performance.

2. When referring to hard drive capacity, MB stands for million bytes and GB stands for billion bytes. Total user-accessible capacity may vary depending on operating environments.

3. For terms and conditions or copies of IBM's limited warranty, call 800-772-2227 in the US Limited warranty includes International Warranty Service in those countries where this statement of product is sold by IBM or IBM Business Partners (registration required).

4. Energy Star Compliance: The EPA, as a matter of policy, does not endorse any particular company or its products.

5. Battery life (and recharge times) will vary based on screen brightness, applications, features, power management, battery conditioning and other references. CD-ROM or hard disk drive usage may also have a significant impact on battery life.

6. Actual specifications may vary slightly depending on features and components.

Network Communication Hub (3Com USRobtics)

A 3Com USRobotics Enterprise Network Hub was selected. Data communication equipment is the single most critical link in any network whether it is the central point of attachment between remote users and a backbone network, regardless the size of the backbone or location or if all users are in the same physical location. As data communication equipment goes so goes the network. At one time remote computing meant having a device in one location and a terminal attached to it by a wire. USRobotics revolutionized that definition by designing the powerful Enterprise Network Hub.

Consider Figure 5.10 which illustrates a network in Dallas and remote users and a remote network, both located in Chicago.

Notice remote users are using their modems to connect directly into the Dallas network via the communications Hub. In this case the remote users use their modem and connect directly to the HUB.

When remote users or remote network(s) are concerned, multiple issues must be considered during the design phase. What follows is the minimum number of issues to be reviewed during the planning stage:

- Security
- Reliability
- Maintenance
- Ease of Use
- Internal Protocol Compatibility
- Expandability
- Internal Design Architecture
- Interface Standard Compatibility.

Security has become the single most important topic in networking, regardless of the type of network or location. Networks can have a considerable degree of security built into the design if proper components are used to implement security. Where data communication equipment is concerned, having a device that can provide a security firewall is best.

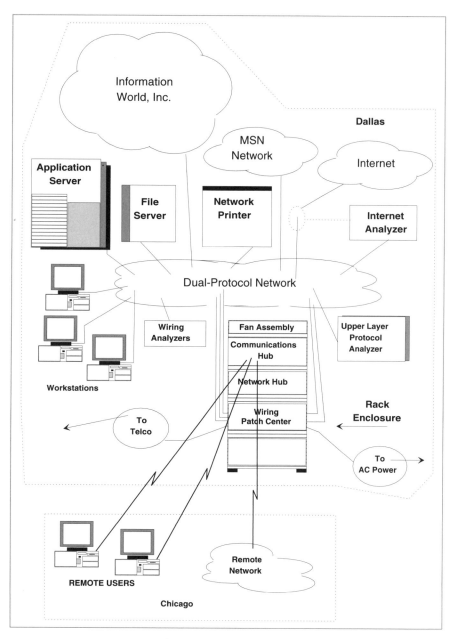

Figure 5.11 shows a secure firewall implemented in the communications hub. Remote users in this illustration are required to sign on to the hub, which is a point of isolation. Other devices on the network require sign-ons and passwords as well.

FIGURE 5.11
Network Firewall

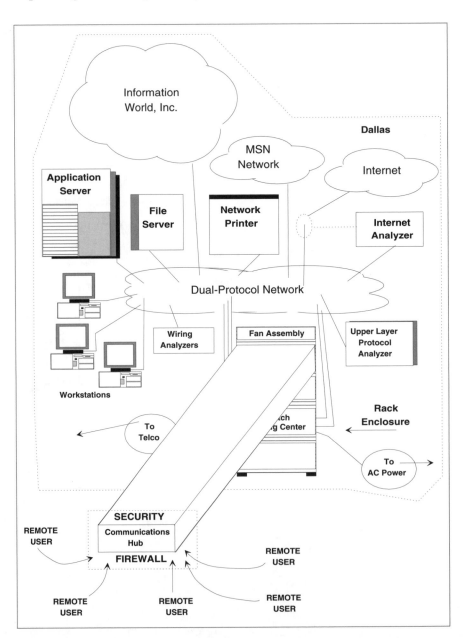

The USRobotics communication hub used in this network has three possible configurations regarding its function in the network. USRobotics refers to this as *gateway application cards*. USRobitcs uses the following terminology and explanation: X.25; NETServer card; API card.

According to USRobotics the X.25 card provides access capability to packet-switched networks. This card uses a EIA-232/V.35 interface connection point.

The NETServer card functions either as a router, as a terminal server or both. Ethernet and Token ring NICs can be used with it. USRobotics refers to this card as the EdgeServe card. It is loaded with WindowsNT. The functionality this card provides is discussed below.

Third, an API card can be used to let customers design their own applications by way of USRobotics software development kits. Figure 5.12 illustrates the Enterprise hub.

FIGURE 5.12
Enterprise
Network Hub

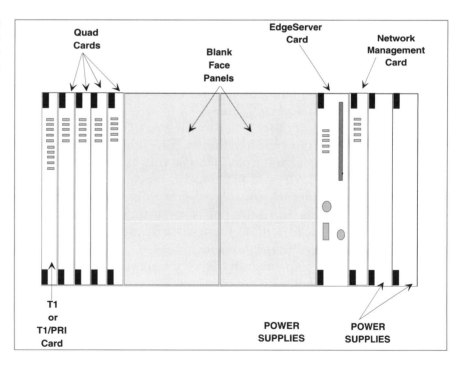

Notice Figure 5.12 shows the hub with blank face panels. These panels can be removed and other cards inserted. A total of 17 slots exist. Slot one is the T1 card. Beginning with slot 2 are analog or digital quad modem cards which have the equivalent of four modems on them. Slots 15 and 16 are the EdgeServer location. Slot 17 is where the network management card is located. The remaining slots house two power supplies. Though not shown in this illustration, the undercradle portion of the hub houses 16 fans to cool the components.

Reliability is another important factor for any communication equipment. The design of the USRobotics hub has reliability built into it. The hub has two power supplies, though only one is required to operate the unit.

Maintenance is another part of the equation for communication equipment. The hub used in this network has remote management capability, local management capability, and easy access for those components that may need removal.

Any communication device requires skill. Most require a fairly advanced level of skill to maximize use. The capability of any communication device has little to do with its ease of use. Ease of use is a design issue. With the hub used here, ease of use is designed in. It can be measured in communication equipment by documentation provided, by how thorough and detailed it is; by accessibility to configure ports, and by ability to use the equipment in a partially failed state (should that occur). The more complex functions a device offers, the simpler the documentation should be. Data communication equipment is complex enough without humans adding another layer of complexity.

Another factor to analyze with data communication equipment is protocol compatibility. This includes evaluation of upper- and lower-layer protocols. Because this hub has the EdgeServer card, NetBEUI, TCP/IP, and IPX upper-layer protocols are supported. Token ring and Ethernet lower-layer protocols are supported as well. Use of Token ring and Ethernet is more than sufficient for this network design because these two protocols are the dominant lower-layer protocols used in networks today.

Expandability is very important with data communication equipment. The design of the Enterprise network hub is such that any size network can be built around this technology. It is possible with the 3Com USRobotics equipment to start a network with one or two Enterprise hubs then continue to add them until racks of them are filled.

Internal design architecture is also crucial to data communication equipment. The internal communications bus and the incoming port architecture are the foundation of the device. These should be capable of handling a complete load on the device without causing hangups or system slowdown.

Interface standard compatibility is another matter to examine when evaluating data communication equipment. In this network, the hub has flexibility regarding how certain connections are made. In some instance options exist to make a connection. This alone makes for ease of use, installation, and maintenance. It also means some existing equipment at your site may be usable. That can save money.

For additional information contact 3Com USRobotics at www.3com.com, or write: 3Com USRobotics, Network Systems Division, 1800 Central Road, Mount Prospect, IL 60056-2293.

Multimedia Components (Creative Labs)

Creative Labs was chosen as the vendor for multi-media equipment. In the past, buying IBM compatibles, or clones, was not a problem. Since multimedia is now primarily and add-on, systems do not depend on multimedia as they do on the hard disk or monitor, for example.

However, some multimedia clone products exist. Many attempt to copy what Creative Labs has already designed. Clones are the incorrect way to invest money. The operational nature of some multimedia software is such that multimedia clone equipment may not have all the capabilities of multimedia.

Today, systems typically have CD-ROMs, speakers, microphones, line outputs for amplifiers, line inputs for peripheral integration, and software that enables users to create, play back, and listen to/see various data streams.

All the desktop systems in this network are IBM 350 series because each one could be customized to deliver a robust workload and because of upgrade capability. It is the same with the Creative Labs equipment.

In each system Creative Labs equipment is the multimedia hardware and software. The system includes an interface board, speakers, necessary cabling, microphone, CD-ROM, infrared remote control, software drivers, and various software titles for viewing and listening.

Creative Labs has designed the benchmark for multimedia systems. Windows95 and NT4.0 acknowledge most, if not all, Creative Labs hardware and software. It is plug-n-play compatible. Another significant aspect of this equipment is its adaptability. Creative Labs is continually upgrading to stay in line with other vendors, but their products support equipment and systems that are not this year's models.

Multimedia is more than a CD-ROM and speakers. Today it typically encompasses a digital video disc (DVD) and enhanced display support. More than at any other time, displays need powerful drivers and memory to store the screen of information to be presented.

Creative Labs is based in California, but has offices worldwide. They can be reached at any of the following addresses: www.soundblaster.com; Creative Labs, 1901 McCarthy Blvd., Milpitas, CA 95035; Creative Technology Ltd., 67 Ayer Rajah Crescent #03-18, Singapore 0513, Malaysia; Creative Labs Technical Support, 1523 Cimarron Plaza, Stillwater, OK 74075; Creative Labs Ltd., Blanchardstown Industrial Park, Blanchardstown, Dublin 15, Ireland.

Infrastructure Equipment (Thomas & Betts)

Because so many parts of the network described here were designed from the ground up I had to select numerous components, computers, printers, the electrical system, cooling, phone wiring, electrical wiring, and network wiring.

Consider the following list of components obtained to make this network possible:

- ALL-LAN Network Cable
- ALL-LAN Patch Panel
- ALL-LAN Jacks
- ALL-LAN Wall Plates
- ALL-LAN to RJ45 Patch Cables
- 4 gang outlet boxes
- 4 gang cover plates
- Twisted-Pair Patch Cables
- Load Centers
- Circuit Breakers
- Wire Strippers
- Ring Terminals
- Zinc Clamp Connectors.

Figure 5.13 represents a detail of the network infrastructure designed and built. The Thomas & Betts equipment was more fundamental to network operation than the network equipment itself; every network that exists requires an electrical and structural environment.

Most people do not consider this level of detail unless they are designing a building with architectural engineers. Most networks designed and installed are built into facilities that already exist.

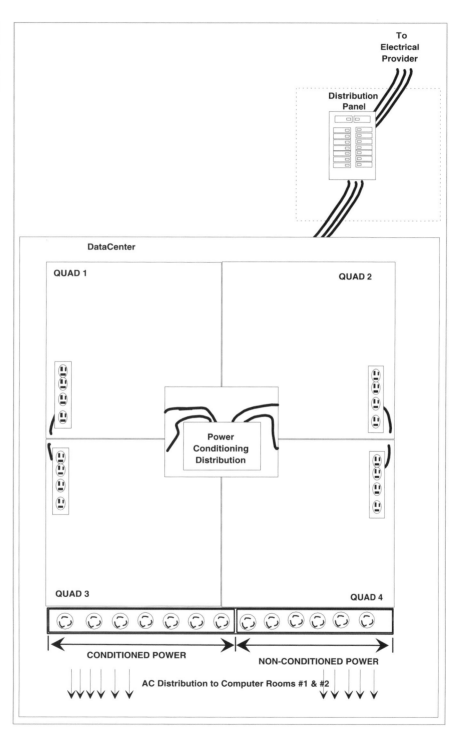

FIGURE 5.13
Components Used in Electrical Wiring

An integral part of the network is the network wiring backbone. ALL-LAN products were chosen for their superior capability.

ALL-LAN cable is characterized at 300 MHz. It features rugged shielded construction for reliable operation. The horizontal or home-run cable for the ALL-LAN Interconnection System is a 4-pair, 24 AWG solid copper core wire. Each pair is individually foiled and the cable has an overall braid, a construction that allows high-frequency signals to be transmitted without noticeable signal corruption or degradation. This cable accommodates all existing systems while allowing for the anticipated bandwidth of future systems. Cable specifications include:

Jacket	T&B Impedance	# of Cable Pairs & Specification	Gauge
Plenum	PWCS-300N4-95	100 Ohm 4 pair	24AWG
PVC	PWCS-300V4-95	100 Ohm 4 pair	24 AWG
Patch	PWCS-300A6-95	100 Ohm 4 pair	26 AWG
LSH	PWCS-300L3-95	100 Ohm 4 pair	23 AWG
Patch	PWCS-300A4-95	100 Ohm 4 pair	24 AWG

In some connections ALL-LAN connections were on one end of a cable and RJ45 connectors on the other. Overall the network backbone is based upon ALL-LAN cable.

To learn more about ALL-LAN and other Thomas & Betts equipment, visit www.thomasbetts.com or write to Thomas & Betts Corporation, 8155 T&B Boulevard, Memphis, TN 38125.

Ethernet and SCSI Adapters (Adaptec Corporation)

In the initial phase of network design it appeared that devices using SCSI were going to be part of the network and Adaptec SCSI adapters were selected. Information on the SCSI and Ethernet adapters used in this network follows.

The Adaptec AHA-2940 SCSI adapter is used in this network. Some of this product family highlights include:

- 20 MByte/sec UltraSCSI data transfer rate
- High-performance bus master architecture for improved system performance

- Compatibility with more than 200 systems and peripherals from major manufacturers
- Compatible with all major operating systems
- Easy plug-and-play installation.

The AHA-2940 Ultra host adapter delivers UltraSCSI speed for demanding professional applications and high-performance peripherals. With its bus mastering architecture and advanced SCSI features, the AHA-2940 Ultra host adapter improves system performance, especially in multitasking environments. In addition, the AHA-2940 Ultra adapter offers unsurpassed system and peripheral compatibility.

Double the data transfer speed Using UltraSCSI technology: the AHA-2940 Ultra host adapter doubles the maximum data transfer rate on the SCSI bus from 10 MByte/sec to 20 MByte/sec. By increasing the throughput rate between peripherals and the desktop system, the AHA-2940 Ultra adapter accelerates system performance and user productivity.

In addition to UltraSCSI speed, the AHA-2940 Ultra host adapter features a high-performance bus mastering architecture that regulates data movement directly between peripherals and system memory. The onboard Adaptec PhaseEngine RISC processor takes over I/O processing from the CPU, which frees it for other tasks. The result is lower CPU utilization and noticeably faster response time.

The AHA-2940 Ultra host adapter makes true multitasking possible. SCSI technology offers unique features, including disconnect/reconnect, tagged command queuing, and multithreaded I/O, that allow the system CPU to access data on multiple peripheral devices simultaneously.

All Adaptec host adapters are rigorously tested with hundreds of different SCSI peripherals and systems, which makes them the most compatible and reliable host adapters in the marketplace. The AHA-2940 Ultra adapter is also fully compatible with all popular desktop and network operating systems, including DOS, Windows, Windows NT, Windows 95, OS/2, NetWare, and UNIX.

Installing the AHA-2940 Ultra host adapter is quick and easy. Insert the host adapter in the PCI slot and the system BIOS will assign resources to it. Using the SCSISelect utility, users can then fine tune the performance of the adapter by making on-screen choices from the utility menu. Software automatically determines what hardware is present, loads the correct drivers, and modifies system configuration files. Completely compatible with Windows 95, the

AHA-2940 Ultra host adapter utilizes advanced plug-and-play features that automatically assign IDs and control termination.

The AHA-2940 Ultra kit provides everything necessary for connecting high-performance SCSI peripherals to PCs and workstations. It features the AHA-2940AU host adapter board with an internal cable, complete user documentation and Adaptec EZ-SCSI software for simple installation. Kit contents include:

- AHA-2940AU PCI-to-UltraSCSI host adapter board
- Adaptec 7800 Family Manager Set software drivers for Windows NT, Windows 95, OS/2 2.x and 3.x, NetWare 3.x and 4.x, SCO UNIX 3.2.x, and UNIXWare 1.x and 2.x. Adaptec EZ-SCSI software for DOS, Windows, Windows NT, Windows 95, and Windows for Workgroups includes applications such as: SCSI Backup (Backup Basics), QuickScan, CD Player, Photo CD Viewer (Magic Lantern), Advanced Power Management, SCSI Interrogator, SCSI Disk Partitioner, SCSITutor, SCSIBench. There is device support for hard disks, removable disks, MO, CD-ROM, CD-Recordable, Photo CD, and tape drives and scanners
- Standard, 3-position internal SCSI ribbon cable
- Complete user documentation.

AHA-2040 technical specifications

Computer Bus:

  PCI local-bus

Interface Protocol:

  Bus master DMA

Host Bus Data Transfer Rate:

  Up to 133 MB/sec burst rate

Peripheral Bus:

  8-bit Ultra SCSI

SCSI Synchronous Data Rate:

  20 MB/sec

SCSI Asynchronous Data Rate:

  6 MB/sec

Device Protocol:

  SCSI-1, SCSI-2, SCSI-3, UltraSCSI

continued on next page

HA-2040 technical specifications (continued)

Advanced SCSI Features:

Advanced SCSI Programming Interface (ASPI) compliant, multi-threaded I/O (up to 255 tasks simultaneously), scatter/gather, tagged queuing, disconnect/reconnect, synchronous and asynchronous Fast and Wide, Bootable from attached disks

External Connector:

50-pin high-density

Electrical Drivers:

Single-ended, active, programmable via SCSISelect

Hard Disk Capacity:

Extended translation supports drive capacity up to 8 gigabytes per disk

Device Support:

Supports up to seven (7) disks under DOS 5.0

Electrical Termination:

Single-ended, active, software-controlled

I/O Operating Environment:

Windows 95, Windows 3.1, Windows NT, Windows for Workgroups, DOS, IBM OS/2 2.x and 3.x, NetWare 3.12 and 4.x, SCO UNIX 3.2.x, UNIXWare 1.x and 2.x

MTBF:

544,264.3 hours (Bellcore, TR-NWT-000332, Method I, QL-I) Physical and environmental specifications:

Length:

4.75" (12 cm)

Height:

3.5" (8.75 cm)

Operating Temperature:

0°C to 55°C

Storage Temperature:

−55°C to 85°C

Humidity (operating):

10% to 90%, non condensing

Another Adaptec component used in the network is the AHA-2940 UW (ultrawide). The product highlights for this adapter are:

- 40 MByte/sec Ultra Wide SCSI data transfer rate

- Connection for up to 15 SCSI peripheral devices
- Design for true multitasking
- Compatibility with hundreds of systems and peripherals from major manufacturers.

The AHA-2940 Ultra Wide host adapter is the ideal PCI-to-SCSI host adapter for entry-level servers and workstations. It moves data fast—up to 40 Mb/sec. and it connects up to 15 SCSI devices for expanded storage capacity. In addition, the AHA-2940 Ultra Wide adapter delivers unrivaled system and peripheral compatibility.

Combining UltraSCSI speed and 16-bit wide SCSI data transfers, the AHA-2940 Ultra Wide host adapter moves data on the SCSI bus at a maximum rate of 40 Mb/sec. By increasing the throughput rate between peripherals and the system CPU, the AHA-2940 Ultra Wide adapter accelerates system performance and user productivity.

The AHA-2940 Ultra Wide host adapter delivers expanded connectivity to meet the storage capacity requirements of server environments. It supports up to 15 SCSI devices simultaneously. Both 8-bit and 16-bit devices can be configured in any combination for maximum configuration flexibility.

The AHA-2940 Ultra Wide host adapter makes true multitasking possible. SCSI technology offers unique features, including disconnect/reconnect, tagged command queuing, and multithreaded I/O, that allow the system CPU to move data to and from multiple peripheral devices simultaneously.

All Adaptec host adapters are rigorously tested with hundreds of different SCSI peripherals and systems, which makes them the most compatible and reliable host adapters in the marketplace. The AHA-2940 Ultra Wide adapter is fully compatible with all popular desktop and network operating systems, including Microsoft Windows 3.1, DOS, Windows NT, Windows 95, OS/2, NetWare, and UNIX. Under Windows 95, the AHA-2940 Ultra Wide adapter utilizes advanced plug-and-play features that automatically assign IDs and control termination.

The AHA-2940 Ultra Wide kit provides everything necessary for connecting high-performance SCSI peripherals to workstations and entry-level servers. It features the AHA-2940 UW host adapter board with internal SCSI cables, and complete user documentation. The kit also includes Adaptec EZ-SCSI software for simple installation and the SCSISelect utility for easy on-screen performance tuning.

The AHA-2940 Ultra Wide complete kit includes:

- AHA-2940 UW PCI-to-Wide UltraSCSI host adapter board
- Adaptec 7800 Family Manager Set software drivers for Windows NT, Windows 95, OS/2 2.x and 3.x, Netware 3.x and 4.x, SCO UNIX 3.2.x and UNIXware 1.x and 2.x
- Adaptec EZ-SCSI software for Windows NT, Windows 95, Windows for Workgroups, and DOS
- Applications such as: SCSI Tape Backup (Backup Basics), QuickScan, CD Player, photo CD Viewer (Magic Lantern), Advanced Power Management, SCSI Interrogator, SCSI Disk Partitioner, SCSITutor, SCSIBench
- Provides device support for hard disks, removable disks, MO, CD-ROM, CD-recordable, Photo CD and tape drives and scanners
- One 3-position, 68-pin UltraSCSI internal ribbon cable
- One 3-position, 50-pin UltraSCSI internal ribbon cable
- Complete user documentation
- Five-year warranty card.

Technical specifications for the AHA-2940 UW

Computer bus:

PCI local-bus

Interface Protocol:

Bus master DMA

Host Bus Burst Data Rate:

133 MByte/sec

Peripheral Bus:

8-bit and 16-bit Wide UltraSCSI

SCSI Synchronous Data Rate:

40 MByte/sec

SCSI Asynchronous Data Rate:

3.3 MByte/sec

Device Protocol:

SCSI-1, SCSI-2, SCSI-3, Wide UltraSCSI

Advanced SCSI Features:

Multithreaded I/O (up to 255 tasks simultaneously)

Scatter/gather

Disconnect/reconnect

Tagged command queuing

Synchronous and asynchronous data transfer

continued on next page

Technical specifications for the AHA-2940 UW

External Connector:

68-pin high-density

Hard Disk Capacity:

Extended translation supports drive capacity up to 8 GB per disk

Device Support:

Up to 15 devices under DOS 5.0 and above

Electrical Termination:

Automatic, active, programmable via SCSISelect

Operating Environment:

Microsoft Windows 3.x, DOS, Windows NT, Windows 95, OS/2 2.x and 3.x, NetWare 3.12 and 4.x, SCO UNIX 3.2.x, and UNIXWare 1.x and 2.x.

AHA-2940 UW Physical and Environmental Specifications

Length:

6.87" (17.0 cm)

Height:

3.87" (9.5 cm)

Operating Temperature:

0°C to 55°C

Storage Temperature:

–55°C to 85°C

Humidity (operating):

10% to 90%, non condensing

MTBF:

494,641 hours, per Bellcore TR-NWT-000332,Issue 4, Method 1

Another Adaptec product used in the network is the COgent 4 port Ethernet adapter. Product highlights include:

- Four connectors supporting four separate network segments, all at full bandwidth
- Each of four channels operating at independent speeds for maximum flexibility (10 Mbps, 20 Mbps, 100 Mbps, 200 Mbps)
- Full Duplex Fast Ethernet on UTP, for up to 800 Mbps throughput on one adapter

- NWay AutoSensing of maximum line speed on 10/100 TX adapters
- Duralink Failover offers FDDI-like port resiliency for optimum availability.

Adaptec's Cogent Quartet adapters are the ultimate performance solution for PCI servers operating on Fast Ethernet and Ethernet networks. With four channels on a single board and Full Duplex support, these adapters have the features today's 32-bit Fast Ethernet and Ethernet servers need to handle users' graphics, multimedia, database, and mission-critical applications.

These adapters provide ample bandwidth for even the most demanding networks. They support up to four network segments on separate channels for a cumulative throughput of up to 800 Mbps (depending on model). The Quartet adapters multiply flexibility, performance, and cabling compatibility by four, and provide easy migration paths from Ethernet to Fast Ethernet network solutions.

The key features and benefits of the 4 port Ethernet adapters follow.

Scalability

Using the Quartet adapter, I.S. organizations can increase the total network bandwidth without the need to buy a new server. Though the PCI bus offers 132 Mbps of bandwidth, typically only a limited number of slots are available, thereby restricting the number of segments a server can handle. The Quartet adapters solve this problem by providing the power of four Fast Ethernet, or Ethernet segments on a single adapter. These adapters use an on-board PCI-to-PCI bridge chip to extend the machine's internal bus. Multiple Quartets can be installed on each server for even greater overall bandwidth.

Flexible Configuration

The Quartet adapters support all four network channels at full cable bandwidth. Each channel is fully independent and is automatically configured by the system BIOS. Each of the adapters' four ID nodes can be customized at load time.

The AutoSense feature of the 10/100 Mbps models allows the adapters to automatically detect the network's maximum line speed. No adapter configuration is necessary. For maximum flexibility, the

AutoSense feature is compatible with all 10 and 100 Mbps devices, including those without NWay line speed negotiation.

With the Quartet T4 model, cabling plant upgrades are not necessary. They run on any UTP cable currently running 10Base-T and can be used in the future to run at 100 Mbps, providing an easy migration path.

Resilient, Redundant Links

Duralink Failover drivers included with each 10/100 TX adapter ensure the integrity of mission-critical Ethernet server links. Duralink Failover establishes an FDDI-like port resiliency with both active and hot-standby links. In the event that the active link fails, the standby link is automatically activated to preserve the network link and maintain the server's availability. Duralink Manager, also included, is a data compilation tool that simplifies adapter monitoring and configuration.

Full Duplex Mode

Full Duplex Fast Ethernet (FDFE) and Full Duplex Ethernet (FDE) capabilities double the cumulative system throughput in Fast Ethernet and Ethernet networks. Servers using the Quartet adapters can handle, receive, and transmit requests simultaneously, over multiple ports so workstations benefit from much faster service.

Designed for Performance

The Quartet adapters' efficient bus master design minimizes CPU utilization for optimum throughput. Independent transmit and receive FIFO buffers (First In, First Out memory) for each port onboard, and a powerful DMA capability mean consistently high performance, even during periods of peak network activity.

The following is a Cogent-to-Adaptec Model Number Conversion Chart:

Cogent PCI Quartet

New Model # Pro	Previous Model # other	Bus Speed	Interface Pentium, 486,	Pentium
4 x ANA-6944A/TX N/A	PCI 10/100	RJ-45 (4) Mbps	X	X
4 x ANA-6944/T4	EM440T4-PCI	PCI 10/100 Mbps	RJ-45 (4)	X
ANA-6940/TX	EM400TX-PCI	PCI 4 x 100 Mbps	RJ-45 (4)	X
ANA-6904/BNC	EM964BNC	PCI 4 x 10 Mbps	BNC (4)	X
ANA-6904	EM964TP	PCI 4 x 10 Mbps	RJ-45 (4)	X

4 port Ethernet adapter technical specifications

Systems Supported:

PCI Local Bus systems based on Intel, DEC Alpha, MIPS, and PowerPC processors

Bus Interface:

PCI, 32-bit bus master (PCI 2.1 for ANA-6944A/TX)

Ethernet Controller:

DECchip LAN coprocessor chip (4)

FIFO Buffer Memory:

10 Mbps models: 256 Bytes transmit, 256 Bytes receive (per port)

100 Mbps models: (24 Kb transmit, 4 Kb receive per port)

Hardware Interrupts:

PCI interrupt A, supports shared interrupts

Base IO or Memory Address:

Assigned by BIOS

PCI Configuration Space:

Supports DWORD, WORD and BYTE access

Reliability:

Calculated MTBF>100,000 hours

continued on next page

4 port Ethernet adapter technical specifications (continued)

Power Requirements:

+5 volts @ 2 Amp. max. (ANA-6904)

+5 volts @ 3.5 Amp. max. (all other models)

Environmental Operating Range:

Temperature: 0°C to 50°C

Relative Humidity:

5% to 85% non-condensing

Altitude:

3000m max.

Interface Connections:

10 Mbps models

RJ-45 female (4), or BNC (4)

RJ-45 supports CAT 3, 4, and 5 UTP and Type 1 STP

BNC supports RG-58 coax cable

100 Mbps models

RJ-45 female (4)

T4 model supports CAT 3, 4, and 5 UTP and Type 1 STP for 10Base-T and 100Base-T4 operation

TX models support CAT 3, 4, and 5 UTP and Type 1 STP for 10Base-T operation, and CAT 5 UTP and Type 1 STP for 100Base-T operation

Full Duplex support on all RJ-45 connectors on all models for 10Base-T operation; additional Full Duplex support on TX models for 100Base-TX operation

Dimensions:

9.75" x 4" to conform to PCI Long Card specifications (ANA-6904 models)

12" x 4.2" to conform to PCI Long Card specifications (ANA-6944 models)

Standards Compliance:

IEEE 802.3 10Base-2

IEEE 802.3 10Base-T

IEEE 802.3u 100Base-TX

IEEE 802.3u 100Base-T4

FCC Class A

CE Class A

continued on next page

4 port Ethernet adapter technical specifications

Drivers Available:

3.5" diskette - Novell NetWare 3.x, 4.x, and SFT III, Windows for Workgroups (NDIS 3.0), Windows 95, Windows NT for Intel, DEC Alpha, PowerPC, and MIPS platforms, DOS NDIS (NDIS 2.0), OS/2 Warp (NDIS 2.0), MS LAN Manager, Artisoft LANtastic, Banyan VINES DOS client, FTP PC/TCP, DEC Path-Works, Sun Solaris, SCO OpenServer, SCO UNIXWare (not all drivers are available for every adapter); Duralink for NetWare and Windows NT servers.

Duralink:

3.5" diskette—Duralink Failover and Duralink Manager for ANA-6944A/TX (Cogent EM 440TX PCI) at no charge

Diagnostic LEDs:

Link Integrity for each channel (4)

Network Activity for each channel (4)

Warranty:

Adaptec's Cogent adapters are protected by a limited lifetime warranty.

For additional information about these and other Adaptec product, contact Adaptec at one of the following addresses:

- Adaptec Asia, Block 1002, Jalan Bukit Merah, #06-07, Singapore 159456, Tel: (65) 273-7300, Fax: (65) 273-0163.
- Adaptec Japan, Ltd., Kiocho Hills, 4F, 3-32 Kiocho, Chiyoda-ku, Tokyo, 102, Japan, Tel: (81) 3-5276-9882, Fax: (81) 3-5276-9884;
- Adaptec Europe, Dreve Richelle 161, Bldg. A, 2nd Floor, B1410 Waterloo, Belgium, Tel: (32) 2-352-34-11, Fax: (32) 2-352-34-00.

Additional sales offices are located in the following countries:

- France: Tel: {33) 1-3452-3434, Fax: (33) 1-3452-3432;
- Germany: Tel: (49) 89-4564060, Fax: (49) 89-4560615;
- United Kingdom: Tel: (44) 1252-811200, Fax: (44) 1252-811212;
- Latin America (Miami): Tel: (305) 265-1387, Fax: (305) 265-0399;
- Adaptec, Inc., 691 South Milpitas Boulevard, Milpitas, California 95035, Tel: (408) 945-8600, Fax: (408) 262-2533.

For literature call: 1-800-934-2766 (USA and Canada) or (510) 732-3829; for pre-sales support: 1-800-442-7274 (USA and Canada) or (408) 957-7274. The World Wide Web address is: http://www.adaptec.com; Internet ftp server: ftp.adaptec.com. The adaptec USA

Bulletin Board Service (BBS) is at: (408) 945-7727 (up to 28,800 bps, using 8 bits, 1 stop bit, no parity); interactive fax number is: (303) 684-3400.

Adaptec, the Adaptec logo, AHA, SCSISelect, EZ-SCSI, SCSI Interrogator, SCSI Tape Backup, SCSITutor, ThreadMark and Magic Lantern are trademarks of Adaptec, Inc., which may be registered in some jurisdictions. Microsoft, Windows, the Windows logo and Windows 95 are registered trademarks and Windows NT and the Windows NT logo are trademarks of Microsoft Corporation used under license. All other trademarks used are owned by their respective owners.

Information supplied by Adaptec, Inc. is believed to be accurate and reliable at the time of printing, but Adaptec, Inc. assumes no responsibility for any errors that may appear in this document. Adaptec, Inc. reserves the right, without notice, to make changes in product design or specifications. Information is subject to change without notice.

Network Security & Virus Protection Software (McAfee)

Computer and network security is probably the single most important issue today and its importance is growing exponentially. Viruses, bots, and all sorts of antidata objects exist within the Internet. Most people have no idea how vulnerable parts of the Internet are. Even "service providers" are more vulnerable than they will admit. There is no *magic program* or anything else that can make networks safe. Good programs exist, the ones chosen and implemented in this network are an example; however, no single program can make a network 100% immune.

Remember this during the design phase of the network. Networks can have security designed into them from the outset. Security in a network needs to be factored into every area from electricity provision to telephone access and every other aspect that categorizes the network.

McAfee software suite was selected partly because of the number of anti-virus programs and the information available; also because of the frequency with which McAfee updates anti-virus software. McAfee now has more than 250 documents available on viruses; they claim to have information about the 1,000 most common viruses. The following software packages were selected and are used in this network:

- VirusScan
- Desktop Security Suite
- Commuter
- QuickBackup
- McAfee Service Desk
- NetShield
- WEBScan
- PCCrypto.

These products have been implemented to varying degrees on each system. Each program's benefits and highlights are presented here.

VirusScan

This program operates with Windows 3.1, 95, Windows NT4.0, DOS, and OS/2. It is software that, once installed, operates automatically upon power-up and can be used at will once a system is operational. It requires minimal space but does a professional job and is NCSAA certified.

Desktop Security Suite

This program also operates with Windows 3.1, 95, and NT4.0. The suite of programs includes anti-virus software, backup abilities, and encryption technology. The virus program is VirusScan. QuickBackup operates with Zip, Jaz, the Internet, or rewritable CD-ROMs. The backup program enables backup hourly or on demand. The cryptographic part of the suite provides 160-bit encryption and enables users to encrypt files to be sent over the Internet. The PC cryptographic part also permits network traffic to be encrypted between Windows-based computers and those running UNIX.

Commuter

Commuter is more than just a communication software; it also includes virus protection, desktop storage management, electronic mail, personal information organizer, calendar, to-do-list, and a contact manager.

QuickBackup

This program works with Windows95 and NT4.0. It enables transparent backup of files to SCSI, Zip, and Jaz drives. An icon-driven program makes for ease of use. The program installs quickly and provides encryption protection and Internet support.

Service Desk

The powerful service desk product is actually multiple products in one box. It works with Windows 3.1, 95, and Windows NT4.0 and lets customer support personnel have access to information about the customer and make a remote connection to a system reporting problem. The package comes with the ability to distribute software and also includes a system diagnostic part for support personnel to use with customers.

NetShield

NetShield uses McAfee's proprietary code, called Code Trace, Code Matrix and Code Poly. The product actually operates in an NT environment in native mode and takes full advantage of NT's server/client remote task distribution capability. Its product supports real-time scanning while operation of other tasks occur.

WEBScan

The WEBscan product is designed to detect viruses within a browser. It examines downloads and e-mail attachments, making it a powerful addition to any desktop or laptop system communicating in networks. It also provides a cybersitter that blocks out unwanted web sites and chat groups. Coverage of the program includes examination of .doc, lzip. exe. zrc. arj. and other file types.

PCCrypto

PCCrypto is used to secure documents and other data files created by anyone using computers. It can encrypt graphics, spreadsheets, and text documents. It uses a 160-bit blowfish encryption mechanism.

The package consumes a minimal amount of space and is one of the most powerful tools of its kind.

Author's Policy

You should initially dedicate a system for testing software. Then install McAfee VirusScan. Then scan each diskette you have, even new diskettes out of the box. Every diskette received from a manufacturer must be scanned. Multiply shrink-wrapped diskettes of new software with a virus once brought by benchmark system to its knees. It was and is my benchmark system. It took me two days to recover the system. Consider when you insert a new program on diskette in your system.

McAfee has other products that may meet your needs. Contact them at: Internet: www.mcafee.com; McAfee, 2710 Walsh Avenue, Santa Clara, CA 95051, (408) 988-3832; McAfee Canada, 178 Main Street, Unionville, Ontario, Canada L3R 2G9; McAfee France S. A., 50 rue de Londres, 75008 Paris, France; McAfee (UK) Ltd., Hayley House, London Road, Bracknell, Berkshire, GR12 2TH U.K.; McAfee Europe B. V., Orlypein 81 - Busitel 1, 1043 DS Amsterdam, Netherlands; McAfee Deutschland GmbH, Industriestrasse 1, D-82110 Germering, Germany.

Network Tape Drive (Sony)

The ability to store large amounts of data and retrieve information quickly is critical in today's applications. Tape storage and retrieval has been revolutionized by Sony's Memory in Cassette (MIC) architecture. The MIC consists of a memory chip built into the data cartridge which holds the system's log and other user-definable information. Applications that benefit from MIC's capabilities include hierarchical storage management, video server, film editing, and real-time data acquisition.

SDX-300C Features and specifications include:

- **High Speed Data Transfer.** With a recording density of 116 KBPI, the SDX-300C offers a sustained data transfer rate of 3.0 MB/s (native) to over 6 MB/s (compressed). The drive uses a fast/wide SCSI with a burst transfer rate of 20 MB/s.

- **Large Cartridge Capacity.** The SDX-300C family can store 25 GB (native) or 50 GB (compressed) on a single 8-mm size data cartridge.
- **System Design Convenience.** The SDX-300C family includes a fast/wide SCSI interface with a 68-pin single-ended or differential interface or an 80-pin SCA connector and a self-cooling design.
- **Exceptional Reliability.** Utilizing Sony technology expertise in 8-mm tape recording, the SDX-300C products are designed to provide 200,000 hour MTBF, an average head life of 50,000 hours and an average of 30,000 media uses.
- **Memory-in-Cassette.** Incorporating a flash memory chip within the data cartridge, the SDX-300C provides ultrafast media load and fast file search as well as the ability for applications to read and write to the memory chip.
- **Media Compatibility.** The SDX-300C family is designed exclusively for use with Sony's Advanced Metal Evaporated (AME) media technology incorporating pure cobalt metallization with a super-durable "diamond-like carbon coating" (DLC). AME tape is available with or without Memory-In-Cassette (MIC).
- **Specifications.** 2:1 data compression. MTBF, head life and media use specifications are averages based on normal office environmental conditions. Actual experience may vary.

Drive Type

   3.5" 8mm tape drive

Media

   170 meter Advanced-Metal Evaporated (AME) tape:

   SDX-T3N (without MIC)

   SDX-T3C (with MIC)

Interface

   SCSI-2 Fast/Wide, Single-ended or Differential

Data Compression (SDX-300C)

   IBM's Adaptive Lossless Data Compression (ALDC)

Capacity

   25 GB (native)

   50 GB (compressed)

continued on next page

Sustained Transfer Rate

3 MB/s (native)

6 MB/s (compressed)

Burst Transfer Rate

Asynchronous: 5.0 MB/s

Synchronous: 20.0 MB/s

Linear Recording Density

116,000 BPI

Recording Block Length

Variable or fixed

Average Media Load Time

20 seconds (without MIC)

10 seconds (with MIC)

Average Access Time

55 seconds (without MIC)

27 seconds (with MIC)

Search Speed

60"/sec (without MIC)

120"/sec (with MIC)

Rewind Speed

120"/sec (150 times nominal)

Drum Rotational Speed

4,800 RPM

Buffer Size

4 MB

Uncorrectable Error Rate

Less than 10–17 bits

MTBF

200,000 Power On Hours (POH)

Average R/W Head Life

50,000 Tape Contact Hours

Media Uses

30,000 end-to-end passes

Vibration (operating)

.25G peak, half sine wave of 50 to 500 Hz (swept)

continued on next page

Shock (operating)

> 5.0G peak, half sine wave of 3 ms duration

Altitude

> 10,000 feet

Maximum Wet Bulb Temperature

> 26°C

Operating Temperature

> 5°C–40°C (40°F–104°F)

Storage Temperature

> –40°C–70°C (–40°F–158°F)

Operating Humidity

> 20% to 80% (non-condensing)

Power Requirement

> DC 5V ± 5%, DC 12V ± 10% (internal)
>
> AC 100–200/220–240V (external)

Power Consumption

> 12 watts (average, internal)
>
> 21 watts (average, external)

Dimensions

> 1.62" H x 4.0" W x 6.10" D (41.1 x 101.6 x 154.9 mm)—internal
>
> 2.28" H x 7.44" W x 10.31" D (57.9 x 189 x 261.9 mm) —external

Weight

> 1lb 11oz (765 g) -internal
>
> 4lb 14oz (2.2 kg) -external

Models

> SDX-300C 68-pin Single Ended
>
> SDX-302C 80-pin SCA
>
> SDX-310C 68-pin Differential
>
> SDX-S300C/NB External Single Ended

Specifications reflect 2:1 data compression. MTBF, head life and media use specifications are averages based on normal office environmental conditions. Actual experience may vary. Nonmetric weights and measurements are approximate.

Electrical Cable (Belden)

As mentioned earlier, even the electrical part of the network infrastructure had to be designed. Because of the complexity of the network, I built my own electrical infrastructure. This meant selecting
and sizing the wire. There was a great need for extension cords. I
decided to build them with 10 gauge SO cable and selected Belden
wire. To find out more about Belden's electrical and data communications wire visit www.belden.com, or write to: Belden Wire & Cable,
1411 North West 11 Street, Richmond, IN 47374.

Computer Cabling (Belkin)

There was a need in the network for special cabling and adapters.
Belkin has a wide variety of peripheral cabling and accessories.
    A brief list of the Belkin components I used includes:

- DB9 female/female gender bender
- DB9 male/male gender bender
- DB15 female/female gender bender
- DB15 male/male gender bender
- SCSI-2 interface cable
- SCSI DB68 terminator
- DB25 male/male gender bender
- DB25 female/female gender bender
- IEEE 1284 printer cable 20'
- IEEE 1284 printer cable 35'
- DB25 Serial cable
- DB9 serial cable
- Super VGA monitor extension cable.

All these cables and accessories, and others, were used in this network. Belkin makes the best computer and printer cables on the market and also offers the best-designed benders.
    Further information on Belkin can be obtained by visiting
www.belkin.com or writing to: Belkin Components, 501 West Walnut
Street, Compton, CA 90220-5030.

Infrared Network Interface (JetEye)

The JetEye infrared network interface, by Extended Systems, enables portable workstations to be moved about and perform network printing via their infrared port. It is probably one of the most cost-effective methods available for network connection to meet the need for printing.

The JetEye features include:

- Line-of-sight infrared transmission for any infrared portable computer
- Supports Windows NT, Windows 95, Windows 98, TCP/IP, NetWare, LAN Manager, and LAN Server
- Supports operating distances up to three feet away.

The JetEye used in this network is dedicated to the ThinkPads which are remote portable workstations. Each has been configured to operate with the JetEye infrared network interface. For more information, contact: Extended Systems, 5777 North Meeker Avenue, Boise, ID 83713, 800-235-7576.

Power Protection (Tripplite)

Power protection in any computing, network, or peripheral equipment is not optional unless you can afford to throw away any or all of your equipment, replace it, and not be negatively impacted by down time.

The following items were needed adequately to protect the network components:

- Data Shield Parallel Dataline Surge Suppressors
- Data Shield 10BASE-T Surge Suppressors
- Data Shield Dial-up Line Surge Suppressors
- Data Shield AUI 802.3 Surge Suppressors
- Data Shield DB9 Surge Suppressors
- Data Shield DB-25 Serial Surge Suppressors.

The data shield protectors are used at all points in the network, with serial, parallel, 10BASE-T, AUI, modem cable, and DB-9 connections. Various electrical protection equipment also has telephone line spike/surge protection that is used to protect all incoming telephone lines.

Tripplite has other power protection equipment; to find out more, visit www.tripplite.com or write to: Tripplite, 500 North Orlean, Chicago, IL 60610.

Summary

This chapter presented the equipment used in the network discussed. It is important to do most of the initial network planning on marker board and/or paper. Once this is done one can begin to acquire equipment and build the network. It is best to design the network, acquire the equipment, then build the network. This approach makes the installation, operation, and maintenance much easier.

The following chapter goes into detail about the network, the equipment used, how it works, and other topics.

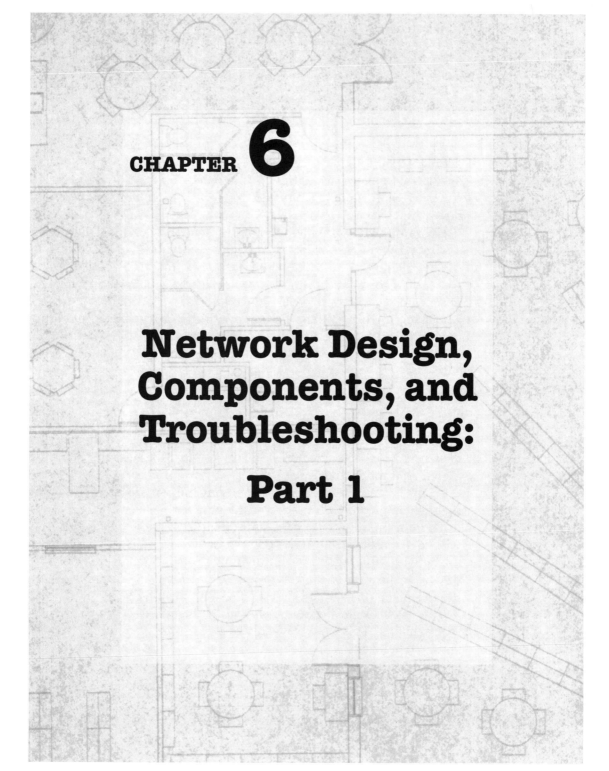

Network Design, Components, and Troubleshooting:

Part 1

Networks' origins can be identified to one of three possible groups:

- De Facto
- De Jure
- La De FactJure

The world of networking is full of de facto network designs. Those discovered after the network existed. Put another way, the only design that existed was a lack of network design. The de jure networks were designed before the network components were assembled. This is what I advocate.

Hybrid networks are about 50-50 de facto and de jure. They generally represent power struggles among the individuals behind them.

This chapter and the next present an explanation about the network I designed and built. Bear in mind I designed this network for myself, to meet the purpose I have, and for no other reason. It is a good example of what can be done with the proper pieces of equipment in place.

Network Design

The network design explained in this chapter is based more on principle than on given pieces of technology. The purpose of the network design is to meet current needs and be flexible enough to sustain growth, not for anyone else's criteria.

Before examining the components of the network, consider the highlighted network view shown in Figure 6.1.

There numerous network components are shown here but they will be discussed. The figure *does* show the overall logical design of the network. It is a good beginning for understanding overall network design. Inspection of the figure might indicate a single point of failure in a given place, but redundancies have been built into it.

This is the logical network design because it was driven by user requirements. This network enables users to exchange files, e-mail, and remote logons with systems such as servers, search network server repositories, and network printing.

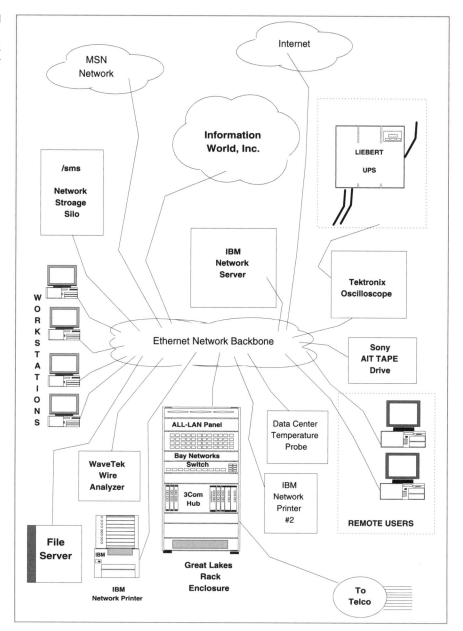

FIGURE 6.1
Highlighted
Network View

Component Overview

Before examining each component, this section provides a list the parts of the network. The list includes a variety of components and is in no particular order; it is a list of the vendor components used in this network.

- Temperature probe (Fluke)
- Oscilloscope (Tektronix)
- Network rack enclosure (Great Lakes Cabinets)
- Network analyzer (Hewlett-Packard)
- Network hubs (BAY Networks)
- ALL-LAN patch panel (Thomas & Betts)
- Network interface cards (Adaptec)
- Network wiring (Thomas & Betts)
- Wiring tester (WaveTek)
- Power protection (Liebert)
- Test equipment (Hewlett-Packard Internet Advisor)
- Microsoft software
- Software suite (McAfee)
- Network server (IBM)
- Network storage silo (SMS Data Products Group)
- Inline patch panel (Hubbell)
- Network Printer (IBM)
- Enterprise network Hub (USRobotics)
- Personal computers (IBM)
- Multimedia support (Creative Labs)
- Miscellaneous equipment.

Temperature Probe (Fluke)

One important aspect of network planning and of post-installation maintenance is knowing the temperature of the operating environment.

Figure 6.2 is an initial reading at the beginning of a business day in the network data center. The temperature reading is displayed in Fahrenheit degrees.

Figure 6.3 was taken with the same instrument, in the same location, a couple of hours after all equipment was powered-on and operating. The temperature has risen approximately four degrees.

Figure 6.4 was taken with the same instrument, in the same place, at a later time during the same day. The temperature now has climbed six degrees. Since the initial reading a short time earlier in the day the room temperature has risen ten degrees.

FIGURE 6.2
Temperature
Reading #1

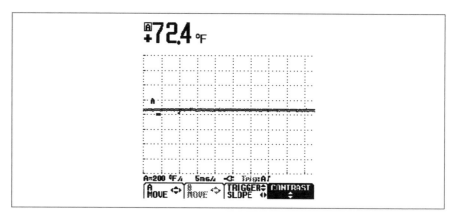

FIGURE 6.3
Temperature
Reading #2

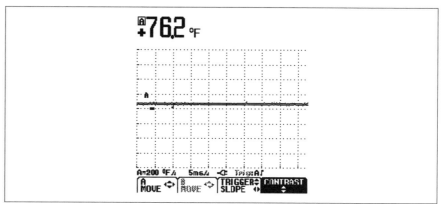

FIGURE 6.4
Temperature
Reading #3

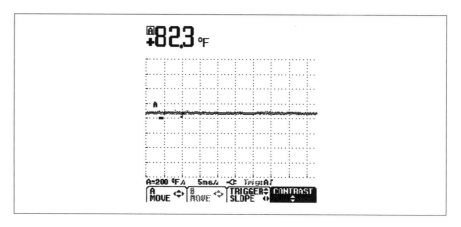

At the time of this reading no cooling fans, blowers, or air circulation were operating. The room was an average room with normal central air conditioning and ventilation.

Now, consider Figure 6.5.

FIGURE 6.5
Temperature
Reading #4

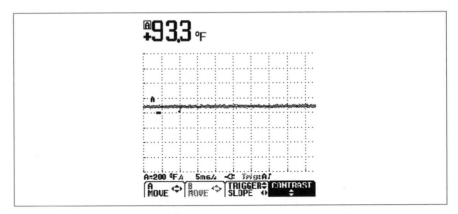

Before the middle of the day the room temperature is at 93.3 degrees. At this point air blowers and cooling fans started up, and there was increased airflow to the room where the readings were taken. This temperature is far above what should be normal operating temperature.

In certain places where equipment is concentrated area temperature can be much higher than the room temperature 15–20 feet away. These prove a point that air flow, cooling, and air circulation equipment are important to maintain stable and normal operating temperatures throughout a room wherein equipment is concentrated.

This is a good example of why rack-mount cabinets are important. With well-designed rack-mount cabinets, equipment can be placed so that blowers and fans can create a positive air flow and maintain temperatures at a level safe for the equipment and personnel working with it.

Parallel to the idea of monitoring temperature is another important aspect of network design. Free space around equipment for air flow is a recommendation many vendors supply with the specifications for their equipment. Be sure to ask for this information if it is not stated with each piece of equipment you plan to install in your network.

For more information about Fluke instruments, visit www.fluke. com; or write: FLUKE Corporation, P. O. Box 9090, Everett, WA 98206; or, FLUKE Europe B. V., P. O. Box 680, 7600 AR, Alemelo, Netherlands.

Oscilloscope/Digital Multimeter (Tektronix)

Due to the complexity of the network electrical planning, implementation, and maintenance I needed a powerful tool to work with a range of readings an oscilloscope and a digital multimeter. I also needed the ability to upload readings onto a computer for storage and printout. The Tektronix model THS720P TekScope IsolatedChannel Scope/DMM includes two devices in one: an oscilloscope and digital multimeter. These are implemented as distinct and separate functions. In addition, the oscilloscope has two channels, which makes for powerful analysis.

The tool is a 100 MHz bandwidth and 500 MS/s sample rate digital real-time oscilloscope and a true RMS digital multimeter. The scope and meter modes can operate simultaneously and independently on the same or separate signals. Some of the features included are: cursors, video trigger, voltage and resistance measurements, storage of waveforms, data, and instrument setups. It can be used to test correct operation of motors, transformer efficiency, power-supply performance, and to measure the effect of neutral current. The functions and specifications of the Tektronix scope are summarized in the chart below.

Bandwidth—100 MHz

Sample Rate (Each Channel)—500 MS/s

Channels—Two

Sensitivity—5 mV to 50 V/div

(to 500 V/div with 10X probe)

Position Range— ±10 div

DC Gain Accuracy— ±2%

Vertical Resolution—8 Bits

Record Length—2500 points

Time/Division Range—5 ns to 50 s/div

Horizontal Accuracy— ±200 ppm

Roll Mode— >/= 0.5 s/div

Autorange—User-selectable

Trigger Modes—Auto, Normal

Trigger Types—Edge, Pulse, Video, Motor, External.

Video Trigger Formats and Field Rates—Odd field, even field, and line

continued on next page

Motor Trigger—Triggers on 3- and 5-level pulse-width modulated power signal

External Trigger Input—5 MHz TTL compatible

Harmonics—Up to 31st (30hz-450hz)

Waveform Processing—Add, Subtract, Multiply, Calculate Watts = V x I

Waveform Storage—10 waveforms

Acquisition Modes—Sample, Envelope, Average, Peak Detect

Cursor Measurements—DELTAVolts, DELTATime, 1/DELTATime (Hz), Degree (phase)

Cursor Types—Horizontal Bars, Vertical Bars, Paired (volts @ time)

Display System—Interpolation: Sin(x)/x

Mode—Vector, Dot, Vector Accumulate, Dot Accumulate

Forma—YT and XY

Automatic Meassurements

Period	Frequency
+Width	Rise Time
−Width	Fall Time
+Duty Cycle	+Overshoot
−Duty Cycle	−Overshoot
High	Max
Low	Min
Peak-to-Peak	Amplitude
Mean	RMS
Cycle Mean	Cycle RMS
Burst	Width

Power Measurements

W	True power
VA	Apparent power
VAR	Reactive power
V	Volts (RMS, Peak)
A	Amps (RMS, Peak)
THD-F	Total harmonic distortion as a percentage of the fundamental
THD-R	Total harmonic distortion of the RMS of the input signal
PF	Power Factor
DPF	Displacement Power Factor

continued on next page

PHI   Phase difference between the voltage and current

DMM Specifications

    DC Voltage Ranges—400.0 mV to 880 V.

    DC Volts Accuracy—±(0.5% of reading + 5 counts)

    True RMS AC Voltage Ranges—400.0 mV to 640 V

    Maximum Float Voltage—600 VRMS each channel (probe-dependent)

    Resolution—4000 count, 3-3/4 digits

    AC Volts Accuracy—±(2% of reading + 5 counts)

    Resistance Range—400.0 Ohm to 40.00 MOhm

    Resistance Accuracy—

        ±(0.5% of reading + 2 counts); 40 MOhm

        ±(2% of reading + 5 counts)

    Diode Test Range—0–2 V

    Continuity Check—Audible tone when <Ohm50 Ohm

    Modes—Min, Max, DELTAMax-Min, Avg, Hold

    Non-volatile Storage—10 DMM screenshots

    External Trigger Input—5 MHz TTL compatible

    Vertical Zoom Capability—2X, 5X, 10X

    dB Scale—Selectable, referenced from 1 mV to 10 V

    dBm Scale—Selectable, referenced from

    50 Ohm to 600 Ohm

General Specifications

    Setups—10 front-panel

    Safety Certification—UL 3111-1 Listed, CSA Certified, complies with EN61010-1

    Power—NiCad rechargeable battery pack and AC adapter

    Battery Life—Approx. 2 hours from full charge

    Display—Backlit LCD

    Display Resolution—320 x 240

In order to set up a baseline for future reference for the electrical characteristics for the network I took sample readings prior to network equipment implementation.

Figure 6.6 is a random voltage reading in the data center, before set up of the Liebert UPS power conditioning equipment. Notice the VAC is 119.4 and the frequency reading is 59.95. Approximately thirty minutes later another reading was made.

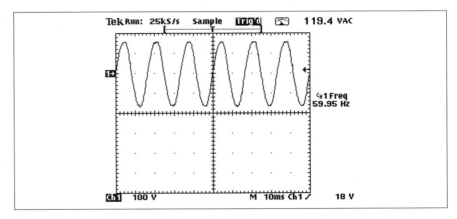

FIGURE 6.6
Baseline Electrical
Reading #1

Figure 6.7 shows a reading of 121.2 VAC and a waveform of 118.4 RMS VAC. Still another reading was taken a short time later in the same place, with the same tool.

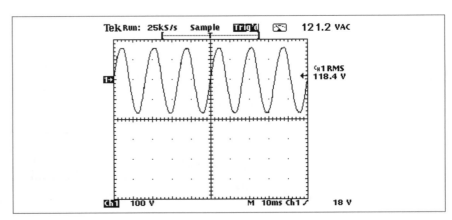

FIGURE 6.7
Baseline Electrical
Reading #2

Figure 6.8 shows a VAC reading of 120.3 VAC and a 59.95 frequency reading.

These readings are very close and this environment has relatively stable power from the utility company.

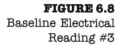

FIGURE 6.8
Baseline Electrical
Reading #3

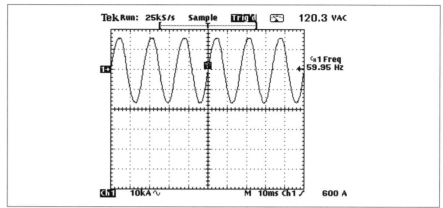

I recommend baseline readings at your site. Your site might require ten times the number of readings to establish a better snapshot of its electrical characteristics equipment. Regardless how many snapshots are needed, this is a valuable tool to establish a baseline for power quality; continue to make readings like these periodically to have a good reference over time.

Network Analyzer (Internet Advisor: Hewlett-Packard)

This network is like others; a network analyzer is required for adequate information to be obtained to maintain it properly. If you are relatively new to networking you may want to refer back to this section later since it contains information considered advanced. Consider the information here about this tool.

The HP Internet Advisor (J2522B) provides comprehensive Ethernet testing. It is a portable, full-featured network-analysis solution that allows users to install, support and maintain LAN, WAN and ATM networks by providing features that allow troubleshooting in any network. Some of these features are:

- Portable platform with rugged built-in 486 PC
- Commentators to help solve network problems quickly and effectively
- 7-layer decoding of all major protocols
- Comprehensive network statistics
- Traffic generation.

Internet Advisor Mainframe Characteristics:

- Intel486 DX4, 100 MHz processor
- 16 MB of PC memory
- VGA color display, 26.4 cm (10.4 inch) diagonal or active matrix display (as an optional feature)
- 814 MB hard drive (as standard) or 1.4 GB hard drive (as an option)
- 3.5" flexible disk drive
- PCMCIA slot (Type I/II)
- Built-in mouse
- Serial, parallel and external VGA monitor ports
- Windows 95.

Internet Advisor General Specifications

- 10 Mbps data rate
- 2 RJ-45 connectors with hub logic allow for testing in switched environments
- AUI connector for universal Ethernet testing through external transceivers

Hardware Filtering

- Hardware timestamp with 100 ns resolution

Internet Advisor Physical Characteristics

- Weight 6.2 kg (13.7lbs)
- Dimensions: 8.5H x 30W x 29D cm (3.4"H x 12"W x 11.5"D)
- Display: 26.5 cm diagonal (10.4") passive DSTNcolor LCD VGA; optional 26.5 cm diagonal (10.4") active matrix TFT color VGA

Internet Advisor Operating Conditions

- Temperature:
  - Operating 5°C–40°C (41°F–104°F)
  - Non-operating –25°C – +60°C (–13°F–140°F)

- Humidity:
  - Operating 20% to 80% relative humidity to 40° C non-condensing
- Storage:
  - 10% to 90% relative humidity to 60°C non-condensing
- Power Requirements:
  - 100–240 VAC, 50–60 Hz, 75 Watts max.
- Warranty:
  - 3 years
- Regulatory Compliances:
  - Bears the CE and CSA marks

The particular advisor I used was:

- HP J2522B Internet Advisor LAN—Ethernet
- Opt 221 26.4 cm active matrix color display
- HP J2514A deluxe carrying case
- HP J2533A Token ring-parallel port adapter (International)
- HP J2531A internet reporter—LAN.

Figure 6.9 provides a lot of information. The name of the screen is at the top of the figure: node discovery measurement. The names of the network computers participating in the network: Brains, Cherokee, Muscle, Silo, and The-Hostage.

The IP addresses shown correlate to the systems on the network. Further information about these systems includes what they are doing: broadcast, etc.

Figure 6.10 shows additional network information, another snapshot of nodes on the network at a later time. Notice the systems participating on the network are Brains, Muscle, Silo, The-Hostage, Cherokee, Fat Boy, Mony, The-Kid, and Angel.

The difference between Figure 6.9 and 6.10 is the time when the reading was taken. This level of information is powerful for measuring network loads, and network nodes using the network, and for obtaining tangible information to create baseline readings for reference.

FIGURE 6.9
Initial Network
Information

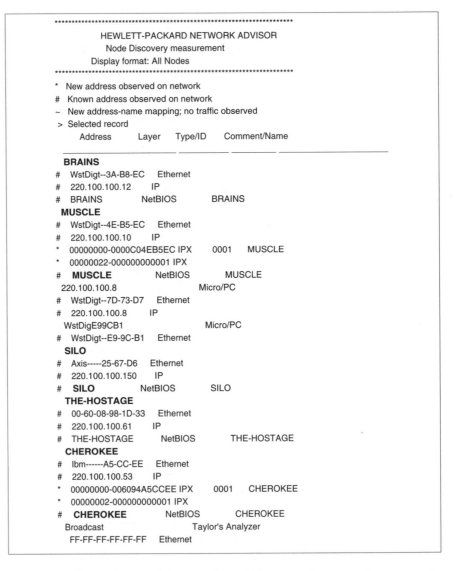

```
*********************************************************************
                    HEWLETT-PACKARD NETWORK ADVISOR
                     Node Discovery measurement
                     Display format: All Nodes
*********************************************************************
  *  New address observed on network
  #  Known address observed on network
  ~  New address-name mapping; no traffic observed
  >  Selected record
        Address          Layer      Type/ID     Comment/Name
        _____      _____    _____     _____

   BRAINS
  #  WstDigt--3A-B8-EC     Ethernet
  #  220.100.100.12        IP
  #  BRAINS             NetBIOS            BRAINS
   MUSCLE
  #  WstDigt--4E-B5-EC     Ethernet
  #  220.100.100.10        IP
  *  00000000-0000C04EB5EC IPX       0001    MUSCLE
  *  00000022-000000000001 IPX
  #  MUSCLE             NetBIOS            MUSCLE
     220.100.100.8                     Micro/PC
  #  WstDigt--7D-73-D7     Ethernet
  #  220.100.100.8         IP
     WstDigE99CB1                      Micro/PC
  #  WstDigt--E9-9C-B1     Ethernet
   SILO
  #  Axis-----25-67-D6     Ethernet
  #  220.100.100.150       IP
  #  SILO               NetBIOS            SILO
   THE-HOSTAGE
  #  00-60-08-98-1D-33     Ethernet
  #  220.100.100.61        IP
  #  THE-HOSTAGE        NetBIOS            THE-HOSTAGE
   CHEROKEE
  #  Ibm------A5-CC-EE     Ethernet
  #  220.100.100.53        IP
  *  00000000-006094A5CCEE IPX       0001    CHEROKEE
  *  00000002-000000000001 IPX
  #  CHEROKEE           NetBIOS            CHEROKEE
     Broadcast                         Taylor's Analyzer
      FF-FF-FF-FF-FF-FF     Ethernet
```

Figure 6.11 shows the addition of Fat-Boy and others on the network.
The previous hosts are also participating on the network. This figure
also shows the protocols in use: NetBIOS, Ethernet, and IP.

To put this information into perspective, consider Figure 6.12.

FIGURE 6.10
Additional
Network
Information

```
*************************************************************************


              HEWLETT-PACKARD NETWORK ADVISOR

        Node Discovery measurement
          Run started on Mar 13, 1998 @ 19:13:34
          Run stopped on Mar 13, 1998 @ 19:14:59
          10 nodes observed
          Display format: Observed Nodes
          Print:      All displayed records


*************************************************************************


        *  New address observed on network
        #  Known address observed on network
        ~  New address-name mapping; no traffic observed
        >  Selected record


              Address       Layer     Type/ID     Comment/Name
          _____ _____ _____ _____


          220.100.100.8               Micro/PC
        #  WstDigt--7D-73-D7    Ethernet
        #  220.100.100.8       IP
        *> FAT BOY          NetBIOS       FAT BOY
        >  ANGEL
        *> Ibm------45-43-F3    Ethernet
        *> 220.100.100.41      IP           ANGEL
          BRAINS
        #  WstDigt--3A-B8-EC    Ethernet
        #> 220.100.100.12      IP           BRAINS
        #  BRAINS           NetBIOS       BRAINS
          CHEROKEE
        #  Ibm------A5-CC-EE    Ethernet
        #  220.100.100.53      IP
        *> 00000000-006094A5CCEE IPX     0001    INFO
        *  00000002-000000000001 IPX
        #  CHEROKEE         NetBIOS       CHEROKEE
          MUSCLE
        #  WstDigt--4E-B5-EC    Ethernet
        #> 220.100.100.10      IP           THE-KID
        *  00000000-0000C04EB5EC IPX     0001    MUSCLE
        *  00000022-000000000001 IPX
        #  MUSCLE           NetBIOS       MUSCLE
        >  RENEGADE
        *> WstDigt--93-73-D7    Ethernet
        *> RENEGADE         NetBIOS       RENEGADE
          SILO
        #  Axis-----25-67-D6    Ethernet
        #> 220.100.100.150     IP           SILO
        #  SILO             NetBIOS       SILO
          THE-HOSTAGE
        #  00-60-08-98-1D-33    Ethernet
        #  220.100.100.61      IP
        *> 00000000-006008981D33 IPX
        #  THE-HOSTAGE          NetBIOS       THE-HOSTAGE
          WstDigE99CB1                Micro/PC
        #  WstDigt--E9-9C-B1    Ethernet
        *> 220.100.100.19      IP
        *> 00000000-0000C0E99CB1 IPX     0001    MONY
        *> MONY             NetBIOS       MONY
        >  *new 220.100.100.77
        *> 00-00-D1-0F-E2-9B    Ethernet
        *> 220.100.100.77      IP
```

FIGURE 6.11
Network
Information
Take #2

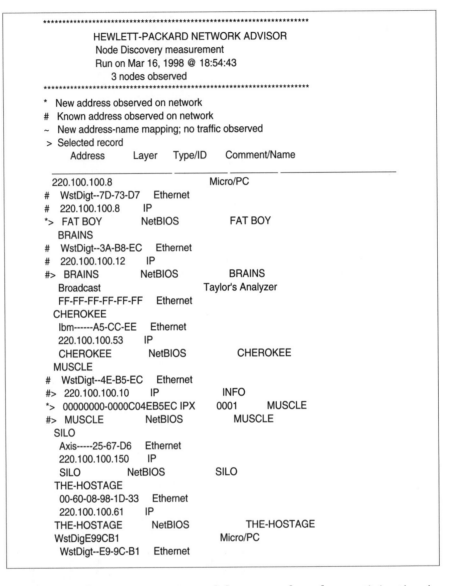

```
**********************************************************************
                    HEWLETT-PACKARD NETWORK ADVISOR
                      Node Discovery measurement
                      Run on Mar 16, 1998 @ 18:54:43
                           3 nodes observed
**********************************************************************
  *   New address observed on network
  #   Known address observed on network
  ~   New address-name mapping; no traffic observed
  >  Selected record
         Address       Layer     Type/ID     Comment/Name
      _____  _____  _____

     220.100.100.8                           Micro/PC
  #   WstDigt--7D-73-D7     Ethernet
  #   220.100.100.8         IP
  *>  FAT BOY           NetBIOS              FAT BOY
     BRAINS
  #   WstDigt--3A-B8-EC     Ethernet
  #   220.100.100.12        IP
  #>  BRAINS            NetBIOS              BRAINS
     Broadcast                           Taylor's Analyzer
      FF-FF-FF-FF-FF-FF     Ethernet
     CHEROKEE
       Ibm------A5-CC-EE    Ethernet
       220.100.100.53       IP
       CHEROKEE         NetBIOS              CHEROKEE
     MUSCLE
  #   WstDigt--4E-B5-EC     Ethernet
  #>  220.100.100.10        IP               INFO
  *>  00000000-0000C04EB5EC IPX      0001        MUSCLE
  #>  MUSCLE            NetBIOS              MUSCLE
     SILO
       Axis-----25-67-D6    Ethernet
       220.100.100.150      IP
       SILO             NetBIOS              SILO
     THE-HOSTAGE
       00-60-08-98-1D-33    Ethernet
       220.100.100.61       IP
       THE-HOSTAGE      NetBIOS              THE-HOSTAGE
     WstDigE99CB1                         Micro/PC
       WstDigt--E9-9C-B1    Ethernet
```

Figure 6.12 shows an overview of the network nodes participating in the network I designed. The ME-HP node is surrounded by a high-lighted box. The Internet Advisor is capable of listening to the communication of all nodes on this network. Consider the information presented here in Table 6.1.

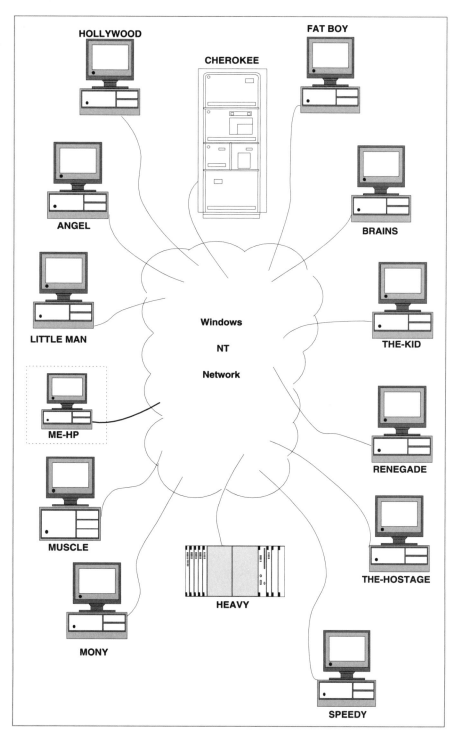

FIGURE 6.12
Overview of
Network Nodes

TABLE 6.1
Network
Commentator
for Ethernet

TCP:	**Close Connection**	[Normal] Mar 13@19:45:05.8432606
	220.100.100.53	<--> 220.100.100.10
	Cherokee	Muscle
	Port: 1144	LOC-SRV 135
	Tx Packets: 6	5
	Low Window: 0	0
	Retrans: 0	0
	Connection Duration: 0:00:00.0081942	
	Frame Number(s): 220	
TCP:	**Close Connection**	[Normal] Mar 13@19:45:05.8527809
	220.100.100.53	<--> 220.100.100.10
	Cherokee	Muscle
	Port: 1145	1034
	Tx Packets: 6	5
	Low Window: 0	0
	Retrans:0	0
	Connection Duration: 0:00:00.0068831	
	Frame Number(s): 231	
NOV:	**Routing Information Reply**	[Normal] Mar 13@19:45:10.5468778
	To Node: FF-FF-FF-FF-FF-FF, Broadcast	
	00000000-006094A5CCEE	---> 00000000-FFFFFFFFFFFF
	Network number: 00000002	
	Number of hops: 1	Number of ticks: 2
	Frame Number: 235	
NOV:	**General Service Query**	[Normal] Mar 13@19:45:40.0371709
	From Node: 00-00-C0-E9-9C-B1, WstDigE99CB1	
	00000000-0000C0E99CB1	---> 00000000-FFFFFFFFFFFF
	Server Type: File Server	
	Frame Number: 272	
NOV:	**Nearest Service Query**	[Normal] Mar 13@19:46:05.1400663
	From Node: 00-00-C0-4E-B5-EC, MUSCLE	
	00000000-0000C04EB5EC ---> 00000000-FFFFFFFFFFFF	
	Server Type: File Server	
	Frame Number: 314	
NOV:	**Nearest Service Query**	[Normal] Mar 13@19:46:05.852107
	From Node: 00-00-C0-4E-B5-EC, MUSCLE	
	00000000-0000C04EB5EC	---> 00000000-FFFFFFFFFFFF
	Server Type: File Server	
	Frame Number: 319	
NOV:	**Nearest Service Query**	[Normal] Mar 13@19:46:06.57323
	From Node: 00-00-C0-4E-B5-EC, MUSCLE	
	00000000-0000C04EB5EC	---> 00000000-FFFFFFFFFFFF

continued on next page

Table 6.1 (continued)

Server Type: File Server
Frame Number: 321

NOV: Nearest Service Query   [Normal]   Mar 13@19:46:07.2943876
From Node: 00-00-C0-4E-B5-EC, MUSCLE
00000000-0000C04EB5EC   ---> 00000000-FFFFFFFFFFFF
Server Type: File Server
Frame Number: 322

NOV: Nearest Service Query   [Normal]   Mar 13@19:46:08.0155127
From Node: 00-00-C0-4E-B5-EC, MUSCLE
00000000-0000C04EB5EC   ---> 00000000-FFFFFFFFFFFF
Server Type: File Server
Frame Number: 325

NOV: Nearest Service Query   [Normal]   Mar 13@19:46:08.7365608
From Node: 00-00-C0-4E-B5-EC, MUSCLE
00000000-0000C04EB5EC   ---> 00000000-FFFFFFFFFFFF
Server Type: File Server
Frame Number: 326

NOV: Nearest Service Query   [Normal]   Mar 13@19:46:09.4577
From Node: 00-00-C0-4E-B5-EC, MUSCLE
00000000-0000C04EB5EC   ---> 00000000-FFFFFFFFFFFF
Server Type: File Server
Frame Number: 327

NOV: Nearest Service Query   [Normal]   Mar 13@19:46:10.1788107
From Node: 00-00-C0-4E-B5-EC, MUSCLE
00000000-0000C04EB5EC   ---> 00000000-FFFFFFFFFFFF
Server Type: File Server
Frame Number: 329

NOV: Routing Information Reply   [Normal]   Mar 13@19:46:10.5455269
To Node: FF-FF-FF-FF-FF-FF, Broadcast
00000000-006094A5CCEE   ---> 00000000-FFFFFFFFFFFF
Network number: 00000002
Number of hops: 1 Number of ticks: 2
Frame Number: 330

NOV: Nearest Service Query   [Normal]   Mar 13@19:46:10.8999035
From Node: 00-00-C0-4E-B5-EC, MUSCLE
00000000-0000C04EB5EC   ---> 00000000-FFFFFFFFFFFF
Server Type: File Server
Frame Number: 331

NOV: Nearest Service Query   [Normal]   Mar 13@19:46:11.6210437
From Node: 00-00-C0-4E-B5-EC, MUSCLE
00000000-0000C04EB5EC   ---> 00000000-FFFFFFFFFFFF

continued on next page

Table 6.1 (continued)

Server Type: File Server
Frame Number: 332

NOV: General Service Query   [Normal]   Mar 13@19:46:12.3421574
From Node: 00-00-C0-4E-B5-EC, MUSCLE
00000000-0000C04EB5EC   ---> 00000000-FFFFFFFFFFFF
Server Type: File Server
Frame Number: 333

NOV: General Service Query   [Normal]   Mar 13@19:46:13.0632036
From Node: 00-00-C0-4E-B5-EC, MUSCLE
00000000-0000C04EB5EC   ---> 00000000-FFFFFFFFFFFF
Server Type: File Server
Frame Number: 334

NOV: General Service Query   [Normal]   Mar 13@19:46:13.7843639
From Node: 00-00-C0-4E-B5-EC, MUSCLE
00000000-0000C04EB5EC   ---> 00000000-FFFFFFFFFFFF
Server Type: File Server
Frame Number: 335

NOV: General Service Query   [Normal]   Mar 13@19:46:14.5054544
From Node: 00-00-C0-4E-B5-EC, MUSCLE
00000000-0000C04EB5EC   ---> 00000000-FFFFFFFFFFFF
Server Type: File Server
Frame Number: 344

TCP: Close Connection   [Normal]   Mar 13@19:46:27.4038468
220.100.100.8   <--> 220.100.100.150
220.100.100.8 SILO
Port: 1043 NETBIOS 139
Tx Packets: 10   8
Low Window: 0   0
Retrans: 0   0
Connection Duration: 0:00:02.0613844
Frame Number(s): 407

NOV: Nearest Service Query   [Normal]   Mar 13@19:46:39.9998894
From Node: 00-00-C0-E9-9C-B1, WstDigE99CB1
00000000-0000C0E99CB1   ---> 00000000-FFFFFFFFFFFF
Server Type: File Server
Frame Number: 472

NOV: Routing Information Reply   [Normal]   Mar 13@19:47:10.544317
To Node: FF-FF-FF-FF-FF-FF, Broadcast
00000000-006094A5CCEE   ---> 00000000-FFFFFFFFFFFF
Network number: 00000002
Number of hops: 1   Number of ticks: 2
Frame Number: 488

continued on next page

Table 6.1 (continued)

TCP:	**Reset Connection**	[Warning] 13@19:47:19.720187
	220.100.100.12	---> 220.100.100.53
	BRAINS	CHEROKEE
	Port: NETBIOS 139	1111
	Tx Packets: 1	0
	Low Window: 0	0
	Retrans: 0	0
	Connection Duration: 0:00:00.0	
	Frame Number(s): 489	
NOV:	**General Service Query**	[Normal] Mar 13@19:47:39.960695
From Node: 00-00-C0-E9-9C-B1, WstDigE99CB1		
00000000-0000C0E99CB1	---> 00000000-FFFFFFFFFFFF	
	Server Type: File Server	
	Frame Number: 562	
TCP:	**Reset Connection**	[Warning] Mar 13@19:47:47.6089335
	220.100.100.41	---> 220.100.100.53
	CHEROKEE	
	Port: NETBIOS 139	1136
	Tx Packets: 1	0
	Low Window: 0	0
	Retrans: 0	0
	Connection Duration: 0:00:00.0	
	Frame Number(s): 566	
TCP:	**Close Connection**	[Normal] Mar 13@19:48:07.5697698
	220.100.100.19	<--> 220.100.100.150
	SILO	
	Port: 1029	NETBIOS 139
	Tx Packets: 10	8
	Low Window: 0	0
	Retrans: 0	0
	Connection Duration: 0:00:02.0748997	
	Frame Number(s): 658	
NOV:	**Routing Information Reply**	[Normal] Mar 13@19:48:10.5430294
	To Node: FF-FF-FF-FF-FF-FF, Broadcast	
	00000000-006094A5CCEE	---> 00000000-FFFFFFFFFFFF
	Network number: 00000002	
	Number of hops:	1 Number of ticks: 2
	Frame Number: 697	
TCP:	**Reset Connection**	[Warning] Mar 13@19:48:31.2433202
	220.100.100.77	---> 220.100.100.53
	CHEROKEE	

continued on next page

Table 6.1 (continued)

	Port: NETBIOS 139	1143
	Tx Packets: 1	0
	Low Window: 0	0
	Retrans: 0	0
	Connection Duration: 0:00:00.0	
	Frame Number(s): 1545	
NOV:	**Nearest Service Query** [Normal] Mar 13@19:48:39.9249748	
	From Node: 00-00-C0-E9-9C-B1, WstDigE99CB1	
	00000000-0000C0E99CB1 ---> 00000000-FFFFFFFFFFFF	
	Server Type: File Server	
	Frame Number: 1858	
TCP:	**Reset Connection** [Warning] Mar 13@19:48:49.3872264	
	220.100.100.61 ---> 220.100.100.53	
	THE-HOSTAGE CHEROKEE	
	Port: NETBIOS 139 1139	
	Tx Packets: 1 0	
	Low Window: 0 0	
	Retrans: 0 0	
	Connection Duration: 0:00:00.0	
	Frame Number(s): 1899	
NOV:	**Nearest Service Query** [Normal] Mar 13@19:49:01.7757016	
	From Node: 00-00-C0-4E-B5-EC, MUSCLE	
	00000000-0000C04EB5EC ---> 00000000-FFFFFFFFFFFF	
	Server Type: File Server	
	Frame Number: 1920	
NOV:	**Nearest Service Query** [Normal] Mar 13@19:49:02.4938427	
	From Node: 00-00-C0-4E-B5-EC, MUSCLE	
	00000000-0000C04EB5EC ---> 00000000-FFFFFFFFFFFF	
	Server Type: File Server	
	Frame Number: 1921	
NOV:	**Nearest Service Query** [Normal] Mar 13@19:49:03.2149768	
	From Node: 00-00-C0-4E-B5-EC, MUSCLE	
	00000000-0000C04EB5EC ---> 00000000-FFFFFFFFFFFF	
	Server Type: File Server	
	Frame Number: 1922	
NOV:	**Nearest Service Query** [Normal] Mar 13@19:49:03.936104	
	From Node: 00-00-C0-4E-B5-EC, MUSCLE	
	00000000-0000C04EB5EC ---> 00000000-FFFFFFFFFFFF	
	Server Type: File Server	
	Frame Number: 1923	

continued on next page

Table 6.1 (continued)

NOV: Nearest Service Query   [Normal] Mar 13@19:49:04.6572385
    From Node: 00-00-C0-4E-B5-EC, MUSCLE
00000000-0000C04EB5EC   ---> 00000000-FFFFFFFFFFFF
    Server Type: File Server
    Frame Number: 1924

NOV: Nearest Service Query   [Normal] Mar 13@19:49:05.3783097
    From Node: 00-00-C0-4E-B5-EC, MUSCLE
    00000000-0000C04EB5EC   ---> 00000000-FFFFFFFFFFFF
    Server Type: File Server
    Frame Number: 1925

NOV: Nearest Service Query   [Normal] Mar 13@19:49:06.0994503
    From Node: 00-00-C0-4E-B5-EC, MUSCLE
    00000000-0000C04EB5EC   ---> 00000000-FFFFFFFFFFFF
    Server Type: File Server
    Frame Number: 1926

NOV: Nearest Service Query   [Normal] Mar 13@19:49:06.8205179
    From Node: 00-00-C0-4E-B5-EC, MUSCLE
    00000000-0000C04EB5EC   ---> 00000000-FFFFFFFFFFFF
    Server Type: File Server
    Frame Number: 1927

NOV: Nearest Service Query   [Normal] Mar 13@19:49:07.5416253
    From Node: 00-00-C0-4E-B5-EC, MUSCLE
    00000000-0000C04EB5EC   ---> 00000000-FFFFFFFFFFFF
    Server Type: File Server
    Frame Number: 1932

NOV: Nearest Service Query   [Normal] Mar 13@19:49:08.2627509
    From Node: 00-00-C0-4E-B5-EC, MUSCLE
    00000000-0000C04EB5EC   ---> 00000000-FFFFFFFFFFFF
    Server Type: File Server
    Frame Number: 1933

NOV: General Service Query   [Normal] Mar 13@19:49:08.9838831
    From Node: 00-00-C0-4E-B5-EC, MUSCLE
    00000000-0000C04EB5EC   ---> 00000000-FFFFFFFFFFFF
    Server Type: File Server
    Frame Number: 1934

NOV: General Service Query   [Normal] Mar 13@19:49:09.7049542
    From Node: 00-00-C0-4E-B5-EC, MUSCLE
    00000000-0000C04EB5EC   ---> 00000000-FFFFFFFFFFFF
    Server Type: File Server
    Frame Number: 1935

continued on next page

Table 6.1 (continued)

NOV: General Service Query   [Normal]   Mar 13@19:49:10.426067
       From Node: 00-00-C0-4E-B5-EC, MUSCLE
       00000000-0000C04EB5EC   ---> 00000000-FFFFFFFFFFFF
       Server Type: File Server
       Frame Number: 1937

NOV: Routing Information Reply   [Normal]   Mar 13@19:49:10.5417939
       To Node: FF-FF-FF-FF-FF-FF, Broadcast
       00000000-006094A5CCEE   ---> 00000000-FFFFFFFFFFFF
       Network number: 00000002
       Number of hops: 1 Number of ticks: 2
       Frame Number: 1938

NOV: General Service Query   [Normal]   Mar 13@19:49:11.1471537
       From Node: 00-00-C0-4E-B5-EC, MUSCLE
       00000000-0000C04EB5EC   ---> 00000000-FFFFFFFFFFFF
       Server Type: File Server
       Frame Number: 1939

NOV: General Service Query   [Normal]   Mar 13@19:49:39.8876314
       From Node: 00-00-C0-E9-9C-B1, WstDigE99CB1
       00000000-0000C0E99CB1   ---> 00000000-FFFFFFFFFFFF
       Server Type: File Server
       Frame Number: 2002

Notice in Table 6.1 a wide variety of information is obtained. The protocol used is identified: NOV (for Novell) and TCP (for TCP/IP). NetBIOS is also in use. IP addresses are shown, as are functions performed: General Service Query and Close Connection among others. A time stamp indicates the hour. This information gives a wealth of insight to differing aspects of the network operation. This level of information is critical after the network is designed and installed. What is *helpful* is to see the information that can be obtained before network design. In the case of my network, the HP Internet Advisor is indispensable.

The Internet Advisor can also give information the 802.3/Ethernet decode. What follows is a detailed view of information on all frames. We will then consider the synthesis of this level of information.

```
************************************************************
*****            HEWLETT PACKARD NETWORK ADVISOR    *****
*****                                                *****
*****     Measurement:  802.3/Ethernet Decode       *****
*****     Print Type:   All Frames                   *****
*****     Open Views:   Detailed                     *****
*****     Display Mode: Viewing All Frames           *****
*****     Print Date:   03/13/98                     *****
*****     Print Time:   20:4:31                      *****
*****                                                *****
************************************************************
```

```
Frame: 1 Time: Mar 13@20:02:56.9192136 Length: 64
Destination address     Broadcast          Broadcast
Source address          220.100.100.8      Individual, global
Type                    08-06 ARP
Data size               46
Frame check sequence     8E-69-77-43
```

```
Frame: 2 Time: Mar 13@20:02:58.4297056 Length: 64
Destination address     Broadcast          Broadcast
Source address          220.100.100.8      Individual, global
Type                    08-06              ARP
Data size               46
Frame check sequence     1E-DE-8C-55
```

```
Frame: 3 Time: Mar 13@20:02:59.9403448 Length: 64
Destination address     Broadcast          Broadcast
Source address          220.100.100.8      Individual, global
Type 0                  8-06               ARP
Data size               46
Frame check sequence     E-69-77-43
```

```
Frame: 4 Time: Mar 13@20:03:01.6672512 Length: 65
Destination address     03-00-00-00-00-01 Group, local
Source address          220.100.100.8      Individual, global
Length                  47                 47
Frame check sequence     F4-31-89-29
```

```
Frame: 5 Time: Mar 13@20:03:01.6676236 Length: 65
Destination address 2   20.100.100.8       Individual, global
Source address          CHEROKEE           Individual, global
Length                  47
Data size               47
Frame check sequence     3A-9A-CD-F5
```

```
Frame: 6 Time: Mar 13@20:03:01.6679466 Length: 64
```

```
Destination address    CHEROKEE         Individual, global
Source address         220.100.100.8    Individual, global
Length                 3
Data size              3
Padding:
00-06-04-00-01-00-00-C0 7D-73-D7-DC-64-64-08-00
00-00-00-00-00-DC-64-64 4D-02-53-BF-8B-50-18-15
38-81-A1-00-00-00-00-00 23-FF-53
Frame check sequence   20-62-02-76
```

```
Frame: 7 Time: Mar 13@20:03:01.6681270 Length: 64
Destination address    220.100.100.8    Individual, global
Source address         CHEROKEE         Individual, global
Length                 3
Data size              3
Padding:
00-00-00-00-00-00-00-00 00-00-00-00-00-00-00-00
00-00-00-00-00-00-00-00 00-00-00-00-00-00-00-00
00-00-00-00-00-00-00-00 00-00-00
Frame check sequence   66-1B-6E-95
```

```
Frame: 8 Time: Mar 13@20:03:01.6683975 Length: 64
Destination address    CHEROKEE         Individual, global
Source address         220.100.100.8    Individual, global
Length                 4
Data size              4
Padding:
00-FF-EF-0A-17-30-00-00 00-30-00-43-48-45-52-4F
4B-45-45-20-20-20-20-20 20-20-20-46-41-54-20-42
4F-59-20-20-20-20-20-20 20-20
Frame check sequence   47-41-9D-7D
```

```
Frame: 9 Time: Mar 13@20:03:01.6685602 Length: 64
Destination address    220.100.100.8    Individual, global
Source address         CHEROKEE         Individual, global
Length                 4
Data size              4
Padding:
00-00-00-00-00-00-00-00 00-00-00-00-00-00-00-00
00-00-00-00-00-00-00-00 00-00-00-00-00-00-00-00
00-00-00-00-00-00-00-00 00-00
Frame check sequence   49-07-D3-43
```

```
Frame: 10 Time: Mar 13@20:03:01.6688476 Length: 64
Destination address    CHEROKEE         Individual, global
Source address         220.100.100.8    Individual, global
Length                 18
Data size              18
Padding:
00-00-00-00-00-00-DC-64 64-4D-02-53-BF-8B-50-18
```

```
15-38-81-A1-00-00-00-00 00-23-FF-53
Frame check sequence   93-AD-15-BE
```

```
Frame: 11 Time: Mar 13@20:03:01.6690630 Length: 64
Destination address    220.100.100.8    Individual, global
Source address         CHEROKEE         Individual, global
Length                 4
Data size              4
Padding:
00-00-00-00-00-00-00-00 00-00-00-00-00-00-00-00
00-00-00-00-00-00-00-00 00-00-00-00-00-00-00-00
00-00-00-00-00-00-00-00 00-00
Frame check sequence   BF-EA-F4-CD
```

```
Frame: 12 Time: Mar 13@20:03:01.6691318 Length: 64
Destination address    220.100.100.8    Individual, global
Source address         CHEROKEE         Individual, global
Length                 18
Data size              18
Padding:
00-00-00-00-00-00-00-00 00-00-00-00-00-00-00-00
00-00-00-00-00-00-00-00 00-00-00-00
Frame check sequence   A4-37-97-40
```

```
Frame: 13 Time: Mar 13@20:03:01.6694761 Length: 64
Destination address    CHEROKEE         Individual, global
Source address         220.100.100.8    Individual, global
Length                 4
Data size              4
Padding:
00-FF-EF-0A-17-30-00-00 00-30-00-43-48-45-52-4F
4B-45-45-20-20-20-20-20 20-20-20-46-41-54-20-42
4F-59-20-20-20-20-20-20 20-20
Frame check sequence   FD-84-2C-50
```

```
Frame: 14 Time: Mar 13@20:03:01.6701895 Length: 190
Destination address    CHEROKEE         Individual, global
Source address         220.100.100.8    Individual, global
Length                 172              Partial packet store
Data size              86
Sliced data
```

```
Frame: 15 Time: Mar 13@20:03:01.6706443 Length: 123
Destination address    220.100.100.8    Individual, global
Source address         CHEROKEE         Individual, global
Length                 105              Partial packet store
Data size              86
Sliced data
```

```
Frame: 16 Time: Mar 13@20:03:01.6710735 Length: 64
Destination address    CHEROKEE           Individual, global
Source address         220.100.100.8      Individual, global
Length                 4
Data size              4
Padding:
00-FF-EF-0A-17-30-00-00 00-30-00-43-48-45-52-4F
4B-45-45-20-20-20-20-20 20-20-20-46-41-54-20-42
4F-59-20-20-20-20-20-20 20-20
Frame check sequence   5D-42-26-5E
```

```
Frame: 17 Time: Mar 13@20:03:01.6725487 Length: 189
Destination address    CHEROKEE           Individual, global
Source address         220.100.100.8      Individual, global
Length                 171                Partial packet store
Data size              86
Sliced data
```

```
Frame: 18 Time: Mar 13@20:03:01.6833829 Length: 130
Destination address    220.100.100.8      Individual, global
Source address         CHEROKEE           Individual, global
Length                 112                Partial packet store
Data size              86
Sliced data
```

```
Frame: 19 Time: Mar 13@20:03:01.6838061 Length: 64
Destination address    CHEROKEE           Individual, global
Source address         220.100.100.8      Individual, global
Length                 4
Data size              4
Padding:
00-FF-EF-0A-17-30-00-00 00-30-00-43-48-45-52-4F
4B-45-45-20-20-20-20-20 20-20-20-46-41-54-20-42
4F-59-20-20-20-20-20-20 20-20
Frame check sequence   AB-AF-01-D0
```

```
Frame: 20 Time: Mar 13@20:03:01.6843194 Length: 145
Destination address    CHEROKEE           Individual, global
Source address         220.100.100.8      Individual, global
Length                 127                Partial packet store
Data size              86
Sliced data
```

```
Frame: 21 Time: Mar 13@20:03:01.6953938 Length: 568
Destination address    220.100.100.8      Individual, global
Source address         CHEROKEE           Individual, global
Length                 550                Partial packet store
Data size              86
Sliced data
```

```
Frame: 22 Time: Mar 13@20:03:01.6967575 Length: 64
Destination address    CHEROKEE           Individual, global
Source address         220.100.100.8      Individual, global
Length                 4
Data size              4
Padding:
00-FF-EF-0A-17-30-00-00 00-30-00-43-48-45-52-4F
4B-45-45-20-20-20-20-20 20-20-20-46-41-54-20-42
4F-59-20-20-20-20-20-20 20-20
Frame check sequence   EB-22-14-CC
```

```
Frame: 23 Time: Mar 13@20:03:01.7274710 Length: 64
Destination address    CHEROKEE           Individual, global
Source address         220.100.100.8      Individual, global
Length                 18
Data size              18
Padding:
FF-53-4D-42-25-00-00-00 00-00-00-80-00-00-00-00
00-00-00-00-00-00-00-00 01-08-BB-14
Frame check sequence   F9-E9-49-5B
```

```
Frame: 24 Time: Mar 13@20:03:01.7276453 Length: 64
Destination address    220.100.100.8      Individual, global
Source address         CHEROKEE           Individual, global
Length                 4
Data size              4
Padding:
00-00-00-00-00-00-00-00 00-00-00-00-00-00-00-00
00-00-00-00-00-00-00-00 00-00-00-00-00-00-00-00
00-00-00-00-00-00-00-00 00-00
Frame check sequence   A4-57-F8-98
```

```
Frame: 25 Time: Mar 13@20:03:03.3579381 Length: 64
Destination address    Broadcast          Broadcast
Source address         220.100.100.8      Individual, global
Type                   08-06 A            RP
Data size              46
Frame check sequence   20-1A-22-FA
```

```
Frame: 26 Time: Mar 13@20:03:03.5655960 Length: 65
Destination address    03-00-00-00-00-01           Group, local
Source address         220.100.100.8      Individual, global
Length                 47
Data size              47
Frame check sequence   E5-04-DF-65
```

```
Frame: 27 Time: Mar 13@20:03:03.5668637 Length: 65
```

```
Destination address    220.100.100.8      Individual, global
Source address         SILO               Individual, global
Length                 47
Data size              47
Frame check sequence   99-9F-D2-6F
```

```
Frame: 28 Time: Mar 13@20:03:03.5672027 Length: 64
Destination address    SILO               Individual, global
Source address         220.100.100.8      Individual, global
Length                 3
Data size              3
Padding:
00-06-04-00-01-00-00-C0 7D-73-D7-DC-64-64-08-00
00-00-00-00-00-DC-64-64 4D-20-20-20-46-41-54-20
42-4F-59-20-20-20-20-20 20-20-20
Frame check sequence   AD-D6-F0-E6
```

```
Frame: 29 Time: Mar 13@20:03:03.5678517 Length: 64
Destination address    220.100.100.8      Individual, global
Source address         SILO               Individual, global
Length                 3
Data size              3
Padding:
FF-FF-FF-FF-FF-FF-FF-FF FF-FF-FF-FF-FF-FF-FF-FF
FF-FF-FF-FF-FF-FF-FF-FF FF-FF-FF-FF-FF-FF-FF-FF
FF-FF-FF-FF-FF-FF-FF-FF FF-FF-FF
Frame check sequence   56-42-97-30
```

```
Frame: 30 Time: Mar 13@20:03:03.5681241 Length: 64
Destination address    SILO               Individual, global
Source address         220.100.100.8      Individual, global
Length                 4
Data size              4
Padding:
00-FF-EF-0A-17-31-00-00 00-31-00-53-49-4C-4F-20
20-20-20-20-20-20-20-20 20-20-20-46-41-54-20-42
4F-59-20-20-20-20-20-20 20-20
Frame check sequence   45-C9-1F-6B
```

```
Frame: 31 Time: Mar 13@20:03:03.5762576 Length: 64
Destination address    220.100.100.8      Individual, global
Source address         SILO               Individual, global
Length                 4
Data size              4
Padding:
FF-FF-FF-FF-FF-FF-FF-FF FF-FF-FF-FF-FF-FF-FF-FF
FF-FF-FF-FF-FF-FF-FF-FF FF-FF-FF-FF-FF-FF-FF-FF
FF-FF-FF-FF-FF-FF-FF-FF FF-FF
Frame check sequence   B5-8D-1C-0D
```

```
Frame: 32 Time: Mar 13@20:03:03.5765530 Length: 64
Destination address     SILO              Individual, global
Source address          220.100.100.8     Individual, global
Length                  18
Data size               18
Padding:
00-00-00-00-00-00-DC-64 64-4D-20-20-20-46-41-54
20-42-4F-59-20-20-20-20 20-20-20-20
Frame check sequence    34-5F-09-87
```

```
Frame: 33  Time: Mar 13@20:03:03.5768360 Length: 64
Destination address     220.100.100.8     Individual, global
Source address          SILO              Individual, global
Length                  4
Data size               4
Padding:
10-65-00-00-40-06-E3-53 DC-64-64-96-DC-64-64-0C
00-8B-04-95-BC-08-EC-B0 02-47-4D-3C-50-10-10-00
1B-60-00-00-FF-FF-FF-FF FF-FF
Frame check sequence    5E-04-1A-D6
```

```
Frame: 34 Time: Mar 13@20:03:03.5772064 Length: 64
Destination address     220.100.100.8     Individual, global
Source address          SILO              Individual, global
Length                  18
Data size               18
Padding:
FF-FF-FF-FF-FF-FF-FF-FF FF-FF-FF-FF-FF-FF-FF-FF
FF-FF-FF-FF-FF-FF-FF-FF FF-FF-FF-FF
Frame check sequence    AD-5B-8C-60
```

```
Frame: 35 Time: Mar 13@20:03:03.5774858 Length: 64
Destination address     SILO              Individual, global
Source address          220.100.100.8     Individual, global
Length                  4
Data size               4
Padding:
00-FF-EF-0A-17-31-00-00 00-31-00-53-49-4C-4F-20
20-20-20-20-20-20-20-20 20-20-20-46-41-54-20-42
4F-59-20-20-20-20-20-20 20-20
Frame check sequence    04-FA-BD-01
```

```
Frame: 36 Time: Mar 13@20:03:03.8540212 Length: 71
Destination address     CHEROKEE          Individual, global
Source address          220.100.100.8     Individual, global
Length                  53
Data size               53
Frame check sequence    50-18-B5-38
```

```
Frame: 37 Time: Mar 13@20:03:03.8543697 Length: 71
Destination address    220.100.100.8      Individual, global
Source address         CHEROKEE           Individual, global
Length                 53
Data size              53
Frame check sequence 14-F9-A7-A2
```

```
Frame: 38 Time: Mar 13@20:03:03.8547697 Length: 64
Destination address    CHEROKEE           Individual, global
Source address         220.100.100.8.     Individual, global
Length                 18
Data size              18
Padding:
4F-20-20-20-20-20-20-20 20-20-20-20-20-46-41-54
20-42-4F-59-20-20-20-20 20-20-20-20
Frame check sequence   DE-8D-26-6E
```

```
Frame: 39 Time: Mar 13@20:03:03.8549544 Length: 64
Destination address    220.100.100.8      Individual, global
Source address         CHEROKEE           Individual, global
Length                 4
Data size              4
Padding:
00-00-00-00-00-00-00-00 00-00-00-00-00-00-00-00
00-00-00-00-00-00-00-00 00-00-00-00-00-00-00-00
00-00-00-00-00-00-00-00 00-00
Frame check sequence   09-8A-C6-5F
```

```
Frame: 40 Time: Mar 13@20:03:03.8552476 Length: 64
Destination address    CHEROKEE           Individual, global
Source address         220.100.100.8      Individual, global
Length                 18
Data size              18
Padding:
FF-53-4D-42-71-00-00-00 00-00-01-80-00-00-00-00
00-00-00-00-00-00-00-00 01-08-00-00
Frame check sequence   FC-6F-C1-6A
```

```
Frame: 41 Time: Mar 13@20:03:03.8554348 Length: 64
Destination address    220.100.100.8      Individual, global
Source address         CHEROKEE           Individual, global
Length                 4
Data size              4
Padding:
00-00-00-00-00-00-00-00 00-00-00-00-00-00-00-00
00-00-00-00-00-00-00-00 00-00-00-00-00-00-00-00
00-00-00-00-00-00-00-00 00-00
Frame check sequence   7F-7D-CA-E9
```

```
Frame: 42 Time: Mar 13@20:03:03.8557614 Length: 64
Destination address    CHEROKEE           Individual, global
Source address         220.100.100.8      Individual, global
Length                 3
Data size              3
Padding:
0B-0E-00-FF-EF-14-00-00 00-04-00-00-00-05-30-4F
20-20-20-20-20-20-20-20 20-20-20-20-46-41-54-20
42-4F-59-20-20-20-20-20 20-20-20
Frame check sequence   3C-F0-22-3F
```

```
Frame: 43 Time: Mar 13@20:03:03.8559136 Length: 64
Destination address    220.100.100.8      Individual, global
Source address         CHEROKEE           Individual, global
Length                 3
Data size              3
Padding:
00-00-00-00-00-00-00-00 00-00-00-00-00-00-00-00
00-00-00-00-00-00-00-00 00-00-00-00-00-00-00-00
00-00-00-00-00-00-00-00 00-00-00
Frame check sequence   66-1B-6E-95
```

```
Frame: 44 Time: Mar 13@20:03:04.8565401 Length: 64
Destination address    Broadcast          Broadcast
Source address         220.100.100.8      Individual, global
Type                   08-06              ARP
Data size              46
Frame check sequence   36-08-6B-61
```

```
Frame: 45 Time: Mar 13@20:03:06.3670765 Length: 64
Destination address    Broadcast          Broadcast
Source address         220.100.100.8      Individual, global
Type                   08-06              ARP
Data size              46
Frame check sequence   20-1A-22-FA
```

```
Frame: 46 Time: Mar 13@20:03:06.7809019 Length: 64
Destination address    Broadcast          Broadcast
Source address         BRAINS             Individual, global
Type                   08-06              ARP
Data size              46
Frame check sequence   CE-8F-B9-E2
```

```
Frame: 47 Time: Mar 13@20:03:06.7812445 Length: 64
Destination address    BRAINS             Individual, global
Source address         220.100.100.8      Individual, global
Type                   08-06              ARP
Data size              46
Frame check sequence   8A-03-34-7C
```

```
Frame: 48 Time: Mar 13@20:03:06.7816335 Length: 126
Destination address      220.100.100.8      Individual, global
Source address           BRAINS             Individual, global
Type                     08-00              IP
Data size                86
Sliced data
```

```
Frame: 49 Time: Mar 13@20:03:06.7823637 Length: 105
Destination address      BRAINS             Individual, global
Source address           220.100.100.8      Individual, global
Type                     08-00              IP
Data size                86
Sliced data
```

```
Frame: 50 Time: Mar 13@20:03:06.7834375 Length: 140
Destination address      20.100.100.8       Individual, global
Source address           BRAINS             Individual, global
Type                     08-00              IP
Data size                86
Sliced data
```

```
Frame: 51 Time: Mar 13@20:03:06.7841119 Length: 97
Destination address      BRAINS             Individual, global
Source address           220.100.100.8      Individual, global
Type                     08-00              IP
Data size                9
Frame check sequence     6B-39-72-1F
```

```
Frame: 52 Time: Mar 13@20:03:06.7974856 Length: 161
Destination address      220.100.100.8      Individual, global
Source address           BRAINS             Individual, global
Type                     08-00              IP
Data size                86
Sliced data
```

```
Frame: 53 Time: Mar 13@20:03:06.7990992 Length: 687
Destination address      BRAINS             Individual, global
Source address           220.100.100.8      Individual, global
Type                     08-00              IP
Data size                86
Sliced data
```

```
Frame: 54 Time: Mar 13@20:03:06.8081367 Length: 140
Destination address      220.100.100.8      Individual, global
Source address           BRAINS             Individual, global
Type                     08-00              IP
Data size                86
```

Sliced data

```
Frame: 55 Time: Mar 13@20:03:06.8088484 Length: 97
Destination address    BRAINS           Individual, global
Source address         220.100.100.8    Individual, global
Type                   08-00            IP
Data size              79
Frame check sequence   C0-B3-14-66
```

This snapshot from the network is of 55 frames. The destination and source address identify the directional flow of data. This is important because knowing this can help you understand *how* and *what* two nodes are communicating on a network. The level of information obtained can also help understand the flow of data between hosts. Length of data frames and the type also provide information about the hosts communicating and this information can be used to deduce network traffic loads at given intervals. Having information that includes date and times of the traffic provides a reference point for aspects of network maintenance such as future planning for expansion, adding or removing various segments of the network and so forth. See this chapter for additional information the Internet Advisor obtained during the operation and maintenance of my network. Contact Hewlett-Packard for additional information by visiting www.hp.com; or write Hewlett Packard, 5070 Centennial Blvd., Colorado Springs, CO 80919.

6.6 Rack Enclosure (Great Lakes Cabinets)

In order to accommodate all the network equipment, four cabinets were required: three 72" and one 48".

Figure 6.13 shows a front view of the rack enclosure with blower at the bottom and fan tray at the top. The circulation of this cabinet met the needs of the equipment used.

Figure 6.14 is similar to Figure 6.13; chassis support brackets run the length of the cabinet. As Figures 6.13 and 6.14 show, there are vertical panel mounting rails in the front and rear of the enclosure. It is possible to mount equipment in the enclosure without rear vertical panel mounting rails and chassis support brackets. This is a judgment call you need to make. The enclosure is sturdy enough to hold considerable weight.

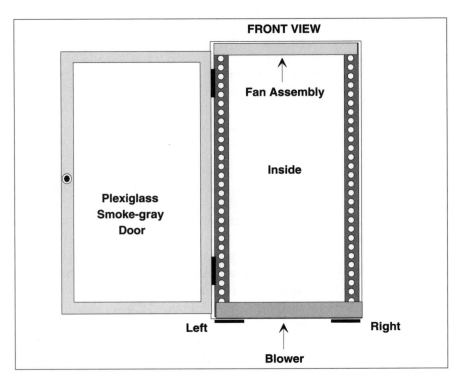

FRONT VIEW

Fan Assembly

Inside

Plexiglass
Smoke-gray
Door

Left

Right

Blower

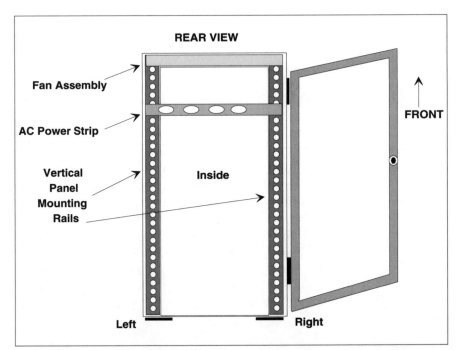

REAR VIEW

Fan Assembly

AC Power Strip

Vertical
Panel
Mounting
Rails

Inside

FRONT

Left

Right

Great Lakes Cabinets has a variety of options for the cabinets they offer. My decision to use front and rear vertical mounting rails resulted from concerns about the weight of the equipment mounted in the enclosure. Your situation could differ, but front and rear vertical rails and chassis support brackets connecting them makes the enclosure even stronger.

Figure 6.15 shows four cabinets and other equipment. Most of the network equipment was rack-mounted in these cabinets. However, some network equipment is not rack mountable. A unique benefit of the Great Lakes Cabinets is that both sides can be worked on inside with relative ease because of the space between the mounting rails and the side walls. Both sides of the enclosure are vented to assist in air circulation. The front and rear doors are keyed, lockable and removable. This flexibility makes the cabinet accessible from every side. The top has machined holes to aid in circulation.

The Great Lakes Cabinets arrived at the network location in a tractor-trailer. Each cabinet weighed approximately 250 lbs. Great Lakes Cabinets shipping included all parts required to assemble the enclosure with a minimum of tools.

For more information, contact Great Lakes Cabinets, P. O. Box 551, Edinboro, PA 16412.

Be sure you know that your facility can accommodate the weight of the equipment. These cabinets arrived within a day of another pallet of equipment and together they weighed over 1000 lbs. and required approximately 10 sq. ft. of floor space.

Commercial Desktop Computers (IBM)

The commercial desktop series PCs used include the PC350 and XL series. The general specifications for the base system units (model 350s) used in this network include:

- 200 MHz Pentium MMX Processor
- 2.6 GB Hard Disk (additional 3.0 GB hard drive)
- 16MB Non-parity EDO Memory (additional 48 MB RAM)
- 3 1/2" floppy disk drive.

Figure 6.16 illustrates these systems and other select network components.

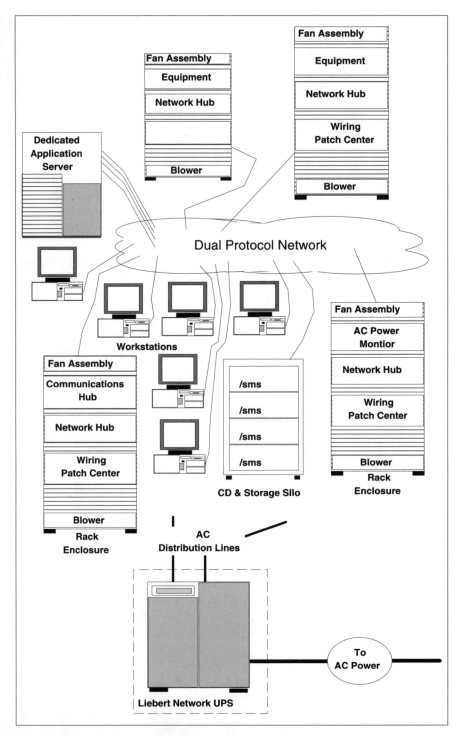

FIGURE 6.15
Conceptual View
of the Network
with Cabinets

FIGURE 6.16
Conceptual View
of Commercial
Desktops
and Network

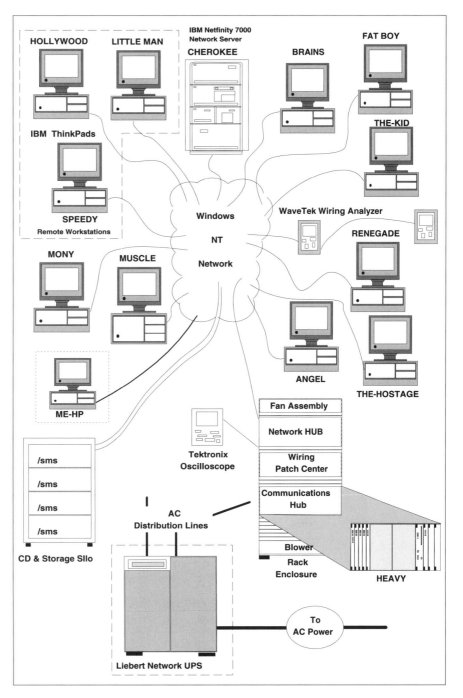

Figure 6.16 shows multiple desktops and a network server. The system named *Muscle* in this figure is also a server, a dedicated file server. More information on these systems include the following specifications.

Units used in this network employ a PCI Busmaster controller and S.M.A.R.T. capabilities. These systems include: PCI enhanced IDE hard drives, universal serial bus ports, infrared, and 64-bit PCI graphics, and wake on LAN capability.

Functionality of the Universal Serial Bus (USB) makes peripheral connectivity easier. The hot-connect ability enables peripheral devices to be connected in seconds and can be added or removed without reconfiguring or rebooting. Each USB port permits up to 127 USB-capable devices.

Some of the PCs used in this network have the capability for Symmetrical Multi-Processing (SMP) when dual processors are used, an L2 external CPU cache of 256KB and pipeline burst L3 cache. The BIOS type is 256KB flash, SurePath.

The systems can accommodate up to 192MB RAM at a speed of 60ns deployed by 72-pin SIMMs. Their hard disk size average seek time is 12ms with a latency of approximately 5.8ms. They support RAID and hot-swappable drive bays.

The graphics capabilities of these systems employ an S3 Trio64 V+Graphics type chipset. The result is SVGA graphics and data width of 64-bit video RAM. Graphic resolution (with the standard video RAM) is: 1280 x 1024 16 colors. The maximum resolution (with a maximum video RAM) is: 1280 x 1024 with 65,536 colors. The graphics bus interface uses PCI architecture.

The systems have a 200 Watt power supply type for either 110 or 220 volts with a universal manual switch. The heat and sound emissions are 48dB. The typical weight of each cabinet is 28lbs, height 6.3", width 16.5", and depth 17.6".

Systems used in this network include the following security features:

- Boot sequence control
- Boot without keyboard or mouse
- Cover key lock
- Diskette boot inhibit
- Diskette write protect (switch)
- Diskette I/O control
- Hard disk I/O control
- Parallel I/O control

- Power-on password
- Secure fixed DASD
- Secure removable media
- Serial I/O control
- Setup utility password (administrator password)
- U-Bolt tie-down support.

The systems specifications used in this network also include the following product approvals and/or certifications according to IBM: BABT (UK); CE; CISPR-22 Class B; CSA C22.2 No. 950 (Canada); DEMKO (EN 60950); EIF (SETI) (EN 60950); Energy Saving Law (refer to N-B 1-9174-001); FCC Class B (US); IECEE CB Certificate and report to IEC-950 Second Edition; ISO 9241-3 Compliant; JATE; NEMKO (EN 60950); NS/G/1234/J/100003 (Telecommunications Safety only: no approval mark); OVE (EN 60950); Power Line Harmonics (refer to N-B 2-4700-017); SEMKO (EN 60950); TUV-GS (EN 60950); TUV-GS - ZH1/618; UL-1950 First Edition; VCCI Class 2 (Japan).

In addition, IBM's current warranty is for a limited warranty period and is type 3—three year: first year on-site, second and third years carry-in; 3 years parts and labor.

The IBM desktop systems used in this network came with pre-installed software. Some of these systems were reconfigured to meet the needs of the network. However, all legal and ethical respect was given to manufacturers of hardware and software products. Each system used in this network is either covered by a site license or has a dedicated piece of software for each system; each system has one user. In the case of servers, workstations, and so forth, each manufacturer's legal guidelines were followed. These matters should be factored into any network design. Using an unpaid piece of software, unless it is clear that it is freeware, is stealing. Consider this when you design your network.

Model 658842U 266 MHz Pentium II Characteristics

The IBM PC 300XL is designed with the latest technology to handle demanding business applications in a networked environment. These are high-end systems that deliver value and 2.5GB hard drive to keep you ahead of the curve with the performance disk that power users demand. The IBM PC 300XL series includes open bay models which can be custom-configured via the Authorized Assembler Program (AAP).

Standard Features

- **Processors.** Pentium(R) II processors—233MHz, 266MHz or 300MHz with unified 512KB L2 Cache
- **Memory.** 32 MB non-parity EDO Memory (Expandable Memory to 384MB) 32MB, expandable to 384MB (3 DIMMs), EDO/60ns
- **Hard Drives.** 2.5GB or 4.2GB EIDE with S.M.A.R.T. or 4.3GB Wide Ultra SCSI with S.M.A.R.T. or open bay PCI bus master EIDE controller on planar, SCSI models include a SCSI-2 Fast and Wide PCI bus master adapter
- **Graphics and Video Resolution.** S3 Trio64V2; 64-bit; 2MB std./max. video DRAM; 256 colors @ 1280x1024
- **Network Features.** LANClient Control Manager supported, Wake on LAN, Plug-In and Go, Flash over LAN (BIOS/CMOS), plug-and-play, CID
- **Network Interface.** Integrated Intel EtherExpress 10/100Mbps Ethernet with Wake on LAN
- **CD-ROM.** Models available with 16X-8X (variable speed) CD-ROM (Variable read rate. Actual playback speed will vary and is often less than the maximum possible.)
- **Audio.** Models available with Crystal 4236B audio chip, 16-bit, supports Sound Blaster Pro applications
- **Diskette Drive.** 3.5" 1.44MB standard
- **Slots.** 3 shared PCI/ISA , 2 ISA
- **Bays.** Three 3.5", two 5.25"
- **BIOS.** Flash ROM
- **Architecture.** PCI local bus, ISA data bus
- **Ports.** Serial (16550), enhanced parallel (ECP/EPP), two USB ports, SVGA video, EIDE controller, 10/100 Ethernet RJ-45, IrDA-2-compliant infrared, audio mic-in and line-out mini-jacks, keyboard, mouse
- **Keyboard/Mouse.** IBM cameo 104-key (rubber dome) and enhanced mouse
- **Power Supply.** 200 Watts
- **Security Features.** IBM AssetCare: serialization and laser etching of memory and processors, third-party registration available through Retainagoup Limited
- **IBM AntiVirus and ConfigSafe.** Vital Product Data (VPD) support, cover key lock, sliding front door lock, U-bolt anchor support, secure access openings, secure removable media, secure fixed DASD, diskette write protect, power-on password, configura-

tion/administrator password, keyboard/mouse password, Wake
on LAN password prompt, boot sequence control, diskette boot
inhibit, boot without keyboard/mouse, mouse-disable, I/O controls

- **Software and Tools.** Windows 95 or Windows NT 4.0 preload
available on models with a hard drive Lotus SmartSuite license,
Microsoft NetMeeting (Windows 95 preload models only), LAN-
Client Control Manager (downloadable via internet), IBM Netfin-
ity Manager software, Intel LANDesk Client Manager, Artisoft
CoSession, QAPlus System Support CD (Ready to Configure) with
additional software/drivers
- **Limited Warranty.** Three-year parts and one-year labor

Legal Notices

1. MHz only measures internal clock speed, not application performance. Many factors affect application performance.
2. When referring to hard drive capacity, MB stands for million
bytes and GB stands for billion bytes. Total user-accessible capacity may vary depending on operating environments.
3. For terms and conditions or copies of IBM's limited warranty, call
800-772-2227 in the US Limited warranty includes International
Warranty Service in those countries where this statement of product is sold by IBM or IBM Business Partners (registration
required).
4. Energy Star Compliance: The EPA, as a matter of policy, does not
endorse any particular company or its products.
5. Battery Life (and recharge times) will vary based on screen brightness, applications, features, power management, battery conditioning and other references. CD-ROM or hard disk drive usage
may also have a significant impact on battery life.
6. Actual specifications may vary slightly depending on features
and components.

For more information on IBM products visit: www.IBM.com or write
International Business Machines, Armonk, New York.

Remote Workstations (IBM ThinkPads)

Multiple remote workstations were required to work with this network. Figure 6.17 illustrates these systems and the network.

FIGURE 6.17
Conceptual View
of Remote
Workstations

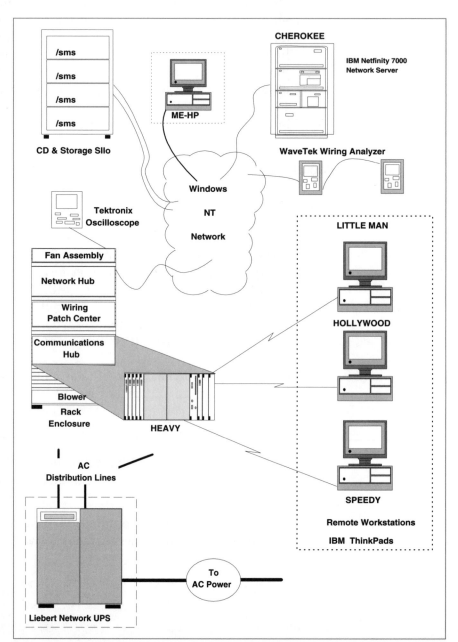

FIGURE 6.17 Conceptual View of Remote Workstations

Remote workstations were used because mobile use was required. IBM ThinkPads were chosen for features, reliability, and value for the money. Typical specifications for the ThinkPads used in this network follows.

ThinkPad 765D

166 MHz Pentium with MMX technology1	The latest power, connectivity and configuration flexibility to optimize effectiveness and maximize investment return. High performance features include: large 13.3" or 12.1" high-resolution displays with superb graphics, the latest Pentium processors with MMX technology, large hard drives, integrated infrared, and advanced multimedia.

13.3" TFT 1024x768 65,536 colors

3GB Hard
 Disk
 RAM
2/32MB
 Non-parity
 EDO Memory
 (Expandable
 to 104MB);
8X CD-ROM
 MPEG-1

Microsoft Windows 95

Standard features:

      Pointing device type: TrackPoint III

      Standard diskette size: 3.5" 1.44MB

      Optional diskette size: 3.5" 2.88MB

Diskette drive configuration:

      External

Keyboard type standard:

      Full size 84 key (tilt/palm rest space)

      Keyboard type(s) selectable:

continued on next page

ThinkPad 765D (continued)

Numeric Keypad:	Integrated
Product approvals/ certifications 4:	CISPR-22 Class B; CSA C22.2 No. 950 (Canada); FCC Class B – Part 15; IEC-950; JATE; NOM (Mexico); SASO; UK-PTT; UL-1950; VCCI Class 2 (Japan)
Warranty:	
Limited warranty period and type 3:	Three year (system battery: one year) Customer Carry-in Repair or provided by ThinkPad EasyServ (North America only)
Weight and dimensions:	

Weight: 7.7 lbs
Height: 2.2"
Width: 11.7"
Depth: 9.3"

Legal Notices

1. MHz only measures internal clock speed, not application performance. Many factors affect application performance.
2. When referring to hard drive capacity, MB stands for million bytes and GB stands for billion bytes. Total user-accessible capacity may vary depending on operating environments.
3. For terms and conditions or copies of IBM's limited warranty, call 800-772-2227 in the US Limited warranty includes International Warranty Service in those countries where this statement of product is sold by IBM or IBM Business Partners (registration required).
4. Energy Star Compliance: The EPA, as a matter of policy, does not endorse any particular company or its products.
5. Battery life (and recharge times) will vary based on screen brightness, applications, features, power management, battery conditioning and other references. CD-ROM or hard disk drive usage may also have a significant impact on battery life.
6. Actual specifications may vary slightly depending on features and components.

Data Communications Network HUB
(3Com USRobotics)

A USRobotics enterprise network hub was selected. Data communication equipment is the single most critical link in any network because it is the central point of attachment between remote users and a backbone network, regardless of the size of the backbone or location. It is also true if all users are in the same physical location. At one time remote computing meant having a device in one location and a terminal attached to it by a wire. USRobotics revolutionized that definition by designing the powerful enterprise network hub.

Figure 6.18 illustrates the network designed here in Dallas and remote users and a remote network, both located in Chicago.

Notice remote users connect directly into the Dallas network via the communications hub with their modems.

When remote users or remote network(s) are concerned, multiple issues must be considered during the design network phase. Issues to be reviewed during planning include, at a minimum:

- Security
- Reliability
- Maintenance
- Ease of use
- Internal protocol compatibility
- Expandability
- Internal design architecture
- Interface standard compatibility.

Security has become the most important topic in networking, regardless of the type of network or its location. Networks can have a considerable degree of security built into the design if proper components are used to implement security. Where data communication equipment is concerned, having a device that can provide a security firewall is best.

Figure 6.19 shows a secure firewall implemented in the communications hub. Remote users in this illustration are required to sign on to the hub. It is a point of isolation. Other devices on the network require sign-ons and passwords as well.

The USRobotics communication hub used in this network has three possible configurations regarding its function in the network. USRobotics refers to this as *gateway application cards*. USRobitcs uses the following terminology:

- X.25
- NETServer card
- API Card.

FIGURE 6.18
Data
Communications
Hub

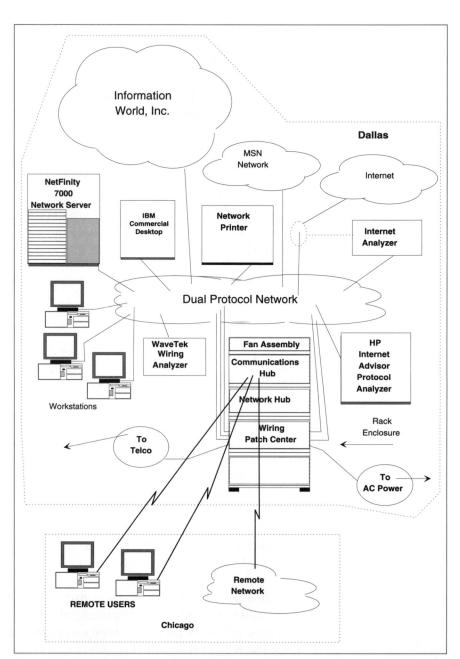

FIGURE 6.19
Network Firewall

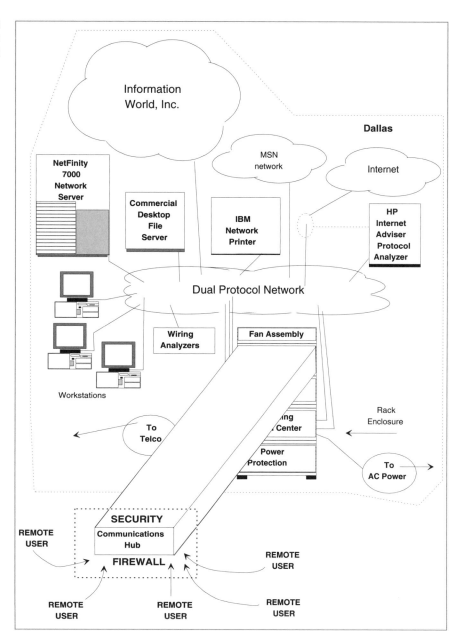

The X.25 card provides access capability to packet-switched networks. This card uses a EIA-232/V.35 interface connection point.

The NETServer card functions as a router, a terminal server or both. Ethernet and token ring NICs can be used with it. USRobotics refers to this card as the EdgeServe card; it has Windows NT loaded onto it.

An API card, which can also be used to let customers design their own applications by way of USRobotics software development kits. Figure 6.20 illustrates the Enterprise hub.

FIGURE 6.20
Network Hub

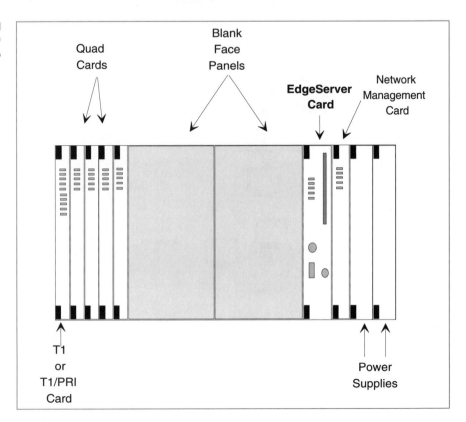

It shows the hub with blank face panels. These panels can be removed and other cards inserted. A total of 17 slots exist. Slot one is the T1 card. Beginning with slot 2 are analog or digital quad modem cards which have the equivalent of four modems on them. Slots 15 and 16 are the EdgeServer location. Slot 17 is where the network management card is located. The remaining slots house two power supplies. Though not shown in this illustration, the undercradle portion of the hub houses approximately 16 fans to cool the components.

Reliability is another important factor for any communication equipment. The design of the USRobotics hub has reliability built into it: the hub has two power supplies, though only one is required to operate the unit.

Maintenance is another part of the equation for communication equipment. The hub used in this network has both remote and local management capability, and easy access to components that may need removal.

Any communication device requires skill. Most require a fairly advanced level of skill to maximize use. The capability of any communication device has little to do with its ease of use. The hub used in this network has ease of use designed into it. Ease of use can be measured in communication equipment by documentation provided, by how thorough and detailed it is; by accessibility to configure ports, and by ability to use the equipment in a partially failed state (should that occur). The more complex functions a device offers, the simpler the documentation should be. The fact is that data communication equipment is complex enough without humans adding another layer of complexity.

Another factor to analyze with data communication equipment is protocol compatibility. This includes evaluation of upper- and lower-layer protocols. Because this hub has the EdgeServer card, NetBEUI, TCP/IP, and IPX upper-layer protocols are supported. Token ring and Ethernet lower-layer protocols are supported as well. Use of token ring and Ethernet here is more than sufficient because these two protocols are the dominant lower-layer protocols used in networks today.

Expandability is very important with data communication equipment. The design of the USRobotics enterprise network hub is such that any size network can be built around this technology. It is possible with the USRobotics equipment to start a network with one or two enterprise hubs then continue to add them until racks of them are filled.

Internal design architecture is the pivot upon which all communication transactions hinge. The internal communications bus and the incoming port architecture are the foundation of the device. These should be capable of handling a complete load on the device without causing hangups or system slowdown.

Interface standard compatibility is another matter to examine when you are evaluating data communication equipment. In this network, the hub has flexibility regarding how certain connections are made. In some instances options exist to make a connection. This alone makes for ease of use, installation, and maintenance. It also means existing equipment at your site may be usable. That can save money.

   The 3Com USRobotics enterprise network hub EdgeServer card has the following attributes:

- 1.44 floppy drive
- Mouse port
- Keyboard port
- Display port
- SCSI port
- Minimum of 800 MB hard drive
- Minimum 100 MHz processor
- 10BASE-T capability.

The EdgeServer card also has Microsoft Windows NT Server 4.0. Conceptually the card and some of its functionality appear as in Figure 6.21.

   The advantages of having NT Server on the EdgeServer card are many. When remote users access the communications hub for information purposes only, they can be stopped there and not access other systems that are part of the network. Remote users who require access to other systems can use the EdgeServer as a *gateway* to access the network behind it. The EdgeServer card can function as an excellent firewall to protect the assets behind it while permitting access.

   Still another powerful feature of the EdgeServer card is the SCSI port located on its back. This feature makes it possible to connect a CD-ROM drive. Documentation is provided with the Enterprise network hub, but is also provided via CD, which makes it convenient to access when manuals are not easily accessible.

   A network management card is also part of the hub's component configuration. The card supports Ethernet and token ring as lower-layer protocols. It is a separate card and provides a console port that can be used for:

- **Remote Access.** It can be dialed into from a remote site
- **Local Access.** Management has access locally with a RJ45 and DB-25 cable with a null-modem adapter provided with the hub
- **Software download** is also possible to aid in the management aspect of the hub.

The network management card supports 10BASE-T, 10BASE-5, and 10BASE-2 connection points for Ethernet-cable flexibility. Token ring cable support includes shielded twisted pair (also called IBM type 1) and unshielded twisted pair (also called IBM type 3).

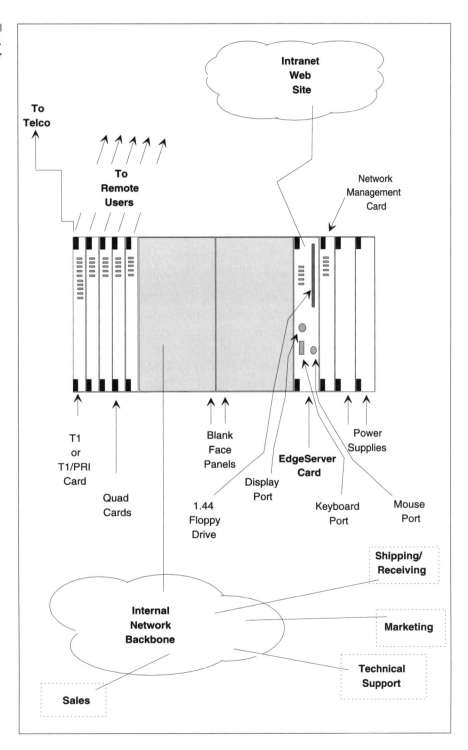

FIGURE 6.21
Hub Functionality

The network management card does not run SNMP management agents directly on the card, however the support for SNMP is not compromised. The network management card technically functions as a proxy agent; the functionality and management ability with SNMP operation features the same support.

The enterprise hub used in this network has a T1 card. It operates as a Primary Rate Interface (PRI). The T1 card is managed by a Total Control Manager (TCM). It is SMP based and works with MS-Windows. The card itself is easily configurable. A dumb terminal, remote PC, LAN PC, or direct-connect PC can work with configuration management parameters. Its operands function within the SNMP MIB standards; both GET and SET operations can be issued against the T1 card.

The T1 front panel features LEDS to indicate the operational status of the card. Those LEDs include:

- **Alarm.** This LED is activated upon existence of any of the following states: alarm indication signal, frame slip, out of frame, excessive CRC errors, change of frame alignment, line format violation, or frame alignment error.
- **Carrier.** This LED indicates whether or not a carrier is present; an unframed signal LED indicates if an Out-Of-Frame condition exists; when a Loss-of-Signal condition occurs; and if a signal is reported "not present."
- **Loopback.** This LED indicates if a test is in operation, initiated from the local telephone company.
- **Run/Fail.** This LED indicates operational mode of the T1 card; that is, if it is operating normally or in a "critical" mode due to a hardware and/or software fail condition.

The Enterprise network hub modems are either analog or digital. Consider Figure 6.22.

This illustration shows the enterprise network hub with analog modems (quad cards) connected to analog telephone lines. The gateway interface card in this illustration shows a generic connectivity to a network. The gateway connectivity portion of the Enterprise network hub does not necessarily require a Windows NT Serves, but this implementation is popular.

Figure 6.23 shows a different hub implementation.

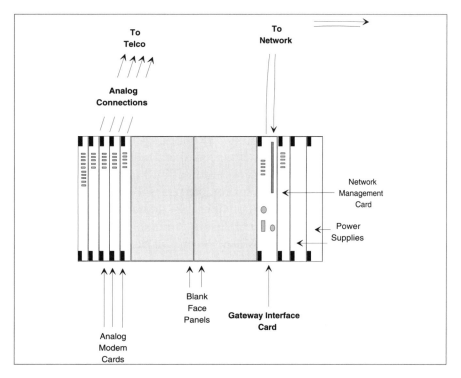

FIGURE 6.22
Network Hub
Analog
Functionality

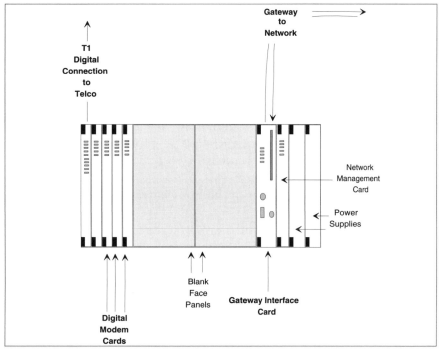

FIGURE 6.23
Network
Hub Digital
Functionality

This shows a T1 link to the telephone company. It also shows digital modem use after a signal is in the hub. The gateway aspect of the hub indicates users can have access outbound to a network if one is configured. Technically remote user's network access is configurable for either analog or digital modem connectivity.

The enterprise network hub is but one of many products offered by 3Com USRobotics. For additional information visit: www.usr.com; or write to: 3Com USRobotics, Corporate Systems Division, 8100 North McCormick Blvd., Skokie, IL 60076.

The data communication hub used in this network provides robust throughput for remote users. Because of its ability to implement security well a considerable degree of secure access has been obtained. Internal (local) users are also able to access the network because it functions as a node on the network, it is *seen* by other systems as a Windows NT node on the network.

Ethernet Network Hubs (Bay Networks)

Most networks have some form of hub or device that serves as the vehicle for the lower-layer network protocols. Bay Networks has been in business a long time; they were previously known as Wellfleet.

The hubs in this network are the Bay Stack 350T and 303. These are sufficient for the operation of the network. The inherent design permits them to be "stacked." They are RJ-45, multi-port, stackable, rack-mount enclosures. Figure 6.24 illustrates how these appear inside the rack enclosure.

This illustration shows two hubs with cable connections in the front. This makes for ease of the hubs since they can be easily accessed. An RJ-45-type cable is used connect two or more of these hubs. In this case two are used and one cable is used to connect them.

The rear of the hubs is where AC cabling is made. Consider Figure 6.25.

These hubs are straightforward. They have LEDs on the front to indicate the status of each port. The documentation and support from Bay is very good. Any previous familiarity with network hubs makes these hubs easy to use.

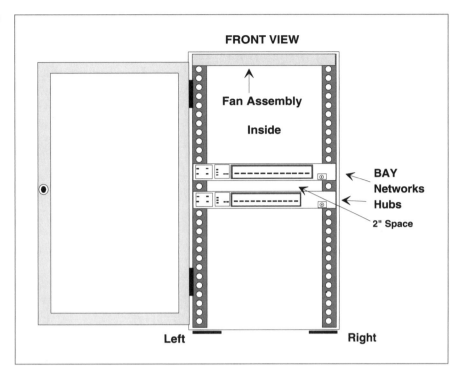

FIGURE 6.24
Bay Networks
Hubs

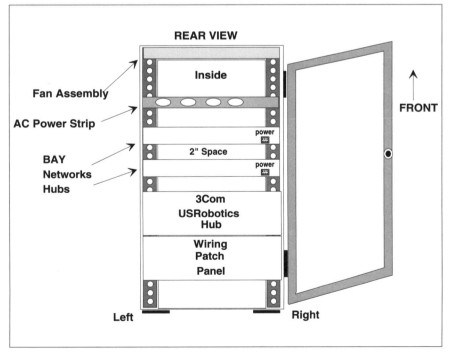

FIGURE 6.25
Rear View of Bay
Networks Hubs

Patch Panel (Hubbell Wiring)

If wiring of any network is not planned, chaos exists. With that thought in mind, the design for wiring in this network was examined from multiple angles: was the cable maker reliable? Would reconfiguration be easy once equipment was installed? How would one know which cables go where? With this level of thought and multiple designs on the marker board Hubbell rack enclosures and wiring were chosen.

Figure 6.26 shows an inside view of the enclosure from the rear. The inline panel has RJ-45 female connectors on what is considered the back side.

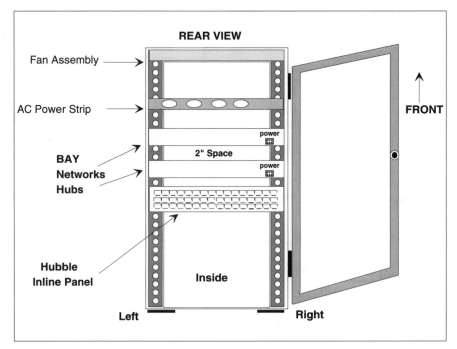

FIGURE 6.26
Inline Panel
Access from
the Rear

Figure 6.27 shows front and rear views of the inline panel.

Many rack-mount panels are available with a RJ-45 female connectors on the front but 110 connectors on the rear. This is neither good or bad. Some environments require this type of rear connection point for each connection.

Hubbell offers a patch panel with all connection points wired straight through. With a rack enclosure full, working inside the rear is difficult; working with all the equipment from the front is much easier.

FIGURE 6.27
Hubbell Inline
Panel

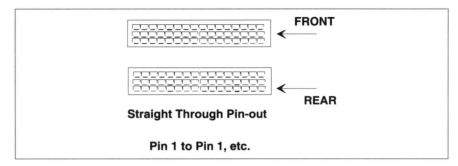

Figure 6.28 shows a side view of the rack enclosure. There are US-Robotics enterprise network hub, Bay Networks hubs, and the Hubbell inline panel, PC, and printer connections. Look closely at the area of dotted-line rectangular box. This illustrates how any combination of connections can be achieved from the front of the enclosure. All equipment is connected into the rear of the inline panel. Actual physical configuration is then made via patch cables from the front. In this network a 48 port inline panel is used, though Hubbell has larger panels.

FIGURE 6.28
Inline Panel Patch
(Side View)

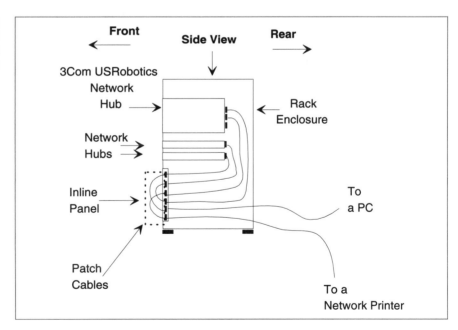

This example of component and wiring design illustrates designing ease-of-use, flexibility, and expandability into the network from the outset. Go one step further with Figure 6.28 and consider this: with a

WaveTek Cable Tester, any cable can be tested *from the front of all equipment* with relative ease. The same is true for troubleshooting or monitoring upper-layer protocols. The Hewlett-Packard Internet Advisor can be easily connected to the inline panel to monitor network traffic and other operating parameters. To make life even better, Hubbell wiring is color-coded. During the installation of this equipment colors, numbers, and labels were assigned to all ports, equipment, and other entry points to the network. There is no reason why a network design should not be documented completely from the very beginning. A well-designed network will be such that anyone who understands the technology would be able to perform any applicable work function.

To get answers to questions about inline panels, wiring, fiber connections, surface mount housing, jacks, or other components required to design your network, contact: Hubbell, Corporate Headquarters, 14 Lord's Hill Road, Stonington, CT 06378, 800-626-0005; or visit www.hubbell-premise.com or www.hubbell-canada.com. Other offices are Hubbell Ltd., Ronald Close, Woburn Road Industrial Estate, Kempston, Bedford, MK42 7SH,U.K., 44-1234-855444; or Hubbell-Taian Co., Ltd., 12 Floor, 66, Sec. 2, Chien-Kuo North Road, Taipei, Taiwan, 886-2-515-0855; or Hubbell Canada, Inc., 870 Brock Road South, Pickering, Ontario,L1W 1Z8, Canada, phone: 905-839-1138.

Network Wiring (Thomas & Betts)

This network design includes enhanced components many dismiss during the planning stage. The core network is based on ALL-LAN wiring, along with other custom cables from Thomas & Betts.

The characteristic of this cable is a high frequency bandwidth ability. The cable itself is jacketed with PVC, then aluminum shielding; four pairs of twisted-pair wire are wrapped with aluminum shielding. The intense shielding of each pair of cables makes the high bandwidth possible. Specifications of the ALL-LAN cable include the following information.

The channel and link performance is significantly beyond existing Cat5 specifications, including superior ACR performance at frequencies from 30 MHz to 300 MHz (>16dB); EMC compliance in all protocols through 300 MHz and beyond without using multi-level encoding non-RJ45-based connectivity. ALL-LAN has a low profile: .650" x

.695" x 1.525". It is a full 360° connector shielding with a cable jack that has only three components. It is easy to field-install and the integral strain relief accommodates cable up to .320 IDCs, compatible with 23-26 AWG wire.

There is a unique latch with damage-free unmating at pullout forces greater that 30 lbs. Its durability is greater than 2,500 cycles.

Figure 6.29 provides additional cable specifications.

FIGURE 6.29
ALL-LAN Cable
Specifications

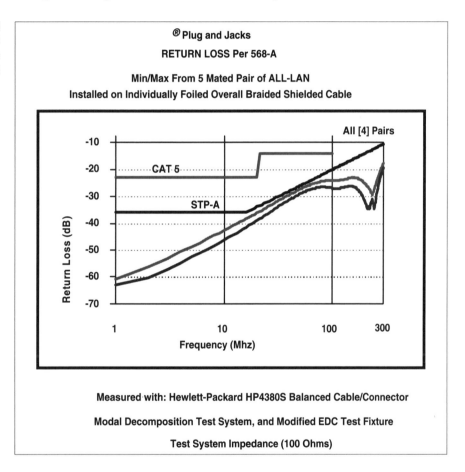

Figure 6.30 shows even more statistics displaying the attenuation of the ALL-LAN cable.

FIGURE 6.30
ALL-LAN Cable
Statistics

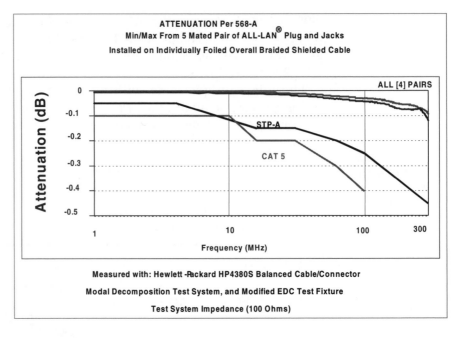

FIGURE 6.30
ALL-LAN Cable
Statistics

Figure 6.31 shows additional information about ALL-LAN with regard to NEXT and Attenuation.

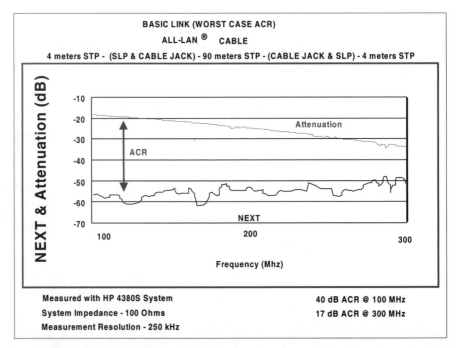

FIGURE 6.31
ALL-LAN Cable
NEXT and
Attenuation
Statistics

ALL-LAN cable was used from the devices to the hubs; PCs, servers, printers, and all the connections were made with ALL-LAN. The main network patch panel is an ALL-LAN panel with ALL-LAN connectors and cabling. It serves the primary network wiring backbone.

Figure 6.32 is still another example of statistical information on ALL-LAN cable.

FIGURE 6.32
ALL-LAN Basic Link (Worst Case NEXT)

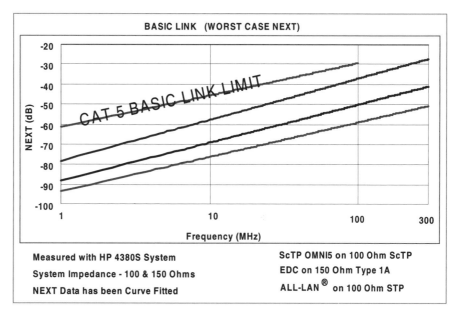

This shows ALL-LAN correlated data with respect to the CAT 5 basic link limit rate. It further presents ALL-LAN in the perspective of the performance of standard CAT 5.

Thomas & Betts provided the information shown in Figures 6.29–6.32. Their representatives were more than able to answer questions I had in the preparation for my network. Contact them for more information; visit www.tnb.com.

Network Power Infrastructure (Thomas & Betts)

Another aspect of the network is the network power infrastructure. Many installations build a network within an existing facility. Probably it is the exception to design and build a facility and network at the same time. If you are building a network in an existing facility it would serve you well to do some site planning with the facilities manager. In most cases facilities managers are versed not in the electrical, structural, air and cooling capabilities of the facility.

In my case, I built the entire infrastructure from the ground up. Because of the scope of my project, I met with Thomas & Betts representatives on more than one occasion. The representatives brought out some topics that had not been discussed before in regard to the facility I built.

The final result was my decision to use the following Thomas & Betts products to make the facility functional.

- Load centers
- Circuit breakers
- Dual gang cover plates
- Metal box housings for receptacles and switches
- Wire wrap ties
- Metal couplings to secure wiring
- NEMA twist lock cover plates
- 6 Gauge connectors
- 8 Gauge connectors
- Quad boxes.

Without the power infrastructure, networks will not operate. With this in mind you should be aware of how critical it is to know the infrastructure and be prepared to make changes if any are required.

Network Server (IBM NetFinity 7000)

The network server is another critical component of the network. I chose a NetFinity 7000 to be the server-of-choice. Specifications are:

- Three 200MHZ pentium processors
- ¾ GB RAM (750 MB RAM)
- 39 MB hard disk (RAID support)
- RAID implemented
- Two 200 Watt power supplies
- 512 Kb L2 Cache
- Network management interface board
- Ethernet network interface card
- IBM's standard software bundle.

FIGURE 6.33
Netfinity 7000
Network Server

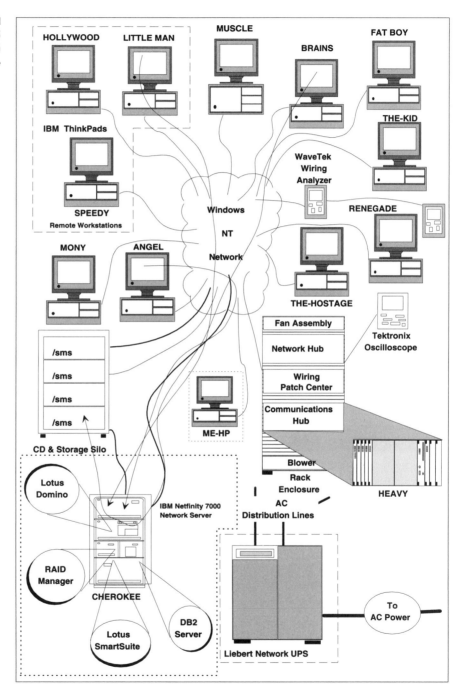

Figure 6.33 shows a conceptual view of how the Netfinity 7000 is implemented and features it provides to users, both local and remote:

- DB2 server
- Lotus Domino
- Lotus SmartSuite
- RAID manager.

These applications are for users except the RAID manager, which is for the user with administrative privileges. Figure 6.33 shows three users accessing the system: Angel, Little Man, and Brains. These are names I gave my computers on the network. All of these systems can access the Netfinity 7000 as well as all other systems shown in the network diagram. In addition users can also access the Network silo.

The Netfinity 7000 used in this network includes the following configuration, the result of a diagnostic report.

```
Diagnostics Report For \\Cherokee
-------------------------------------------------------------------
OS Version Report
-------------------------------------------------------------------
Microsoft (R) Windows NT (TM) Server
Version 4.0 (Build 1381: Service Pack 3) x86 Multiprocessor Free
Registered Owner: Ed Taylor
Product Number: 51222-270-1251174-59767
-------------------------------------------------------------------
System Report
-------------------------------------------------------------------
System: AT/AT COMPATIBLE
Hardware Abstraction Layer: MPS 1.4 - APIC platform
BIOS Date: 10/20/97
BIOS Version: BIOS Version 1.00.14.CDO
Processor list:
  0: x86 Family 6 Model 1 Stepping 9 GenuineIntel ~198 Mhz
  1: x86 Family 6 Model 1 Stepping 9 GenuineIntel ~198 Mhz
  2: x86 Family 6 Model 1 Stepping 9 GenuineIntel ~198 Mhz
-------------------------------------------------------------------
Video Display Report
-------------------------------------------------------------------
BIOS Date: 01/07/94
BIOS Version: CL-GD542X VGA BIOS Version 1.41
Adapter:
  Setting: 640 x 480 x 256
          60 Hz
  Type: cirrus compatible display adapter
  String: Cirrus Logic Compatible
  Memory: 512 KB
  Chip Type: CL 5424
  DAC Type: Integrated RAMDAC
```

```
Driver:
  Vendor: Microsoft Corporation
  File(s): cirrus.sys, vga.dll, cirrus.dll, vga256.dll, vga64K.dll
Version: 4.00, 4.0.0
------------------------------------------------------------------
Drives Report
------------------------------------------------------------------
C:\ (Local - NTFS) CHEROKEE Total: 0KB, Free: 0KB
D:\ (Removable - FAT) Total: 1,045,200KB, Free: 1,045,184KB
E:\ (Local - NTFS) CHEROKEE-E Total: 37,556,692KB, Free: 36,256,336KB
G:\ (CDROM - CDFS) IE_DISP_R1_0 Total: 189,020KB, Free: 0KB
H:\ (CDROM - CDFS) PUBS1310 Total: 366,396KB, Free: 0KB
I:\ (CDROM - CDFS) ROCKYSERVICEP Total: 178,218KB, Free: 0KB
------------------------------------------------------------------
Memory Report
------------------------------------------------------------------
Handles: 2,088
Threads: 169
Processes: 28
Physical Memory (K)
  Total: 785,840
  Available: 707,232
  File Cache: 15,748
------------------------------------------------------------------
Services Report
------------------------------------------------------------------
Alerter                                      Running (Automatic)
Computer Browser                             Running (Automatic)
EventLog (Event log)                         Running (Automatic)
Server                                       Running (Automatic)
Workstation (NetworkProvider)                Running (Automatic)
License Logging Service                      Running (Automatic)
TCP/IP NetBIOS Helper                        Running (Automatic)
Messenger                                    Running (Automatic)
Netfinity Support Program                    Running (Automatic)
Net Logon (RemoteValidation)                 Running (Automatic)
Norton SpeedDisk                             Running (Automatic)
Plug and Play (PlugPlay)                     Running (Automatic)
Remote Access Connection Manager (Network)   Running (Automatic)
Remote Access Server (Network)               Running (Automatic)
Remote Procedure Call (RPC) Locator          Running (Automatic)
Remote Procedure Call (RPC) Service          Running (Automatic)
Spooler (SpoolerGroup)                       Running (Automatic)
Telephony Service                            Running (Manual)
------------------------------------------------------------------
Drivers Report
------------------------------------------------------------------
AFD Networking Support Environment (TDI)     Running (Automatic)
aic78xx (SCSI miniport)                      Running (Boot)
Remote Access Mac (NDIS)                     Running (Automatic)
atapi (SCSI miniport)                        Running (Boot)
Beep (Base)                                  Running (System)
Cdfs (File system)                           Running (Disabled)
```

```
Cdrom (SCSI CDROM Class)                            Running (System)
cirrus (Video)                                      Running (System)
Disk (SCSI Class)                                   Running (Boot)
Diskperf (Filter)                                   Running (Boot)
Intel 82557-based PRO Adapter Driver (NDIS)         Running (Automatic)
Fastfat (Boot file system)                          Running (Disabled)
Floppy (Primary disk)                               Running (System)
i8042 Keyboard and PS/2 Mouse Port Driver           Running (System)
  (Keyboard Port)
ipsraidn (SCSI miniport)                            Running (Boot)
Keyboard Class Driver (Keyboard Class)              Running (System)
KSecDD (Base)                                       Running (System)
Modem (Extended base)                               Running (Boot)
Mouse Class Driver (Pointer Class)                  Running (System)
Msfs (File system)                                  Running (System)
Mup (Network)                                       Running (Manual)
NetBEUI Protocol (PNP_TDI)                          Running (Automatic)
Microsoft NDIS System Driver (NDIS)                 Running (System)
Microsoft NDIS TAPI driver (NDIS)                   Running (System)
Remote Access WAN Wrapper (NDISWAN)                 Running (Automatic)
NetBIOS Interface (NetBIOSGroup)                    Running (Automatic)
WINS Client(TCP/IP) (PNP_TDI)                       Running (Automatic)
NetFin (Extended base)                              Running (Automatic)
Npfs (File system)                                  Running (System)
Ntfs (File system)                                  Running (Disabled)
Null (Base)                                         Running (System)
NWLink IPX/SPX Compatible Transport Protocol        Running (Automatic)
  (PNP_TDI)
NWLink NetBIOS (PNP_TDI)                            Running (Automatic)
NWLink SPX/SPXII Protocol                           Running (Manual)
Parallel (Extended base)                            Running (Automatic)
Parport (Parallel arbitrator)                       Running (Automatic)
ParVdm (Extended base)                              Running (Automatic)
Remote Access Auto Connection Driver                Running (Automatic)
  (Streams Drivers)
Remote Access ARP Service (PNP_TDI)                 Running (Automatic)
Rdr (Network)                                       Running (Manual)
Scsiscan (SCSI Class)                               Running (System)
Serial (Extended base)                              Running (Automatic)
Srv (Network)                                       Running (Automatic)
TCP/IP Service (PNP_TDI)                            Running (Automatic)
-----------------------------------------------------------------------
IRQ and Port Report
-----------------------------------------------------------------------
Devices                      Vector        Level        Affinity
-----------------------------------------------------------------------
MPS 1.4 - APIC platform        8             8          0x00000007
MPS 1.4 - APIC platform        0             0          0x00000007
MPS 1.4 - APIC platform        1             1          0x00000007
MPS 1.4 - APIC platform        2             2          0x00000007
MPS 1.4 - APIC platform        3             3          0x00000007
MPS 1.4 - APIC platform        4             4          0x00000007
MPS 1.4 - APIC platform        5             5          0x00000007
MPS 1.4 - APIC platform        6             6          0x00000007
```

```
MPS 1.4 - APIC platform          7        7        0x00000007
MPS 1.4 - APIC platform          8        8        0x00000007
MPS 1.4 - APIC platform          9        9        0x00000007
MPS 1.4 - APIC platform          10       10       0x00000007
MPS 1.4 - APIC platform          11       11       0x00000007
MPS 1.4 - APIC platform          12       12       0x00000007
MPS 1.4 - APIC platform          13       13       0x00000007
MPS 1.4 - APIC platform          14       14       0x00000007
MPS 1.4 - APIC platform          15       15       0x00000007
MPS 1.4 - APIC platform          16       16       0x00000007
MPS 1.4 - APIC platform          17       17       0x00000007
MPS 1.4 - APIC platform          18       18       0x00000007
MPS 1.4 - APIC platform          19       19       0x00000007
MPS 1.4 - APIC platform          20       20       0x00000007
MPS 1.4 - APIC platform          21       21       0x00000007
MPS 1.4 - APIC platform          22       22       0x00000007
MPS 1.4 - APIC platform          23       23       0x00000007
MPS 1.4 - APIC platform          24       24       0x00000007
MPS 1.4 - APIC platform          25       25       0x00000007
MPS 1.4 - APIC platform          26       26       0x00000007
MPS 1.4 - APIC platform          27       27       0x00000007
MPS 1.4 - APIC platform          28       28       0x00000007
MPS 1.4 - APIC platform          29       29       0x00000007
MPS 1.4 - APIC platform          30       30       0x00000007
MPS 1.4 - APIC platform          31       31       0x00000007
MPS 1.4 - APIC platform          32       32       0x00000007
MPS 1.4 - APIC platform          33       33       0x00000007
MPS 1.4 - APIC platform          34       34       0x00000007
MPS 1.4 - APIC platform          35       35       0x00000007
MPS 1.4 - APIC platform          36       36       0x00000007
MPS 1.4 - APIC platform          37       37       0x00000007
MPS 1.4 - APIC platform          38       38       0x00000007
MPS 1.4 - APIC platform          39       39       0x00000007
MPS 1.4 - APIC platform          40       40       0x00000007
MPS 1.4 - APIC platform          41       41       0x00000007
MPS 1.4 - APIC platform          42       42       0x00000007
MPS 1.4 - APIC platform          43       43       0x00000007
MPS 1.4 - APIC platform          44       44       0x00000007
MPS 1.4 - APIC platform          45       45       0x00000007
MPS 1.4 - APIC platform          46       46       0x00000007
MPS 1.4 - APIC platform          47       47       0x00000007
MPS 1.4 - APIC platform          61       61       0x00000007
MPS 1.4 - APIC platform          65       65       0x00000007
MPS 1.4 - APIC platform          80       80       0x00000007
MPS 1.4 - APIC platform          193      193      0x00000007
MPS 1.4 - APIC platform          225      225      0x00000007
MPS 1.4 - APIC platform          253      253      0x00000007
MPS 1.4 - APIC platform          254      254      0x00000007
MPS 1.4 - APIC platform          255      255      0x00000007
i8042prt                         1        1        0xffffffff
i8042prt                         12       12       0xffffffff
Serial                           4        4        0x00000000
Serial                           3        3        0x00000000
```

E100B	9	9	0x00000000
Floppy	6	6	0x00000000
aic78xx	11	11	0x00000000
aic78xx	10	10	0x00000000
aic78xx	5	5	0x00000000
aic78xx	15	15	0x00000000
atapi	0	14	0x00000000
ipsraidn	11	11	0x00000000

Devices	Physical Address	Length

Devices	Physical Address	Length
MPS 1.4 - APIC platform	0x00000000	0x0000000010
MPS 1.4 - APIC platform	0x00000020	0x0000000002
MPS 1.4 - APIC platform	0x00000040	0x0000000004
MPS 1.4 - APIC platform	0x00000048	0x0000000004
MPS 1.4 - APIC platform	0x00000061	0x0000000001
MPS 1.4 - APIC platform	0x00000070	0x0000000002
MPS 1.4 - APIC platform	0x00000080	0x0000000010
MPS 1.4 - APIC platform	0x00000092	0x0000000001
MPS 1.4 - APIC platform	0x000000a0	0x0000000002
MPS 1.4 - APIC platform	0x000000c0	0x0000000010
MPS 1.4 - APIC platform	0x000000d0	0x0000000010
MPS 1.4 - APIC platform	0x000000f0	0x0000000010
MPS 1.4 - APIC platform	0x00000400	0x0000000010
MPS 1.4 - APIC platform	0x00000461	0x0000000002
MPS 1.4 - APIC platform	0x00000464	0x0000000002
MPS 1.4 - APIC platform	0x00000480	0x0000000010
MPS 1.4 - APIC platform	0x000004c2	0x000000000e
MPS 1.4 - APIC platform	0x000004d0	0x0000000002
MPS 1.4 - APIC platform	0x000004d4	0x000000002c
MPS 1.4 - APIC platform	0x00000c84	0x0000000001
i8042prt	0x00000060	0x0000000001
i8042prt	0x00000064	0x0000000001
Parport	0x00000378	0x0000000003
Serial	0x000003f8	0x0000000007
Serial	0x000002f8	0x0000000007
E100B	0x0000e4e0	0x0000000014
Floppy	0x000003f0	0x0000000006
Floppy	0x000003f7	0x0000000001
aic78xx	0x0000ec00	0x0000000100
aic78xx	0x0000e800	0x0000000100
aic78xx	0x0000dc00	0x0000000100
aic78xx	0x0000d800	0x0000000100
atapi	0x000001f0	0x0000000008
atapi	0x000003f6	0x0000000001
ipsraidn	0x0000fc00	0x0000000100
cirrus	0x000003b0	0x000000000c
cirrus	0x000003c0	0x0000000020

DMA and Memory Report

Devices	Channel	Port

| Floppy | 2 | 0 |

```
------------------------------------------------------------------
Devices                         Physical Address     Length
------------------------------------------------------------------
MPS 1.4 - APIC platform         0xfec00000           0x00000400
MPS 1.4 - APIC platform         0xfec08000           0x00000400
E100B                           0xfe0ff000           0x00000014
E100B                           0xfe0ff000           0x00000014
aic78xx                         0xfe8ff000           0x00001000
aic78xx                         0xfe8fe000           0x00001000
aic78xx                         0xfe1ff000           0x00001000
aic78xx                         0xfe1fe000           0x00001000
ipsraidn                        0xfeafe000           0x00002000
cirrus                          0x000a0000           0x00020000
------------------------------------------------------------------
Environment Report
------------------------------------------------------------------
System Environment Variables
  ComSpec=C:\WINNT\system32\cmd.exe
  NUMBER_OF_PROCESSORS=3
  OS=Windows_NT
  Os2LibPath=C:\WINNT\system32\os2\dll;
  Path=E:\Notes;C:\WINNT\system32;C:\WINNT;C:\WNETFIN
  PROCESSOR_ARCHITECTURE=x86
  PROCESSOR_IDENTIFIER=x86 Family 6 Model 1 Stepping 9, GenuineIntel
  PROCESSOR_LEVEL=6
  PROCESSOR_REVISION=0109
  windir=C:\WINNT
Environment Variables for Current User
  TEMP=C:\TEMP
  TMP=C:\TEMP
------------------------------------------------------------------
Network Report
------------------------------------------------------------------
Your Access Level: Admin & Local (total control)
Workgroup or Domain: INFO
Network Version: 4.0
LanRoot: INFO
Logged On Users: 1
Current User (1): Administrator
  Logon Domain: INFO
  Logon Server: CHEROKEE
Transport: NetBT_E100B1, 00-60-94-A5-CC-EE, VC's: 0, Wan: Wan
Transport: Nbf_E100B1, 00-60-94-A5-CC-EE, VC's: 0, Wan: Wan
Transport: NwlnkNb, 00-60-94-A5-CC-EE, VC's: 0, Wan: Wan
Character Wait: 3,600
Collection Time: 250
Maximum Collection Count: 16
Keep Connection: 600
Maximum Commands: 5
Session Time Out: 45
Character Buffer Size: 512
Maximum Threads: 17
Lock Quota: 6,144
Lock Increment: 10
```

```
Maximum Locks: 500
Pipe Increment: 10
Maximum Pipes: 500
Cache Time Out: 40
Dormant File Limit: 45
Read Ahead Throughput: 4,294,967,295
Mailslot Buffers: 3
Server Announce Buffers: 20
Illegal Datagrams: 5
Datagram Reset Frequency: 60
Bytes Received: 3,395
SMB's Received: 33
```

The Cherokee, as the network server is called in my network, is more than capable of not only providing applications to network users, but also performing certain file server functions. Implementation of RAID with the server makes it a strong component in the network, and a safe server to use for sensitive data.

Figure 6.34 highlights the high-speed network connections it utilizes.

The Netfinity 7000 uses an Adaptec quad card. This four-port Ethernet adapter is a good match for the server and this network. It enables the server to maximize its potential to the network users requiring its resources.

Summary

This chapter presented some of the network components used in the network I designed. It is important to do most of the preliminary planning work on marker board and/or paper. Once this is done one can begin to acquire equipment and build the network.

The next chapter continues to list and explain components used in this network. All this equipment is integrated in such a way that the network yields benefits beyond the benefits of each single piece.

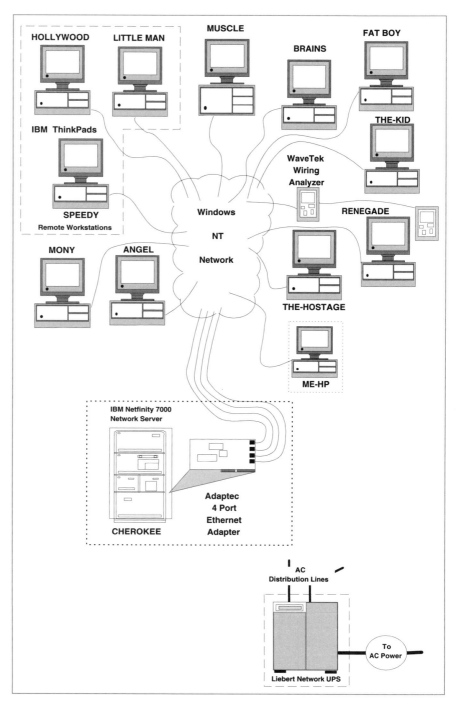

FIGURE 6.34
High-Speed
Network
Connection

CHAPTER **7**

Network Design, Components, and Troubleshooting: Part 2

The previous chapter began explaining considerations
and components regarding network design. This chapter concludes presentation of that information.

Operating System Software

The network presented in Chapters 5 and 6 included the Windows 95
and Windows NT workstation operating systems. In order to understand the operation of these systems consider the information extract-
ed from two workstations on the network. The first report is a system
summary report from Fat-Boy (a Windows 95-based computer on the
network). The second report is a report from Angel (a Windows NT
workstation on the network).

Windows95 System Resource Report from Fat-Boy

```
******************** SYSTEM SUMMARY ********************
Windows version: 4.00.950 Computer Name: FAT-BOY
Processor Type: Pentium
System BUS Type: ISA
BIOS Name: IBM
BIOS Date: 05/29/96
BIOS Version: Unknown
Machine Type: IBM PC/AT
Math Co-processor: Not Present
Registered Owner: Ed Taylor
Registered Company: Information World, Inc.
******************** IRQ SUMMARY ********************
IRQ Usage Summary:3#dr 00 - System timer
01 - Standard 101/102-Key or Microsoft Natural Keyboard
02 - Programmable interrupt controller
03 - Sportster 33600 Fax PC Plug and Play
04 - Communications Port (COM3)
05 - Creative Labs Sound Blaster 16 Plug and Play
06 - Standard Floppy Disk Controller
07 - ECP Printer Port (LPT1)
08 - System CMOS/real time clock
09 - PCI Card
09 - S3
10 - SMC EtherEZ (8416)
11 - IBM MPEG Interactive Video Player
12 - Standard PS/2 Port Mouse
13 - Numeric data processor
14 - Standard Dual PCI IDE Controller
14 - Primary IDE controller (single fifo)
15 - Standard Dual PCI IDE Controller
15 - Secondary IDE controller (single fifo) 3F
******************** I/O PORT SUMMARY ********************
I/O Port Usage Summary:3 # 0000h-001Fh - Direct Memory Access
    Controller
0020h-0021h - Programmable interrupt controller
002Eh-002Fh - Motherboard resources
0040h-0043h - System timer
0060h-0060h - Standard 101/102-Key or Microsoft Natural Keyboard
0061h-0061h - System speaker
```

```
0064h-0064h - Standard 101/102-Key or Microsoft Natural Keyboard 3
**************** System Resource Report
3F 0070h-0071h - System CMOS/real time clock 3 # 0081h-0083h -
Direct Memory Access Controller
0087h-0087h - Direct memory access controller
0089h-008Bh - Direct memory access controller
008Fh-008Fh - Direct memory access controller
00A0h-00A1h - Programmable interrupt controller
00C0h-00DFh - Direct memory access controller
00F0h-00FFh - Numeric data processor
0100h-0100h - Creative SB32 PnP
0170h-0177h - Standard Dual PCI IDE Controller
0170h-0177h - Secondary IDE controller (single fifo)
01F0h-01F7h - Primary IDE controller (single fifo)
01F0h-01F7h - Standard Dual PCI IDE Controller
0200h-0207h - Gameport Joystick
0200h-0203h - IBM MPEG Interactive Video Player
0220h-023Fh - SMC EtherEZ (8416)
0240h-024Fh - Creative Labs Sound Blaster 16 Plug and Play
0270h-0273h - IO read data port for ISA Plug and Play enumerator
02F8h-02FFh - Sportster 33600 Fax PC Plug and Play
0300h-0301h - Creative Labs Sound Blaster 16 Plug and Play
0376h-0376h - Standard Dual PCI IDE Controller
0376h-0376h - Secondary IDE controller (single fifo)
0388h-038Bh - Creative Labs Sound Blaster 16 Plug and Play
03B0h-03BBh - S3
03BCh-03BEh - ECP Printer Port (LPT1)
03C0h-03DFh - S3
03E8h-03EFh - Communications Port (COM3)
03F0h-03F5h - Standard Floppy Disk Controller
03F6h-03F6h - Primary IDE controller (single fifo)
03F6h-03F6h - Standard Dual PCI IDE Controller
0660h-0663h - Creative Advanced Wave Effects Synthesis for AWE 32
0CF8h-0CFFh - PCI bus
1000h-101Fh - PCI Card
FFF0h-FFF7h - Standard Dual PCI IDE Controller
FFF8h-FFFFh - Standard Dual PCI IDE Controller 3F
******************* UPPER MEMORY USAGE SUMMARY
Memory Usage Summary: 3 #00000000h-0009FFFFh - System board extension
                     for PnP BIOS
000A0000h-000AFFFFh - S3
000B0000h-000BFFFFh - S3
000C0000h-000C7FFFh - S3
000E0000h-000FFFFFh - System board extension for PnP BIOS
00100000h-00FFFFFFh - System board extension for PnP BIOS
40000000h-43FFFFFFh - S3
**************** System Resource Report ************************
DMA USAGE SUMMARY
DMA Channel Usage Summary:3#
02 - Standard Floppy Disk Controller
03 - Creative Labs Sound Blaster 16 Plug and Play
04 - Direct memory access controller
06 - Creative Labs Sound Blaster 16 Plug and Play
07 - IBM MPEG Interactive Video Player3F
```

```
******************* MEMORY SUMMARY *******************
640 KB Total Conventional Memory
32288 KB Total Extended Memory
******************* DISK DRIVE INFO *******************
A:  Floppy Drive, 3.5" 1.44M  80 Cylinders   2 Heads
512 Bytes/Sector   18 Sectors/TrackC:  Fixed Disk  1664960K
Total  935744K Free 826 Cylinders   64 Heads
512 Bytes/Sector   63 Sectors/TrackD:  CD-ROM Drive
******************* SYSTEM DEVICE INFO *******************
Class: Other devices
Device: Creative SB32 PnP
Resources:
I/O: 0100h-0100h  Class: Other devices  Device: IBM MPEG Interactive
                  Video Player
Resources:
IRQ: 11
I/O: 0200h-0203h
DMA: 07 Class: Other devices   Device: PCI Card
Resources: IRQ: 09
I/O: 1000h-101Fh  Class: Network adapters  System Resource Report
****************************
Device: SMC EtherEZ (8416)
Resources: IRQ: 10
I/O: 0220h-023Fh  Class: Network adapters Device: Dial-Up Adapter
No resources used. DISABLED DEVICE    Class: Ports (COM & LPT)
Device: Generic IRDA Compatible Device
No resources used. Class: Ports (COM & LPT) Device: ECP Printer Port
                   (LPT1)
Resources:
IRQ: 07
I/O: 03BCh-03BEh
Device drivers:
C:\WINDOWS\SYSTEM\lpt.vxd
File size: 0 bytes.
Manufacturer: Microsoft Corporation
File version: 4.00.950
Copyright: Copyright _ Microsoft Corp. 1992-1995 Class: Ports (COM &
           LPT)
Device: Communications Port (COM3)
Resources: IRQ: 04
I/O: 03E8h-03EFh
Device drivers: C:\WINDOWS\SYSTEM\serial.vxd
File size: 18572 bytes.
Manufacturer: Microsoft Corporation
File version: 4.00.950
Copyright: Copyright  Microsoft Corp. 1992-1995
C:\WINDOWS\SYSTEM\serialui.dll
File size: 12032 bytes.
Manufacturer: Microsoft Corporation
File version: 4.00.950
Copyright: Copyright Microsoft Corp. 1993-1995
Class: Mouse  Device: Standard PS/2 Port Mouse
Resources: IRQ: 12
```

```
*********************** System Resource Report******************
Device drivers: C:\WINDOWS\SYSTEM\mouse.drv
File size: 7712 bytes.
Manufacturer: Microsoft Corporation
File version: 9.01.0.000
Copyright: Copyright Microsoft Corp. 1990-1995
C:\WINDOWS\SYSTEM\msmouse.vxd
File size: 15804 bytes.
Manufacturer: Microsoft Corporation
File version: 4.00.950
Copyright: Copyright Microsoft Corp. 1988-1995
Class: Hard disk controllers Device: Secondary IDE controller (single
        fifo)
Resources: IRQ: 15
I/O: 0170h-0177h
I/O: 0376h-0376h Class: Hard disk controllers Device: Primary IDE
                        controller (single fifo)
Resources: IRQ: 14
I/O: 01F0h-01F7h
I/O: 03F6h-03F6h
*DISABLED DEVICE* Class: Hard disk controllers
Device: Standard IDE/ESDI Hard Disk Controller
No resources used. Class: Hard disk controllers Device: Standard Dual
                        PCI IDE Controller
Resources:
IRQ: 14
IRQ: 15
I/O: 01F0h-01F7h
I/O: 03F6h-03F6h
I/O: 0170h-0177h
I/O: 0376h-0376h
I/O: FFF0h-FFF7h
I/O: FFF8h-FFFFh
Class: Floppy disk controllers  Device: Standard Floppy Disk
        Controller
Resources: IRQ: 06
*************************System Resource Report******************
I/O: 03F0h-03F5h   DMA: 02 Class: Display adapters Device: S3
Resources:   IRQ: 09
I/O: 03B0h-03BBh
I/O: 03C0h-03DFh
MEM: 000C0000h-000C7FFFh
MEM: 000A0000h-000AFFFFh
MEM: 000B0000h-000BFFFFh
MEM: 40000000h-43FFFFFFh
Device drivers:
C:\WINDOWS\SYSTEM\orchid.cp0
Driver file possibly missing.
No version information.
C:\WINDOWS\SYSTEM\orchidf.cp0
Driver file possibly missing.
No version information.
C:\WINDOWS\SYSTEM\s3.drv
File size: 57632 bytes.
```

Manufacturer: Microsoft Corporation
File version: 4.00.950
Copyright: Copyright _ Microsoft Corp. 1992-1995
C:\WINDOWS\SYSTEM\s3.vxd
File size: 17087 bytes.
Manufacturer: Microsoft Corporation
File version: 4.00.950
Copyright: Copyright _ Microsoft Corp. 1988-1995
C:\WINDOWS\SYSTEM\supervga.drv
File size: 52320 bytes.
Manufacturer: Microsoft Corporation
File version: 4.00.950
Copyright: Copyright Microsoft Corp. 1991-1995
Class: CDROM Device: TEAC CD-56E
No resources used. Class: Monitor Device: Plug and Play Monitor (VESA
                   DDC)
No resources used. Class: Modem Device: Sportster 33600 Fax PC Plug
                   and Play
Resources:System Resource Report
IRQ: 03 I/O: 02F8h-02FFh Class: Modem Device: Courier Dual Standard
     V.34 Ready Fax
No resources used. Class: System devices
Device: I/O read data port for ISA Plug and Play enumerator
Resources: I/O: 0270h-0273h
Class: System devices Device: PCI standard ISA bridge
No resources used. Class: System devices Device: PCI standard host CPU
                   bridge
No resources used. Class: System devices Device: Motherboard resources
Resources: I/O: 002Eh-002Fh
Class: System devices Device: Motherboard resources
No resources used. Class: System devices Device: System board
                   extension for PnP BIOS
Resources: MEM: 000E0000h-000FFFFFh Class:
System devices Device: System board extension for PnP BIOS
Resources: MEM: 00000000h-0009FFFFh
MEM: 00100000h-00FFFFFFh Class: System devices Device: PCI bus
Resources: I/O: 0CF8h-0CFFh
Device drivers:
C:\WINDOWS\SYSTEM\pci.vxd
File size: 24535 bytes.
****************System Resource Report**********************
Manufacturer: Microsoft Corporation File version: 4.00.950
Copyright: Copyright Microsoft Corp. 1988-1995 Class: System devices
Device: Numeric data processor
Resources: IRQ: 13
I/O: 00F0h-00FFh Class: System devices Device: System speaker
Resources: I/O: 0061h-0061h Class: System devices
Device: System CMOS/real time clock
Resources: IRQ: 08
I/O: 0070h-0071h Class: System devices Device: System timer
Resources: IRQ: 00
I/O: 0040h-0043h Class: System devices Device:
Direct memory access controller
Resources:

```
I/O: 0000h-001Fh
I/O: 0081h-0083h
I/O: 0087h-0087h
I/O: 0089h-008Bh
I/O: 008Fh-008Fh
I/O: 00C0h-00DFh
DMA: 04  Class: System devices Device: Programmable interrupt
        controller
Resources: IRQ: 02
I/O: 0020h-0021h
I/O: 00A0h-00A1h Class: System devices
Device: Advanced Power Management support System Resource Report No
        resources used.
Class: System devices  Device: Plug and Play BIOS
No resources used.
Device drivers:
 C:\WINDOWS\SYSTEM\VMM32\bios.vxd
No version information.Class: System devices Device: System board
No resources used. Class:
Keyboard Device: Standard 101/102-Key or Microsoft Natural Keyboard
Resources: IRQ: 01
I/O: 0060h-0060h
I/O: 0064h-0064h
Device drivers:
C:\WINDOWS\SYSTEM\keyboard.drv
File size: 12688 bytes.
Manufacturer: Microsoft Corporation
File version: 4.00.950
Copyright: Copyright Microsoft Corp. 1991-1995
C:\WINDOWS\SYSTEM\VMM32\vkd.vxd
No version information.
 *DISABLED DEVICE* Class: Sound, video and game controllers
Device: Gameport Joystick
No resources used.
Device drivers:
C:\WINDOWS\SYSTEM\vjoyd.vxd
File size: 20590 bytes.
Manufacturer: Microsoft Corporation
File version: 4.00.950
Copyright: Copyright Microsoft Corp. 1994-1995
C:\WINDOWS\SYSTEM\msjstick.drv
File size: 7744 bytes.
Manufacturer: Microsoft Corporation
File version: 4.0.950
Copyright: Copyright Microsoft Corp. 1991-1995
Class: Sound, video and game controllers Device: Creative Advanced
Wave Effects Synthesis for AWE 32
****************System Resource Report************************
I/O: 0660h-0663h Device drivers:
C:\WINDOWS\SYSTEM\sbawe.vxd
File size: 40014 bytes.
Manufacturer: Creative Technology Ltd.
File version: 4.00.466
Copyright: Copyright (c) 1993-95 Creative Technology Ltd.
```

```
C:\WINDOWS\SYSTEM\sbawe32.drv
File size: 23216 bytes.
Manufacturer: Creative Technology Ltd.
File version: 4.00
Copyright: Copyright (c) 1993-95 Creative Technology Ltd.
C:\WINDOWS\SYSTEM\synthgm.sbk
File size: 34832 bytes.
No version information. Class: Sound, video and game controllers
Device: Creative Labs Sound Blaster 16 Plug and Play
Resources: IRQ: 05
I/O: 0240h-024Fh
I/O: 0300h-0301h
I/O: 0388h-038Bh
DMA: 03
DMA: 06
Device drivers:
C:\WINDOWS\SYSTEM\cspman.dll
File size: 17776 bytes.
Manufacturer: Creative Technology Ltd.
File version: 4.00
Copyright: Copyright Creative Technology Ltd. 1994-1995
C:\WINDOWS\SYSTEM\sb16.vxd
File size: 54363 bytes.
Manufacturer: Creative Technology Ltd.
File version: 4.00.493
Copyright: Copyright Creative Technology Ltd. 1994-1995
C:\WINDOWS\SYSTEM\sbfm.drv
File size: 4128 bytes.
Manufacturer: Creative Technology Ltd.
File version: 4.00
Copyright: Copyright Creative Technology Ltd. 1994-1995
C:\WINDOWS\SYSTEM\sb16snd.drv
File size: 46000 bytes.
Manufacturer: Creative Technology Ltd.
File version: 4.00
Copyright: Copyright Creative Technology Ltd. 1994-1995
C:\WINDOWS\SYSTEM\wfm0200.acv
****************System Resource Report*****************
File size: 13456 bytes. Manufacturer: Creative Technology Ltd.
File version: 4.00
Copyright: Copyright Creative Technology Ltd.
C:\WINDOWS\SYSTEM\wfm0200a.csp
File size: 2238 bytes.
No version information.
C:\WINDOWS\SYSTEM\wfm0201.acv
File size: 5184 bytes.
Manufacturer: Creative Technology Ltd.
File version: 4.00
Copyright: Copyright Creative Technology Ltd.
C:\WINDOWS\SYSTEM\wfm0201a.csp
File size: 6776 bytes.
No version information.
C:\WINDOWS\SYSTEM\wfm0202.acv
File size: 9056 bytes.
```

```
No version information.
C:\WINDOWS\SYSTEM\wfm0202a.csp
File size: 9004 bytes.
No version information.
C:\WINDOWS\SYSTEM\wfm0203.acv
File size: 9056 bytes.
Manufacturer: Creative Technology Ltd.
File version: 4.00
Copyright: Copyright Creative Technology Ltd.
C:\WINDOWS\SYSTEM\wfm0203a.csp
File size: 9004 bytes.
No version information. Class: Sound, video and game controllers
Device: Gameport Joystick
Resources:
I/O: 0200h-0207h
Device drivers:
C:\WINDOWS\SYSTEM\vjoyd.vxd
File size: 20590 bytes.
Manufacturer: Microsoft Corporation
File version: 4.00.950
Copyright: Copyright  Microsoft Corp. 1994-1995
C:\WINDOWS\SYSTEM\msjstick.drv
File size: 7744 bytes.
Manufacturer: Microsoft Corporation
File version: 4.0.950
Copyright: Copyright  Microsoft Corp. 1991-1995
Class: Disk drives System Resource Report
Device: GENERIC IDE  DISK TYPE: No resources used.
Class: Disk drives Device: GENERIC NEC  FLOPPY DISK
No resources used. Class: Printer Device: HP ColorPro
No resources used.
Device drivers:
C:\WINDOWS\SYSTEM\HPPLOT.DRV
Driver file possibly missing.
No version information.
C:\WINDOWS\SYSTEM\HPPLOT.HLP
Driver file possibly missing.
No version information. Class: Printer Device: IBM Network Printer 17
                            PCL
No resources used.
Device drivers:
C:\WINDOWS\SYSTEM\IBMPCL.HLP
File size: 26652 bytes.
No version information.
C:\WINDOWS\SYSTEM\IBMPCLR.DLL
File size: 9504 bytes.
Manufacturer: The IBM Printing Systems Company
File version: 3.10
Copyright: Licensed Materials—Property of IBM. Copyright IBM Corp. 1
C:\WINDOWS\SYSTEM\MTETAB.DLL
File size: 3840 bytes.
Manufacturer: Softel vdm
File version: 2.00
Copyright: Copyright Softel vdm 1995
```

```
C:\WINDOWS\SYSTEM\IBMPCLFI.DLL
File size: 592 bytes.
Manufacturer: IBM CORP.
File version: 3.10.130
Copyright: Copyright IBM Corporation, 1996. Copyright Microsoft
C:\WINDOWS\SYSTEM\IBM4317F.HLP
File size: 27094 bytes.
No version information.
C:\WINDOWS\SYSTEM\IBMPCL.DRV
File size: 7104 bytes.
Manufacturer: The IBM Printing Systems Company
File version: 3.10
*************** System Resource Report*************************
Copyright: Licensed Materials—Property of IBM. Copyright IBM Corp. 1
Class: Printer Device: HP ColorPro
No resources used.
Device drivers:
C:\WINDOWS\SYSTEM\HPPLOT.DRV
Driver file possibly missing.
No version information.
C:\WINDOWS\SYSTEM\HPPLOT.HLP
Driver file possibly missing.
No version information. Class: Printer Device: IBM 2390 PS/1
No resources used.
Device drivers:
C:\WINDOWS\SYSTEM\IBM239X.DRV
File size: 30560 bytes.
Manufacturer: Microsoft Corporation
File version: 4.00.950
Copyright: Copyright Microsoft Corp. 1991-1995
C:\WINDOWS\SYSTEM\UNIDRV.DLL
File size: 416 bytes.
Manufacturer: Microsoft Corporation
File version: 4.00.950
Copyright: Copyright Microsoft Corp. 1991-1995
C:\WINDOWS\SYSTEM\UNIDRV.HLP
File size: 15343 bytes.
No version information.
C:\WINDOWS\SYSTEM\ICONLIB.DLL
File size: 12176 bytes.
Manufacturer: Microsoft Corporation
File version: 4.00.950
Copyright: Copyright Microsoft Corp. 1991-1995
Class: Printer Device:No resources used. Class:
Printer Device: IBM 4019 LaserPrinter PS39
No resources used.
Device drivers:
C:\WINDOWS\SYSTEM\IB401939.SPD
File size: 10431 bytes.
No version information.
************System Resource Report******************************
C:\WINDOWS\SYSTEM\PSCRIPT.DRVFile size: 65520 bytes.
Manufacturer: Microsoft Corporation
File version: 4.00.950
```

```
Copyright: Copyright Microsoft Corp. 1991-1995
C:\WINDOWS\SYSTEM\PSCRIPT.HLP
File size: 20439 bytes.
No version information.
C:\WINDOWS\SYSTEM\PSCRIPT.INI
File size: 328 bytes.
No version information.
C:\WINDOWS\SYSTEM\TESTPS.TXT
File size: 2640 bytes.
No version information.
C:\WINDOWS\SYSTEM\APPLE380.SPD
File size: 6046 bytes.
No version information.
C:\WINDOWS\SYSTEM\FONTS.MFM
File size: 30183 bytes.
No version information.
C:\WINDOWS\SYSTEM\ICONLIB.DLL
File size: 12176 bytes.
Manufacturer: Microsoft Corporation
File version: 4.00.950
Copyright: Copyright Microsoft Corp. 1991-1995
C:\WINDOWS\SYSTEM\PSMON.DLL
File size: 28672 bytes.
Manufacturer: Microsoft Corporation
File version: 4.00.950
Copyright: Copyright Microsoft Corp. 1981-1995 Class: Printer
Device: IBM 2390 PS/1
No resources used.
Device drivers:
C:\WINDOWS\SYSTEM\IBM239X.DRV
File size: 30560 bytes.
Manufacturer: Microsoft Corporation
File version: 4.00.950
Copyright: Copyright Microsoft Corp. 1991-1995
C:\WINDOWS\SYSTEM\UNIDRV.DLL
File size: 416 bytes.
Manufacturer: Microsoft Corporation
File version: 4.00.950
Copyright: Copyright Microsoft Corp. 1991-1995
C:\WINDOWS\SYSTEM\UNIDRV.HLP
File size: 15343 bytes.
**********System Resource Report************************
No version information.
C:\WINDOWS\SYSTEM\ICONLIB.DLL
File size: 12176 bytes.
Manufacturer: Microsoft Corporation
File version: 4.00.950
Copyright: Copyright Microsoft Corp. 1991-1995
Class: Printer Device: Apple LaserWriter Plus
No resources used.
Device drivers:
C:\WINDOWS\SYSTEM\APPLE380.SPD
File size: 6046 bytes.
No version information.
```

```
C:\WINDOWS\SYSTEM\PSCRIPT.DRV
File size: 65520 bytes.
Manufacturer: Microsoft Corporation
File version: 4.00.950
Copyright: Copyright Microsoft Corp. 1991-1995
C:\WINDOWS\SYSTEM\PSCRIPT.HLP
File size: 20439 bytes.
No version information.
C:\WINDOWS\SYSTEM\PSCRIPT.INI
File size: 328 bytes.
No version information.
C:\WINDOWS\SYSTEM\TESTPS.TXT
File size: 2640 bytes.
No version information.
C:\WINDOWS\SYSTEM\FONTS.MFM
File size: 30183 bytes.
No version information.
C:\WINDOWS\SYSTEM\ICONLIB.DLL
File size: 12176 bytes.
Manufacturer: Microsoft Corporation
File version: 4.00.950
Copyright: Copyright Microsoft Corp. 1991-1995
C:\WINDOWS\SYSTEM\PSMON.DLL
File size: 28672 bytes.
Manufacturer: Microsoft Corporation
File version: 4.00.950
Copyright: Copyright _ Microsoft Corp. 1981-1995 Class: Printer
Device: IBM 4019 LaserPrinter PS39
No resources used.
Device drivers:
C:\WINDOWS\SYSTEM\IB401939.SPD
*************** System Resource Report ***************
File size: 10431 bytes.
No version information.
C:\WINDOWS\SYSTEM\PSCRIPT.DRV
File size: 65520 bytes.
Manufacturer: Microsoft Corporation
File version: 4.00.950
Copyright: Copyright Microsoft Corp. 1991-1995
C:\WINDOWS\SYSTEM\PSCRIPT.HLP
File size: 20439 bytes.
No version information.
C:\WINDOWS\SYSTEM\PSCRIPT.INI
File size: 328 bytes.
No version information.
C:\WINDOWS\SYSTEM\TESTPS.TXT
File size: 2640 bytes.
No version information.
C:\WINDOWS\SYSTEM\APPLE380.SPD
File size: 6046 bytes.
No version information.
C:\WINDOWS\SYSTEM\FONTS.MFM
File size: 30183 bytes.
No version information.
```

```
C:\WINDOWS\SYSTEM\ICONLIB.DLL
File size: 12176 bytes.
Manufacturer: Microsoft Corporation
File version: 4.00.950
Copyright: Copyright Microsoft Corp. 1991-1995
C:\WINDOWS\SYSTEM\PSMON.DLL
File size: 28672 bytes.
Manufacturer: Microsoft Corporation
File version: 4.00.950
Copyright: Copyright Microsoft Corp. 1981-1995
```

Windows NT Workstation Report from Angel

```
Microsoft Diagnostics Report For \\ANGEL
-------------------------------------------------------------------
OS Version Report
-------------------------------------------------------------------
Microsoft (R) Windows NT (TM) Workstation
Version 4.0 (Build 1381: Service Pack 1) x86 Uniprocessor Free
Registered Owner: ANGEL, Information World, Inc.
Product Number: 17597-OEM-0023333-22375
-------------------------------------------------------------------
System Report
-------------------------------------------------------------------
System: AT/AT COMPATIBLE
Hardware Abstraction Layer: PC Compatible Eisa/Isa HAL
BIOS Date: 07/24/97
BIOS Version: BIOS Version 0.11.01.DUOM- Beta
Processor list:
   0:  x86 Family 6 Model 3 Stepping 3 GenuineIntel ~265 Mhz
-------------------------------------------------------------------
Video Display Report
-------------------------------------------------------------------
BIOS Date: 07/21/97
BIOS Version: S3 86C775/86C785 Video BIOS. Version 1.01.11-C2.08.05
             S3 86C775/86C785 Video BIOS. Version 1.01.11-C2.08.05
             S3 86C775/86C785 Video BIOS. Version 1.01.11-C2.08.05
             S3 86C775/86C785 Video BIOS. Version 1.01.11-C2.08.05
Adapter:
   Setting: 640 x 480 x 256
           60 Hz
   Type: s3mini compatible display adapter
   String: S3 Compatible Display Adapter
   Memory: 2 MB
   Chip Type: S3 Trio64V2
   DAC Type: S3 SDAC
Driver:
   Vendor: S3 Incorporated
   File(s): s3mini.sys, s3disp.dll
   Version: 1.03.10, 4.0.0
Drives Report
-------------------------------------------------------------------
C:\  (Local - FAT) ANGEL Total: 1,023,824KB, Free: 783,600KB
```

```
        Serial Number: 1939 - BFE
        Bytes per cluster: 512
        Sectors per cluster: 32
        Filename length: 255
D:\  (Local - FAT) ANGEL-D Total: 2,096,320KB, Free: 2,090,208KB
        Serial Number: 2651 - C03
        Bytes per cluster: 512
        Sectors per cluster: 64
        Filename length: 255
E:\  (Local - FAT)  Total: 999,632KB, Free: 999,616KB
        Serial Number: 3055 - C06
        Bytes per cluster: 512
        Sectors per cluster: 32
        Filename length: 255
------------------------------------------------------------------
Memory Report
------------------------------------------------------------------
Handles: 1,281
Threads: 124
Processes: 19
Physical Memory (K)
    Total: 32,180
    Available: 6,072
    File Cache: 6,784
Kernel Memory (K)
    Total: 5,104
    Paged: 4,184
    Nonpaged: 920
Commit Charge (K)
    Total: 21,316
    Limit: 67,788
    Peak: 22,084
Pagefile Space (K)
    Total: 44,032
    Total in use: 640
    Peak: 640
    C:\pagefile.sys
        Total: 44,032
        Total in use: 640
        Peak: 640
------------------------------------------------------------------
Services Report
------------------------------------------------------------------
Alerter                                  Stopped    (Manual)
    C:\WINNT40\System32\services.exe
    Service Account Name: LocalSystem
    Error Severity: Normal
    Service Flags: Shared Process
    Service Dependencies:
        LanmanWorkstation
Computer Browser                         Running    (Automatic)
    C:\WINNT40\System32\services.exe
    Service Account Name: LocalSystem
    Error Severity: Normal
```

```
                          Service Flags: Shared Process
                          Service Dependencies:
                              LanmanWorkstation
                              LanmanServer
                              LmHosts
                      ClipBook Server                          Stopped   (Manual)
                          C:\WINNT40\system32\clipsrv.exe
                          Service Account Name: LocalSystem
                          Error Severity: Normal
                          Service Flags: Own Process
                          Service Dependencies:
                              NetDDE
                      DHCP Client (TDI)                        Stopped   (Disabled)
                          C:\WINNT40\System32\services.exe
                          Service Account Name: LocalSystem
                          Error Severity: Normal
                          Service Flags: Shared Process
                          Service Dependencies:
                              Tcpip
                              Afd
                              NetBT
                      IBM DMI Service Layer (DMI Service Layer)  Running  (Automatic)
                          C:\sva\dmi\bin\dmislsrv.exe
                          Service Account Name: LocalSystem
                          Error Severity: Normal
                          Service Flags: Own Process, Interactive
                      EventLog (Event log)                     Running   (Automatic)
                          C:\WINNT40\system32\services.exe
                          Service Account Name: LocalSystem
                          Error Severity: Normal
                          Service Flags: Shared Process
                      Server                                   Running   (Automatic)
                          C:\WINNT40\System32\services.exe
                          Service Account Name: LocalSystem
                          Error Severity: Normal
                          Service Flags: Shared Process
                          Group Dependencies:
                              TDI
                      Workstation (NetworkProvider)            Running   (Automatic)
                          C:\WINNT40\System32\services.exe
                          Service Account Name: LocalSystem
                          Error Severity: Normal
                          Service Flags: Shared Process
                          Group Dependencies:
                              TDI
                      PC System Monitor                        Running   (Automatic)
                          C:\sva\dmi\bin\lm78cint.exe
                          Service Account Name: LocalSystem
                          Error Severity: Normal
                          Service Flags: Own Process, Interactive
                          Group Dependencies:
                              DMI Service Layer
                      TCP/IP NetBIOS Helper                    Running   (Automatic)
                          C:\WINNT40\System32\services.exe
```

```
                       Service Account Name: LocalSystem
                       Error Severity: Normal
                       Service Flags: Shared Process
                       Group Dependencies:
                          NetworkProvider
                  Messenger                              Running   (Automatic)
                       C:\WINNT40\System32\services.exe
                       Service Account Name: LocalSystem
                       Error Severity: Normal
                       Service Flags: Shared Process
                       Service Dependencies:
                          LanmanWorkstation
                          NetBios
                  Network DDE (NetDDEGroup)             Stopped   (Manual)
                       C:\WINNT40\system32\netdde.exe
                       Service Account Name: LocalSystem
                       Error Severity: Normal
                       Service Flags: Shared Process
                       Service Dependencies:
                          NetDDEDSDM
                  Network DDE DSDM                       Stopped   (Manual)
                       C:\WINNT40\system32\netdde.exe
                       Service Account Name: LocalSystem
                       Error Severity: Normal
                       Service Flags: Shared Process
                  Net Logon (RemoteValidation)           Stopped   (Manual)
                       C:\WINNT40\System32\lsass.exe
                       Service Account Name: LocalSystem
                       Error Severity: Normal
                       Service Flags: Shared Process
                       Service Dependencies:
                          LanmanWorkstation
                          LmHosts
                  Norton SpeedDisk                       Running   (Automatic)
                       C:\Program Files\Norton Speed Disk Trial\SDSRV.EXE
                       Service Account Name: LocalSystem
                       Error Severity: Normal
                       Service Flags: Own Process
                  NT LM Security Support Provider        Stopped   (Manual)
                       C:\WINNT40\System32\SERVICES.EXE
                       Service Account Name: LocalSystem
                       Error Severity: Normal
                       Service Flags: Shared Process
                  Plug and Play (PlugPlay)               Running   (Automatic)
                       C:\WINNT40\system32\services.exe
                       Service Account Name: LocalSystem
                       Error Severity: Normal
                       Service Flags: Shared Process
                  Remote Access Autodial Manager        Running   (Automatic)
                       C:\WINNT40\system32\rasman.exe
                       Service Account Name: LocalSystem
                       Error Severity: Normal
                       Service Flags: Shared Process
                       Service Dependencies:
```

```
                        RasMan
             Remote Access Connection Manager (Network)    Running   (Manual)
                C:\WINNT40\system32\rasman.exe
                Service Account Name: LocalSystem
                Error Severity: Normal
                Service Flags: Shared Process, Interactive
                Service Dependencies:
                   tapisrv
             Remote Access Server (Network)         Stopped   (Manual)
                C:\WINNT40\system32\rassrv.exe
                Service Account Name: LocalSystem
                Error Severity: Normal
                Service Flags: Own Process
                Service Dependencies:
                   LanmanServer
                   RasMan
                   NetBios
                   NetBT
             Directory Replicator                   Stopped   (Manual)
                C:\WINNT40\System32\lmrepl.exe
                Service Account Name: LocalSystem
                Error Severity: Normal
                Service Flags: Own Process
                Service Dependencies:
                   LanmanWorkstation
                   LanmanServer
             Remote Procedure Call (RPC) Locator    Stopped   (Manual)
                C:\WINNT40\System32\LOCATOR.EXE
                Service Account Name: LocalSystem
                Error Severity: Normal
                Service Flags: Own Process
             Remote Procedure Call (RPC) Service    Running   (Automatic)
                C:\WINNT40\system32\RpcSs.exe
                Service Account Name: LocalSystem
                Error Severity: Normal
                Service Flags: Own Process
             Schedule                               Stopped   (Manual)
                C:\WINNT40\System32\AtSvc.Exe
                Service Account Name: LocalSystem
                Error Severity: Normal
                Service Flags: Own Process
             Spooler (SpoolerGroup)                 Running   (Automatic)
                C:\WINNT40\system32\spoolss.exe
                Service Account Name: LocalSystem
                Error Severity: Normal
                Service Flags: Own Process, Interactive
             Telephony Service                      Running   (Manual)
                C:\WINNT40\system32\tapisrv.exe
                Service Account Name: LocalSystem
                Error Severity: Normal
                Service Flags: Own Process
             UPS                                    Stopped   (Manual)
                C:\WINNT40\System32\ups.exe
                Service Account Name: LocalSystem
```

```
      Error Severity: Normal
      Service Flags: Own Process
------------------------------------------------------------------
Drivers Report
------------------------------------------------------------------
Abiosdsk (Primary disk)              Stopped   (Disabled)
      Error Severity: Ignore
      Service Flags: Kernel Driver,
      Shared Process
AFD Networking Support Environment (TDI) Running   (Automatic)
      C:\WINNT40\System32\drivers\afd.sys
      Error Severity: Normal
      Service Flags: Kernel Driver,
      Shared Process
Aha154x (SCSI miniport)              Stopped   (Disabled)
      Error Severity: Normal
      Service Flags: Kernel Driver,
       Shared Process
Aha174x (SCSI miniport)              Stopped   (Disabled)
      Error Severity: Normal
      Service Flags: Kernel Driver,
       Shared Process
aic78xx (SCSI miniport)              Stopped   (Disabled)
      C:\WINNT40\system32\drivers\aic78xx.sys
      Error Severity: Normal
      Service Flags: Kernel Driver,
      Shared Process
Always (SCSI miniport)               Stopped   (Disabled)
      Error Severity: Normal
      Service Flags: Kernel Driver,
      Shared Process
ami0nt (SCSI miniport)               Stopped   (Disabled)
      Error Severity: Normal
      Service Flags: Kernel Driver,
      Shared Process
amsint (SCSI miniport)               Stopped   (Disabled)
      Error Severity: Normal
      Service Flags: Kernel Driver,
      Shared Process
Arrow (SCSI miniport)          Stopped   (Disabled)
      Error Severity: Normal
      Service Flags: Kernel Driver,
      Shared Process
Remote Access Mac (NDIS)             Running   (Automatic)
      C:\WINNT40\system32\drivers\asyncmac.sys
      Error Severity: Normal
      Service Flags: Kernel Driver,
      Shared Process
atapi (SCSI miniport)                Stopped   (Disabled)
      Error Severity: Normal
      Service Flags: Kernel Driver,
       Shared Process
Atdisk (Primary disk)                Stopped   (Disabled)
      Error Severity: Ignore
```

```
                         Service Flags: Kernel Driver,
                         Shared Process
                      ati (Video)                            Stopped   (Disabled)
                         Error Severity: Ignore
                         Service Flags: Kernel Driver,
                         Shared Process
                      Beep (Base)                            Running   (System)
                         Error Severity: Normal
                         Service Flags: Kernel Driver,
                         Shared Process
                      BusLogic (SCSI miniport)          Stopped   (Disabled)
                         Error Severity: Normal
                         Service Flags: Kernel Driver,
                         Shared Process
                      Busmouse (Pointer Port)           Stopped   (Disabled)
                         Error Severity: Ignore
                         Service Flags: Kernel Driver,
                         Shared Process
                      Cdaudio (Filter)                       Stopped   (System)
                         Error Severity: Ignore
                         Service Flags: Kernel Driver,
                         Shared Process
                      Cdfs (File system)                     Running   (Disabled)
                         Error Severity: Normal
                         Service Flags: File System Driver, Shared Process
                         Group Dependencies:
                           SCSI CDROM Class
                      Cdrom (SCSI CDROM Class)               Running   (System)
                         Error Severity: Ignore
                         Service Flags: Kernel Driver,
                         Shared Process
                         Group Dependencies:
                           SCSI miniport
                      Changer (Filter)                       Stopped   (System)
                         Error Severity: Ignore
                         Service Flags: Kernel Driver,
                         Shared Process
                      cirrus (Video)                         Stopped   (Disabled)
                         Error Severity: Ignore
                         Service Flags: Kernel Driver,
                         Shared Process
                      Cpqarray (SCSI miniport)          Stopped   (Disabled)
                         Error Severity: Normal
                         Service Flags: Kernel Driver,
                         Shared Process
                      cpqfws2e (SCSI miniport)               Stopped   (Disabled)
                         Error Severity: Normal
                         Service Flags: Kernel Driver,
                         Shared Process
                      cs32ba11 (Base)                        Running   (System)
                         C:\WINNT40\System32\drivers\cs32ba11.SYS
                         Error Severity: Normal
                         Service Flags: Kernel Driver,
                         Shared Process
```

```
dac960nt (SCSI miniport)              Stopped   (Disabled)
   Error Severity: Normal
   Service Flags: Kernel Driver,
   Shared Process
dce376nt (SCSI miniport)              Stopped   (Disabled)
   Error Severity: Normal
   Service Flags: Kernel Driver,
   Shared Process
Delldsa (SCSI miniport)              Stopped   (Disabled)
   Error Severity: Normal
   Service Flags: Kernel Driver,
   Shared Process
Dell_DGX (Video)                      Stopped   (Disabled)
   Error Severity: Ignore
   Service Flags: Kernel Driver,
   Shared Process
Disk (SCSI Class)                    Running   (Boot)
   Error Severity: Ignore
   Service Flags: Kernel Driver,
   Shared Process
   Group Dependencies:
      SCSI miniport
Diskperf (Filter)                  Stopped   (Disabled)
   Error Severity: Normal
   Service Flags: Kernel Driver,
   Shared Process
DptScsi (SCSI miniport)               Stopped   (Disabled)
   Error Severity: Normal
   Service Flags: Kernel Driver,
   Shared Process
dtc329x (SCSI miniport)              Stopped   (Disabled)
   Error Severity: Normal
   Service Flags: Kernel Driver,
   Shared Process
Intel 82557-based PRO Adapter Driver (NDIS) Running (Automatic)
   C:\WINNT40\System32\drivers\e100b.sys
   Error Severity: Normal
   Service Flags: Kernel Driver,
Shared Process
et4000 (Video)                        Stopped   (Disabled)
   Error Severity: Ignore
   Service Flags: Kernel Driver,
Shared Process
Fastfat (Boot file system)               Running   (Disabled)
   Error Severity: Normal
   Service Flags: File System Driver,
   Shared Process
Fd16_700 (SCSI miniport)               Stopped   (Disabled)
   Error Severity: Normal
   Service Flags: Kernel Driver,
   Shared Process
Fd7000ex (SCSI miniport)              Stopped   (Disabled)
   Error Severity: Normal
   Service Flags: Kernel Driver,
```

```
                    Shared Process
      Fd8xx (SCSI miniport)                   Stopped   (Disabled)
          Error Severity: Normal
          Service Flags: Kernel Driver,
          Shared Process
      flashpnt (SCSI miniport)                Stopped   (Disabled)
          Error Severity: Normal
          Service Flags: Kernel Driver,
          Shared Process
      Floppy (Primary disk)             Running   (System)
          Error Severity: Ignore
          Service Flags: Kernel Driver,
          Shared Process
      Ftdisk (Filter)             Stopped   (Disabled)
          Error Severity: Ignore
          Service Flags: Kernel Driver,
          Shared Process
      i8042 Keyboard and PS/2 Mouse Port
          Driver (Keyboard Port) Running          (System)
          System32\DRIVERS\i8042prt.sys
          Error Severity: Normal
          Service Flags: Kernel Driver,
          Shared Process
      Inport (Pointer Port)                 Stopped   (Disabled)
          Error Severity: Ignore
          Service Flags: Kernel Driver,
          Shared Process
      Jazzg300 (Video)                      Stopped   (Disabled)
          Error Severity: Ignore
          Service Flags: Kernel Driver,
          Shared Process
      Jazzg364 (Video)                      Stopped   (Disabled)
          Error Severity: Ignore
          Service Flags: Kernel Driver,
          Shared Process
      Jzvx1484 (Video)                      Stopped   (Disabled)
          Error Severity: Ignore
          Service Flags: Kernel Driver,
          Shared Process
      Keyboard Class Driver (Keyboard Class)  Running   (System)
          System32\DRIVERS\kbdclass.sys
          Error Severity: Normal
          Service Flags: Kernel Driver,
          Shared Process
      KSecDD (Base)                         Running   (System)
          Error Severity: Normal
          Service Flags: Kernel Driver,
          Shared Process
      LM78                                  Running   (Automatic)
          \??\C:\WINNT40\system32\drivers\lm78nt.sys
          Error Severity: Normal
          Service Flags: Kernel Driver,
          Shared Process
      mga (Video)                           Stopped   (Disabled)
```

```
                    Error Severity: Ignore
                    Service Flags: Kernel Driver,
                    Shared Process
        mga_mil (Video)                             Stopped    (Disabled)
                    Error Severity: Ignore
                    Service Flags: Kernel Driver,
                    Shared Process
        mitsumi (SCSI miniport)                     Stopped    (Disabled)
                    Error Severity: Normal
                    Service Flags: Kernel Driver,
                    Shared Process
        mkecr5xx (SCSI miniport)                    Stopped    (Disabled)
                    Error Severity: Normal
                    Service Flags: Kernel Driver,
                    Shared Process
        Modem (Extended base)                       Stopped    (Manual)
                    Error Severity: Ignore
                    Service Flags: Kernel Driver,
                    Shared Process
        Mouse Class Driver (Pointer Class)          Running    (System)
                    System32\DRIVERS\mouclass.sys
                    Error Severity: Normal
                    Service Flags: Kernel Driver,
                    Shared Process
        Msfs (File system)                          Running    (System)
                    Error Severity: Normal
                    Service Flags: File System Driver,
                    Shared Process
        Mup (Network)                               Running    (Manual)
                    C:\WINNT40\System32\drivers\mup.sys
                    Error Severity: Normal
                    Service Flags: File System Driver,
                    Shared Process
        Ncr53c9x (SCSI miniport)                    Stopped    (Disabled)
                    Error Severity: Normal
                    Service Flags: Kernel Driver,
                    Shared Process
        ncr77c22 (Video)                            Stopped    (Disabled)
                    Error Severity: Ignore
                    Service Flags: Kernel Driver,
                    Shared Process
        Ncrc700 (SCSI miniport)                     Stopped    (Disabled)
                    Error Severity: Normal
                    Service Flags: Kernel Driver,
                    Shared Process
        Ncrc710 (SCSI miniport)                     Stopped    (Disabled)
                    Error Severity: Normal
                    Service Flags: Kernel Driver,
                    Shared Process
        Microsoft NDIS System Driver (NDIS)
                    Service Flags: Kernel Driver,
                    Shared Process
        Microsoft NDIS TAPI driver (NDIS)           Running    (System)
                    C:\WINNT40\system32\drivers\ndistapi.sys
```

```
                 Error Severity: Normal
                 Service Flags: Kernel Driver,
                 Shared Process
Remote Access WAN Wrapper (NDISWAN)     Running   (Automatic)
                 C:\WINNT40\system32\drivers\ndiswan.sys
                 Error Severity: Normal
                 Service Flags: Kernel Driver,
                 Shared Process
NetBIOS Interface (NetBIOSGroup)     Running   (Manual)
                 C:\WINNT40\System32\drivers\netbios.sys
                 Error Severity: Normal
                 Service Flags: File System Driver,
                 Shared Process
                 Group Dependencies:
                     TDI
WINS Client(TCP/IP) (PNP_TDI)        Running   (Automatic)
                 C:\WINNT40\System32\drivers\netbt.sys
                 Error Severity: Normal
                 Service Flags: Kernel Driver,
Shared Process
                 Service Dependencies:
                     Tcpip
NetDetect                            Stopped   (Manual)
                 C:\WINNT40\system32\drivers\netdtect.sys
                 Error Severity: Normal
                 Service Flags: Kernel Driver,
                 Shared Process
Npfs (File system)                   Running   (System)
                 Error Severity: Normal
                 Service Flags: File System Driver,
                 Shared Process
Ntfs (File system)                   Stopped   (Disabled)
                 Error Severity: Normal
                 Service Flags: File System Driver,
                 Shared Process
Null (Base)                          Running   (System)
                 Error Severity: Normal
                 Service Flags: Kernel Driver,
                 Shared Process
Oliscsi (SCSI miniport)              Stopped   (Disabled)
                 Error Severity: Normal
                 Service Flags: Kernel Driver,
                 Shared Process
Parallel (Extended base)             Running   (Automatic)
                 Error Severity: Ignore
                 Service Flags: Kernel Driver,
                 Shared Process
                 Service Dependencies:
                     Parport
                 Group Dependencies:
                     Parallel arbitrator
Parport (Parallel arbitrator)        Running   (Automatic)
                 Error Severity: Ignore
                 Service Flags: Kernel Driver,
```

```
                    Shared Process
        ParVdm (Extended base)                Running   (Automatic)
           Error Severity: Ignore
           Service Flags: Kernel Driver,
           Shared Process
           Service Dependencies:
              Parport
           Group Dependencies:
              Parallel arbitrator
        PCIDump (PCI Configuration)           Stopped   (System)
           Error Severity: Ignore
           Service Flags: Kernel Driver,
           Shared Process
        Pcmcia (System Bus Extender)          Stopped   (Disabled)
           Error Severity: Normal
           Service Flags: Kernel Driver,
           Shared Process
        PIIXIDE (SCSI miniport)               Running   (Boot)
           C:\WINNT40\system32\drivers\PIIXIDE.SYS
           Error Severity: Normal
           Service Flags: Kernel Driver,
           Shared Process
        PnP ISA Enabler Driver (Base)         Stopped   (System)
           Error Severity: Ignore
           Service Flags: Kernel Driver,
           Shared Process
        psidisp (Video)                       Stopped   (Disabled)
           Error Severity: Ignore
           Service Flags: Kernel Driver,
           Shared Process
        Ql10wnt (SCSI miniport)               Stopped   (Disabled)
           Error Severity: Normal
           Service Flags: Kernel Driver,
           Shared Process
        qv (Video)                            Stopped   (Disabled)
           Error Severity: Ignore
           Service Flags: Kernel Driver,
           Shared Process
        Remote Access Auto Connection Driver
           (Streams Drivers) Running          (Automatic)
           C:\WINNT40\system32\drivers\rasacd.sys
           Error Severity: Normal
           Service Flags: Kernel Driver,
           Shared Process
        Remote Access ARP Service (PNP_TDI)   Running   (Automatic)
           C:\WINNT40\system32\drivers\rasarp.sys
           Error Severity: Normal
           Service Flags: Kernel Driver,
            Shared Process
           Service Dependencies:
              TCPIP
        Rdr (Network)                         Running   (Manual)
           C:\WINNT40\System32\drivers\rdr.sys
           Error Severity: Normal
```

```
                    Service Flags: File System Driver,
                    Shared Process
                 s3 (Video)                            Stopped    (Disabled)
                    Error Severity: Ignore
                    Service Flags: Kernel Driver,
                    Shared Process
                 S3Inc (Video)                         Running    (System)
                    System32\DRIVERS\s3mini.sys
                    Error Severity: Normal
                    Service Flags: Kernel Driver,
                    Shared Process
                 Scsiprnt (Extended base)              Stopped    (Automatic)
                    Error Severity: Ignore
                    Service Flags: Kernel Driver,
                    Shared Process
                    Group Dependencies:
                      SCSI miniport
                 Scsiscan (SCSI Class)                  Stopped    (System)
                    Error Severity: Ignore
                    Service Flags: Kernel Driver,
                    Shared Process
                    Group Dependencies:
                      SCSI miniport
                 Serial (Extended base)                 Running    (Automatic)
                    Error Severity: Ignore
                    Service Flags: Kernel Driver,
                    Shared Process
                 Sermouse (Pointer Port)               Stopped    (Disabled)
                    Error Severity: Ignore
                    Service Flags: Kernel Driver,
                    Shared Process
                 Sfloppy (Primary disk)                Stopped    (System)
                    Error Severity: Ignore
                    Service Flags: Kernel Driver,
                    Shared Process
                    Group Dependencies:
                      SCSI miniport
                 Simbad (Filter)                       Stopped    (Disabled)
                    Error Severity: Normal
                    Service Flags: Kernel Driver,
                    Shared Process
                 slcd32 (SCSI miniport)                Stopped    (Disabled)
                    Error Severity: Normal
                    Service Flags: Kernel Driver,
                    Shared Process
                 Sparrow (SCSI miniport)                Stopped    (Disabled)
                    Error Severity: Normal
                    Service Flags: Kernel Driver,
                    Shared Process
                 Spock (SCSI miniport)                  Stopped    (Disabled)
                    Error Severity: Normal
                    Service Flags: Kernel Driver,
                    Shared Process
                 Srv (Network)                          Running    (Manual)
```

```
                    C:\WINNT40\System32\drivers\srv.sys
                    Error Severity: Normal
                    Service Flags: File System Driver,
                    Shared Process
              symc810 (SCSI miniport)              Stopped    (Disabled)
                    Error Severity: Normal
                    Service Flags: Kernel Driver,
                    Shared Process
              T128 (SCSI miniport)                 Stopped    (Disabled)
                    Error Severity: Normal
                    Service Flags: Kernel Driver,
                    Shared Process
              T13B (SCSI miniport)                 Stopped    (Disabled)
                    Error Severity: Normal
                    Service Flags: Kernel Driver,
                    Shared Process
              TCP/IP Service (PNP_TDI)             Running   (Automatic)
                    C:\WINNT40\System32\drivers\tcpip.sys
                    Error Severity: Normal
                    Service Flags: Kernel Driver,
                    Shared Process
              tga (Video)                          Stopped    (Disabled)
                    Error Severity: Ignore
                    Service Flags: Kernel Driver,
                    Shared Process
              tmv1 (SCSI miniport)                Stopped   (Disabled)
                    Error Severity: Normal
                    Service Flags: Kernel Driver,
                    Shared Process
              Ultra124 (SCSI miniport)           Stopped   (Disabled)
                    Error Severity: Normal
                    Service Flags: Kernel Driver,
                    Shared Process
              Ultra14f (SCSI miniport)           Stopped   (Disabled)
                    Error Severity: Normal
                    Service Flags: Kernel Driver,
                    Shared Process
              Ultra24f (SCSI miniport)           Stopped   (Disabled)
                    Error Severity: Normal
                    Service Flags: Kernel Driver,
                    Shared Process
              v7vram (Video)                      Stopped   (Disabled)
                    Error Severity: Ignore
                    Service Flags: Kernel Driver,
                     Shared Process
              VgaSave (Video Save)                Running   (System)
                    C:\WINNT40\System32\drivers\vga.sys
                    Error Severity: Ignore
                    Service Flags: Kernel Driver,
                    Shared Process
              VgaStart (Video Init)              Stopped    (System)
                    C:\WINNT40\System32\drivers\vga.sys
                    Error Severity: Ignore
                    Service Flags: Kernel Driver,
```

```
                     Shared Process
     Wd33c93 (SCSI miniport)                   Stopped    (Disabled)
        Error Severity: Normal
        Service Flags: Kernel Driver,
        Shared Process
     wd90c24a (Video)                          Stopped    (Disabled)
        Error Severity: Ignore
        Service Flags: Kernel Driver,
        Shared Process
     wdvga (Video)                             Stopped    (Disabled)
        Error Severity: Ignore
        Service Flags: Kernel Driver,
        Shared Process
     weitekp9 (Video)                        Stopped    (Disabled)
        Error Severity: Ignore
        Service Flags: Kernel Driver, Shared Process
     Xga (Video)                                Stopped    (Disabled)
        Error Severity: Ignore
        Service Flags: Kernel Driver, Shared Process
     -----------------------------------------------------------------
     IRQ and Port Report
     -----------------------------------------------------------------
     Devices                   Vector Level  Affinity
     -----------------------------------------------------------------
     i8042prt                       1       1 0xffffffff
     i8042prt                      12      12 0xffffffff
     Serial                         4       4 0x00000000
     cs32ba11                      55       7 0x00000001
     E100B                         10      10 0x00000000
     Floppy                         6       6 0x00000000
     PIIXIDE                        0      14 0x00000000
     PIIXIDE                        0      15 0x00000000
     -----------------------------------------------------------------
     Devices                   Physical Address  Length
     -----------------------------------------------------------------
     i8042prt                  0x00000060  0x0000000001
     i8042prt                  0x00000064  0x0000000001
     Parport                   0x000003bc  0x0000000003
     Serial                    0x000003f8  0x0000000007
     cs32ba11                  0x00000530  0x0000000008
     cs32ba11                  0x00000388  0x0000000004
     E100B                     0x0000ff40  0x0000000014
     Floppy                    0x000003f0  0x0000000006
     Floppy                    0x000003f7  0x0000000001
     LM78                      0x00000295  0x0000000002
     PIIXIDE                   0x000001f0  0x0000000008
     PIIXIDE                   0x0000ffa0  0x0000000008
     PIIXIDE                   0x00000170  0x0000000008
     PIIXIDE                   0x0000ffa8  0x0000000008
     S3Inc                     0x000003c0  0x0000000010
     S3Inc                     0x000003d4  0x0000000008
     VgaSave                   0x000003b0  0x000000000c
     VgaSave                   0x000003c0  0x0000000020
     VgaSave                   0x000001ce  0x0000000002
```

```
--------------------------------------------------------------------------
DMA and Memory Report
--------------------------------------------------------------------------
Devices                         Channel    Port
--------------------------------------------------------------------------
cs32ball                          1         0
cs32ball                          0         0
Floppy                            2         0
--------------------------------------------------------------------------
Devices                         Physical Address   Length
--------------------------------------------------------------------------
E100B                           0xffbef000   0x00000014
E100B                           0xffbef000   0x00000014
S3Inc                           0x000a0000   0x00010000
S3Inc                           0x000c0000   0x00008000
VgaSave                         0x000a0000   0x00020000
--------------------------------------------------------------------------
Environment Report
--------------------------------------------------------------------------
System Environment Variables
    ComSpec=C:\WINNT40\system32\cmd.exe
    Os2LibPath=C:\WINNT40\system32\os2\dll;
    Path=C:\WINNT40\SYSTEM32;C:\WINNT40;C:\SVA\DMI\BIN
    windir=C:\WINNT40
    OS=Windows_NT
    PROCESSOR_ARCHITECTURE=x86
    PROCESSOR_LEVEL=6
    PROCESSOR_IDENTIFIER=x86 Family 6 Model 3 Stepping 3,GenuineIntel
    PROCESSOR_REVISION=0303
    NUMBER_OF_PROCESSORS=1
    help=c:\ipfwin\help
    ipf_path=c:\ipfwin
Environment Variables for Current User
    TEMP=C:\TEMP
    TMP=C:\TEMP
--------------------------------------------------------------------------
Network Report
--------------------------------------------------------------------------
Your Access Level: Admin & Local (total control!)
Workgroup or Domain: INFO
Network Version: 4.0
LanRoot: INFO
Logged On Users: 1
Current User (1): Administrator
  Logon Domain: ANGEL
  Logon Server: ANGEL
 Transport: NetBT_E100B1,00-60-94-45-43-F3, VC's: 0, Wan: Wan
Character Wait: 3,600
Collection Time: 250
Maximum Collection Count: 16
Keep Connection: 600
Maximum Commands: 5
Session Time Out: 45
Character Buffer Size: 512
```

```
Maximum Threads: 17
Lock Quota: 6,144
Lock Increment: 10
Maximum Locks: 500
Pipe Increment: 10
Maximum Pipes: 500
Cache Time Out: 40
Dormant File Limit: 45
Read Ahead Throughput: 4,294,967,295
Mailslot Buffers: 3
Server Announce Buffers: 20
Illegal Datagrams: 5
Datagram Reset Frequency: 60
Log Election Packets: False
Use Opportunistic Locking: True
Use Unlock Behind: True
Use Close Behind: True
Buffer Pipes: True
Use Lock, Read, Unlock: True
Use NT Caching: True
Use Raw Read: True
Use Raw Write: True
Use Write Raw Data: True
Use Encryption: True
Buffer Deny Write Files: True
Buffer Read Only Files: True
Force Core Creation: True
512 Byte Max Transfer: False
Bytes Received: 1,028
SMB's Received: 9
Paged Read Bytes Requested: 0
Non Paged Read Bytes Requested: 0
Cache Read Bytes Requested: 0
Network Read Bytes Requested: 0
Bytes Transmitted: 1,133
SMB's Transmitted: 9
Paged Read Bytes Requested: 0
Non Paged Read Bytes Requested: 0
Cache Read Bytes Requested: 0
Network Read Bytes Requested: 0
Initally Failed Operations: 0
Failed Completion Operations: 0
Read Operations: 0
Random Read Operations: 0
Read SMB's: 0
Large Read SMB's: 0
Small Read SMB's: 0
Write Operations: 0
Random Write Operations: 0
Write SMB's: 0
Large Write SMB's: 0
Small Write SMB's: 0
Raw Reads Denied: 0
Raw Writes Denied: 0
```

```
Network Errors: 0
Sessions: 2
Failed Sessions: 0
Reconnects: 0
Core Connects: 0
LM 2.0 Connects: 0
LM 2.x Connects: 0
Windows NT Connects: 2
Server Disconnects: 0
Hung Sessions: 0
Use Count: 2
Failed Use Count: 0
Current Commands: 0
Server File Opens: 0
Server Device Opens: 0
Server Jobs Queued: 0
Server Session Opens: 0
Server Sessions Timed Out: 0
Server Sessions Errored Out: 0
Server Password Errors: 0
Server Permission Errors: 0
Server System Errors: 0
Server Bytes Sent: 249
Server Bytes Received: 477
Server Average Response Time: 0
Server Request Buffers Needed: 0
Server Big Buffers Needed: 0
```

The requirements of the network meant Windows 95 and NT workstation were determined to be the best operating systems to use. Consider some highlights of the Windows NT workstation.

Windows NT version 4 could be the standard by which other operating systems are judged. It has the look and feel of an interface of Windows 95. This version of NT has robust features and is seperated into the NT server and the NT workstation.

Common characteristics between them are:

- Advanced file handling systems
- Back-up capabilities
- C2 security
- Graphical user interface tools
- Network capabilities
- Remote access capabilities
- TCP/IP.

More detailed information can be obtained from Microsoft by visiting www.microsoft.com.

Network Printer

An IBM model 17 was determined to be the best printer for the network. The following features and functions factored into that reasoning during the decision process.

- 17 pages per minute
- 600 x 600 resolution
- Up to 5 addressable input trays
- 4MB RAM (optional to 66 MB)
- PCL5e standard language (postscript, IPDS, SCS optional)
- Auto language switching with options
- Auto I/O switching
- Standard parallel with two network interface slots.

The following options were added to make the printer capable of meeting the needs of all users on the network.

- 75 envelope feeder
- Ethernet interface
- Token ring interface
- 24 MB RAM
- Postscript language option level 2
- 500-sheet second paper tray
- Duplex unit
- 10-bin secured mailbox unit.

This printer arrived on a pallet weighing approximately 250 lbs (entire pallet weight). The printer itself is 40.9 lbs (18.6 kg). With all options installed the dimensions are: 31" height, 25" front-to-back, and 17" wide and weight about 65 lbs. (These are my measurements made including space for rear cabling, etc. and are approximations.)

The printer was chosen because of its flexibility and power. It supports IPDS and SCS character strings. This is valuable because if the network should need a system which uses either of these character strings for printing the printer can already handle the job.

Intelligent Printer Data Stream (IPDS) is used between an IBM host and a printer; generally this refers to an SNA environment. This data stream is used with an all-points addressable printer. IPDS can intermix text and graphics—both vector- and raster-based. An SCS character string is a protocol used with printers and certain terminals in the SNA environment. LU1 and LU6.2 can use this data stream. One unique aspect of this data stream is its lack of data-flow control functions. The significance of the Model 17 printer should not be overlooked. When the need arises for a host running MVS and VTAM the *current* printer can be used. Here is another example of building success into the network.

Because the printer is on the network all network users can take advantage of it. If might be off-site, want to work on the network from a remote location, print something to someone and have that document secure. The printer makes this possible (see Figure 7.1).

FIGURE 7.1
Remote Users
Using the
Network Printer

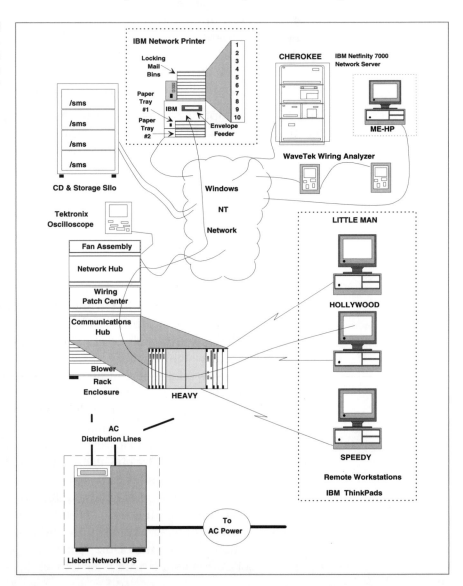

Figure 7.1 shows a remote user connecting via a switched line to the network. The "network" in this example is viewed as the equipment in the rack enclosure. However, the network includes all devices participating in it. This example shows *Hollywood* sending a file to the network printer. All the remote users have the same capability to interact with the network printer.

Users onsite where the printer is installed have free access to it, with the exception of those who require secured access through the mailbox feature.

Electrical Considerations for the Network Printer

Knowing actual electrical printer requirements is important. Consider the information here, actual readings I took specifically for the purpose of use here as an example. I used the Tektronix THS720P Oscilloscope for these readings.

Figure 7.2 shows the voltage and frequency readings of the line supplying voltage to the printer. These readings were taken minutes prior to turning on the printer.

FIGURE 7.2
Baseline Voltage
Readings

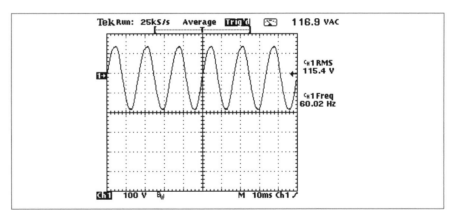

Figure 7.3 shows not only the voltage and frequency reading, but also the amperage reading as shown by channel 2 (ch2), 5.249 amps. This reading was taken upon immediate power-on of the printer.

Figure 7.4 shows amperage and voltage readings when the drum cycled to heat itself back to printing temperature; the amperage draw is 6.961 amps.

FIGURE 7.3
Amperage and
Voltage Readings
Upon Power-on

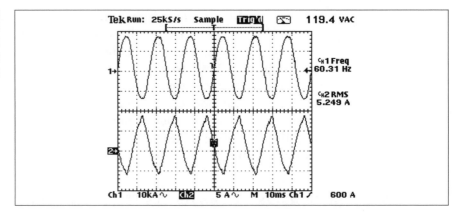

FIGURE 7.4
Amperage and
Voltage Readings
with Drum
Heating

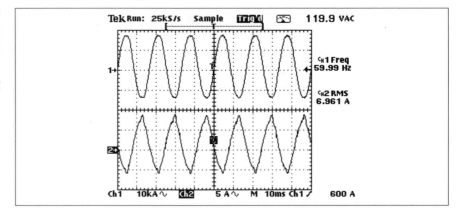

Figure 7.5 shows still another reading made while monitoring the oscilloscope for a period of about 10 minutes. This is a "random" reading; there was no meaningful correlation to anything I did. I was surprised at the reading, but it is real and is actual documentation of a real event in the electrical considerations for this printer. No other devices were drawing current on the line when I took these readings. The oscilloscope itself was running on battery power. Consider Figure 7.6.

I decided to take a temperature reading while measuring the environment around the printer. I repositioned the temperature probe near the printer. The temperature of the area near the printer was 77.9° Fahrenheit.

FIGURE 7.5
Random
Amperage and
Voltage Readings

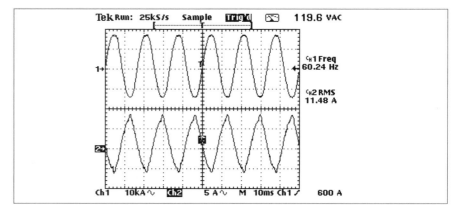

FIGURE 7.6
Temperature
Readings Near
the Printer

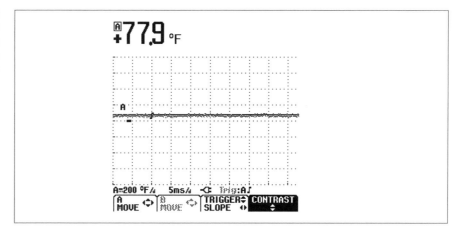

The significance of this electrical information should not be understated. You need to know the electrical requirements of your network equipment. You may think that computers and network devices don't use much electricity, and for the most part this is true. However, electrical requirements for each device should be known. This information is presented as an aid to planing for a network printer.

Author's Comment

The IBM Model 17 printer arrived on a pallet as described previously. From time of delivery until the printer was operational one person day elapsed. I estimate about 2 hours for unpacking the printer and reading material IBM recommends before beginning. Assembling the various components (accessories) for the printer was easy. IBM designed the printer so that minimal tools are needed to install it. It will probably require longer to configure the printer and integrate the network workstations and servers than to set up the printer.

The weight and amount of space the printer requires is also important to consider. This information should encourage you to think through plans before receiving equipment at your site.

For further information, visit www.ibm.com.

Network and Computer Security (McAfee)

Computer and network security are vital. Viruses, bots, and all sorts of anti-data objects exist within the Internet. Most people have no idea how vulnerable parts of the Internet are. Even "service providers" are more vulnerable than they will admit. There is no *magic program* or anything else that can make networks safe. Good programs exist, the ones chosen and implemented in this network are an example; but no single program can make your network 100% immune.

Remember this during the design phase of your network. Security in your network needs to be factored into every area from electricity provision to telephone access and every other aspect that categorizes your network.

The McAfee software suite was selected because of a number of anti-virus programs and the amount of information available and useful. McAfee also continuously updates the antivirus software. McAfee has over 250 documents available on viruses and information about the 1,000 most common viruses. When the security analysis for this network was complete, the following software packages were selected:

- VirusScan
- Desktop Security Suite
- Commuter
- QuickBackup
- McAfee Service Desk
- NetShield
- WEBScan
- PCCrypto.

These products have been implemented to varying degrees on each system. Each program's benefits and highlights are presented here.

VirusScan

This program, arguably the most popular antivirus software in the marketplace, operates with Windows 3.1, 95, Windows NT4.0, DOS, and OS/2. Once installed, it operates automatically upon power-up. It can be used at will once a system is operational, requires minimal space, does a professional job and is NCSAA certified.

Desktop Security Suite

This also operates with Windows 3.1, 95, and NT4.0. It includes antivirus software, backup abilities, and encryption technology. The virus program is VirusScan. QuickBackup operates with Zip, Jaz, the Internet, or rewritable CD-ROMs. The backup program enables back-up hourly or on demand. The cryptographic part of the suite provides 160-bit encryption and enables users to encrypt files before sending them over the Internet. The PC cryptographic part permits network traffic to be encrypted between Windows-based computers and those running UNIX.

Commuter

Commuter is not only a communication software, but also includes virus protection, desktop storage management, electronic mail, a personal information organizer, calendar, to-do-list, and a contact manager.

QuickBackup

This backup program works with Windows 95 and NT4.0. It enables transparent backup of files to SCSI, Zip, and Jaz drives. An icon-driven program makes for ease of use. The program installs quickly, works well and provides encryption protection and Internet support.

Service Desk

The powerful service desk product is actually multiple products in one box. It works with Windows 3.1, 95, and NT4.0, letting customer support personnel have access to information about customers and make a remote connection to a system reported with a problem. The package comes with the ability to distribute software and also includes a system-diagnostic part for support personnel to use with customers.

NetShield

Netshield uses McAfee's proprietary code, Code Trace, Code Matrix and Code Poly. The product operates in an NT environment in native mode and takes full advantage of NT's server/client remote task distribution capability. It supports real-time scanning during operation of other tasks.

WEBScan

The WEBScan product is designed to detect viruses within a browser. It examines downloads and e-mail attachments, making it a powerful addition to any desktop or laptop system communicating in networks today. It also provides a cybersitter that blocks out unwanted websites and chat groups. The program includes examination of .doc, lzip., exe., zrc., arj. and other file types.

PCCrypto

PCCrypto is used to secure documents and other data files created by anyone using computers. It can encrypt graphics, spreadsheets, and text documents using a 160-bit blowfish encryption mechanism. The package consumes a minimal amount of space and is one of the most powerful, tools of its kind on the market.

Author's Policy

McAfee has other products that may meet your needs. They can be reached at: www.mcafee.com; or write, McAfee, 2710 Walsh Avenue, Santa Clara, CA 95051, (408) 988-3832; or McAfee Canada, 178 Main Street, Unionville, Ontario, L3R 2G9 Canada; or McAfee France S. A., 50 rue de Londres, 75008 Paris, France; or McAfee (UK) Ltd., Hayley House, London Road, Bracknell, Berkshire, GR12 2TH, U.K.; or McAfee Europe B. V., Orlypein 81 - Busitel 1, 1043 DS Amsterdam, Netherlands; or McAfee Deutschland GmbH, Industriestrasse 1, D-82110 Germering, Germany.

Multimedia Components (Creative Labs)

In the arena of multimedia, Creative Labs wrote the book on how-to-do-it. Since multimedia is currently primarily an add-on, systems do not depend on multimedia as they do the hard disk or monitor.

However, some multimedia clone products exist. Many attempt to copy what Creative Labs has already designed. But multimedia "clone" equipment may not be able to execute all exploits of multimedia.

Today, systems typically have CD-ROMs, speakers, microphones, line outputs for amplifiers, line inputs for peripheral integration, and software that enables users to create, play back, and listen to and see various data streams.

All the desktop systems in this network are IBM 350 series; selected these because each one would be customized to deliver a robust workload. Another reason for choosing this series was the upgrade capability. It is the same with Creative Labs equipment.

In each system Creative Lab's equipment is the multimedia hardware and software. One has a package of multimedia equipment which includes an interface board, speakers, necessary cabling, microphone, CD-ROM, infrared remote control, software drivers, and various software titles for viewing and listening.

Windows 95 and NT4.0 acknowledge most Creative Labs hardware and software. It is plug-and-play compatible. Creative Labs is continually upgrading its equipment to stay in line with other vendors; the equipment also supports products that are not this year's model.

Multimedia is more than a CD-ROM and speakers; today it typically encompasses a digital video disc (DVD) and enhanced display support. More than at any other time, displays need powerful drivers and memory to store the screen of information to be presented.

Creative Labs is based in California, but has offices worldwide. You can visit www.soundblaster.com or write Creative Labs, 1901 McCarthy Blvd., Milpitas, CA 95035; or Creative Technology Ltd., 67 Ayer Rajah Crescent #03-18, Singapore 0513, Malaysia; or Creative Labs Technical Support, 1523 Cimarron Plaza, Stillwater, OK 74075; or Creative Labs Ltd., Blanchardstown Industrial Park, Blanchardstown, Dublin 15, Ireland.

Network Storage (SMS Data Products Group)

Network storage is an important topic today and will become more so in the years ahead. Factors influencing my decision to use SMS products included the simplicity of their products; installation and operation are easy. This is a boon, because networking is complex enough without adding complexity to the network.

The knowledge and helpfulness of SMS personnel also influenced my decision. So did the fact that SMS has been in business for close to 20 years. This industry (networking as it is known today) is a relatively new phenomenon. For this company to have been in business in this area since the mid-70s says something about the company itself.

Figure 7.7 shows the SMS server, connected to the network and the network server. It has dual port connectivity and supports 10/100 Ethernet speeds. The connection to the network server is SCSI. The system used in this network has not only CDs but also a barracuda hard drive, recordable CD, and a Jaz drive.

Figure 7.8 shows an SMS system connected to the Netfinity 7000 and the Netfinity connected to the network via a four-port network adapter. I configured the silo to operate this way. As the illustration shows, the network users can access the silo if they have access through the Cherokee.

SMS has a variety of network products; those used in this example are representative of what the company offers. For further information visit www.sms.com; or write SMS Data Products Group, 1501 Farm Credit Drive, McLean, VA 22102, 800-331-1767.

Network Wiring Analyzer (Wavetek)

Networks require wiring to function. My network needed a powerful wiring analyzer to make sure the wiring used was in proper working order and met specifications. The WaveTek LANTek PROL XL is a powerful tool consisting of battery-powered, hand-held units. It comes with software that enables the information captured about a given piece of cable to be uploaded onto a computer and saved and/or printed for further analysis.

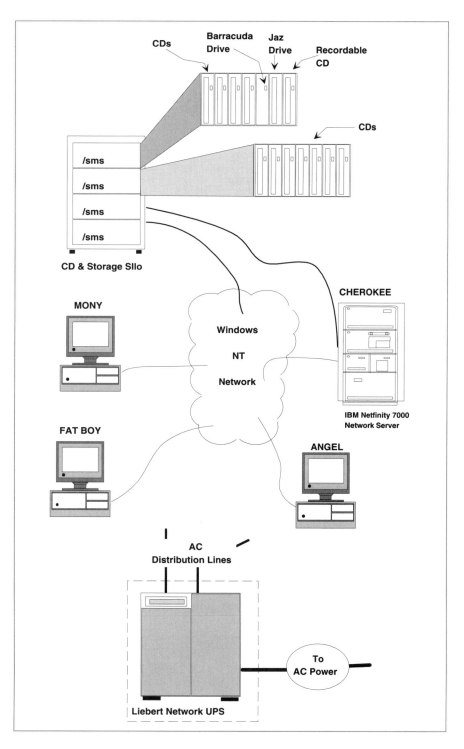

FIGURE 7.7
Network Storage

FIGURE 7.8
Network Storage
Connections

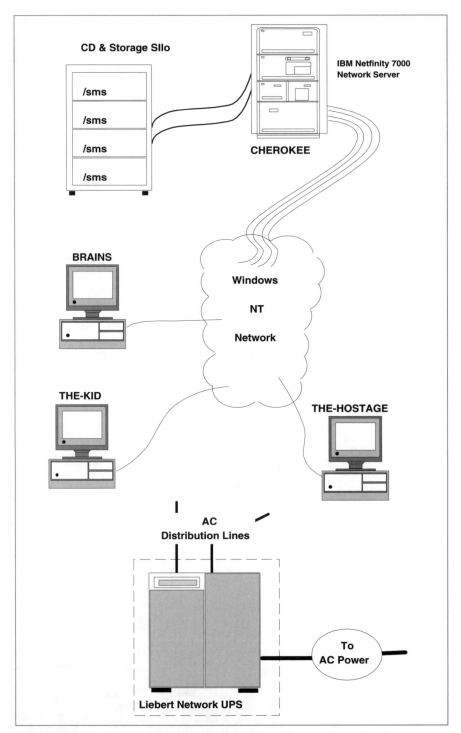

FIGURE 7.8
Network Storage
Connections

Figure 7.9 shows a test of a 10BASE-T cable. The line mapping, dual NEXT, worst case NEXT, attenuation, capacitance, length, loop resistance, and ACR readings are presented. This level of information is excellent and should be gotten on all cabling being installed into a network. If this information is obtained and saved, it can be used at a later date for reference.

FIGURE 7.9

Test #1 Reading

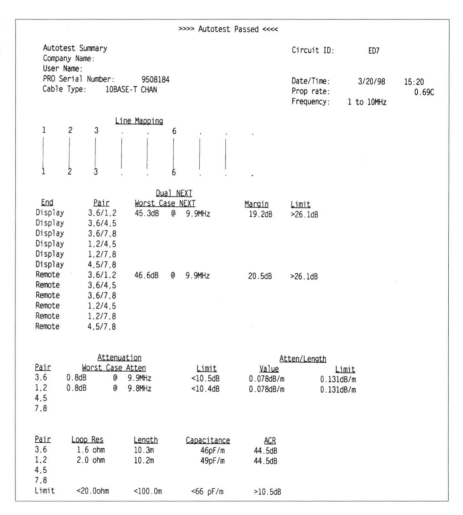

Figure 7.10 shows TIA CAT 5 cable results. The line mapping, dual NEXT, and other information provided are details for each pair of cable tested. Again, this information is invaluable when troubleshooting network wiring.

FIGURE 7.10
TIA CAT 5 Cable
Results

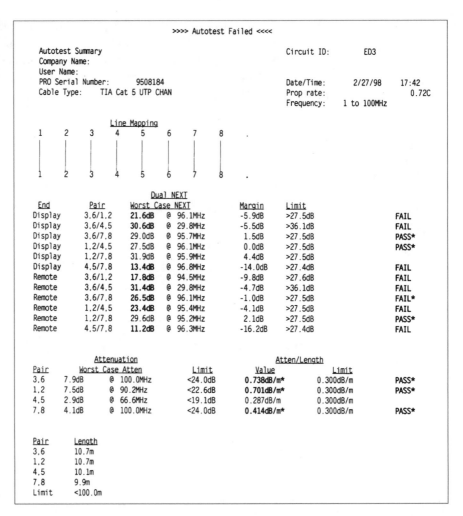

Figure 7.11 shows statistics for 10BASE-T cabling used in the network. Notice the display information and that provided by the remote end of the wire. The attenuation, loop resistance, and capacitance are pertinent when calculating the requirements for various needs of the network.

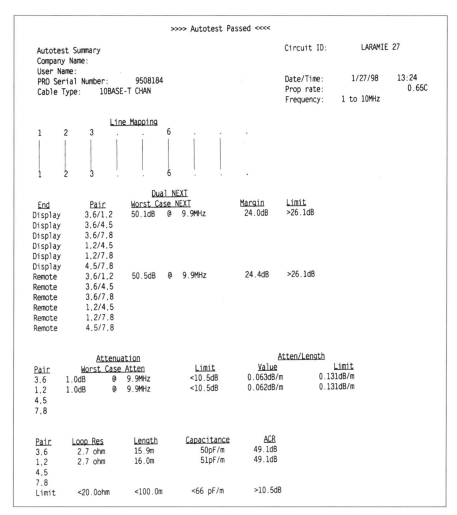

FIGURE 7.11
10BASE-T
Statistics

Figure 7.12 shows enhanced details for category 5 cable at both ends, from the display to the remote. Notice the statistics for the dual NEXT and worst-case dual NEXT readings. There is also a *fail* condition indicated to the right of the test results. I purposely used a cable to force a *fail* condition in order to show the in-depth results obtainable by the LANTek PRO XL.

FIGURE 7.12
Category 5
Statistics

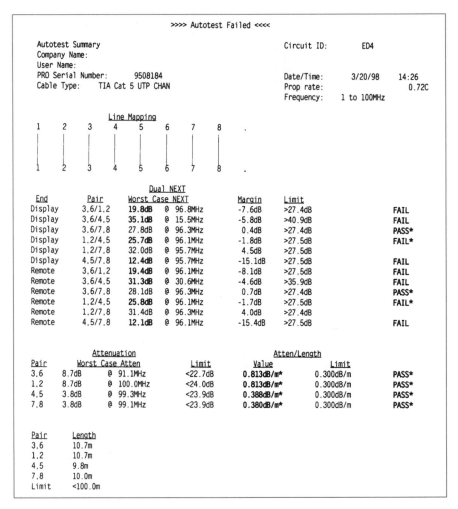

Figure 7.13 shows the results from measurement of a single pair. The line mapping and other statistics can serve as baseline information against which future information is measured during testing and evaluation.

Figure 7.14 is a detailed report for 10BASE-T. Notice the line mapping, attenuation and capacitance differ from those in other reports.

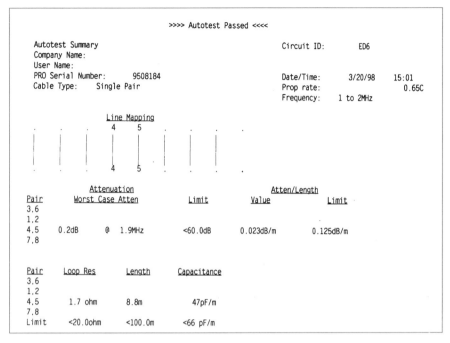

Many more tests can be obtained; it is a powerful tool invaluable during the initial phases of network installation and for performing tests during the life of the network. Additional information is available at www.wavetek.com; or write WaveTek Instruments and Datacommunications Division, 9045 Balboa Avenue, San Diego, CA 92123; or call 800-854-2708.

Troubleshooting Network Analyzer (Hewlett-Packard)

To design a network requires both abstract and practical skills. To keep a network operational at its peak is another thing. Obtaining information about an operational network is important. To be sure the information is accurate is more important.

Figure 7.15 is an actual snapshot on the network nodes participating at the time I took this sample with the HP Internet Advisor. Consider the following information. It is a network stack decode performed by the Internet Advisor. Notice it explains some functions of the *Cherokee*.

FIGURE 7.14
10BASE-T
Detailed Report

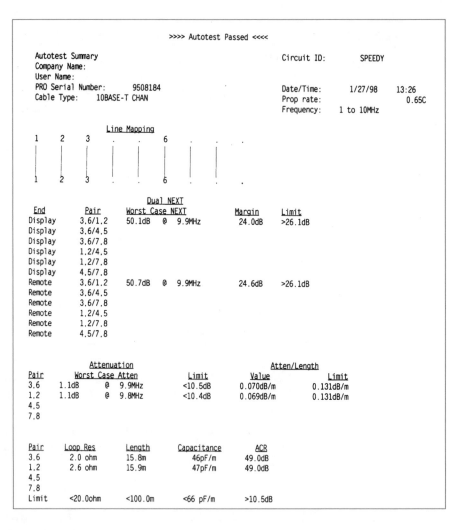

```
                              >>>> Autotest Passed <<<<

Autotest Summary                            Circuit ID:       SPEEDY
Company Name:
User Name:
PRO Serial Number:      9508184             Date/Time:    1/27/98    13:26
Cable Type:   10BASE-T CHAN                 Prop rate:                0.65C
                                            Frequency:    1 to 10MHz

                    Line Mapping
   1     2     3     .     .     6     .     .     .

   |     |     |     |     |     |     |     |     |

   1     2     3     .     .     6     .     .     .

                         Dual NEXT
   End       Pair     Worst Case NEXT          Margin      Limit
   Display   3,6/1,2   50.1dB   @   9.9MHz      24.0dB     >26.1dB
   Display   3,6/4,5
   Display   3,6/7,8
   Display   1,2/4,5
   Display   1,2/7,8
   Display   4,5/7,8
   Remote    3,6/1,2   50.7dB   @   9.9MHz      24.6dB     >26.1dB
   Remote    3,6/4,5
   Remote    3,6/7,8
   Remote    1,2/4,5
   Remote    1,2/7,8
   Remote    4,5/7,8


                  Attenuation                     Atten/Length
   Pair      Worst Case Atten      Limit        Value          Limit
   3,6    1.1dB     @   9.9MHz    <10.5dB     0.070dB/m      0.131dB/m
   1,2    1.1dB     @   9.8MHz    <10.4dB     0.069dB/m      0.131dB/m
   4,5
   7,8


   Pair    Loop Res     Length      Capacitance      ACR
   3,6     2.0 ohm      15.8m         46pF/m        49.0dB
   1,2     2.6 ohm      15.9m         47pF/m        49.0dB
   4,5
   7,8
   Limit   <20.0ohm    <100.0m       <66 pF/m      >10.5dB
```

FIGURE 7.15
Network Node
Discovery

```
..................................................................
                HEWLETT-PACKARD NETWORK ADVISOR

               Node Discovery measurement

                    10 nodes observed
..................................................................

        Address      Layer    Type/ID    Comment/Name
       _____  _____  _____  _____

    #   WstDigt--7D-73-D7    Ethernet
    #   220.100.100.8        IP
        FAT BOY              NetBIOS          FAT BOY


        BRAINS
    #   WstDigt--3A-B8-EC    Ethernet
    #   220.100.100.12       IP
        BRAINS               NetBIOS          BRAINS


        Broadcast
        FF-FF-FF-FF-00-00    Ethernet     All IP Stations
        Broadcast                         Taylor's Analyzer
        FF-FF-FF-FF-FF-FF    Ethernet


        CHEROKEE
        Ibm------A5-CC-EE    Ethernet
        220.100.100.53       IP
        CHEROKEE             NetBIOS          CHEROKEE


        MUSCLE
    #   WstDigt--4E-B5-EC    Ethernet
    #>  220.100.100.10       IP               BRAINS
    #>  MUSCLE               NetBIOS          MUSCLE


    >   RENEGADE
    *>  WstDigt--93-73-D7    Ethernet
    *>  220.100.100.79       IP           RENEGADE
    *>  RENEGADE             NetBIOS      RENEGADE


        SILO
        Axis-----25-67-D6    Ethernet
        220.100.100.150      IP
        SILO           NetBIOS            SILO


    >   SILO-1
    *>  Axis-----32-41-35    Ethernet
    *>  220.100.100.175      IP
    *>  SILO-1         NetBIOS            SILO-1


    >   SILO-2
    *>  Axis-----32-41-3F    Ethernet
    *>  220.100.100.180      IP
    *>  SILO-2         NetBIOS            SILO-2


        THE-HOSTAGE
    #   00-60-08-98-1D-33    Ethernet
    #   220.100.100.61       IP
    *>  00000000-006008981D33 IPX    0001    INFO
        THE-HOSTAGE          NetBIOS          THE-HOSTAGE


    >   THE-KID
    *>  00-00-D1-0F-E2-9B    Ethernet
    *>  220.100.100.77       IP

    *>  THE-KID              NetBIOS          THE-KID
        WstDigE99CB1                     Micro/PC
    #   WstDigt--E9-9C-B1    Ethernet
    *>  220.100.100.19       IP

    *>  00000000-0000C0E99CB1 IPX   0001         MONY
    >   *new 220.100.100.41
    *>  Ibm------45-43-F3    Ethernet
    *>  220.100.100.41       IP
```

```
******************************************************************
*****             HEWLETT PACKARD NETWORK ADVISOR         *****
*****                                                     *****
*****     Measurement:  Brief Network Stack Decode        *****
*****     Print Type:   All Frames                        *****
*****     Open Views:   Summary                           *****
*****     Display Mode: Viewing All Frames                *****
*****     Print Date:   03/20/98                          *****
*****     Print Time:   16:40:27                          *****
******************************************************************
1     36:18.087 WellfleetE8-8F-1C 01-80-C2-00-00-00 LLC C S=42 D=42 UI
2     36:20.025 WellfleetE8-8F-1C 01-80-C2-00-00-00 LLC C S=42 D=42 UI
3     36:22.025 WellfleetE8-8F-1C 01-80-C2-00-00-00 LLC C S=42 D=42 UI
4     36:24.004 00000000-CHEROKEE 00000000-Broadcast IPX RIP Response:
      1   network
5     36:24.025 WellfleetE8-8F-1C 01-80-C2-00-00-00 LLC C S=42 D=42 UI
6     36:26.025 WellfleetE8-8F-1C 01-80-C2-00-00-00 LLC C S=42 D=42 UI
7     36:28.025 WellfleetE8-8F-1C 01-80-C2-00-00-00 LLC C S=42 D=42 UI
8     36:29.413 WstDigt—93-73-D7 Broadcast ARP C PA=[220.100.100.10]
9     36:30.025 WellfleetE8-8F-1C 01-80-C2-00-00-00 LLC C S=42 D=42 UI
10    36:30.915 WstDigt—93-73-D7 Broadcast ARP C PA=[220.100.100.10]
11    36:32.025 WellfleetE8-8F-1C 01-80-C2-00-00-00 LLC C S=42 D=42 UI
12    36:32.418 WstDigt—93-73-D7 Broadcast ARP C PA=[220.100.100.10]
13    36:34.025 WellfleetE8-8F-1C 01-80-C2-00-00-00 LLC C S=42 D=42 UI
14    36:36.025 WellfleetE8-8F-1C 01-80-C2-00-00-00 LLC C S=42 D=42 UI
15    36:38.025 WellfleetE8-8F-1C 01-80-C2-00-00-00 LLC C S=42 D=42 UI
16    36:40.025 WellfleetE8-8F-1C 01-80-C2-00-00-00 LLC C S=42 D=42 UI
17    36:42.025 WellfleetE8-8F-1C 01-80-C2-00-00-00 LLC C S=42 D=42 UI
18    36:44.025 WellfleetE8-8F-1C 01-80-C2-00-00-00 LLC C S=42 D=42 UI
19    36:46.025 WellfleetE8-8F-1C 01-80-C2-00-00-00 LLC C S=42 D=42 UI
20    36:48.086 WellfleetE8-8F-1C 01-80-C2-00-00-00 LLC C S=42 D=42 UI
21    36:50.024 WellfleetE8-8F-1C 01-80-C2-00-00-00 LLC C S=42 D=42 UI
22    36:52.025 WellfleetE8-8F-1C 01-80-C2-00-00-00 LLC C S=42 D=42 UI
23    36:52.552 IP Multicast    Broadcast     BOOTP Request
24    36:54.024 WellfleetE8-8F-1C 01-80-C2-00-00-00 LLC C S=42 D=42 UI
25    36:56.024 WellfleetE8-8F-1C 01-80-C2-00-00-00 LLC C S=42 D=42 UI
26    36:58.024 WellfleetE8-8F-1C 01-80-C2-00-00-00 LLC C S=42 D=42 UI
27    37:00.024 WellfleetE8-8F-1C 01-80-C2-00-00-00 LLC C S=42 D=42 UI
28    37:02.024 WellfleetE8-8F-1C 01-80-C2-00-00-00 LLC C S=42 D=42 UI
29    37:04.024 WellfleetE8-8F-1C 01-80-C2-00-00-00 LLC C S=42 D=42 UI
30    37:06.024 WellfleetE8-8F-1C 01-80-C2-00-00-00 LLC C S=42 D=42 UI
31    37:08.024 WellfleetE8-8F-1C 01-80-C2-00-00-00 LLC C S=42 D=42 UI
32    37:09.487 CHEROKEE  Broadcast  ARP C PA=[220.100.100.10]
33    37:10.024 WellfleetE8-8F-1C 01-80-C2-00-00-00 LLC C S=42 D=42 UI
34    37:10.987 CHEROKEE  Broadcast   ARP C PA=[220.100.100.10]
35    37:12.024 WellfleetE8-8F-1C 01-80-C2-00-00-00 LLC C S=42 D=42 UI
36    37:12.487 CHEROKEE  Broadcast   ARP C PA=[220.100.100.10]
37    37:13.987 CHEROKEE  Broadcast   ARP C PA=[220.100.100.10]
38    37:14.024 WellfleetE8-8F-1C 01-80-C2-00-00-00 LLC C S=42 D=42 UI
39    37:15.487 CHEROKEE  Broadcast   ARP C PA=[220.100.100.10]
40    37:16.024 WellfleetE8-8F-1C 01-80-C2-00-00-00 LLC C S=42 D=42 UI
41    37:16.987 CHEROKEE  Broadcast   ARP C PA=[220.100.100.10]
42    37:17.539 CHEROKEE       220.100.100.255  NETB Datagram
43    37:18.086 WellfleetE8-8F-1C 01-80-C2-00-00-00 LLC C S=42 D=42 UI
```

```
44   37:18.487 CHEROKEE  Broadcast     ARP C PA=[220.100.100.10]
45   37:18.851 00000000-CHEROKEE 00000000-Broadcast SMB C
46   37:19.347 CHEROKEE 03-00-00-00-00-01 NETB Datagram CHEROKEE-
     JSPNRMPTGSBSSDIR
47   37:19.987 CHEROKEE  Broadcast     ARP C PA=[220.100.100.10]
48   37:20.024 WellfleetE8-8F-1C 01-80-C2-00-00-00 LLC C S=42 D=42 UI
49   37:21.487 CHEROKEE  Broadcast     ARP C PA=[220.100.100.10]
50   37:21.846 CHEROKEE  03-00-00-00-00-01 NETB Name query SILO-1
51   37:21.846 00000000-CHEROKEE 00000000-Broadcast NETB Find Name
     SILO-1
52   37:22.024 WellfleetE8-8F-1C 01-80-C2-00-00-00 LLC C S=42 D=42 UI
53   37:22.409 00000000-CHEROKEE 00000000-Broadcast NETB Find Name
     SILO-1
54   37:22.971 00000000-CHEROKEE 00000000-Broadcast NETB Find Name
     SILO-1
55   37:22.987 CHEROKEE  Broadcast     ARP C PA=[220.100.100.10]
56   37:24.003 00000000-CHEROKEE 00000000-Broadcast IPX RIP Response:
     1 network
57   37:24.024 WellfleetE8-8F-1C 01-80-C2-00-00-00 LLC C S=42 D=42 UI
58   37:24.487 CHEROKEE Broadcast      ARP C PA=[220.100.100.10]
59   37:25.987 CHEROKEE Broadcast      ARP C PA=[220.100.100.10]
60   37:26.024 Wellfleet E8-8F-1C 01-80-C2-00-00-00 LLC C S=42 D=42 UI
61   37:27.487 CHEROKEE Broadcast      ARP C PA=[220.100.100.10]
62   37:28.024 Wellfleet E8-8F-1C 01-80-C2-00-00-00 LLC C S=42 D=42 UI
63   37:28.346 CHEROKEE 220.100.100.255 NETB C ID=33218 Query Name=
     JSPNRMPTGSBSSDIR
64   37:28.987 CHEROKEE Broadcast      ARP C PA=[220.100.100.10]
65   37:29.096 CHEROKEE 220.100.100.255  NETB C ID=33218 Query Name=
     JSPNRMPTGSBSSDIR
66   37:29.648 CHEROKEE 03-00-00-00-00-01 SMB C Transaction name
67   37:29.846 CHEROKEE 220.100.100.255  NETB C ID=33218 Query Name=
     JSPNRMPTGSBSSDIR
68   37:30.024 Wellfleet E8-8F-1C 01-80-C2-00-00-00 LLC C S=42 D=42 UI
69   37:30.487 CHEROKEE Broadcast      ARP C PA=[220.100.100.10]
70   37:30.846 CHEROKEE 220.100.100.255  NETB C ID=33220 Query
     Name=SILO-1
71   37:30.851 CHEROKEE Broadcast      ARP C PA=[220.100.100.175]
72   37:31.300 CHEROKEE Broadcast      ARP C PA=[220.100.100.8]
73   37:31.987 CHEROKEE Broadcast      ARP C PA=[220.100.100.10]
74   37:32.024 Wellfleet E8-8F-1C 01-80-C2-00-00-00 LLC C S=42 D=42 UI
75   37:33.487 CHEROKEE Broadcast      ARP C PA=[220.100.100.10]
76   37:34.024 Wellfleet E8-8F-1C 01-80-C2-00-00-00 LLC C S=42 D=42 UI
77   37:34.987 CHEROKEE Broadcast      ARP C PA=[220.100.100.10]
78   37:36.024 Wellfleet E8-8F-1C 01-80-C2-00-00-00 LLC C S=42 D=42 UI
79   37:36.487 CHEROKEE Broadcast      ARP C PA=[220.100.100.10]
80   37:37.987 CHEROKEE Broadcast      ARP C PA=[220.100.100.10]
81   37:38.024 Wellfleet E8-8F-1C 01-80-C2-00-00-00 LLC C S=42 D=42 UI
82   37:39.487 CHEROKEE Broadcast      ARP C PA=[220.100.100.10]
83   37:40.023 Wellfleet E8-8F-1C 01-80-C2-00-00-00 LLC C S=42 D=42 UI
84   37:40.987 CHEROKEE Broadcast      ARP C PA=[220.100.100.10]
85   37:42.023 Wellfleet E8-8F-1C 01-80-C2-00-00-00 LLC C S=42 D=42 UI
86   37:42.467 WstDigt—93-73-D7 Broadcast ARP C PA=[220.100.100.53]
87   37:42.487 CHEROKEE Broadcast      ARP C PA=[220.100.100.10]
88   37:43.987 CHEROKEE Broadcast      ARP C PA=[220.100.100.10]
```

```
89   37:44.023 Wellfleet E8-8F-1C 01-80-C2-00-00-00 LLC C S=42 D=42 UI
90   37:45.487 CHEROKEE  Broadcast     ARP C PA=[220.100.100.10]
91   37:46.023 Wellfleet E8-8F-1C 01-80-C2-00-00-00 LLC C S=42 D=42 UI
92   37:46.986 CHEROKEE  Broadcast     ARP C PA=[220.100.100.10]
93   37:48.085 Wellfleet E8-8F-1C 01-80-C2-00-00-00 LLC C S=42 D=42 UI
```

Additional information can be obtained by the Internet Advisor (IA). This shows Ethernet vital signs for frames between 688 and 742 and the time when the capture was taken.

ETHERNET Vital Signs Measurement

Frame Range: 688..742

	Threshold	Current	Average	Peak	Total
NETWORK COUNTS (Pre-Filter)					
Utilization %	40	0.00	0.00	0.08	
Frames	700	0	0	5	54
Local coll	35	0	0	0	0
Late coll	0	0	0	0	0
Remote coll	35	0	0	0	0
Remote late coll	0	0	0	0	0
Bad FCS	0	0	0	0	0
Runt	0	0	0	0	0
Misaligns	0	0	0	0	0
BUFFER COUNTS (Post-Filter)					
Utilization %	40	0.00	0.00	0.08	
Frames	700	0	0	5	54
Runts (good FCS)	0	0	0	0	0
Jabbers	0	0	0	0	0
Jabber (bad FCS)	0	0	0	0	0
Dribble frms	35	0	0	0	0
Broadcasts	25	0	0	3	16
Multicasts	2	0	0	2	38
Buff Overwrites	100	0	0	0	0

Start Time: Mar 20 98 @ 16:58:54

Sample Time: Mar 20 98 @ 17:00:00

Having this information filed for future reference can be invaluable in establishing a clear baseline.

Consider the following information.

```
ETHERNET Connection Stats
Sample Date Time Src. Address Dst. Address Frames Bytes Errors Stn 1
      Fr Stn 2 Fr Fr lost
1 Mar 20 98 17:01:43 Network Total 1,64,0,1,0,0
1 Mar 20 98 17:01:43 WellfleetE8-8F-1C 01-80-C2-00-00-00",1,64,0,1,0
2 Mar 20 98 17:01:53 Network Total 9,858,0,9,0,0
2 Mar 20 98 17:01:53 Wellfleet E8-8F-1C 01-80-C2-00-00-00",6,384,0,6,0
2 Mar 20 98 17:01:53 WstDigt—93-73-D7 Broadcast",2,128,0,2,0
2 Mar 20 98 17:01:53 Wellfleet E8-8F-10 Broadcast",1,346,0,1,0
3 Mar 20 98 17:02:03 Network Total 23,1786,0,23,0,0
3 Mar 20 98 17:02:03 Wellfleet E8-8F-1C 01-80-C2-00-00-00",11,704,0,
  11,0
3 Mar 20 98 17:02:03 WstDigt—93-73-D7 Broadcast",11,736,0,11,0
3 Mar 20 98 17:02:03 Wellfleet E8-8F-10 Broadcast",1,346,0,1,0
4 Mar 20 98 17:02:13 Network Total 31,2330,0,31,0,0
4 Mar 20 98 17:02:13 Wellfleet E8-8F-1C 01-80-C2-00-00-00",16,1024,0,
  16,0
4 Mar 20 98 17:02:13 WstDigt—93-73-D7 Broadcast",14,960,0,14,0
4 Mar 20 98 17:02:13 Wellfleet E8-8F-10 Broadcast",1,346,0,1,0
```

With such information in hand, utilization and per-node access percentages can be calculated.

The following information presents details about the MS protocol by frame. This is one of the many protocol decodes the HP IA is capable of performing. The Internet Advisor decodes the frames and makes interpretation of this information easy.

```
*************************************************************************
*****                                                     *****
*****         HEWLETT PACKARD NETWORK ADVISOR             *****
*****                                                     *****
*****    Measurement:  MS Windows Stack Decode            *****
*****    Print Type:   Frames 1 to 40                     *****
*****    Open Views:   Summary Detailed                   *****
*****    Display Mode: Viewing All Frames                 *****
*****    Print Date:   03/20/98                           *****
*****    Print Time:   17:14:11                           *****
*************************************************************************
```

```
16   46:31.278 CHEROKEE 03-00-00-00-00-01 NETB Name query RENEGADE
Frame: 16 Time: Mar 20@16:46:31.2788912 Length: 65
           ***** DETAILED FORMAT *****
NetBIOS (NetBEUI)
Header Length        44
Delimiter            EFFF
Command              0A        NAME_QUERY
Optional Data 1      00        Reserved field
 Name Type           00        Unique name type
 Session Number      00        Error: Session number of 0 invalid
Transmit Correlator  0000      Reserved field
Response Correlator  001F
Destination Name     RENEGADE
```

```
Source Name          CHEROKEE
```

```
18 46:31.288 00000000-CHEROKEE 00000000-Broadcast NETB Find Name
RENEGADE
Frame: 18 Time: Mar 20@16:46:31.2883590 Length: 102
           ***** DETAILED FORMAT *****
Novell NetBios (IPX/SPX)
Connection Control Flag  00
                    0.......          Non-System Packet
                    .0......          Non Send ACK
                    ..0.....          Not Attention
                    ...0....          Not End of Message
                    ....0...          No Rsend Needed
Operation          1               Find Name
Name Type Flag        00
                    0.......          Unique Name
                    .0......          Name Not Used
                    .....0..          Name Not Registered
                    ......0.          Name Not Duplicated
                    .......0          Name Not Deregistered
Operation          1               Find Name
Name Claim String     RENEGADE
```

```
19 46:31.850 00000000-CHEROKEE 00000000-Broadcast NETB Find Name
RENEGADE
Frame: 19     Time: Mar 20@16:46:31.8507519 Length: 102
           ***** DETAILED FORMAT *****
Novell NetBios (IPX/SPX)
Connection Control Flag  00
                    0.......          Non-System Packet
                    .0......          Non Send ACK
                    ..0.....          Not Attention
                    ...0....          Not End of Message
                    ....0...          No Rsend Needed
Operation          1               Find Name
Name Type Flag        00
                    0.......          Unique Name
                    .0......          Name Not Used
                    .....0..          Name Not Registered
                    ......0.          Name Not Duplicated
                    .......0          Name Not Deregistered
Operation          1               Find Name
Name Claim String     RENEGADE
```

```
21 46:32.413 00000000-CHEROKEE 00000000-Broadcast NETB Find Name
RENEGADE

Frame: 21     Time: Mar 20@16:46:32.4132375 Length: 102

           ***** DETAILED FORMAT *****
Novell NetBios (IPX/SPX)
Connection Control Flag  00
                    0.......          Non-System Packet
                    .0......          Non Send ACK
```

```
                    ..0.....          Not Attention
                    ...0....          Not End of Message
                    ....0...          No Rsend Needed
Operation              1              Find Name
Name Type Flag00
                    0.......          Unique Name
                    .0......          Name Not Used
                    .....0..          Name Not Registered
                    ......0.          Name Not Duplicated
                    .......0          Name Not Deregistered
Operation              1              Find Name
Name Claim String       RENEGADE
```

The information above can be helpful when troubleshooting network problems. This level of detail provides per-node communication functions.

The HP Internet Advisor provides complete seven-layer decoding and analysis of protocols. Consider the following captured statistics.

Novell Vital Signs Measurement				
Threshold	**Current**	**Average**	**Peak**	**Total**
Network Util % 10	0.00	2.16	23.81	
IPX Util % 10	0.00	0.00	0.15	
Network Packets 1200	0	37	368	1573
IPX Packets 1000	0	0	13	37
IPX Packet Size 1000	0	8	151	
Local Tx Rate 1000	0	0	13	37
Remote Tx Rate 1000	0	0	0	0
Burst Mode 500	0	0	0	0
RIP Frames 10	0	0	0	0
SAP Frames 10	0	0	1	2
Read Rq Pkts 500	0	0	0	0
Write Rq Pkts 500	0	0	0	0
Busy Server % 4	0.00	0.00	0.00	
Buffer Overwrites 100	0	0	0	0
Start Time: Mar 23 98 @ 15:16:58				
Sample Time: Mar 23 98 @ 15:18:47				

These statistics provide valuable insight to Novell protocol operation in the network. Additional information can also be obtained about IPX/SPX protocol.

As mentioned, the IA can decode multiple protocol stacks. Consider the following.

```
********************************************************************
*****            HEWLETT PACKARD NETWORK ADVISOR          *****
*****                                                     *****
*****     Measurement:  Network Stack Decode              *****
*****     Print Type:   All Frames                        *****
*****     Open Views:   Summary Detailed                  *****
*****     Display Mode: Viewing All Frames                *****
*****     Print Date:   03/23/98                          *****
*****     Print Time:   15:12:47                          *****
********************************************************************
```

```
1 29.464599 MUSCLE 03-00-00-00-00-01  NETB Datagram MUSCLE->
  JSPNRMPTGSBSSDIR
Frame: 1     Time: Mar 23@15:10:29.4645992 Length: 75
            ***** DETAILED FORMAT *****
NetBIOS
Header Length          44
Delimiter              EFFF
Command                08                DATAGRAM
Optional Data 1        00                Reserved field
Optional Data 2        0000              Reserved field
Transmit Correlator    0000              Reserved field
Response Correlator    0000              Reserved field
Destination Name       JSPNRMPTGSBSSDIR
Source Name            MUSCLE
 802.2
Destination SAP        F0                NetBios
Source SAP             F0                NetBios
Command/Response       ....-...0         Command
Type                   03                Unnumbered
Poll                   ...0-....
Modifier               000.-00..         Information
 802.3/Ethernet
Destination address    03-00-00-00-00-01 Group, local
Source address         MUSCLE            Individual, global
Length                 57
Frame check sequence   7C-32-0E-3B
> Data size            57
```

```
2 30.339447 WstDigt-93-73-D7 Broadcast  ARP C PA=[220.100.100.10]
Frame: 2     Time: Mar 23@15:10:30.3394479 Length: 64
            ***** DETAILED FORMAT *****
ARP/RARP
Hardware               1                 Ethernet
Protocol               08-00             IP
HW addr length         6
Phys addr length       4
Operation              1                 ARP Request
Sender HW addr         00-00-C0-93-73-D7
Sender internet addr   220.100.100.79
```

```
Target HW addr            00-00-00-00-00-00
Target internet addr      220.100.100.10
 802.3/Ethernet
Destination address       Broadcast              Broadcast
Source address            WstDigt—93-73-D7       Individual, global
Type                      08-06                  ARP
Frame check sequence      BF-A0-DC-C2
> Data size               46
```

```
3 30.339769 MUSCLE WstDigt—93-73-D7 ARP R PA=MUSCLE HA=0000C04EB5EC
Frame: 3     Time: Mar 23@15:10:30.3397692 Length: 64
             ***** DETAILED FORMAT *****
ARP/RARP
Hardware                  1                      Ethernet
Protocol                  08-00                  IP
HW addr length            6
Phys addr length          4
Operation                 2                      ARP Reply
Sender HW addr            00-00-C0-4E-B5-EC
Sender internet addr      220.100.100.10
Target HW addr            00-00-C0-93-73-D7
Target internet addr      220.100.100.79
 802.3/Ethernet
Destination address       WstDigt—93-73-D7       Individual, global
Source address            MUSCLE                 Individual, global
Type                      08-06                  ARP
Frame check sequence      F4-93-C6-3E
> Data size               46
```

```
4  30.340128 WstDigt—93-73-D7 MUSCLE NETB C ID=32878 Query Name=FAT
   BOY
Frame: 4     Time: Mar 23@15:10:30.3401281 Length: 96
             ***** DETAILED FORMAT *****
NetBIOS
Service Type :                                   Name Service
Name_Trn_ID               32878
Packet Type :                                    Name Query Request
Opcode, NM_Flags, Rcode   01-00                  See Bit Fields Below
 Response Flag            0.......               Request Packet
 Opcode                   .0000...               Query
 Auth. Answer Flag        .....0..               False
 Truncation Flag          ......0.               False
 Recursion Desired Flag   .......1               True
 Recursion Available Flag 0.......               False
 Reserved                 .00.....
 Broadcast Flag           ...0....               False
 Rcode                    ....0000
Qdcount                   1                      No. Of Entries In Question
 Section
Ancount                   0                      No. Of Entries In Answer
 Section
Nscount                   0                      No. Of Entries In Authority
 Section
Arcount                   0                      No. of Entries In Additional
```

```
 Records Section
Name Length              32
Question_Name            FAT BOY              NetBIOS Name
Question_Type            32                   General Name Service
  Resource Record
Question_Class           1                    Internet Class
  UDP
Source port              137                  NETBIOS
Destination port         137                  NETBIOS
Length                   58
Checksum                 A2-72
  IP
Version                  4
Internet header length   5                    (32 bit words)
Precedence               000.-....            Routine
Delay                    ...0-....            Delay normal
Throughput               ....-0...            Throughput normal
Reliability              ....-.0..            Reliability normal
Total Length             78
Identification           40459
May / Do Not Fragment    .0..-....            Fragmentation allowed
Last / More Fragments    ..0.-....            fast fragment
Offset                   0
Time To Live             128
Next Protocol            17                   UDP
Checksum                 1B-71
Source                   220.100.100.79
Destination              MUSCLE
> Data size              58
  802.3/Ethernet
Destination address      MUSCLE               Individual, global
Source address           WstDigt—93-73-D7 Individual, global
Type                     08-00                IP
Frame check sequence     B6-8F-A8-0E
> Data size              78
```

```
5  30.341308 MUSCLE WstDigt—93-73-D7 NETB R ID=32878 Query Name=
   FAT BOY
Frame: 5     Time: Mar 23@15:10:30.3413080 Length: 108
             ***** DETAILED FORMAT *****
  NetBIOS
Service Type : Name Service
Name_Trn_ID  32878
Packet Type : Positive Name Query Response
Opcode, NM_Flags, Rcode  85-80             See Bit Fields Below
 Response Flag           1.......           Response Packet
 Opcode                  .0000...           Query
 Auth. Answer Flag       .....1..           True
 Truncation Flag         ......0.           False
 Recursion Desired Flag  .......1           True
 Recursion Available Flag 1.......          True
 Reserved                .00.....
 Broadcast Flag          ...0....           False
 Rcode                   ....0000
```

```
Qdcount                   0                No. Of Entries In Question
 Section
Ancount                   1                No. Of Entries In Answer
 Section
Nscount                   0                No. Of Entries In Authority
 Section
Arcount                   0                No. of Entries In Additional
 Records Section
Name Length               32
RR_Name                   FAT BOY          NetBIOS Name
RR_Type                   32               General Name Service
 Resource Record
RR_Class                  1                Internet Class
TTL                       0
Rdlength                  6
NB_Flags                  60-00            See Bit Fields Below
 Group Flag               0.......         Unique Name
 Owner Node Type          .11.....         Reserved Bit(s) Not Zero
 Reserved Bits            ...0000000000000
Sliced Data (Truncated)   Sliced Data
 UDP
Source port               137              NETBIOS
Destination port          137              NETBIOS
Length                    70               Partial packet store
Checksum                  7D-66            Checksum not checked
 IP
Version                   4
Internet header length    5                (32 bit words)
Precedence                000.-....        Routine
Delay                     ...0-....        Delay normal
Throughput                ....-0...        Throughput normal
Reliability               ....-.0..        Reliability normal
Total Length              90               Partial packet store
Identification            63241
May / Do Not Fragment     .0..-....        Fragmentation allowed
Last / More Fragments     ..0.-....        Last fragment
Offset                    0
Time To Live              128
Next Protocol             17               UDP
Checksum                  C2-66
Source                    MUSCLE
Destination               220.100.100.79   RENEGADE
> Data size               66
 802.3/Ethernet
Destination address       WstDigt—93-73-D7 Individual, global
Source address            MUSCLE           Individual, global
Type                      08-00            IP
> Sliced data
> Data size               86
```

```
6 30.341872 WstDigt—93-73-D7 Broadcast    ARP C PA=[220.100.100.8]
Frame: 6     Time: Mar 23@15:10:30.3418728 Length: 64
             ***** DETAILED FORMAT *****
ARP/RARP
```

```
Hardware                    1                  Ethernet
Protocol                    08-00              IP
HW addr length              6
Phys addr length            4
Operation                   1                  ARP Request
Sender HW addr              00-00-C0-93-73-D7
Sender internet addr        220.100.100.79
Target HW addr              00-00-00-00-00-00
Target internet addr        220.100.100.8
 802.3/Ethernet
Destination address         Broadcast          Broadcast
Source address              WstDigt-93-73-D7 Individual, global
Type                        08-06              ARP
Frame check sequence        35-E7-B6-AA
> Data size                 46
```

```
7 32.467583 MUSCLE   Broadcast NETB C ID=33902 Query Name=
 JSPNRMPTGSBSSDIR
Frame: 7     Time: Mar 23@15:10:32.4675834 Length: 96
             ***** DETAILED FORMAT *****
NetBIOS
Service Type :  Name Service
Name_Trn_ID  33902
Packet Type :  Name Query Request
Opcode, NM_Flags, Rcode  01-10                 See Bit Fields Below
 Response Flag           0.......              Request Packet
 Opcode                  .0000...              Query
 Auth. Answer Flag       .....0..              False
 Truncation Flag         ......0.              False
 Recursion Desired Flag  .......1              True
 Recursion Available Flag 0.......             False
 Reserved                .00.....
 Broadcast Flag          ...1....              True
 Rcode                   ....0000
Qdcount                  1                     No. Of Entries In Question
 Section
Ancount                  0                     No. Of Entries In Answer
 Section
Nscount                  0                     No. Of Entries In Authority
 Section
Arcount                  0                     No. of Entries In Additional
 Records Section
Name Length              32
Question_Name            JSPNRMPTGSBSSDIR NetBIOS Name
Question_Type            32                    General Name Service
 Resource Record
Question_Class           1                     Internet Class
 UDP
Source port              137                   NETBIOS
Destination port         137                   NETBIOS
Length                   58
Checksum                 73-97
 IP
Version                  4
```

```
Internet header length      5                   (32 bit words)
Precedence                  000.-....           Routine
Delay                       ...0-....           Delay normal
Throughput                  ....-0...           Throughput normal
Reliability                 ....-.0..           Reliability normal
Total Length                78
Identification              64009
May / Do Not Fragment       .0..-....           Fragmentation allowed
Last / More Fragments       ..0.-....           Last fragment
Offset                      0
Time To Live                128
Next Protocol               17                  UDP
Checksum                    BE-C2
Source                      MUSCLE
Destination                 220.100.100.255
> Data size                 58
  802.3/Ethernet
Destination address         Broadcast           Broadcast
Source address              MUSCLE              Individual, global
Type                        08-00               IP
Frame check sequence        EC-E8-DB-13
> Data size          7      8
```

```
8 33.218765 MUSCLE Broadcast NETB C ID=33902 Query Name=
  JSPNRMPTGSBSSDIR
Frame: 8     Time: Mar 23@15:10:33.2187650 Length: 96
             ***** DETAILED FORMAT *****

NetBIOS
Service Type : Name Service
Name_Trn_ID    33902
Packet Type :  Name Query Request
Opcode, NM_Flags, Rcode    01-10              See Bit Fields Below
 Response Flag             0.......           Request Packet
 Opcode                    .0000...           Query
 Auth. Answer Flag         .....0..           False
 Truncation Flag           ......0.           False
 Recursion Desired Flag    .......1           True
 Recursion Available Flag 0.......            False
 Reserved                  .00.....
 Broadcast Flag            ...1....           True
 Rcode                     ....0000
Qdcount                    1                  No. Of Entries In Question
 Section
Ancount                    0                  No. Of Entries In Answer
 Section
Nscount                    0                  No. Of Entries In Authority
 Section
Arcount                    0                  No. of Entries In Additional
 Records Section
Name Length                32
Question_Name              JSPNRMPTGSBSSDIR NetBIOS Name
Question_Type              32                 General Name Service
 Resource Record
Question_Class             1                  Internet Class
```

```
  UDP
Source port                 137                NETBIOS
Destination port            137                NETBIOS
Length                      58
Checksum                    73-97
  IP
Version                     4
Internet header length      5                  (32 bit words)
Precedence                  000.-....          Routine
Delay                       ...0-....          Delay normal
Throughput                  ....-0...          Throughput normal
Reliability                 ....-.0..          Reliability normal
Total Length                78
Identification              64265
May / Do Not Fragment       .0..-....          Fragmentation allowed
Last / More Fragments       ..0.-....          Last fragment
Offset                      0
Time To Live                128
Next Protocol               17                 UDP
Checksum                    BD-C2
Source                      MUSCLE
Destination                 220.100.100.255
> Data size                 58
  802.3/Ethernet
Destination address         Broadcast          Broadcast
Source address              MUSCLE             Individual, global
Type                        08-00              IP
Frame check sequence        D1-A1-D2-5B
> Data size                 78
```

```
9 33.344719 WstDigt-93-73-D7 Broadcast ARP C PA=[220.100.100.8]
Frame: 9     Time: Mar 23@15:10:33.3447195 Length: 64
             ***** DETAILED FORMAT *****

ARP/RARP
Hardware                    1                  Ethernet
Protocol                    08-00              IP
HW addr length              6
Phys addr length            4
Operation                   1                  ARP Request
Sender HW addr              00-00-C0-93-73-D7
Sender internet addr        220.100.100.79
Target HW addr              00-00-00-00-00-00
Target internet addr        220.100.100.8
  802.3/Ethernet
Destination address         Broadcast          Broadcast
Source address              WstDigt-93-73-D7   Individual, global
Type                        08-06              ARP
Frame check sequence        35-E7-B6-AA
> Data size                 46
```

```
10  33.969839 MUSCLE  Broadcast  NETB C ID=33902 Query Name=
    JSPNRMPTGSBSSDIR
Frame: 10    Time: Mar 23@15:10:33.9698393 Length: 96
             ***** DETAILED FORMAT *****
```

```
NetBIOS
Service Type :  Name Service
Name_Trn_ID  33902
Packet Type : Name Query Request
Opcode, NM_Flags, Rcode  01-10           See Bit Fields Below
 Response Flag            0.......        Request Packet
 Opcode                   .0000...        Query
 Auth. Answer Flag        .....0..        False
 Truncation Flag          ......0.        False
 Recursion Desired Flag   .......1        True
 Recursion Available Flag 0.......        False
 Reserved                 .00.....
 Broadcast Flag           ...1....        True
 Rcode                    ....0000
Qdcount                  1               No. Of Entries In Question
 Section
Ancount                  0               No. Of Entries In Answer
 Section
Nscount                  0               No. Of Entries In Authority
 Section
Arcount                  0               No. of Entries In Additional
 Records Section
Name Length              32
Question_Name            JSPNRMPTGSBSSDIR NetBIOS Name
Question_Type            32              General Name Service
 Resource Record
Question_Class           1               Internet Class
 UDP
Source port              137             NETBIOS
Destination port         137             NETBIOS
Length                   58
Checksum                 73-97
 IP
Version                  4
Internet header length   5               (32 bit words)
Precedence               000.-....       Routine
Delay                    ...0-....       Delay normal
Throughput               ....-0...       Throughput normal
Reliability              ....-.0..       Reliability normal
Total Length             78
Identification           64521
May / Do Not Fragment    .0..-....       Fragmentation allowed
Last / More Fragments    ..0.-....       Last fragment
Offset                   0
Time To Live             128
Next Protocol            17              UDP
Checksum                 BC-C2
Source                   MUSCLE
Destination              220.100.100.255
> Data size              58
 802.3/Ethernet
Destination address      Broadcast       Broadcast
Source address           MUSCLE          Individual, global
Type                     08-00           IP
```

```
Frame check sequence        B1-95-93-E7
> Data size                 78
```

The previous data capture with the Internet Advisor provides a wealth of information in 10 frames of this sequence. NetBIOS, ARP, and RARP protocols are presented. Both destination and source addresses are shown. In addition, data size and type of frame are indicated. This level of tracing is valuable to repositories of information for baseline setting and future planning.

Another valuable insight into network traffic is knowledge of what nodes are consuming the majority of the network's bandwidth. Consider the following information. The "top talkers" is a data capture of nodes talking on the network at a given instance.

ETHERNET Top Talkers				
Node	**Frames Xmt**	**Bytes Xmt**	**Frames Rcv**	**Bytes Rcv**
BRAINS	1042	213602	1696	1637371
THE-HOSTAGE	989	1150866	502	60320
Axis-----32-41-35	710	690040	341	34497
MUSCLE	498	87757	474	155264
WstDigt--93-73-D7	312	39480	439	358026
220.100.100.8	299	27109	474	280046
Axis-----32-41-3F	290	321964	144	14717
WstDigE99CB1	162	28951	132	12120
00-00-D1-0F-E2-9B	73	18028	77	11554
Ibm------45-43-F3	27	5389	28	4564
Broadcast	0	0	65	9613
03-00-00-00-00-01	0	0	29	5029
01-00-5E-00-01-18	0	0	1	65

TCP/IP ETHERNET Commentator

```
Commentating on: TCP/IP
TCP: Close Connection      [Normal]  Mar 23@14:11:56.7437798
     220.100.100.79        <--> 220.100.100.8
                           220.100.100.8
     Port: 1034            NETBIOS 139
     Tx Packets: 4         3
     Low Window: 0         0
     Retrans:    0         0
     Connection Duration: 0:00:00.0088922
```

```
                        Frame Number(s): 82
       TCP: Close Connection       [Normal]  Mar 23@14:12:01.7474972
            220.100.100.79         <--> 220.100.100.19
            Port: 1035             NETBIOS 139
            x Packets:  4          3
            Low Window: 0          0
            Retrans:    0          0
            Connection Duration: 0:00:00.0047942
                        Frame Number(s): 94
       TCP: Close Connection       [Normal]  Mar 23@14:12:01.760128
            220.100.100.79         <--> 220.100.100.175 SILO
            Port: 1036             NETBIOS 139
            Tx Packets: 4          4
            Low Window: 0          0
            Retrans:    0          0
            Connection Duration: 0:00:00.0114625
                        Frame Number(s): 107
       TCP: Close Connection       [Normal]  Mar 23@14:12:01.7635736
            220.100.100.79         <--> 220.100.100.12
                                   BRAINS
            Port: 1037             NETBIOS 139
            Tx Packets: 4          3
            Low Window: 0          0
            Retrans:    0          0
            Connection Duration: 0:00:00.0036442
                        Frame Number(s): 113
       TCP: Close Connection       [Normal]  Mar 23@14:12:06.7530549
            220.100.100.79         <--> 220.100.100.61
                                   THE-HOSTAGE
            Port: 1038             NETBIOS 139
            Tx Packets: 4          3
            Low Window: 0          0
            Retrans:    0          0
            Connection Duration: 0:00:00.0033536
                        Frame Number(s): 123
       TCP: Close Connection       [Normal]  Mar 23@14:12:06.7564388
            220.100.100.77         <--> 220.100.100.79
            Port: NETBIOS 139      1039
            Tx Packets: 4          5
            Low Window: 0          0
            Retrans:    0          0
            Connection Duration: 0:00:53.1002132
                        Frame Number(s): 130
       TCP: Close Connection       [Normal]  Mar 23@14:12:11.7688309
            220.100.100.79         <--> 220.100.100.180
            Port: 1040             NETBIOS 139
            Tx Packets: 4          4
            Low Window: 0          0
            Retrans:    0          0
            Connection Duration: 0:00:00.0113425
                        Frame Number(s): 140
       TCP: Close Connection       [Normal]  Mar 23@14:13:29.096155
            220.100.100.8          <--> 220.100.100.12
            220.100.100.8          BRAINS
```

```
Port: 1041              NETBIOS 139
Tx Packets: 11          8
Low Window: 0           0
Retrans:    0           0
Connection Duration: 0:00:02.3622054
Frame Number(s): 217
```

Still another powerful insight to network monitoring is that information which comments on TCP protocol. Various details can be deduced from this and, depending upon your site, more precise information can be gathered.

The Internet Advisor also provides information on crucial vital signs measurement.

TCP/IP Vital Signs Measurement					
Frame Range: 7..874					
	Threshold	**Current**	**Average**	**Peak**	**Total**
Network Util %	10	0.00	0.00	20.12	
IP Util %	5	0.00	0.00	17.34	
Network Packets	1200	0	0	226	867
IP Packets	800	0	0	205	641
IP Broadcast	10	0	0	2	8
IP Fragment	5	0	0	0	0
ICMP Redirects	1	0	0	0	0
ICMP Unreach	10	0	0	0	0
Low TTL	1	0	0	0	0
IP Packet Size	18000	0	0	1084	
SNMP Get/Set Pkts	10	0	0	0	0
SNMP Trap Pkts	10	0	0	0	0
DNS Packets	10	0	0	0	0
ARP Packets	10	0	0	6	38
Low Window	5	0	0	0	0
Reset Connections	5	0	0	0	0
Routing Packets	50	0	0	0	0
Buffer Overwrites	100	0	0	0	0
Start Time: Mar 23 98 @ 14:08:47					
Sample Time: Mar 23 98 @ 14:29:13					

The information provided in this capture can be used to fine-tune the network and to plan for additional network traffic loads.

Many more network *captures* can be obtained with the Internet Advisor. More information about the Internet Advisor can be obtained by visiting www.hp.com; or write Hewlett-Packard, 5070 Centennial Blvd., Colorado Springs, CO 80919.

Network Tape Drive (Sony)

With most networks, multiple devices operate them. During the planning stage of my network, I determined a Sony tape drive would be the best solution for backup purposes.

Figure 7.16 shows the tape drive connected to *The-Kid*. This system has an SCSI interface and is also connected to the network. *The-Kid* is running NT Workstation; consequently it has the tape backup software built into it and requires no further software to perform backups. This particular tape drive is capable of 50 GB of storage and uses tape with a chip on it and onboard RAM which makes access quick.

Contact Sony for further information and consider this type of setup to provide back-up storage for your network. Visit Sony on the Web at www.sony.com; or write Sony Electronics, 3300 Zanker, San Jose, CA 95134.

Power Protection (Liebert)

This network involves a lot of equipment. Rather than attempt to use isolated pieces of power protection, I determined the best approach would be to use a uninterruptable power supply. I selected Liebert because of their reputation, quality, product reliability, and personnel.

My network needs could be met well with a 15 kVA UPS. Chapter 4 presented information to help you determine what size UPS you need. One important aspect of power protection is pre-site planning. Consider the following pre-site visit checklist made available by Liebert. Some of the checklist needs to be completed prior to receiving your UPS or other power conditioning equipment; other aspects of this checklist must be performed after receipt of the UPS. This is the checklist I used; you will need to use the appropriate one for your environment.

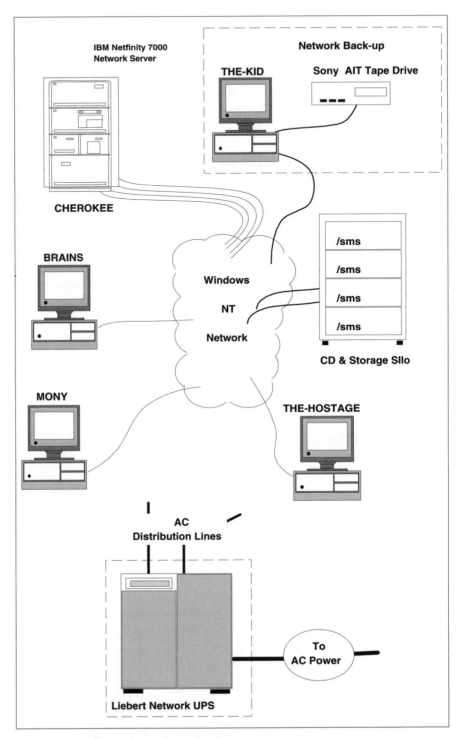

FIGURE 7.16
Network Back-up

Liebert Pre-Site Visit Checklist

1.0 Documentation

1.1 Ensure that the installing contractor has the installation and handling instructions for the equipment to be installed.

1.2 Ensure the installing contractor has proper wire lists for the equipment to be installed and that all information on the wire list is understood.

1.3 Review proper wiring requirements. If it is a 4 wire+ ground, ensure neutral is bonded at the server entrance. If it is a 3 wire + ground, ensure a bond is placed between neutral and ground (IAW NED) in the control cabinet and GFI time delay is set to 30 cycles (.5 seconds).

2.0 Inspection of the UPS System

2.1 Verify that all ordered items are received (options, spares, and ancillary equipment).

2.2 Check for shipping damage internally and externally. (If any damage is noted, contact the Liebert sales representative and note on explanation sheet.)

2.3 Discuss proper removal of orange shipping brackets (when applicable).

3.0 UPS System Installation

3.1 Ensure that there is required clearance for all the cabinet doors to open fully on all system sections.

3.2 Ensure that there is a minimum of 36" in front of the breakers to perform maintenance.

3.3 Ensure that there is adequate clearance above the unit to allow exhaust air to flow without restriction (refer to installation manual).

3.4 Ensure that there is adequate ventilation and/or cooling (refer to installation manual).

3.5 Ensure that the UPS is installed in a clean, cool, and dry location.

3.6 Ensure that the battery system has a minimum of 36" of clearance for service access.

Conceptual Use of the Network UPS

The Liebert UPS I used in this network appears conceptually like Figure 7.17.

FIGURE 7.17
Network Power
Protection

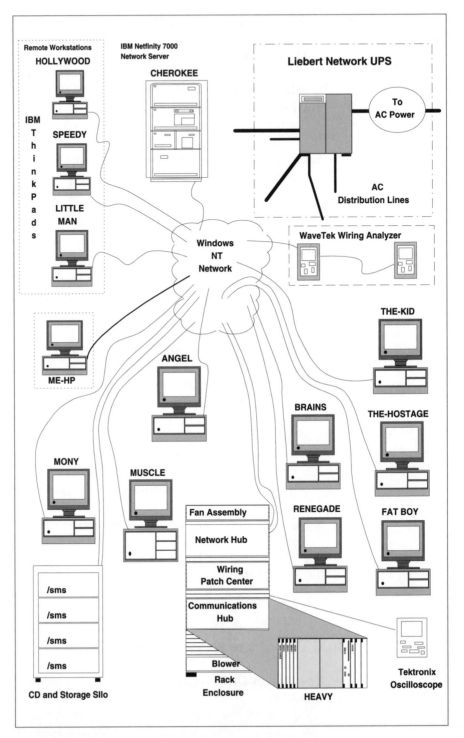

FIGURE 7.17
Network Power
Protection

This shows the complete network environment and the Liebert UPS, which provides coverage for the entire network. The following specifications for the UPS protecting the network are of interest.

Liebert not only has state-of-the-art power protection equipment and qualified personnel, they have a wealth of information assimilated to assist customers and potential customers. During my research a valuable piece of information was made available by Liebert. The following is that report and is reprinted here with all credit due to the Liebert Corporation.

Network UPS Details

Additional information about the UPS used in this network includes examination of the LCD display on the front. The panel menu is easy to use and appears like Figure 7.18.

FIGURE 7.18
Control Panel
Highlighted View

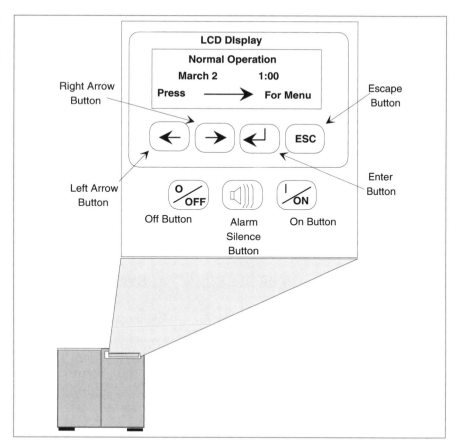

This interface to the UPS is significant because the design of the menus and the information provided through them is easily understandable by those who are familiar with UPSs and electrical information.

Because of the importance of UPS and other power conditioning equipment, it is worth your while to read the following information provided by Liebert.

Liebert Site Power Audit (Sample Report)

Acme Computer Company Co. contracted Liebert Global Services (LGS) to evaluate the electrical environment at an automobile dealership. The automobile dealership had complaints about the performance of Acme's data processing system installed at their site. LGS was contracted to determine whether or not these problems could be attributed to power quality or electrical system problems.

Standards For Evaluation

LGS subscribes to the industry-wide standards used for the evaluation of the electrical systems for computer installations, which are:

> Federal Information Processing Standards Publication 94, "Guideline on Electrical Power for ADP Installations", published by the U.S. Department of Commerce/ National Bureau of Standards, 1983.
>
> Institute of Electrical and Electronic Engineers Standard 1100-1992, "Grounding and Powering Sensitive Electronic Equipment", 1992.
>
> Both of these standards conform to the requirements of the National Electric Code (NFPA 70).

Elements of the Electrical System Which Were Inspected

- Building transformer, grounding, and power distribution
- Isolation transformers for computer equipment
- Distribution panels for computer equipment
- Grounding of isolation transformer, distribution panels and power receptacles
- Power conditioning equipment
- Cable runs.

Building Transformer, Grounding, and Power Distribution

The site is a large automobile dealership consisting of several different buildings located on 26 acres. These buildings include the main showroom, parts building, service building, body shop, truck center, and used car center. All buildings contain computer terminals and printers which communicate with the mainframe computer located in the parts building.

A 1000 KVA, 20/0.48KV transformer sits on a concrete pad immediately outside and adjacent to the parts building. The nameplate of this transformer has been painted over, so no other details regarding its composition were available. The building transformer is grounded according to the National Electric Code. The transformer and building ground rods are located between the building transformer and outside wall of the parts building. Grounding electrode conductor cables from the building transformer and building steel are attached to ground rods with a screw-down compression fitting. These fittings have worked loose over the years, allowing the grounding electrode conductor cables to rotate freely about the ground rods. These connections should be remade. Welding the grounding electrode conductor cables directly to the ground rod is much more effective.

Power enters the parts building via underground conduit and terminates at the facility's main distribution panel. Power from this panel is distributed throughout the parts building and distributed to the other buildings, as well.

Isolation Transformers for Computer Equipment

Isolation transformers are used to step down the 480 VAC building power to 208/120 VAC as required by the computer equipment. It is recommended that these transformers be designed specifically for computer applications, contain Faraday electrostatic shields, and have only computer-type loads attached to them. Additionally, they must be grounded in accordance with section 250-26 of the National Electric Code.

The isolation transformers feeding the computer equipment at the automobile dealership are general-purpose type, which do not contain Faraday electrostatic shields and do not provide a high degree of noise immunity. Additionally, the distribution panels fed by these transformers contain non-computer circuits such as lighting, coffee machines etc. This allows the proliferation of electrical noise in computer power circuits which can result in data corruption.

Distribution Panels for Computer Equipment

Acme recommends the use of an isolated ground system for their equipment. Proper wiring of these circuits is well documented in the IEEE 1100-1992 and FIPS 94 publications noted earlier. The automobile dealership is in the process of upgrading parts of their electrical system to meet the recommendations of Acme. For example, the electrical service providing power to the computer equipment in the office area of the main showroom building has been renovated in the last several months. As part of this renovation, a new isolation transformer, a new distribution panel, and isolated ground receptacles were specified. Specific problems with how this system was wired will be discussed in the next section of this report.

There are many distribution panels in this facility's electrical system which feed power to computer terminals. Most of these panels are not wired in accordance with the practices defined in IEEE 1100-1992 and FIPS 94. For example, one of the problems noted during the evaluation is that electrical panels are not dedicated to computer loads. Large panels which serve the computer terminals also serve facility lighting and HVAC, coffee machines and refrigerators, and many other non-computer type loads. This allows easy coupling of electrical noise from non-computer loads into computer load power circuits.

Main Showroom Office Power Distribution System

The power system feeding this office has been recently renovated. Isolated ground receptacles are being used, however the entire system has not been properly wired. Some of the problems encountered during the inspection are as follows:

1. Distribution panels designed for isolated ground systems usually have three busbars. The first is a ground busbar which is electrically connected to the chassis of the distribution panel. The second is the isolated ground busbar which is electrically isolated from the chassis of the distribution panel. The third is a neutral busbar which is also electrically isolated from the chassis of the distribution. The distribution panel for this office has only an isolated ground busbar and a neutral busbar.

2. The distribution panel for this office contains 11 branch circuit breakers but has only seven conduits leaving it. This indicates that circuits are being shared in the same conduit. This practice is not recommended as it eliminates any advantage gained by the isolated ground system.

3. The computer hub and network equipment which serve the entire showroom building are located in the room adjacent to the electrical equipment. There are only two circuits feeding all this equipment. Because there are not enough power receptacles on those two circuits, terminal strips are being used to power the computer equipment. It is recommended to add at least two more circuits to this area and eliminate the terminal strips.

4. Figure 7.19 illustrates how the showroom office electrical system was wired before the inspection. A ground loop existed which could create performance problems. The loop can be visualized by following the source ground wire (which is also connected to building steel) through the ground connection in the transformer, to the isolated ground busbar in the distribution panel, to the neutral busbar in the distribution panel, back to the neutral connection in the transformer cabinet, and finally back to building steel through the grounding electrode conductor (G.E.C.). The loop was eliminated after wiring corrections were made.

Figure 7.19 shows wiring changes to existing office electrical systems.

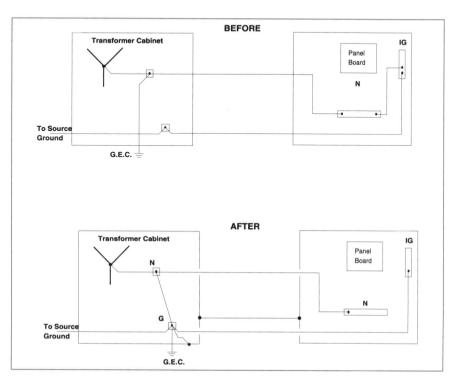

FIGURE 7.19
Wiring Changes

5. PVC conduit is used between the transformer cabinet and the distribution panel. No ground conductor is present to ground the distribution panel cabinet to building steel. The cabinet is in fact "floating," creating a personnel safety hazard. The automobile dealership maintenance personnel were advised to connect the cabinet of the distribution panel to a solid ground point.

6. The solid, bare copper ground conductor connecting the transformer to its source ground was replaced with a larger stranded, insulated conductor.

7. The bare, stranded ground conductor connected between the transformer ground and the isolated ground busbar in the distribution panel was too short, so an extension was wire-nutted in. This reflects poor workmanship during the renovation and is not acceptable.

Isolation Transformers, Distribution Panels, and Power Receptacles

Various isolation transformers are used in this facility to step down the 480 VAC building power to 208/120 VAC which is used by the computer system. These transformers are all general-purpose type, which are not designed for sensitive computer loads. None have the Faraday electrostatic shields which are required to isolate noise in the power system. These transformers have their neutral-to-ground bonds made in the distribution panel which the transformers feed. This is acceptable to code, however better system performance is achieved when the neutral-to-ground bond is made directly in the transformer cabinet.

The distribution panels in this facility are very old. Computer circuits are mixed with other building loads such as lighting and HVAC. As stated earlier this is not a recommended practice for a computer environment. The wiring in the distribution panels is very disorderly. Noise can easily be transferred from non-computer circuits to computer circuits. Color codes are not consistent. For example: there are blue and brown cables attached to the neutral bus. A professionally wired distribution panel will have all circuit conductors correctly color coded and the cables neatly run and wire-tied. Neutral busbars should have only white cables attached. Ground busbars should have only green cables attached. Isolated ground busbars should have only green/yellow cables attached. This is not the case at this site. Blue and brown cables are attached to the neutral bus. The wiring is haphazardly installed, making it difficult to trace circuits. In one case, the panel covering the branch circuit breakers has an opening where a circuit breaker is missing. An individual may inadvertently place a finger through the opening, touch an energized busbar inside the distribution panel and receive an electrical shock.

The automobile dealership has elected to use conduit as equipment safety ground instead of running a ground wire from the distribution panel to the power receptacle. This practice is not recommended by IEEE 1100-1992 or FIPS 94. It does not allow for the lowest ground impedance possible, nor does it minimize the influence of electrical noise. There is certainly no guarantee that the impedance of conduit is low enough to trip a circuit breaker should a phase-to-ground fault occur. To summarize, using conduit as an equipment safety ground conductor does not prevent the proliferation of electrical noise and could pose a personnel safety hazard.

Power Conditioning Equipment

With the exception of small UPS systems located at the mainframe, no other power conditioning is installed. Three transient voltage spike suppression (TVSS) units are installed by the distribution panel that feeds the main computer room, but they are not currently wired in. Power conditioners or UPS systems by themselves cannot be used as a remedy for poor wiring or a poor grounding system. They rely on solid wiring foundations in order to work correctly.

Cable Runs

During the inspection of this facility it was noted on several occasions that the communication cables going to the computer terminals were run physically in parallel with, and in the same raceway, as power cables. The power cables have strong magnetic fields which can introduce noise into the communication cables, resulting in data corruption. The practice of running communication cables together with power cables must be avoided. Where communication cables and power cables meet, they should cross at ninety-degree angles to minimize the effects of radiated electrical noise.

Harmonics

A harmonic study was done at the main showroom office distribution panel to determine whether or not harmonic distortion was a contributing factor to the performance problems encountered at this facility. Although significant amounts of third harmonic currents are expected to be, and are, present at this facility, it was determined that the 2% voltage distortion measured is not a contributing factor to the performance problems of the computer system.

Background—The Zero Signal Reference Grid

Both the IEEE-1992 and FIPS 94 standards pay great attention to a grounding concept referred to as a zero signal reference grid (ZSRG). The idea of the zero signal reference grid is to develop a grounding system that will prevent the proliferation of undesirable electrical noise. The intent is to provide an extraordinarily low ground path impedance (at all frequencies) to all computer equipment attached to a common system. For example, if an individual were to take a volt-ohm meter and measure across the ground pins of any two power receptacles in the system, a measurement of zero ohms and zero volts would always be read. Of course, creating a zero impedance grounding system is impossible, but the ground impedance should still be kept as low as possible. Data centers that are able to concentrate all their operations in relatively small areas can install a zero signal reference grid and have it work very effectively. Problems due to electrical noise are rare.

On the other hand, large facilities, such as this automobile dealership, which have components of a common computer system located in several different buildings, are more likely to experience problems due to electrical noise. The reason for this is that all the different pieces of computer equipment located in the different buildings have different ground potentials. A zero signal reference grid is impossible to build at this type of facility. For example, if a volt-ohm meter were connected to the ground plug of a power receptacle in the main computer room and to a ground plug of a power receptacle in the main showroom office area substantial resistance would be measured. In addition, substantial voltage differences could be read.

All this becomes more complicated when communication cables are connected between different pieces of computer equipment sitting at different ground potentials. The communication cables contain signal ground cables and/or shields which sit at chassis or ground potential. If the ground potentials of the interconnected pieces of computer equipment are not the same (a likely scenario), current will flow through the grounding system into the communication cable's signal ground and/or shields and return to the grounding system. Magnetic fields are generated and common-mode noise voltages are induced into other conductors in the communication cables. The result is data corruption or equipment malfunction.

Neutral-to-Ground Measurements

A Fluke 87 digital voltmeter was placed at the neutral and ground pins of a power receptacle of a Lexmar laser printer in the main showroom office area. When the laser printer started to print, a 7.0 volt peak-to-peak voltage disturbance was recorded from neutral to ground. Manufacturers who recommend isolated ground systems usually like to see 1.0 Volt RMS (2.8 volts peak-to-peak) or less neutral-to-ground voltage. This test was repeated (with the same results) at another Lexmar laser printer to ensure that the power supply in the first laser printer was operating properly. The Lexmar laser printer is putting substantial amounts of noise onto the grounding system and should be investigated.

Conclusion

The purpose of LGS's visit to the automobile dealership was to determine whether or not the Acme data processing system was experiencing problems due to an inadequate electrical system. The electrical system at this site is not conducive to computer operations. The methods used for distributing power are far outdated. Having computer equipment which shares a common system in different buildings provides additional problems. It is impossible to achieve a zero signal reference grid when the entire computer room is scattered across several buildings. As computer technology (processor speeds) improve, the symptoms are like to worsen. Below are our recommendations:

1. Replacing all the computer power circuits with dedicated computer grade transformers, a dedicated distribution panel for computer loads, and a correctly installed isolated ground system will help, but may not solve all problems. The effect of this new system will be limited because the noise problem is due to computer equipment connected at different ground potentials in different buildings.

2. Replacing the current communication cables with fiber optics would offer more desired results. Fiber optics convert electrical impulses into light. They help eliminate the ground loop problems due to computer equipment operating at different ground potentials. This solution provides excellent noise isolation and is commonplace in industrial settings.

Data corruption due to electrical noise can be a very difficult problem to diagnose and resolve. Many times the best solution is an environmental design which eliminates and isolates the sources of electrical noise. A well-designed and installed power distribution system which is dedicated only to computer equipment is the best way to minimize the amount and effect of electrical noise. Data corruption due to noise currents that are present on communication links is not easily eliminated. The most common method of eliminating noise on communication links is to replace the wire cables with fiber optic links. If this is not possible the source of the electrical noise must be removed.

This information was provided by Liebert Corporation. It is a sample of the quality of information resources they have to offer consult Chapter 4 for considerable detail about electrical considerations and the Liebert UPS used in this network.

Computer Cables and Accessories (Belkin)

Today many computers that operate with laser printers, plotters, and the like require special cables. Cables, gender changes, and other ancillary devices are critical in the connectivity of computers and peripheral devices. This network required considerable numbers of cables and accessories.

The list of Belkin components I used includes:

- IBM/PC Hayes Modem Gold Premium DB25 F/M 6'
- Hayes Modem Gold DB25 F/M 10'
- Super VGA Monitor Extension Cable M/M 10'
- Serial DB25 M/F 10'
- IEEE 1284 A-B Cable Centronics 36P 35'
- IEEE 1284 A-B Cable Centronics 36P 20'
- IEEE 1284 A-B Cable Centronics 36P 20'
- Gender Changer DB9-F/DB9-F
- Gender Changer DB15-M/DB15-M
- Gender Changer DB25P/DB25P
- SCSI 2 Interface Cable DB50P-M/DB50P-M 12'
- Micro DB68P Terminator (Active SCSI)
- SCSI-III Differential Terminator DB68P Single Ended.

For additional information visit www.belkin.com; or write Belkin Components, 501 West Walnut Street, Compton, CA 90220.

Software Troubleshooting Tools

Windows 95 and NT have commands available that can provide valuable information in the troubleshooting of computers and networks.

Figure 7.20 is a diagnostic command used on Muscle. The checkdisk command reveals the information shown in the figure. If any corrupt files are discovered a notation will be made and presented in the report the command is capable of generating.

FIGURE 7.20
Diagnostic
Information for
Muscle

```
The type of the file system is FAT.
Volume  MUSCLE   created 6/10/97 4:26 AM
Volume Serial Number is 0833-E695


CHKDSK is verifying files and directories...

0 percent completed.
1 percent completed.
20 percent completed.
25 percent completed.
50 percent completed.
75 percent completed.
100 percent completed.

File and directory verification completed.

146631680 bytes total disk space.
7503872 bytes in 159 hidden files.
6094848 bytes in 186 directories.
350224384 bytes in 2907 user files.
1782808576 bytes available on disk.

32768 bytes in each allocation unit.
65510 total allocation units on disk.
54407 allocation units available on disk.
```

Figure 7.21 shows the results of the scan disk function that is a part of the Windows program. It is used for disk maintenance. Notice that Fat-Boy has one lost allocation unit found in one chain. If this lost allocation unit were corrected there would be an additional 32,768 bytes freed for use.

Figure 7.22 shows the Windows NT NETstat statistics command issued against Brains. The result is shown in the number of bytes received from other workstations, the number of server message blocks received and transmitted, the number of connections made, and other information.

FIGURE 7.21
Windows
Diagnostics for
Fat-Boy

Volume **FAT-BOY**   created 02-22-1997 7:50p
Volume Serial Number is 3155-1AFF
Errors found, F parameter not specified
Corrections will not be written to disk

1 lost allocation units found in 1 chains.
    32,768 bytes disk space would be freed

1,704,951,808 bytes total disk space
  20,840,448 bytes in 217 hidden files
  13,565,952 bytes in 414 directories
  708,608,000 bytes in 7,659 user files
  961,904,640 bytes available on disk

    32,768 bytes in each allocation unit
    52,030 total allocation units on disk
    29,354 available allocation units on disk

    655,360 total bytes memory
    615,152 bytes free

FIGURE 7.22
Windows NT
NetStat Command

Workstation Statistics for \\BRAINS

Statistics since 3/25/98 10:46 AM

Bytes received   181134
Server Message Blocks (SMBs) received   339
Bytes transmitted   33830
Server Message Blocks (SMBs) transmitted   339
Read operations   36
Write operations   0
Raw reads denied   0
Raw writes denied   0

Network errors   0
Connections made   34
Reconnections made   0
Server disconnects   2

Sessions started   36
Hung sessions   0
Failed sessions   0
Failed operations   0
Use count   87
Failed use count   1

The command completed successfully.

Figure 7.23 shows the NETstat server command issued against Muscle. Notice those workstations connected.

FIGURE 7.23
Windows NT NET
Command

```
Server Name          Remark

------------------------------------------------------------------------
\\BRAINS
\\FAT BOY            ED TAYLOR
\\MUSCLE
\\RENEGADE
The command completed successfully.
```

Figure 7.24 shows the NET SHARE command issued against Muscle. Notice the *shares* available on the system. This identifies those shares that users throughout the network can access. A host of other commands can be used at the command line within Windows NT and Windows-based computers. Figure 7.25 is an example of this.

FIGURE 7.24
Windows NT Net
Share Command

```
Share name   Resource              Remark

------------------------------------------------------------------------
REPL$        C:\WINNT\System32\Repl\Export
print$       C:\WINNT\System32\spool\DRIVERS Printer Drivers
IPC$                               Remote IPC
C$           C:\                   Default share
D$           D:\                   Default share
ADMIN$       C:\WINNT                 Remote Admin
anybody      D:\                   thismeansu
MUSCLE -  D
             D:\               D - MUSCLE
MUSCLE - A   A:\                  its the A drive dummy
MUSCLE - C   C:\                  STRONG MAN
MUSCLE - D   D:\                  U GOT IT
MUSCLE-E     E:\                  18-E
U-GOT-ME     C:\                  U  GOT  ME
DOTMAN       LPT1:             Spooled  DOT MAN
The command completed successfully.
```

Figure 7.25 shows the results of the Ping command. From a command line within Windows NT I issued a Ping command against Brains to test the accessibility of a given host. The results inform me that 32 bytes were received from Brains whose IP address is 220.100.100.12 in less that 10ms.

FIGURE 7.25
Windows NT Ping
Command

Pinging brains [220.100.100.12] with 32 bytes of data:

Reply from 220.100.100.12: bytes=32 time=10ms TTL=128
Reply from 220.100.100.12: bytes=32 time<10ms TTL=128
Reply from 220.100.100.12: bytes=32 time<10ms TTL=128
Reply from 220.100.100.12: bytes=32 time<10ms TTL=128

Software commands can be helpful in diagnosing network problems. The trick is to understand the information available from these commands. Many additional commands are available in Windows NT and Windows. Take time to review the documentation with the software and explore this aspect of system support.

Miscellaneous Devices/Tools

Deep exploration of the design of a network reveals that some things must be extensively looked for or created.

External CD-ROM

In this network existed a need for an external CD-ROM that could connect via SCSI to the USRobotics hub, laptops, and Hewlett-Packard internet advisor.

A Sony CD-ROM, model PRD-650WN was used. Whether or not this particular device will be available as you read this, is a different story. Should this specific device not be available, some vendor will make an SCSI-attach CD-ROM. This device works well; the technology is genuine Sony and Adaptec for the SCSI PCMCIA card and the device is a must-have for network installers and administrators.

Wire Testers

A cable tester is necessary to check AC cables, data cables of all sorts, RJ45 wire, RJ11 wire, RJ11 wall connectors, and so forth. Do not assume that because something is "new" it is "good." No equipment or cable in this network was discovered "bad," but that does not mean you should not test cables and connection points.

Fluke meters provide AC test ability. This same equipment can be used to obtain anmperage readings, cable test, and so on. I ordered two devices specifically to check cable: one was for RJ45 and the other for RJ11 wire.

Break-out AC Test Cable

I make my own extension cords. Any single one of them could be used to supply voltage and current to multiple dryers, ovens, or other high amperage devices. Electricity demands respect; you can give it or it will be taken.

Who knows if my break-out AC test wire is UL Listed or not; but the cables work. I bought 10 gauge SO-type wire—two conductor with ground. Connect a regular 110 volt three-prong connector on one end. On the other end put one or two pairs of regular electrical outlets in a metal box with enclosed top. Carefully take about 6–8 inches of outer sheath off the conductors. Three conductors should be exposed with insulation. Tape these ends where the cuts were made; clamp an AMP probe around the hot wire without going into any danger areas and get the amperage pull off the line. I do not recommend that you do this. I am only describing what I did. This level of information assisted me in the design phase of ground floor of the network. I had to go back and draw four clean lines to the breaker box to accommodate the new equipment.

Again make it your business to know the electrical part of your network. If you do not have the education and background for this then get somebody who does. You cannot afford not to have this base covered.

Summary

This and the previous chapter covered almost all the aspects of network design. Do not forget to factor in time for interacting with the companies with whom you decide to do business. If you have established relationships that is all the better, but if you do not, factor in additional time.

Remember: network design is similar to designing a house. Once the foundation is laid things are in "cement" and not easily moved. Do your homework. You should be able to work through the majority of your network on the marker board and/or on paper first. If you do so, you may find it a bit less expensive.

CHAPTER **8**

APPN
Technology and
Blueprints

Advanced Peer-to-Peer Networking (APPN) is a peer-oriented architecture that predates most of the personal computers (PCs) in use today. Though most current applications are peer-oriented, this has not always been the case.

In 1986 IBM announced support for T2.1 nodes with the System 36 (S/36). That same year IBM introduced its SNA Type 2.1 Node Reference Manual, number SC30-3422. It defined the beginnings of APPN implementations. Nodes can be understood best by knowing the services they provide or characteristics that represent them. Both architectural design and characteristics supported define a node type.

It is best to view APPN from this abstract viewpoint because it does not really matter which host or model number a device is. The core of APPN is that it uses LU6.2. The question to ask is: "Which functions/features are supported by a certain device with respect to APPN?"

Origins and Evolution

Version 1

Version 1 can be characterized by low entry networking end nodes or APPN end nodes. According to the IBM Type 2.1 Architecture Manual #SC30-3422, published 1991, these two references to end nodes are synonymous.

IBM documentation also states, "a T2.1 node is that node which uses protocols that require less system requirements." A T2.1 node provides peer connectivity, and session-level connectivity using LU6.2 protocols.

APPN version 1 can best be described as an evolution. According to the Type 2.1 Architecture Manual, three types of nodes were identifiable with T2.1 architecture:

- APPN Network Node (NN)
- APPN End Node (APPN EN)
- LEN End Node (LEN EN).

APPN NNs:

- Are capable of performing intermediate session routing
- Perform directory searches and route selection
- Provide LU-LU service for local LUs.

Consider Figure 8.1.

FIGURE 8.1
Conceptual
View of a
Network Node

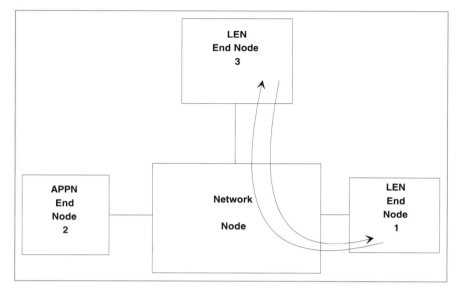

APPN ENs:

- Can perform limited directory services
- Can register their LUs with an NN
- Can be attached to multiple NNs.

Consider Figure 8.2.

FIGURE 8.2
Conceptual
View of Two
APPN End Nodes

LEN ENs:

- Cannot register LUs with an NN
- Must have predefined remote LUs via the system
- Use T2.1 protocols *without* APPN enhancements.

Consider Figure 8.3.

FIGURE 8.3
Conceptual
View of Two
LEN End Nodes

Traces of version 1 can be seen through IBM product offerings from 1986 to 1992. An example of one such offering supporting APPN is the AS/400, announced in 1988. Other products were announced during that period, but a significant break with version 1 came in 1992.

APPN Version 2

APPN version 2 can be identified by IBM's APPN Architecture Reference number SC30-3422, published in March 1993. Here, IBM clearly defines extensions to earlier APPN and LEN networking.

IBM started to bring APPN together in 1992 with the announcement of VTAM 4.1. (shipped in May 1993), which permits VTAM to participate with other nodes in an APPN network and appear as another peer node. Technically this capability was available in VTAM 3.2; support for causal connections came with VTAM 3.3.

Correlations with T2.1 Architecture

APPN has its roots in T2.1 architecture and has evolved into its present state; IBM will probably continue to enhance it.

APPN simplifies network definition, permits dynamic route selection and provides a distributed directory service. This function determines remote LUs that may be known locally only by name. This means manual definition for routes or location of remote LUs is not required.

APPN implementations can select routes based upon user defined criteria. A component in each NN called a control point (CP) is used to determine the best route from the initiating LU to the destination LU. APPN also supports intermediate session routing of data through the NN for sessions that do not originate or terminate with that NN. Transmission priority is established based upon the class of service specified by the user.

Node Types

APPN's approach to networking parallels that of client/server. This architectural nature lends APPN to a "peer" oriented network. Discussion follows of the pivotal questions of what node types exist, what functions they perform, and what additional APPN option sets exist.

APPN Node Types

APPN Network Node (NN)

A major role of the NN is performing the function of *server*. In this context, other nodes participate as *clients*. This concept of client/server is similar but not identical to TCP/IP clients/servers. An NN functions as a server to the end nodes attached to it. The NN and its attached end nodes are considered a domain. NN services include:

- Directory services
- Route services
- Intermediate LU-LU Routing
- End node management services
- LU-LU session services
- Support for any APPN or LEN node attachment with the same network ID
- Function as a *server* for its clients
- Support for SNA subarea boundary nodes.

APPN End Node

In light of the client/server parallel of APPN, an end node functions like a client. End nodes support LU6.2. Without an NN, ENs can only communicate via LU-LU sessions with the partner LU located in an adjacent node. However, with an NN a EN can communicate with remote LUs. These types of nodes have the ability to inform an NN of their local LUs. ENs can have active links to multiple nodes at any given time, but an EN can have CP-CP sessions with only one NN at a given instance. ENs can have attachments to multiple NNs in case one NN fails. Examine Figure 8.4.

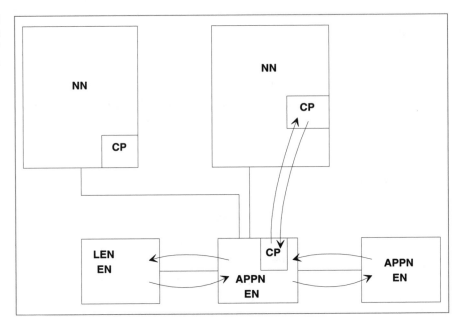

FIGURE 8.4
Conceptual View
of CP-CP Session

This type of node can make a connection to any LEN or APPN-type node. An EN cannot have CP-CP sessions with another EN.

LEN End Node

This type of node implements basic T2.1 protocols; no APPN enhancements are included. A LEN EN is not capable of having a CP-CP session. Connections with destinations must be predefined. A LEN EN communicates with remote LUs via system definition. At system definition time the CP name of the adjacent node is defined and local LUs can then be accessed. The LEN EN accesses some remote LUs by the services provided via the NN server functions. Consider Figure 8.5.

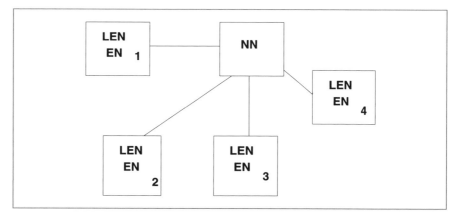

FIGURE 8.5
LEN ENs Defined
to the NN

Peripheral Border Node

These nodes do not support intermediate network routing, but do support the following:

- Directory services
- Session establishment
- Route selection
- Session establishment of LUs between adjacent subnetworks.

Figure 8.6 is an example of this type of node.

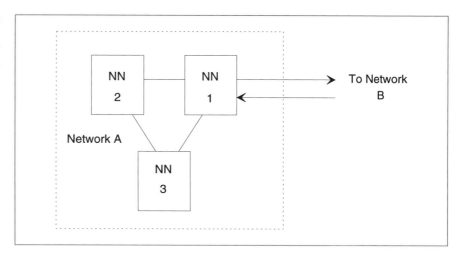

FIGURE 8.6
Conceptual View
of a Peripheral
Border Node

Extended Border Node

This type of node supports intermediate network routing, but the subnetworks must be predefined. The nodes provide the following:

- Directory services
- Session establishment
- Route selection
- The partitioning of a subnetwork into two or more clusters.

Figure 8.7 depicts four networks with a LU-LU session between peripheral networks via intermediate networks with extended boundary node function support.

FIGURE 8.7
Conceptual View
of an Extended
Border Node

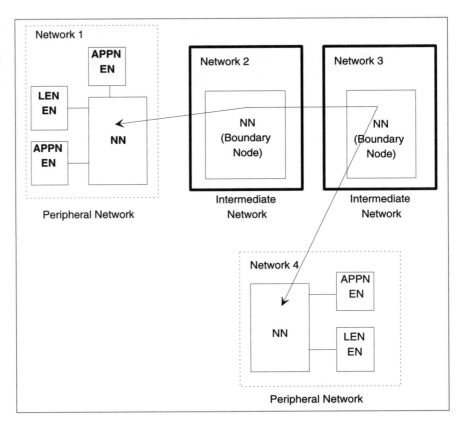

APPN-Subarea Interchange Node (IN)

This is a T5 node in SNA feature/function. It permits connectivity between APPN networks and SNA networks. An IN achieves this by mapping routing, directory, session setup, and route selection for both network types. Figure 8.8 is an example of this.

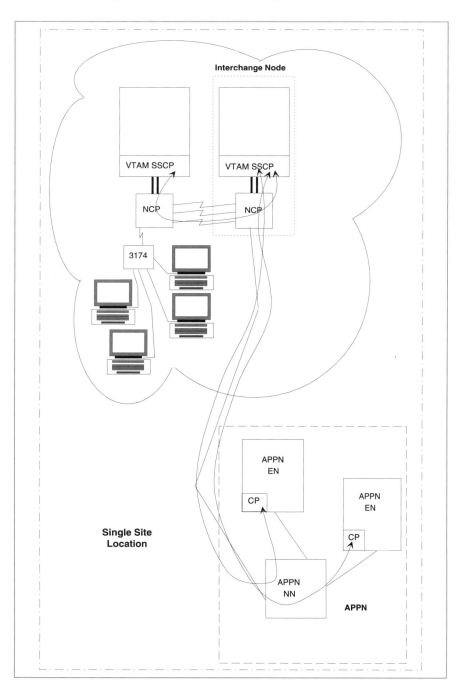

FIGURE 8.8
APPN and
Subarea SNA
via an
Interchange Node

Migration Data Host

Beginning with VTAM 4.1 a host node can:

- Emulate a APPN End Node in an APPN network
- Support subarea connections
- Perform Cross Domain Resource Manager functions.

It does not participate in broadcast searches in APPN networks. The migration data host is primarily a host dedicated to processing applications. It functions not only as an EN in an APPN network, but also to support subarea connections in traditional SNA.

High-Performance Routing (HPR) Node

HPR is fundamentally an extension to APPN as defined by IBM. Operationally, HPR is implemented into APPN network nodes or APPN end nodes. Practically, HPR implemented in APPN provides a high-performance method to perform routing and the realization of the routing function is enhanced because of the high-speed links that connect. HPR, in APPN, provides a method to control congestion in the network and it enables enhanced throughput in the network. HPR in APPN is also able to perform routing of sessions away from nodes or links that have become unavailable.

A key component of HPR is Rapid Transport Protocol (RTP). This is connection-oriented and full-duplex. These characteristics enable higher speeds within the bandwidth in which the technology is used. A function of RTP is the non-disruptive path switch, a sort of dynamic path allocation ability. Another key function of RTP is the error recovery it employs from end to end. This is performed in all network links. A byproduct of end-to-end error recovery is the congestion control mechanism built into RTP.

Another key component of HPR is Automatic Network Routing (ANR). This minimizes storage and processing requirements for routing functions, including fast packet switching. Many functions that make ANR possible occur at RTP connection endpoints. Another characteristic of ANR is lack of session awareness. The result of this is the absence of the requirement for maintenance of routing tables related to session connectors. ANR is characteristically a source routing protocol. Required routing information is carried in the network header in each packet. This could be viewed as routing-on-the-fly.

APPN Node Structure

At the core of APPN lie the three nodes previously mentioned:

- APPN Network Node
- APPN End Node
- LEN End Node.

These nodes are built around the structure displayed in Figure 8.9.

FIGURE 8.9
Conceptual View
of APPN Node
Structure

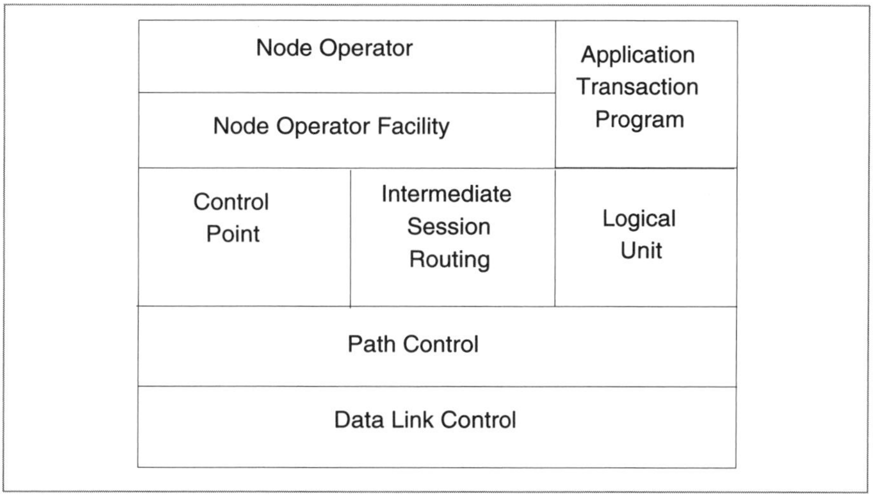

Node Operator	Application Transaction Program
Node Operator Facility	

Control Point	Intermediate Session Routing	Logical Unit

Path Control

Data Link Control

Components of the node are:

- Data link control
- Path control
- Logical unit
- Intermediate session routing
- Control point
- Node operator facility.

Each of these is explained below, along with subcomponents and multiple functions.

Data Link Control (DLC)

DLC is the interface with the link connection and provides data link protocols. The function of DLC is to establish communication between nodes, maintain the synchronization between nodes, give acknowledgments, perform error recovery when required, and sequence data flow. Figure 8.10 shows how the DLC appears conceptually.

FIGURE 8.10
Conceptual
View of Data
Link Control

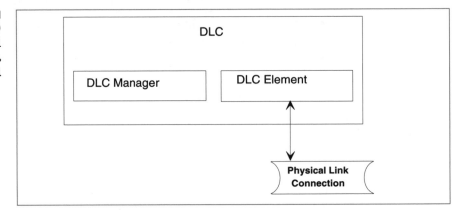

This part of the node is responsible for communication with a physical link and consists of two components. The DLC element is responsible for:

- Moving data to the physical medium
- Performing retransmissions
- Moving data to and from other DLC elements
- Managing the DLC and Path Control boundary
- Receiving traffic from the session.

Figure 8.11 depicts the relationship of the element within the node.

FIGURE 8.11
The Role of the
Element

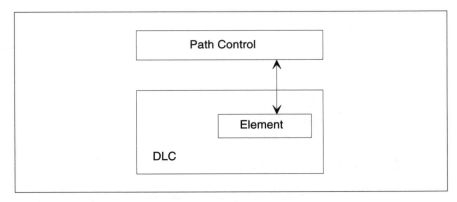

The DLC Manager performs the following functions:

- Activating the DLC element
- Deactivating the DLC element
- Activating links
- Deactivating links
- Passing parameters to the CP when a station becomes operative or otherwise
- Controlling the boundary between the CP and the DLC.

Figure 8.12 depicts the relationship of the manager with other node components.

FIGURE 8.12
Functionality of the Manager

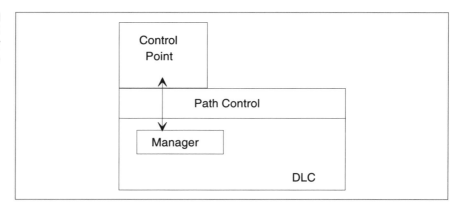

Figure 8.13 shows how the DLC communicates with the medium, internally, with the session, and with the control point.

Path Control (PC)

The PC component in the node also has two components; an element and a manager. Functions include:

- Element functions:
  - Error checking on messages received from the DLC element
  - Generation of segments for outbound messages
  - Message conversion from messages received from the DLC
  - Prioritizing message transmission to the DLC component
  - Routing messages between the PC manager, Half Session (HS), Session Connector (SC), and the DLC component.

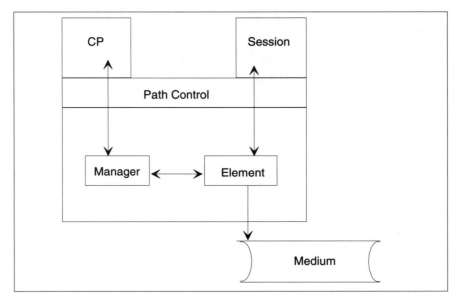

FIGURE 8.13
Functionality of
DLC as a Whole

Figure 8.14 shows how the PC component appears and its relationship to the DLC component.

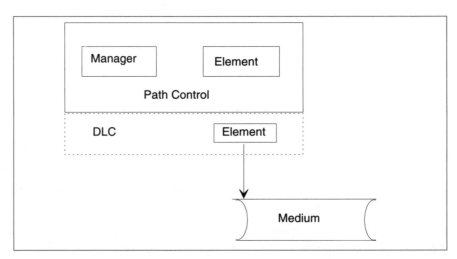

FIGURE 8.14
Conceptual
View of the
Path Control

- Manager functions include:
    - Session connection
    - Session disconnection
    - Stopping outbound data traffic upon notification
    - Interaction with the CP.

Figure 8.15 shows the relationship of the PC with the CP and the parts that aid in session establishment.

FIGURE 8.15
PC, CP, and
Session
Establishment
Relationship

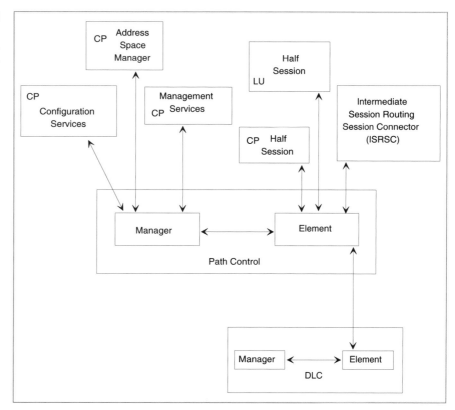

General characteristics of the PC include routing messages between destination nodes and LUs residing in the same node. The PC routes messages from the DLC to the appropriate component, such as: the CP, LU, or the ISR component.

Logical Unit (LU)

The LU has many ports that enable it to communicate with the PC, LUs in another node, and other components within the same node. Figure 8.16 is a conceptual view of an LU's correlation to the APPN node structure as a whole.

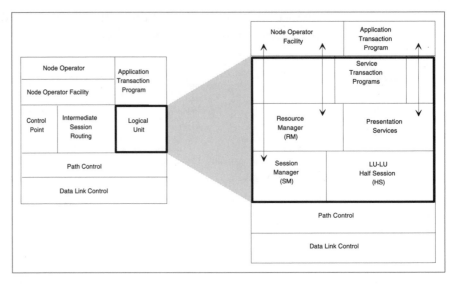

FIGURE 8.16
The LU with Respect to the Node Structure

The LU serves as a port (addressable point) for application transaction programs. The components that make up a LU include:

- LU-LU half session
- Session manager
- Presentation service component
- Resource manager
- Service transaction programs.

LU-LU Half Session

This part of the LU is comprised of two components: data flow control and transmission control. The half session component controls local and remote LU communications. The data flow control part of the half session performs the following functions:

- Creates Request/Response Headers (RH)
- Insures proper RH parameters are in place
- Insures proper Function Management (FM) profile for the session
- Manages bracket protocol
- Flushes rejected brackets
- Is responsible for generating chaining.

The transmission control part of the LU performs these functions:

- Session level pacing
- Examining received sequence numbers for possible BIU errors

- Reassembling RUs
- Enforcing the exchange of cryptography verification when it is used
- Enciphering session cryptography when used
- Deciphering session cryptography when required
- Providing reassembly for RUs that have been segmented.

Session Manager

The session manager performs these functions:

- Sending the BIND
- Being the recipient of the BIND
- Creating half-session instances
- Connecting half sessions to the path control
- Supplying session parameters during the BIND exchange
- Negotiating parameters during the BIND exchange
- Informing the resource manager when session outage occurs.

Presentation Services Component

The presentation services component performs the following functions:

- Calling a transaction program
- Loading a transaction program
- Keeping the send or receive state alive with the transaction program
- Putting data into logical records
- Mapping transaction program data into mapped conversation records
- Confirming logical record length
- Generating FM headers for an ATTACH and providing error information.

Other functions exist, but those listed cover the major operations of the LU component.

Resource Manager (RM)

The resource manager works in conjunction with presentation services and conversations flowing between transaction programs. Basic functions of the RM include:

- Creating presentation service instances
- Destroying presentation service instances
- Creating conversation resources
- Connecting conversation resources to the half session and to presentation services
- Destroying conversation resources
- Maintaining data structures
- Enforcing session level security
- Generating the FM Header 12 (Security Header).

Service Transaction Programs (STPs)

These programs make up the transaction services layer and can be used to Change the Number of Sessions (CNOS). They also interact with the Node Operator Facility.

Intermediate Session Routing (ISR)

Figure 8.17 shows the structure of the ISR facility.

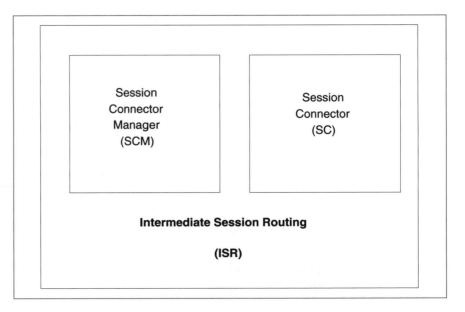

FIGURE 8.17
Conceptual View
of ISR Component

The ISR consists of two components: the Session Connector (SC) and the Session Connector Manager (SCM). An SC is allocated for each session and performs the following functions:

- Routing
- Pacing
- Reassembly of Basic Information Units (BIUs)
- Monitoring the session for errors
- Performing intermediate reassembly.

This component is responsible for routing session traffic through intermediate nodes.

The SCM performs the following functions:

- Intermediate BIND and UNBIND processing
- Creating, initializing, and eliminating session connectors
- Connecting SCs to the PC
- Buffer reservation.

Figure 8.18 shows the correlation between the components of the ISR and other components in the node.

FIGURE 8.18
ISR
Communication
with Other
Components

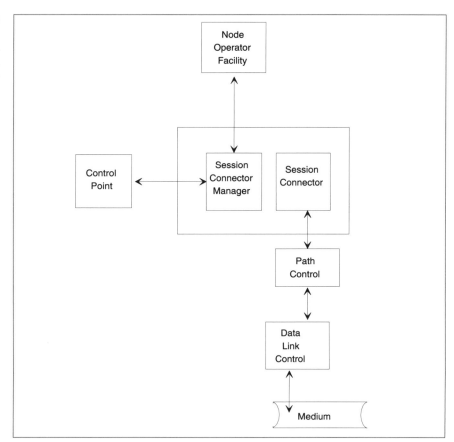

Control Point (CP)

The CP manages resources within a node; using CP-to-CP sessions to exchange management information. According to IBM documentation, the CP may be merged with the LU; this is an implementation issue. For our purposes the CP is treated as a separate entity.

Another way of defining the CP is based on the IBM APPN Architecture Manual, #SC30-3422, which states:

> (1) A component of an APPN or LEN node that manages the resources of that node. In an APPN node, the CP is capable of engaging in CP-CP sessions with other APPN nodes. In an APPN network node, the CP provides services to adjacent end nodes in the APPN network. (2) A component of a node that manages resources of that node and optionally provides services to other nodes in the network. Examples are a system services control point (SSCP) in a type 5 node, a physical unit control point (PUCP) in a type 4 subarea node, a network node control point (NNCP) in an APPN network node, and an end node control point (ENCP) in an APPN or LEN end node. An SSCP and an NNCP can provide services to other nodes.

The focus here is upon the components within the CP and their function. Figure 8.19 is a conceptual example of how the CP appears.

The following explanation will be helpful.

Configuration Services (CS)

This component manages physical link connections of the node itself. Functions include:

- **Link Activation.** The CS exchanges information with the DLC. Exchange Identification parameters (XIDs) are passed to insure each node's abilities are understood. Figure 18.19 shows the CS relative to the DLC and the PC.
- **Link Deactivation.** When a link is deactivated the CS performs cleanup functions then notifies the appropriate components within the node.
- **Link queries** are performed.
- **Exchange of XID3** can occur if link or node characteristics change while the link is active.
- **Link definition is verified.** The CS saves this definition when activating and deactivating the link.

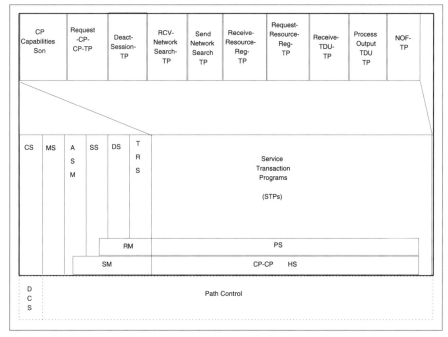

Management Services (MS)

This component handles alert level locally. Other components in the node log alert information in the local node. This component communicates with a number of other components within the node such as the ISR, NOF, and the PC.

Address Space Manager (ASM)

The ASM handles the address spaces related to each local Transmission Group (TG) within a node. In APPN, a TG is synonymous with a *link*. In each address space a Local Form Session Identifier (LSFID) is defined. Additionally, one address space correlates with a TG (link).

The ASM performs these functions:

- Designating session addresses
- Activating an address space
- Deactivating an address space
- Freeing address spaces upon request
- Routing nonrelated session data
- Pacing BINDs via adaptive pacing
- Assembling BINDs received as segments.

The ASM communicates with the PC, NOF, and other components within the node.

Session Services (SS)

SS primarily focus upon initialization and termination of sessions, CP-CP and LU-LU. Specific functions include:

- Procedure Correlation Identifiers (also known as Fully Qualified Procedure Correlation Identifiers, FQPCIDs)
- Initiation of sessions
- CP-CP session activation
- CP-CP session deactivation
- Termination of sessions
- Monitoring of the active number of sessions.

Directory Services (DS)

The DS functions depend upon whether the node is NN or EN. The DS maintains the node directory within that node, except in LEN end nodes. It provides the ability to search and update directories in other nodes throughout the network. Other functions it performs include:

- **End Node Searches.** In ENs, three types of searches can be identified: a search initiated locally, a search initiated from a remote node, and the sending of a search request to an NN. In this latter case the NN actually performs the search; it functions as a proxy.
- **Network Node Searches.** DS examines its own directory for resources owned by that node or by associated end nodes.
- **End Node Updates.** Local directory updates are performed via system definition.
- **Network Node Updates.** There are three ways these are achieved: as a result of systems definition; dynamic updates occur as a result of communication with the NN server's client nodes; after network search completion updates may be performed by data cached during the search.
- **End Node Registration and Deletion.** This function occurs only if the end node is authorized for it.
- **Network Node Directory Maintenance.** An NN performs updates and deletions based upon information received from nodes whose registration applies.

Topology and Routing Services

This component of the CP has three primary functions:

- **Class of Service Manager (COSM).** The COSM keeps the database updated. It notifies Route Selection Services when a class of service changes.
- **Route Selection Service (RSS).** This component functions differently in NNs and ENs. In an NN, the RSS determines preferred routes within the network and what transmission priority to use on selected routes. It also updates the topology database to reflect the most current topology. It specifies routes computed by the COS requested. The TG from origin to destination is selected by the RSS. In an EN, RSS selects a TG and transmission priority.
- **Topology Database Manager (TDM).** Functions are based on the node type. In an EN it maintains the topology database. In an NN it broadcasts to the network once changes are made locally. It performs a "periodic broadcast," a broadcast throughout the network in intervals of approximately five 24-hour days. It also *deletes* resources from the database if no data have been received about a resource in 15 days. It responds to remote queries.

Service Transaction Programs (STPs)

STPs in an APPN node exchange information over CP-CP sessions. They do not exist in LEN ENs. Transaction Programs include:

- **CP Capabilities/Sent Outside the Node (SON).** This is the only SS TP used to attach a remote node. Its purpose is two-fold: it sends the PC capabilities to another participating node, and it performs processing for session outage.
- Request_CP_CP_TP. When the SS wishes to start a CP-CP session with another node, this TP is used to invoke the Request CP Capabilities TP.
- Deact_Session_TP. This deactivates a CP-CP session to a specific node.
- Receive_Network_Search_TP. They receive a locate search from an adjacent APPN node.
- Send_Network_Search_TP. This is an APPN node that sends a locate search request/reply to a remote directory service.
- Receive_Resource_Registration_TP. This occurs when an APPN NN sends registration and deletion variables to an APPN EN pertaining to specified resources.

- `Request_Resource_Registration_TP`. This is an instance in which an APPN EN sends registration and delete information to the target APPN NN.
- `Receive_TDU_TP`. Here an NN TRS communicates with a `TDP_TP` receiving information from an adjacent node.
- `Process_Output_TDU_TP`. TDM sends a signal to the `Process_Output_TDU_TP` when a local node wants to broadcast topology information.
- `NOF_TP`. This is involved in the startup of a node operator facility.

Node Operator Facility (NOF)

This component initializes the CP and ISR upon starting the node. It is the user interface for the CP, ISR, and LUs Through it the following functions can be achieved:

- Activating links
- Deactivating links
- Creating LUs
- Deleting LUs
- Ascertaining status information
- Retrieving database information
- Defining:
  - Directory information
  - Local and remote LUs
  - Node characteristics
  - Session limits
  - Transaction programs
  - Links
  - Starting TPs
  - Determining other CP names.

More details are provided about the NOF later in this chapter.

Directory Services (DS)

The concept behind the DS component is the responsibility for resource searches both for the local node and for those throughout an APPN network. DS are responsible for the registration of resources to NNs where they function as servers for DS.

The DS component of the CP has three major functions:

1. Directory database
2. Maintaining CP Status
3. Network Search.

Figure 8.20 shows these three components of the DS.

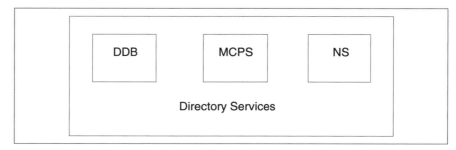

FIGURE 8.20
Conceptual View
of Directory
Service
Components

DDB   MCPS   NS

Directory Services

The Directory Database (DDB) function performs lookup and maintenance for directory services.

The maintain control point status function keeps a log of other CPs wishing to communicate with the CP in that node. In NNs it keeps track of end nodes (clients) and it also maintains information on other NNs with which it can establish CP-CP sessions.

The network search function component sends and receives research search requests to and from other nodes in the network.

Understanding the terminology is important for examining the DS component.

Directory Service Terminology

- **Authorized Node.** When this term is used in conjunction with DS it means information sent about itself is accepted. An unauthorized node cannot use certain protocols and is refused the ability to register its LUs in the distributed directory.
- **Border Node.** This is an NN connecting APPN networks that maintain different databases reflecting their topology. Peripheral border nodes support directory services, session setup, and route selection between networks of different identifiers. This type of node does not support intermediate routing. An extended border node provides session setup, directory services, and routing through a boundary of different networks when these networks have different topologies.

- **Central Directory Server (CDS).** This function resides in an NN. It differs from that of DS because the CDS maintains all resource information within a network. More than one CDS can exist in a network.
- **CP Send and Receive Session.** The DS uses CP-CP sessions between APPN EN and the NN server. This session carries the `Locate_Search` function.
- **Distributed Directory Database (DDD).** Directories of resources exist throughout the APPN network. The DDD is the collective whole of the databases throughout the network.
- **Local Directory Database (LDD).** This refers specifically to the local directory database in a given node.
- **Locate Search.** This is the method by which a DS finds resources not in the node. A locate search can be one of the following:
  - **Broadcast Search.** This is sent throughout the entire network.
  - **Directed Search.** This is sent to a known location for verification.
  - **Domain Search.** This is an NN communication with client ENs to verify resources in a given location.
- **DS User.** This is a component in a node which uses the DS.
- **Subnetwork.** This is a collection of nodes which have common characteristics such as a network address or database.

DS Functions

The function of the DS component is present in each T2.1 node; the degree to which it is exploited is contingent upon the node itself. DS functions in an NN include:

1. Maintaining a database of local resources and resources that have been cached because of a locate search function.
2. Providing the ability to determine the location of a specified resource.
3. Registering resources in a domain via the NOF or an EN (client).
4. Deactivating CP-CP sessions if the node is in a state of deadlock with respect to sending a locate search.
5. Providing support for intermediate nodes in locate searches.

DS in an APPN EN provide these functions:

1. Once notification of a CP-CP session failure has occurred DS cleans up any outstanding searches.

2. Locate resource searches with the NN are sent and received.
3. Resources are registered with the NN.
4. CP-CP sessions with the NN are supported.
5. A DD of local resources and adjacent node resources is maintained.

Directory Database (DD) Function

The DD is a distributed database containing lists of resources throughout the APPN network. For example, ENs keep information about their resources in their DD. An NN maintains an NOF. The NOF defines directory entries of resources in that node and in the nodes it serves. A major function of DD is keeping the database within the storage requirements for that node. In the DD various entries exist.

Types of Entries

Fundamentally, the directory database maintains information about its own resources. The following types of entries may be found.

Domain entries include resources in that domain, but located in one of the client nodes (end nodes). Other domain entries maintain information about resources in other domains as its name implies. Other network entries keep information about resources that can be reached by a different net ID.

Origination of Entries

As mentioned previously, a distributed directory is the individual, local databases viewed as a whole. Information gets into these directories by one of the following means:

1. NOF definition
2. APPN EN registration with an NN server via a CP-CP session.
3. Entry through the caching function as a result of the locate search function.

The Network Search Function (NSF)

The NSF maintains the protocols used while searching the distributed database. It also maintains control of the transport directory services, and also enforces logic with regard to the sending of directory service messages. Its primary purpose is location of network resources and control flow throughout the network of requests and replies.

Within the NSF a need may arise to send a request to another node asking for information about the directory in that node. When this is the case the message that flows is called a Locate Search. Locate searches can be identified as one-hop, directed, or broadcast.

The one-hop search is a locate search request exchanged between an APPN EN and an NN.

A directed search traverses a predefined path from one NN to another. The originating NN calculates a CP-CP path to the target node and adds routing information to the search. This works because each NN on the path uses this information to select the next hop. This search ensures that the most direct route to the destination node is obtained.

The broadcast search is used by NN to send a locate search request to multiple CPs. The two dominant types of broadcast searches are domain and network.

The domain broadcast search sends a locate search for the resource to adjacent APPN ENs. Because the possibility exists that more than one reply will return, the directory service uses the first positive reply.

The network broadcast search is sent to all NN nodes and is used to ascertain a resource location which cannot otherwise be found. It is used as the last attempt because this type of search permeates the network with requests for the location of the resource.

Locate searches can carry nondirectory service information. Which is used by the CP components for transport control data. The user is an application. For example, session services could use this to transport information variables. Information capable of being transported as nondirectory service information includes:

- Fully Qualified Procedure Correlation Identifier (FQPCID)
- Destination LU
- Mode name
- Class of Service (COS)
- Originating LU
- Endpoint vectors.

Central Directory Server (CDS)

The CDS resides in an APPN network. More than one can exist. The CDS accepts registration of resources from other network nodes.

Once information is received from the registrations of other nodes a central directory is maintained.

Directory Entry Contents

The contents of a directory entry depends upon node type. The contents of directory entries includes:

- **Resource name**
- **Resource type:** NN Control Point, EN Control Point, LU information
- **EN Control Point** uses a pointer to an adjacent CP status control block
- **Information about the hierarchy:** LU entries for NN servers, adjacent entries for an LU entry, the "child" LU entries for adjacent EN Control Points
- **Classification:** home, cached, or registered information regarding whether or not the resource can be or has been registered with the CDS.

Topology and Routing Services (TRS)

TRS is present in each NN and in a lesser form (with respect to functionality) in APPN ENs, and LEN ENs. In NNs TRS creates and maintains the class of service database and is responsible for maintaining a copy of the network topology database.

In end nodes the TRS creates and maintains the local topology database. It is also responsible for the class of service table.

The TRS consist of three components: Class-of-Service Manager; Route Selection Service; and Topology Database Manager (TDM).

Figure 8.21 shows these three components.

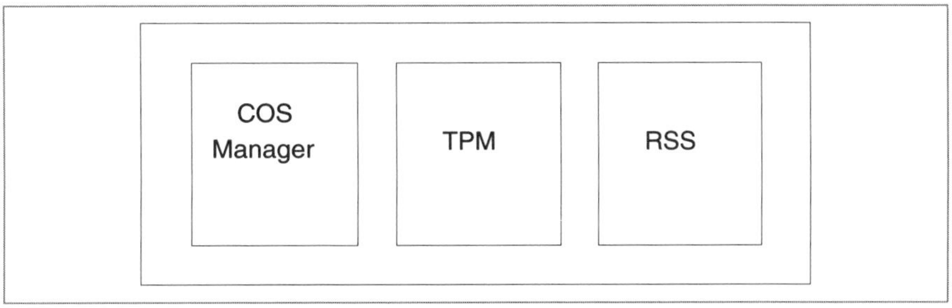

FIGURE 8.21
Conceptual View of Topology and Routing Services Components

The class-of-service manager enables translation of a mode name to a COS name. This is a base function for NNs, but is optional for ENs.

Route selection service computes routes. It selects the path from origin to destination. It computes the most efficient route between nodes in an APPN network.

The TDM maintains the COS and topology databases. In NNs it maintains the network topology database and, on one or the other ends, it maintains local topology information.

Class-of-Service (COS) Database

The COS database exists in all NNS and in those end nodes which support them. It contains:

- Mode names which include a pointer to a COS name
- COS names which have COS definitions representing characteristics of the node, transmission priority, and assigned weight
- Weight index structure for computing the actual transmission group weight.

Each COS entry in the COS database contains such basic information as:

- COS name
- Transmission priority
- Transmission group characteristics;
- Security level
- Cost per byte
- Propagation delay
- Other characteristics.

Route Selection Service

A route in APPN is a path between two end points. It includes the intermediate components that may exist, for example, links, NNs, domains, and transmission groups.

To determine the best route in an APPN network the following minimum criteria are used:

- Route characteristics must be known
- All possible routes are calculated
- If a resource is not acceptable it must be excluded; hence, determining this factor about resources must be performed

- All resources that will be used during the route must be accounted for and calculated accordingly.

Topology Database

The topology database contains information about the logical structure of the APPN network: about all nodes in the network, transmission groups, intermediate transmission groups, as well as other pertinent information.

The two types of topology databases are: network and local.

Network Topology Database

A network topology database is maintained in all NNs. It includes information on NN connections to other NNs and connections to virtual routing nodes. Each NN participating in the APPN network is aware of this database because the database is on each NN.

The structure of the network topology database includes two categories:

- A node table, which contains information about the node such as:
  - CP name
  - Network ID
  - Characteristics
  - Resource Sequence Number
- A TG table, which contains information about transmission groups. Some of that information includes:
  - CP-CP session support
  - Status
  - A pointer to the TG vector
  - A pointer to the weight (amount of resource requirement).

Local Topology Database

Local topology databases are located in end nodes. They contain information about each end point attached to that node and are created and maintained by the topology database manager. The local topology database is used:

- When no CP-CP session to an NN exists
- To establish sessions to predefined LUs
- To send information to the NN for the route selection process.

Configuration Services (CS)

CS is responsible for managing local node resources like links to other nodes. A conceptual view of CS is shown in Figure 8.22.

FIGURE 8.22
Conceptual View
of Configuration
Services

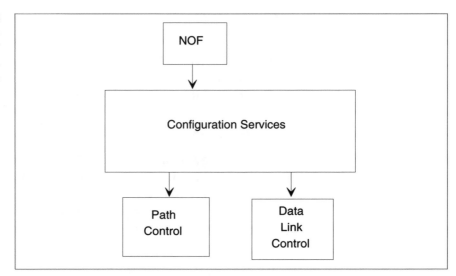

CS performs a number of functions, including:

- Node configuration definition:
    - Data link type
    - Ports
    - Adjacent nodes
    - Adjacent links
- Link activation
- Link deactivation
- Nonactivation of an XID exchange.

Upon node initialization, CS receives the node name, network id, link station support information, and information concerning TGs.

Through CS the NOF defines the basic node configuration. First comes the data link type. This CP component communicates with the data link control manager for definition purposes. Ports are also defined by the NOF via CS. They are considered hardware.

Port type is defined: switched, non-switched, or shared access facility. Information includes buffer size, limits, timeout values, transmission group characteristics, and any associated DLC process.

Link stations may be defined at activation time or their parameters can be negotiated; either way they must match. Nodes require system definitions for their local link station. These definitions include:

- Role: primary or secondary
- Address or defined as negotiable
- Inactivity timer
- Retry limit on mode setting
- Modem delay limits.

Management Service (MS)

The concept of management services is implemented in each T2.1 node and is known as Control Point Management Services (CPMS). The CPMS is a component of the CP in T2.1 nodes. Its functionality is straightforward.

The NOF sends messages to the CPMS. These are converted into local management services where they are carried out by the receiving component in the T2.1 node.

With respect to the CP, management services interact with each of the following:

- Session services
- Configuration services
- Session manager
- Resource manager
- Address space manager
- Topology and routing services
- Directory services
- Presentation services.

Some information CPMS receives from CP components, other components are listed below. Some information must be solicited, some need not be:

1. Information about currently active sessions; problems detected in a node by the CP
2. Domain information
3. Information about currently active LU6.2 sessions
4. Information about session conversations
5. Unsolicited information about problems related to this component
6. Information about routing

7. Locating network resources for the CPMS

8. Providing LU6.2 protocol boundary information.

The LU session manager provides information about currently active sessions. The LU resource manager provides information about conversations across an LU6.2 session. The LU management service component provides unsolicited information about the LU. The session connection manager provides information about data passing through the node.

The path control manager reports unsolicited information about any problems detected at this component.

The data link control manager provides a vehicle for testing resources such as links and modems.

Other management information is ascertainable; the point is that management services actually interact with all T2.1 node components, not only with the CP.

Address Space Manager (ASM)

The ASM resides in NNs and APPN ENs. Fundamental functions of the ASM include:

- Managing session addresses (also known as Local Form Session Identifiers LSFID); these addresses are used for routing data traffic and local path control
- Managing flow control of session activation messages (the BIND)
- Informing the appropriate session manager component when a link fails
- Routing session activation and deactivation messages.

The ASM is created upon initialization of the node by the NOF. Then the ASM is notified by the NOF of the CP name, network ID, and the nature of the BIND assembly supported.

Functions of the ASM

For communication to occur between LUs or CPs and other CPs a Local Form Session Identifier (LFSID) must be allocated by the ASM. By performing this function the ASM achieves address control in the node. The ASM bases the LFSID on the path control instance identifier for that session. The ASM maintains an address space list and a list of assigned LFSIDs in use.

Address spaces are defined by the ASM in relation to the transmission group attached to the node. The ASM assigns an address space consisting of a number large enough to allocate enough LFSIDs for that TG.

Whenever a TG is activated or deactivated, the ASM is informed. At that time the ASM creates or destroys the tables used to control that TG's address space. ASM handles the assigned address space by dividing it into groups. These groups consist of 256 LFSIDs. However, the ASM only allocates the LFSIDs as necessary.

LFSIDs

LFSIDs are 17-bit session identifiers used by the path control to route session traffic. They have two components:

1. **A one bit assignor indicator**—Every ASM in the nodes connected by a TG selects an LFSID from the TG address space with a different value so no duplication exists.
2. **A 16-bit session identifier** that is further broken into an 8-bit identifier considered high and an 8-bit identifier considered low.

LFSIDs assigned to a session maintain their active state as long as the session exists. The ASM is the component that terminates the association of the LFSID and the session once the ASM receives notification of an UNBIND or response to UNBIND is delivered from the path control component.

This LFSID is used because on each session hop between two endpoints each node uses distinct session identifiers for a session; consequently, the term Local Form Session Identifier (LFSID) is used.

For further information on the topic, refer to IBM's APPN Reference Manual number SC30-3422.

Session Services (SS)

The SS functional part of the CP aids in: generating unique session identifiers, LU-LU session initiation and deactivation, and CP-CP session activation and deactivation.

Figure 8.23 identifies the relationship of SSs with other components.

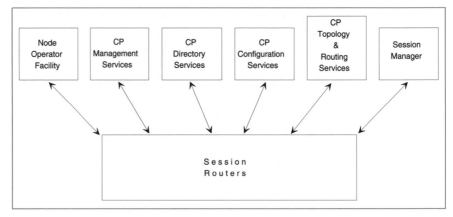

FIGURE 8.23
Session Services
Relationships to
Other Components

Full-Qualified Path Control Identifier (FQPCID)

The session identifiers generated by this part of the CP should not be confused with the LFSIDs generated by the ASM mentioned previously.

Session services assign a *network* unique session identifier, known more commonly as the FQPCID. This FQPCID performs the following functions:

- Correlates request and replies between APPN nodes
- Identifies a session for problem determination
- Identifies a session for auditing, accounting, performance, and other purposes
- Identifies a session for cleanup or to perform recovery actions.

The FQPCID is assigned at the originating node; is a fixed length, and contains an 8-byte session-identifier field that includes the network qualified name which generated it.

LU-LU Session Initiation/Deactivation

With APPN NNs, APPN ENs, and LEN ENs, LUs can initiate sessions and respond to a session initiation request from another LU or CP. The session activation request (also called a BIND) is sent by a particular LU; that LU is considered the Primary LU (PLU). The BIND recipient is called the Secondary LU (SLU). The LUs go into session once the BIND is sent, received by the target, and the target LU send a response (RSP) to the BIND back to the sending LU. This is an active session.

An example of information specified in a BIND request includes:

- The network-qualified name of the PLU
- The network-qualified name of the SLU
- The route through the network to the SLU
- The FQPCID
- The maximum Request/Response Unit size.

A session is stopped when a UNBIND is sent to the target and the target responds with a response (RSP) back to the originator of the UNBIND. This is session deactivation, or an inactive session.

Sometimes the terms PLU and SLU are replaced by the terms Origin LU (OLU) and Destination LU (DLU).

CP-CP Session Activation/Deactivation

CP sessions are always LU6.2. This means that given a CP in two nodes the possibility for contention exists. Contention is best explained as both CPs attempting to establish a session with the other at the same time. The question of how to overcome this scenario needs to be considered.

Contention can be overcome by "contention winners" and "losers." Each CP has contention winner LUs defined and generally the same number of contention losers defined. Because CP-CP sessions are established in parallel each CP has winner and loser LUs defined.

Establishment of CP-CP sessions begins when the SS notifies directory services that a session is pending active. The directory service then queues network operations that may involve the CP session LU. SS also notifies the resource manager to attempt activation of a winner LU with the destination LU in the target node. SS is once again invoked to assign a FQPCID having a mode name of CPSVCMG.

The following information is some of what flows across CP-CP sessions:

- Topology database updates
- Session activity
- Requests for data management support
- Replies to requests for data management support
- Resource search capability.

CP-CP session deactivation may occur for one of two reasons. Normal deactivation usually means the node, or its partner, no longer requires the session. An abnormal CP-CP session termination could be the result of protocol violation during the session or a link failure, or in remote cases, both.

Node Operator Facility (NOF)

The NOF is the interface between an operator and the T2.1 node. Its purpose is to permit a way for operators to control node operation. A node operator can be human; a command list for execution; or a transaction program.

Any of these node operators can perform node operator functions. A human operator can execute a specific dialog between the NOF and the individual and make changes possibly not anticipated or possible with a program.

A command list is a file with a list of node operator commands to be executed. The NOF interpreter logs the commands and responses from the NOF and maintains this log for future reference.

Transaction program control is used in remote operations and works by a transaction program's actually issuing commands against the NOF which is in a remote location.

A graphic display of these three ways to communicate with the NOF are presented in Figure 8.24.

FIGURE 8.24
A Perspective of the Node Operator Facility

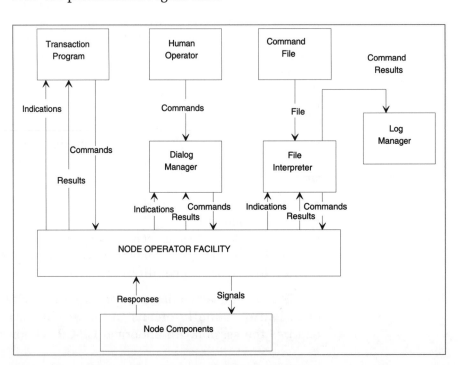

NOF Functions

Node operator facility functions include:

- Creating other components in the node
- Issuing commands to initialize the node
- Converting commands to signals capable of being understood by components within the node
- Starting a log of commands issued and the results of issuing these commands
- Receiving results from node components
- Routing signals to the appropriate node components
- Managing unsolicited messages from any node components.

Upon initialization the NOF creates the following components in order:

1. Address space manager
2. Session services
3. Directory services
4. Configuration services
5. Management services
6. Topology and routing services
7. Session connector manager
8. Session manager of the control point (CP).

Commands Listing and Function

When a command is entered and received, the NOF parses the command into an understandable form. At this time the syntax is verified.

The following node operator commands are architecturally defined.

- `CHANGE_SESSION_LIMIT`—Changes the session limit
- `DEFINE_ADJACENT_NODE`—Defines an adjacent node to a local node
- `DEFINE_CLASS_OF_SERVICE`—Changes or updates the COS
- `DEFINE_CONNECTION_NETWORK`—Defines a connection network to the local APPN node
- `DEFINE_DIRECTORY_ENTRY`—Defines or updates directory entries
- `DEFINE_DLC`—Defines a data link control
- `DEFINE_ISR_TUNING`—Adds or updates the session connector manager

- `DEFINE_LINK_STATION`—Defines a connection to a link station
- `DEFINE_LOCAL_LU`—Defines a new LU
- `DEFINE_MODE`—Create a new mode definition for a local LU
- `DEFINE_NODE_CHARS`—Defines or updates current characteristics in the local node
- `DEFINE_PARTNET_LU`—Defines/changes a local LU
- `DEFINE_PORT`—Defines a port to a local node
- `DEFINE_TP`—Defines or changes a local LU's operation with a local transaction program
- `DELETE_ADJACENT_NODE`—Removes a definition of an adjacent node
- `DELETE_CLASS_OF_SERVICE`—Removes a COS definition
- `DELETE_CONNECTION_NETWORK`—Removes a connection network from a local node
- `DELETE_DIRECTORY_ENTRY`—Removes an entry from the directory services directory
- `DELETE_DLC`—Removes a data link control instance
- `DELETE_ISR_TUNING`—Removes one or more session connector managers
- `DELETE_LINK_STATION`—Removes adjacent a link station definition
- `DELETE_LOCAL_LU`—Removes a local LU from a node
- `DELETE_MODE.`—Removes a mode definition from a local LU
- `DELETE_PARTNER_LU`—Removes a definition a local LU uses with a remote LU
- `DELETE_PORT`—Removes a port definition in the local node
- `DELETE_TP`—Removes a local transaction program definition
- `INITIALIZE_SESSION_LIMIT`—Initializes the number of sessions allowed
- `QUERY_CLASS_OF_SERVICE`—Used to obtain the values defined for a COS
- `QUERY_CONECTION_NETWORK`—Obtains the status of a connection network
- `QUERY_DLC`—Obtains the status of a specific data link control instance within a node
- `QUERY_ISR_TUNING`—Ascertains information about the session connector manager
- `QUERY_LINK_STATION`—Obtains the status within the node of an adjacent link station
- `QUERY_PORT`—Obtains the status of a port within the node
- `QUERY_STATISTICS`—Obtains detailed information about a link station

- `RESET_SESSION_LIMIT`—Resets the number of sessions allowed
- `START_DLC`—Starts a specified data link
- `START_LINK_STATION`—Establishes communication between a local link station and an adjacent link station
- `START_NODE`—Brings up the SNA node
- `START_PORT`—Starts a specified port and local link stations using
- `START_TP`—Requests a local LU to start a TP in a node
- `STOP_DLC`—Stops the named data link control
- `STOP_LINK_STATION`—Stops communication with a specified adjacent link station
- `STOP_PORT`—Stops a specified port and associated local link stations.

APPN Concepts and Traditional SNA

APPN and SNA are philosophically different. APPN is peer-oriented, using LU6.2 protocols and is implemented across a variety of equipment. SNA has been hierarchical in nature. This meant VTAM was involved in practically all session establishment. This began changing with VTAM 3.2 and is more prevalent with VTAM 4.1.

APPN and traditional SNA are becoming less clear-cut. They are evolving into a cooperative way of networking when both are present in one environment. This section explores differences between the two and examples of areas where they are coming together.

APPN Structure

APPN builds upon different types of nodes that provide services such as routing, database maintenance, directory services, and end-user services. The growth in different types of nodes that comprise APPN is changing. No longer is an APPN network considered implemented with mid-range and PS/2 systems. Now, APPN can be implemented with SNA via VTAM support.

APPN uses LU6.2, an independent LU, capable of initiating a BIND (request for a session with another LU).

SNA Structure

SNA has been built around hardware architecture and envisioning that VTAM would become the centerpiece of software for the network.

SNA has been hierarchical (some call it subarea SNA) in nature, but it has had support for peer operations. Now, those peer operations are expanding by embracing APPN via VTAM and the NCP.

SNA uses LU6.2, but primarily utilizes other LU types such as LU1, 2, and 3. These LUs are dependent upon VTAM for session establishment. It is necessary to ask how LU2s can be implemented into an APPN network and access a VTAM host.

APPN–SNA Mixture

Subarea SNA supports dependent logical units. SNA's roots are in this functionality. This means that an LU requesting a session with a VTAM application must have the services of VTAM (SSCP) or help via the NCP boundary function. LUs residing on nodes adjacent to VTAM or the NCP traverse the VTAM or NCP boundary function.

If VTAM is configured as an end node, it cannot perform intermediate session routing. However, nodes can attach to VTAM using the boundary function of SNA. Consequently, dependent LUs must access VTAM via this boundary function.

Two terms need clarification and explanation: dependent logical unit requester (DLUR) and dependent logical unit server (DLUS). An implementation of DLUR and DLUS provides the following scenario.

When APPN nodes are mixed in networks with nodes such as PU2.0 devices, the need exists for the PU2.0 to have SSCP-PU sessions and SSCP-LU sessions. Once support for these two sessions is achieved, a dependent LU-LU session can be accomplished from the PU2.0 device and a subsystem application.

To realize this in APPN and mixed subarea SNA, the data must be encapsulated within a LU6.2 session and passed to the SSCP and PU, respectively. When this happens, the T2.0 node no longer needs to be directly attached, or a data link switched, to the SSCP thus providing SSCP access. Integration of PU2.0 and PU2.1 APPN and subarea-dependent LU can be achieved.

Figure 8.25 depicts an APPN network and a subarea network with VTAM functioning as a composite network node.

As a result of the implementation shown in Figure 8.25 session establishment can occur between any LU in the subarea network and any LU in the APPN network. In this case APPN VTAM must be implemented and convert subarea to APPN protocols and vice versa.

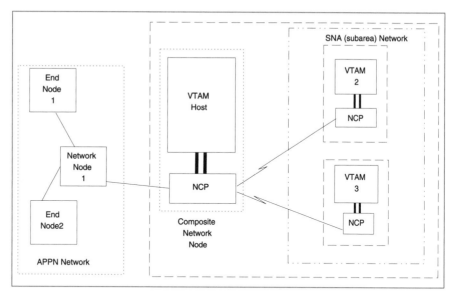

FIGURE 8.25
An APPN and
SNA Mixed
Network

Blueprint #1

APPN can be implemented numerous ways.

In Figure 8.26 two LEN end nodes are communicating via an APPC between Dallas and Houston. This peer-oriented network design shows two hosts in geographically different locations sharing information.

APPN Blueprint #2

In Figure 8.27 a VTAM and NCP host is acting as an intermediate node, operating as another LEN end node. This means the CP information session flow is between end nodes and therefore making the routing function more efficient.

APPN Blueprint #3

APPN can also be implemented as Figure 8.28 shows.

FIGURE 8.26
APPN
Blueprint #1

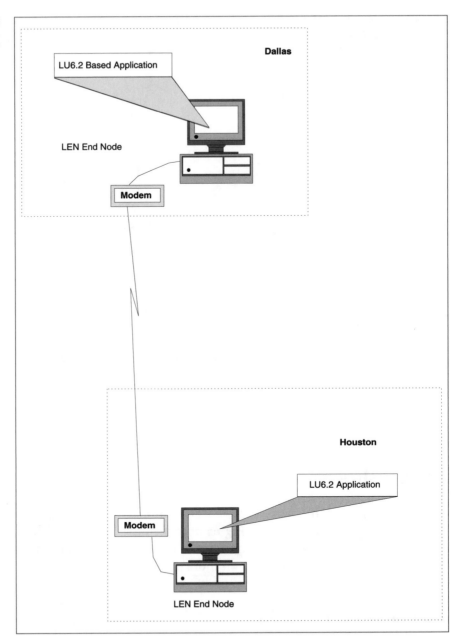

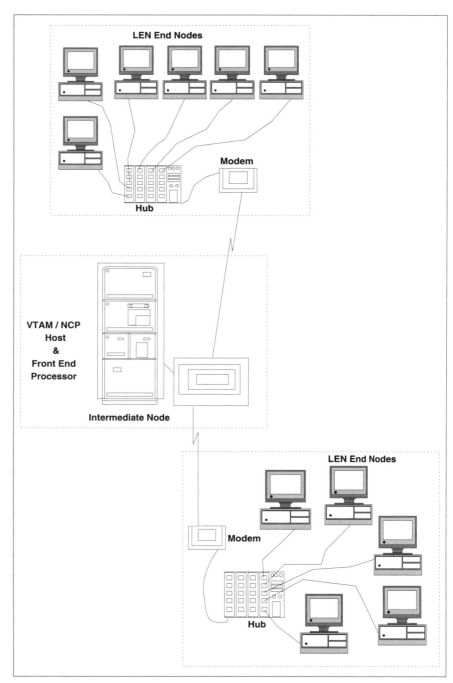

FIGURE 8.27
APPN
Blueprint #2

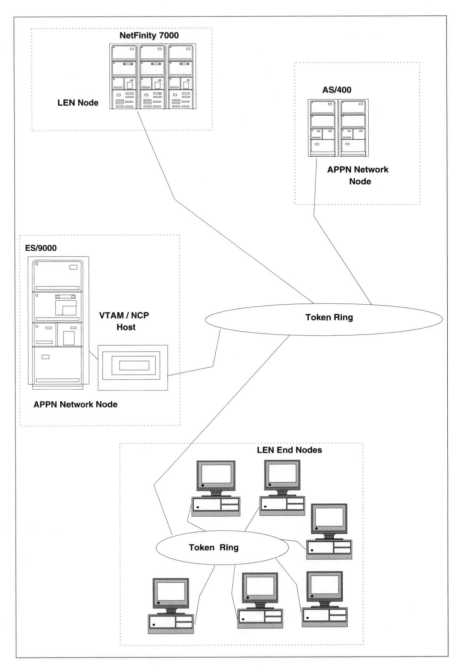

FIGURE 8.28
APPN
Blueprint #3

Multiple hosts are connected via token ring technology in a single facility. LEN end nodes are intermixed with two network nodes. In this implementation, the LEN EN users located on the isolated token ring are using data stored on the Netfinity 7000 enterprise server. This illustration shows that APPN nodes cannot exchange configuration and topology data. LEN end nodes cannot exchange this level of network information in a APPN network environment. Here the VTAM/NCP network node performs routing functions enabling the LEN end node users on the isolated token ring network to communicate with the Netfinity 7000 data server. The VTAM/NCP hosts maintain the topology and routing functions in the network.

APPN Blueprint #4

Figure 8.29 shows an APPN and a subarea SNA network together. The APPN network is superimposed on the SNA environment. The VTAM and NCP hosts in this illustration are working as APPN network nodes. These hosts serve as links between the end node in the lower portion of the illustration and the LEN end node in the upper right portion of the example. The APPN network nodes in the illustration operate with their CP performing routing and topology information exchange. Due the vast traffic load in the network, the configuration shows a VTAM and NCP host connected to the APPN network nodes. The blueprint itself has enabled increased routing loads. This blueprint is a good example to use for environments where multiple hosts are used, a VTAM network host is to be implemented, and growth is anticipated.

APPN Blueprint #5

APPN supports high performance routing. Some installations require this type of technology and implementation.

Figure 8.30 shows an HPR APPN subnet. Notice the multiple network nodes connected through a variety of links. The result of this blueprint is a maximized throughput for routing data.

Two APPN subnets are connected via the HPR subnet. Multiple connections link the APPN subnet on the bottom to the HPR subnet. This blueprint is a good example of how to build a multifaceted network with multiple network links to connect the subnets. It can be used when the APPN subnets are geographically dispersed or in the same location.

FIGURE 8.29
APPN
Blueprint #4

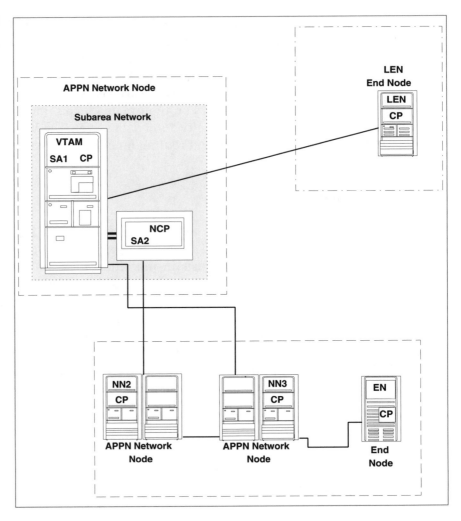

FIGURE 8.29 APPN Blueprint #4

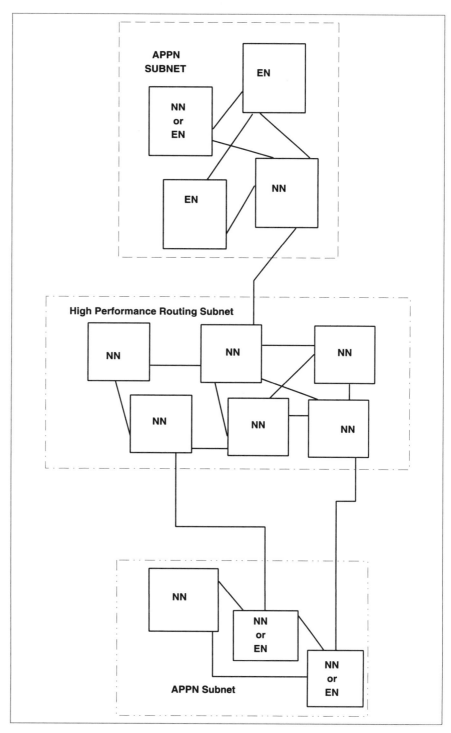

FIGURE 8.30
APPN
Blueprint #5

APPN Blueprint #6

Figure 8.31 shows numerous hosts, both SNA oriented and APPN.

FIGURE 8.31
APPN
Blueprint #6

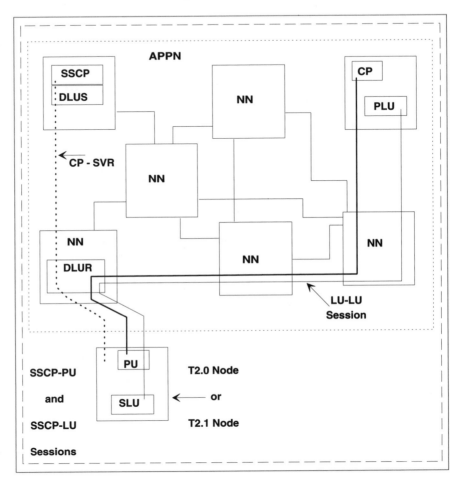

The VTAM host implements the SSCP to perform network management functions and for session setup and management. Both the SSCP-PU and SSCP-LU sessions are established via the network node.

There are multiple APPN nodes. The VTAM host has been traditionally SNA-oriented by design and implementation. However, beginning with VTAM versions and releases in the 1990's support for APPN existed. Consequently, VTAM nodes can be SNA subarea, APPN-oriented, or configured to operate in both SNA subarea and APPN.

Blueprint 6 is a good example of a network host design structure for program load distribution. The blueprint can be used to build a base network backbone with potential for growth.

APPN Blueprint #7

Blueprint 7 is a further example of a varied host configuration.

Figure 8.32 shows four networks, each with multiple hosts. Extended border nodes have interconnect functionality. One characteristic of this blueprint and the extended border node support is that LU-LU session support is present so that these sessions do not have to terminate within the APPN-oriented network nodes. A transparent LU-LU session support is the result. Notice the SLU in Network C communicates with the PLU in Network B through Network D, which is native APPN. The extended border node function in the nodes of Network D make this possible.

Peripheral border nodes are also part of Blueprint 7. These nodes interconnect APPN networks identified via network identifiers to support LU-LU sessions. A characteristic of this type of session is that the LU-LU sessions have partner LUs in their native networks.

Blueprint 7 shows an implementation that could be used with geographically dispersed networks. It includes networks that are a mix between APPN and subarea SNA. Figure 8.32 shows a logical depiction of the APPN blueprint; actual implementation may be with a wide variety of hardware devices. Devices implementing this blueprint are capable of performing functions such as the extended border node and the peripheral border node.

Blueprint 7 should be considered when a heavily mixed APPN and SNA subarea network is needed. If you are beginning to work with a network plan prior to implementation, Blueprint 7 can be used to expand and implement a network in geographically dispersed environments and with many different types of devices.

APPN Blueprint #8

Blueprint 8 is a good working example of an APPN implementation where APPN network data are routed through the subarea SNA.

FIGURE 8.32
APPN
Blueprint #7

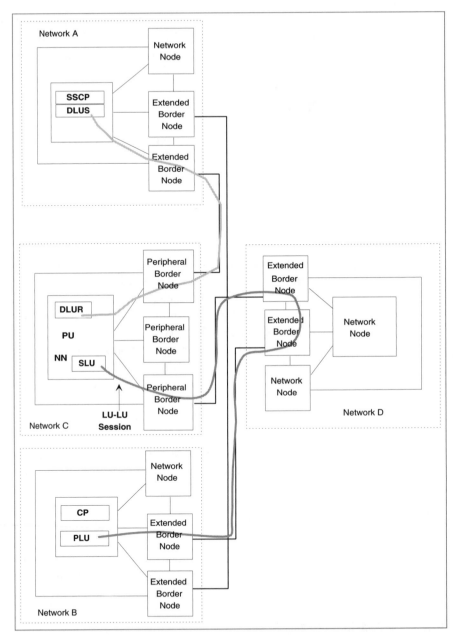

Figure 8.33 shows two APPN networks, each with a network node, one network node is identified as #1 and one identified as #4. These nodes are shown with CP-CP sessions communicating with each other; that is, node 4 is communicating with node 1 with a CP-CP

session. This communication occurs via subarea SNA network connections by way of node 2 and node 3.

FIGURE 8.33
APPN
Blueprint #8

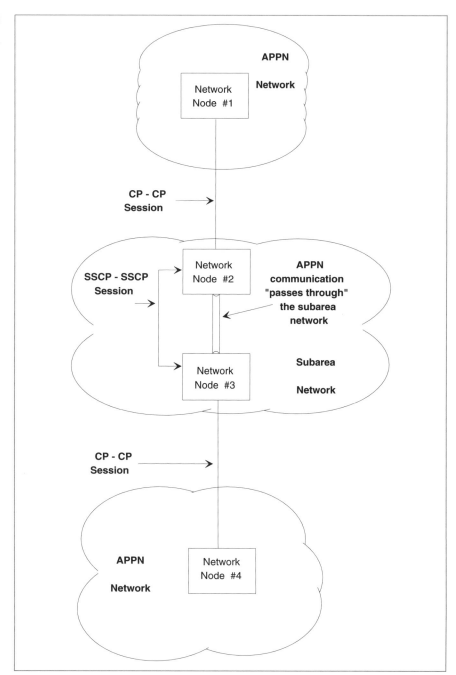

FIGURE 8.33
APPN
Blueprint #8

Figure 8.33 shows node 3 and node 2 communicating in an SSCP session. The result of this implementation creates a pass through situation for the CP-CP session to occur between nodes 1 and 4. This figure also presents an ideal example of a large SNA subarea network and large data repositories; APPN networks have also been designed and implemented around the subarea SNA. A built-in benefit of this blueprint is the ability to utilize existing SNA subarea bandwidth to support APPN traffic.

Blueprint 8 can be used with networks from the planning stage or with networks already implemented. It can be sized as needed. The scaling of this blueprint is basically limited to the hardware and software used. This design can support a few hundred or tens of thousands of users. In fact, if the backbone of this blueprint is carried to its logical conclusion it can support hundreds of thousands of users on a global basis.

Blueprint #9

Figure 8.34 shows a physical and logical description of an APPN network utilizing the benefits of VTAM and NCP hosts in a subarea SNA network. Notice the VTAM-based hosts are acting as interchange nodes. Interchange nodes permit connectivity between APPN networks and SNA networks. An interchange node achieves this functionality by mapping routing, directory, session setup, and route selection for both network types. In essence, an interchange node will convert APPN protocols into SNA subarea protocols and vice versa.

The physical depiction of the APPN and subarea SNA network is shown in the upper part of Figure 8.34. Communication between NN1, NN2 and NN3, NN4 is achieved through the interchange node function of the VTAM host. Any combination of communication between NN1, NN2, NN3, and NN4 is possible.

The logical interpretation, the APPN interpretation, shows the interchange nodes as simply NNA and NNB. The VTAM and NCP function becomes transparent and a unit: the logical operation seems to be one host.

Blueprint 9 can easily be scaled to large networks. It can also be implemented where existing SNA subarea networks exist. One consideration when implementing this type network is the version and release of those software components which will create the functionality in the interacting nodes. This blueprint can also be used to build from scratch. Its benefit lies in the integrator or network designer. It is a powerful exploitation of subarea SNA and APPN.

FIGURE 8.34
APPN
Blueprint #9

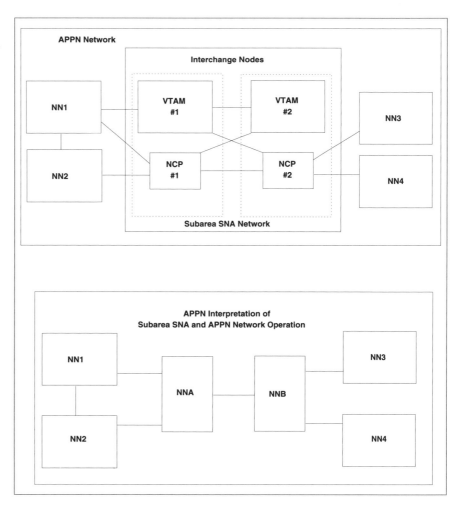

APPN Blueprint #10

A common scenario for many installations is a network that already exists in a wide variety of locations or will exist after installation of all the network equipment. Figure 8.35 is an example of a blueprint to consider.

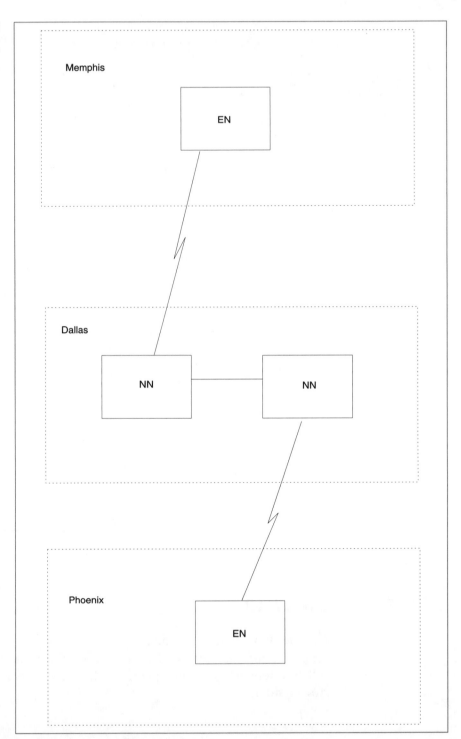

As Figure 8.35 shows, remote end nodes are communicating via network nodes. These nodes, in geographically separate locations, have been included in a tri-city network. this example can be expanded to include many different cities. A unique benefit of this blueprint is that it can be superimposed on an existing network without significant displacement of the existing components. Furthermore, if a remote network is in place it may be possible to incorporate this type of network blueprint into existing operations and thus expand the network's reach.

If this blueprint is a viable approach for your location, it is a good idea to understand the capabilities of all existing equipment in your network. This may reveal latent capabilities you were not aware of.

Regardless which blueprint seems to be right for you, consider these blueprints as "beginning" points. Let them serve as templates and guides to point you in the direction of the best network growth and equipment utilization.

Summary

This chapter has presented the essence of APPN architecture and technology as well as blueprint ideas for designing and implementing APPN networks.

APPN has its own peer-oriented architecture. SNA is hierarchical in nature. VTAM 4.1 is a tool to bring together APPN and subarea SNA. It was enhanced in VTAM 4.2.

The T2.1 architecture consists of many components. T2.1 node components are the components that make up the node itself and those components that comprise the CP.

APPN and subarea SNA are different. Neither is better; they are different. Much more information is available about APPN. Consult your IBM representative.

CHAPTER 9

Windows NT Technology and Blueprints

The purpose of this chapter is to introduce Windows NT. There are explanations of aspects of NT technology and Windows NT blueprints to use guides to designing an NT-based network.

Windows NT is a Microsoft product whose origins date back to 1988. Characteristics of the original design intent are that it is compatible with a variety of hardware platforms and operating systems, is easily adaptable to internationalization, is portable, and is a system with high security standards.

Before examining NT blueprints consider the NT components, features, and functions.

Workstation and Server Operational Overview

Windows NT is two products workstation and server. The workstation product is currently marketed and sold as an operating system, as is the server product.

The operational idea behind Windows NT is the peer concept. This can also be viewed by considering the workstation as the client and the server as the server. Both are not required to function. An ordinary user who chooses a workstation for an operating system does not need the server product. However, if this workstation user decides to participate in a network using NT server, then the workstation component required for the NT network operation is already present.

NT server is also sold as a standalone operating system. In most instances the NT server does not function merely as a standalone operating system; it is used to operate on a system in which the product enables server functionality.

Together workstation and server function in a physically networked environment and no additional software is required to make communication between hosts running the workstation product and the host(s) running the server product function. This is so because workstation and server include upper-layer protocols, so adding upper-layer software is not required. A network adapter, drivers for the adapter, cabling, and a network hub/concentrator are required to make the systems running workstation and server operate in the network. In fact, these components make up the network.

Figure 9.1 shows NT server on the Netfinity and NT workstation on two different systems beneath. One NT workstation is connected to the network, the other is considered a standalone system. The standalone workstation could be integrated into the network with a network adapter card, driver, and cabling to the patch panel interface. Notice the Netfinity system has NT server operating on it. That is the network server and also functions as a *workstation*. Administration of the server can be performed locally (a user working on it) or remotely (a user working on another computer on the network—assuming the server is configured for remote administration).

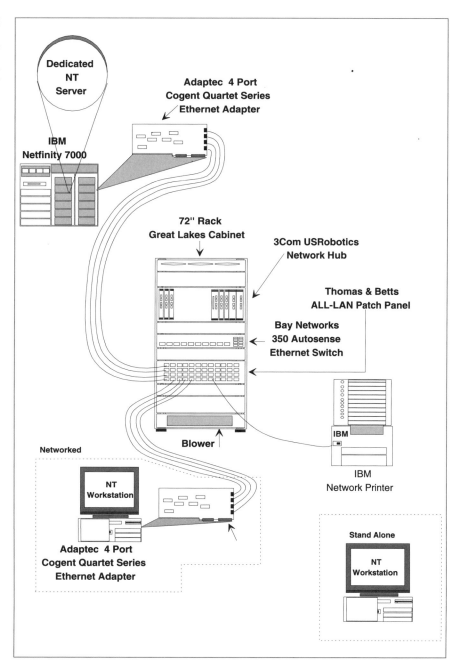

FIGURE 9.1
Windows NT
Workstation and
Server

NT is essentially a hybrid operating system. Its appearance and operation are a mix of earlier versions of Windows and UNIX.

Terminology

Account	A method of record keeping that can maintain statistical information about users on a given system or network
Account Policy	A given set of rules or permissions that explain what a users can and cannot do; for example, reading, writing, and deleting files is defined in a user account policy. The term is used in NT, UNIX, and other large computer operating system environments
Application Server	Typically a term used to refer to a system that maintains application software that may be distributed to users throughout a network.
Architecture	A term that is increasingly used in the computer/network industry to refer to the design of something. That something may be a program, network, operating system, or other such structural component of reference. An architect is one who designs various aspects of computers and/or networks.
Auditing	A term used to refer to the detection and recording of security-related events in the NT operating system.
Authentication	The process used at login time to verify a password and/or user profile
Backup Domain Controller	That computer which acts as an alternate computer for the system that keeps the security policy and the domain's database, and authenticates the network logins
Boot Loader	The program used in the beginning setup of NT that defines the system startup such as the location for the operating system's file. Once the boot loader is created, each time the system is booted, the boot loader file is checked to see if any changes have been made.
Boot Partition	That part of a hard or floppy disk, CD-ROM, or other medium used in computing which maintains basic system level information required to bridge the system's operation from firmware instructions in BIOS to the actual operating system. The boot partition is formatted either in File Allocation Table (FAT), New Technology File System (NTFS), or High Performance File System (HPFS).

continued on next page

Terminology continued

Cold Boot	Refers to a system being turned off physically (electrical power removed) and then turned back on. This is in contrast to a system that is cycled or rebooted by way of pressing a certain key stroke sequence.
Computer Name	A unique name used to identify a computer or network device; in NT up to fifteen characters can be used in naming as long as they are unique on a given network part
Configuration Registry	The program storage that keeps a database of a computer's configuration. In contrast, a computer's `autoexec.bat`, `config.sys`, `win.ini`, and `system.ini` are similar but primarily used on other operating systems
Connected User	Refers to a person or program using the resources of a given computer on a network
Data Link Control (DLC)	A low-level (data link; ios layer 2) protocol interface in NT to enable the connectivity between NT and IBM's SNA network equipment
Default	Refers to a set of conditions or parameters used if no choice is indicated to make a selection when such an option is given. A default printer is one that is used when no other selection is made
Dial-up Networking	Refers to a computer connected to a network via a telephone line
Disabled User Account	Refers to a user account that does not permit logons
Disk Configuration Information	Refers to NT registry information that contains disk configuration details such as the assigned drive letters, stripe sets, mirror sets, volume sets, and stripe sets with parity
Domain	In the context of NT this is a computer, or computers, that share a common database and security policy for a given logical configuration. It is a method of identification as well as control. The term trust is used to further explain the functional description of a domain.
Domain Controller	That system used in a collection of NT server and workstation-based computers that maintains the security policy for those computers and network devices assigned to it; it also maintains the master database of functional information for those computers and devices. Domain controllers and servers can validate a logon; however, a domain controller is required to be contacted in order to make changes to passwords.

continued on next page

Terminology continued

Domain Name	Refers to a collection of computers and devices in the network
Ethernet	A lower-layer protocol that operates functionally at layers two and one in the OSI model
Event	A significant occurrence in an NT workstation or server operating system
Event Log	A file maintained in NT-based systems that records significance occurrences and can be viewed
FAT File System	A file maintained on a medium such as a hard or floppy disk which keeps track of the space segments on the storage medium
Group	A specific account that lists (contains) other accounts called members. The notion of groups or groupings is a way to make certain common capabilities available to the members in that group. In NT server, groups are managed via the User Manager.
Global Account	A user's own home domain account
Global Group	A way to identify a collection of users that can access resources in the domain where those users reside (identified) and also access resources outside the domain
Hardware Compatibility List	A list of hardware that tested and approved by Microsoft as operational with a given operating system such as Windows NT 4.0 or 5.0.
High-Performance File System	A file system designed to work with IBM's OS/2 version 1.2
Kernel	Refers to the the innermost part of an operating system, includes such functions as memory, files, and device management. It also includes the management of overall system resource allocation.
Local Account	A way to identify a user in a non-trusted domain; a functional description in terms of the user's global account.
Local Group	Refers to a collection of users with rights to access only one NT workstation. Where NT server is concerned this means the identified collection of users can only access the server in their domain.
NetBEUI	A netBIOS Extended User Interface protocol which is fast but not routable

continued on next page

Terminology continued

NTFS	The file system designed specifically for Windows NT operating systems; it is an object-oriented file system that treats files as objects that have system and user attributes.
Permission	Rules that apply to objects on a per-user basis and dictate what functions can be performed with that object, for example the ability to read, write, or delete a file
Personal Group	Program items associated with a given logon ID; it becomes logically attached to that ID once the user is logged on.
Personal User Profile	The characteristics assigned to each user by the administrator that identify the abilities and limitations of each user. As each user signs on and makes changes to settings, an update is made to invoke the next time that user logs onto the system.
Primary Domain Controller	Performs security policy functions, maintains the master database and authenticates domain logons for a given domain
Remote Access Service	That portion of Windows NT software component which enables connectivity between two computers over telephone lines
Right	Implies what a user can do to system level actions, contrast with permissions applicable to specific objects
SAM	Security Accounts Manager
SAM Database	Maintained information including account names, passwords, and security policy settings
Shared Directory	A directory to which network users can connect
Shared Resource	Anything on the network considered to be of value and available to more than one user
Trust Relationship	The ability for interaction between multiple domains that have been configured to trust one another. This means that certain user accounts can access other domains that are deemed trusted. Domains that trust acknowledge and approve the logon requests of users that are identified in a another (different) domain.
User Account	Information defined to an NT system which includes a user's password, name and groups to which the user can have access; the rights and privileges of the user.
User Manager	Refers to an NT tool used to administer accounts, groups, and security policies

continued on next page

Terminology continued	
User Rights Policy	The management definition of user rights to accounts and groups.

NT File Structure Support

Windows NT supports four types of file systems:

- File Allocation Table (FAT)
- New Technology File System (NTFS)
- High Performance File System (HPFS)
- CD-ROM File System (CDFS).

At this time, NT is unique in its operation and relation to supporting file systems. During the installation phase of NT either FAT, NTFS, or HPFS must be selected as the default file system support. This makes NT a powerful operating system because of its file-system support selectability. The impact of this is displayed in a positive way in a single environment which must support FAT and NTFS.

FAT

Not too long ago the FAT file system was the default file system on personal computers and notebooks. This was because the DOS was the dominant operating system on these computers, and it used the FAT for file management. In the past 20 years there has been evolution and revolution. Now, multiple operating systems work with personal computers. However, because of the dominance of DOS and MS Windows applications continued support for the FAT file system is needed.

The FAT file system is the only file system supported by Windows NT where floppy disk drives are used. Before reviewing more information about FAT and other file systems, we need to understand some terminology.

Contiguous Sector	Storage locations on media in consecutive locations
Cluster	The basic unit of space allocated on a disk; a cluster may contain one or more sectors
	continued on next page

FAT Terminology continued	
Directory	A logical, hierarchical form of file organization used on various forms of media
Fragmented File	A file stored on a disk in non-contiguous sectors
Sector	The smallest logical storage unit used on a physical storage medium
Track	Storage is comprised of sectors; the largest logical unit of storage on physical storage media
Volume	The division or part of a physical storage medium. The hard drives in computers are generally referred to by letters such as C, D, E, etc.

NTFS

The New Technology File System is NT's native file system. However, at the installation of NT the desired file system support can be selected. One aspect of NTFS is its user ability in overall security procedures of NT environments.

NTFS has what is referred to as a master file table. This includes administrative information, a description of the MFT itself, and a mirror record used as a back-up source in case the first record is lost or corrupted in some manner. The MFT and the backup MFT are located not only in the boot sector but also in the logical center portion of the disk drive.

The NTFS MFT also maintains a log file which is used primarily for fault tolerance and file recovery. At the core of NTFS is its operational nature, which is object- and attribute-based. Basic terms and concepts need to be understood in light of this file system.

Attributes	These are characteristics ascribed to files that can be categorized as system-defined and user-defined. Attributes include reading, sharing, hidden, archive, and other functions or abilities that can be performed or not performed on a given file.
Boot Sector	This part of a boot drive is read upon startup. It contains files that are used in the initial startup of a system.

continued on next page

NTFS Terminology continued

File Attributes	These are the name, data, and other information ascribed to files or a given directory. Generally, these are all attributes of files and directories.
Log File	This type of file contains information required to recover a system in the event of a system crash. It also maintains information regarding the state of the file system in use.
Mirror File	This file contains the backup copy of a user-created file or record and is kept by the operating system. It has the information needed to restore a file or record.
Master File Table (MFT)	This is the NTFS primary table for storing NTFS file objects and attributes.
Non-resident Attributes	This is information relevant to NTFS files that is not stored in the MFT table.
Object	A file in an NTFS
Resident Attributes	Characteristics of a file that can physically fit into the MFT table
System Files	These are files that contain parameters required for the proper startup and operation of an operating system.
Unicode	This is standard used to represent characters in NT and is similar to ASCII character representation. ASCII character representation uses 8 bits to represent characters, which translates into a possible 256 characters. Unicode uses a 16-bit method for character representation, hence 65,536 different characters can be represented. Therefore, Unicode can easily be used to accommodate the needs of a wide range of languages including Japanese, Chinese, and others.

What follows are types of attributes and their contents that relate to files in the NTFS file system.

Attribute List	All attributes for files considered to be large.
Bitmap	Refers to those bit-maps in use for the MFT or the directory.
Data	Refers to an actual data file.
Extended Attributes or Extended Attribute Information	Characteristics used in reference to OS/2-based file servers not used by NT.

continued on next page

NTFS Attributes continued	
Filename	The long filename stored by way of unicode characters as the standard MS-DOS filename.
Index Allocation	Allocation specific to the type of directory implemented
Index Root	Used to implement directories.
Security Descriptor	Is reference to characteristics includes access, ownership, and other characteristics

The NTFS is particularly advantageous in recovery from system crashes. Not all data may be recovered from a crash due to anomalies such as input/output problems, but the NTFS is suited to a high degree of probable recovery. Disk mirroring and parity striping on disks also contribute to recovery from system crashes. Hot-fixing, also a characteristic of NTFS, is the ability of NTFS to move a disk's sector data and mark the sector on the disk as bad. Hot-fixing is transparent to the user and eliminates the manual intervention required in some systems before this aspect of NT was available.

High Performance File System (HPFS)

IBM's OS/2 was once considered a possible contender for the next-generation operating system in the marketplace. It is still around but prevalent in market share when compared to Microsoft's operating systems.

OS/2 used the HPFS file system. The idea behind support for this in earlier versions of NT was upgradeability. Users working with OS/2 would not have problems using NT. This is not such an issue now.

CD-ROM File System

This file system is native to NT. It supports what have traditionally been called *long file names*. Long file name supports enable read-only CDs good candidates for boot media.

Architecture and Conceptual Overview

At the most basic level Windows NT is the division of software into workstation and server. The workstation software can operate well in a stand-alone environment, as can the server software. However, the server software is generally thought of as software used with a dedicated system to serve the needs of others in a network (see Figure 9.2).

FIGURE 9.2
NT Workstations
and Servers

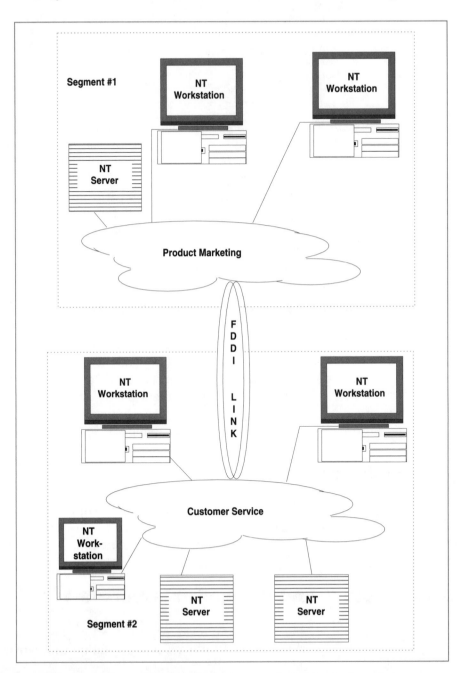

Figure 9.2 is a simple network with two segments. Multiple NT workstations are located on each segment. Each of these workstations can operate independently of the network; however they interact with other network workstations and servers because of the architectural design compatibility between NT workstations and servers. Two NT server systems are also located in this network.

NT workstation comes with the networking component and can easily be configured to operate in a networked environment. NT Server software is capable of supporting a variety of workstations in a networked environment.

In Figure 9.3 the server software operates on an IBM Netfinity 7000. This is a typical real-world approach to using NT Server along with multiple workstations. Notice two /SMS network storage silos are located in the network as well. Each workstation participating in the network can access the /SMS storage silos. The workstations can also function well as standalones. As part of the network, they can interact with all the benefits of the network. These illustrations and explanations are typical of NT architecture from an implementation perspective.

NT is capable of supporting a significant number of resources. The standard server version of NT has supports 2 GB of RAM per process address limit; the Enterprise Edition supports 3 GB of RAM without any new APIs—thus no additional overhead.

Windows NT architecture is thought of as modular because it contains multiple components.

Figure 9.4 shows NT from a component architecture perspective. The following distinct components can be identified:

- NT Executive Services
  - Object manager
  - Security reference monitor
  - Process manager
  - Local procedure call facility
  - Virtual memory manager
  - I/O manager
  - System services
- Kernel
- Hardware Abstraction Layer (HAL)
- WIN32 Subsystem (Application Environment Subsystems).

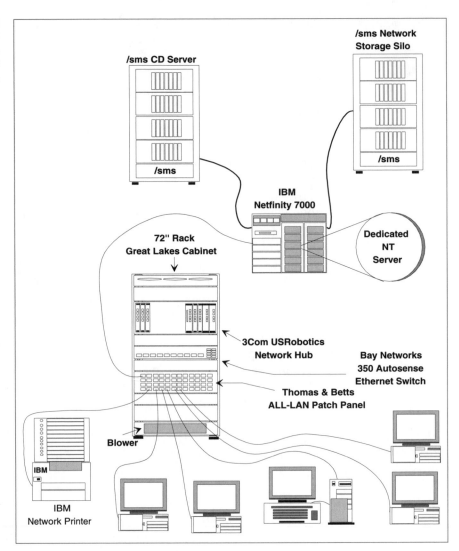

FIGURE 9.4
Windows NT
Architecture

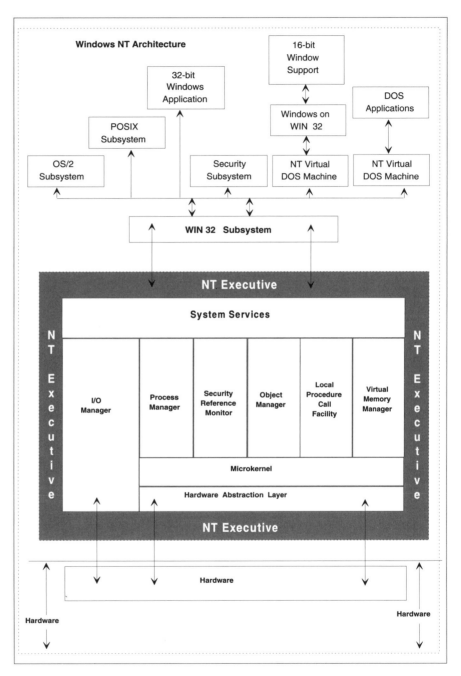

NT Executive Services

The NT executive is the highest order of control within the operating system. It can be subdivided into smaller components:

- Object manager
- Security reference monitor
- Process manager
- Local procedure call facility
- Virtual memory manager
- I/O manager.

Object Manager

The object manager creates, deletes, and modifies objects, which are nothing more than abstract data types used as operating system resources. Objects can be ports (physical) or threads (logical). The object manager also works in the system to clean up stray objects that could exist if a program crashes. Another function of the object manager is to keep track of the resources used. For example, one resource used by objects is memory. The object manager keeps objects in line with system resources and facilitates a balanced system.

Process Manager

The process manager is involved in all processes and threads. General consensus defines a process as that which has an identifiable virtual address space, one or more threads, some system resources, and executable program code. When an application is started in NT, the object manager is called on to start a process which sequentially creates an initial thread.

Security Reference Monitor

This is the core of NT security. Logon and local security authority processes are used in the implementation of security with NT.

Virtual Memory Manager (VMM)

The VMM translates a system's process memory address into actual memory addresses. It manages virtual memory. Virtual memory in personal computers operates on the same principles as in large computers. Some aspects may be augmented or enhanced, but the foundation of the idea is the same.

NT's modular design makes it robust. It has a great degree of hardware independence. Hardware platforms NT can operate on include:

- X86 uniprocessor computers
- X86 multiprocessor computers
- AXP RISC architecture
- AXP RISC multiprocessor computers
- MIPS RISC architecture
- MIPS RISC multiprocessor architecture
- Motorola PowerPC.

Another powerful aspect of NT is its use of unicode rather than ASCII for a character set. Since unicode is based on 16 bits (meaning this character set can represent 65,536 characters) it is more powerful than its ASCII counterpart which uses 8 bits yielding only 256 characters. Multicharacter languages such as Japanese, Chinese, Russian, and Swedish can be supported.

Kernel

The NT kernel is part of the NT Executive. For practical purposes, the kernel is referred to as the microkernel. However, the microkernel is *not* the same as kernel mode. The kernel is that part of NT code that comprises the most fundamental and core aspects of NT. *Microkernel* refers to that part of NT code which has been reduced to the single most important code which the operating system uses.

The term microkernel (within the context of its use in the Microsoft camp) has roots at Carnegie Mellon University in the mid-80s. A project was then under way called MACH (Micro-Kernel architecture). The name may be awkward, but the idea brought with it an architecture for an operating system which limited functions of that system to a *micro-kernel*. This is the core feature of NT operating system: a very small collection of routines, considered the core, upon which all other routines are built. This type of design makes the operating system relatively portable in different operating environments. Because NT adapted this philosophy, the operating system can support 32-bit windows programs and UNIX- or DOS-styled programs.

Within NT, Interprocess Communication (IPC) functionality is possible. This is the ability for any process or program to communicate with another operating alongside it. Many operating systems do not provide this ability. From a processor viewpoint, the notion of privileged levels of operation is common. Intel processors have *rings* of processor protection.

Figure 9.5 shows four boxes, each inside the other. The center box is level 0, the core of a processor's operation, and the safest, or most protected. This is where the operating system kernel runs. Notice the *rings* going outward, away from the center of the processor. Levels 1 and 2 are where operating system services are performed. The outermost *ring* is where applications run.

FIGURE 9.5
Processor Rings
of Protection

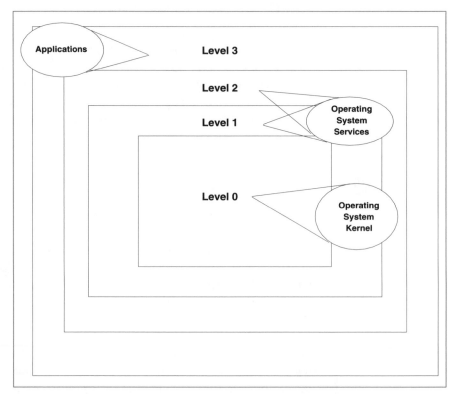

You have encountered something similar in the message *general protection fault*. The processor has detected a violation in a level of protection. First, the general protection fault message is being generated at almost the lowest (or most crucial) level in a computer. This message is an indicator that some combination of programs or functions have merged to create a low-level error. It also indicates when whether the set of conditions causing the message to be generated is a state making the entire system is unstable.

Windows NT has *user mode* and *kernel mode.* Figure 9.6 illustrates this.

FIGURE 9.6
User Mode and
Kernel Mode

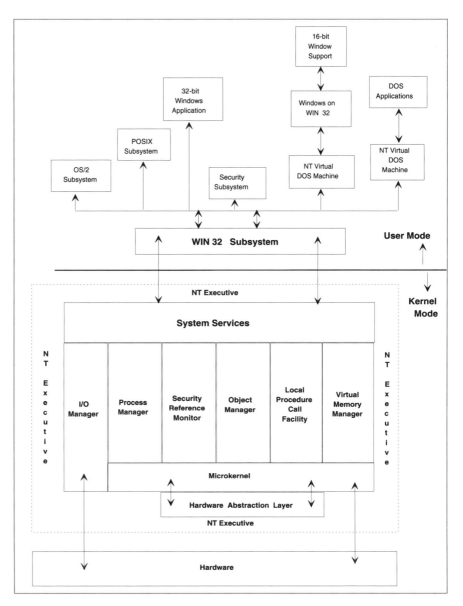

User and kernel modes are akin to the privileged and unprivileged modes processors use. They define the level or degree to which programs running in the computer have access to resources such as hardware and other programs.

The easiest way to describe user and kernel modes in NT is this: only the microkernel, HAL, and the device drivers run in the kernel mode. All other parts of NT run in user mode. The kernel mode applications are kept from incidental mishaps by the inherent design of the microprocessor. On the other hand, user mode applications are kept secure because of the design of the NT operating system.

The kernel basically dispatches and schedules threads used in the operating system. Each thread is assigned a priority number ranging from 0 to 31. A *thread* is an executable object that belongs to a process. An *object* can be something as "concrete" as a device port or application. The function of the kernel is to dispatch threads to run on processors based upon the priority numbers assigned to them.

The microkernel itself is part of the NT Executive. It operates in kernel mode and communicates with the NT Executive via low-level primitives. In a basic way, the microkernel is that part which controls the entire system. Because NT is based on preemptive multitasking it controls time slices and manages to pass control to other processes.

In summary, the microkernel operates in a privileged processor mode. In this mode the microprocessor is responsible for protecting the operating system kernel. The end result is that the operating system kernel runs in a safe environment where system crashes are not the norm.

Hardware Abstraction Layer (HAL)

The HAL is a Dynamic Load Library (DLL) used between a system's hardware and the operating system software. It is that software that serves as the interface between the hardware and the operating system itself.

The purpose of HAL is to keep NT from being concerned with I/O interrupts; it thereby makes NT easily portable. Technically, HAL is the only part of NT that talks directly with hardware. All other NT components talk indirectly. The kernel, device drivers, and I/O manager talk to the hardware through HAL.

Because of HAL, NT is considered portable between different operating systems. HAL also provides support for Symmetrical Multi-Processing (SMP). The result is that NT can be used on Intel, MIPS, Alpha processors and others.

Because of HAL there is a hardware compatibility list with the NT operating system. For the most part NT is compatible with many vendor's hardware; because of HAL the question of compatibility is an issue. I have been using NT version 4.0. During the development of the network I discovered some hardware components that NT would not (or could not) acknowledge. I realized the problem was the fundamental inability of NT to *know* a certain piece of hardware existed. Now NT and this piece of hardware are compatible.

Application Environment Subsystem

The Application Environment Subsystem is that part above the *WIN 32 Subsystem*. The WIN 32 Subsystem is the main subsystem for NT. It includes WIN 32-bit Application Program Interfaces (APIs). As well as 32-bit programs, the WIN 32 Subsystem supports application programs for other operating environments.

Input/Output (I/O) Manager

This part of NT handles input and output processing. The I/O manager coordinates all system I/O: drivers, installable file systems, network directors, and caching memory management.

Local Procedure Call (LPC) Facility

This part of NT works as an interface between all clients and servers on an NT system. The functionality of LPC is similar to that of a Remote Program Call (RPC) facility. However, LPC and RPC are not equals because LPC permits exchange of information between two thread processes on a local machine and RPC does not.

Administration Concepts

Administration of NT involves understanding the following concepts.

Workgroups

The concept of a workgroup exists in Windows NT. Technically a workgroup is a logical grouping of computers on the network. Multiple workgroups are possible in NT. For example, it is possible to have a workgroup named support and one named sales. Now assume six computers are listed under the workgroup named support. Assume one NT server is in the support workgroup. In this example, the support users can access the server in this group.

Assume six users and a server are listed under the sales workgroup. The users in the sales workgroup can access this server. However, a distinction is made between the support and sales workgroups. Security is implemented on each server; this means any user wanting to access either the support or sales server must have a valid account on that server. Generally computers that are a part of a workgroup can access the server(s) in that workgroup.

Domains

A domain in NT is slightly different from one in workgroups. A domain is a collection of computers that share a common *user policy* and *security account database*. A domain may exist with seven workstations and one server. In the context of a domain, all seven workstations share the same user policy. In this sense the user policy is a "global" setting applicable to all workstations. The same is true for the security database; that is, all seven workstations share it. A domain could be considered a workgroup with centralized security.

The way these functions are implemented in a domain is via a *domain controller*. A domain controller is identified during the installation phase of NT Server. Functions of a domain controller include managing the security and policy database for all users in the domain. Two types of domain controllers exist: primary and backup. A primary domain controller performs all the functions required to make the domain work effectively. The backup domain controller is like a mirror image of the primary domain controller and exists in case a failure occurs in the primary domain controller. It is a good idea to have a backup domain controller in the domain if a primary domain controller has been defined.

Two primary domain controllers cannot exist in the same domain. One will win out if two do exist initially. The two will go into a contention mode and the workstations in the domain will quickly acknowledge one and not the other.

One last note about domain controllers and domains. A domain controller is identified and defined during the installation phase of NT. It cannot be defined at any other time. This is a very important aspect of the setup phase of the network.

Trust Relationships

A trust relationship among domains simply means two or more domains *trust* the other. This does not mean that all users in one domain will have automatic access to resources in the other domain. Further definition of access is required. In addition, a global domain is required for operation when multiple domains exist. Its purpose is to facilitate coordination of domains and users within various domains.

Another concept to remember about domains is that trust relationships among them are one-way, not two-way. For example, user A in domain A may trust resource B in domain B; this does not however mean that resource B in domain B trusts user A in domain A.

The simplest way to think of trust and domains is illustrated in these three examples. First, a master domain has domains that have trust relationships with it. Second, two domains have bi-directional trust relationships. This could loosely be called peer-to-peer trust. Third, three or more domains have multiple trust relationships with more than one domain.

User Attributes

NT users have associated attributes, typified by the following list:

- Account
- Password
- Group memberships
- Account policy
- User rights
- User profile.

This information is used by administrators to customize a wide variety of user profiles. Some users may have much broader abilities than others due to their work requirements. This degree of information in user profiles enables considerable control over user access and provides system security.

The account and password for NT users are similar to those on other operating systems; they are a way to provide unique identifiers to users and a level of security.

NT *group memberships* are a way to assign resources to a collection of users. For example, assume the group "work" exist and has seven users. Now suppose an eighth user is to be added. With the implementation of *groups* this eighth user would have all the same abilities and limitations as the previous seven members of this group. The use of groups is powerful because multiple groups can be defined in a given domain. Groups are an administrative way to associate users with other users who need similar privileges. The scope of *how* groups are implemented is determined on a site-by-site basis by the network administrator. Since a network needs an administrator it is wise to learn more. Consult NT books mentioned later in this chapter which provide excellent information.

Account policy is a feature of NT not always used in implementations; though when security is of greater importance, this feature is generally useful. The account policy enables a more complex implementation. For example, the password age, length, and history, and any account lockout on failed logon attempts are manipulated.

User rights are basically definitions of what users can or cannot do to the operating system: they may include changing the system time, restoring files and directories, shutting down the system, taking ownership of files, forcing a shutdown of a remote system, backing up files and directories, accessing a given computer from the network, managing the audit and security log of systems, and controlling logons (either remotely or locally).

The *user profile* specifies the program groups available. This collection of program groups indicates accessible options that are available.

Workstation and Server Commonalities

Windows NT is clearly delineated into two parts. This section highlights those aspects/parts the workstation and server have in common.

Both the NT workstation and server used what is considered advanced file systems. NT supports the NTFS and FAT. NTFS supports long file names, file level compression, file data forking support (required for Macintosh systems), international filenames, software level sector support for fault tolerance, and file level security permissions.

FAT support makes NT backward-compatible with DOS. Floppy drives use FAT and RISC systems using NT use FAT in the boot partition.

Both workstation and server support TCP/IP. NetBIOS is supported also as defined in RFCs 1001 and 1002. This means logical naming at a session level is possible. The NetBIOS interface also supports

Dynamic Data Exchange (DDE). DDE enables sharing data embedded within documents.

NT workstation and server also share the Dynamic Host Configuration Protocol (DHCP) client. This means NT stations can participate in an environment to obtain DNS addresses, IP addresses, gateway addresses, and netmasks.

NT provides support for SNMP. This makes workstations and servers capable of participating in environments that use management tools such as OpenView, SunNet Manager, and SystemView.

NT workstation and server both support Remote Access Service (RAS). In NT version 4 this is a point-to-point tunneling protocol. This function of NT enables a virtual network to be created over a wide distance. NT data encryption makes this a popular service.

Both workstation and server provide support for C2-level security. Protecting data on a system is achieved by Access Control Lists (ACLs) which enable directory and file level security maintenance.

NT workstation and server are administered the same way. Administration tools include:

- DHCP Manager
- Disk Manager
- Event Viewer
- Performance Monitor
- RAS Administrator
- Server Manager
- User Manager
- WINS Manager.

The DHCP manager is used to configure the station to obtain required information upon startup. There is also the DHCP server service, which permits remote control of DHCP servers.

The disk manager is the tool for creating disk partitions, mirrored disks, and volume set disk partitioning.

The event viewer enables a user to view events on local and remote systems. Information such as the system log, security log, and application log can be obtained.

The performance monitor provides a method for real-time monitoring. It also makes it possible to send administrative alerts to remote systems possible, monitor performance counters, and maintain performance logs.

The RAS administrator is a configuration tool used to designate certain users privileged to gain access to a network node. It can also be used to configure remote stations.

The server manager tool is used to create domain systems for workstations (NT), standalone servers, and domain controllers. It is also used to determine the status of servers and users logged on.

The user manager enables the creation and management of user accounts. When it is used on a domain controller, interdomain trust relationships are set up by this tool. This is the tool for setting up user rights, system-wide passwords, and auditing functions.

The Windows Internet Name Service (WINS) manager manages the WINS server service. This function of NT can be used to manage a local or a remote host. The basic purpose of WINS is dynamic name resolution.

Networking and Services in Windows NT

Important aspects of NT are its networking ability and services built into the operating system. Fundamental to NT is the intent that its design be used in a networked environment. The following protocols and services supported in Windows NT are bundled as part of the operating systems; administrators select which ones they want to use in any given instance:

- TCP/IP
- User protocols and applications
- Administrative utilities
- Dynamic Host Configuration Protocol (DHCP)
- Windows Internet Naming Service (WINS)
- Domain Name System (DNS)
- NetBEUI
- IPX/SPX
- DLC
- STREAMS
- Remote Procedure Call (RPC)
- Service Advertising Protocol (SAP)
- Workstation
- NetBIOS
- Client service for NetWare
- Server
- Remote Access Service (RAS)
- LMHosts.

TCP/IP

TCP/IP is covered in much greater depth in Chapters 11 and 12. If you need more information now, refer to that chapter. It is appropriate to examine here some TCP/IP aspects as they relate to Windows NT.

In Figure 9.7 NT and TCP/IP are illustrated together. The layers of TCP/IP are represented in NT. However, not all functional aspects of TCP/IP are bundled into NT as a single unit, meaning all aspects have to be used or none can be used. For example, TCP and UDP are integral to NT because these transport-layer protocols are required for using protocols and applications that reside above them. The same is true for the layer in TCP/IP where IP, ICMP, and the routing protocols reside. These components are required in order for TCP/IP to operate.

However, on the upper layers where applications reside, choices to use different components can be made.

FIGURE 9.7
Windows NT
and TCP/IP

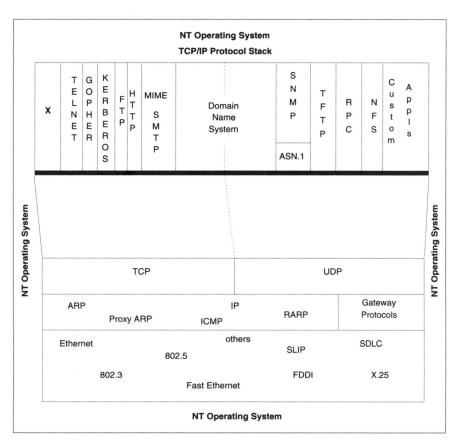

User Protocols and Applications

One example of a user protocol and application is File Transfer Protocol (FTP). FTP itself is an application divided into two parts: client and server. From a user aspect FTP is merely seen as an application that enables file transfers from one system to another.

Telnet is another protocol and application supported in NT. Like FTP, it consists of a client and a server. The Telnet client is used to initiate a session between two hosts. A Telnet server answers a Telnet client's request. Other TCP/IP protocols and applications are also used with NT.

Administrative Utilities

Network administrative utilities, also part of NT, are actually commands that can be issued on the NT server or workstation command line. They are helpful tools in obtaining information used to manage the NT network. Examples of these utilities include:

- **ARP (address resolution protocol):** when entered on a command line of an NT workstation or server this yields the following data:

  ```
  Interface: 220.100.100.10 on Interface 2
  Internet Address Physical Address Type
  220.100.100.53 00-60-94-a5-cc-ee dynamic
  ```

- **Hostname:** When entered on an NT workstation or server command line this yields the following:

  ```
  Microsoft® Windows NT™
  © Copyright 1985-1996 Microsoft Corp.
  C:\>hostname
  BRAINS
  C:\>hostname?
  ```

- `sethostname`: Use the Network Control Panel Applet to set hostname. `hostname -s` is not supported.

  ```
  C:\>
  ```

- `ipconfig`: When this command is entered on the command line of NT workstation or server it yields the following information:

  ```
  Windows NT IP Configuration
  Ethernet adapter SMCISA1:
  IP Address. . . . . . . . : 220.100.100.10
  ```

```
Subnet Mask . . . . . . . . : 255.255.255.0
Default Gateway . . . . . . :
Ethernet adapter NdisWan5:
IP Address. . . . . . . . . : 0.0.0.0
Subnet Mask . . . . . . . . : 0.0.0.0
Default Gateway . . . . . . :
```

- nbstat: When this command is entered on an NT workstation or server command line the following information is obtained, depending upon which argument is used with the command:

  ```
  C:\>nbtstat
  ```

  Displays protocol statistics and current TCP/IP connections using NBT (NetBIOS over TCP/IP).

  ```
  NBTSTAT [-a RemoteName] [-A IP address] [-c] [-n]
      [-r] [-R] [-s] [-S] [interval] ]
  ```

-a	(adapter status) Lists the remote machine's name table given its name
-A	(Adapter status) Lists the remote machine's name table given its IP address
-c	(cache) Lists the remote name cache including the IP addresses
-n	(names) Lists local NetBIOS names
-r	(resolved) Lists names resolved by broadcast and via WINS
-R	(Reload) Purges and reloads the remote cache name table
-S	(Sessions) Lists sessions table with the destination IP addresses
-s	(sessions) Lists sessions table converting destination IP addresses to host names via the host's file.
RemoteName	Remote host machine name
IP address	Dotted decimal representation of the IP address
interval	Redisplays selected statistics, pausing interval seconds between each display; press **Ctrl+C** to stop redisplaying statistics.

```
C:\>
---------------------------------------------------------------------
Node IpAddress: [220.100.100.10] Scope Id: []
      NetBIOS Local Name Table
Name          Type      Status
---------------------------------------------------------------------
Registered Registered Registered Registered
MUSCLE       <20> UNIQUE
MUSCLE       <00> UNIQUE
INFO         <00> GROUP
MUSCLE       <06> UNIQUE
MUSCLE       <03> UNIQUE
INFO         <1E> GROUP
---------------------------------------------------------------------
NetBIOS Names Resolution and Registration Statistics
---------------------------------------------------------------------
Resolved By Broadcast    = 1
Resolved By Name Server  = 23
Registered By Broadcast  = 7
Registered By Name Server = 2
---------------------------------------------------------------------
NetBIOS Names Resolved By Broadcast
---------------------------------------------------------------------
SILO
---------------------------------------------------------------------
NetBIOS Connection Table
Local        State     In/Out    Remote     Input     Output
Name                             Host
---------------------------------------------------------------------
Connected        OutListening                 Listening
MUSCLE       <00>      CHEROKEE     <20>          14KB      16KB
MUSCLE       <03>
ADMINISTRATOR <03>
---------------------------------------------------------------------
Node IpAddress: [220.100.100.10] Scope Id: []
    NetBIOS Local Name Table
Name          Type      Status
---------------------------------------------------------------------
Registered Registered Registered Registered Registered
MUSCLE       <20> UNIQUE
MUSCLE       <00> UNIQUE
INFO         <00> GROUP
MUSCLE       <06> UNIQUE
MUSCLE       <03> UNIQUE
INFO         <1E> GROUP
```

- netstat: Depending upon which argument is issued against this command, a variety of information can be obtained. Consider the following:

```
C:\>netstat ? > n
```

Displays protocol statistics and current TCP/IP network connections:

```
NETSTAT [-a] [-e] [-n] [-s] [-p proto] [-r] [interval]
```

-a	Displays all connections and listening ports. (Server-side connections are normally not shown).
-e	Displays Ethernet statistics. This may be combined with the -s option.
-n	Displays addresses and port numbers in numerical form
-p	proto Shows connections for the protocol specified by proto; proto may be TCP or UDP. If used with the -s option to display per-protocol statistics, proto may be TCP, UDP, or IP.
-r	Displays the contents of the routing table
-s	Displays per-protocol statistics; by default, statistics are shown for TCP, UDP and IP; the -p option may be used to specify a subset of the default.
interval	Redisplays selected statistics, pausing interval seconds between each display. Press **CTRL+C** to stop redisplaying statistics. If omitted, netstat will print the current configuration information once.

```
C:\>type n
C:\>
Active Connections
Proto Local Address        Foreign Address       State
TCP   CHEROKEE:1027        0.0.0.0:0             LISTENING
TCP   CHEROKEE:135         0.0.0.0:0             LISTENING
TCP   CHEROKEE:135         0.0.0.0:0             LISTENING
TCP   CHEROKEE:13991       0.0.0.0:0             LISTENING
TCP   CHEROKEE:1025        0.0.0.0:0             LISTENING
TCP   CHEROKEE:1025        localhost:1027        ESTABLISHED
TCP   CHEROKEE:1027        localhost:1025        ESTABLISHED
TCP   CHEROKEE:137         0.0.0.0:0             LISTENING
TCP   CHEROKEE:138         0.0.0.0:0             LISTENING
TCP   CHEROKEE:nbsession   0.0.0.0:0             LISTENING
```

```
TCP  CHEROKEE:nbsession    220.100.100.19:1035  SYN_RECEIVED
TCP  CHEROKEE:nbsession    220.100.100.61:1042  SYN_RECEIVED
TCP  CHEROKEE:nbsession    220.100.100.77:1038  SYN_RECEIVED
UDP  CHEROKEE:135          *:*
UDP  CHEROKEE:13991        *:*
UDP  CHEROKEE:nbname       *:*
UDP  CHEROKEE:nbdatagram   *:*
```

- `ping`: When this command is entered on a command line of an NT workstation or server the following information can be obtained, depending upon the arguments used against it.

   Usage: `ping [-t] [-a] [-n count] [-1 size] [-f] [-i TTL] [-v TOS] [-r count] [-s count] [[-j host-list] | [-k host-list]] [-w timeout] destination-list`

   Options:

`-t`	Ping the specified host until interrupted
`-a`	Resolve addresses to hostnames
`-n count`	Number of echo requests to send
`-1 size`	Send buffer size
`-f Set`	Don't Fragment flag in packet
`-i TTL`	Time To Live
`-v TOS`	Type Of Service
`-r count`	Record route for count hops
`-s count`	Timestamp for count hops
`-j host-list`	Loose source route along host-list
`-k host-list`	Strict source route along host-list
`-w timeout`	Timeout in milliseconds to wait for each reply.

```
Pinging cherokee [220.100.100.53] with 32 bytes of data:
Reply from 220.100.100.53: bytes=32 time=20ms TTL=128
Reply from 220.100.100.53: bytes=32 time<10ms TTL=128
Reply from 220.100.100.53: bytes=32 time<10ms TTL=128
Reply from 220.100.100.53: bytes=32 time<10ms TTL=128
-------------------------------------------------------------
Pinging brains [220.100.100.12] with 32 bytes of data:
Reply from 220.100.100.12: bytes=32 time=10ms TTL=128
Reply from 220.100.100.12: bytes=32 time<10ms TTL=128
Reply from 220.100.100.12: bytes=32 time<10ms TTL=128
Reply from 220.100.100.12: bytes=32 time<10ms TTL=128
```

- route

  `C:\>route`

  Manipulates network routing tables.

  ```
  ROUTE [-f] [command [destination] [MASK netmask] [gateway]
  [METRIC metric]]
  ```

-f	Clears the routing tables of all gateway entries; if this is used in conjunction with one of the commands, the tables are cleared prior to running the command.
-p	When used with the ADD command, makes a route persistent across boots of the system. By default, routes are not preserved when the system is restarted. When used with the PRINT command, displays the list of registered persistent routes. This is ignored for all other commands, which always affect the appropriate persistent routes.
-command	Specifies one of four commands
PRINT	Prints a route
ADD	Adds a route
DELETE	Deletes a route
CHANGE	Modifies an existing route
-destination	Specifies the host
-MASK	If the MASK keyword is present, the next parameter is interpreted as the netmask parameter
-netmask	If this is provided, it specifies a subnet mask value to be associated with this route entry. If no specification, the default is to 255.255.255.255.
-gateway	Specifies gateway
-METRIC	Specifies the metric/cost for the destination

All symbolic names used for destination are looked up in the network database file NETWORKS. The symbolic names for gateway are looked up in the host name database file HOSTS. If the command is to print or delete, wildcards may be used for the destination and gateway, or the gateway argument may be omitted.

```
C:\>
Active Routes:
Network Address Netmask Gateway Address Interface Metric
127.0.0.0       255.0.0.0       127.0.0.1       127.0.0.1       1
220.100.100.0   255.255.255.0   220.100.100.8 220.100.100.8   1
220.100.100.8   255.255.255.255 127.0.0.1       127.0.0.1       1
220.100.100.255 255.255.255.255 220.100.100.8 220.100.100.8   1
224.0.0.0       224.0.0.0       220.100.100.8 220.100.100.8   1
255.255.255.255 255.255.255.255 220.100.100.8 220.100.100.8   1
```

- tracert: Depending upon which argument is issued on the command line, the following information is obtained:

```
C:\>tracert
```

Usage: tracert [-d] [-h maximum_hops] [-j host-list] [-w timeout] target_name
Options:

-d	Do not resolve addresses to hostnames
-h maximum_hops	Maximum number of hops to search for target
-j host-list	Loose source route along host-list
-w timeout	Wait timeout milliseconds for each reply.

```
C:\>
Tracing route to renegade [220.100.100.79] over a maximum of 30 hops:
    1 One of the IP options is invalid.
Trace complete.
```

Dynamic Host Configuration Protocol (DHCP)

DHCP has its roots in the Internet and RFCs that make the constituent parts what they are. In Windows NT, variations exist with regard to DHCP concepts and terminology. For that reason, native DHCP information is presented here, followed by information specific to Windows NT.

DHCP Considerations

DHCP was designed to supply DHCP clients with the configuration parameters defined in the host requirements RFCs. After obtaining parameters via DHCP, a DHCP client should be able to exchange packets with any other host in the Internet.

Not all of these parameters are required for a newly initialized client. A client and server may negotiate transmission of parameters required by the client or specific to a particular subnet.

DHCP allows but does not require the configuration of client parameters not directly related to the IP protocol. DHCP also does not address registration of newly configured clients with the DNS. The original design intent of DHCP was not to configure routers.

DHCP Terms

- **DHCP client.** A DHCP client is an Internet host using DHCP to obtain configuration parameters such as a network address.
- **DHCP server.** A DHCP server is an Internet or internet host that returns configuration parameters to DHCP clients.
- **BOOTP relay agent.** A BOOTP relay agent or relay agent is an Internet host or router that passes DHCP messages between DHCP clients and DHCP servers. DHCP is designed to use the same relay agent behavior specified in the BOOTP protocol.
- **binding.** A binding is a collection of configuration parameters, including at least an IP address, associated with or bound to a DHCP client. Bindings are managed by DHCP servers.

DHCP Design Intent

The original design intent of DHCP specifies:

- DHCP should be a mechanism rather than a policy. DHCP must allow local system administrators control over configuration parameters where desired; this means local system administrators should be able to enforce local policies concerning allocation and access to local resources where desired.
- Clients should require no manual configuration. Each client should be able to discover appropriate local configuration para-

meters without user intervention and incorporate those parameters into its own configuration.

- Networks should require no manual configuration for individual clients. Under normal circumstances a network manager should not have manually to enter any per-client configuration parameters.
- DHCP should not require a server on each subnet. To allow for scale and economy, DHCP must work across routers or through the intervention of BOOTP relay agents.
- A DHCP client must be prepared to receive multiple responses to a request for configuration parameters. Some installations may include multiple, overlapping DHCP servers to enhance reliability and increase performance.
- DHCP must coexist with statically configured, non-participating hosts and with existing network protocol implementations.
- DHCP must work with the BOOTP relay agent behavior as described by RFCs 951 and 1542.
- DHCP must provide service to existing BOOTP clients.

DHCP requirements include the following, specific to the transmission of network layer parameters:

- Guarantee that any network address will not be in use by more than one DHCP client at a time
- Retain DHCP client configuration across DHCP client reboot. A DHCP client should, whenever possible, be assigned the same configuration parameters (e.g., network address) in response to each request
- Retain DHCP client configuration across server reboots
- Assign the same configuration parameters to a DHCP client despite restarts of the DHCP mechanism
- Allow automated assignment of configuration parameters to new clients so they may avoid hand configuration
- Support fixed or permanent allocation of configuration parameters to specific clients.

DHCP and NT

DHCP is used the same way in Windows NT as in the Internet and in intranets. It is designed around a client/server method of communication. A DHCP server and DHCP clients are required to be in the NT network for proper operation to be performed. The basic purpose of a DHCP server in an NT network is to provide IP addresses to NT clients who request them. In addition to allocation of DHCP addresses, a DHCP server is able to provide statistics about the network. The significance of DHCP servers cannot be understated.

In an environment with numerous hosts including one that is portable and moved frequently, a DHCP server is beneficial. In such an environment, the DHCP server administers configuration information without requiring human intervention. DHCP also provides a security function by allocating IP addresses because these addresses can be revoked by a network administrator. Furthermore, the length of time when IP addresses are valid is controllable and therefore another angle of security is achieved.

DHCP assigns addresses to requesting clients because of a range of addresses. This assignment of an IP address to a requesting client on behalf of a DHCP server is considered a *loan* from the DHCP server's perspective.

Windows Internet Naming Service (WINS)

The purpose of WINS is to map NetBIOS computer names to IP addresses in a TCP/IP network. WINS itself is based on RFCs 1001 and 1002. These define a NetBIOS name resolution over TCP/IP. NetBIOS is a session-layer protocol which in years past was the protocol used in Microsoft networks. Now TCP/IP is built into Windows NT and is becoming the protocol of choice.

WINS provides a centralized management approach. With the WINS manager, WINS servers can be managed and replication partners set up. WINS also provides dynamic name registration, release, and renewal for clients using the service. Another advantage of WINS is the ability it affords to browse in resources in a computer network separated by a router without the need for a domain controller. Furthermore, broadcast traffic is reduced because a WINS server supplies an IP address for each name query message received.

Domain Name System (DNS)

The organization of the domain system is specified in RFCs and is dominant throughout the Internet. The information here reflects much of the RFC specifications. DNS is designed to avoid many of the the complicated problems found in general-purpose database systems. Assumptions include:

1. The size of the total database will initially be proportional to the number of hosts using the system, but will eventually grow to be proportional to the number of users on those hosts as mailboxes and other information are added to the domain system.

2. Most of the data in the system will change very slowly (e.g., mailbox bindings, host addresses), but the system should be able to deal with subsets that change more rapidly (in a time frame measured in seconds or minutes).

3. The administrative boundaries used to distribute responsibility for the database will usually correspond to organizations that have one or more hosts. Each organization that has responsibility for a particular set of domains will provide redundant name servers, either on the organization's own hosts or on other hosts that the organization arranges to use.

4. Clients of the domain system should be able to identify trusted name servers they prefer to use before accepting referrals to name servers outside of this "trusted" set.

5. Access to information is more critical than are instantaneous updates or guarantees of consistency. Hence the update process allows updates to percolate out through the users of the domain system rather than guaranteeing that all copies are simultaneously updated. When updates are unavailable due to network or host failure, the usual course is to believe old information while continuing efforts to update it. The general model is that copies are distributed with timeouts for refreshing. The distributor sets the timeout value and the recipient of the distribution is responsible for performing the refresh. In special situations, very short intervals can be specified, or the owner can prohibit copies.

6. In any system that has a distributed database, a particular name server may be presented with a query that can only be answered by some other server. The two general approaches to dealing with this problem are "recursive", in which the first server pursues the query for the client at another server, and "iterative", in which the server refers the client to another server and lets the client pursue the query. Both approaches have advantages and disadvantages, but the iterative approach is preferred for the datagram style of access. The domain system requires implementation of the iterative approach, but allows the recursive approach as an option.

7. The domain system assumes that all data originate in master files scattered through the hosts that use the domain system. These

master files are updated by local system administrators. Master files are text files that are read by a local name server, and hence become available through the name servers to users of the domain system. The user programs access name servers through standard programs called resolvers.

8. The standard format of master files allows them to be exchanged between hosts (via FTP, mail, or some other mechanism); this facility is useful when an organization wants a domain, but doesn't want to support a name server. The organization can maintain the master files locally using a text editor, transfer them to a foreign host which runs a name server, and then arrange with the system administrator of the name server to get the files loaded.

9. Each host's name servers and resolvers are configured by a local system administrator [RFC 1033]. For a name server, this configuration data includes the identity of local master files and instructions on which non-local master files are to be loaded from foreign servers. The name server uses the master files or copies to load its zones. For resolvers, the configuration data identify the name servers which should be the primary sources of information.

10. The domain system defines procedures for accessing the data and for referrals to other name servers. The domain system also defines procedures for caching retrieved data and for periodic refreshing of data defined by the system administrator.

    A system administrator provides:

    *   The definition of zone boundaries
    *   Master files of data
    *   Updates to master files
    *   Statements of the refresh policies desired.

    The domain system provides:

    *   Standard formats for resource data
    *   Standard methods for querying the database
    *   Standard methods for name servers to refresh local data from foreign name servers.

Elements of DNS

The DNS has three major components: domain name space and resource records, name servers, and resolvers.

Domain Name Space and Resource Records, are specifications for a tree-structured name space and data associated with the names. Conceptually, each node and leaf of the domain name space tree names a set of information, and query operations are attempts to extract specific types of information from a particular set. A query names the domain name of interest and describes the type of resource information desired. For example, the Internet uses some of its domain names to identify hosts; queries for address resources return Internet host addresses.

Name Servers are server programs which hold information about the domain tree's structure and set information. A name server may cache structure or set information about any part of the domain tree, but in general a particular name server has complete information about a subset of the domain space, and pointers to other name servers that can be used to lead to information from any part of the domain tree. Name servers know the parts of the domain tree for which they have complete information; a name server is said to be an authority for these parts of the name space. Authoritative information is organized into units called *zones*, and these zones can be automatically distributed to the name servers which provide redundant service for the data in a zone.

Resolvers are programs that extract information from name servers in response to client requests. Resolvers must be able to access at least one name server and use that name server's information to answer a query directly, or pursue the query using referrals to other name servers. A resolver will typically be a system routine that is directly accessible to user programs; hence no protocol is necessary between the resolver and the user program.

These three components roughly correspond to the three layers or views of the domain system. Consider a detailed explanation here that correlates this.

- From the user's point of view, the domain system is accessed through a simple procedure or OS call to a local resolver.
- The domain space consists of a single tree and the user can request information from any section of the tree.
- From the resolver's point of view, the domain system is composed of an unknown number of name servers. Each name server has one or more pieces of the whole domain tree's data, but the resolver views each of these databases as essentially static.
- From a name server's point of view, the domain system consists of separate sets of local information called zones. The name serv-

er has local copies of some of the zones. The name server must periodically refresh its zones from master copies in local files or foreign name servers. The name server must concurrently process queries that arrive from resolvers.

In the interests of performance, implementations may couple these functions. For example, a resolver on the same machine as a name server might share a database consisting of the the zones managed by the name server and the cache managed by the resolver.

Domain Name Space and Resource Records

The domain name space is a tree structure. Each node and leaf on the tree corresponds to a resource set (which may be empty). The domain system makes no distinctions between the uses of the interior nodes and leaves, and the term "node" refers to both. Each node has a label, which is 0 to 63 octets in length. Brother nodes may not have the same label, although the same label can be used for nodes which are not brothers. One label is reserved, and that is the null (i.e., zero length) label used for the root.

The domain name of a node is the list of the labels on the path from the node to the root of the tree. By convention, the labels that compose a domain name are printed or read left to right, from the most specific (lowest, farthest from the root) to the least specific (highest, closest to the root).

Internally, programs that manipulate domain names should represent them as sequences of labels, where each label is a length octet followed by an octet string. Because all domain names end at the root, which has a null string for a label, these internal representations can use a length byte of zero to terminate a domain name.

By convention, domain names can be stored with arbitrary case, but domain name comparisons for all present domain functions are done in a case-insensitive manner, assuming an ASCII character set, and a high-order zero bit. This means that you are free to create a node with label "A" or a node with label "a," but not both as brothers; you could refer to either using "a" or "A." When you receive a domain name or label, you should preserve its case. The rationale for this choice is that we may someday need to add full binary domain names for new services; existing services would not be changed.

When a user needs to type a domain name, the length of each label is omitted and the labels are separated by dots ("."). Since a complete domain name ends with the root label, this leads to a printed form which ends in a dot. We use this property to distinguish between:

- A character string which represents a complete domain name (often called *absolute*). For example, "joejones.ISI.EDU."
- A character string that represents the starting labels of a domain name which is incomplete, and should be completed by local software using knowledge of the local domain (often called *relative*). For example, "joejones" used in the ISI.EDU domain.

Relative names are taken either relative to a well-known origin, or to a list of domains used as a search list. Relative names appear mostly at the user interface, where their interpretation varies from implementation to implementation, and in master files, where they are relative to a single origin domain name. The most common interpretation uses the root "." as either the single origin or as one of the members of the search list, so a multilabel relative name is often one where the trailing dot has been omitted to save typing.

To simplify implementations, the total number of octets that represent a domain name (i.e., the sum of all label octets and label lengths) is limited to 255. A domain is identified by a domain name, and consists of that part of the domain name space that is at or below the domain name which specifies the domain. A domain is a subdomain of another domain if it is contained within that domain. This relationship can be tested by seeing if the subdomain's name ends with the octet containing domain's name. For example, A.B.C.D is a subdomain of B.C.D, C.D, D, and " ".

DNS technical specifications do not mandate a particular tree structure or rules for selecting labels; the goal is to be as general as possible, so that DNS can be used to build arbitrary applications. In particular, the system was designed so that the name space did not have to be organized along the lines of network boundaries, name servers, etc. The rationale for this is not that the name space should have no implied semantics, but rather that the choice of implied semantics should be left open to be used for the problem at hand, and that different parts of the tree can have different implied semantics. For example, the IN-ADDR.ARPA domain is organized and distributed by network and host address because its role is to translate from network or host numbers to names; NetBIOS domains [RFC 1001, RFC 1002] are flat because that is appropriate for the application.

However, there are some guidelines that apply to the "normal" parts of the name space used for hosts, mailboxes, etc., that will make the name space more uniform, provide for growth, and minimize problems as software is converted from the older host table. The political decisions about the top levels of the tree originated in RFC

920. Current policy for the top levels is discussed in [RFC 1032]. MILNET conversion issues are covered in [RFC 1031].

Lower domains which will eventually be broken into multiple zones should provide branching at the top of the domain so that the eventual decomposition can be done without renaming. Node labels which use special characters, leading digits, etc., are likely to break older software which depends on more restrictive choices.

Before the DNS can be used to hold naming information for some kind of object, two needs must be met:

- For a convention for mapping between object names and domain names; this describes how information about an object is accessed.
- For RR types and data formats for describing the object.

The DNS can be quite simple or fairly complex. Very often, the designer must take into account existing formats and plan for upward compatibility for existing usage. Multiple mappings or levels of mapping may be required. For hosts, the mapping depends on the existing syntax for host names which is a subset of the usual text representation for domain names, together with RR formats for describing host addresses, etc. Because we need a reliable inverse mapping from address to host name, a special mapping for addresses into the IN-ADDR.ARPA domain is also defined.

For mailboxes, the mapping is slightly more complex. The usual mail address `<local-part>@<mail-domain>` is mapped into a domain name by converting `<local-part>` into a single label (regardless of dots it contains), converting `<mail-domain>` into a domain name using the usual text format for domain names (dots denote label breaks), and concatenating the two to form a single domain name. Thus the mailbox `HOSTMASTER@SRI-NIC.ARPA` is represented as a domain name by `HOSTMASTER.SRI-NIC.ARPA`. An appreciation for the reasons behind this design also must take into account the scheme for mail exchanges [RFC 974].

A typical user is not concerned with defining these rules, but should understand that they are usually the result of numerous compromises between desires for upward compatibility with old usage, interactions between different object definitions, and the inevitable urge to add new features when defining the rules. The way the DNS is used to support some object is often more crucial than the restrictions inherent in the DNS.

The following figure shows a part of the current domain name space, and is used in many examples. Note that the tree is a very small subset of the actual name space.

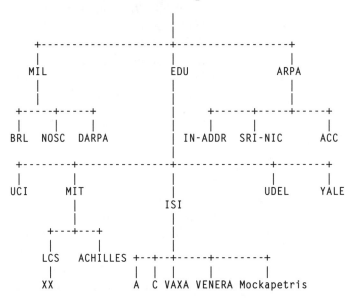

In this example, the root domain has three immediate subdomains: MIL, EDU, and ARPA. The LCS.MIT.EDU domain has one immediate subdomain named XX.LCS.MIT.EDU. All of the leaves are also domains.

NetBEUI

NetBEUI is a protocol of evolution. NetBIOS, a session-layer protocol, was developed in the early 1980s for IBM. One of its purposes was to make networking APIs available to user applications so that they could obtain and provide network services. Inherent in NetBIOS was a transport-layer protocol known as NetBIOS Frames Protocol (NBFP). This transport aspect of NetBIOS eventually became known as NetBIOS Extended User Interface (NetBEUI). NetBEUI became known as the protocol of choice to transport data traffic among small LANs.

As a result, NetBEUI became the transport protocol for Microsoft networks. A confusion still exists today between NetBIOS and NetBEUI. NetBIOS is a protocol, still widely used, that can be intermixed and used with IPX/SPX and TCP/IP. Since NetBIOS is a session-layer protocol it can utilize the transport-layer protocols found in IPX/SPX and TCP/IP. NetBEUI, on the other hand, is tied to NetBIOS. NetBEUI is a relatively small protocol (compared to the size of other protocols) and operationally it is quick. Because of the design of NetBEUI operations it is not well suited for medium to large networks; its true forte is small networks.

IPX/SPX

IPX/SPX is a Novell network protocol supported by Windows NT. Before we examine the operating of IPX/SPX with NT, we should consider some IPX/SPX information.

NetWare can be evaluated by its layers compared to the OSI model. Figure 9.8 best exemplifies this.

FIGURE 9.8
IPX/SPX
by Layers

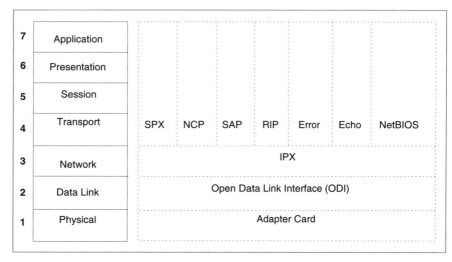

At the lowest layer is support for adapter cards. NetWare supports multiple adapter cards including: Ethernet, Token ring, ARCnet, 802.3, FDDI, and others.

The next layer is called the Open Data Link Interface (ODI). This is a specification for the data-link layer providing hardware and thus media protocol independence. Some drawings of the NetWare protocol stack do not show this layer but nevertheless it is there. The ODI standard was the fruition of joint work among multiple corporations including Apple and Novell. Technically, the specification is more than just a data link specification, because it defines four independent yet cohesive subcomponents. Before examining the details of ODI consider Figure 9.9 showing the sublayers where ODI operates.

FIGURE 9.9
Closeup of ODI

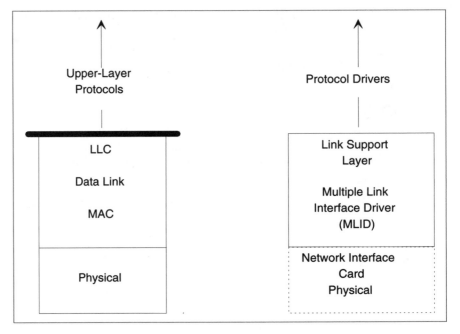

ODI is shown compared to the OSI layers, particularly the data-link layer as it is broken into the MAC and LLC sublayers.

Internet Packet Exchange (IPX)

IPX operates at layer three compared to the OSI model. It is a datagram protocol based upon a best-effort delivery system. As Figure 9.8 shows the correlation is directly with the network layer. It operates where packet delivery is accomplished on a best-effort delivery mechanism. In other words, packet delivery has no relationship to other packets. This means there is no logical order of delivery.

IPX is connectionless oriented; no acknowledgements are sent from the receiving hosts to the originating host to indicate receipt of packets. Because of this connectionless-oriented nature, acknowledgement and related topics are left to higher-level protocols or programs to perform. This protocol is faster than those above it as shown in Figure 9.8.

Even though IPX operates at network layer three compared to the OSI model, it does perform transport-layer functions and this sense of one-to-one correlation between NetWare and the OSI model is not accurate.

Sequenced Packet Exchange (SPX)

SPX operates above IPX. It is a connection-oriented protocol. Specialized applications can be built using this as the base protocol. One characteristic of SPX is insured packet delivery; capability of recovering from lost data and errors that may occur in the data being passed from origin to destination. Another characteristic that makes the protocol robust is that it does not acknowledge each packet but waits until the maximum number of outstanding packets is reached. In Net-Ware this is referred to as a *window*. Operationally, SPX performs some functions as the transport layer is the OSI model and after it is finished makes a program call to IPX for packet delivery. SPX and IPX operate together to some degree. A perspective on its relationship to the NetWare model is shown in Figure 9.8.

NetWare Core Protocol (NCP)

NCP is a defined protocol which is the procedure that file servers' operating systems utilize to respond to requests and to accept requests made. NCP controls client and server operations by defining interactions between them. The NCP provides a service similar to that of SPX in that it performs some packet error checking. It also has built-in session control between entities. The NCP uses a number placed inside the request field of an NCP packet to request a given service. The reason for this is that NetWare services are given a number by a NetWare file server. Details of this protocol are Novell proprietary information and few details can be provided. It is not the general consensus that the NCP is the shell used on workstations.

Service Advertising Protocol (SAP)

This protocol resides on top of IPX. It uses IPX to perform its function. SAP does as its name implies; it functions with nodes that provide services to *advertise* available services. Available services include print and file servers. Gateway servers could be included in this as well. Those nodes that provide services broadcast SAP information periodically.

Router Information Protocol (RIP)

RIP is the routing information protocol used on NetWare networks. Functions performed by RIP include location of the best (fastest) route from a workstation to a network. RIP is used by routers to exchange information about routes, respond to requests from routers and workstations, and perform periodic routing table broadcasts among routers.

Error Protocol

This protocol is used among peer protocols. Programs that attempt to communicate with a host on a different network use NCP and IPX to attempt to reach that network. If that network is unreachable, an error packet is generated by a router and sent back to the requesting host regarding the state of the route to the target host. Interestingly, this function is portrayed in Figure 9.8 above the IPX layer, but functionally it seems to operate at the IPX layer.

Echo

Understanding echo is similar to understanding Ping in TCP/IP. This protocol is used to investigate the ability to check a path en route to a target destination. If the path is functional and the target node accessible, the echo protocol in the target node is built so that it literally echoes the packet back to the destination.

Review

NetWare is complex. It consist of multiple parts that perform different functions. Some are used in special situations whereas others are used in most installations. Many variations on the NetWare protocol stack exist. This has been a discussion of the components of NetWare, but has not addressed NetWare functionality in different environments.

Open Data Interface (ODI) Concepts

ODI is a concept for protocol independence. Its roots are in the philosophy of providing a consistent interface to multiple transport layer protocols so that network hardware independence can be achieved and greater implementation and flexibility can be realized.

ODI actually consists of three parts, or subcomponents: multiple protocol interface, link-support layer, and multiple-link interface driver.

The protocol part of the specification calls for support for a diverse blend of protocols. In fact, if any protocol is coded against this OSI specification then independence is achievable. The protocol drivers must operate at the network layer and above.

The next part of the specification is the link-support layer, whose primary purpose is routing between protocol drivers and multiple-link interface drivers. Figure 9.10 provides a closer view of the link support layer and its interaction with the layers above and below it.

FIGURE 9.10
Closeup View
of Link-Layer
Support

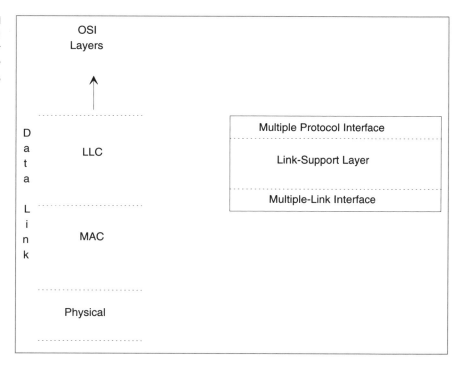

Figure 9.10 shows two interfaces. One provides a connectivity point with the network layer, and is called the *multiple-protocol interface.* As its name implies the interface is designed to operate with multiple protocols at the network layer and above. This interface was designed for developers creating program code so that they would have a standard interface into which to program regardless of the protocol.

The multiple-link interface is backed by the same philosophy as the multiple-protocol interface. This interface was designed so data-link-layer protocol developers would have a standard to code against.

The link-support layer performs a number of functions including: coordinating numbers assigned to multiple-link interface drivers after these drivers have been identified with the link-support layer; managing the protocol stack identification assigned to network protocol

drivers; managing individual network protocol drivers via their identification numbers even though frames can be grouped according to
MAC frame type; and being capable of manipulating media identification using specific frame formatting.

The fundamental purpose of media identification and protocol
identification is so packets can be routed from a given upper-layer
protocol stack to the correct lower-layer protocol interface without
rebooting the system.

The purpose of the Multiple Link Interface Driver (MLID) is to pass
data to and from the network media. The specification calls for these
drivers to be protocol-independent.

Implementing ODI

ODI is implemented differently according to operating system, device
driver, network protocol, and NetWare version. The functionality
behind it is a three-fold concept. The first concept is illustrated in
Figure 9.11.

FIGURE 9.11
Multiple
Upper-Layer
Protocols -1
Network Adapter

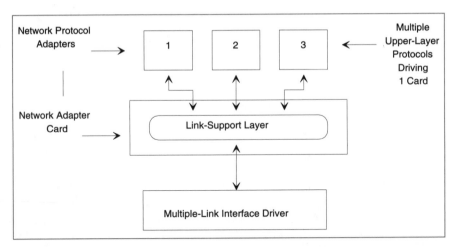

Figure 9.11 shows multiple upper-layer protocol drivers against one
network interface card. This is possible because of the ODI concept.

Figure 9.12 is the converse of Figure 9.11. In figure 9.12 one network protocol driver is used against the link-support layer and three
multiple-link interface drivers are used.

Figure 9.13 is another example of how the ODI concept is implemented.

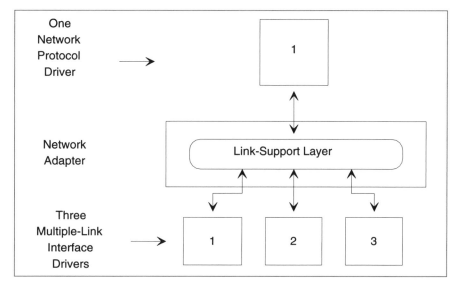

FIGURE 9.12
ODI Converse
Implementation

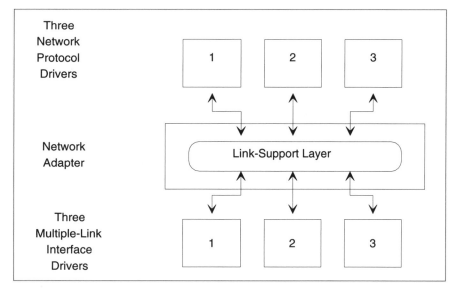

FIGURE 9.13
Multiple NPDs
and MLIDs

In Figure 9.13 multiple network protocol drivers are hooked into the link-support layer to drive three multiple-link interface drivers. Three is not a magic number with this concept; it could be two or four just as easily.

How ODI is Managed

An ODI implementation is managed through a configuration file with three basic components: protocol, link support, and link driver.

These components contain parameters that control the ODI operating environment. The protocol parameters are used in the logical *BIND* which is created between the upper-layer network protocol and the multiple-link interface driver. Link support reflects storage used at this part of the layer. The link driver parameters reflect the characteristics of the interface board used. Other configuration parameters may be required by different environments and because of that variety the environment manuals need to be used as references.

IPX

IPX is used to define addressing schemes in internetwork and intranetwork environments. NetWare network segments use numbers primarily for routing purposes. This section explores IPX packet structure and provides additional information concerning its function in a NetWare network.

IPX Packet Structure

IPX packets are carried in the data portion of a MAC frame. The focus here is upon the IPX protocol, its structure, and contents. Figure 9.14 illustrates the IPX packet structure, components, and the relationship to a MAC frame. Inside the IPX packet are field names.

FIGURE 9.14
IPX Packet
Structure

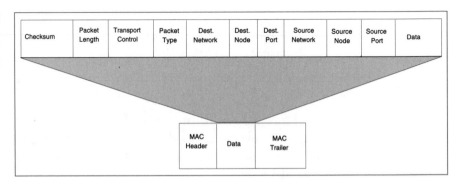

Sockets and Ports

Novell refers to destination and source sockets. These *sockets* are understood better by their function as ports. Henceforth, where Novell makes reference to a socket the term *port* is used, unless significant meaning is changed and then clarification of this is provided. The term socket actually refers to a network, host, and port number just as in TCP/IP protocols.

IPX Field Explanation

Each field in the IPX packet has significant meaning. Explanation of those meanings follows.

- **Checksum.** This field is responsible for performing packet level checking.
- **Packet Length.** This field contains the internetwork packet length, the header and the data section.
- **Transport Control.** This field is used by routers between internetworks. Primarily this is used by NetWare-based routers.
- **Packet Type.** This field indicates the service provided by the packet regardless of whether this service is required or merely offered.

     The packet type is indicated by a value that tells the specific service provided. The values and corresponding services include:
   - 0 Unknown type of packet
   - 1 Routing Information Packet (RIP)
   - 2 Echo packet
   - 3 Error packet
   - 4 Packet exchange packet
   - 5 Sequenced packet protocol packet
   - 16–31 Designated experimental protocols
   - 17 NetWare Core Protocol (NCP)
- **Destination Network.** This field identifies the target network. Each network in a NetWare environment requires unique network numbers.
- **Destination Node.** This address identifies nodes on a given network.
- **Destination Port.** This indicates a *process* or *function* address.
- **Source Network.** This field identifies the network (by number) on which the source host is located.
- **Source Node.** This indicates a given node address. In any particular instance a host may function either as a source or as a destination.

- **Source Port.** This is the port number that originally submitted the packet onto the network.
- **Data.** This field includes user data and other information from higher layers.

IPX is the heart of NetWare. All protocols operating above it move down the protocol stack and are enveloped in this packet. IPX is similar to TCP/IP in this regard; for example, regardless of whether TCP or UDP protocols are used, they are enclosed into an IP packet.

IPX Addressing

IPX uses an addressing scheme similar to that of TCP/IP. An address is assigned to a NetWare network, addresses are assigned to each node on a given network, and the network protocol used by nodes on the network has identifiable ports or access points. In TCP/IP the combination of a network, host, and port address creates what is called a socket. In NetWare, sockets to refer to the parallel concept of a port.

In NetWare the network address is comprised of a four-byte value. Host addresses use six bytes. The socket address is a two-byte address. The socket address is that address on which a server will listen and receive requests. Examples of identified sockets are:

File Servers
    451h NetWAre Core Protocol
Routers
    452h Service Advertising Protocol
    453h Routing Information Protocol
Workstations
4000h–6000h   Used for the interaction with file servers and other network communications

455h NetBIOS
456 Diagnostics

Additional addressing is used in such environments as the LANRES product, but these addresses affect the aspect of communication with NetWare actually located in a different network. The addressing affects NetWare indirectly.

Sequence Packet Exchange (SPX)

SPX is a connection-oriented protocol that applications requiring such services can use to operate in a NetWare network. By default, SPX uses IPX. However, SPX has a completely different set of functions.

SPX Packet Structure

An SPX packet has its own fields that perform functions in a manner different from that of IPX, but SPX utilizes IPX as it goes down the protocol stack.

Figure 9.15 shows the SPX datagram behind an IPX header inside a MAC frame. This is how it appears at the data-link layer.

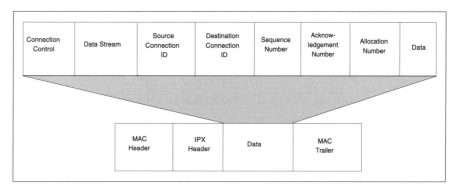

FIGURE 9.15
SPX Packet
Structure

SPX Field Contents

Fields and their purposes in an SPX packet include:

- **Connection Control.** This field controls bi-directional data flow between connections.
- **Datastream.** This field indicates the type of data found in the packet.
- **Source Connection ID.** This field identifies the originating point of the packet. It is also responsible for multiplexing packets of data as they leave the node if this function is required.
- **Destination Connection ID.** This field identifies the target point for the packet. The destination point may perform demulitplexing if required.
- **Sequence Number.** This field is responsible for maintaining a packet count: the sending side and the receiving side both maintain counts.

- **Acknowledgement Number.** This field performs packet orientation functions. It indicates sequence numbers of the SPX packets that should be received.
- **Allocation Number.** This is used to indicate the number of outstanding receive buffers in a given direction at one time.
- **Data.** This field contains data used by the application requiring the SPX protocol.

SPX itself is considered a transport protocol that uses IPX as a delivery service from origin to destination. Packets exchanged between origin and destination SPX points have sequence numbers assigned to them. By these numbers can help check for out-of-sequence, duplicate, or missing packets.

Not all applications require SPX, but some that do are as gateways and applications requiring session-oriented services.

Even though this much detail is generally not presented with IPX/SPX operation in the same explanation with NT, the operational aspect of IPX/SPX is much the same as in native mode. In fact, the NWLink IPX/SPX-compatible transport is Microsoft's "hook" that supports IPX/SPX. Setup and operation of the NWLink is oriented to the native functions of IPX/SPX.

Data Link Control (DLC)

DLC is a protocol used to enable Windows NT connectivity to SNA networks. It allows low levels of communication to be established; upper-layer applications in NT networks can than communicate with SNA environments. It is a protocol that requires enabling for SNA interconnectivity and back office application use.

STREAMS

The purpose of this protocol is to provide support and utilities to use to work with UNIX-based, or styled, STREAMS drivers and protocols to an NT environment.

Remote Procedure Call (RPC)

RPC services are basically a set of dynamic load libraries that operate as run-time DLLs. They support distributed applications in a networked environment. RPC is implemented in an NT environment by using a name service provider that locates and registers servers on an NT network. Support for the Distributed Computing Environment (DCE) cell directory service and the microsoft locator is provided.

Service Advertising Protocol (SAP)

The SAP support provided by NT is a service used to handle the NetWare compatible service advertisements which are generally native to NetWare.

Workstation

This service is part of NT that operates simply as a client. Its primary responsibilities include directory sharing and file maintenance, among others.

NetBIOS

NetBIOS, the network-basic input/output system, is an interface that some programs require to interact with Windows 95, NT, OS/2 and some UNIX environments. Its operational nature is higher up in the layers of a network; it enables requests for lower-layer network services to be answered and achieved.

Client Service for NetWare

This service is provided to enable workstations and servers to interact with NetWare networks and workstations for file and print sharing and with other NetWare services. This service must be enabled in order for interoperation with NetWare.

Computer Browser

This service is what makes possible the viewing of other computers in the network. Without this service network computers/systems are not visible.

Server

This is a service that enables the computer to operate as a server to clients on a network. It must be enabled for the network to function as a server.

Remote Access Service (RAS)

This is a feature that enables remote workstations to participate in the network as if they were physically attached to it. This service must be configured on the system operating as a server and on the systems operating as workstations in order for dial-up or switched connections to operate.

LMHosts

This is considered a service as well. Technically, it is a file that maps systems with IP addresses to NetBIOS computer names for those systems using NetBIOS in their network; this is particularly true for computers using NetBIOS outside the local subnet wherein the LMHosts file is located.

NT Server Selection

Selecting a network server is no trivial task. It is important to spend a good amount of time and money to obtain the right server for your operations. If you intend to run only one server in your network, you should know as much as possible about its strengths and limitations. You should also know what the current and foreseeable requirements are for your network and the server to be positioned in it. This information may take time to obtain, but it will be worthwhile.

Because of the nature and purpose of the network I designed the IBM Netfinity 7000 is the best solution. Now that the server has been obtained, configured, and operational for some time, I also believe this is the best server available in the marketplace regardless of the size of the network in which a server is to be placed.

Figure 9.16 illustrates a front view of the Netfinity 7000.

FIGURE 9.16
Netfinity 7000
Front View

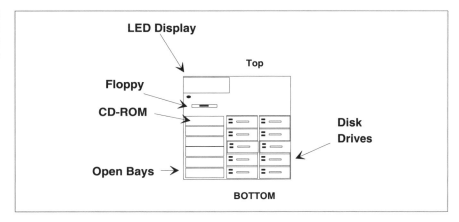

From the front, the Netfinity is very accessible. Disk drives can be easily removed and inserted (without any tools). The open bays are ready accessible, just behind a front panel that can also be removed without any tools. The LED display is one of Netfinity's jewels. During boot, the display constantly reflects the status of the system. Different LEDs immediately above it reveal any status information about devices such as power supplies, etc.

Figure 9.17 shows front and rear views of the Netfinity 7000. The front view shows the system fans easily accessible once the top cover is removed. The top cover can be removed without any tools, as two strong thumb screws more than secure the top cover.

The rear of the Netfinity 7000 shows the power supplies, connection points, and vacant slots. The system's power supplies can be easily replaced. Three are in the design, but two are more than sufficient. Since the place exists for a third, I recommend having a third on hand, just in case. The system is easily accessible from the open slots at the top and is clearly marked.

Consider the inside view of Figure 9.18.

With the removal of a single panel the Netfinity is very accessible. From the top all memory is accessible. The memory card can be removed without any tools and upgrades made literally in minutes. The same is true for the processors. The processor card can be removed, upgraded, and re-inserted in minutes. The open slots, which are numbered, are easy to work with when inserting interface boards.

The Netfinity 7000 has numerous strengths regardless of the configuration. One strength is that it is basically a plug-and-go system. From the time the box arrived until the system was operational was less than half a business day. In fact, assuming you have power, network cables, and other required components available, it is entirely possible the Netfinity can be up and running in a less than an hour after arrival. This is an incredible testimony to the design engineering of the system from end to end.

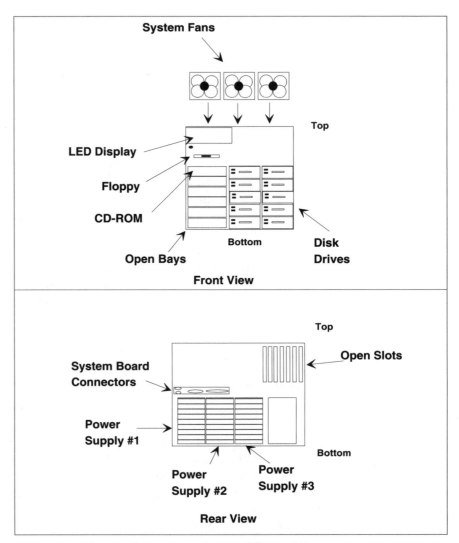

FIGURE 9.17
Netfinity 7000
Front and Rear
Views

The upgradeability of the Netfinity 7000 is impressive. The basic system can be enhanced to accommodate multiple processors, gigabytes of memory, multiple power supplies, large amounts of storage and other commercial requirements. A unique aspect of the Netfinity 7000 is that is basically offered as a *shell*, and then it can be dressed to the degree deemed appropriate by the user. The design alone almost guarantees a good return on the investment.

FIGURE 9.18
Netfinity 7000
Top View

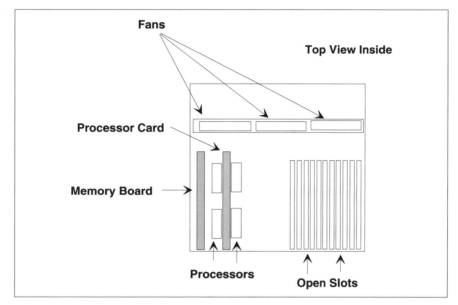

Another powerful aspect of the Netfinity 7000 is the people behind it. But when you are about to invest tens of thousands of dollars (if not hundreds of thousands) the support and warranty on your investment become important. Working with people who have correct answers, make things happen when they should, and see work through to the end is important and cannot be understated. You are not just buying a server, you are investing in a company by way of their product.

Firsthand experience with the Netfinity 7000, research and review of other vendor equipment, indicate the Netfinity 7000 is the server of choice for Windows NT. It is easily serviceable, upgradeable, well-designed, and has the backing of the IBM corporation. You should seriously consider this server for your Windows NT network.

NT Network Peripherals

Another key part of any NT network is the network peripherals. Most networks today are increasingly intermixed with audio, video, data, and multimedia.

Network Storage Products

The demand for storage of these various forms of information take puts heavy loads on systems whose architecture is 5–8 years old. The norm now is for ever-increasing amounts of online storage.

Figure 9.19 depicts one aspect of the network I designed. The /SMS storage products are probably the second-most important components of the network after the Netfinity 7000. The /SMS products make large numbers of CDs, DVDs, and vast amounts of data, video, and multimedia available to the entire network. Figure 9.20 shows a different implementation of the same equipment.

FIGURE 9.19
NT Network
Peripherals of
Choice

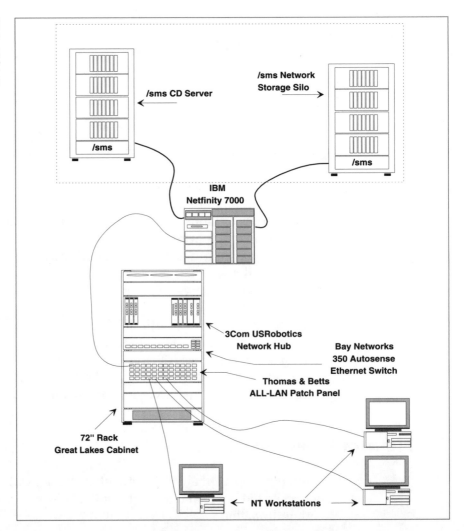

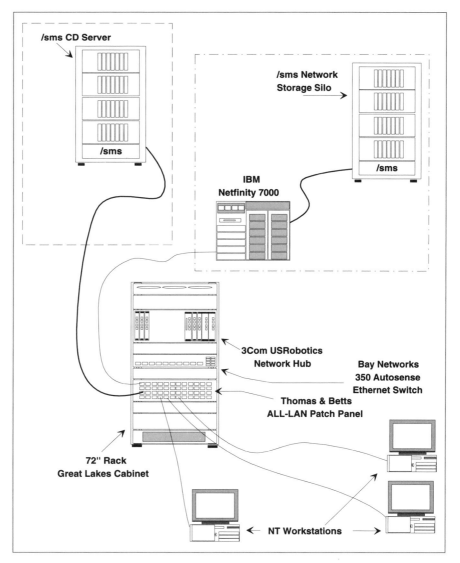

FIGURE 9.20
Network
Peripheral
Implementations

One silo is connected to the IBM Netfinity 7000. The other is directly connected to the network via the patch panel, where it is then connected to the Bay Network's hub. The multiple ways /SMS can connect devices to a network enable load balancing from many different angles. For example, the Netfinity 7000 can accommodate the silo as shown in the illustration without any degradation. The other silo can be connected to the network because it has a Fast Ethernet connectivity module than enables it to function as a standalone device. This level of modularity of the /SMS device connectivity makes for an attractive network peripheral.

Two factors make /SMS products network peripherals of choice: flexibility and simplicity. The ease-of-use is a refreshing experience. It is possible to break these systems down into bays of seven devices and implement them in an entirely different modular fashion.

/SMS personnel are professionals at all levels. /SMS products may be peripheral in the network but the value they deliver is high. At the center of networks is information in some form or the other. The /SMS products make that information accessible. From that perspective, these products *are* the network because they house the essence of the network.

Network Tape Drive

Most networks today require some form of backup ability. I determined early on that this network needed a superior method for backup and selected a Sony AIT tape drive.

Figure 9.21 shows the tape drive connected to an NT workstation. From that workstation alone, I can back up any device on the network. The beauty behind this design is that it offloads another function to a workstation that can be monitored and controlled like a standalone workstation or even managed remotely. Any way the actual function of backup is performed, the Sony AIT tape drive is a superior product. Its medium has memory in the cassette; this makes for quick searches and location of stored data. The native amount of storage the device is designed to accommodate is 25 GB, and 50 GB when compressed. This is an ideal device to back up any devices on the network whether they are workstations or servers.

Network Printing

Another critical aspect of network operation is network printing.

Figure 9.22 shows the IBM Model 17 network printer used in this network. It supports dual network interface cards, token ring and Ethernet simultaneously. It can accommodate large amounts of on-board memory, duplexing support, and multiple paper trays—including an envelope feeder that feeds and prints envelopes as simply as paper. The printer also has a secure mail bin. This may well be the best network printer on the market for its size, price, and maintenance costs.

It has a small footprint, but large operational ability. Remember that this printer can connect to one of IBM's largest mainframes or work with a standalone PC, or anywhere between these extremes.

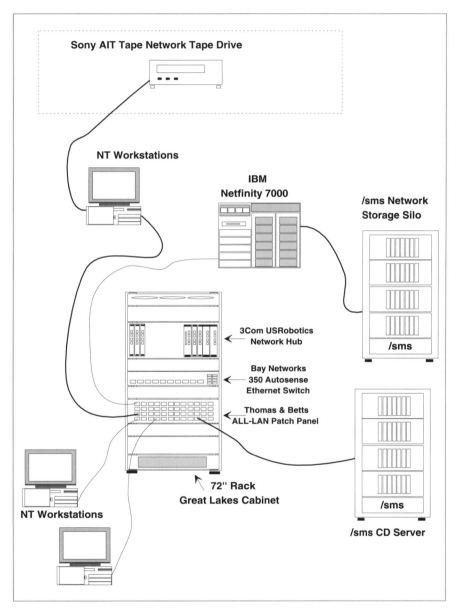

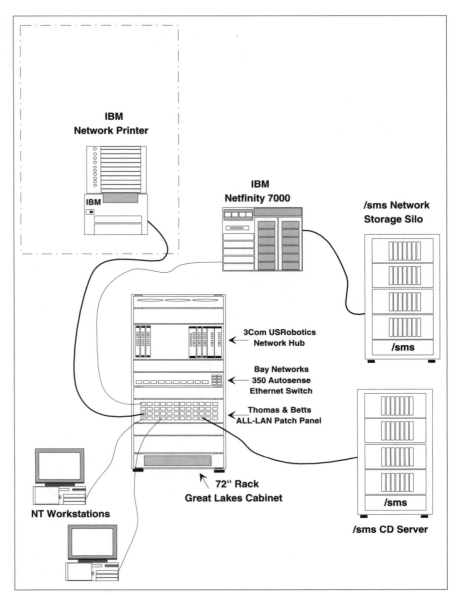

FIGURE 9.22
Network Printer

NT Administration

NT is a powerful operating system with many different ways an administrator can obtain information about servers and workstations in a network. The best way to perform administration is to do so prior to implementation, to determine which protocol will be used, security levels, domains to be named, workgroups to be identified, any remote access service to be used, and so forth. If there is this level of information in the early stages of network planning, you will be better off.

Network Server Administration Information

You should obtain a diagnostic report immediately after stabilizing each server, domain controller, and backup domain controller. Consider the information obtained in the diagnostic report from the primary server in this network, the IBM Netfinity 7000.

Microsoft Diagnostics Report for \\CHEROKEE (Netfinity 7000)

```
---------------------------------------------------------------------
OS Version Report
---------------------------------------------------------------------
Microsoft (R) Windows NT (TM) Server
Version 4.0 (Build 1381: Service Pack 3) x86 Multiprocessor Free
Registered Owner: Ed Taylor
Product Number: 00000-000-0000000-00000
---------------------------------------------------------------------
System Report
---------------------------------------------------------------------
System: AT/AT COMPATIBLE
Hardware Abstraction Layer: MPS 1.4 - APIC platform
BIOS Date: 10/20/97
BIOS Version: BIOS Version 1.00.14.CD0

Processor list:
   0: x86 Family 6 Model 1 Stepping 9 GenuineIntel ~198 Mhz
   1: x86 Family 6 Model 1 Stepping 9 GenuineIntel ~198 Mhz
   2: x86 Family 6 Model 1 Stepping 9 GenuineIntel ~198 Mhz

---------------------------------------------------------------------
Video Display Report
---------------------------------------------------------------------
BIOS Date: 01/07/94
BIOS Version: CL-GD542X VGA BIOS Version 1.41

Adapter:
   Setting: 640 x 480 x 256
           60 Hz
   Type: cirrus compatible display adapter
   String: Cirrus Logic Compatible
   Memory: 512 KB
   Chip Type: CL 5424
   DAC Type: Integrated RAMDAC
```

```
Driver:
  Vendor: Microsoft Corporation
  File(s): cirrus.sys, vga.dll, cirrus.dll, vga256.dll, vga64K.dll
  Version: 4.00, 4.0.0
-------------------------------------------------------------------
 Drives Report
-------------------------------------------------------------------
C:\ (Local - NTFS) CHEROKEE Total: 0KB, Free: 0KB
  Serial Number: 84D - 3C0E
  Bytes per cluster: 512
  Sectors per cluster: 1
  Filename length: 255
E:\ (Local - NTFS) CHEROKEE-E Total: 37,556,692KB, Free: 36,551,268KB
  Serial Number: D810 - 991E
  Bytes per cluster: 512
  Sectors per cluster: 8
  Filename length: 255
F:\ (CDROM - CDFS) 970124_0928 Total: 87,898KB, Free: 0KB
  Serial Number: E2AC - 877E
  Bytes per cluster: 2048
  Sectors per cluster: 1
  Filename length: 110
G:\ (CDROM - CDFS) WPDC_CD_ROM Total: 350KB, Free: 0KB
  Serial Number: 1A06 - CF48
  Bytes per cluster: 2048
  Sectors per cluster: 1
  Filename length: 221
H:\ (CDROM - CDFS) ESSENTIAL JAVA Total: 29,696KB, Free: 0KB
  Serial Number: E262 - 782C
  Bytes per cluster: 2048
  Sectors per cluster: 1
  Filename length: 221
I:\ (CDROM - CDFS) Total: 336,534KB, Free: 0KB
  Serial Number: 625 - 760C
  Bytes per cluster: 2048
  Sectors per cluster: 1
  Filename length: 221
J:\ (CDROM - CDFS) QUEINSTNT Total: 98,532KB, Free: 0KB
  Serial Number: 47B0 - EDF0
  Bytes per cluster: 2048
  Sectors per cluster: 1
  Filename length: 221
K:\ (CDROM - CDFS) LIEBERT 98 Total: 277,286KB, Free: 0KB
  Serial Number: C64F - F728
  Bytes per cluster: 2048
  Sectors per cluster: 1
  Filename length: 110
L:\ (CDROM - CDFS) WSU Total: 111,374KB, Free: 0KB
  Serial Number: 2331 - 84AB
  Bytes per cluster: 2048
  Sectors per cluster: 1
  Filename length: 221
-------------------------------------------------------------------
Memory Report
```

```
------------------------------------------------------------------
Handles: 1,517
Threads: 143
Processes: 19

Physical Memory (K)
  Total: 785,840
  Available: 720,664
  File Cache: 14,544

Kernel Memory (K)
  Total: 7,748
  Paged: 5,108
  Nonpaged: 2,640

Commit Charge (K)
  Total: 24,292
  Limit: 772,144
  Peak: 25,928

Pagefile Space (K)
  Total: 24,576
  Total in use: 448
  Peak: 448

  C:\pagefile.sys
   Total: 12,288
   Total in use: 256
   Peak: 256

  E:\pagefile.sys
   Total: 12,288
   Total in use: 192
   Peak: 192
------------------------------------------------------------------
Services Report
------------------------------------------------------------------
Alerter                                        Running (Automatic)
  C:\WINNT\System32\services.exe
  Service Account Name: LocalSystem
  Error Severity: Normal
  Service Flags: Shared Process
  Service Dependencies:
   LanmanWorkstation
Computer Browser                               Running (Automatic)
  C:\WINNT\System32\services.exe
  Service Account Name: LocalSystem
  Error Severity: Normal
  Service Flags: Shared Process
  Service Dependencies:
   LanmanWorkstation
   LanmanServer
   LmHosts
ClipBook Server                                Stopped  (Manual)
```

```
                C:\WINNT\system32\clipsrv.exe
                Service Account Name: LocalSystem
                Error Severity: Normal
                Service Flags: Own Process
                Service Dependencies:
                 NetDDE
             DHCP Client (TDI)                           Stopped (Disabled)
                C:\WINNT\System32\services.exe
                Service Account Name: LocalSystem
                Error Severity: Normal
                Service Flags: Shared Process
                Service Dependencies:
                 Tcpip
                 Afd
                 NetBT
             EventLog (Event log)                        Running (Automatic)
                C:\WINNT\system32\services.exe
                Service Account Name: LocalSystem
                Error Severity: Normal
                Service Flags: Shared Process
             Server                                      Running (Automatic)
                C:\WINNT\System32\services.exe
                Service Account Name: LocalSystem
                Error Severity: Normal
                Service Flags: Shared Process
                Group Dependencies:
                 TDI
             Workstation (NetworkProvider)               Running (Automatic)
                C:\WINNT\System32\services.exe
                Service Account Name: LocalSystem
                Error Severity: Normal
                Service Flags: Shared Process
                Group Dependencies:
                 TDI
             License Logging Service                     Running (Automatic)
                C:\WINNT\System32\llssrv.exe
                Service Account Name: LocalSystem
                Error Severity: Normal
                Service Flags: Own Process
             TCP/IP NetBIOS Helper                       Running (Automatic)
                C:\WINNT\System32\services.exe
                Service Account Name: LocalSystem
                Error Severity: Normal
                Service Flags: Shared Process
                Group Dependencies:
                 NetworkProvider
             Messenger                                   Running (Automatic)
                C:\WINNT\System32\services.exe
                Service Account Name: LocalSystem
                Error Severity: Normal
                Service Flags: Shared Process
                Service Dependencies:
                 LanmanWorkstation
                 NetBios
```

```
Network DDE (NetDDEGroup)                           Stopped  (Manual)
  C:\WINNT\system32\netdde.exe
  Service Account Name: LocalSystem
  Error Severity: Normal
  Service Flags: Shared Process
  Service Dependencies:
   NetDDEDSDM
Network DDE DSDM                                     Stopped  (Manual)
  C:\WINNT\system32\netdde.exe
  Service Account Name: LocalSystem
  Error Severity: Normal
  Service Flags: Shared Process
Net Logon (RemoteValidation)                        Running (Automatic)
  C:\WINNT\System32\lsass.exe
  Service Account Name: LocalSystem
  Error Severity: Normal
  Service Flags: Shared Process
  Service Dependencies:
   LanmanWorkstation
   LanmanServer
   LmHosts
NT LM Security Support Provider                      Stopped  (Manual)
  C:\WINNT\System32\SERVICES.EXE
  Service Account Name: LocalSystem
  Error Severity: Normal
  Service Flags: Shared Process
Plug and Play (PlugPlay)                             Running (Automatic)
  C:\WINNT\system32\services.exe
  Service Account Name: LocalSystem
  Error Severity: Normal
  Service Flags: Shared Process
Remote Access Autodial Manager                      Stopped (Disabled)
  C:\WINNT\system32\rasman.exe
  Service Account Name: LocalSystem
  Error Severity: Normal
  Service Flags: Shared Process
  Service Dependencies:
   RasMan
Remote Access Connection Manager (Network)          Running (Automatic)
  C:\WINNT\system32\rasman.exe
  Service Account Name: LocalSystem
  Error Severity: Normal
  Service Flags: Shared Process, Interactive
  Service Dependencies:
   tapisrv
Remote Access Server (Network)                      Running (Automatic)
  C:\WINNT\system32\rassrv.exe
  Service Account Name: LocalSystem
  Error Severity: Normal
  Service Flags: Own Process
  Service Dependencies:
   LanmanServer
   RasMan
   NetBios
```

```
        NetBT
        Nbf
        NwlnkIpx
Directory Replicator                     Stopped  (Manual)
  C:\WINNT\System32\lmrepl.exe
  Service Account Name: LocalSystem
  Error Severity: Normal
  Service Flags: Own Process
  Service Dependencies:
   LanmanWorkstation
   LanmanServer
Remote Procedure Call (RPC) Locator      Running (Automatic)
  C:\WINNT\System32\LOCATOR.EXE
  Service Account Name: LocalSystem
  Error Severity: Normal
  Service Flags: Own Process
  Service Dependencies:
   LanmanWorkstation
   Rdr
Remote Procedure Call (RPC) Service      Running (Automatic)
  C:\WINNT\system32\RpcSs.exe
  Service Account Name: LocalSystem
  Error Severity: Normal
  Service Flags: Own Process
Schedule                                 Stopped  (Manual)
  C:\WINNT\System32\AtSvc.Exe
  Service Account Name: LocalSystem
  Error Severity: Normal
  Service Flags: Own Process
Spooler (SpoolerGroup)                   Running (Automatic)
  C:\WINNT\system32\spoolss.exe
  Service Account Name: LocalSystem
  Error Severity: Normal
  Service Flags: Own Process, Interactive
Telephony Service                        Running  (Manual)
  C:\WINNT\system32\tapisrv.exe
  Service Account Name: LocalSystem
  Error Severity: Normal
  Service Flags: Own Process
UPS                                      Stopped  (Manual)
  C:\WINNT\System32\ups.exe
  Service Account Name: LocalSystem
  Error Severity: Normal
  Service Flags: Own Process
------------------------------------------------------------------
Drivers Report
------------------------------------------------------------------
Abiosdsk (Primary disk)                  Stopped (Disabled)
  Error Severity: Ignore
  Service Flags: Kernel Driver, Shared Process
AFD Networking Support Environment (TDI) Running (Automatic)
  C:\WINNT\System32\drivers\afd.sys
  Error Severity: Normal
  Service Flags: Kernel Driver, Shared Process
```

```
Aha154x (SCSI miniport)                          Stopped (Disabled)
  Error Severity: Normal
  Service Flags: Kernel Driver, Shared Process
Aha174x (SCSI miniport)                          Stopped (Disabled)
  Error Severity: Normal
  Service Flags: Kernel Driver, Shared Process
aic78xx (SCSI miniport)                          Running  (Boot)
  C:\WINNT\System32\DRIVERS\aic78xx.sys
  Error Severity: Normal
  Service Flags: Kernel Driver, Shared Process
Always (SCSI miniport)                           Stopped (Disabled)
  Error Severity: Normal
  Service Flags: Kernel Driver, Shared Process
amiOnt (SCSI miniport)                           Stopped (Disabled)
  Error Severity: Normal
  Service Flags: Kernel Driver, Shared Process
amsint (SCSI miniport)                           Stopped (Disabled)
  Error Severity: Normal
  Service Flags: Kernel Driver, Shared Process
Arrow (SCSI miniport)                            Stopped (Disabled)
  Error Severity: Normal
  Service Flags: Kernel Driver, Shared Process
Remote Access Mac (NDIS)                         Running (Automatic)
  C:\WINNT\system32\drivers\asyncmac.sys
  Error Severity: Normal
  Service Flags: Kernel Driver, Shared Process
atapi (SCSI miniport)                            Running  (Boot)
  C:\WINNT\System32\DRIVERS\atapi.sys
  Error Severity: Normal
  Service Flags: Kernel Driver, Shared Process
Atdisk (Primary disk)                            Stopped (Disabled)
  Error Severity: Ignore
  Service Flags: Kernel Driver, Shared Process
ati (Video)                                      Stopped (Disabled)
  Error Severity: Ignore
  Service Flags: Kernel Driver, Shared Process
Beep (Base)                                      Running  (System)
  Error Severity: Normal
  Service Flags: Kernel Driver, Shared Process
BusLogic (SCSI miniport)                         Stopped (Disabled)
  Error Severity: Normal
  Service Flags: Kernel Driver, Shared Process
Busmouse (Pointer Port)                          Stopped (Disabled)
  Error Severity: Ignore
  Service Flags: Kernel Driver, Shared Process
Cdaudio (Filter)                                 Stopped  (System)
  Error Severity: Ignore
  Service Flags: Kernel Driver, Shared Process
Cdfs (File system)                               Running (Disabled)
  Error Severity: Normal
  Service Flags: File System Driver, Shared Process
  Group Dependencies:
   SCSI CDROM Class
Cdrom (SCSI CDROM Class)                          Running  (System)
```

```
                      Error Severity: Ignore
                      Service Flags: Kernel Driver, Shared Process
                      Group Dependencies:
                       SCSI miniport
Changer (Filter)                                     Stopped  (System)
                      Error Severity: Ignore
                      Service Flags: Kernel Driver, Shared Process
cirrus (Video)                                       Running  (System)
                      Error Severity: Normal
                      Service Flags: Kernel Driver, Shared Process
Cpqarray (SCSI miniport)                             Stopped (Disabled)
                      Error Severity: Normal
                      Service Flags: Kernel Driver, Shared Process
cpqfws2e (SCSI miniport)                             Stopped (Disabled)
                      Error Severity: Normal
                      Service Flags: Kernel Driver, Shared Process
dac960nt (SCSI miniport)                             Stopped (Disabled)
                      Error Severity: Normal
                      Service Flags: Kernel Driver, Shared Process
dce376nt (SCSI miniport)                             Stopped (Disabled)
                      Error Severity: Normal
                      Service Flags: Kernel Driver, Shared Process
Delldsa (SCSI miniport)                              Stopped (Disabled)
                      Error Severity: Normal
                      Service Flags: Kernel Driver, Shared Process
Dell_DGX (Video)                                     Stopped (Disabled)
                      Error Severity: Ignore
                      Service Flags: Kernel Driver, Shared Process
Disk (SCSI Class)                                    Running  (Boot)
                      Error Severity: Ignore
                      Service Flags: Kernel Driver, Shared Process
                      Group Dependencies:
                       SCSI miniport
Diskperf (Filter)                                    Stopped (Disabled)
                      Error Severity: Normal
                      Service Flags: Kernel Driver, Shared Process
DptScsi (SCSI miniport)                              Stopped (Disabled)
                      Error Severity: Normal
                      Service Flags: Kernel Driver, Shared Process
dtc329x (SCSI miniport)                              Stopped (Disabled)
                      Error Severity: Normal
                      Service Flags: Kernel Driver, Shared Process
Intel 82557-based PRO Adapter Driver (NDIS)    Running (Automatic)
                      C:\WINNT\System32\drivers\e100b.sys
                      Error Severity: Normal
                      Service Flags: Kernel Driver, Shared Process
et4000 (Video)                                       Stopped (Disabled)
                      Error Severity: Ignore
                      Service Flags: Kernel Driver, Shared Process
Fastfat (Boot file system)                           Stopped (Disabled)
                      Error Severity: Normal
                      Service Flags: File System Driver, Shared Process
Fd16_700 (SCSI miniport)                             Stopped (Disabled)
                      Error Severity: Normal
```

```
                  Service Flags: Kernel Driver, Shared Process
Fd7000ex (SCSI miniport)                          Stopped (Disabled)
   Error Severity: Normal
                  Service Flags: Kernel Driver, Shared Process
Fd8xx (SCSI miniport)                             Stopped (Disabled)
   Error Severity: Normal
                  Service Flags: Kernel Driver, Shared Process
flashpnt (SCSI miniport)                          Stopped (Disabled)
   Error Severity: Normal
                  Service Flags: Kernel Driver, Shared Process
Floppy (Primary disk)                             Running  (System)
   Error Severity: Ignore
                  Service Flags: Kernel Driver, Shared Process
Ftdisk (Filter)                                   Stopped (Disabled)
   Error Severity: Ignore
                  Service Flags: Kernel Driver, Shared Process
i8042 Keyboard and PS/2 Mouse Port Driver (Keyboard Port) Running
(System)
   System32\DRIVERS\i8042prt.sys
   Error Severity: Normal
                  Service Flags: Kernel Driver, Shared Process
Inport (Pointer Port)                             Stopped (Disabled)
   Error Severity: Ignore
                  Service Flags: Kernel Driver, Shared Process
ipsraidn (SCSI miniport)                          Running  (Boot)
   C:\WINNT\system32\drivers\ipsraidn.sys
   Error Severity: Normal
                  Service Flags: Kernel Driver, Shared Process
Jazzg300 (Video)                                  Stopped (Disabled)
   Error Severity: Ignore
                  Service Flags: Kernel Driver, Shared Process
Jazzg364 (Video)                                  Stopped (Disabled)
   Error Severity: Ignore
                  Service Flags: Kernel Driver, Shared Process
Jzvx1484 (Video)                                  Stopped (Disabled)
   Error Severity: Ignore
                  Service Flags: Kernel Driver, Shared Process
Keyboard Class Driver (Keyboard Class)            Running  (System)
   System32\DRIVERS\kbdclass.sys
   Error Severity: Normal
                  Service Flags: Kernel Driver, Shared Process
KSecDD (Base)                                     Running  (System)
   Error Severity: Normal
                  Service Flags: Kernel Driver, Shared Process
mga (Video)                                       Stopped (Disabled)
   Error Severity: Ignore
                  Service Flags: Kernel Driver, Shared Process
mga_mil (Video)                                   Stopped (Disabled)
   Error Severity: Ignore
                  Service Flags: Kernel Driver, Shared Process
mitsumi (SCSI miniport)                           Stopped (Disabled)
   Error Severity: Normal
                  Service Flags: Kernel Driver, Shared Process
mkecr5xx (SCSI miniport)                          Stopped (Disabled)
```

```
                Error Severity: Normal
                Service Flags: Kernel Driver, Shared Process
        Modem (Extended base)                      Running (Boot)
                Error Severity: Ignore
                Service Flags: Kernel Driver, Shared Process
        Mouse Class Driver (Pointer Class)         Running (System)
         System32\DRIVERS\mouclass.sys
                Error Severity: Normal
                Service Flags: Kernel Driver, Shared Process
        Msfs (File system)                         Running (System)
                Error Severity: Normal
                Service Flags: File System Driver, Shared Process
        Mup (Network)                              Running (Manual)
         C:\WINNT\System32\drivers\mup.sys
                Error Severity: Normal
                Service Flags: File System Driver, Shared Process
        NetBEUI Protocol (PNP_TDI)                 Running (Automatic)
         C:\WINNT\System32\drivers\nbf.sys
                Error Severity: Normal
                Service Flags: Kernel Driver, Shared Process
        Ncr53c9x (SCSI miniport)                   Stopped (Disabled)
                Error Severity: Normal
                Service Flags: Kernel Driver, Shared Process
        ncr77c22 (Video)                           Stopped (Disabled)
                Error Severity: Ignore
                Service Flags: Kernel Driver, Shared Process
        Ncrc700 (SCSI miniport)                    Stopped (Disabled)
                Error Severity: Normal
                Service Flags: Kernel Driver, Shared Process
        Ncrc710 (SCSI miniport)                    Stopped (Disabled)
                Error Severity: Normal
                Service Flags: Kernel Driver, Shared Process
        Microsoft NDIS System Driver (NDIS)        Running (System)
                Error Severity: Normal
                Service Flags: Kernel Driver, Shared Process
        Microsoft NDIS TAPI driver (NDIS)          Running (System)
         C:\WINNT\system32\drivers\ndistapi.sys
                Error Severity: Normal
                Service Flags: Kernel Driver, Shared Process
        Remote Access WAN Wrapper (NDISWAN)        Running (Automatic)
         C:\WINNT\system32\drivers\ndiswan.sys
                Error Severity: Normal
                Service Flags: Kernel Driver, Shared Process
        NetBIOS Interface (NetBIOSGroup)           Running (Automatic)
         C:\WINNT\System32\drivers\netbios.sys
                Error Severity: Normal
                Service Flags: File System Driver, Shared Process
                Group Dependencies:
                 TDI
        WINS Client(TCP/IP) (PNP_TDI)              Running (Automatic)
         C:\WINNT\System32\drivers\netbt.sys
                Error Severity: Normal
                Service Flags: Kernel Driver, Shared Process
                Service Dependencies:
```

```
            Tcpip
NetDetect                                    Stopped  (Manual)
  C:\WINNT\system32\drivers\netdtect.sys
  Error Severity: Normal
  Service Flags: Kernel Driver, Shared Process
Npfs (File system)                           Running  (System)
  Error Severity: Normal
  Service Flags: File System Driver, Shared Process
Ntfs (File system)                           Running (Disabled)
  Error Severity: Normal
  Service Flags: File System Driver, Shared Process
Null (Base)                                  Running  (System)
  Error Severity: Normal
  Service Flags: Kernel Driver, Shared Process
NWLink IPX/SPX Compatible Transport Protocol (PNP_TDI) Running (Auto-
matic)
  C:\WINNT\System32\drivers\nwlnkipx.sys
  Error Severity: Normal
  Service Flags: Kernel Driver, Shared Process
NWLink NetBIOS (PNP_TDI)                      Running (Automatic)
  C:\WINNT\System32\drivers\nwlnknb.sys
  Error Severity: Normal
  Service Flags: Kernel Driver, Shared Process
  Service Dependencies:
   NwlnkIpx
NWLink SPX/SPXII Protocol                     Running  (Manual)
  C:\WINNT\System32\drivers\nwlnkspx.sys
  Error Severity: Normal
  Service Flags: Kernel Driver, Shared Process
  Service Dependencies:
   NwlnkIpx
Oliscsi (SCSI miniport)                       Stopped (Disabled)
  Error Severity: Normal
  Service Flags: Kernel Driver, Shared Process
Parallel (Extended base)                      Running (Automatic)
  Error Severity: Ignore
  Service Flags: Kernel Driver, Shared Process
  Service Dependencies:
   Parport
  Group Dependencies:
   Parallel arbitrator
Parport (Parallel arbitrator)                 Running (Automatic)
  Error Severity: Ignore
  Service Flags: Kernel Driver, Shared Process
ParVdm (Extended base)                        Running (Automatic)
  Error Severity: Ignore
  Service Flags: Kernel Driver, Shared Process
  Service Dependencies:
   Parport
  Group Dependencies:
   Parallel arbitrator
PCIDump (PCI Configuration)                   Stopped  (System)
  Error Severity: Ignore
  Service Flags: Kernel Driver, Shared Process
```

```
Pcmcia (System Bus Extender)                    Stopped (Disabled)
  Error Severity: Normal
  Service Flags: Kernel Driver, Shared Process
PnP ISA Enabler Driver (Base)                   Stopped  (System)
  Error Severity: Ignore
  Service Flags: Kernel Driver, Shared Process
psidisp (Video)                                 Stopped (Disabled)
  Error Severity: Ignore
  Service Flags: Kernel Driver, Shared Process
Ql10wnt (SCSI miniport)                         Stopped (Disabled)
  Error Severity: Normal
  Service Flags: Kernel Driver, Shared Process
qv (Video)                                      Stopped (Disabled)
  Error Severity: Ignore
  Service Flags: Kernel Driver, Shared Process
Remote Access Auto Connection Driver (Streams Drivers) Running (Auto-
matic)
  C:\WINNT\system32\drivers\rasacd.sys
  Error Severity: Normal
  Service Flags: Kernel Driver, Shared Process
Remote Access ARP Service (PNP_TDI)             Running (Automatic)
  C:\WINNT\system32\drivers\rasarp.sys
  Error Severity: Normal
  Service Flags: Kernel Driver, Shared Process
  Service Dependencies:
   TCPIP
Rdr (Network)                                   Running  (Manual)
  C:\WINNT\System32\drivers\rdr.sys
  Error Severity: Normal
  Service Flags: File System Driver, Shared Process
s3 (Video)                                      Stopped (Disabled)
  Error Severity: Ignore
  Service Flags: Kernel Driver, Shared Process
Scsiprnt (Extended base)                        Stopped (Automatic)
  Error Severity: Ignore
  Service Flags: Kernel Driver, Shared Process
  Group Dependencies:
   SCSI miniport
Scsiscan (SCSI Class)                           Running  (System)
  Error Severity: Ignore
  Service Flags: Kernel Driver, Shared Process
  Group Dependencies:
   SCSI miniport
Serial (Extended base)                          Running (Automatic)
  Error Severity: Ignore
  Service Flags: Kernel Driver, Shared Process
Sermouse (Pointer Port)                         Stopped (Disabled)
  Error Severity: Ignore
  Service Flags: Kernel Driver, Shared Process
Sfloppy (Primary disk)                          Stopped  (System)
  Error Severity: Ignore
  Service Flags: Kernel Driver, Shared Process
  Group Dependencies:
   SCSI miniport
```

```
Simbad (Filter)                               Stopped (Disabled)
  Error Severity: Normal
  Service Flags: Kernel Driver, Shared Process
slcd32 (SCSI miniport)                        Stopped (Disabled)
  Error Severity: Normal
  Service Flags: Kernel Driver, Shared Process
Sparrow (SCSI miniport)                       Stopped (Disabled)
  Error Severity: Normal
  Service Flags: Kernel Driver, Shared Process
Spock (SCSI miniport)                         Stopped (Disabled)
  Error Severity: Normal
  Service Flags: Kernel Driver, Shared Process
Srv (Network)                                 Running (Automatic)
  C:\WINNT\System32\drivers\srv.sys
  Error Severity: Normal
  Service Flags: File System Driver, Shared Process
symc810 (SCSI miniport)                       Stopped (Disabled)
  Error Severity: Normal
  Service Flags: Kernel Driver, Shared Process
T128 (SCSI miniport)                          Stopped (Disabled)
  Error Severity: Normal
  Service Flags: Kernel Driver, Shared Process
T13B (SCSI miniport)                          Stopped (Disabled)
  Error Severity: Normal
  Service Flags: Kernel Driver, Shared Process
TCP/IP Service (PNP_TDI)                      Running (Automatic)
  C:\WINNT\System32\drivers\tcpip.sys
  Error Severity: Normal
  Service Flags: Kernel Driver, Shared Process
tga (Video)                                   Stopped (Disabled)
  Error Severity: Ignore
  Service Flags: Kernel Driver, Shared Process
tmv1 (SCSI miniport)                          Stopped (Disabled)
  Error Severity: Normal
  Service Flags: Kernel Driver, Shared Process
Ultra124 (SCSI miniport)                      Stopped (Disabled)
  Error Severity: Normal
  Service Flags: Kernel Driver, Shared Process
Ultra14f (SCSI miniport)                      Stopped (Disabled)
  Error Severity: Normal
  Service Flags: Kernel Driver, Shared Process
Ultra24f (SCSI miniport)                      Stopped (Disabled)
  Error Severity: Normal
  Service Flags: Kernel Driver, Shared Process
v7vram (Video)                                Stopped (Disabled)
  Error Severity: Ignore
  Service Flags: Kernel Driver, Shared Process
VgaSave (Video Save)                          Stopped  (System)
  C:\WINNT\System32\drivers\vga.sys
  Error Severity: Ignore
  Service Flags: Kernel Driver, Shared Process
VgaStart (Video Init)                         Stopped  (System)
  C:\WINNT\System32\drivers\vga.sys
  Error Severity: Ignore
```

```
         Service Flags: Kernel Driver, Shared Process
Wd33c93 (SCSI miniport)                                    Stopped (Disabled)
    Error Severity: Normal
         Service Flags: Kernel Driver, Shared Process
wd90c24a (Video)                                           Stopped (Disabled)
    Error Severity: Ignore
         Service Flags: Kernel Driver, Shared Process
wdvga (Video)                                              Stopped (Disabled)
    Error Severity: Ignore
         Service Flags: Kernel Driver, Shared Process
weitekp9 (Video)                                           Stopped (Disabled)
    Error Severity: Ignore
         Service Flags: Kernel Driver, Shared Process
Xga (Video)                                                Stopped (Disabled)
    Error Severity: Ignore
         Service Flags: Kernel Driver, Shared Process
------------------------------------------------------------------------------
IRQ and Port Report
------------------------------------------------------------------------------
Devices                    Vector Level Affinity
------------------------------------------------------------------------------
MPS 1.4 - APIC platform         8    8 0x00000007
MPS 1.4 - APIC platform         0    0 0x00000007
MPS 1.4 - APIC platform         1    1 0x00000007
MPS 1.4 - APIC platform         2    2 0x00000007
MPS 1.4 - APIC platform         3    3 0x00000007
MPS 1.4 - APIC platform         4    4 0x00000007
MPS 1.4 - APIC platform         5    5 0x00000007
MPS 1.4 - APIC platform         6    6 0x00000007
MPS 1.4 - APIC platform         7    7 0x00000007
MPS 1.4 - APIC platform         8    8 0x00000007
MPS 1.4 - APIC platform         9    9 0x00000007
MPS 1.4 - APIC platform        10   10 0x00000007
MPS 1.4 - APIC platform        11   11 0x00000007
MPS 1.4 - APIC platform        12   12 0x00000007
MPS 1.4 - APIC platform        13   13 0x00000007
MPS 1.4 - APIC platform        14   14 0x00000007
MPS 1.4 - APIC platform        15   15 0x00000007
MPS 1.4 - APIC platform        16   16 0x00000007
MPS 1.4 - APIC platform        17   17 0x00000007
MPS 1.4 - APIC platform        18   18 0x00000007
MPS 1.4 - APIC platform        19   19 0x00000007
MPS 1.4 - APIC platform        20   20 0x00000007
MPS 1.4 - APIC platform        21   21 0x00000007
MPS 1.4 - APIC platform        22   22 0x00000007
MPS 1.4 - APIC platform        23   23 0x00000007
MPS 1.4 - APIC platform        24   24 0x00000007
MPS 1.4 - APIC platform        25   25 0x00000007
MPS 1.4 - APIC platform        26   26 0x00000007
MPS 1.4 - APIC platform        27   27 0x00000007
MPS 1.4 - APIC platform        28   28 0x00000007
MPS 1.4 - APIC platform        29   29 0x00000007
MPS 1.4 - APIC platform        30   30 0x00000007
MPS 1.4 - APIC platform        31   31 0x00000007
```

```
MPS 1.4 - APIC platform      32   32 0x00000007
MPS 1.4 - APIC platform      33   33 0x00000007
MPS 1.4 - APIC platform      34   34 0x00000007
MPS 1.4 - APIC platform      35   35 0x00000007
MPS 1.4 - APIC platform      36   36 0x00000007
MPS 1.4 - APIC platform      37   37 0x00000007
MPS 1.4 - APIC platform      38   38 0x00000007
MPS 1.4 - APIC platform      39   39 0x00000007
MPS 1.4 - APIC platform      40   40 0x00000007
MPS 1.4 - APIC platform      41   41 0x00000007
MPS 1.4 - APIC platform      42   42 0x00000007
MPS 1.4 - APIC platform      43   43 0x00000007
MPS 1.4 - APIC platform      44   44 0x00000007
MPS 1.4 - APIC platform      45   45 0x00000007
MPS 1.4 - APIC platform      46   46 0x00000007
MPS 1.4 - APIC platform      47   47 0x00000007
MPS 1.4 - APIC platform      61   61 0x00000007
MPS 1.4 - APIC platform      65   65 0x00000007
MPS 1.4 - APIC platform      80   80 0x00000007
MPS 1.4 - APIC platform     193  193 0x00000007
MPS 1.4 - APIC platform     225  225 0x00000007
MPS 1.4 - APIC platform     253  253 0x00000007
MPS 1.4 - APIC platform     254  254 0x00000007
MPS 1.4 - APIC platform     255  255 0x00000007
i8042prt                      1    1 0xffffffff
i8042prt                     12   12 0xffffffff
Serial                        4    4 0x00000000
Serial                        3    3 0x00000000
E100B                         9    9 0x00000000
Floppy                        6    6 0x00000000
aic78xx                      11   11 0x00000000
aic78xx                      10   10 0x00000000
aic78xx                       5    5 0x00000000
aic78xx                      15   15 0x00000000
atapi                         0   14 0x00000000
ipsraidn                     11   11 0x00000000
-----------------------------------------------------------------
Devices          Physical Address    Length
-----------------------------------------------------------------
MPS 1.4 - APIC platform   0x00000000 0x0000000010
MPS 1.4 - APIC platform   0x00000020 0x0000000002
MPS 1.4 - APIC platform   0x00000040 0x0000000004
MPS 1.4 - APIC platform   0x00000048 0x0000000004
MPS 1.4 - APIC platform   0x00000061 0x0000000001
MPS 1.4 - APIC platform   0x00000070 0x0000000002
MPS 1.4 - APIC platform   0x00000080 0x0000000010
MPS 1.4 - APIC platform   0x00000092 0x0000000001
MPS 1.4 - APIC platform   0x000000a0 0x0000000002
MPS 1.4 - APIC platform   0x000000c0 0x0000000010
MPS 1.4 - APIC platform   0x000000d0 0x0000000010
MPS 1.4 - APIC platform   0x000000f0 0x0000000010
MPS 1.4 - APIC platform   0x00000400 0x0000000010
MPS 1.4 - APIC platform   0x00000461 0x0000000002
MPS 1.4 - APIC platform   0x00000464 0x0000000002
```

```
MPS 1.4 - APIC platform        0x00000480 0x0000000010
MPS 1.4 - APIC platform        0x000004c2 0x000000000e
MPS 1.4 - APIC platform        0x000004d0 0x0000000002
MPS 1.4 - APIC platform        0x000004d4 0x000000002c
MPS 1.4 - APIC platform        0x00000c84 0x0000000001
i8042prt                       0x00000060 0x0000000001
i8042prt                       0x00000064 0x0000000001
Parport                        0x00000378 0x0000000003
Serial                         0x000003f8 0x0000000007
Serial                         0x000002f8 0x0000000007
E100B                          0x0000e4e0 0x0000000014
Floppy                         0x000003f0 0x0000000006
Floppy                         0x000003f7 0x0000000001
aic78xx                        0x0000ec00 0x0000000100
aic78xx                        0x0000e800 0x0000000100
aic78xx                        0x0000dc00 0x0000000100
aic78xx                        0x0000d800 0x0000000100
atapi                          0x000001f0 0x0000000008
atapi                          0x000003f6 0x0000000001
ipsraidn                       0x0000fc00 0x0000000100
cirrus                         0x000003b0 0x000000000c
cirrus                         0x000003c0 0x0000000020
-----------------------------------------------------------------------
DMA and Memory Report
-----------------------------------------------------------------------
Devices            Channel  Port
-----------------------------------------------------------------------
Floppy                2        0
-----------------------------------------------------------------------
Devices            Physical Address   Length
-----------------------------------------------------------------------
MPS 1.4 - APIC platform        0xfec00000 0x00000400
MPS 1.4 - APIC platform        0xfec08000 0x00000400
E100B                          0xfe0ff000 0x00000014
E100B                          0xfe0ff000 0x00000014
aic78xx                        0xfe8ff000 0x00001000
aic78xx                        0xfe8fe000 0x00001000
aic78xx                        0xfe1ff000 0x00001000
aic78xx                        0xfe1fe000 0x00001000
ipsraidn                       0xfeafe000 0x00002000
cirrus                         0x000a0000 0x00020000
-----------------------------------------------------------------------
Environment Report
-----------------------------------------------------------------------
 System Environment Variables
  ComSpec=C:\WINNT\system32\cmd.exe
  NUMBER_OF_PROCESSORS=3
  OS=Windows_NT
  Os2LibPath=C:\WINNT\system32\os2\dll;
  Path=C:\WINNT\system32;C:\WINNT
  PROCESSOR_ARCHITECTURE=x86
  PROCESSOR_IDENTIFIER=x86 Family 6 Model 1 Stepping 9, GenuineIntel
  PROCESSOR_LEVEL=6
  PROCESSOR_REVISION=0109
```

```
    windir=C:\WINNT
Environment Variables for Current User
  TEMP=C:\TEMP
  TMP=C:\TEMP
--------------------------------------------------------------------
Network Report
--------------------------------------------------------------------
Your Access Level: Admin & Local
Workgroup or Domain: INFO
Network Version: 4.0
LanRoot: INFO
Logged On Users: 1
Current User (1): Administrator
Logon Domain: INFO
Logon Server: CHEROKEE
Transport: NetBT_E100B1, 00-60-94-A5-CC-EE, VC's: 0, Wan: Wan
Transport: Nbf_E100B1, 00-60-94-A5-CC-EE, VC's: 0, Wan: Wan
Transport: NwlnkNb, 00-60-94-A5-CC-EE, VC's: 0, Wan: Wan
Character Wait: 3,600
Collection Time: 250
Maximum Collection Count: 16
Keep Connection: 600
Maximum Commands: 5
Session Time Out: 45
Character Buffer Size: 512
Maximum Threads: 17
Lock Quota: 6,144
Lock Increment: 10
Maximum Locks: 500
Pipe Increment: 10
Maximum Pipes: 500
Cache Time Out: 40
Dormant File Limit: 45
Read Ahead Throughput: 4,294,967,295
Mailslot Buffers: 3
Server Announce Buffers: 20
Illegal Datagrams: 5
Datagram Reset Frequency: 60
Log Election Packets: False
Use Opportunistic Locking: True
Use Unlock Behind: True
Use Close Behind: True
Buffer Pipes: True
Use Lock, Read, Unlock: True
Use NT Caching: True
Use Raw Read: True
Use Raw Write: True
Use Write Raw Data: True
Use Encryption: True
Buffer Deny Write Files: True
Buffer Read Only Files: True
Force Core Creation: True
512 Byte Max Transfer: False
Bytes Received: 1,678
```

```
SMB's Received: 17
Paged Read Bytes Requested: 0
Non Paged Read Bytes Requested: 0
Cache Read Bytes Requested: 0
Network Read Bytes Requested: 0
Bytes Transmitted: 1,948
SMB's Transmitted: 17
Paged Read Bytes Requested: 0
Non Paged Read Bytes Requested: 1,600
Cache Read Bytes Requested: 0
Network Read Bytes Requested: 0
Initally Failed Operations: 0
Failed Completion Operations: 0
Read Operations: 0
Random Read Operations: 0
Read SMB's: 0
Large Read SMB's: 0
Small Read SMB's: 0
Write Operations: 15
Random Write Operations: 0
Write SMB's: 0
Large Write SMB's: 0
Small Write SMB's: 0
Raw Reads Denied: 0
Raw Writes Denied: 0
Network Errors: 0
Sessions: 3
Failed Sessions: 0
Reconnects: 0
Core Connects: 0
LM 2.0 Connects: 0
LM 2.x Connects: 0
Windows NT Connects: 3
Server Disconnects: 0
Hung Sessions: 0
Use Count: 4
Failed Use Count: 0
Current Commands: 0
Server File Opens: 93
Server Device Opens: 0
Server Jobs Queued: 0
Server Session Opens: 0
Server Sessions Timed Out: 0
Server Sessions Errored Out: 8
Server Password Errors: 0
Server Permission Errors: 0
Server System Errors: 0
Server Bytes Sent: 132,078
Server Bytes Received: 116,973
Server Average Response Time: 0
Server Request Buffers Needed: 0
Server Big Buffers Needed: 0
```

NT Workstation System Information

Consider the following administrative information on a typical work-station on the network. Notice similarities exist between the server information listed previously and the information that follows for the workstation named ANGEL.

Diagnostics Report for \\ANGEL (IBM XL Series Workstation)

```
-------------------------------------------------------------------------
OS Version Report
-------------------------------------------------------------------------
Microsoft (R) Windows NT (TM) Workstation
Version 4.0 (Build 1381: Service Pack 1) x86 Uniprocessor Free
Registered Owner: Angel, Information World, Inc.
Product Number: 17597-OEM-0023333-22375
-------------------------------------------------------------------------
System Report
-------------------------------------------------------------------------
System: AT/AT COMPATIBLE
Hardware Abstraction Layer: PC Compatible Eisa/Isa HAL
BIOS Date: 07/24/97
BIOS Version: BIOS Version 0.11.01.DUOM- Beta
Processor list:
  0: x86 Family 6 Model 3 Stepping 3 GenuineIntel ~265 Mhz
-------------------------------------------------------------------------


-------------------------------------------------------------------------
Video Display Report
-------------------------------------------------------------------------
BIOS Date: 07/21/97
BIOS Version: S3 86C775/86C785 Video BIOS. Version 1.01.11-C2.08.05

Adapter:
  Setting: 640 x 480 x 256
      60 Hz
  Type: s3mini compatible display adapter
  String: S3 Compatible Display Adapter
  Memory: 2 MB
  Chip Type: S3 Trio64V2
  DAC Type: S3 SDAC
Driver:
  Vendor: S3 Incorporated
  File(s): s3mini.sys, s3disp.dll
  Version: 1.03.10, 4.0.0
-------------------------------------------------------------------------
Drives Report
-------------------------------------------------------------------------
C:\ (Local - FAT) ANGEL Total: 1,023,824KB, Free: 783,664KB
D:\ (Local - FAT) ANGEL-D Total: 2,096,320KB, Free: 2,090,208KB
```

```
E:\ (Local - FAT) Total: 999,632KB, Free: 999,616KB
------------------------------------------------------------------------
Memory Report
------------------------------------------------------------------------
Handles: 1,300
Threads: 127
Processes: 19
Physical Memory (K)
  Total: 32,180
  Available: 5,752
  File Cache: 6,844
------------------------------------------------------------------------
Services Report
------------------------------------------------------------------------
Computer Browser                                     Running  (Automatic)
IBM DMI Service Layer (DMI Service Layer)            Running  (Automatic)
EventLog (Event log)                                 Running  (Automatic)
Server                                               Running  (Automatic)
Workstation (NetworkProvider)                        Running  (Automatic)
PC System Monitor                                    Running  (Automatic)
TCP/IP NetBIOS Helper                                Running  (Automatic)
Messenger                                            Running  (Automatic)
Norton SpeedDisk                                     Running  (Automatic)
Plug and Play (PlugPlay)                             Running  (Automatic)
Remote Access Autodial Manager                       Running  (Automatic)
Remote Access Connection Manager (Network)           Running  (Manual)
Remote Procedure Call (RPC) Service                  Running  (Automatic)
Spooler (SpoolerGroup)                               Running  (Automatic)
Telephony Service                                    Running  (Manual)
------------------------------------------------------------------------
Drivers Report
------------------------------------------------------------------------
AFD Networking Support Environment (TDI)             Running  (Automatic)
Remote Access Mac (NDIS)                             Running  (Automatic)
Beep (Base)                                          Running  (System)
Cdfs (File system)                                   Running  (Disabled)
Cdrom (SCSI CDROM Class)                             Running  (System)
cs32ba11 (Base)                                      Running  (System)
Disk (SCSI Class)                                    Running  (Boot)
Intel 82557-based PRO Adapter Driver (NDIS)          Running  (Automatic)
Fastfat (Boot file system)                           Running  (Disabled)
Floppy (Primary disk)                                Running  (System)
i8042 Keyboard and PS/2 Mouse Port Driver (Keyboard Port) Running
(System)
Keyboard Class Driver (Keyboard Class)               Running  (System)
KSecDD (Base)                                        Running  (System)
LM78                                                 Running  (Automatic)
Mouse Class Driver (Pointer Class)                   Running  (System)
Msfs (File system)                                   Running  (System)
Mup (Network)                                        Running  (Manual)
Microsoft NDIS System Driver (NDIS)                  Running  (System)
Microsoft NDIS TAPI driver (NDIS)                    Running  (System)
Remote Access WAN Wrapper (NDISWAN)                  Running  (Automatic)
NetBIOS Interface (NetBIOSGroup)                     Running  (Manual)
```

```
WINS Client(TCP/IP) (PNP_TDI)                         Running  (Automatic)
Npfs (File system)                                    Running  (System)
Null (Base)                                           Running  (System)
Parallel (Extended base)                              Running  (Automatic)
Parport (Parallel arbitrator)                         Running  (Automatic)
ParVdm (Extended base)                                Running  (Automatic)
PIIXIDE (SCSI miniport)                               Running  (Boot)
Remote Access Auto Connection Driver (Streams Drivers) Running (Auto-
matic)
Remote Access ARP Service (PNP_TDI)                   Running  (Automatic)
Rdr (Network)                                         Running  (Manual)
S3Inc (Video)                                         Running  (System)
Serial (Extended base)                                Running  (Automatic)
Srv (Network)                                         Running  (Manual)
TCP/IP Service (PNP_TDI)                              Running  (Automatic)
VgaSave (Video Save)                                  Running  (System)
-----------------------------------------------------------------------
IRQ and Port Report
-----------------------------------------------------------------------

Devices             Vector Level   Affinity
-----------------------------------------------------------------------
i8042prt               1     1    0xffffffff
i8042prt              12    12    0xffffffff
Serial                 4     4    0x00000000
cs32ball              55     7    0x00000001
E100B                 10    10    0x00000000
Floppy                 6     6    0x00000000
PIIXIDE                0    14    0x00000000
PIIXIDE                0    15    0x00000000
-----------------------------------------------------------------------
Devices             Physical Address  Length
-----------------------------------------------------------------------
i8042prt            0x00000060   0x0000000001
i8042prt            0x00000064   0x0000000001
Parport             0x000003bc   0x0000000003
Serial              0x000003f8   0x0000000007
cs32ball            0x00000530   0x0000000008
cs32ball            0x00000388   0x0000000004
E100B               0x0000ff40   0x0000000014
Floppy              0x000003f0   0x0000000006
Floppy              0x000003f7   0x0000000001
LM78                0x00000295   0x0000000002
PIIXIDE             0x000001f0   0x0000000008
PIIXIDE             0x0000ffa0   0x0000000008
PIIXIDE             0x00000170   0x0000000008
PIIXIDE             0x0000ffa8   0x0000000008
S3Inc               0x000003c0   0x0000000010
S3Inc               0x000003d4   0x0000000008
VgaSave             0x000003b0   0x000000000c
VgaSave             0x000003c0   0x0000000020
VgaSave             0x000001ce   0x0000000002
-----------------------------------------------------------------------
DMA and Memory Report
-----------------------------------------------------------------------
```

```
Devices              Channel  Port
-----------------------------------------------------------------------------
cs32ba11                1     0
cs32ba11                0     0
Floppy                  2     0
-----------------------------------------------------------------------------
Devices              Physical Address Length
-----------------------------------------------------------------------------
E100B                0xffbef000  0x00000014
E100B                0xffbef000  0x00000014
S3Inc                0x000a0000  0x00010000
S3Inc                0x000c0000  0x00008000
VgaSave              0x000a0000  0x00020000
-----------------------------------------------------------------------------
Environment Report
-----------------------------------------------------------------------------
System Environment Variables
  ComSpec=C:\WINNT40\system32\cmd.exe
  Os2LibPath=C:\WINNT40\system32\os2\dll;
  Path=C:\WINNT40\SYSTEM32;C:\WINNT40;C:\SVA\DMI\BIN
  windir=C:\WINNT40
  OS=Windows_NT
  PROCESSOR_ARCHITECTURE=x86
  PROCESSOR_LEVEL=6
  PROCESSOR_IDENTIFIER=x86 Family 6 Model 3 Stepping 3, GenuineIntel
  PROCESSOR_REVISION=0303
  NUMBER_OF_PROCESSORS=1
  help=c:\ipfwin\help
  ipf_path=c:\ipfwin
Environment Variables for Current User
  TEMP=C:\TEMP
  TMP=C:\TEMP
-----------------------------------------------------------------------------
Network Report
-----------------------------------------------------------------------------
Your Access Level: Admin & Local
Workgroup or Domain: INFO
Network Version: 4.0
LanRoot: INFO
Logged On Users: 1
Current User (1): Administrator
 Logon Domain: ANGEL
 Logon Server: ANGEL
Transport: NetBT_E100B1, 00-60-94-45-43-F3, VC's: 2, Wan: Wan
Character Wait: 3,600
Collection Time: 250
Maximum Collection Count: 16
Keep Connection: 600
Maximum Commands: 5
Session Time Out: 45
Character Buffer Size: 512
Maximum Threads: 17
Lock Quota: 6,144
Lock Increment: 10
```

```
Maximum Locks: 500
Pipe Increment: 10
Maximum Pipes: 500
Cache Time Out: 40
Dormant File Limit: 45
Read Ahead Throughput: 4,294,967,295
Mailslot Buffers: 3
Server Announce Buffers: 20
Illegal Datagrams: 5
Datagram Reset Frequency: 60
Bytes Received: 16,527
SMB's Received: 58
```

It is a good idea to obtain administrative information about the network as soon as the network is operational. Windows NT has built-in commands that can be issued against a command to obtain information. Commands and information that can be obtained this way include:

NETstat Command

The NETstat command issued with a ? afterwards yields the following information. Consider Figure 9.23.

FIGURE 9.23
Windows NT
NETstat
Command

```
C:\>netstat ?

Displays protocol statistics and current TCP/IP network connections.

NETSTAT [-a] [-e] [-n] [-s] [-p proto] [-r] [interval]

   -a        Displays all connections and listening ports. (Server-side
             connections are normally not shown).
   -e        Displays Ethernet statistics.  This may be combined with the -s
             option.
   -n        Displays addresses and port numbers in numerical form.
   -p proto  Shows connections for the protocol specified by proto; proto
             may be tcp or udp.  If used with the -s option to display
             per-protocol statistics, proto may be tcp, udp, or ip.
   -r        Displays the contents of the routing table.
   -s        Displays per-protocol statistics.  By default, statistics are
             shown for TCP, UDP and IP; the -p option may be used to specify
             a subset of the default.
   interval  Redisplays selected statistics, pausing interval seconds
             between each display.  Press CTRL+C to stop redisplaying
             statistics.  If omitted, netstat will print the current
             configuration information once.


C:\>
```

Numerous command line arguments can be issued against this command, and each yields different administrative details.

NETstat Command for Interface Statistics

Figure 9.24 shows information obtained about an interface in one of the network computers.

FIGURE 9.24
Windows NT
NETstat
Command

Interface Statistics		
	Received	**Sent**
Bytes	199411	339017
Unicast packets	687	977
Non-unicast packets	455	189
Discards	0	0
Errors	0	0
Unknown protocols	850	

This illustration yields the byte, unicast packet, non-unicast packet, discards, errors, and unknown protocol counts for this given interface. It reflects a given interface for a given instance in time.

NETstat Command for Active Sessions

The NETstat command can also obtain the number of active sessions for a given interface board (see Figure 9.25).

FIGURE 9.25
Windows NT
NETstat
Command
Active Sessions

Active Connections

Proto	Local Address	Foreign Address	State
TCP	127.0.0.1:1026	127.0.0.1:1027	ESTABLISHED
TCP	127.0.0.1:1027	127.0.0.1:1026	ESTABLISHED
TCP	220.100.100.53:139	220.100.100.8:1029	ESTABLISHED
TCP	220.100.100.53:139	220.100.100.10:1043	ESTABLISHED
TCP	220.100.100.53:139	220.100.100.12:1040	ESTABLISHED

Notice Figure 9.25 shows TCP as the protocol in use, the local IP addresses, the foreign or destination address, and the state of the connection. The actual meaning of this information is that these *sessions* are established.

NETstat Command for Comprehensive Statistics

This NETstat command can be used to obtain the kind of comprehensive that Figure 9.26 shows.

FIGURE 9.26
Comprehensive
NETstat
Command

IP STATISTICS	
Packet Receieved	
Received Header Errors	= 1004
Received Address Errors	= 0
Datagrams Forwarded	= 0
Unknown Protocols Received	= 0
Received PAckets Discarded	= 0
Received Packets Delivered	= 0
Output Requests	= 1004
Routing Discards	= 1136
Discarded Output Packets	= 0
Output Packet No Route	= 0
Reassembly Required	= 0
Reassembly Successful	= 0
Reassembly Failures	= 0
Datagrams Successfully Fragmented	= 0
Datagrams Failing Fragmentation	= 0
Fragments Created	= 0

ICMP Statistics	Sent	Receieved
Messages	0	0
Errors	0	0
Destination Unreachable	0	0
Time Exceeded	0	0
Parameter Problems	0	0
Source Quenchs	0	0
Redirects	0	0
Echos	0	0
Echo Replies	0	0
Timestamp	0	0
Timestamp Replies	0	0
Address Masks	0	0
Address Mask Replies	0	0

TCP Statistics	
Active Opens	= 13
Passive Opens	= 10
Failed Connection Attempts	= 0
Reset Connections	= 2
Current Connections	= 5
Segments Received	= 579
Segments Sent	= 649
Segments Retransmitted	= 0

UDP Statistics	
Datagrams Received	= 414
No Ports	= 11
Receive Errors	= 0
Datagrams Sent	= 487

Figure 9.26 indicates IP, ICMP, TCP, and UDP statistics. This command can be issued for any and all workstations and servers participating in the network.

NETstat Command for View

Another piece of information obtainable via the NETstat command is a list of views in a given system. Consider Figure 9.27.

```
C:\>net view
Server Name          Remark

-----------------------------------------------------------------------
\\ANGEL
\\BRAINS
\\CHEROKEE
\\FAT BOY           ED TAYLOR
\\MONY              taylor
\\MUSCLE
\\RENEGADE
\\SILO              AXIS StorPoint CD, CD-ROM Server, V4.13
\\THE-HOSTAGE
\\THE-KID
The command completed successfully.


C:\>
```

NETstat Command for Users

Another piece of information obtainable via the NETstat command is a list of users in a given system. Consider Figure 9.28.

NETstat Active Connections

This command is the same as that shown in Figure 9.25. However, consider Figure 9.29.

FIGURE 9.28
Windows NT NET
User Command

```
C:\>net user

User accounts for \\CHEROKEE

----------------------------------------------------------------
Administrator         ANGEL               BRAINS
FAT BOY               Guest               HEAVY
HOLLYWOOD             LITTLE MAN              MONY
MUSCLE               RENEGADE             SPEEDY
taylor               THE HOSTAGE          THE KID
The command completed successfully.


C:\>
```

FIGURE 9.28
Windows NT NET
User Command

FIGURE 9.29
Windows NT NET
Command Active
Sessions

```
Active Connections

  Proto  Local Address        Foreign Address      State
  TCP    CHEROKEE:1027          0.0.0.0:0           LISTENING
  TCP    CHEROKEE:135           0.0.0.0:0           LISTENING
  TCP    CHEROKEE:135           0.0.0.0:0           LISTENING
  TCP    CHEROKEE:1026          0.0.0.0:0           LISTENING
  TCP    CHEROKEE:1026          localhost:1027      ESTABLISHED
  TCP    CHEROKEE:1027          localhost:1026      ESTABLISHED
  TCP    CHEROKEE:137           0.0.0.0:0           LISTENING
  TCP    CHEROKEE:138           0.0.0.0:0           LISTENING
  TCP    CHEROKEE:nbsession     0.0.0.0:0           LISTENING
  TCP    CHEROKEE:nbsession     FAT:1029            ESTABLISHED
  TCP    CHEROKEE:nbsession     MUSCLE:1043         ESTABLISHED
  TCP    CHEROKEE:nbsession     BRAINS:1040         ESTABLISHED
  UDP    CHEROKEE:135           *:*
  UDP    CHEROKEE:nbname        *:*
  UDP    CHEROKEE:nbdatagram    *:*
```

Notice the command yields different information when issued against a different system. In Figure 9.29 the command was issued on the Netfinity 7000.

Windows NT CMD

The CMD command is an NT command.

Notice the information available in Figure 9.30. The CMD is the Windows NT command interpreter. The different switches available yield different results.

FIGURE 9.30
Windows NT CMD

Starts a new instance of the Windows/NT command interpreter

CMD [/X I /Y] [/A I /U] [/Q] [[/C I /K] string]

/C   Carries out the command specified by string and then terminates
/K   Carries out the command specified by string but remains
/Q   Turns the echo off
/A   Causes the output of internal commands to a pipe or file to be ANSI
/U   Causes the output of internal commands to a pipe or file to be Unicode
/T:fg Sets the foreground/background colors (see COLOR /? for more info)
/X   Enable extensions to the Windows NT version of CMD.EXE
/Y   Disable extensions to the Windows NT version of CMD.EXE

Note that multiple commands separated by the command separator '&&'
are accepted for string if surrounded by quotes

Command Extensions are enabled by default. You may also disable
extensions for all invocations of the command processor by setting the
following value in the registry to 0

    HKEY_CURRENT_USER\Software\Microsoft\Command Processor\EnableExtensions

The command extensions involve changes and/or additions to the following
commands:

    DEL or ERASE
    COLOR
    CD or CHDIR
    MD or MKDIR
    PROMPT
    PUSHD
    POPD
    SET
    SETLOCAL
    ENDLOCAL
    IF
    FOR
    CALL
    SHIFT
    GOTO
    START (also includes changes to external command invocation)
    ASSOC
    FTYPE

To get specific details, type HELP commandname to view the specifics.

All the commands presented here provide valuable information to a network administrator. They are not all the tools an administrator has available, but they are a considerable portion of the utilities that provide useful information.

The Registry

Windows NT employs what is called the *registry*. There is no way I can do justice to this topic here in detail. Many books on NT include dozens of pages on the registry. Simply put, the registry is the replacement for the .ini files of times past. Actually, it is much more than this. Data in the registry encompass everything from device adapters to software configuration and system configuration.

The registry is actually a database that can be divided into six subtrees. In addition, there are global and user-preferred values. Global registry entries affect hardware settings, local machine settings, system-wide software settings, and other system-wide parameters. User-preferred values focus on individual settings or preferences.

The bottom of the subtree contains what is called *root keys*. The six root keys are:

```
HKEY_CLASSES_ROOT
HKEY_CURRENT_USER
HKEY_LOCAL_MACHINE
HKEY_USERS
HKEY_CURRENT_CONFIG
HKEY_DYN_DATA
```

The naming convention of these registry root keys was designed to make future reference to these components easy. Each root key maintains data about different system functions or components. For example, classes_root contains information about object linking and embedding, files, class, and various associations. This information is used by system and application components. The current_user root key maintains user settings and profiles for the user currently logged on. The local_machine root key maintains local machine hardware, memory, display, hard drives, network adapters and so forth. The users root key maintains data about all user profiles. The current config root key contains data about the actual configuration of the system as it is operating; this includes device setup, control values, and so forth. The dyn data root key contains dynamic data required by internal registry functions.

The registry is not intuitively obvious. In fact, it is somewhat obscure. It is also available in Windows 95. To invoke the editor and the registry, type `regedit` at a DOS prompt or on the `RUN` command line under the pop-up menu. I do not recommend that anyone edit without a very good understanding of the consequences.

Experience has taught me that changes are required in various parts of the registry. These must be made with surgical precision. If you encounter trouble in the network as you set up and configure it, it is possible changes will be required in the registry.

High-Speed Server Connections

NT-based networks typically have one or more NT servers. My network was designed with three NT servers. An important part of a server's use is the ability to transfer data. During the design phase of your network, you should consider data (video, voice, or multimedia) transfer from the server to each user and server connectivity to the network.

Adaptec four-part network adapters ("quad cards") were selected for their design. Their inherent architecture makes for high-speed connections. Adaptec refers to these interface boards as Cogent Quartet Series network adapters. Both Cogent and Quartet are trademarked names and the property of the Adaptec Corporation. These boards are known as ANA-6944A. Figure 9.31 illustrates how these interface boards were implemented into the server in the network I designed and built.

Figure 9.32 shows a closeup of the Adaptec board. It has four ports for network connectivity, thus providing a high level of redundancy. This level of throughput is also required to realize potential benefit from the high-end servers on the market today.

Adaptec is a pioneer in the area of SCSI device control. They have a wide range of products for desktop computers, networking, and telecommunication equipment. You should contact Adaptec during the planning phase of your network and let their technical support division assist you. Contact Adaptec Corporation to obtain more information at: www.adaptec.com or call 800-442-7274.

FIGURE 9.31
High-Speed Server
Connections

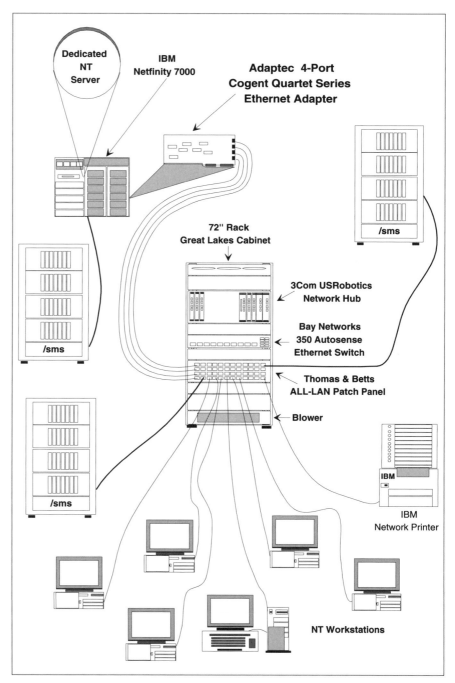

FIGURE 9.32
High Speed
Network Interface
Board

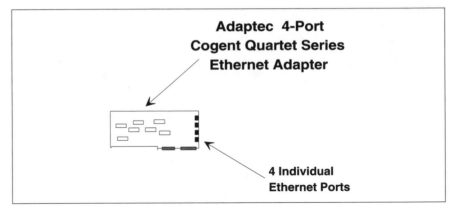

Highlights of Windows NT Server, Enterprise Edition

Windows NT Server, Enterprise Edition, the newest member of the Windows NT Server family, builds on the strengths and broad functionality of Windows NT Server, extending scalability, availability, and manageability. The Enterprise Edition also provides the best platform for building and deploying large-scale distributed applications.

Together, all of the following new capabilities make Windows NT Server, Enterprise Edition the easiest operating system for your largest and most mission-critical enterprise servers:

- There is a cluster-ready operating system, with Microsoft Cluster Server (MSCS); when this feature is used on a validated cluster configuration, two-node high-availability clusters are provided on standard PC server hardware.
- There is support for up to eight-processor symmetric multiprocessing (SMP) servers for higher scalability. Support for larger SMP servers is available from selected system vendors.
- There is more application RAM that improves performance by increasing the amount of memory available to memory-intensive applications.
- Microsoft Message Queue Server, Enterprise Edition, provides assured delivery of messages between applications running on multiple machines across a network with unlimited concurrent users, intelligent routing, and support for third-party gateways to IBM's MQSeries servers.

Windows NT Server, Enterprise Edition, brings the higher scalability and availability required of enterprise servers to the world's most popular server operating system. In addition, the Windows NT Server platform offers unparalleled flexibility and choice, and significant IT lifecycle cost savings, along with enterprise-class support options from Microsoft.

Cluster-ready for higher availability, Windows NT Server is a reliable operating system, thanks to built-in features such as application isolation, disk mirroring, and file directory journaling. The Enterprise Edition builds on this reliable platform with Microsoft Cluster Server, which lets you connect two servers into a "cluster" for higher availability and easier manageability of your server resources. Microsoft Cluster Server monitors the health of standard applications and servers, and can automatically recover mission-critical data and applications from many common types of failure—usually in less than a minute. A graphical management console lets you visually monitor the status of all resources in the cluster. MSCS can even be used to move workload around within the cluster with simple point-and-click actions. Use this capability for manual balancing of processing loads, or to unload servers for planned maintenance without taking important data and applications offline. With Microsoft Cluster Server, higher levels of service are delivered to users while greater control is maintained over the management of critical server resources.

In support of larger SMP servers Windows NT Server is designed to deliver excellent scalability on standard SMP servers from a variety of system vendors. It is licensed for use on SMP servers with up to four processors. Windows NT Server, Enterprise Edition is licensed for use on SMP servers with up to eight processors for even higher scalability. Versions of Windows NT Server, Enterprise Edition for even larger SMP servers are available from selected system vendors. As more eight-processor SMP servers for Windows NT Server, Enterprise Edition enter the marketplace, they will become cost-effective standards for enterprises that are consolidating workloads from smaller servers to simplify their environments. Larger SMP servers running Windows NT Server, Enterprise Edition will also represent a powerful upgrade path for enterprise applications that are growing to handle more users and more data.

Windows NT Server was designed to support servers with up to 4 GB of RAM. As the price of RAM continues to fall, it has now become cost-effective to run large, memory-intensive applications on servers with multiple gigabytes of RAM. To support this need, Windows NT Server, Enterprise Edition includes a feature for 4 GB Memory Tuning (4GT). This allows memory-intensive applications running on the

Enterprise Edition to utilize up to 50% more RAM on 32-bit Intel architecture servers. 4GT does this by reducing the potential RAM allocated to the Windows NT kernel from 2 GB to 1 GB, and increasing the potential RAM allocated to applications from 2 GB to 3 GB. The result can dramatically improve performance for applications such as decision support or data mining.

Corporate and professional developers will find that Windows NT Server, Enterprise Edition is an ideal platform for creating enterprise-class distributed applications. It includes all the strengths of today's Windows NT Server: a secure, robust environment containing a rich array of distributed computing services accessible through familiar, standard APIs, and supported by a wealth of visual development tools. Building on this, Windows NT Server, Enterprise Edition, includes Microsoft's newest distributed application tool—Microsoft Message Queue Server (MSMQ), Enterprise Edition.

MSMQ is store-and-forward middleware that provides assured delivery of messages between applications running on multiple machines across a network. The Enterprise version of MSMQ offers no limits on concurrent users, automatic least-cost routing, and the ability to connect to IBM MQSeries and other messaging systems through optional gateways from Level 8 systems. MSMQ is an ideal environment for building large-scale distributed applications that encompass mobile systems or communicate across occasionally unreliable networks.

Windows NT Server, Enterprise Edition builds on the foundation of Windows NT Server, a multipurpose server operating system built on a reliable, secure, microkernel architecture. It has become the best-selling, fastest-growing server operating system because of three key strengths:

- Windows NT Server is designed to work with your existing investment in IT. The Windows NT Directory Service provides a single network logon to all servers and applications, centralized administration of user accounts, and replication to ensure no single point of failure for network authentication. In addition, Windows NT Server has built-in support for all of the most important networking and UNIX standards, including Internet/intranet protocols like TCP/IP, HTTP, and DNS. The optional Microsoft SNA Server application extends integration to IBM mainframes and AS/400 environments. Windows NT Server shares the same user interface, management tools, and developer environment as 32-bit Microsoft Windows-based desktops.

- Comprehensive support for the server tier of your information technology is built in. Windows NT Server includes fast file/print services and offers a complete suite of communications services, such as remote access and multiprotocol routing. It is ready with Internet/intranet services including Web, FTP, Gopher, content indexing, and site management. In addition, Windows NT Server is an excellent distributed applications platform with the inclusion of Microsoft Transaction Server (MTS) and MSMQ. MTS is a component-based application platform for quickly building scalable, manageable distributed-transaction applications. A limited version of MSMQ will be a standard feature of Windows NT Server with the release of Internet Information Server (IIS) 4.0.
- Ease of use starts with fast installation and configuration, and continues with a complete suite of graphical, remoteable management tools. Windows NT Server is designed to increase the productivity of users, administrators, and developers by adhering to all of the familiar Windows interface, usage, and development standards. By design, it is the easiest server operating system for the most demanding business needs.

Windows NT Server, Enterprise Edition technical features include:

Microsoft Cluster Server (MSCS)

When run on a validated configuration this provides automatic recovery from server and application failures. It also lets you do "rolling upgrades" on your servers, performing standard maintenance without taking important data and applications offline. Manage clusters through a graphical administration console that treats all the servers in a cluster as a single environment. Use the cluster administration console to monitor the status of your server applications and move workload around to balance loads.

Choose from standard set of clustering services that are available on clusters from many different hardware vendors; no hardware vendor lock-in is required for your investment in cluster-enabled applications and training.

Microsoft Cluster Server includes a standard, cross-platform API for developing and supporting cluster-aware applications. Use the cluster API to create applications that are more reliable, easier to install, easier to manage, able to upgrade without downtime, and recover from failures more rapidly. Also use the MSCS APIs to create scalable, cluster-aware applications that can automatically balance loads across multiple servers within the cluster. Microsoft Cluster Server is designed to support advanced "shared nothing" applications that can scale smoothly across large numbers of servers.

Microsoft Message Queue Server (MSMQ)

MSMQ is the foundation for distributed applications you can depend on. It provides reliable delivery of messages and data across your network, even if the network and servers are occasionally unavailable or unreliable.

Managing applications based on MSMQ is dramatically easier than with older store-and-forward middleware. Queues are managed through an integrated directory, permitting rapid and flexible reconfiguration of your distributed environment even while applications are running.

Automatic least-cost routing chooses the best route for message delivery, and intelligent rerouting automatically routes around unavailable network segments for fast, assured delivery. MSMQ provides a rich variety of delivery capabilities, from efficient fire-and-forget to the most reliable levels requiring absolute confirmation of message and delivery status.

Connect MSMQ applications to message queues managed by legacy systems, such as IBM MQSeries, through optional gateways from Level 8 Systems.

4 Gigabyte (GB) Memory Tuning

Standard Windows NT Server applications can now access up to 3 GB of RAM, a 50% increase over the standard Windows NT Server 2-GB limit. This can provide excellent performance for data-warehouse and decision-support applications that do massive amounts of "slicing and dicing."

Well-designed multithreaded applications written with the standard Microfost Win32 API can scale smoothly by simply increasing the amount of RAM all up to 3 GB and the number of processors in SMP servers.

Up to 8-Way SMP Server Support

Server support scales smoothly from uniprocessors up to eight-way SMP servers, and across servers from dozens of vendors, with no change to your investment in training, data, and applications.

Windows NT Server, Enterprise Edition offers a unique ability to simplify corporate data centers by consolidating server workloads on a smaller number of larger servers because it runs on large "super servers" with up to eight-way SMP.

Microsoft Transaction Server (MTS)

MTS provides component-based transaction middleware similar to a TP Monitor, but easier to use and easier to integrate with Windows-based desktops. When distributed applications are based on MTS, your important inventory and financial records stay consistent across all locations, even when processing transactions from multiple locations and multiple time zones.

MTS provides component-based access to distributed transaction services, while automatically managing security and threading. Applications are built quickly and scale smoothly.

Microsoft Message Queue Server Standard Edition

A limited version of MSMQ is part of Windows NT Server, Standard Edition. This version has a limit on the number of concurrent users.

Windows 95 User Interface

The Windows 95 UI is integrated with Windows NT Server 4.0, making the server interface easier to use and consistent with Windows 95 and Windows NT Workstation 4.0 operating systems. Universal Inbox provides access to all information sources through the Messaging API (MAPI).

Administrative Wizards

Administrative wizards group the common server management tools into a single place and walk you through the steps required for each task. Windows NT Server 4.0 includes the following wizards: Add User Accounts, Group Management, Managing File and Folder Access, Add Printer, Add/Remove Programs, Install New Modem, Network Client Administrator, and License.

Task Manager

This provides detailed information on each application and process running on the system, as well as graphical memory and CPU usage readouts for easy status-checking at a glance.

Network Monitor

This examines network traffic to and from the server at the packet level and captures that information for later analysis.

Microsoft Internet Information Server (IIS)

IIS is integrated with Windows NT Server 4.0 and offers a fast Web server on Windows NT Server, World Wide Web, Gopher, FTP services, Internet Service Manager and an Internet Database Connector.

Microsoft Internet Explorer

This embraces existing HTML standards while advancing HTML with improvements such as online video, backgrounds, Secure Sockets Layer (SSL) support, and support for Internet shopping applications.

Microsoft Front Page

This enables nonprogrammers and experienced developers alike to create and manage professional-quality Web sites.

Microsoft Index Server

This helps users find information on distributed servers within their corporate intranet.

Distributed Component Object Model (DCOM)

DCOM-enabled applications can share components across networks including the Internet.

Remote Access Service (RAS) Multilink Aggregation Channel

This enables clients dialing into Windows NT Server 4.0 to combine all available dial-up lines, providing increased bandwidth.

Point-to-Point Tunneling Protocol (PPTP)

PPTP enables users to extend secure private networks across the Internet.

MultiProtocol Router (MPR)

This eliminates the need for dedicated routers by enabling small- and medium-sized sites to deploy Windows NT Server 4.0 as a low-cost LAN-LAN routing solution; it provides LAN-LAN routing for IPX/SPX, TCP/IP, and AppleTalk.

Telephony Application Programming Interface (TAPI) and Unimodem

These provide the technologies required by fax applications, the Windows Messaging Subsystem (Microsoft Exchange Client), MSN and trade, the Microsoft Network online service, and Microsoft Internet Explorer.

Domain Name System (DNS) Server Integration with Windows Internet Name Service

This allows access to resources on the network or over the Internet using DNS names. DNS features include: a graphical administration utility, interoperability with the notify protocol, and reverse Windows NT Server 4.0 referrals.

Scalability

This supports as many as 5,000 concurrent database clients and databases of 100 GB or more.

It provides for transaction rates of more than 12,000 TPC-Cs for less than $500,000. It supports more than 3,000 applications today, with 4,000 expected within the next 12 months.

Windows 95 Remote Program Load

This boots Windows 95-based diskless clients from a server running Windows NT Server 4.0.

Policy Desktop Configuration

This controls desktop configurations, giving a common desktop look and functionality across workstations.

Cryptography APIs

These allow developers to create custom encryption solutions.

Minimum Requirements for Enterprise Edition

A pentium 90 MHz or higher processor for Intel or compatible systems Systems with Alpha processor for RISC systems is required with:

- 64 MB of memory (RAM)
- 500 MB of available hard disk space
- Microsoft SQL Server 6.5 is required to run Microsoft Message Queue Server
- VGA, Super VGA, or video graphics adapter compatible with Windows NT Server 4.0 CD-ROM drive
- Microsoft mouse or compatible pointing device.

Windows NT can be implemented numerous ways. Different implementations yield different advantages. The following blueprints are guides that can be used to use as templates to build a network.

NT Blueprint #1

The first blueprint for a Windows NT network is rather basic but powerful.

Figure 9.33 shows a dedicated NT server, numerous workstations, and a network printer. This sample blueprint is powerful enough to meet the needs of many smaller installations. Some of the features of this implementation include: file sharing, a central file server, e-mail, network printing, and workstation sharing among users where rights and permissions are granted.

FIGURE 9.33
Windows NT
Blueprint #1

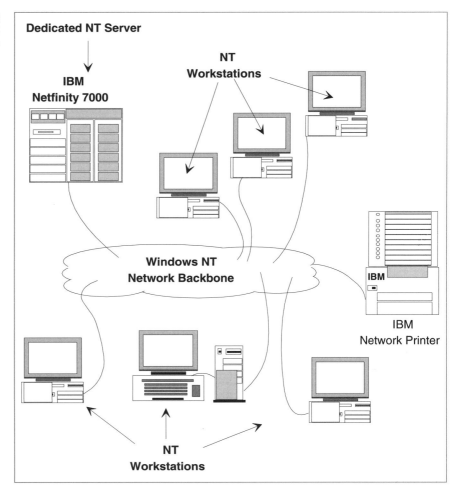

Blueprint #2

Blueprint 2 is a step beyond the first example.

Figure 9.34 shows two dedicated network servers, workstations, and a network printer. In this blueprint, one server is a dedicated file server and the other a dedicated application server. All the workstations on the network have access to the servers. This network blueprint could easily sustain a large number of users and large database, and enable scalable growth. This particular blueprint is an ideal way to begin a network if future plans may involve considerable expansion.

FIGURE 9.34
Windows NT
Blueprint #2

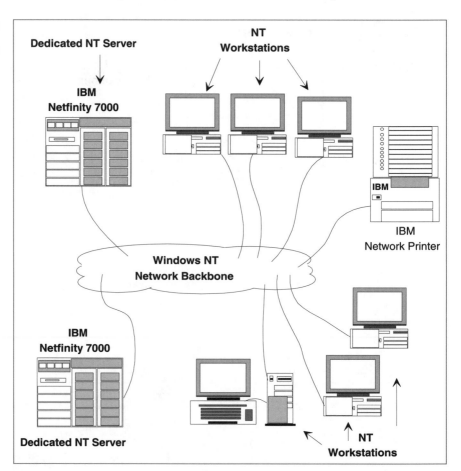

NT Blueprint #3

NT blueprint 3 reveals a design different from its predecessors, consider Figure 9.35.

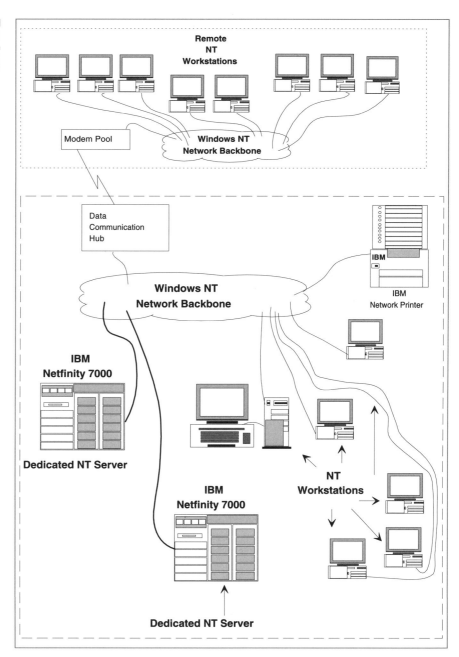

FIGURE 9.35
Windows NT
Blueprint #3

Notice two network servers exist on the major network backbone along with workstations, a printer, and a data communication hub.

In this blueprint, the addition of a data communication hub enables remote users on an NT network to access the servers on the major network backbone. This blueprint could be used with a entity needing remote network support in the same geographical area or it could be implemented to integrate widely dispersed networks. The benefit of this blueprint is the leverage portrayed by the remote users' accessing the pre-existing servers on the major network backbone. This yields a cost saving and, implemented appropriately, enables load balancing. This particular blueprint can also be scaled to support large numbers of users.

NT Blueprint #4

Blueprint 4 provides additional equipment and implementation differences. Consider Figure 9.36.

The equipment shown includes a rack cabinet, communication hub, network hub, patch panel, workstations, network printer, high speed network adapters, storage silo, and network server.

This blueprint illustrates a need for a rack cabinet. In fact, almost every blueprint shown requires enough equipment to require a rack cabinet. A rack cabinet not only makes for order with equipment and wiring, but also promotes ease of maintenance and proper cooling. A patch panel makes for easy patch wiring with all sorts of equipment. The network hub can be patched with equipment such as workstations, servers, printers, and data communications equipment.

The high-speed network adapter shown is one way to design growth capability into the network. Not all ports on the network adapter are required, but they are used and provide enhanced throughput ability. The high-speed adapter in this blueprint allows for greater bandwidth in the architecture.

Notice the network silo is attached to the network server. By integrating a network silo into the design, much-increased storage capacity is possible. All sorts of online information can be made available. In this illustration the network silo is connected to the network server; however, from the view of a workstation user, the network silo is just another node on the network.

Blueprint 4 provides great flexibility for expansion and change, and support for remote users. This blueprint is a good one to use for networks where 500 to 1,000 users participate.

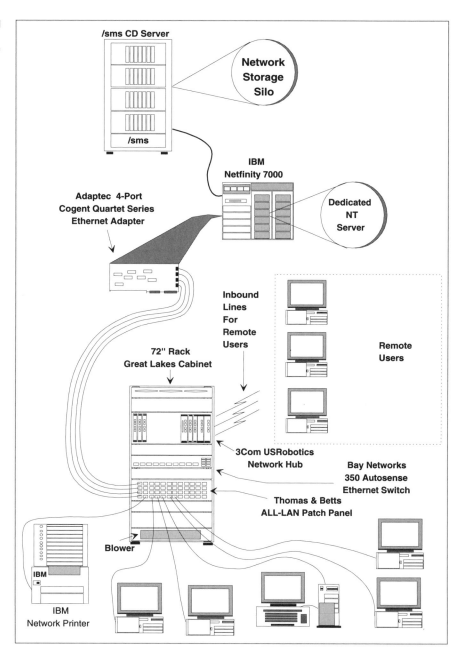

FIGURE 9.36
Windows NT
Blueprint #4

NT Blueprint #5

Network blueprint 5 expands the scope of NT network design (see Figure 9.37).

FIGURE 9.37
Windows NT
Blueprint #5

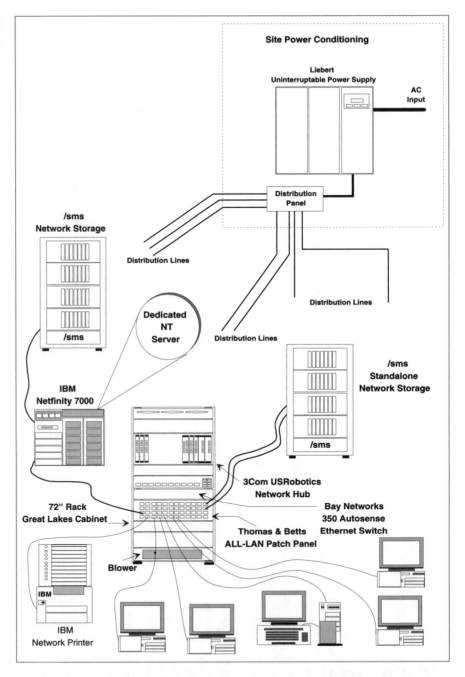

Figure 9.37 shows a comprehensive network design with AC voltage
planning and design included. Examine Figure 9.37 again.

Blueprint 5 shows a Liebert UPS providing power conditioning for the entire site. Notice that the network site's electrical provision is distributed through the Liebert UPS. A single input comes from the site's AC distribution panel. As in the case of the network I designed, this distribution panel is designed and implemented for the entire site. Consequently, all the network equipment AC power is delivered from the Liebert UPS. This design is a powerful departure from the previous blueprints because all the network equipment is protected by the UPS and the equipment can also operate for a certain amount of time without electrical power.

This blueprint also shows two network silos, a network server, workstations, and other equipment as in other blueprints. Notice one silo is connected to the network server and one is connected to the network patch panel itself. The purpose of this is network load balancing. This blueprint showing the network silo connected to the network server is one way for the silo to be connected. Because of the flexibility of the silo shown, it can also be connected directly to the network itself.

One practical way this blueprint operates is for the local workstation users to access the silo connected to the network server and the remote users to access the silo connected to the network patch panel. In this blueprint either the local or the remote users can access either silo, and significant impairment would not be realized unless the number of users presented significant traffic loads.

NT Blueprint #6

Blueprint 6 shows a network design well suited for medium- to large-size networks.

Figure 9.38 shows a network segmented into two parts. Each part shares some components: a rack enclosure, network hub, network patch panel, data communication hub, network server, network silo, and workstations.

With a dual-segment network, multiple objectives can be accomplished. Network maintenance can be achieved, as can backup of workstations, servers, and other network devices. A level of redundancy is possible if the network is planned in advance to include such an advantage. The ability to move resources for interim load balancing is also another benefit from such design.

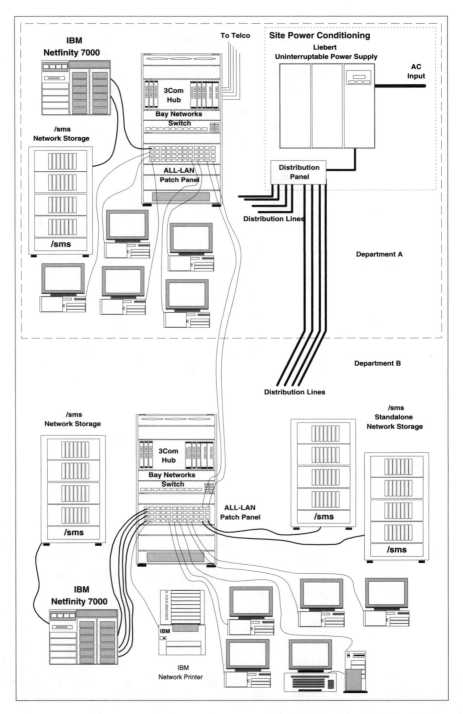

FIGURE 9.38
Windows NT
Blueprint #6

Blueprint 6 shows complete site power conditioning by the Liebert UPS. This approach to power conditioning and auxiliary power is advantageous because the design can eliminate ground loops and other undesirable power nuances. With a single UPS to provide power conditioning and backup power, the entire site can be managed better

This blueprint is well suited for entities that may be in campus-like settings or span large amounts of space.

NT Blueprint #7

Blueprint 7 presents a different perspective on network design.

Figure 9.39 is labeled to reflect a network that provides data, video, and multimedia information. Notice how many SMS network silos and Netfinity servers are shown. This presents a blueprint design where the information and server requirements are large. The illustration shows multiple remote users and shows single-site power conditioning.

This blueprint is an excellent example of how Internet service provider networks are designed. If your entity requires a lot of information online and multiple servers consider this blueprint to use in building your facility.

NT Blueprint #8

Blueprint 8 is a good example for businesses/entities with multiple locations.

Figure 9.40 shows a data center and multiple remote sites. The data center has a single method for power conditioning, numerous network silos, and two network servers. Multiple users are connected to the network at the data center location and remotely.

Three remote connections are shown in this illustration. Each of these sites uses NT as the network backbone. The sites use RAS. NT's RAS makes a powerful connectivity method for a site predominantly NT-oriented.

A benefit of these remote sites is that they are mirror images of each other. This promotes ease of maintenance and software management. This blueprint design is excellent to use when multiple remote sites need connectivity into the network. It enables almost endless numbers of remote sites to be integrated. The actual restrictions of network size have more to do with design, hardware, and money than with NT architecture itself. This is a good blueprint to consider for migration if you are working with a sizable network.

FIGURE 9.39
Windows NT
Blueprint #7

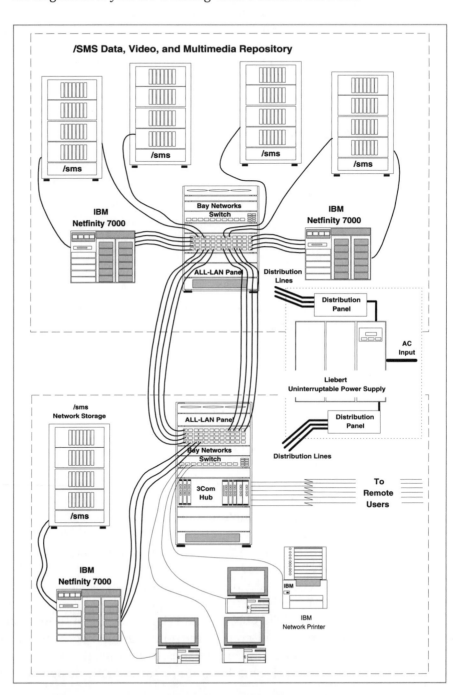

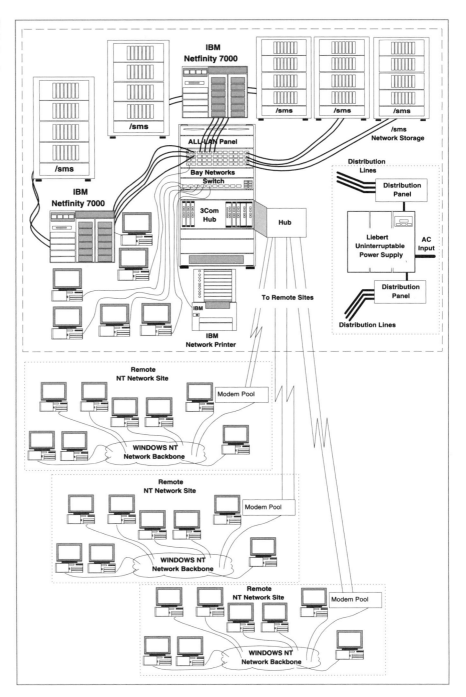

FIGURE 9.40
Windows NT
Blueprint #8

NT Blueprint #9

Blueprint 9 shows a different way to integrate multiple geographic locations (see Figure 9.41).

FIGURE 9.41
Windows NT
Blueprint #9

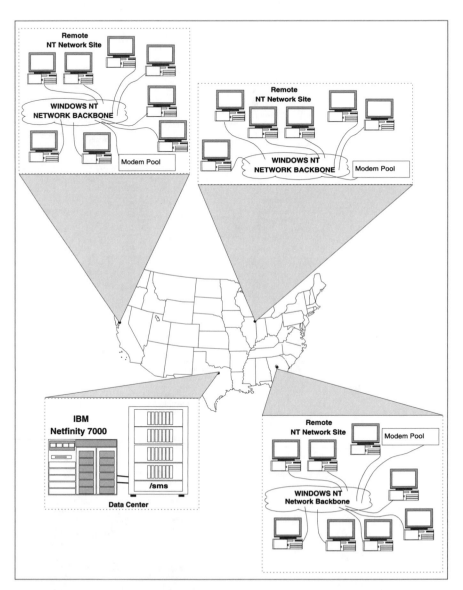

Figure 9.41 shows four distinct different locations where networks are implemented. One location has a data center, three others have the same networks. This blueprint is purposely left *open* in the sense of

connectivity. So that any location can interact with any other location. Another example of these network connections could be their integration into the data center. These sites could also be integrated by integrating some into the data center and the others into other locations.

This blueprint is a good tool to use with different-size network environments. In fact, it could be used with networks small enough to fit into what might be considered simple groups and powerful enough to support expanded implementations around the globe.

This blueprint is a good example of a tool to use when network size can change and requirements may vary from time to time. There is great flexibility in the implementation.

NT Blueprint #10

Blueprint 10 is an example of a good baseline to use with large networks.

Figure 9.42 shows multiple servers and network silos in multiple locations around the country. The end result is a logical network. This is a good example of how the Internet *appears* and is *implemented*. With this blueprint, many different access points could be used. In fact, the blueprint could be expanded to have two, four, six, or more sites just like those shown.

This is a good example of how to build a large network. If it is designed and implemented well, one logical network is the result. This is just the beginning of how the technology can be exploited. This blueprint could be used with other blueprints superimposed on it. With that in mind, hybrid blueprints could easily emerge. Consider this idea when you begin the planning stage of your network.

Summary

Windows NT is not a technology just for the desktop; it is for the enterprise, regardless of size. This chapter presented basic information about NT. Many well-written books on this technology exist. Investigate and invest some money in some of them.

Designing NT networks should include such aspects as load balancing, power conditioning, network silos, remote access, network printing and other topics presented in this chapter. The blueprints are meant to help in the initial phases of network planning. They can be used and expanded to meet the needs of your facility and users.

These blueprints presented basic information. Preplanning networks is of the utmost importance. Windows NT is no trivial technology to attempt to harness. This chapter in conjunction with others in this book should provide information to help you along the way.

FIGURE 9.42
Windows NT
Blueprint #10

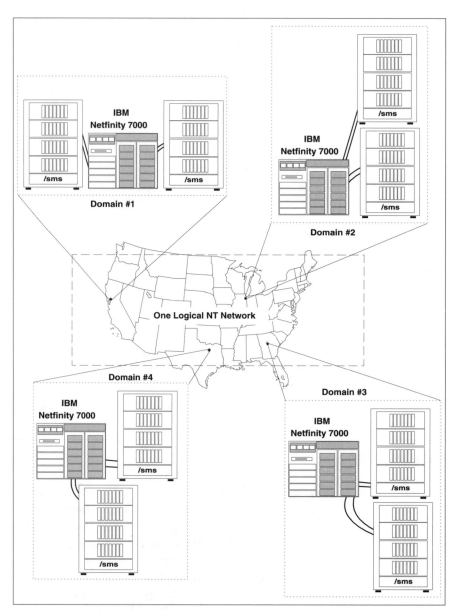

CHAPTER 10

Systems Network Architecture (SNA) Blueprints

SNA is a complex topic. Those whose background is not in SNA will find this chapter helpful. Those whose background includes experience in SNA, will find this chapter particularly enlightening. There is background information here for the benefit of all readers. The blueprints are based on the terms, concepts, and architecture presented in the early part of the chapter.

SNA networks are built from hardware and software components, they vary in size; the different blueprints bear this out. Before we examine blueprints, we need to consider some reference material.

Hardware Architecture

An Evolutionary Perspective

The development that occurred at IBM during the 1940s and 50s, led to the creation of the System/360 (S/360) hardware architecture. An overview of hardware offerings preceding the S/360 is in order.

During the '40s, '50s, and even into the '60s IBM had approximately a half-dozen popular mainframe computers, each with their own strengths. Other systems existed, but six were fundamentally solid-state devices. A fundamental problem with these systems was that little was interchangeable among them.

This meant their programming, support, sales, and technical sales advisors each concentrated on a single area of expertise. Usually there was no overlap from one type of system to another. This was costly and increasingly a problem for IBM and customers had to contend with this if they had more than one type of machine within a given corporation. Examples of these machines and their forte include:

- **IBM 604.** This was an electronic calculating punch card machine, first available in approximately 1948. The strength of this machine, and its major selling points were: speed, a pluggable circuitry, and its components concentrated in a small physical location. From the users' point of view its speed was important.
- **IBM 650.** This machine was available circa 1954, though it was announced in 1953. The machine's strength was two-fold: it was a magnetic-drum storage machine and it concentrated on meeting the needs of general computing. It was extremely successful.
- **IBM 701.** This machine was announced in 1952. Its input/output was fast. It focused on increased processing speed. The 701 system had its power in scientific and related areas of computation; it was not a general-purpose machine.
- **IBM 702.** This system announced in 1953 made its debut in approximately 1955. Its origins were in the late 1940s. It focused on ease of character handling.

- **IBM 1401.** This system was announced in 1959 and gained a large market share after shipping began in 1960. It had increased speed, a fast printer, and other peripherals such as tape and card processing capabilities that made it popular. Its strengths lay in its multiple components' selective capabilities in conjunction with its price.

These systems, and others offered during the '40s, '50s, and early '60s, proved IBM's ability to meet a diversity of needs. However, such diversity in systems led to complexity in terms of one corporation attempting to maintain its position in a technical environment.

After years of planning, designing, and reengineering, 1964 proved a pivotal year in the history of IBM. The System/360 was introduced. This system was unique for multiple reasons; at the heart of the S/360 was now one architecture capable of accommodating what previously achieved by different systems. In addition, the S/360 architecture had different models; customers could begin with a purchase to meet immediate needs and expect a migration path to accommodate changing requirements.

Another appeal of the S/360 architecture was IBM's commitment to upgradeability to later architectures as they were introduced. Now IBM is four architectures removed from the S/360, but a program originally written for the S/360 has been successfully executed on the S/390 architecture.

Technical highlights of each of IBM's hardware architectures are presented below.

System/360 (S/360)

Characteristics and functions of this hardware architecture are listed below. The S/360 hardware architecture is presented by component, with synopsis of component characteristics and functions.

S/360 components included: central processing unit (CPU), channels, control unit(s), devices such as terminals, printers, tape and disk drives, as well as card punch and readers, and main storage.

CPU characteristics and functions included:

- Single processor architecture; models introduced later supported multiple processors
- Five classes of interrupts
- Interrupt priority
- 16 general-purpose 32-bit registers

- Optional four 64-bit floating point registers
- Dynamic address translation on selected models
- Supervisor facilities including a timer, direct control capabilities, storage protection, and support for multisystem operation
- ASCII and EBCDIC character set support.
- 24-bit addressing
- Channel-to-channel adapters used for interconnection of multiple processors.

Channel characteristics and functions:

- A data path to/from control units and devices
- Use of a protocol for data transfer
- Selector channels used with tape and disk devices for high speed data transfer; it uses one subchannel
- Byte multiplexor channels interleave I/O operations. Slower operating devices are used with this type of channel; which can logically support up to 256 subchannels.

Control Unit(s)

These serve as an *interface between* devices such as terminal, card reader, card punch, and printer.

Devices

These include terminals, printers, card punches, and card readers. The devices serve as input/output devices. Terminals are used interactively and punched cards used in batch processing.

Main Storage

Main storage in the early models emphasized speed and size. Virtual storage was available in later models.

Consider Figure 10.1, a logical view of the S/360. In a general way, it is basic to PC architecture. Granted that PC architecture has become more complex, but the illustration does provide the rudiments of the PC's beginning.

Figure 10.2 is a physical perspective of the S/360. This view is the essence of systems today, though more components have been inserted into various places. Systems today still have a processor, main storage (RAM), input and output (channels), and peripherals to control other devices.

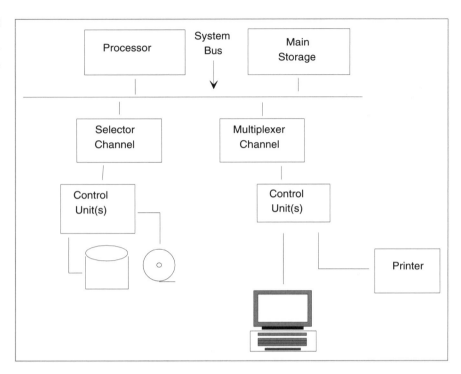

FIGURE 10.1
Logical View
of an S/360

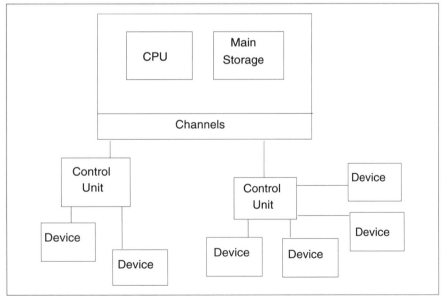

FIGURE 10.2
Physical View
of an S/360

Later S/360 versions had some features and functionality carried over
to the next hardware architectural generation, the S/370.

System/370 (S/370)

This architecture, announced in 1970, was the successor to the S/360. During the six following years IBM refined more than 14 models based on this architecture. Examination here includes features and functions based on the S/370 architecture as a whole, not from inception, but in incremental enhancements. Components and their characteristics and functions are considered.

S/370 components included: CPUs, channels, control unit(s), devices, and storage, both main and virtual.

Central Processing Unit characteristics and functions included:

- User program upgrade support from S/360
- Multiple processor support
- Six classes of interrupts
- Interrupt priority
- 16 general-purpose 32-bit registers
- Four 64-bit floating point registers
- Dynamic Address Translation (DAT) facility
- Extended real addressing an extension to DAT making 64MB addressability of real storage possible
- Dual Address Space (DAS) facility, supporting semiprivileged programs
- Supervisor facilities including a timer, direct control capabilities, storage protection, and support for multisystem operation
- Optional vector facility offering on selected models
- EBCDIC character set support
- Removal of ASCII support as in the S/360
- 24-bit addressing
- Two page sizes: 2K and 4K bytes
- Two segment sizes: 64K and 1M byte
- Multiprocessing with one operating system
- Approximately 50 new instructions more than on the S/360
- Translation look aside buffer to minimize DAT use.

Channel characteristics and functions were:

- Three types of channels supported: selector, byte, and block multiplexor
- Support for two byte channel bus width extension
- An associated set of subchannels for each channel
- Channel protocol for data transfer

- Data transfer rates of 1.5 MB and 3 MB achievable depending on channel bus width
- Suspend and resume facility for programmed control of channel program execution
- Removal of 16-byte channel prefetching from S/360 channels.

Control Unit(s)

These served as an *interface between* devices such as a terminal, card reader, card punch, and printer.

Devices

These included terminals, printers, card punches, and card readers; all serve as input/output devices. Terminals are used interactively whereas punched cards are used in batch processing.

Storage

- Main, with addressability of up to 64 MB
- Virtual, with addressability of up to 16 MB beyond that of main storage.

Figure 10.3 shows S/370 architecture which followed the S/360.

370/Extended Architecture (370/XA)

This architecture was announced in 1981, following the S/370 and what IBM called "S/370 compatible realized in the 4300 series of systems." From 1981–1988 370/XA was the hardware architecture implemented in IBM's mainframes.

370/XA components included: CPUs, a channel subsystem, control unit(s), devices, and three storage addressing types: absolute, real, and virtual.

CPU characteristics and functions included:

- Two addressing modes of operation: 24-bit and 31-bit
- 2 GB addressability with 31 bit-addressing mode
- 13 new instructions
- Multiple processor support
- Six classes of interrupts
- Interrupt priority

FIGURE 10.3
A Conceptual
View of S/360

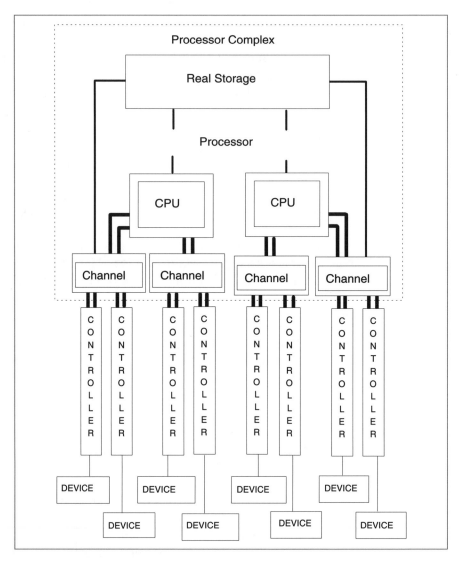

FIGURE 10.3
A Conceptual
View of S/360

- 16 general-purpose 32-bit registers
- Four 64-bit floating point registers
- Dynamic Address Translation (DAT) facility
- Extended real addressing, an extension to DAT permitting 64MB real storage addressability
- Dual Address Space (DAS) facility, supporting semiprivileged programs
- Supervisor facilities including timer, direct control capabilities, storage protection, and support for multisystem operation

- Optional vector facility offering on selected models
- EBCDIC character set support
- Dynamic I/O reconnect
- 24-bit addressing
- Two page sizes: 2K and 4K bytes
- Two segment sizes: 64K and 1M byte
- Multiprocessing with one operating system
- Approximately 50 new instructions more than with over the S/360
- Translation look aside buffer to minimize DAT use.

Channel subsystem characteristics and functions were:

- A processor that interfaces I/O devices and processors
- Preprocessing of data between I/O devices and processors
- A channel path (the physical path between the channel subsystem and a device)
- Subchannel numbers, a one-to-one relationship with an I/O device
- Path independent addressing for I/O devices
- Implementation of paths enabling dynamic data routing from I/O device to processor
- A channel path identifier (CHIPID) associated with devices such as control units
- Path management performed by the channel subsystem
- Increased Channel Command Word (CCW) support for direct use of 31-bit addressing in channel programs
- 13 I/O instructions added
- Two types channels supported: byte and block multiplexor
- Subchannels are owned by the channel as in S/370
- Channel protocol used for data transfer
- Data transfer rates of 1.5 MB and 3 MB achievable, depending on the channel bus width
- Suspend and resume facility for programmed control of channel program execution
- Removal of 16-byte channel prefetching.

Figure 10.4 is a view of a channel subsystem.

Control Unit(s)

These serve as an *interface between* devices such as terminal, card reader, card punch, and printer.

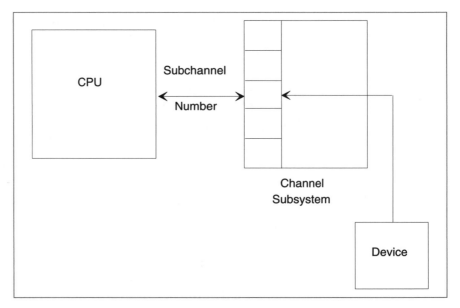

FIGURE 10.4
370/XA Channel
Subsystem

Devices

These terminals, printers, card punches, and card readers; they serve as input/output devices. Terminals are used interactively whereas punched cards are used in batch processing.

Storage (By Addressing Scheme)

- **Absolute.** This is an address to main storage. In essence, the term is synonymous with main storage. This type of address is storage where no transformations are performed on the contents. 2 GB of absolute storage are possible.
- **Real.** This also refers to an address in main storage and is used when multiple processors are accessing the same main storage. A CPU prefix number distinguishes processors so storage order is maintained.
- **Virtual.** This address reflects an abstract location. Virtual storage does not exist in reality, but is a concept, achieved by main storage, secondary storage, and processor speed as the fundamental components that make virtual storage possible.

Look at Figure 10.5. This architectural advancement brought about more segregated system component functions. This is a representation of 370/XA architecture.

FIGURE 10.5
370/XA
Architecture

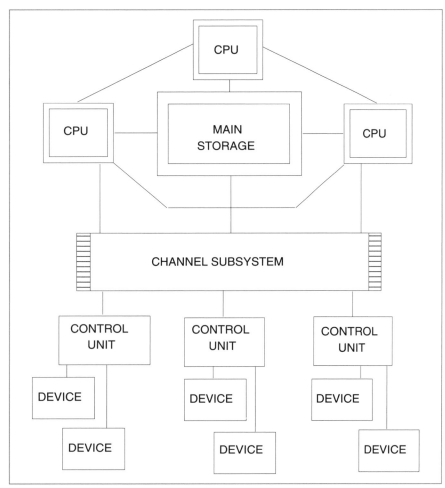

Other functionality was added to 370/XA before the announcement of Enterprise System Architecture, but the highlights above constitute the bulk of additions to the XA architecture.

Enterprise System Architecture/370 (ESA/370)

ESA/370 was announced in 1988 and succeeded 370/XA. This architecture built upon advances made in 370/XA and S/370. Different hardware-related functions were implemented. From a system standpoint considerable advances were made. Highlights of ESA/370 include: addressing, storage, and machine-dependent support.

Addressing

Key enhancements in ESA/370 include 16 new access registers. To provide the hardware capability for a program to address up to 16 spaces. A home address space is the name of a translation mode that permits the control program to gain control quickly where principle control blocks are maintained. A private space is supported to prevent use of the translation lookaside buffer for common segments. This private space support enhances security functions.

Storage

In ESA/370 a major enhancement was made in how the system handles storage. The storage management subsystem is designed to stage data. An I/O boundary exists and multiple places where data can be are possible. With a storage subsystem, the framework is in place for a particular processor complex to capitalize on this feature.

Figure 10.6 depicts the storage hierarchy, which is significant. Today, PCs typically have a similar arrangement. Even the implementation of cache to the processor and RAM is being phased in to a greater degree with each new model.

In addition, the System Control Element (SCE) works with the storage hierarchy, by routing data through the CPU's main and expanded storage and the channels. The SCE keeps track of changes made to data and is the key component for moving data throughout the hierarchy. Figure 10.7 is a logical view of the SCE.

Notice the centralized connection of the SCE and the other system components.

Machine-Dependent Support

A feature known as the Logical Partitioned Mode (LPAR) is a machine-dependent function, but is tied to hardware and a software component known as the Processor Resource/Systems Manager (PR/SM), pronounced *prism*. For a machine to function in LPAR mode it must be supported by that system and selected at power-up time.

LPAR permits a system to run four logical partitions, each running an operating system simultaneously and all independent of each other. Figure 10.8 depicts a logical view of a LPAR configured system.

The logical partitioning of a processor includes the processor's resources such as storage, channels, and the processor itself. Isolation of the LPARs is enforced via hardware. PR/SM is an IBM-supplied option that some machines can take advantage of to offer LPAR. It is implemented in microcode, IBM's term synonymous with firmware.

FIGURE 10.6
IBM's Storage
Hierarchy

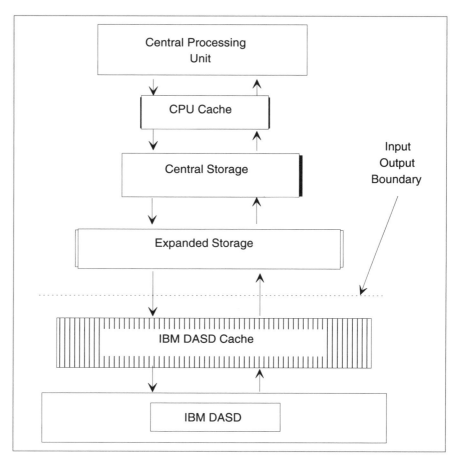

ESA/370 architecture differs from that of 370/XA because of the storage, addressing, and machine-dependent enhancements offered.

From a physical view little differs; however, Figure 10.9 depicts ESA/370 with two processors.

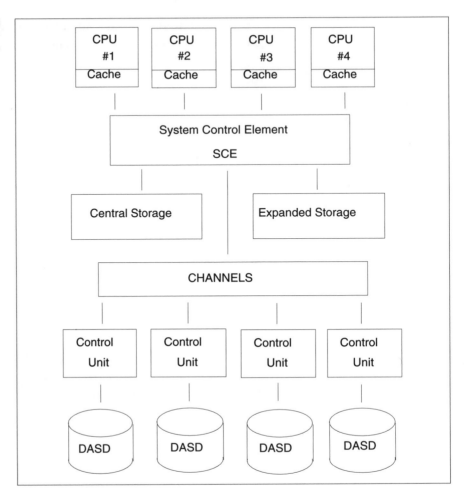

FIGURE 10.7
SCE Logical View

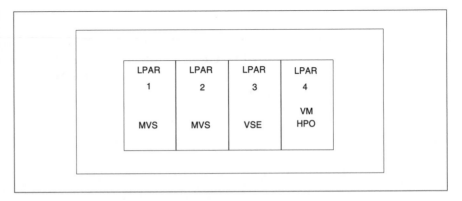

FIGURE 10.8
A Logical
View of LPAR

FIGURE 10.9
ESA/370

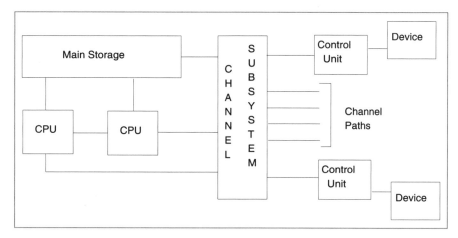

System/390 (S/390)

S/390, also known as Enterprise System/390, was announced September 1990. The announcement was broad in scope, encompassing a new processor line, channel subsystem, many software changes, and sweeping networking-related support. The hardware highlights include: S/390 enhancements, ES/9000 processors, Enterprise Systems Connection Architecture (ESCON), and networking support.

S/390 Enhancements

- **Storage Override Protection.** This provides reliability of program execution by keeping any different application from executing simultaneously within that same address space.
- **Program Event Recording (PER) Facility 2.** This provides a more focused method of event control when compared to PER 1.
- **Access List Control.** This permits different users different functionality within the same address space.

S/390 builds on the framework of ESA/370. Some documents refer to S/390 an ESA/390 simultaneously. IBM documentation uses ESA/390 to refer to those environments which include one or more of the following:

- ESCON
- Common cryptographic architecture
- An environment providing data spaces for VM.

ES/9000 Processors

Initially 18 processors were announced. These included both air- and water-cooled models. A view of a ES/9000 processor physically divided into two logical independent complexes is shown in Figure 10.10.

FIGURE 10.10
A Conceptual
View of a
Partitioned
ES/9000

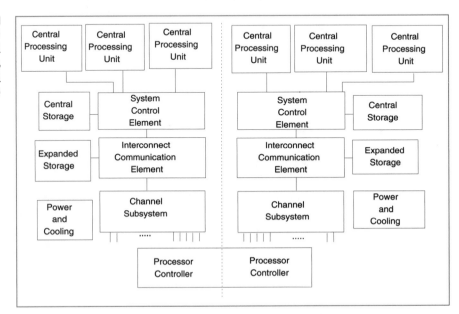

This is a typical example of the functional processors implemented into partitioned scenarios. Physically, the system is viewed as a single processor.

ESCON

IBM's greatest contribution to the S/390 announcement was the new fiber channel subsystem called, ESCON. Figure 10.11 depicts an example of a possible ESCON configuration.

Here two ESCON directors are shown. An ESCON director is the focal point for dynamic connectivity used in IBM's fiber channel environment. The director in Figure 10.11 is attached to two processors and control units with devices connecting to the director.

Fundamental highlights of ESCON include:

- Switched point-to-point connections
- Point-to-point connections
- ESCON cable distance support of 23 kilometers

- ESCON cable distance support with daisy-chained directors of 43 kilometers
- Data transfer rates up to 17 MB/sec
- 1,024 devices assignable to any addressable path
- Lighter cable weights
- Serial data transfer
- Photon transfer versus electron transfer as in parallel channels.

FIGURE 10.11
ESCON
Configuration

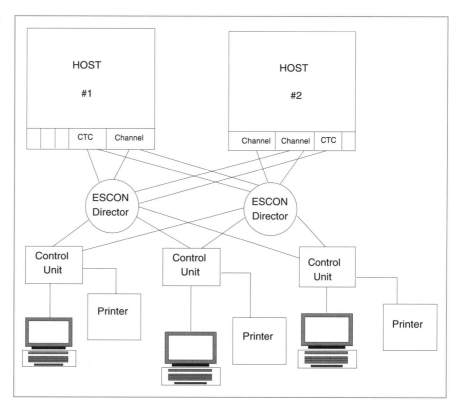

ESCON and parallel channels sum up the operational nature of transmission methods. Data transmission is achieved by moving either electrons or photons. Regardless of the physical implementation, moving anything in the computer, networking, or internetworking community is done in one of these ways. Remember the maxim "Matter is neither created or destroyed." I add to that statement: "...it is merely rearranged."

Networking Support

The S/390 announcement includes devices and support for networking technologies for other-than-native IBM networking solutions. A brief, but not exhaustive, list of these offerings and some of their features includes:

- VTAM Version 3 Release 4
  - T2.1 node multi-tail support
  - Dynamic NETID
  - FDDI support
  - ESCON channel support
  - T2.1 boundary function support
  - Dynamic I/O
  - Support for program selectivity of data encryption
- 3745 Enhancements
  - Buffer chaining channel adapter
  - 32-line capacity
  - Memory expansion
- 3174 Enhancements
  - X.21/X.25 switched autocall and autodisconnect
  - Systems management support with NetView
  - Multi-host Token Ring gateway support
- 3172 Enhancements
  - Model 002
  - Up to two ESCON connections
  - Up to two parallel channel connections
  - FDDI support
  - Remote CTC controller function
  - LAN gateway functionality
- NCP Version 5 Releases 3.1 and 4
  - Buffer chaining channel adapter support
  - Increased network management with token ring
  - Dynamic NETID
  - Reduced storage requirements for explicit routes
  - Additional options for T1 support
- 8209 Token Ring Attachment Module
  - Connection of two token ring networks into one logical ring
  - Source and destination filtering
  - Custom filter support.

Other software and hardware support was introduced with the S/390 announcement, but is too wide ranging to list here. For a detailed list of product offerings as part of this announcement, contact an IBM representative.

Hardware Components

Processors

IBM processors are grouped into what IBM calls series. There are different series based on different architectures. For example, the ES/9000 series is based upon ESA/390 or S/390 architecture. Processor series IBM has and has offered include: ES/9000, 3090, 4300, 303X, 308X, and 9370.

Processor series have models. For example, the announcement of the ES/9000 included 18 models. Some of these models were: 120, 130, 150, 170, 190, 210, 260, 320, 330, 340, 440, 480, 500, 580, 620, 720, 820, and 900.

Each of these models has different support levels in terms of processing capability and there are other areas of difference such as cooling method (water or air).

The processor series IBM has offered provide varying functionality. For example, some models in the 9370 series support direct Ethernet network attachment.

Some 308X series have model numbers that indicate a uniprocessor or dual-processor capabilities. In general the model number of a particular series indicates a significant amount about the processor.

Understanding this numbering scheme helps break the number barrier for those new to IBM equipment/environments.

Channels

The saying in IBM circles is that all data inbound to a processor must go through a channel to get to the processor. Channels, a channel subsystem, and channel paths are deeply rooted in the hardware architecture dictating how data are manipulated at the lowest layers in a system. The channels prior to ESCON used copper-stranded cables called *bus* and *tag* cables. These were weighty. The distance that parallel channels (those prior to ESCON) could operate is approximately

200 feet if devices were daisy-chained. A straight run of 400 feet might be obtained under ideal conditions. The bus cable contained signal lines used to transport data. Tag cables controlled data traffic on the bus.

Before the ESCON offering, IBM had parallel channels that moved data in parallel from source to destination point. Three type of channels comprised this offering, but the selector channel support was discontinued in the 1970s. To understand these three channels consider the following:

Selector Channel

The selector channel has one subchannel. However, multiple devices such as tape and disk devices can be connected to this subchannel. Characteristics of this type of channel include:

- It is intended for high speed devices only
- It can accommodate only one data transfer at a time
- Once a logical connection is established between a device and the channel, no interruptions occur for the duration of the data transfer.

Selector channels such as these are outdated and were primarily used in the 1960s and to a reduced degree in the early 1970s. Figure 10.12 shows a selector channel and devices.

Byte Multiplexor Channels

This type of channel is different from selector a channel; the following characterize this type channel:

- It is intended for low-speed devices
- One channel can address up to 256 subchannels
- The subchannels operate in burst mode; once a logical connection is established between a device and the channel the data is pushed to the channel. After release, the next data transfer can occur. This permits interleaving of data at a byte level. Since these channels are designed to operate with slow-speed devices, this operation works quite well, exploiting bandwidth and utilizing available resources.

The follow-up to the selector channel was two other channels that operated differently. Figure 10.13 shows the byte multiplexor channel.

FIGURE 10.12
Selector Channel

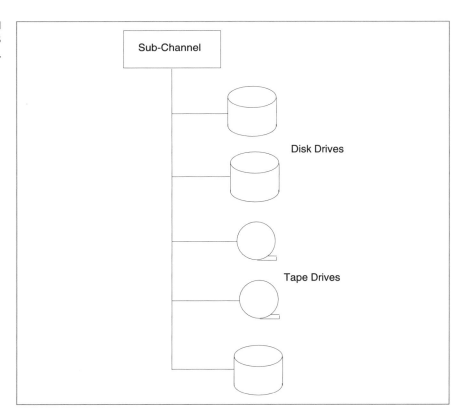

FIGURE 10.13
A View of a
Multiplexer
Channel,
Subchannels,
and Devices

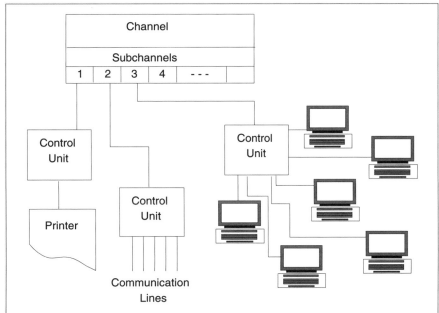

Block Multiplexor Channel

This type of channel was introduced with the S/370 hardware architecture and had the ability to record the address, byte count, status, and control information for an I/O operation. As a result this type of channel could perform a disconnect from a device if no data was being transferred. This meant that high speed devices could have operations that overlapped. In this sense a greater utilization of resources was realized. Figure 10.14 depicts the block multiplexor channel, its subchannels, and a view of how data is interleaved as it is passed to the channel.

FIGURE 10.14
Data Flow
Through a
Block Multiplexer
Channel

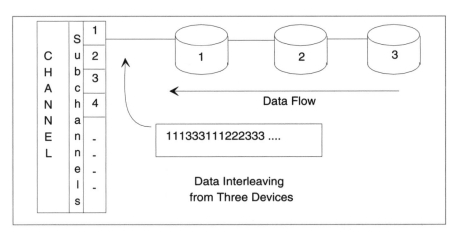

Another type of channel now supported by IBM is the ESCON channel. This is a fiber optic data path. It has channel protocols different from those of the three aforementioned channels. ESCON is referred to as a serial channel, the earlier channels have been renamed parallel channels.

ESCON channels support greater physical cable length because photons are moved, not electrons; no voltage drop is realized. ESCON channels also support dynamic connectivity with the use of ESCON directors. ESCON extenders can be used to lengthen the distance these cables can operate to approximately 43 kilometers. Figure 10.15 is an example of a processor with ESCON channels and a processor in the same complex with parallel channels.

FIGURE 10.15
Serial and
Parallel Channels

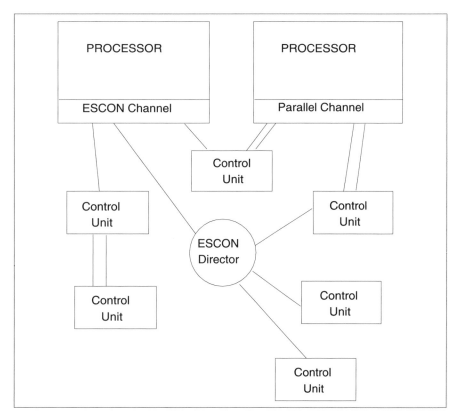

Communication Controller

This device is also known as a Front End Processor (FEP). It is where the Network Control Program (NCP) is located. The communication controller are available in different sizes and models; this dictates the abilities and limitations of the controllers. Communication controllers perform multiple tasks, including:

- Routing
- Flow control
- Being the point where communication lines connect
- Being the location where some specialized programs operate allowing non-SNA equipment to access an SNA network.

A diagram of a processor, channels, and a communications controller appears as Figure 10.16.

FIGURE 10.16
Processors,
Channels, and
Communication
Controller

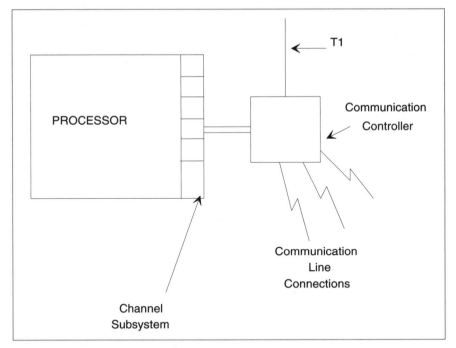

This is one example of how a communication controller is implemented. Later in this chapter the implementation of this device is shown in different scenarios.

Cluster Controller

A cluster controller is the forerunner of the establishment controller explained next. In SNA environments, cluster controllers are used to attach terminals and printers. Different models of cluster controllers exist. A cluster controller model dictates how many devices can be attached to the controller. In SNA drawings where a cluster controller is used it is represented as in Figure 10.17.

FIGURE 10.17
Cluster Controller

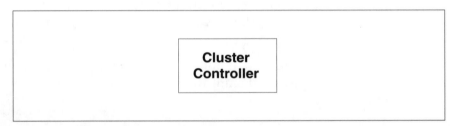

The cluster controller is known in SNA environments a 3274 control unit; the 3274 control unit family has different models, including: 1A, 21A, 31, and 41.

Depending upon the model, local or remote modes of operation are possible.

Beyond the three methods of identification, the operational method of a particular control unit can be designated in several ways:

- An **A** indicator means the control unit is functioning as a channel attached local device.
- The **B** and **D** designators mean the control units are channel-attached using the processor channel program.
- The **C** designator indicates the control unit is operating as a remote unit with SDLC or BSC data-link layer protocols.

The 3274 is still being used today even when the 3174 exists as the replacement for it. Both work well together. Depending upon the need, a 3274 may be as credible as a 3174.

Establishment Controller

This device succeeds the cluster controller. It provides services offered by the cluster controller as well as those used in networking. The establishment controller appears as in Figure 10.18.

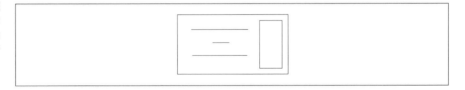

FIGURE 10.18
Establishment
Controller

The establishment controller has numerous models; certain models are capable of performing functions others cannot. A list of these controller models includes:

1L 13R 61R	3R 22L	12L 51R
1R 21L 62R	11L 22R	12R 52R
2R 21R 63R.	11R 23R	

Characteristics and functions the establishment controller offers include:

- Token ring support
- Token ring gateway support
- Muŧi-host support via concurrent communication adapter and the single-link multi-host support
- ISDN support
- PU2.0 support
- PU2.1 support
- APPN support
- Control Unit Terminal (CUT) support
- Distributed Function Terminal (DFT) support
- SDLC support
- X.21 and X.25 support
- Parallel channel support
- ESCON support
- BSC support
- 3270 data stream support
- Printer support
- Response time monitor support
- Common Management Information Protocol (CMIP) support
- Generic alert support
- T2.1 channel command support.

The APPN support offered by the establishment controller is a considerable enhancement of the 3274 cluster controllers, which did not have this support. This device covers a broader range of support than did its predecessor and is positioned to fit into either SNA, APPN networks or both.

Interconnect Controller

This succeeded the cluster controller. It provides services of the cluster controller as well as those used in networking (Figure 10.19).

The interconnect controller is known numerically as the 3172. Three models have been introduced: 001, 002, and 003.

The latter model's forte is its versatility. The model 003 supports the TCP/IP offload function offered by IBM. This means a customer can purchase TCP/IP to run as a VTAM application but select the applications/functions desired and offload TCP, UDP, and IP to the 3172 model 003. In turn only the desired portion of TCP/IP resides as an active application under VTAM. The result is conservation of resources from a processor standpoint.

FIGURE 10.19
Interconnect
Controller

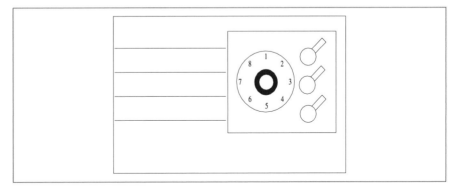

The offload function of TCP/IP to the model 003 means that protocol conversion of TCP and/or UDP is performed on the 3172, not the processor. This also means that IP performs routing functions on the 3172. The benefit is no work on the processor for this function.

The 3172 model 003 communicates effectively with a processor via what IBM calls "Common Link Access to Workstation" protocol. The 3172 003 can achieve this because it implements a claw driver to do so. The benefit to this is the use of the subchannel with regard to data rate transfer.

Other benefits of the 3172 model 003 include its support for data-link layer protocols. This model support: FDDI, Ethernet Version 2, 802.3, Token ring, and Channel protocol (to the processor).

Another powerful aspect of the 3172 is its ability to support not only NetView, but also Simple Network Management Protocol (SNMP). It also provides a system log facility via the Interconnect Control Program (ICP) which can be used for debugging if necessary.

Since its announcement, the 3172 has undergone multiple changes. Some functions available now did not exist at the time of its inception. Other functions have been discontinued due to market conditions.

Direct Access Storage Device (DASD)

This is IBM's term for a disk drive. Significant here are the five delineable DASD offerings. Many IBM DASD units are still working in companies and corporations around the world. For information's sake the focus here is on these different offerings and their fundamental significance.

The first DASD devices (platters) were characterized by removable media. A platter is that piece of the drive where data are stored.

The second DASD devices to appear had more intelligence than their predecessors; they had removable platters, but a great improvement was the increased storage capacity of some models in these offerings.

Then came the DASD offering which brought significant improvement of storage in terms of density and also better diagnostic capabilities. Significant increased performance was also achieved.

The fourth category of DASD offerings from IBM dominated the 1980s. Reliability, performance, speed, and flexibility in regard to implementation characterized this category.

Many in the technical community, including IBM, consider the fifth category of IBM DASD the architectural foundation of the '90s and into the 21st century. The strength of this category includes a robust number of models to select from. Software used in processors supporting the IBM storage hierarchy has also caught up significantly. Leveraging advanced hardware along with supporting software brings synergy to the storage subsystem offered in this current category.

Figure 10.20 depicts how reference to DASD is made in SNA generally. Most references are not to a specific DASD model, unless an in-depth discussion is required.

FIGURE 10.20
Direct Access
Storage Device

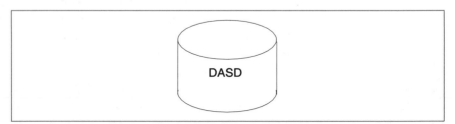

Tape Devices

IBM has two basic groups of tape devices. The fundamental difference between them is that one is reel-based and the other uses cartridges. In many IBM shops tape is a method of backup for data that may be archived. Figure 10.21 shows the general symbols used when reference is made to a disk drive.

FIGURE 10.21
Tape Drive

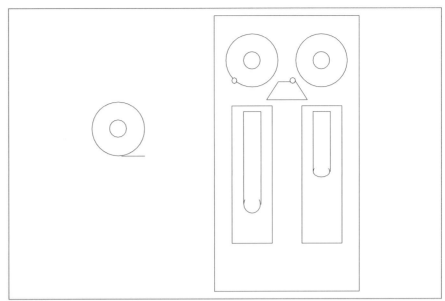

Printers

IBM has different types of printers; these can be categorized by speed and type of technology. Figure 10.22 shows a generic example of a printer. Reference to a printer in this chapter are to this representation. IBM's documentation generally uses this representation for printers. In most cases this symbol suffices to convey the information being discussed.

FIGURE 10.22
Printer

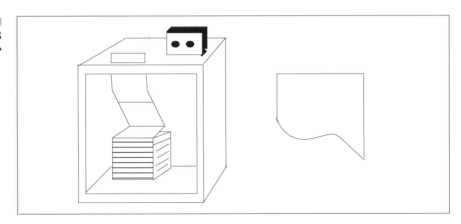

Terminals

Different types of terminals are used in SNA , but most use 3270 data stream. This will be discussed in more detail, but it is important here to understand the general nature of IBM terminals used in SNA.

Terminals are categorized as those which do not support graphics and those which do support graphics.

Another way of expressing differing terminal characteristics is by how many columns and rows they support. A 3278 terminal family exists; four types of 3278 terminals constitute this family, model 2, model 3, model 4, and model 5.

Another terminal type is a 3179G which supports graphic applications. A terminal type 3279 also exists; a later version of the 3278 type.

More will be presented about terminals when issues of SNA, including the type of data stream they support, are discussed later in this chapter. References in this book to a 3270 type terminal appear as in Figure 10.23.

FIGURE 10.23
Terminal

IBM Operating Systems

There are other IBM operating systems that function in the hardware architectural environments explained previously. Some have been excluded purposely because the ones presented here are dominant in market share and presence in the SNA networking environment. The three we are concerned with are: multiple virtual storage, virtual machine, and virtual storage extended.

Each of these is at different versions and releases. They are like the underlying hardware architecture upon which they operate. They have architectural characteristics. Each operating system is presented, with basic characteristics, functions, and other pertinent information.

After the operating systems have been explained, software subsystems that operate under their control will be presented. These software subsystems have considerable market share, but others exist;

the intent is not to present them all but rather to focus upon dominant ones. This section, like the one before, provides the basics for understanding SNA-centered terminology and concepts.

Multiple Virtual Storage (MVS)

MVS has its roots in the first versions of OS/360, designed in the early 1960s. It is generally considered a production-oriented operating system. From a historical viewpoint, the operating system has evolved through many versions and releases, but for our purposes, MVS's immediate predecessor was multiprogramming with a variable number of tasks (OS/MVT). Figure 10.24 illustrates this.

FIGURE 10.24
Conceptual View
of MVS Processor

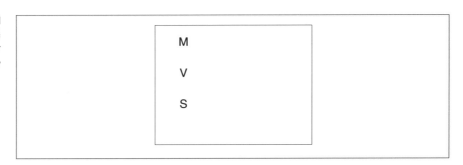

Much has been written about MVS, by IBM and authors not affiliated with the IBM. The intent of this section is to focus on the highlights of MVS. Not all of its features and functions are presented, just those which have made significant impact through the versions and releases of MVS thus far.

MVS operated with S/370 hardware architecture and followed two earlier versions of operating systems known as OS/VS1 and OS/VS2. MVS could address up to 16 MB of virtual storage. It utilized program areas which were names referring to address spaces. MVS is an identifiable amount of memory addresses a program can use. Tied in was the concept of an address-space identifier. Common data areas provided capabilities for the user: program messaging, communication with the operating supervisor, and operating system interaction with the program. I/O buffers were also used to pass data from a telecommunication subsystem to an address space where that data had to be moved for operations to be performed.

A major change for MVS in 1981 had to do with addressability. MVS/XA broke the 16-MB boundary; virtual storage addressability was supported up to 2 GB.

MVS/XA also provided each user with the idea of unique address space and capable of distinguishing between programs and user data in each address space. Cross-memory services allowed a user to access other address spaces as necessary.

The concept of task management meant MVS/XA divided jobs into smaller pieces and processed each "task" as efficiently as possible. Control of this process lay with the supervisor.

MVS/XA was unique in supporting both 24- and 31-bit addressing. Along with MVS/XA came changes in I/O facilities, especially relating to the I/O subsystem, which handled I/O operations independently of the processor.

First, the channel, not the operating system, handled channel-path selection. Then, dynamic reconnection was added to the I/O portion to support dynamic path selection. The number of supported devices increased to 4,096; but a contingent factor was dependence on the I/O configuration program. Support for up to 256 channel paths with eight paths per device also existed under MVS/XA.

MVS/XA brought with it three types of tracing: address space, branch, and explicit software.

The Generalized Trace Facility (GTF) was changed to support 31-bit addressing. Parallel to this was the improved dump facility.

MVS/XA controlled work or managed a resource by identifying a control block. Three types are associated with MVS/XA:

- **Resource.** Represented a DASD or processor, for example
- **System.** Contained system-wide information
- **Task.** Represented one unit of work.

The System Resource Manager (SRM) was used in MVS/XA to make decisions concerning where an address space should remain; in real storage or DASD. The SRM is the primary way "resources" are managed in an MVS/XA environment.

In 1988, MVS/ESA was introduced. Its virtual storage addressability was 16 terabytes. New features and functions made this software the most vigorous architecture to date.

With MVS/ESA data spaces are available that contains data only, no programs. Since data spaces are available, they must be managed. A data-space manager keeps track of those in use in the system and manages them accordingly. A data space may be assigned to one program only or shared. This new type of space available further extends the abilities of virtual storage.

Along with data space is the concept of a hyperspace, data in an address space that has a special classification. Data are processed in an address space, but typically use expanded storage or migrate to auxiliary storage.

An access list also part of MVS/ESA is responsible for determining which data spaces a program is authorized to use. This facility is also exploited by hardware for use with the segment-table descriptor.

The linkage stack is a facility used to retain information about the state of a program during execution when call is given to another program.

The virtual lookaside facility (VLF) can be characterized as curbing time for Partitioned Data Set (PDS) searches and reads. It can also perform multiple reads against the same object. VLF operates in its own address space and assigns names to objects it manages. The naming convention uses three levels: class, major, and minor. This notion of object naming is a way for the VLF to increase retrieval.

Advanced Program-to-Program Communication (APPC) support under MVS enables peer connectivity outside the MVS environment; for example in: AIX for the RISC/6000, S/38, OS/400, VM/ESA, VSE, and OS/2. APPC under MVS by APPC/MVS applications, Time Sharing Option/Extension (TSO/E) users, the Information Management System and even APPC batch jobs. Figure 10.25 shows how this appears conceptually.

FIGURE 10.25
Conceptual View
of APPC/MVS

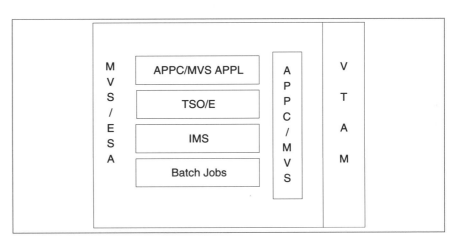

Other functions in MVS/ESA for examination include: Sysplex, the Cross System Coupling Facility (XCF), the Automatic Reconfiguration Facility (ARF), and Hardware Configuration Definition (HCD).

Sysplex is the concept of bringing together one or more MVS systems via hardware and software services. In this scenario they are treated as a single complex and initialized as such. To achieve this Sysplex concept an external clock, the Susplex Timer, must be used to synchronize the systems brought together. The timer's purpose is to synchronize the time across the entire central processing complex.

XCF is software providing control of members and groups, intercommunication among members, and monitoring of members. Put another way, it provides the services necessary for programs in a multisystem environment to communicate successfully.

ARF can be used in a single or multiprocessor configuration environment. In either case it serves to redistribute a workload in the event of failure without operator intervention.

HCD permits simultaneous communication between the channel subsystem and I/O definitions. Prior to MVS version 4 this was a two-step function: first the I/O subsystem was defined via the I/O Control Program (IOCP), then, software was defined by the MVS Control Program (MVSCP). With HCD the two are combined.

Other functions of MVS exist, but are too many to list here. For further information about MVS, contact an IBM representative.

Virtual Machine (VM)

VM/ESA combines the VM/System Product (VM/SP), VM/SP High Performance Option (VM/SP HPO), and VM/SP XA. Some VM/ESA facilities include:

- **APPC/VM VTAM Support (AVS).** This is a facility of VM/ESA that converts APPC/VM into APPC/VTAM protocol for communication throughout an SNA network.
- **Group Control System (GCS).** This facility manages subsystems that permit VM/ESA to interact within an SNA environment.
- **Interactive Problem Control System (IPCS).** This component of VM/ESA provides an operator with on-line capability for problem diagnosis and management.
- **Transparent Services Access Facility (TSAF).** This is a component of VM/ESA that permits communication between programs by name specification instead of user or node ID.

The forte of VM/ESA is its ability to run multiple operating systems on the same processor, a concept is known as Multiple Preferred Guest (MPG). Figure 10.26 demonstrates MPG.

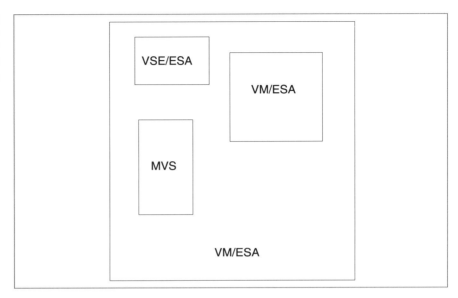

The idea behind the concept of MPG is that totally different operating systems can be executing simultaneously and one MPG fails but does not cause any other MPG to fail.

This type of environment can be advantageous if a production operating system such as MVS/ESA is needed and a development oriented operating system like VM/ESA is also needed. Both of these can execute under the control of a VM/ESA operating system.

VM has its roots in the 1970s as does MVS. Technically, VM has roots in 1965 with what is known as Control Program 40 (CP-40). By the late 1960s evolution of the Control Program was shaping up to what would become known as VM/370. VM/370 was made available in 1972.

A closer view of VM/ESA reveals four components that are the focus of the remainder of this section: Control Program (CP), Conversational Monitoring System (CMS), Group Control System (GCS), and Inter-User Communication Vehicle (IUCV).

The CP is used to manage the actual hardware. It communicates with resources such as the real processor, I/O subsystem, and storage and is responsible for management of these resources. It is the CP that utilizes the physical resources to create the logical (virtual machines).

CP exploits the hardware architecture mentioned previously. In the case of S/390 architecture, many of the resources available with the MVS operating system are available through the platform where CP is in control.

CP has a set of commands that permits the manipulation of physical and logical resources. Some of the commands can be used immediately after logon to perform system management functions.

There are various aspects of CP we should consider. First, CP is software transferred to real storage when the system is booted. One way CP works is by defining internal objects by a "control block". An example of an important control block is the VM Definition Block (VMDBK). This represents a logged-on virtual machine; it is created by the CP when a user logs onto VM.

In VM a CP trace table exists that maintains any events related to problems, system crashes, or the like.

The CP knows the real I/O configuration and correlates real I/O device capabilities to virtual devices. CP with VM/ESA architecture also supports ESCON I/O architecture.

The Conversational Monitoring System (CMS) is another part of VM/ESA. This component operates with the CP but is used as a two-way communication processor between users. IBM has a large manual of valid CMS commands that can be used to perform a number of functions. CMS is an operating system for users of VM.

CMS communication can occur between users and CMS. Users can enter commands to CMS and CMS can issue messages to users. CMS permits a number of user functions, including:

- Communication with other users
- User creation, testing, and debugging of programs
- Work flow control in a VM/ESA system
- File sharing.

The concept of file sharing under CMS is achieved via the Shared File System (SFS) facility, an extension of CMS to provide file management capabilities. According to IBM's *CMS Shared File System Primer* (document number GG24-3709), the features of SFS include:

- A hierarchical file system
- Files can be stored in pools
- User space can be assigned to a spool file
- A file can be located in more than one directory
- Files and directories can be shared with users on other systems
- File and directory locks ensure data integrity when multiple users are involved with the same file and/or directory
- Users can have concurrent access to files and directories
- Files in a file space are stored in a directory.

CMS also has a facility known as XEDIT, a full screen editor that permits users to create, edit, and manipulate files. It runs under the control of CMS. Functions available under XEDIT include:

- CMS file creation
- File editing
- Joining existing files
- Searches in files for specific data
- Creation of XEDIT macros
- A sort function performed on data in a file
- Providing help for users.

The Group Control System (GCS) is a VM component shipped by IBM with each VM/ESA system. It manages subsystems that permit interoperation with IBM's SNA. GCS is a supervisor. IBM's VTAM runs under a GCS group which in turn has a supervisor. Communication between programs in a VM/ESA machine or complex and devices outside it in an SNA network use VTAM.

The Inter-User Communication Vehicle (IUCV) facilitates communication between programs running in two different virtual machines. It is also aided by CMS. The IUCV facilitates the communication between a virtual machine and a CP service. Examples of its functions include:

- Logging errors
- Communication with the system console
- Performing message system service functions
- Other services such as a SPOOL system service.

Figure 10.27 is a conceptual view of two IUCV communication functions.

Much more could be said about the VM environment, but for our purposes this information suffices. IBM has exhaustive documentation about VM and its components; contact IBM for further information.

Virtual Storage Extended (VSE)

VSE/ESA is another of IBM's systems that operate on some S/370 architectures and the ESA/390 architecture. Its strength is in batch processing capabilities. Also, according to IBM documentation, it can support high transaction volumes. VSE/ESA is pregenerated; a generation is not required; IBM ships object code. This is in contrast with MVS/ESA and VM/ESA which must be generated at installation time for site-specific customization. Because VSE/ESA comes this way much planning can be foregone.

FIGURE 10.27
IUCV
Communications

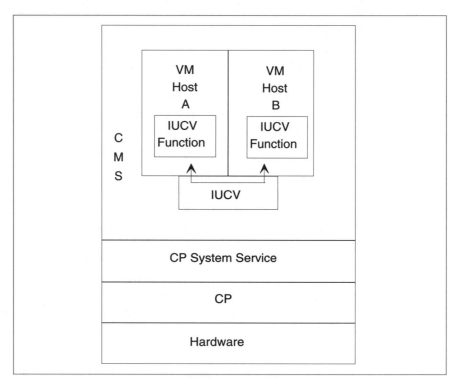

Before examining functionality of VSE/ESA consider its lineage according to IBM's *VSE/ESA Version 1.3 An Introduction Presentation Foil Master* (document number GG24-4008).

DATE	OFFERING
1965	DOS
1972	DOS/Virtual Storage (DOS/VS)
1979	DOS/Virtual Storage Extended (DOS/VSE)
1985	VSE/System Product (VSE/SP) Version 2
1989	VSE/SP Version 4
1990	VSE/ESA Version 1.1
1991	VSE/ESA Version 1.2
1993	VSE/ESA Version 1.3

VSE/ESA can operate in multiple environments, including:

- As the sole operating system on a processor; as a result both local and remote operations can be realized
- Under an LPAR
- As a standalone system; this means it can be run without human intervention, in some cases functioning as a node within a network
- Under VM as a preferred guest.

Major enhancements and features of VSE/ESA include inherent features/functions with VSE/ESA, as well as optional facilities. It is important to understand the breadth of change that VSE has undergone with the advent of its support in ESA. The list is not exhaustive, but the core aspects of this release are presented. VSE/ESA has:

- 31-bit virtual addressing
- Support for data spaces
- Support for more I/O devices
- ESCON support
- ESCON director support
- VTAM version 3 release 4 features for VSE/ESA
- National language support including: Spanish, German, and Japanese
- Addressability up to 2 GB of real storage
- Addressability up to 2 GB of virtual storage
- VSE/ESA POWER operating in a private address space
- Support for the 3172 via VTAM 3.4
- ES/9000 processor support
- ESCON C-T-C adapter support
- Support for virtual disks in storage
- Support for extended functions of the 3990 DASD
- NetView for VES/ESA
- Support for SQL/DS, making a VSE/ESA capable of functioning with Distributed Relational Database Architecture (DRDA) as a server
- 3174 ESCON connectivity.

So many enhancements have made the VSE/ESA operating system more popular in the past few years. Consideration of enhancements to VSE should lead to discussion of its system components. Components to be discussed sequentially are: Librarian, ICCF, POWER, and VSAM.

Librarian

The Librarian is a utility program used to manipulate libraries. It aids in their creation, maintenance, and use. With VSE/ESA the following are included to the Librarian:

- Copy and compare command
- Move command
- LISTD command— a list including the date
- Search command
- Lock and Unlock command to provide data integrity to single library members who may be in the process of being updated
- Backup command supporting the backup of an individual member.

Libraries have one or more sublibraries which in turn consist of members. These members are where data, programs, source code, and other "data" exists in a VSE/ESA system.

Two types of libraries exist in VSE/ESA: System and ICCF. System library's sublibraries can include:

- **Source.** This is source code to be processed.
- **Object.** These modules are generated by the output of a language translator and used for input by a linkage editor.
- **Dump.** If an abnormal termination results, the contents will be sent to this type of member in a sublibrary.
- **Procedure.** This is a set of procedures. It may be a set of job control statements.
- **Phase.** This type of member has a program or sections of a program stored in it; they are ready to run.

Other system-oriented libraries exist; if further information is needed, acquire the appropriate IBM VSE/ESA manual. A list of VSE/ESA documentation can be obtained through any IBM representative.

VSE/Interactive Computing and Control Facility (VSE/ICCF) uses libraries. A considerable number of these libraries exist, frequently-used ones include:

- **Public.** This type of library consists of data that may need to be accessed by a number of users system-wide.
- **Common.** This type of library contains data that all users have interest in.
- **Main.** This is the library attached to an individual who has been logged on.
- **Private.** This type of library contains data limited to one, or a few, users.

ICCF

The ICCF in a sense is the interface between a user and a VSE/ESA system. Technically, it is the subsystem where program development and system administration occurs. Through ICCF libraries, sub-libraries, and members can be created.

POWER

Priority Output Writers and Execution Processors and Input Readers (POWER) is the subsystem that provides networking support, batch job processing, and spooling functions.

Virtual Storage Access Method (VSAM)

This is the access method by which data, programs and the like, are stored, a method of data management. Its supported data organization includes:

- Entry sequenced files (similar to a sequential file)
- Key sequenced data sets (similar to an indexed file)
- Relative record data sets (similar to direct access files)
- Variable length relative record data sets.

VSE/ESA has been put on equal ground with MVS/ESA and VM/ESA. Discussion of these operating systems has tried to convey some of their strengths. The enhancements necessary to place VSE/ESA on the same level as MVS and VM took time. Now IBM has three refined and tested operating systems to meet a wide variety of customer needs.

IBM Software Offerings

IBM has many software subsystems that operate with the previously presented operating systems. This section focuses on:

- VTAM
- Job Entry Subsystem (JES2)
- Network Control Program (NCP)
- NetView
- Time Sharing Option (TSO)
- Customer Information Control System (CICS)
- DATABASE/2 (DB2)

- Remote Spooling Communication System (RSCS)
- Local Area Network Resource Extension Services (LANRES).

Virtual Telecommunication Access Method (VTAM)

VTAM is a software subsystem that operates under the previously described operating systems. It is a critical component in traditional SNA and functions in new ways with IBM's APPN. Practically every application that runs in an MVS host runs as a VTAM application. Applications must be defined to VTAM in such a way that they can be used. The same holds true for hardware and components outside the processor. Figure 16.28 provides a conceptual view of VTAM with peripherals attached.

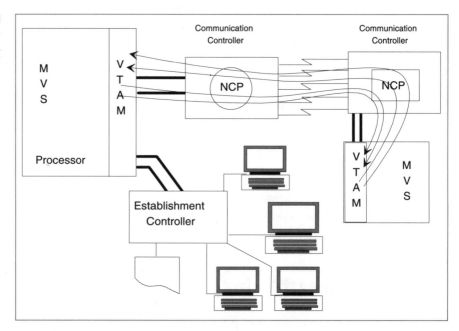

FIGURE 10.28
Conceptual
View of VTAM

One of VTAM's major roles in traditional SNA is aiding in session establishment. When a terminal user requests use of a software subsystem the request is first interpreted by VTAM then passed to the appropriate subsystem.

VTAM is also the centralized point for network component activation and deactivation. VTAM's component known as the System Services Control Point (SSCP) plays a vital role in the area of network management. This role should not be confused with the software that enables network management to be realized; they work together. The SSCP network management role has to do with communicating with hardware and other components throughout the network.

VTAM must know (have defined) software and hardware that operate within an SNA network. VTAM components that must be defined for software and hardware to operate include:

- Application(s)
- Device(s)
- Session operating parameters
- Logon menu (if utilized)
- Communication controller and attached devices.

Applications must be defined to VTAM in order to work. If application Z is loaded into a system, certain parameters about the application must be defined. Different applications have requirements for definition. Consult the IBM VTAM Resource Definition Manuals. Table 10.1 shows a basic example of an application definition.

Table 10.1 shows the following in order from left to right.

TABLE 10.1
Examples of an Application Definition

The name of the application	MYAPP
The VBUILD statement	TYPE=APPL
The name of the application	MYAPP
Definition statement	APPL
Operands	ACBNAME
	AUTH
	DLGMODE
	EAS
	MODETAB
	SSCPFM
	USSTAB

Table 10.1 is an example of how each application that operates under VTAM needs to be defined. Not all the parameters will be the same. The application and VTAM requirements will dictate how the application should be defined, as will the site requirements.

Devices must be defined to VTAM as well. A number of factors dictate how a device is defined, including how the device is physically attached, the data link protocol used, its role in the SNA environment (according to SNA definitions), and others as well. Table 10.2 is an example of a 3174 establishment controller defined to VTAM.

TABLE 10.2
Establishment
Controller
Definitions

MY3174	VBUILD	TYPE=LOCAL
MY3174	PU	CUADDR=
		DLOGMODE=
		DISCNT=
		ISTATUS=
		MAXBFRV=
		PUTYPE=
		USSTAB=
YOUR327401	LU	LOCADDR=
YOUR317406	LU	LOCADDR=

In Table 10.2 the definition of the device can be divided into three parts. VTAM requires a VBUILD statement, Physical Unit (PU) statement, and Logical Unit (LU) statements for those LUs to be used. More information will be provided about the PUs and LUs below.

The statements and parameters in this example are typical. Three factors determine how a device should be defined to VTAM: the architectural capability of the device, how VTAM dictates it must be defined, and how the device is used in a given site.

Session operating parameters must be customized. If a terminal user wants to work with an application, the terminal parameters must be programmed. The location for these session parameters is known as the logon mode table (LOGMODE table).

The LOGMODE table consists of numerous entries, each of which defines the session parameters for a particular type of session. More on sessions can be found below, but this shows how a LOGMODE table appears.

```
*************************************************************
*    THIS IS THE LOGMODE TABLE FOR MY3174         *
*************************************************************
*    LOGMODE TABLE ENTRY FOR 3278-M2 EMULATION      *
*************************************************************
EDMODE     MODETAB
EDMODE2    MODEENT    LOGMODE=EDM2,
                      FMPROF=X'03',
                      TSPROF=X'03',
                      PRIPROT=X'B1',
                      SECPROT=X'90',
```

```
                            COMPROT=X'3080',
                            RUSIZES=X'F8F8',
                            PSERVIC=X'0280000000000000000000200'
      ***************************************************************
      *    LOGMODE TABLE ENTRY FOR 3278-M3 EMULATION      *
      ***************************************************************
      EDMODE3    MODEENT    LOGMODE=EDM3,
                            FMPROF=X'03',
                            TSPROF=X'03',
                            PRIPROT=X'B1',
                            SECPROT=X'90',
                            COMPROT=X'3080',
                            RUSIZES=X'F8F8',
                            PSERVIC=X'0280000000000185020507F00'


      ***************************************************************
             LOGMODE TABLE ENTRY FOR 3278-M4 EMULATION      *
      ***************************************************************
      EDMODE4    MODEENT    LOGMODE=EDM4,
                            FMPROF=X'03',
                            TSPROF=X'03',
                            PRIPROT=X'B1',
                            SECPROT=X'90',
                            COMPROT=X'3080',
                            RUSIZES=X'F8F8',
                            PSERVIC=X'0280000000000185028507F00'
      ***************************************************************
             LOGMODE TABLE ENTRY FOR 3278-M5 EMULATION      *
      ***************************************************************
      EDMODE5    MODEENT    LOGMODE=EDM5,
                            FMPROF=X'03',
                            TSPROF=X'03',
                            PRIPROT=X'B1',
                            SECPROT=X'90',
                            COMPROT=X'3080',
                            RUSIZES=X'F8F8',
                            PSERVIC=X'0280000000000185018847F00'
      ***************************************************************
      EDMODE     MODEEND                        *
      ***************************************************************
```

The logon menu, if utilized, is what users see upon viewing a terminal under the control of VTAM. This logon menu is formally called the unformatted system services (USS) table. This is an example of a USS table.

```
******************* TOP OF DATA *******************************
*********** USSTAB TITLE 'ETUSS TABLE' *********************
ETUSS         USSTAB
LOGON         USSCMD     CMD=LOGON,FORMAT=PL1
              USSPARM    PARM=APPLID
              USSPARM    PARM=LOGMODE
              USSPARM    PARM=DATA
TSO           USSCMD     CMD=TSO,REP=LOGON,FORMAT=PL1
```

```
                   USSPARM    PARM=APPLID,DEFAULT=A01TSO
                   USSPARM    PARM=LOGMODE
                   USSPARM    PARM=DATA
CICS               USSCMD     CMD=CICS,REP=LOGON,FORMAT=PL1
                   USSPARM    PARM=APPLID,DEFAULT=DETTCCICS\
                   USSPARM    PARM=LOGMODE
                   USSPARM    PARM=DATA
JES2               USSCMD     CMD=JES2,REP=LOGON,FORMAT=PL1
                   USSPARM    PARM=APPLID,DEFAULT=JES2
                   USSPARM    PARM=LOGMODE
                   USSPARM    PARM=DATA
USSMSGS
USSMSG MSG=0,TEXT='USSMSG0: @@LUNAME LOGON/LOGOFF IN PROGRESS'
USSMSG MSG=1,TEXT='USSMSG1: @@LUNAME INVALID COMMAND SYNTAX'
USSMSG MSG=2,TEXT='USSMSG2: @@LUNAME % COMMAND UNRECOGNIZED'
USSMSG MSG=3,TEXT='USSMSG3: @@LUNAME % PARAMETER UNRECOGNIZED'
USSMSG MSG=4,TEXT='USSMSG4: @@LUNAME % PARAMETER INVALID'
USSMSG MSG=5,TEXT='USSMSG5: @@LUNAME UNSUPPORTED FUNCTION'
USSMSG MSG=6,TEXT='USSMSG6: @@LUNAME SEQUENCE ERROR'
USSMSG MSG=7,TEXT='USSMSG7: @@LUNAME SESSION NOT BOUND'
USSMSG MSG=8,TEXT='USSMSG8: @@LUNAME INSUFFICIENT STORAGE'
USSMSG MSG=9,TEXT='USSMSG9: @@LUNAME MAGNETIC CARD DATA ERROR'
USSMSG MSG=10,BUFFER=MSG10
USSMSG MSG=11,TEXT='USSMSG11: @@LUNAME SESSION ENDED'
USSMSG MSG=12,TEXT='USSMSG12: @@LUNAME REQ PARAMETER OMITTED'
USSMSG MSG=13,TEXT='USSMSG13: @@LUNAME IBMECHO %'
USSMSG MSG=14,TEXT='USSMSG14: @@LUNAME USS MESSAGE % NOT DEFINED'
MSGBUFF
MSG10  DC (MSG10E-MSG10-2)     DC   C'     ',X'15'  DC   DC   C'    DC
DC     C' USING THE CORRECT    ',X'15'  DC        DC   C'   '    DC
DC     C' VTAM SYNTAX          ',X'15'  DC        DC   C'   '    DC
DC     C' THE MENU OF          ',X'15'  DC        DC   C'   '    DC
DC     C' CHOICE CAN           ',X'15'  DC        DC   C'   '    DC
DC     C' BE DISPLAYED         ',X'15'  DC        DC   C'   '    DC
DC     C'                         '     DC
DC     C' -------------------   ''X'15'  DC
DC     C' -------------------   ',X'15'  DC
DC     C' YOU CAN CREATE YOUR OWN ',X'15'  DC     DC   C'   '    DC
DC     C' MENU                 ',X'15'  DC        DC   C'   '    DC
DC     C' SO USERS LOGON       ',X'15'  DC        DC   C'   '    DC
DC     C' BY APPLICATION NAME  ',X'15'  DC
DC     C'                      '        DC
DC     C' SUCH AS              ',X'15'  DC
DC     C'-------------------   '        DC
DC     C' TSO                  ',X'15'  DC        DC   C'   '    DC
DC     C' CICS                 ',X'15'  DC        DC   C'   '    DC
DC     C' JES2                 ',X'15'  DC        DC   C'   '    DC
DC     C'                      '        DC
DC     C' -------------------  ',X'15'  DC
DC     C' -------------------  ',X'15'  DC
DC     C'                      '        DC
DC     C'                      ',X'15'  DC
END    USSEND
*************** BOTTOM OF DATA ***************************
```

The USS table shown here can be divided into three parts. Its arrangement is based on IBM's VTAM Resource Definition manual. Some flexibility exists, but generally these three parts are present.

First, the name of the application a user wants to access is listed and beside it, parameters required to pass the request to that application. VTAM has 15 messages which constitute the second part. These messages may get generated if certain conditions exist. Third, the contents of what is displayed on the menu must be coded. As long as the table is created and does not violate any VTAM regulations, much flexibility exists.

A communication controller (also called a Front End Processor FEP) has special definitions to VTAM because it has a software program known as the Network Control Program (NCP) operating within it. Because this is so, knowing what is directly and indirectly attached to the FEP is required.

Creating a NCP is site-dependent as with VTAM. Restrictions do apply on how the NCP can be generated. The term generate is often used in the shortened form GEN. Figure 10.29 shows the location of an NCP with reference to other components in the network.

FIGURE 10.29
NCP Location

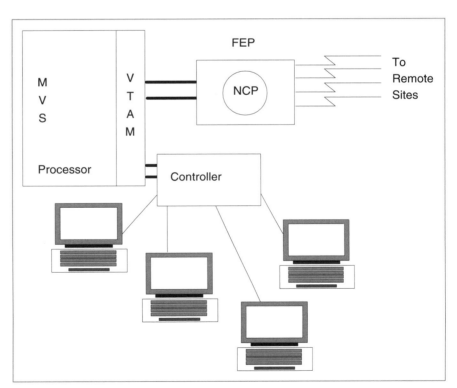

VTAM is a critical component in an SNA network. Understanding is no trivial task. VTAM is the heart and soul of SNA.

Job Entry Subsystem 2 (JES2)

According to IBM, JES2, a spooling subsystem, is a primary subsystem. It operates under the control of VTAM, as does other software often referred to as subsystems. Some subsystems are so large they are practically operating systems themselves, with sub-subsystems.

JES2 receives jobs, schedules them, and controls their output, serving as an interface to the operating system for job processing. When the command is issued to print the job, that command goes to JES2 and the job is subsequently printed.

Figure 10.30 is a conceptual view of JES2.

FIGURE 10.30
JES2

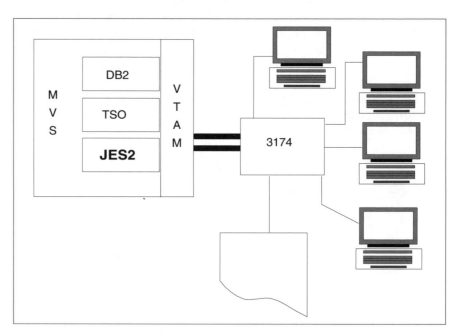

JES2 functions so that data to be processed may literally be spooled to a DASD for buffer storage. Delays can thus be minimized because processing continues and jobs are queued to be processed.

The term Remote Job Entry (RJE) refers to a site not in the same physical facility as the processor complex; it has terminal capabilities and a link to the processor so that jobs may be submitted to JES2. Network Job Entry (NJE) is another term used to refer to a complex of processors dispersed but connected in a network. NJE allows multiple JES2 subsystems to communicate as peers in a network environment. In contrast, RJE permits JES2 interaction with remote workstations.

JES2 is a descendent of the Houston Automatic Spooling Priority (HASP) and originated with IBM employees in Houston to expedite job processing in a typical university environment which had many jobs and short execution times. Early OS/360 spent more time scheduling jobs than for their execution. The benefit of HASP was achieving overlap in scheduling and execution through spooling.

Another job management subsystem is JES3. Originating from IBM's Attached Support Processor (ASP) system, JES3 broadens the scope of job management by managing jobs in the queue, during the execution phase, and after execution for proper outputting; this is accomplished by specially tailored algorithms, furnished by the installation. A fundamental difference between JES2 and JES3 is that JES3 operates in an environment in which one copy of JES3 is the "master" (called the global) and other copies (called locals) operate throughout a processor complex in communication with this master copy.

Network Control Program (NCP)

The NCP is a program that operates on IBM's communication controllers. Like VTAM it plays a critical role in IBM's SNA. The NCP serves two primary functions: routing and flow control, though it serves other functions as well. An NCP must have devices, paths, communication lines, and connections to it defined.

The NCP performs two major functions: it controls data flow through a network with other NCPs and VTAMs and the NCP controls data flow between itself and VTAM.

The NCP also routes data throughout a network. Within a NCP generation a list of routes (explicit and virtual) is defined and a class-of-service can be used to aid in routing data. Depending on how the COS has been implemented, particular data from one source may have higher priority than data from another source.

The NCP also has programs that operate with it on a communications controller. The Network Packet Switched Interface (NPSI) option is a program used to permit connectivity with an X.25 network. The Network Terminal Option (NTO) works in conjunction with an NCP to permit non-SNA devices to connect to the SNA network. NTO's fundamental purpose is to convert a non-SNA protocol into SNA protocol before the data gets routed to the processor.

NetView

NetView is IBM's tool for managing SNA, with origins in the 1970s it was announced in 1986. Before than components were used for selective management of a network. For example, NCCF, the command line interface for NetVeiw, was announced in 1978. At the same time the Network Problem Determination Application (NPDA) program was announced. Both were released in 1979.

NetView has grown to consist of:

- NCCF
- NPDA
- NLDM
- Browse facility
- Status monitor
- Graphic monitor
- Resource Object Data Manager (RODM).

Figure 10.31 is a conceptual view of a VTAM and SNA network.

NCCF is the base of NetView. From it, NetView, VTAM, and MVS system commands can be entered at the command line. Because of this, it is possible to control an SNA network from a remote location.

SNA management is typically accomplished via a console (generally inside a data center), with the capability NCCF provides, remote operation is possible. As long as a connection can be made to the system running NetView and an individual has the authority to execute system-oriented commands, NetView, VTAM, and MVS commands can be issued against the NCCF command prompt.

NPDA is that part of NetVeiw used to manage hardware. It can collect and maintain data about devices throughout the network and has the capability to request data about a particular piece of hardware or accept data sent to it from a given hardware device.

NLDM monitors the session (a logical connection between two end points). With NLDM the following information can be obtained about a session:

- Availability
- Configuration
- Error

- Event
- Explicit route
- Response time
- Session partner
- Trace
- Virtual route.

FIGURE 10.31
Conceptual View
of NetView

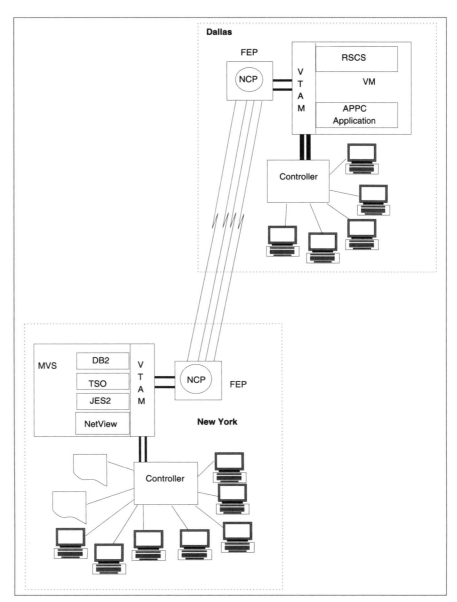

The browse facility enables an operator to view NetView log data, VTAM definitions of devices within the network, command lists, and system-wide definitions.

The status monitor collects information about parts of an SNA network. That data is displayed in columnar form or can be routed to the graphic monitor where the data can be displayed graphically.

The graphic monitor is a menu-driven method for monitoring network operations. It has pull-down menus and displays selected parts of a network in color. Certain colors are also used to highlight problem areas.

The RODM operates in its own address space in memory, serving as a central repository for storing and retrieving information about resources throughout the network. It can obtain execution configuration, and/or status information and can make the data available to those applications which need it because of its object-oriented structure.

NetView can operate under MVS, VM, and VSE. Two commonly used functions of NetView are alerts and response time.

Alerts are messages about the status of a given device. They use IBM's Network Management Vector Transport (NMVT) protocol. Information such as day, date, and time of a failure can be included in an alert. Other status information is also included and can be site-specific.

Response Time Monitor (RTM) is a tool used to measure the time it takes for data to leave a terminal after an Attention Identifier (AID) key is pressed, reach the host application, and return.

NetView has been expanded by IBM to support other platforms such as the RISC/6000. Other capabilities, even participating in network management with TCP/IP-based networks, are possible with NetView.

Time Sharing Option (TSO)

TSO is IBM's interactive facility that operates under MVS. Its three modes of operation are:

- Interactive System Productivity Facility/Program Development Facility (ISPF/PDF)
- Information center facility (ICF)
- Line mode.

The ISPF/PDF main menu is typically what a user sees upon logging onto TSO. Through the ISPF/PDF main menu many choices exist which lead to submenus. Main menu choices and their basic functions include:

- **ISPF PARMS.** Specific parameters for use with ISPF
- **Browse.** Permits viewing only of authorized data sets
- **Edit.** Invokes the editor; with it a user can create a memo, program, or anything one would use an editor for.
- **Utilities.** These lead to another menu with a number of selections that permit disk, data set, and other types of maintenance and utility functions.
- **Foreground.** Causes the language processor to move to the foreground
- **Batch.** Enables a user to submit jobs for batch processing
- **Command.** This takes the user to a TSO line mode of operation. Here valid TSO commands can be entered.
- **Dialog Test.** This function allows a user to perform dialog testing.
- **LM Utility.** This provides an individual with capability to perform maintenance utility functions.
- **Exit.** If selected, this causes ISPF/PDF to terminate.

Other functions are available from the main menu. Some of those listed above have submenus that a provide additional capabilities.

ICF provides users with a main menu similar in appearance to the ISPF/PDF main menu. Functions available to users via ICF include:

- **News.** Obtain news from the system
- **Names.** Get a list of names and phone numbers
- **Chart.** Create a chart or graph
- **PDF.** This enables a user to use program development services
- **Exit.** This causes ICF to terminate.

TSO line mode can be used for various reasons. Valid TSO commands such as LISTCAT can be entered. This command is used to list data sets that are cataloged and accessible to a user.

Another function of TSO line mode is the execution of custom programs. If a customized program such as terminal interaction needs a certain protocol for operation, then a program can be created to execute under line mode.

Figure 10.32 shows a conceptual view of TSO and other subsystems mentioned.

FIGURE 10.32
Conceptual View
of TSO

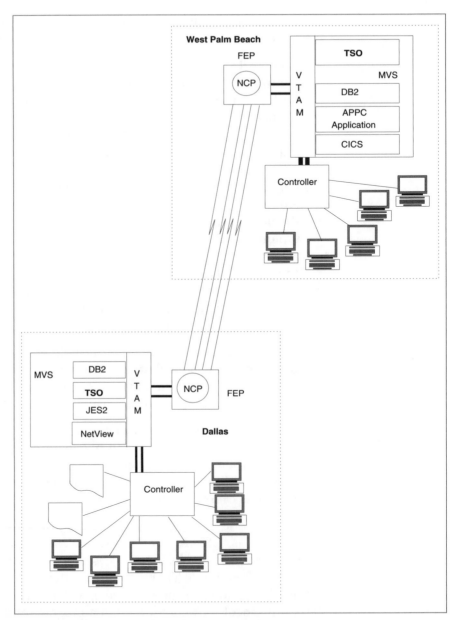

FIGURE 10.32
Conceptual View
of TSO

Customer Information Control System (CICS)

CICS is an on-line transaction processing system supported under
MVS, VM, and VSE operating systems. It has a general orientation
toward business implementations rather than scientific or engineering computations.

CICS might typically be implemented is in a banking environment. If a customer has a bank account and wants to access that account via an automatic teller machine, this could be achieved with transaction programming using CICS. In this case a program in the automatic teller machine communicates with a program running under CICS control in the bank's computer. The program at the teller machine is communicating with the CICS program in real time. The program running under CICS in turn accesses a database that maintains the requesting automatic teller's account balance. After the program under CICS verifies the requesting party's account it communicates with the automatic teller machine, sending it the appropriate response. If the money is available the automatic teller machine dispenses it.

Customized programming is possible under CICS, which makes it attractive to users who need to create on-line processing programs. CICS also supports communication between transaction programs within a single CICS subsystem.

Database 2 (DB2)

DB2 is IBM's relational database application that provides users with flexibility and power via the functions it supports. Those functions include:

- Utilization of a single VTAM conversation to manipulate multiple requests and responses with other DB2 applications throughout a complex
- Support for Distributed Relational Database Architecture (DRDA)
- Support for Structured Query Language (SQL) requests from remote locations
- Site-independence at the same time as capability for interaction with other DB2 sites
- Multi-user support for concurrent access including making updates, deletions, and insertions
- Fitting into SAA via CPI-SQL
- Selective choosing of an audit trail is possible
- Use in an XRF environment
- Support for 10,000 open concurrent data sets per address space
- A maximum of 750 columns in a DB2 table
- Multiple simultaneous index recovery performed on the same table space.

Remote Spooling Communication Subsystem (RSCS)

RSCS is an application that operates under VM to provide data transfer capabilities. IBM lists the following as some of its functions:

- File transfer, message, commands, and mail between VM, MVS, VSE, NJE, and OS/400
- ASCII support to printers and plotters
- IPDS and SCS data stream support
- A gateway programming interface for protocols such as TCP/IP
- Support of 3270-type printers with form control buffering
- The capability to share printers.

RSCS allows VM users to send mail, specific messages, and jobs to other users within an SNA network. VM users use RSCS for printing purposes. The basic functionality of RSCS is that the origin node starts communication with a destination node. Multiple devices may be along the path between the two. Because of the wide protocol support, RSCS can function over multiple types of links.

Local Area Network Resource Extension and Services (LANRES)

LANRES is an application that operates in MVS and VM environments. According to IBM sources, it brings the power behind the S/390 architecture to a NetWare environment by making DASD available to NetWare servers and S/390-based printers available to NetWare clients.

LANRES also permits authorized MVS users to move data to and from a NetWare server. NetWare server files and directories can be listed, created, and/or deleted.

LANRES also makes LAN printers available to MVS users. In effect it brings together NetWare environments with S/390 seamlessly, to take advantage of right-positioning of work loads. Another function LANRES offers is centralization of LAN management to the MVS host. It also permits MVS users to send postscript files to a postscript printer on a LAN.

A LANRES environment might look like Figure 10.33.

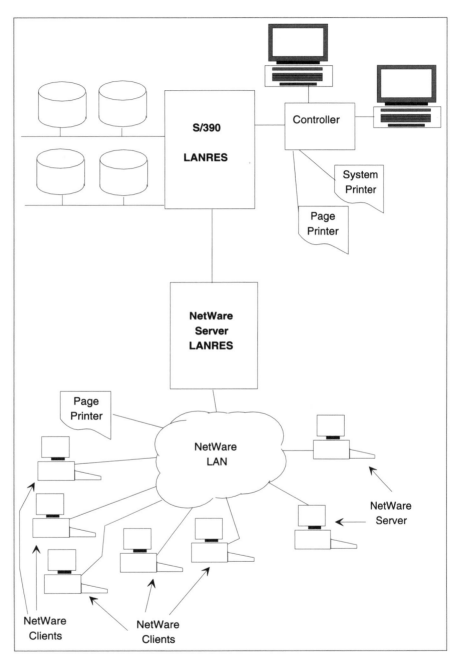

FIGURE 10.33
Conceptual View
of LANRES and
NetWare LANs

LANRES is versatile because of the connectivity solutions it supports:

- ESCON
- Parallel channel
- APPC connection
- Host TCP/IP connection
- VM Programmable Workstation Services (VM PWSCS).

The method of connection dictates how LANRES is configured on the host. Because of the breadth of support for connectivity solutions, requirements, installation, and definitions are site-dependent and directly related to how the product is used. If the product is used with TCP/IP under MVS, LANRES uses sockets and TCP for connectivity. If APPC is used, it connects to APPC MVS via CPI-C, conforming to SAA standards.

   If your software needs have not been covered in this section, contact an IBM representative for additional information.

SNA by Traditional Layers

IBM announced SNA in 1974. This began as a layerd architecture and traditional SNA remains so. Traditional SNA is more hierarchical than peer-oriented. It predates 1992 and the Networking Blueprint announcement. This does not mean the Networking Blueprint replaces the functionality of traditional SNA; rather it provides a different approach to networking. More on the Networking Blueprint will be presented later in this chapter.

   By layers, SNA appears conceptually like Figure 10.34.

   The basic functions at these layers include:

1. The point where a link is made between two or more nodes
2. Movement of data across a link
3. Performing routing and flow control
4. Throttling data movement and performing security functions if required
5. Synchronizing, correlating, and grouping data
6. Formatting data to protocol
7. Providing application-required services.

In many installations this describes the functionality of data flow within the network. This model of networking is considered traditional SNA.

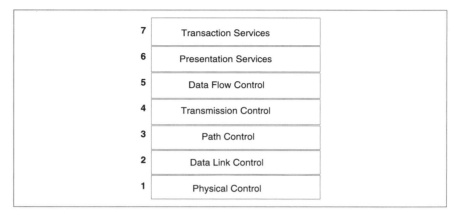

FIGURE 10.34
SNA Traditional
Layers

IBM's Blueprint for Networking

In September 1992 IBM announced the Networking Blueprint. This was a new approach to IBM networking, providing a framework for choices to be made to fit the needs of a situation. Figure 10.35 is a representation of that framework.

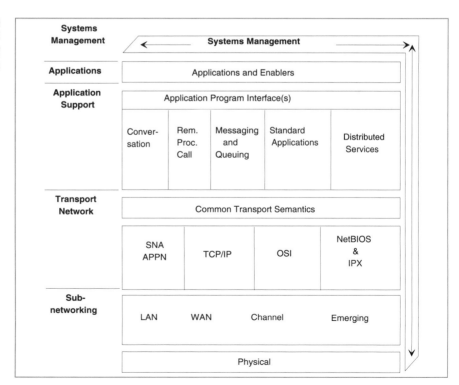

FIGURE 10.35
IBM's Networking
Blueprint

As Figure 10.35 shows the structure of the blueprint is entirely different from the layers of traditional SNA. According to IBM the blueprint structure has four major layers, three switching boundaries, and what IBM calls the systems management plane.

Subnetworking Layer

This layer constitutes the lower layer and is divided into four categories: LAN, WAN, channel and emerging.

These categories can be further divided into protocols. For example, protocols that would generally fall in to the LAN category include Ethernet, Token ring, FDDI, and others.

Protocols applicable to the WAN category could include FDDI, frame relay, SDLC, and others.

Protocols applicable to the channel category could include byte multiplexor channel, block multiplexor channel, and ESCON.

Protocols applicable to the emerging technology category include Asynchronous Transfer Mode (ATM) and Fast Ethernet.

This list is not exhaustive, but conveys the idea behind the supported protocols at this layer. To a considerable degree these can be selected for what best fits the site requirements.

Transport/Networking Layer

This layer is represented by six networking capabilities applied differently according to the following supported protocols: SNA, APPN, TCP/IP, OSI, NetBIOS, and NetWare.

The way this layer functions is contingent on the protocol selected. TCP/IP works in one particular fashion whereas APPN works according to its structural definitions at this layer. Users can choose the protocol.

Application Support Layer

This layer provides service support for applications. The prevalent interfaces and services at this layer are:

- **Conversational (known as CPI-C).** This deals with streams of related interactions.
- **Remote Procedure Call (known as RPC).** This is capable of passing parameters to a subroutine.

- **Message Queue (known as MQI).** This manages the queues that relate messages.

In addition, the following services may apply at this layer:

- Distributed system services
- Vendor applications such as:
  - Telnet for remote login
  - FTP for file transfer
  - SNMP for network management
- Other non-transport layer-dependent applications.

Application Layer

At this layer are applications inherent to the protocols available, including print, mail, file transfer, remote logon and other services.

Switching Boundaries

The applicable switching boundaries include:

- Application Program Interface (API)
- Common Transport Semantics (CTS)
- Subnetwork-Access Boundary (SAB).

The API switching boundary serves a primary purpose, making the underlying architecture transparent.

The CTS switching boundary enables any protocol above it to access any protocol below it.

The SAB switching boundary resides between the transport/network part and the physical part of the blueprint. It makes link services available to the protocols driving the network.

This blueprint indicates a more flexible networking approach than traditional SNA had. Two documents that are good references for learning more about the networking blueprint are:

| #GC31-7057 | Networking Blueprint Executive Overview |
| #GC31-7074 | Multiprotocol Transport Networking (MPTN) Architecture: Formats |

To obtain these and other IBM documents contact an IBM representative or view them at IBM's Web site.

Traditional Concepts

This section explains terms and concepts that make up the core of SNA. SNA as a network protocol is implemented via hardware and software.

Nodes

The term node is used in IBM documentation, and depending upon the context it can take on different meanings. In traditional SNA, sometimes referred to as subarea SNA, different types of nodes exist, including:

- **Host Node.** Also known as a subarea node; it provides end-user services. It is a type 5 node.
- **Communication Controller Node.** This refers to a communication controller (also known as an FEP). It is a type 4 node.
- **Peripheral Node.** This is a cluster or establishment controller. Depending upon the device, it may be a type 2.0 or 2.1 node.

Figure 10.36 shows all three types of nodes.

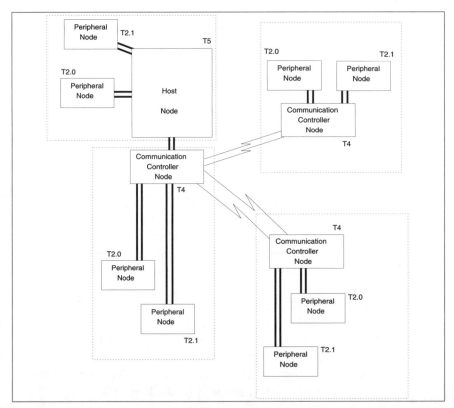

FIGURE 10.36
Conceptual View of Nodes

Subareas

In traditional SNA subareas exist. No areas are defined. A subarea is defined as one of the following:

- A subarea node and peripheral node(s)
- A subarea node
- A subarea node and a communication controller node.

Figure 10.37 depicts these three types of subareas:

FIGURE 10.37
Conceptual View
of Subareas

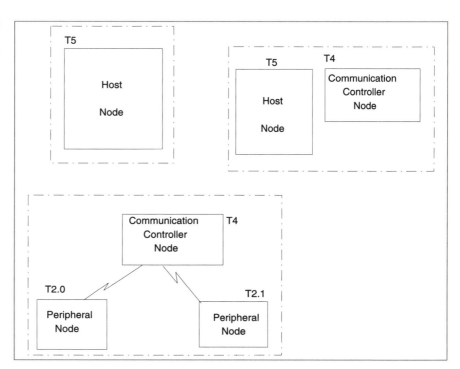

Network Accessible Units (NAUs)

IBM defines an NAU as a:

- System Services Control Point (SSCP)
- Physical Unit (PU)
- Logical Unit (LU).

System Services Control Point (SSCP)

The SSCP is a controlling point in SNA located in the VTAM. Some of its characteristics and functions include:

- Network control
- Session management
- Resource activation
- Resource deactivation
- Focal point for receipt of PU data
- Passing data to/from NetView
- Executing commands.

The SSCP and VTAM might appear as in Figure 10.38.

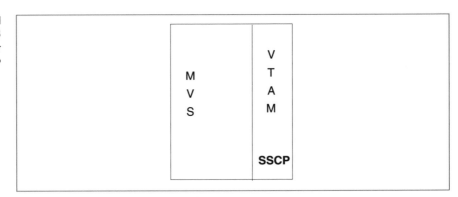

Physical Unit (PU)

A PU pertains more to the functions or capabilities of a node than to describing a particular hardware device. The PU type is architecturally related and part of microcode and software.

Basic characteristics and functions of PUs include:

- A PU is defined in software or microcode
- It receives messages from an SSCP
- PUs provide internal network, not user-related, functions
- Participating entities in an SNA network are known by their node type
- A PU manages links and link stations
- It sets up virtual and explicit routes in certain nodes
- It communicates with one or more control points.

Types of PUs

Four types of PUs are best described by their functional characteristics, PU types 5, 4, 2.0, and 2.1.

A PU type 5 (T5) node is a host subarea node. Practically speaking, it is a processor or can provide T5 functions including:

- Managing subarea resources
- Aiding in session establishment
- Ability to monitor resources.

A PU type 4 (T4) node is a communication controller node. It is an FEP or has the capability to emulate PU 4 functions:

- A control point called a physical unit control point (PUCP).
- Managing its peripheral nodes.
- Communicating with an SSCP.

A PU type 2.0 is a peripheral node, totally dependent upon a T5 node for session establishment. This type node's functions include:

- A control point named the same as PU4
- Communication with a T4 PUCP or an SSCP
- Monitoring its local resources
- Sending status-related data to an SSCP.

For practical purposes it is correct to associate a physical device with a PU, but some devices can act as different PU types depending on how they are GENed. Also, the location where terminals and printers connect on controllers can be considered an LU. The same holds true for PU2.1 devices.

A PU2.1 node is also a peripheral node. Its controlling access is called a control point. It differs from a T2.0 node because it supports peer communications to some degree. It can perform the functions of a T2.0 node, but can also perform functions native to T2.1 architecture. Additional details on T2.1 nodes are provided in Chapter 8.

Logical Unit (LU)

IBM defines a logical unit as an addressable end point. This applies to hardware and software. The type of LUs of concern here and their function (protocol support) are:

- LU0 Create your own program
- LU1 SNA character String printing (SCS)
- LU2 A 3270 data stream

- LU3 A 3270 data stream for printers
- LU6.2 Advanced Program-to-Program Communication (APPC) protocol
- LU7 5250 data stream for AS/400 systems.

The two categories of logical units are dependent and independent. The fundamental difference between the two is that the former requires VTAM for session establishment and the latter does not—after initial download of tables.

Figure 10.39 is an example of hardware, software, and concepts presented to this point and gives a good general perspective of SNA.

FIGURE 10.39
Conceptual View of a Typical SNA Network

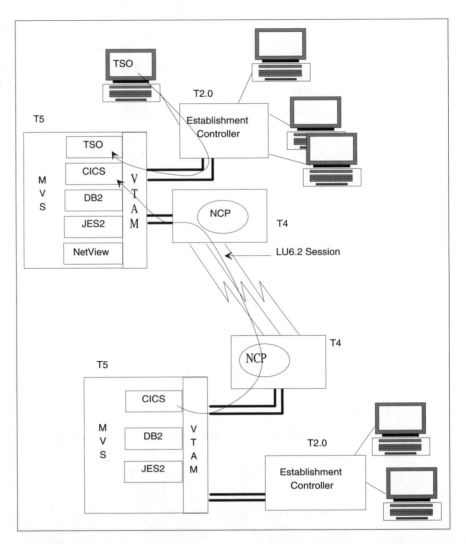

Figure 10.39 shows two processors, software on each, communication controllers, an establishment controller, a cluster controller, printers and terminals. It also shows two CICS subsystems communicating with each other via an LU6.2 session. It shows a terminal communicating with TSO via the LU2 protocol.

Sessions

We know that sessions are defined as logical connections between two end points. The types of sessions to be considered are SSCP-SSCP, SSCP-PU, SSCP-LU, and LU-LU.

The SSCP-SSCP session is an example of two VTAM subsystems communicating with each other. One possible reason would be to set up a session between a terminal user and a software subsystem that is not in the same processor.

An SSCP-PU session is used to activate a device. Other functions are allowing management-related data flows across the session.

An SSCP-LU session can be used by VTAM to vary an active LU or deactivate it.

An LU-LU session could be a terminal user communicating with a software subsystem. In this case the LU-LU session could be described as Primary Logical Unit (PLU) and Secondary Logical Unit (SLU); the former is a software subsystem and the second is the terminal user. This is considered a Dependent Logical Unit (DLU).

The LU-LU session can also be described as independent. When this is the case the LU is referred to as an Independent Logical Unit (ILU).

Link Stations (LS)

An LS is the intelligence in a device defined as that point in a device where the data link is managed. IBM's SNA Technical Overview document # GC30-3073 describes this concept well. Figure 10.40 depicts this based on their model.

Link Stations perform functions including:

- Receiving requests from and responding to the control point
- Controlling link-level data flow
- Moving data from one link station to another via the medium
- Managing error recovery at the link level on the node.

FIGURE 10.40
Conceptual View
of a Link Station

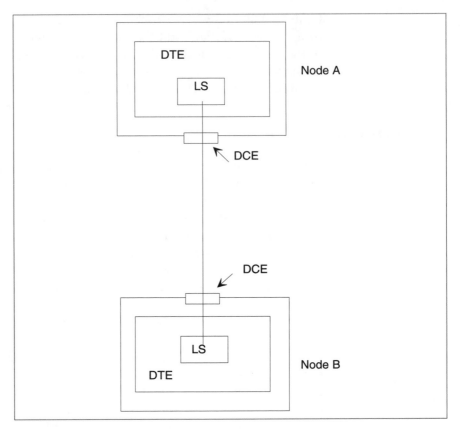

Link

In SNA a link refers to the data link. Types of links include parallel channel, ESCON, frame relay, token ring, SDLC, and Ethernet.

IBM defines a link as that connection between two link stations. This includes the medium, DCEs, and link connection. The link connection consists of the DCEs and transmission medium.

Domains

Another concept in SNA is the domain, that area whose components have a single point for control. In a T5 node the control point is the SSCP. In a T4 node it is the NCP.

Parallel to the concept of domains is that of ownership. In SNA all resources are owned; one needs to determine by which device.

Resources in a given domain are normally owned by a control point in that domain.

Now that the concept of a domain is understood, we consider the concept of cross domain resources, resources in a domain other than that where the requesting party is located.

Figure 10.41 is an example of two different domains.

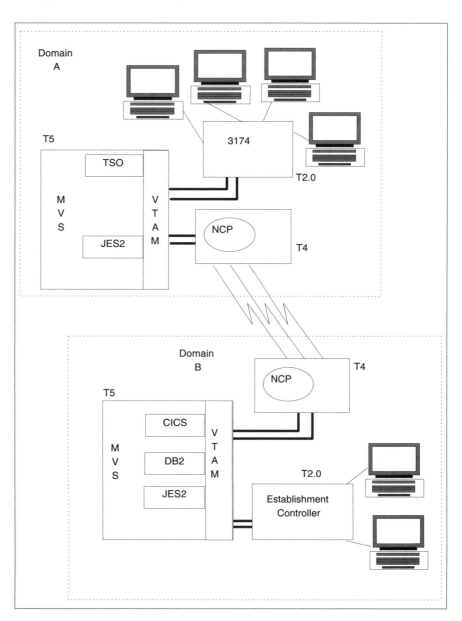

FIGURE 10.41
Conceptual View
Domains

In Figure 10.41 two processors have application subsystems. Each processor owns the applications on the host. If defined appropriately to VTAM, users in domain A can access application subsystems in domain B and vice versa.

SNA Protocol Structure

SNA protocol structure can be explained by layers. Figure 10.42 is a view of what SNA considers as a message unit.

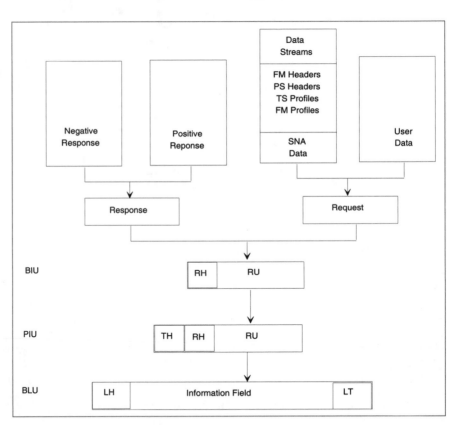

FIGURE 10.42
Structured
View of the
Message Unit

The three distinct components of the message unit are: Basic Link Unit (BLU); Path Information Unit (PIU); and Basic Information Unit (BIU).

Basic Link Unit

The BLU is assembled at the data-link layer of the network. It includes data and protocols passed from layers above it. In front of the BLU is a Link Header (LH). The Information field is next ,with all above it. The Link Trailer is the end of the message unit.

Path Information Unit

PIU consists of the Transmission Header (TH), Request or Response Header (RH), and the Request or Response Unit (RU). The PIU operates at that layer in the network responsible for routing data (message units) through SNA.

Basic Information Unit

The BIU consists of an RH then a Request or Response Unit (RU).

An RU is on top of the BIU. Depending on direction of the message unit flow either a response or some type data—end user or SNA data (including data streams) is sent.

IBM document number GA27-3136 is the source for this information and that to come discussing data streams, profile concepts, function management header concepts, and request and response concepts. For greater detail on these topics the IBM document is the best reference.

SNA Data Streams

IBM has defined data streams used in SNA. An example of a dominant data stream is the 3270 data stream. This is used by terminals and printers that operate with MVS, VM, and VSE operating systems.

The data streams used include:

- SNA Character String (SCS)
- 3270
- General Data Stream Variable (GDS)
- Information Interchange Architecture (IIA)
- Intelligent Printer Data Stream (IPDS).

SNA Character String (SCS)

This is a protocol used with printers and certain terminals. LU1 and LU6.2 can use this data stream. One unique aspect of this data stream is its lack of data flow control functions.

3270

This data stream is characterized by the presence of user-defined data. It also includes commands that aid in LU-LU control. LU2, and LU3 use this data stream for terminals and printers respectively. It can be used by LU6.2 as an option data stream.

General Data Stream

This is used by transaction programs to interpret data records as they are sent and received. It is used by LU6.2.

Information Interchange Architecture

IIA is used by applications exchanging programs to define a collection of data streams. This means that Open Document Architecture (ODA) and Document Content Architecture (DCA) can be used.

Intelligent Printer Data Stream

IPDS is used between a host and a printer, and on an all-points addressable printer. IPDS can intermix text and graphics—both vector and raster-based.

Profile Concepts

Two profiles we need to examine are the transmission service and function management profiles.

Transmission Service Profiles

These profiles provide a variety of services and are used at a developmental and debugging level on the transmission layer in the network. They represent protocols that may be selected at session activation:

- **TS1**—Used with SSCP-PU and SSCP-LU sessions
- **TS2**—Used with LU-LU sessions
- **TS3**—Also used on LU-LU sessions
- **TS4**—Used on LU-LU sessions
- **TS5**—Used on SSCP-PU sessions
- **TS7**—Used on LU-LU sessions
- **TS17**—Used on SSCP-SSCP session.

Function Management Profiles

These include:

- **FM0**—Used on SSCP-PU and SSCP-LU sessions
- **FM2**—Used on LU-LU sessions
- **FM3**—Used on LU-LU sessions
- **FM4**—Used on LU-LU sessions
- **FM5**—Used on SSCP-PU Type 5 and 4 sessions
- **FM6**—Used on SSCP-LU session
- **FM7**—Used on LU-LU sessions
- **FM17**—Used on SSCP-SSCP sessions
- **FM18**—Used on LU-LU sessions
- **FM19**—Used on LU-LU sessions.

Like the transmission service profiles, the function management profiles provide a variety of services based on session type and need. For in-depth information about these profiles refer to IBM manual GA27-31-36.

Function Management Header (FMH) Concepts

The concept behind an FMH is that if a session supports these headers a request header can contain an option indicating the presence of an FMH. If present, the FMH indicates specific functionality. Consider the list of FMHs:

- **FMH1**—Used to select a destination logical unit
- **FMH2**—Used to handle data management for a task
- **FMH3**—Used for the same purposes as FMH2, this does not have a stack reference
- **FMH4**—This header carries logical block commands used to define diferent parameters.
- **FMH5**—This is a LU6.2 Attach header used to carry a request for a conversation. A non-LU6.2 Attach originates from the sending half-session program to the destination manager.
- **FMH6**—This header is used during an active transaction program conversation
- **FMH7**—This provides error information for LU6.2, for non-LU6.2 it is used in a similar fashion.
- **FMH8**—Used with an application called IMS with LU6.1 protocols
- **FMH10**—This prepares a session for sync point processing.
- **FMH12**—This header is used with LU6.2 for security.

Request/Response Header (RH) Concept

These headers are used to perform bit-level operations inside message units. IBM identifies an exhaustive list of RHs to accomplish a variety of tasks:

- Provide a format indicator
- Indicate sense data
- Indicate beginning of chain
- Indicate the end of a chain
- Indicate the types of a response
- Request a larger window
- Indicate the beginning and end of a bracket.

The format of the RH depends on the type of session used. Details provided by these formats are used in the formatting of SNA data.

SNA Commands

SNA commands differ according to the type of LU and session used. Some commonalties exist in theory, but specific commands can differ. Consider the following:

Theory of Command Flow

Assume a terminal user wants to sign on to TSO. What are the theoretical operation and commands that flow between the two?
Figure 10.43 depicts this scenario.

FIGURE 10.43
Conceptual View
of a TSO User

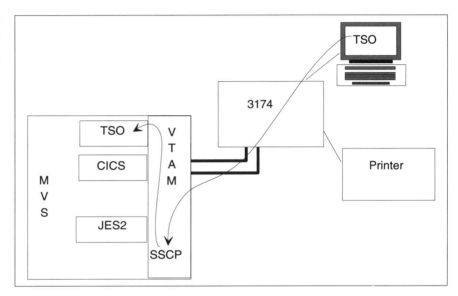

The operation between the terminal user and TSO includes the following:

1. A user enters TSO and is received by VTAM as a character-coded logon.
2. A logon exit is scheduled for the Primary Logical Unit.
3. After receiving control of the logon exit, the PLU passes an open-session request to the SSCP.
4. As a result of the open-session request the BIND command is sent to the Secondary Logical Unit (SLU).
5. Assuming the terminal sends back a positive response, the session is bound.
6. If a negative response is returned, a BIND failure command is generated.

The SNA Command Structure

The IBM SNA format manual GA27-3136 describes SNA commands. These commands fit into the request or response structure just explained. SNA commands and their functions include:

- ACTLU—Activate Logical Unit
- ACTPU—Activate Physical Unit
- DACTLU—Deactivate Logical Unit
- DACTPU—Deactivate Physical Unit
- BIND—Activate a session between LUs
- CDINIT—Cross Domain Initiate sent between two SSCPs
- CINIT—Control Initiate; request the PLU to send a BIND
- LUSTAT—Send status information
- NOTIFY—Synchronize awareness of an SSCP and PLU
- SDT—Start Data Traffic
- SESSEND—LU notification to the SSCP that a session has ended
- UNBIND—Send to UNBIND two LUs.

Flow Control

The following three topics are partially how SNA controls data.

Explicit Route (ER)

In SNA, an ER is a defined set of nodes and transmission groups (TG) of a path. For example, an explicit route could be subarea node X, TG2, subarea node T, TG2, and subarea D. An explicit route is the definition of a path in subarea SNA. It is a physical connection.

Virtual Route (VR)

These routes are logical connections between two end points. A virtual route is mapped atop explicit routes. Consequently, it reflects the characteristics of an explicit route. For example, in most scenarios where multiple FEPs are installed multiple links connect them. These links are physical and defined as explicit. The logical route is then mapped to the route that best fits the need of the session.

Class of Service (COS)

This includes characteristics such as transmission priority, bandwidth, and security. With a class of service the following can be defined:

- Providing response times reflecting high priority
- Reflect best availability
- A class with higher levels of security
- A class for batch processing.

The combination of transmission priority makes flow control possible in the network.

Advance Program-to-Program Communication (APPC)

APPC is IBM's premier peer-oriented protocol and is based on LU6.2. The flexibility of the protocol enables it to be implemented across a variety of platforms.

Origins and Evolution

APPC originated in the early 1980s and evolved from limited support to now being supported by MVS/ESA and many application subsystems operating under VTAM. Benefits of using APPC include:

- One protocol can be used across a variety of architectures.
- It provides security.
- It offers a distributed approach to transaction processing.
- It offers multiple ways to create transaction programs.

APPC is now common among MVS, VM, and VSE operating systems. It is also fundamental to Advanced Peer-to-Peer Networking (APPN). APPC is widespread in the marketplace among third-party vendors.

Conceptual Overview

The idea behind APPC is peer communication between programs. This means that customized programs can be written to utilize the power behind APPC. Consider an example of two banks, one in Dallas and the other in Research Triangle Park. Assume that daily information needs to be exchanged between the bank in Dallas and the one in Research Triangle Park. Figure 10.44 shows an example of two programs exchanging information between the two banking institutions.

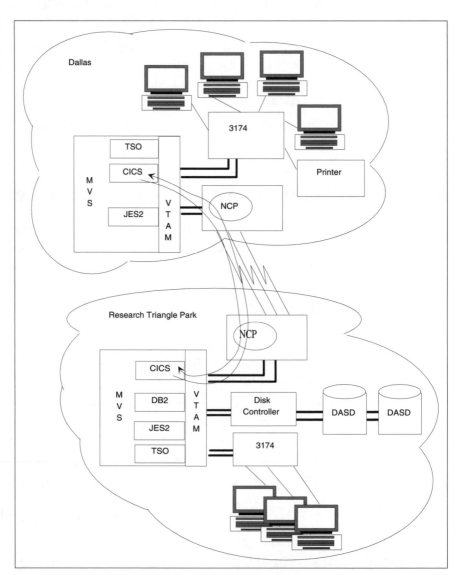

FIGURE 10.44
Conceptual View
of APPC
Implementation

Conversations

Sessions have been explained as being logical connections between two endpoints. A conversation is communication between two or more transaction programs using an LU6.2 session through a defined Independent Logical Unit (ILU). Figure 10.45 explains this concept.

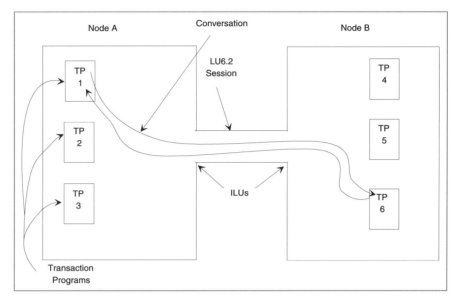

Figure 10.45 shows the following components:

- Node A
- Multiple Transaction Programs (TP)
- A LU6.2 session
- A point where an ILU is defined
- A conversation between two TPs.

Figure 10.45 shows the idea behind a conversation. In this figure any of the transaction programs in Node A can communicate with any of the TPs on Node B.

Two types of conversations exist: basic and mapped. A basic conversation provides a low-level interface for those transactions programs needing support for privileged functions. A mapped conversation is the protocol boundary, like the basic conversation, except it enables arbitrary transmission of message format. System- or user-defined mappers can be used.

Transaction Program

IBM defines a transaction program as a application executed within the LU6.2 protocol. It is typically user-written to meet the needs of a specific installation.

Types of Verbs

APPC is a high-level language using "verbs" to achieve communication. Two categories of verbs exist, conversation and control operator.

Conversation Verbs

The verbs in this category include: mapped, basic and type-independent. Mapped verbs are used by application programs to provide services for programs written in high-level languages. Basic verbs are used by LU service programs to provide end-user services or protocol boundaries for application programs. Type-independent verbs can be used with basic and mapped conversations. They provide a variety of generic services needed by both conversations.

Control Operator Verbs

This category of verbs includes the subcategories Change Number of Session (CNOS), session control, LU definition, and Miscellaneous.

CNOS verbs are used to change the session limit that controls the number of LU–LU sessions per mode name available between two LUs allocated for conversations.

Session control verbs are used to activate and deactivate sessions and deactivate conversation groups.

LU Definition verbs define or modify local LU operating parameters.

Miscellaneous verbs are those verbs needed but not defined in another category.

LU6.2 Session Considerations

Concepts and functions that are a part of APPC include:

- Parallel sessions
- Single sessions
- Session pools

- Session selection
- Session limits
- Contention
- Winners and losers.

Parallel sessions are based on the concept of multiple pairs of sessions communicating with the same pair of LUs. Typically, one pair of TPs uses a session at a given instance. LU6.2 supports multiple concurrent sessions. Applications must be capable of supporting multiple-sessions including the processors and workstations. The concept of multiple-session support is called *parallel sessions*.

Single sessions are defined as LUs that cannot support more than one session against a given LU in a given instance.

Session pools are a collection of named LUs that contain active sessions which can be allocated to different conversations if required.

Session selection is the way a transaction program controls selection of a session. TPs cannot control session selection directly, but do so via the mode name parameter. They can map this to a set of characteristics.

A session limit is the maximum number of sessions that can be active at a given LU at one time.

Contention polarity is allied to the idea that two LUs attempt to initiate a session simultaneously. It is a method of preventing this event by defining multiple LUs for operation as contention winners or losers. Typically, multiple winners losers are defined in each node to prevent a state of contention.

Sync Point Processing

In LU6.2, sync point processing lets transaction programs synchronize their resources at specified time periods called *sync points*. This is important because multiple transaction programs are exchanging data; thus TPs must be in "sync".

Additional concepts in LU6.2 can be found in many books. A helpful one is IBM's *SNA Transaction Programmer's Reference Manual for LU Type 6.2*, document number GC30-3084.

A Perspective on Blueprints

The information in this chapter is the foundation of the blueprints that follow. Almost any SNA network can be viewed in light of the following blueprints. Regardless of the network size, SNA networks contain components and abstract infrastructures that can be identified and explained.

The following blueprints can be used to examine various SNA benefits and structures. The blueprints present successive designs of complexity. Any of them could be augmented in various ways to achieve implementation.

Blueprint #1

This blueprint could be explained by listing the major components: processor, controller, user devices, operating system, communication control subsystem, and application programs.

Figure 10.46 shows a processor, controller, and user devices such as a printer and terminals, as well as applications operating under the MVS operating system.

Blueprint 1 shows an SNA implementation and is typical for small SNA environments. The blueprint is simple, but the implementation could accommodate hundreds of users.

This type of blueprint is good to use with a scenario where large amounts of data entry are performed and databases are maintained. A customer-service center where a large database is used and numerous operators need access to it could be an ideal use of this blueprint. If this scenario were "real" many more controllers would be required to accommodate increased users by way of terminals.

Blueprint 1 is a good place to begin when an SNA network is needed and growth is anticipated. It is the core of most SNA network blueprints. It can be expanded upon and enhanced in every way; additional processors, controllers, printers, terminals, even other equipment can be added to accommodate remote equipment (hardware and software) and users.

Blueprint 1 can use software different from what is shown in the previous figure. A different operating system could be used. Additional software could be used or some of the software referred to in this figure could be replaced with software to meet the needs of a given location.

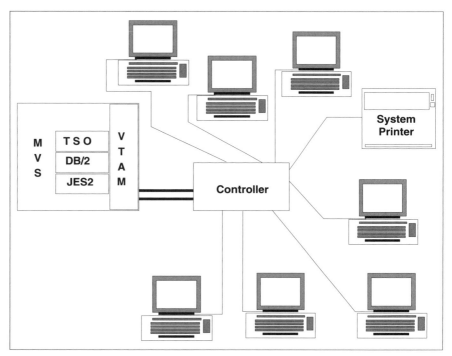

Blueprint 1 is a beginning point in planning SNA networks. Since SNA networks consist of hardware and software, this is an example of hardware and software that can be used. Most SNA networks do not start out to be large. This can be considered the base blueprint for any network planning for SNA.

SNA Blueprint #2

The next blueprint for SNA network design includes expansion of users and functionality of the network. Some may disagree that such figures as Blueprints 1 and 2 are "real" SNA networks.

Figure 10.47 illustrates the next logical extension to growth in an SNA network. Here, there are two sites located within the same geographical plant. Consider this figure as an example of a facility where the data center houses the actual processor and controller used to interface the terminals and printer in site A. Terminal users in site A are the customer service department in a large room of a company where numerous customer-service representatives have cubicles.

FIGURE 10.47
Blueprint #2

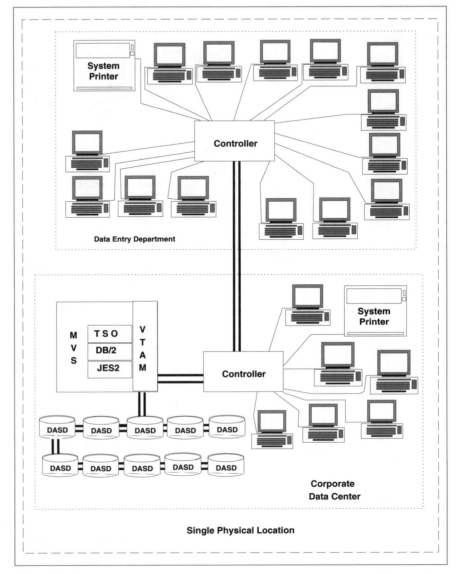

Site B is the technical support for the same company. In this example sites A and B are under the same physical "roof" but are located in entirely different places in the facility. Site B is on the second floor of the physical plant and is a large area where employees have desks and personal computers in addition to the 3270-based terminals as shown in Figure 10.47. There is a lab area as well to test product problems as they are taken by each employee and logged into the company database which is maintained in the SNA network.

Blueprint 2 is an ideal example of a single data center supporting two entirely different divisions within a company. Both customer service and technical support need access to the same database where customer information is maintained; however, each department has entirely different corporate missions with respect to the customer. This blueprint is a good example of how to lay a strong technical foundation in hardware and software that can easily be enhanced and upgraded as demands grow.

Blueprint #3

SNA Blueprint 3 begins to move toward a more complex SNA environment. Figure 10.48 illustrates this.

Notice Figure 10.48 shows the processor (core operations) of the SNA network located in Dallas. This site shows a controller, terminals, and a system printer in the Dallas location, as well as a communication controller which houses the NCP.

This blueprint adds an entirely new twist. The use of a communications device means more complex configuration for the processor's telecommunication access method. Where an NCP is used in conjunction with VTAM, considerable more intelligence is required to make the network function.

This blueprint seems to be fairly simple, but is not. The remote location in San Jose shows a communication controller with an NCP, controller, terminals, and a printer. Technically, the San Jose location has the same functionality as the Dallas location. This structure is common in many locations where SNA networks are implemented.

Blueprint 3 implies numerous topics for consideration. Operation of such an environment presupposes a staff exists to implement and maintain it. Most sites today using this structure have staff capable of implementation and maintainance. However, just because someone is knowledgeable in VTAM does not necessarily imply knowledge ability in NCP. These are two powerful and significant software packages that are complex and require time to master.

This blueprint does not explicitly show any network management. In most sites where this structure adequately reflects the hardware and software, network management is not necessarily required. Knowledgeable staff can extrapolate functionality of the network without any formal network management software. A small enough SNA network, even though it can be physically dispersed, can be implemented and managed to some degree.

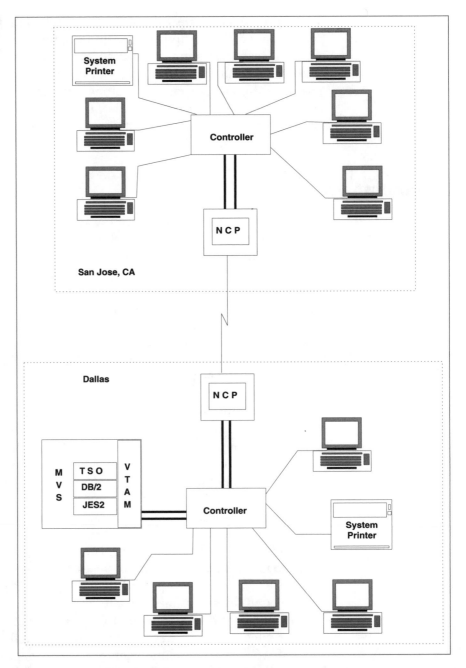

This blueprint also shows a variable not present in the former blue-prints: data link communication through lines outside the facility where the processor lies. Whether or not the link between Dallas and

San Jose is dedicated, the fact that distance separates the processor and the remote site requires consideration.

The matter of distance between locations presents some degree of uncertainty about manageability. All things being equal, no significant problems should arise. However, line quality, maintenance of the data communication lines themselves, and other factors contribute to uncertainty.

This bluepoint implies some degree of accessibility to the NCP at the San Jose site if the processor in Dallas is not functional. It also implies no redundant links between NCPs.

In summary, this blueprint allows link management, remote user operation, and growth in the remote (San Jose) location. This information alone is enough to realize that functional SNA networks are more than simple implementation of hardware and software.

Blueprint #4

This is the first departure from fairly basic SNA blueprints.

Figure 10.49 shows an SNA network where two different locations have considerable equipment. Notice two SNA hosts are used and multiple links are maintained between these locations. This type of implementation generally includes some common functions.

For example, this type of SNA blueprint shows processors in two locations. With this scenario processing can occur in both locations or be batted to one or the other; consequently, load balancing can be achieved. This type of blueprint also enables a network to be created where it appears that both processors are in the same location with respect to the users. In SNA parlance, a cross-domain environment would exist.

This blueprint also implies that personnel capable of working at system-level operation are at both locations. This is important. Though the blueprint may appear simple and straight forward it is complex in installation, operation, and maintenence.

Blueprint 4 could reflect an environment where hundreds of users work with various programs daily. Both locations in this example reflect an environment where users may be working with a database or some office-related function provided under TSO.

This blueprint could reflect two environments located in the same city or zone, or located in different parts of the world.

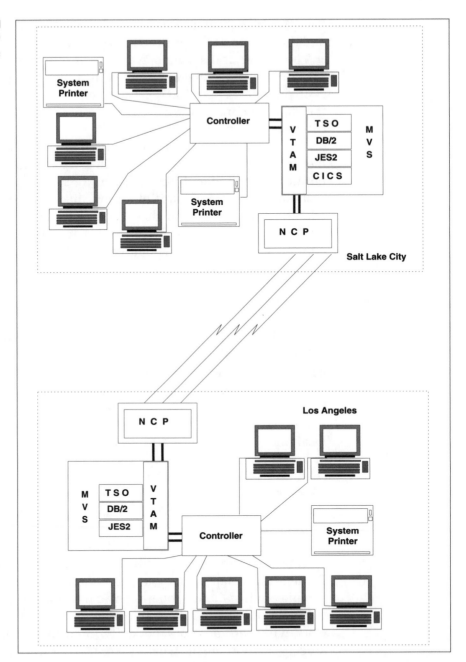

FIGURE 10.49
SNA Blueprint #4

Blueprint #5

SNA blueprint 5 is another step in complexity with building blocks
of SNA hardware and software. Consider Figure 10.50.

FIGURE 10.50
SNA Blueprint #5

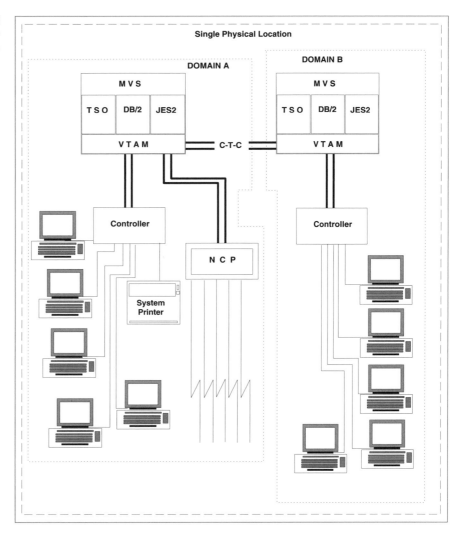

Notice that all the equipment is in the same location. This blueprint is an example of a redundant processor installation. Notice the processors are connected via channels; they are literally tied together at the lowest and therefore the most powerful level.

All data that comes into a host processor, in an SNA environment, goes across a channel. The only question is whether or not this is an ESCON channel or a parallel channel.

Figure 10.50 shows two domains. One has a communication controller and NCP and one does not. This particular implementation may well be configured so that either one of the host processors *owns* the NCP and the other processor is literally the backup processor in regard to ownership of the NCP.

Notice this blueprint shows two processors with the same software. Load balancing can be achieved in regard to the number of users accessing a given host. Users who need access to DB2 may be directed to the host where the communication controller is not connected or owned. TSO users on the other hand may be directed to the host processor where the communication controller is directly connected.

Because of the logical mapping that is possible within system configurations such as this one, distribution of users logging onto the system can be made to either host. VTAM can be configured to direct DB2 users to one processor and TSO users to the other processor. Likewise, JES2 jobs can be distributed equally. Consequently, considerable system resources are consumed at the channel level rather than at the application processing level. This distribution of resources greatly enhances the utilization of all resources, hardware and software.

This blueprint is good to consider where two processors are in the same physical location. It should be considered in conjunction with the reference material available in VTAM and NCP manuals from IBM. Many details provided in IBM manuals will help save time in the planning process.

IBM manuals present details how to program and configure VTAM to direct inbound traffic from the NCP. Logical mappings (and thus operation) are elusive to casual observers of this blueprint who are not schooled in VTAM and NCP configuration capabilities. Consider Figure 10.51.

Notice that inbound traffic to the DB2 application comes through the NCP, across VTAM, then is directed to the other host via VTAM by channel-to-channel (C-T-C). Also, notice the inbound sessions to TSO from the users connected to the processor that does not have the communication controller attached. Examine the print direction from the JES subsystem to the printer controller by the host that also controls the communication controller.

This blueprint provides much flexibility in ownership of resources, both hardware and software. A location with this network blueprint could include banking, insurance, or other database and data entry-intensive operations.

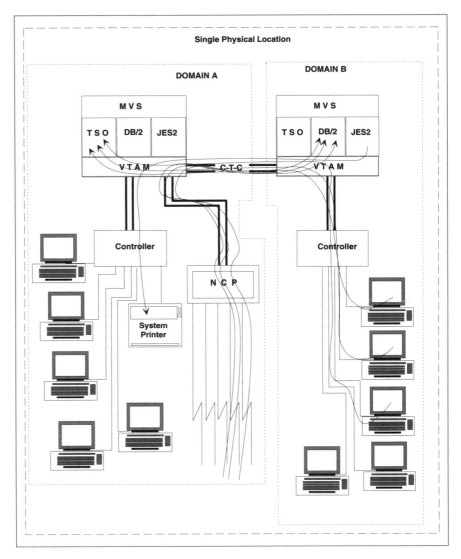

FIGURE 10.51
Software
Perspective of
Blueprint #5

Blueprint #6

Blueprint 6 begins an intensely more complex implementation. It comes from my own experience.

Figure 10.52 shows four processors, four communication controllers, four outbound connections via the communication controllers, and a controller for terminals and printers. Two of the processors have CICS loaded. All of the processors have a copy of DB2 loaded on them. Two of the processors have JES2 loaded on them. The complexity of Blueprint 6 cannot be understated.

FIGURE 10.52
SNA Blueprint #6

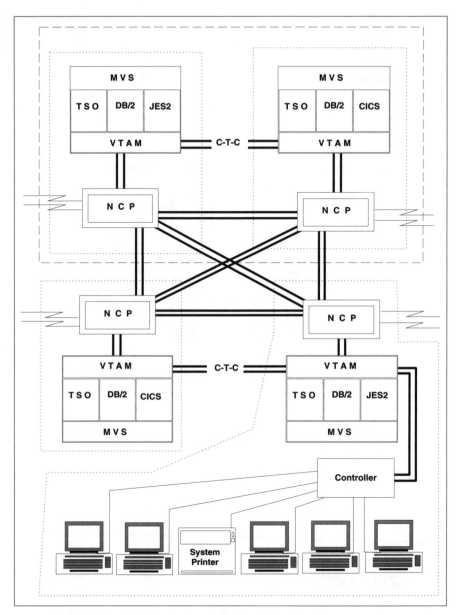

FIGURE 10.52
SNA Blueprint #6

Physically, Blueprint 6 shows all the communication controllers connected via parallel channels. Two of the processors are paired via a C-
T-C connection. The implication of blueprint #6 is that remote users
are routed through the NCPs, and inbound traffic is thus prioritized
with regard to routing in the NCP and not VTAM. This is significant
because this type of blueprint for handling inbound traffic offloads

much routing work to the communication controller rather than passing it back to VTAM on the host processor (see Figure 10.53).

FIGURE 10.53
Highlighted View
of NCP's in SNA
Blueprint #6

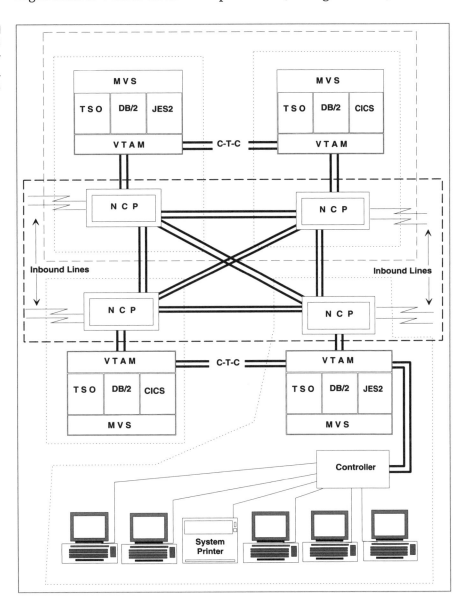

Figure 10.53 shows a highlighted view of the NCPs and the inbound lines from remote users. The parallel channel connections between each communication controller show an explicit path, thus capability

for a logical path, between any of the communication controllers. The consequence of this of scenario is maximum utilization of equipment.

The reason for this type of blueprint is primarily concentrated in routing. Notice two pairs of processors are channel-attached providing maximum routing ability among processors. The blueprint shows how to use routing capabilities in a communication controller and the channels in a processor in the design phase of network planning. Environments being augmented to include additional equipment can also be structured according to this blueprint.

Another benefit from this type of blueprint is that some scalability is possible in each processor. Because each piece of equipment is tuned, smaller processors can be used. The size of a processor may be downsized because of the low level of work due to routing requirements. Some of the *smartest* installations are those wherein each piece of equipment is installed and used so that there is synergy of the equipment as a whole.

Figure 10.54 shows a logical ring environment, a scenario that can be used to create a fault-tolerant environment. One of the host processors could fail and network users might not realize it. If it is configured appropriately a fail-safe environment can easily be achieved.

Blueprint #7

Blueprint 7 highlights current IBM channel systems.

Figure 10.55 shows multiple hosts, ESCON data link connectivity, ESCON directors, ESCON converters, and various equipment typical in such a scenario.

Notice the processors in this blueprint utilize an ESCON subsystem. This is a clear break from previous channel subsystems IBM offered. By definition ESCON is serial delivery of data rather than the parallel transmission used by channel subsystems prior to ESCON.

This blueprint implies some advantages of the ESCON technology. Extended distances can be included in a local setting with SNA processors that use ESCON connectivity. This extended distance capability is a significant improvement over the previous subsystem. ESCON data link connectivity supports data transfer at much higher speeds than did its predecessor. ESCON also provides the advantage of backward capability with previous equipment that may already be in use at a given site; at the same time current technology is integrated to provide enhanced speed.

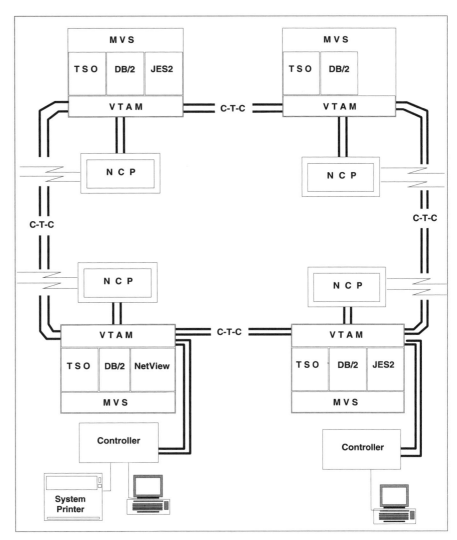

FIGURE 10.54
Logical Ring
View of SNA
Blueprint #6

This blueprint also shows the basics required in most ESCON-based installations. ESCON support is required on behalf of the processor, communications software, and other components used in the network. If compatibility is not possible, then ESCON converters facilitate bridging the gaps among the technology in use.

This blueprint presents the notion of off-load directional data flow at the data link level. This means the ESCON directors are doing much of the *routing* heretofore achieved with other components (software or hardware) in the SNA network. ESCON directors play a major role in a blueprint such as that shown in Figure 10.55. Because this blueprint provides the basics for building a much more dense environment with other components, the directors enable high-speed switching.

FIGURE 10.55
SNA Blueprint #7

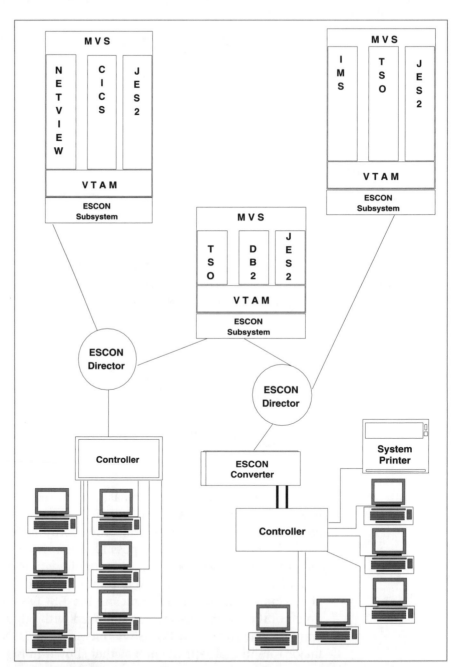

The example shown in Figure 10.55 presents three processors. Each shows different software applications. Assuming users are many, ESCON directors perform much of the routing to the respective processors where work is performed.

Blueprint #8

Blueprint 8 has the following components:

- Multiple processors
- Multiple locations
- Multiple data links among controllers
- Large centralized storage location
- Network management software
- Local print facilities in each location.

Four locations are shown in Figure 10.56 (Dallas, Denver, Phoenix, and Houston). Each location has a processor, links to other locations, software used by that location and a remote location, location print capability, local user support, and remote user support.

This blueprint is a foundation for entities with large databases and data entry personnel in multiple locations. This example could reflect government agencies, large business environments, or even large nonprofit entities. Regardless of *what* the entity is, this example shows a complex blueprint supporting operations for multiple users, multiple time zones, and significant operational size.

This blueprint is typically not implemented *overnight*. For example, the entity represented most likely started with a large single site, then added another location. Subsequently, a third and fourth site were included. The blueprint could be initially designed in network planning to be as this illustration shows.

Benefits of this type blueprint include:

- Redundant links between sites (directly or indirectly)
- Multiple sites have the same application program running
- Logical redundant site operation achievable without great modification
- Personnel at any data center in this blueprint could be moved to another location without major retraining efforts.

The way network management is implemented in this blueprint shows the centralization of management of all sites, while providing distributed update and other support as well.

FIGURE 10.56
SNA Blueprint #8

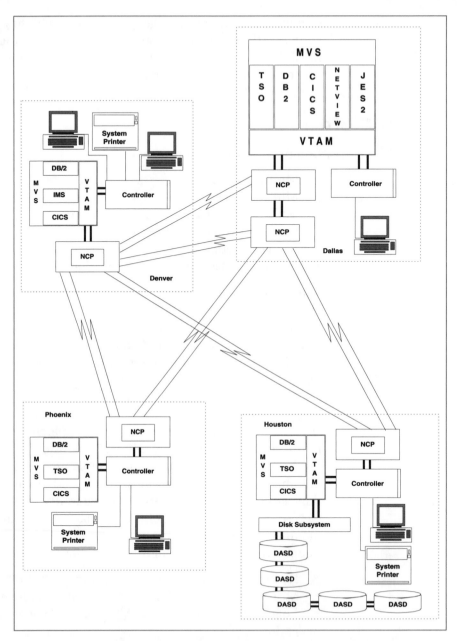

The Dallas location in this example shows two communication controllers. This is a built-in redundant network link ability. Should one of the communication controllers fail in the Dallas location, the other is GENed to take over and maintain operations.

Figure 10.57 is another example of functionality in Blueprint 8.

FIGURE 10.57
Operational
Examples of SNA
Blueprint #8

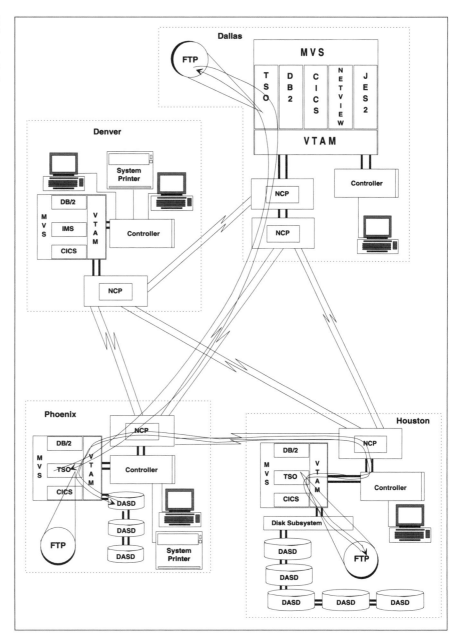

Notice FTP is an application running under TSO in the Dallas,
Phoenix, and Houston, enabling file transfers to be performed
between these environments. A systems person in Dallas could perform a file transfer between the Houston and Phoenix. This ability is

a powerful aspect of the network. Software like this included in the network blueprint during the planning phase can be a great enhancement of overall network operation. This type of program (application) can also significantly reduce costs.

Figure 10.57 shows a slight variation of Figure 10.56. Notice in the Phoenix location in Figure 10.57 that disk drives are shown. Such an augmented network blueprint can provide some degree of redundancy and backup capability. This type of arrangement enables a systems person in another location to perform maintenance functions without physically being in either the Houston or Phoenix location.

This blueprint provides an enormous amount of flexibility for operations, maintenance, management, and growth. Even if one of these physical locations shown in Figure 10.57 were removed, this would still be a good working blueprint from which to build.

Blueprint #9

Blueprint 9 is an example of a real network I worked with. I have seen variations of the operational nature of the blueprint presented here. Consider Figure 10.58.

Some of the highlights of this blueprint include:

- Single host processor
- Large database repository
- Multiple ESCON directors
- Four remote locations
- Redundant remote links
- Centralized network management.

This blueprint is a common scenario found in SNA environments. Whether more or fewer hardware devices are included in this blueprint, it is found worldwide.

This blueprint with a single host processor enables maximum control for operational effectiveness and upgrades as they are necessary. A single processor, assuming it is capable of accommodating the processing power required, can be a good solution. The more diverse and distributed the network environments the harder they are to maintain.

Another aspect of this blueprint is the large database repository. The single location for this repository provides an environment that is fairly easy to secure logically and physically. From a maintenance perspective, having a central repository of DASD enables easier upgrades, maintenance, and implementation and expansion of RAID. Performing backups for the entire database is also easier with a single location for the data repository.

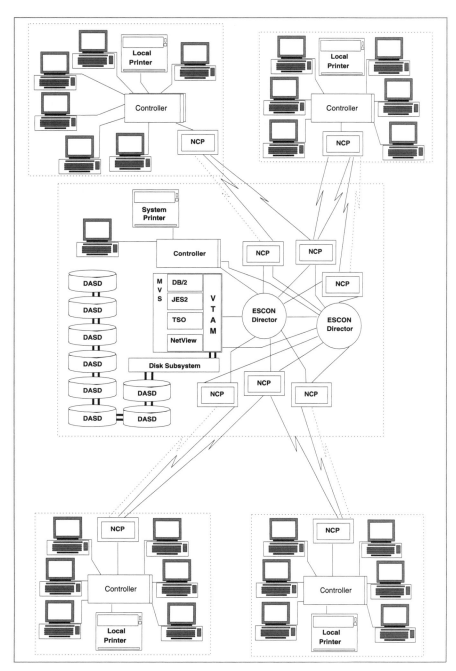

FIGURE 10.58
Blueprint #9

This blueprint shows two ESCON directors. Configuration of these directors and related components enables data-link redundancy within the data center itself. Having a redundant ESCON director can provide great flexibility for any changes required in the data center during operational hours.

The four remote locations shown in this blueprint portray multiple users in each location. Notice the redundant data link between each remote location and the central data center.

Because of the intense data entry from remote locations to the application in the data center, two data links (leased lines) are maintained. The dotted line indicates a switched-line backup that can be used if required due to failure or the need for greater bandwidth from the remote location to the data center.

This blueprint shows NetView as the network management application. This tool enables hardware, software, and link management and can measure usage of system resources such as memory, and CPU requirements during different operational levels, as well as other measurable parameters.

Blueprint #10

This SNA blueprint incorporates technology to make interoperability with non-SNA protocols possible.

Figure 10.59 shows an SNA network in Houston with a basic blueprint similar to Figure 10.60. This blueprint includes a gateway to make TCP/IP network interoperability possible. Host on the TCP/IP network include Sun, IBM, Tandem, and NEC. Each of these hosts uses TCP/IP as a network protocol.

Because there is a gateway between the TCP/IP and SNA, network communication between these diverse environments is possible as are file transfer, remote usage, electronic mail, program-to-program communication, and other functions. The factor what functions are possible is what the gateway vendor supports in the gateway itself.

Another variation on this blueprint is Figure 10.60.

This is similar to Figure 10.59 except Windows NT is used as the method for networking. Notice a gateway appears between the NT network and the SNA network. E-mail, file transfer, remote logons, and other functions users might have available to them are contingent on what is supported in the NT and SNA gateways.

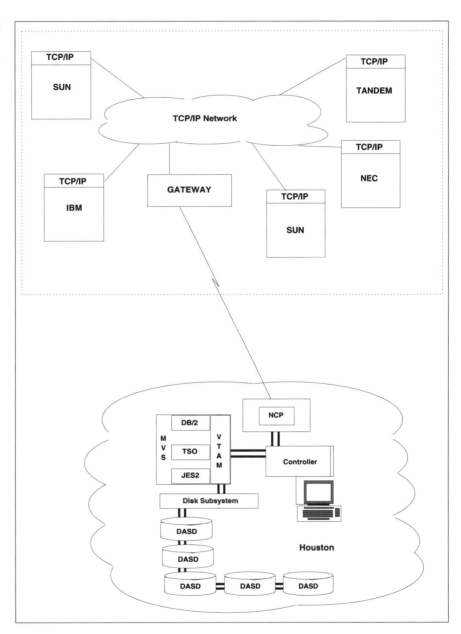

FIGURE 10.59
SNA
Blueprint #10

Blueprint 10 is a guideline for building an SNA network with a great degree of openness for other technologies and protocols not inherently compatible with SNA.

Variations on this blueprint principle could include technology for peer-to-peer program support between SNA and non-SNA networks.

The fundamental principle of this type blueprint is openness toward non-SNA equipment. Because so many different technologies and variations on degrees of integration exist, thet use of openness is the best way to approach an SNA network requiring a more open design scheme.

FIGURE 10.60
Software
Variation of SNA
Blueprint #10

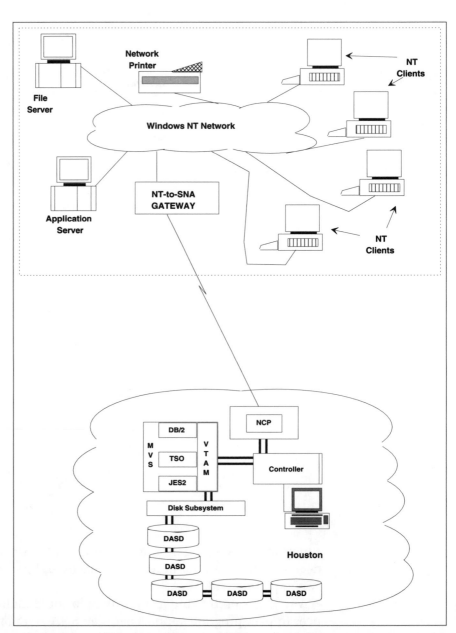

CHAPTER **11**

TCP/IP Blueprints: Part 1

Transmission Control Protocol/Internet Protocol (TCP/IP) is an upper-layer network protocol in widespread use around the world. A presentation of its core components and issues related to TCP/IP, is preceded by a historical perspective.

A Historical Perspective

In the late 1960s a US government entity, the Advanced Research Projects Agency (ARPA) was exploring technologies of all sorts. Then came a need (desire) to create a network based on packet-switching technology to help experiment with what had been built. This would also be a way to use telephone lines to connect scientists and personnel in physically different locations.

By late 1969 the necessary components had come together to create the ARPAnet. In short order a network was created that was capable of exchanging data. Time passed, additions and refinements were made to ARPAnet.

In the 1970s

In 1971 the Defense Advanced Research Projects Agency (DARPA) succeeded ARPA and gained control of the ARPAnet. DARPA's forte was concentration on satellite, radio, and packet-switching technology.

During this same period the ARPAnet used what was called a Network Control Program (NCP). The NCP was so closely tied to the characteristics of ARPAnet, that it had limitations for coping with research, capabilities, and other requirements. The NCP was characteristically slow and had periods when the network was not stable. Since ARPAnet was now officially under DARPA's umbrella, the realization that a new approach to ARPAnet was needed led in a different direction.

Around 1974 DARPA sponsored development for a new set of protocols to replace those currently in use. This led to the development of protocols that were the basis for TCP/IP. The first TCP/IP began to appear in the 1974–1975.

In 1975 the US Department of Defense (DoD) put ARPAnet under the control of the Defense Communication Agency (DCA); the DCA was responsible for operational aspects of the network. It was then that the ARPAnet became the foundation for the Defense Data Network (DDN).

As time passed TCP/IP continued to be enhanced. Many networks emerged to work with and connect to the ARPAnet with TCP/IP protocols. In 1978 TCP/IP was stable enough for a successful public demonstration from a mobile location connecting to a remote location via a satellite.

In the 1980s

From 1978 until 1982 TCP/IP gained momentum and was continually refined. In 1982 multiple strides were made. First, DoD made a policy Statement adopting TCP/IP protocols and making them the overseeing entity for uniting distributed networks. In 1983 DoD formally adopted TCP/IP as the standard the protocol to use when connecting to the ARPAnet.

When DoD formally discontinued support for the NCP and adopted TCP/IP protocol the Internet was born. The term Internet was an outgrowth of internetworking, a technical term used to refer to the interconnection of networks. The term Internet has maintained its association reflecting the multiple networks around the world today.

In the 1990s

The Internet today consists of numerous interconnected networks. The National Research and Education Network (NREN) is now a dominant part of the Internet. Other networks in the Internet include the National Science Foundation network (NSF), NASA, the Department of Education, and educational institutions.

Commercial, educational, and organizations of all types are connected to the Internet. An industry of service providers for the Internet is emerging.

Forces Contributing to the Growth of TCP/IP

Technology

The historical review just completed sheds light on technology of the TCP/IP and the Internet, but does not explain aspects of the Internet that may aid in understanding the technological impact it had on TCP/IP.

The Internet is based on TCP/IP as the US government standardized it. The Internet is worldwide and all sorts of entities are connected to it. Knowing this we can deduce that these entities connected to it are using TCP/IP. This alone accounts for a tremendous amount of TCP/IP in the marketplace.

The 1980s can be characterized as a decade of rapid technological growth. Many companies capitalized on the government endorsement of TCP/IP as the standard for the Internet and began producing related products.

This influx of TCP/IP products spawned the need for additional products. For example, in the 1980s two technologies dominated, PCs and LANs. With the proliferation of PCs and LANs an entirely new industry began emerging. These technological forces seemed to propel TCP/IP forward because TCP/IP and PCs made a good match when implementing LANs. TCP/IP implemented on an individual basis is referred to as an internet (lowercase i).

Market Forces

A factor that contributed to the growth of TCP/IP in the market was corporate downsizing. This was not the only reason for TCP/IP's healthy market share, but it did contribute.

A corporation with headquarters in the northeast had more than 50 satellite offices around the nation. These satellite offices needed independence for daily operations and at the same time connection to the corporate data center. This was achieved by implementing TCP/IP-based LANs in the satellite offices, then connecting them to the data center.

Availability

TCP/IP could be purchased on the shelves of many computer stores by the end of the 1980s. This degree of availability says much for a product which at the beginning of the decade was not readily available to end-users.

The DoD not only encouraged use of TCP/IP, it funded Bolt, Beranek, and Newman to port TCP/IP to UNIX. In addition, DoD encouraged the University of California at Berkeley to include TCP/IP in their BSD UNIX operating system. By acquiring Berkeley UNIX, users got TCP/IP free. It was not long before TCP/IP was added to AT&T's System V UNIX operating system.

Individual Knowledge

By the late 1970s and into the 1980s TCP/IP was in most colleges and many educational institutions. Since it was shipping free with Berkeley UNIX and had availability, it became dominant in learning institutions. Students who graduated from educational institutions with a background in computer science, had usually been exposed to TCP/IP.

These individuals entered the workplace and began penetrating technical and managerial departments. When it came to contributing to a decision about a network protocol, TCP/IP was an obvious choice.

In the 1980s the marketplace paid a premium to those who understood TCP/IP. In the mid-1990s the market has considerable numbers of individuals with varying degrees of TCP/IP knowledge.

All these factors weave together to make TCP/IP the dominant force it is today. Other factors have contributed as well and TCP/IP has become a prevalent upper-layer protocol worldwide.

Layer Analysis

In the early days of the Internet the term gateway became commonplace. It generally meant a connection from a specific location into the Internet. This was adequate at the time, but now confusion abounds about the use of this term.

According to the American Heritage Dictionary the term *gateway* is defined as: "1. An opening, as in a wall or a fence, that may be closed by a gate. 2. A means of access." I believe the original intent of the term's was "a means of access." Today an entire industry called internetworking and integration has appeared and with it specialized devices exist. Once such device is a gateway.

A consensus among integrators and those who integrate heterogeneous networks defines gateway as a device that at a minimum converts upper-layer protocols from one type to another. It can however, convert all seven layers of protocols.

The purpose of explaining this here is that thoughout the presentation on TCP/IP the term gateway may appear. It has such a foothold in the TCP/IP community that it is still used. However, when the term gateway is used in many instances with TCP/IP and the Internet, technically it should be *router*.

Overview and Correlation to the OSI Model

TCP/IP is an upper-layer protocol implemented in software; however some specific implementations have abbreviated TCP/IP protocol stacks implemented in firmware. TCP/IP can operate on different hardware and software platforms and supports more than one data link-layer protocol.

The OSI model is a representation of the layers that *should* exist in a network. Figure 11.1 shows TCP/IP with the OSI model layers to the left.

FIGURE 11.1
TCP/IP and OSI

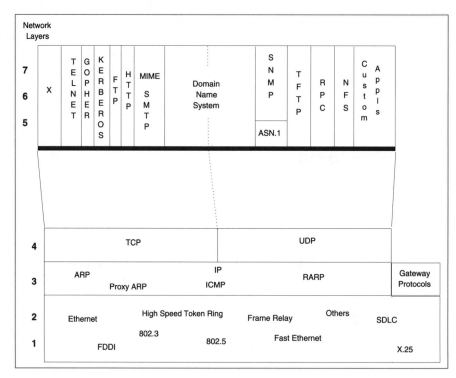

Notice TCP/IP has three layers; network, transport, and the upper three layers combined together functioning as the application layer. TCP/IP is flexible when it comes to the lower two layers and can be implemented in a variety of ways.

TCP/IP can operate with a number of data link-layer protocols. Some are listed in Figure 11.1. The remainder of this section highlights popular components at each layer.

Network Layer Components and Functions

OSI model layer three is the network layer. In TCP/IP it is the lowest layer in the TCP/IP protocol suite. TCP/IP network layer components include:

- **Internet Protocol (IP).** IP has an addressing scheme used to identify the host in which it resides. It is involved in routing functions.
- **Internet Control Message Protocol (ICMP).** ICMP is a required component in each TCP/IP implementation and is responsible for sending messages through the network via the IP header.
- **Address Resolution Protocol (ARP).** ARP dynamically translates IP addresses into physical (hardware interface card) addresses.
- **Reverse Address Resolution Protocol (RARP).** RARP requests its host IP address by broadcasting its hardware address. Typically a RARP server is designated and responds.
- **Routing Information Protocol (RIP).** RIP is a routing protocol used at the network layer. If implemented, it performs routing of packets in the host in which it resides.
- **Open Shortest Path First (OSPF).** This is a routing protocol implemented at the network layer as RIP, but it utilizes knowledge of the internet topology to route messages the quickest way.

Transport Layer Components and Functions

Layer four at the OSI model and in TCP/IP is the transport layer. Transport layer components include:

- **TCP.** This transport-layer protocol is considered reliable and performs retransmissions if necessary.
- **UDP.** This transport-layer protocol is considered unreliable and does not perform retransmissions; this is left up to the application using its services.

Popular Application-Layer Offerings

Above the transport layer in TCP/IP exist a number of popular applications, including:

- **X.** This is a windowing system that can be implemented in a multi-vendor environment.
- **TELNET.** This application provides remote logon services.
- **File Transfer Protocol (FTP).** This application provides file transfer capabilities among heterogeneous systems.
- **Simple Mail Transfer Protocol (SMTP).** This application provides electronic mail services for TCP/IP-based users.

- **Domain Name Service (DNS).** This application is designed to resolve destination addresses in a TCP/IP network. It is an automated method of providing network addresses without having to update host tables manually.
- **Trivial File Transfer Protocol (TFTP).** This UDP application is used best in initialization of network devices where software must be downloaded to a device. Since TFTP is a simple file transfer protocol it meets this need well.
- **Simple Network Management Protocol (SNMP).** This is the way most TCP/IP networks are managed. SNMP is based on an agent and manager arrangement: the agent collects information about a host and the manager maintains status information about hosts participating with agents
- **Network File Server (NFS).** NFS is an application that makes remote directories appear to be part of the directory system to the host which the user is using.
- **Remote Procedure Call (RPC).** This is an application protocol that enables a routine to be called and executed on a server.
- **Custom Applications.** Custom applications can be written using UDP as a transport-layer protocol. By doing so peer communications can be achieved between applications.

TCP/IP Network Requirements

Basic requirements for a TCP/IP network to function include, that *all* participating hosts have TCP/IP operating on each host, to a certain degree; and these must be connected directly or indirectly to a common link (either potentially or actually).

IP Version 4

IP resides at network layer three and routes packets (units of data) from source to destination. Some refer to a packet in the sense of IP as a datagram. An IP datagram is a basic unit moved through a TCP/IP network.

IP is connectionless. It implements two basic functions, fragmentation and addressing. Fragmentation (and reassembly) is accomplished by a field in the IP header and is required when datagrams need to be smaller for passing through a small packet-oriented network.

IPv4 Header Format

The addressing function is also implemented in the IP header, which includes the source and destination address as well as additional information. Figure 11.2 is an example of an IPv4 header.

FIGURE 11.2
IP Version 4
Header

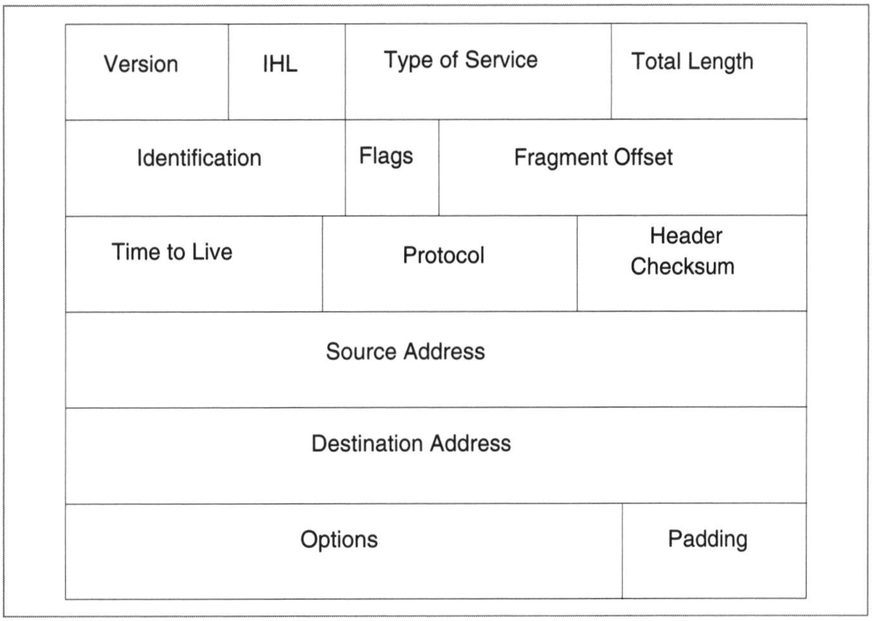

Version	IHL	Type of Service	Total Length
Identification		Flags	Fragment Offset
Time to Live		Protocol	Header Checksum
Source Address			
Destination Address			
Options			Padding

The components in the IP header are:

- **Version.** The version field is used to indicate the format of the IP header.
- **IHL.** IHL stands for internet header length, the length of the internet header in 32-bit words. It points to the beginning of data.
- **Type of Service.** The type of service field specifies how the datagram is treated during its transmission through the network.
- **Total Length.** This field indicates the total length of the datagram; it includes the IP header and data.
- **Flags.** The flag field has three bits, used to indicate if fragmentation is supported, not to fragment, or to indicate more and last fragments.
- **Fragment Offset.** This indicates where in the datagram the fragment belongs (assuming fragmentation has occurred).

- **Time to Live.** This indicates the maximum time a datagram is permitted to stay in the internet system (whether this is a local internet or the Internet). When the value equals zero the datagram is destroyed. Time is measured in units per second, and each entity that processes the datagram must decrease the value by one even if the process time is less than a second.
- **Protocol.** This field determines whether the data should be sent to TCP or UDP in the next layer in the network.
- **Header Checksum.** This is a header checksum only. Some header fields change and the header checksum is recomputed and verified every place the the header is processed.
- **Source Address.** This is the originator of the datagram. It consists of 32 bits.
- **Destination Address.** This is target for the header and data. It too is 32 bits.
- **Options.** Options may or may not appear in datagrams; they must be implemented in IP modules; but they may not be used in any given transmission. A number of variables in the options field exist. The following is a list of those variables including a brief explanation:
  - **No Option.** This option can be used between options to correlate the beginning of a following option on a 32 bit boundary.
  - **Security.** Security is a mechanism used by DoD to provides hosts a way to use security, by means of compartmentation, handling restrictions, and transmission control codes (TCC). The compartmentation value is used when information transmitted is not compartmented. Handling restrictions are defined by the Defense Intelligence Agency. TCC permits segregation of data traffic.
  - **Loose Source and Record Route.** This provides a way for the source of a datagram to supply information for routers to aid in forwarding the datagram. It also serves to record the route information.
  - **Strict Source and Record Route.** This option permits the source of a datagram to supply information used by routers and record the route information.
  - **Record Route.** This is a way to record the route of a datagram as it traverses the network.
  - **Stream Identifier.** This provides a way for a stream identifier to be carried through networks that do not support the stream concept.

- **Timestamp.** This option includes a pointer, overflow, flag field and internet address. It provides the time and date when a router handles the datagram
- **Padding.** The padding is used to ensure the header ends on the 32-bit boundary.

Internet Protocol Version 6 (IPv6)

IPv6 is a new version of the Internet protocol, designed as a successor to IPv4 [RFC 791]. The changes from IPv4 to IPv6 fall primarily into the following categories:

Expanded Addressing Capabilities

IPv6 increases the IP address size from 32 bits to 128 bits, to support more levels of addressing hierarchy, a much greater number of addressable nodes, and simpler autoconfiguration of addresses. The scale-ability of multicast routing is improved by adding a "scope" field to multicast addresses. A new type of address called an "anycast address" is used to send a packet to any one of a group of nodes.

Header Format Simplification

Some IPv4 header fields were dropped or made optional, to reduce the common-case processing cost of packet handling and to limit the bandwidth cost of the IPv6 header.

Improved Support for Extensions and Options

Changes in the way IP header options are encoded allow for more efficient forwarding, less stringent limits on the length of options, and greater flexibility for introducing new options in the future.

Flow Labeling Capability

A new capability is added to enable the labeling of packets belonging to particular traffic "flows" for which the sender requests special handling, such as non-default quality of service or real-time service.

Authentication and Privacy Capabilities

Extensions to support authentication, data integrity, and data confidentiality are specified for IPv6. The basic IPv6 header and the initially-defined IPv6 extension headers and options are, and RFC 791 also discusses packet size issues, the semantics of flow labels and priority, and the effects of IPv6 on upper-layer protocols. The format and semantics of IPv6 addresses are specified separately in RFC 1884. The IPv6 version of ICMP, which all IPv6 implementations are required to include, is specified in RFC 1885.

IPv6 Terminology

The following terms are important in IPv6:

- **Node.** A device that implements IPv6
- **Router.** A node that forwards IPv6 packets not explicitly addressed to itself
- **Host.** Any node that is not a router
- **Upper Layer.** A protocol layer immediately above IPv6. Examples are transport protocols such as TCP and UDP, control protocols such as ICMP, routing protocols such as OSPF, and internet or lower-layer protocols being "tunneled" over (i.e., encapsulated in) IPv6 such as IPX, AppleTalk, or IPv6 itself.
- **Link.** A communication facility or medium over which nodes can communicate at the link layer, i.e., the layer immediately below IPv6. Examples are Ethernets (simple or bridged); PPP links; X.25, Frame Relay, or ATM networks; and internet (or higher) layer *tunnels*, such as tunnels over IPv4 or IPv6 itself.
- **Neighbors.** Nodes attached to the same link
- **Interface.** A node's attachment to a link
- **Address.** An IPv6-layer identifier for an interface or a set of interfaces
- **Packet.** An IPv6 header plus payload
- **Link MTU.** The maximum transmission unit, i.e., maximum packet size in octets, that can be conveyed in one piece over a link.
- **Path MTU.** The minimum link MTU of all the links in a path between a source node and a destination node.

It is possible for a device with multiple interfaces to be configured to forward non-self-destined packets arriving from some set (fewer than all) of its interfaces, and to discard non-self-destined packets arriving from its other interfaces. Such a device must obey the protocol requirements for routers when receiving packets from, and interacting with neighbors over, the former (forwarding) interfaces. It must obey the protocol requirements for hosts when receiving packets from, and interacting with neighbors over, the latter (non-forwarding) interfaces.

IPv6 Header Format

Figure 11.3 presents an IPv6 header format.

FIGURE 11.3
IP Version 6
Header Format

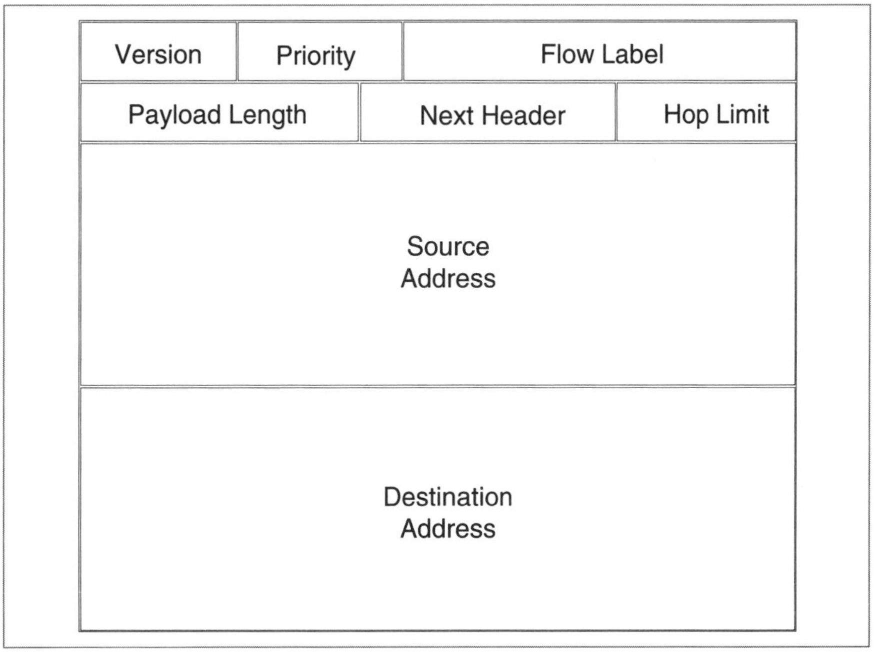

- **Version.** 4-bit Internet protocol version number = 6
- **Priority.** 4-bit priority value
- **Flow Label.** 24-bit flow label
- **Payload Length.** 16-bit unsigned integer, this is the rest of the packet following the IPv6 header, in octets. A zero indicates that the payload length is carried in a Jumbo Payload hop-by-hop option.
- **Next Header.** An 8-bit selector, this identifies the type of header immediately following the IPv6 header, and uses the same values as the IPv4 protocol field.

- **Hop Limit.** An 8-bit unsigned integer, this is decreased by one by each node that forwards the packet. The packet is discarded if the hop limit becomes zero.
- **Source Address.** The 128-bit address of the originator of the packet.
- **Destination Address.** The 128-bit address of the intended recipient of the packet (possibly not the ultimate recipient, if a routing header is present).

IPv6 Extension Headers

In IPv6, optional internet-layer information is encoded in separate headers that may be placed between the IPv6 header and the upper-layer header in a packet. There are a small number of such extension headers, each identified by a distinct Next Header value. As illustrated in these examples, an IPv6 packet may carry zero, one, or more extension headers, each identified by the Next Header field of the preceding header:

```
+---------------+-----------------------
| IPv6 header   | TCP header + data
|               |
| Next Header = |
|    TCP        |
+---------------+-----------------------

+---------------+----------------+------------------------
| IPv6 header   | Routing header | TCP header + data
|               |                |
| Next Header = | Next Header =  |
|   Routing     |    TCP         |
+---------------+----------------+------------------------

+---------------+----------------+------------------+----------------
|IPv6 header    | Routing header | Fragment header  | fragment of TCP
|               |                |                  | header + data
| Next Header = | Next Header =  | Next Header =    |
|   Routing     |   Fragment     |    TCP           |
+---------------+----------------+------------------+----------------
```

With one exception, extension headers are not examined or processed by any node along a packet's delivery path, until the packet reaches the node (or each of the set of nodes, in the case of multicast) identified in the Destination Address field of the IPv6 header. There, normal demultiplexing on the Next Header field of the IPv6 header invokes the module to process the first extension header, or the upper-layer header if no extension header is present. The contents and semantics of each extension header determine whether or not to proceed to the next header. Therefore, extension headers must be processed strictly in the order they appear in the packet; a receiver must not, for example, scan through a packet looking for a particular kind of extension header and process that header prior to processing all preceding ones.

The exception referred to in the preceding paragraph is the Hop-by-Hop Options header, which carries information that must be examined and processed by every node along a packet's delivery path, including the source and destination nodes. When the Hop-by-Hop Options header is present, it must immediately follow the IPv6 header. Its presence is indicated by the value zero in the Next Header field of the IPv6 header.

If, as a result of processing a header, a node is required to proceed to the next header but the Next Header value in the current header is unrecognized by the node, it should discard the packet and send an ICMP Parameter Problem message to the source of the packet, with an ICMP Code value of 2 ("unrecognized Next Header type encountered") and the ICMP Pointer field containing the offset of the unrecognized value within the original packet. The same action should be taken if a node encounters a Next Header value of zero in any header other than an IPv6 header.

Each extension header is an integer multiple of 8 octets long, in order to retain 8-octet alignment for subsequent headers. Multi-octet fields within each extension header are aligned on their natural boundaries, i.e., fields of width n octets are placed at an integer multiple of n octets from the start of the header, with n = 1, 2, 4, or 8.

A full implementation of IPv6 includes the following extension headers: Hop-by-Hop Options, Routing (Type 0), Fragment, Destination Options, Authentication, and Encapsulating Security Payload.

Extension Header Order

When more than one extension header is used in the same packet, it is recommended that those headers appear in the following order:

- IPv6 header
- Hop-by-Hop Options header
- Destination Options header
- Routing header
- Fragment header
- Authentication header

- Encapsulating Security Payload header
- Destination Options header
- Upper-layer header

This way options can be processed by the first destination that appears in the IPv6 Destination Address field plus subsequent destinations listed in the Routing header.

Each extension header should occur at most once, except for the Destination Options header which should occur at most twice (once before a Routing header and once before the upper-layer header). If the upper-layer header is another IPv6 header (in the case of IPv6 being tunneled over or encapsulated in IPv6), it may be followed by its own extensions headers, which are separately subject to the same ordering recommendations.

If and when other extension headers are defined, their ordering constraints relative to the above-listed headers must be specified.

IPv6 nodes must accept and attempt to process extension headers in any order and occurring any number of times in the same packet, except for the Hop-by-Hop Options header which is restricted to appearing immediately after an IPv6 header only. It is strongly advised that sources of IPv6 packets adhere to the above recommended order until and unless subsequent specifications revise that recommendation.

Options

Two of the currently-defined extension headers—the Hop-by-Hop Options header and the Destination Options header—*carry a variable number of type-length-value (TLV) encoded options,* of the following format:

```
+-+-+-+-+-+-+-+-+-+-+-+-+-+-+-+-+- - - - - - - -
| Option Type   | Opt Data Len  | Option Data
+-+-+-+-+-+-+-+-+-+-+-+-+-+-+-+-+- - - - - - - -
```

- **Option Type.** 8-bit identifier of the type of option.
- **Optional Data Length.** 8-bit unsigned integer; length of the option; data field of this option, in octets.
- **Option Data.** Variable-length field; option types specific data.

The sequence of options within a header must be processed in the order they appear in the header; a receiver must not, for example, scan through the header looking for a particular kind of option and process that option prior to processing all preceding ones.

The Option Type identifiers are internally encoded such that their highest-order two bits specify the action that must be taken if the processing IPv6 node does not recognize the Option Type:

00	Skip over this option and continue processing the header.
01	Discard the packet.
10	Discard the packet and, regardless of whether or not the packet's destination address was a multicast address, send an ICMP Parameter Problem, Code 2, message to the packet's source address, pointing to the unrecognized option type.
11	Discard the packet and, only if the packet's destination address was not a multicast address, send an ICMP Parameter Problem, Code 2, message to the packet's source address, pointing to the unrecognized option type.

The third-highest-order bit of the option type specifies whether or not the option data of that option can change en route to the packet's final destination. When an Authentication header is present in the packet, for any option whose data may change en route, its entire option data field must be treated as zero-valued octets when computing or verifying the packet's authenticating value.

0	Option data do not change en route
1	Option data may change en route

Individual options may have specific alignment requirements, to ensure that multi-octet values within option data fields fall on natural boundaries. The alignment requirement of an option is specified using the notation xn+y, meaning the option type must appear as an integer multiple of x octets from the start of the header, plus y octets. For example:

2n	Means any 2-octet offset from the start of the header.
8n+2	Means any 8-octet offset from the start of the header, plus 2 octets.

There are two padding options used when necessary to align subsequent options and to pad out the containing header to a multiple of 8 octets in length. These padding options must be recognized by all IPv6 implementations:

Pad1 option (alignment requirement: none)

```
+-+-+-+-+-+-+-+-+
|       0       |
+-+-+-+-+-+-+-+-+
```

The format of the Pad1 option is a special case—it does not have length and value fields. Pad 1 option is used to insert one octet of padding into the Options area of a header. If more than one octet of padding is required, the PadN option, described next, should be used, rather than multiple Pad1 options.

PadN option (alignment requirement: none)

```
+-+-+-+-+-+-+-+-+-+-+-+-+-+-+-+-+- - - - - - - -
|       1       | Opt Data Len | Option Data
+-+-+-+-+-+-+-+-+-+-+-+-+-+-+-+-+- - - - - - - -
```

The PadN option is used to insert two or more octets of padding into the Options area of a header. For n octets of padding, the Opt Data Len field contains the value n-2, and the option Data consist of n-2 zero-valued octets.

IPv6 Hop-by-Hop Options Header

The Hop-by-Hop Options header is used to carry optional information that must be examined by every node along a packet's delivery path. It is identified by a Next Header value of 0 in the IPv6 header, and has the following format:

```
+-+-+-+-+-+-+-+-+-+-+-+-+-+-+-+-+-+-+-+-+-+-+-+-+-+-+-+-+-+-+-+-+
| Next Header  |  Hdr Ext Len  |                               |
+-+-+-+-+-+-+-+-+-+-+-+-+-+-+-+-+                               +
|                                                              |
.                                                              .
.                          Options                             .
.                                                              .
|                                                              |
+-+-+-+-+-+-+-+-+-+-+-+-+-+-+-+-+-+-+-+-+-+-+-+-+-+-+-+-+-+-+-+-+
```

- **Next Header.** 8-bit selector. This identifies the type of header immediately following the Hop-by-Hop Options header and uses the same values as the IPv4 protocol field.
- **Hdr Ext Len.** 8-bit unsigned integer, the length of the Hop-by-Hop Options header in 8-octet units, not including the first 8 octets
- **Options.** Variable-length field, of length such that the complete Hop-by-Hop Options header is an integer multiple of 8 octets long. It contains one or more TLV-encoded options.

In addition to the Pad1 and PadN options the following Hop-by-Hop option is defined:

Jumbo Payload option: (alignment requirement: 4n + 2)

```
+-+-+-+-+-+-+-+-+-+-+-+-+-+-+-+-+
|     194       |Opt Data Len=4 |
+-+-+-+-+-+-+-+-+-+-+-+-+-+-+-+-+-+-+-+-+-+-+-+-+-+-+-+-+-+-+-+-+
|                     Jumbo Payload Length                      |
+-+-+-+-+-+-+-+-+-+-+-+-+-+-+-+-+-+-+-+-+-+-+-+-+-+-+-+-+-+-+-+-+
```

The Jumbo Payload option is used to send IPv6 packets with payloads longer than 65,535 octets. The jumbo payload length is the length of the packet in octets, excluding the IPv6 header but including the Hop-by-Hop Options header; it must be greater than 65,535. If a packet is received with a Jumbo Payload option containing a jumbo payload length less than or equal to 65,535, an ICMP Parameter Problem message, Code 0, should be sent to the packet's source, pointing to the high-order octet of the invalid Jumbo Payload Length field.

The Payload Length field in the IPv6 header must be set to zero in every packet that carries the Jumbo Payload option. If a packet is received with a valid Jumbo Payload option present and a non-zero IPv6 Payload Length field, an ICMP Parameter Problem message, Code 0, should be sent to the packet's source, pointing to the Option Type field of the Jumbo Payload option. The Jumbo Payload option must not be used in a packet that carries a Fragment header. If a Fragment header is encountered in a packet that contains a valid Jumbo Payload option, an ICMP Parameter Problem Message, Code 0, should be sent to the packet's source, pointing to the first octet of the Fragment header.

An implementation that does not support the Jumbo Payload option cannot have interfaces to links whose link MTU is greater than 65,575 (40 octets of IPv6 header plus 65,535 octets of payload).

IPv6 Routing Header

The Routing header is used by an IPv6 source to list one or more intermediate nodes to be "visited" on the way to a packet's destination. This function is similar to IPv4's Source Route options. The Routing header is identified by a Next Header value of 43 in the immediately preceding header, and has the following format:

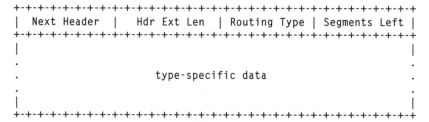

```
+-+-+-+-+-+-+-+-+-+-+-+-+-+-+-+-+-+-+-+-+-+-+-+-+-+-+-+-+-+-+-+-+
|  Next Header  |  Hdr Ext Len  | Routing Type  | Segments Left |
+-+-+-+-+-+-+-+-+-+-+-+-+-+-+-+-+-+-+-+-+-+-+-+-+-+-+-+-+-+-+-+-+
|                                                               |
.                                                               .
.                     type-specific data                       .
.                                                               .
|                                                               |
+-+-+-+-+-+-+-+-+-+-+-+-+-+-+-+-+-+-+-+-+-+-+-+-+-+-+-+-+-+-+-+-+
```

- **Next Header.** 8-bit selector. This identifies the type of header immediately following the Routing header, and uses the same values as the IPv4 Protocol field.
- **Hdr Ext Len.** 8-bit unsigned integer, the length of the Routing header in 8-octet units, not including the first 8 octets
- **Routing Type.** 8-bit identifier of a particular Routing header variant
- **Segments Left.** 8-bit unsigned integer; the number of route segments remaining, i.e., number of explicitly listed intermediate nodes still to be visited before reaching the final destination
- **Type-specific Data.** Variable-length field; its format is determined by the routing type, and its length is such that the complete Routing header is an integer multiple of 8 octets long.

If, while processing a received packet, a node encounters a Routing header with an unrecognized Routing Type value, the required behavior of the node depends on the value of the Segments Left field, as follows:

If segments left is zero, the node must ignore the Routing header and proceed to process the next header in the packet, whose type is identified by the Next Header field in the Routing header.

If segments left is non-zero, the node must discard the packet and send an ICMP Parameter Problem, Code 0, message to the packet's source address, pointing to the unrecognized routing type.

Type 0 Routing header has the following format:

```
+-+-+-+-+-+-+-+-+-+-+-+-+-+-+-+-+-+-+-+-+-+-+-+-+-+-+-+-+-+-+-+-+
| Next Header   |  Hdr Ext Len  |Routing Type=0 | Segments Left |
+-+-+-+-+-+-+-+-+-+-+-+-+-+-+-+-+-+-+-+-+-+-+-+-+-+-+-+-+-+-+-+-+
|    Reserved   |            Strict/Loose Bit Map               |
+-+-+-+-+-+-+-+-+-+-+-+-+-+-+-+-+-+-+-+-+-+-+-+-+-+-+-+-+-+-+-+-+
|                                                               |
+                                                               +
|                                                               |
+                           Address 1                           +
|                                                               |
+                                                               +
|                                                               |
+-+-+-+-+-+-+-+-+-+-+-+-+-+-+-+-+-+-+-+-+-+-+-+-+-+-+-+-+-+-+-+-+
|                                                               |
+                                                               +
|                                                               |
+                           Address 2                           +
|                                                               |
+                                                               +
|                                                               |
+-+-+-+-+-+-+-+-+-+-+-+-+-+-+-+-+-+-+-+-+-+-+-+-+-+-+-+-+-+-+-+-+
.                               .                               .
.                               .                               .
.                               .                               .
+-+-+-+-+-+-+-+-+-+-+-+-+-+-+-+-+-+-+-+-+-+-+-+-+-+-+-+-+-+-+-+-+
|                                                               |
+                                                               +
|                                                               |
+                          Address[n]                           +
|                                                               |
+                                                               +
|                                                               |
+-+-+-+-+-+-+-+-+-+-+-+-+-+-+-+-+-+-+-+-+-+-+-+-+-+-+-+-+-+-+-+-+
```

- **Next Header.** 8-bit selector. This identifies the type of header immediately following the Routing header, and uses the same values as the IPv4 Protocol field.
- **Hdr Ext Len.** 8-bit unsigned integer, the length of the Routing header in 8-octet units, not including the first 8 octets. For the Type 0 Routing header, Hdr Ext Len is equal to two times the number of addresses in the header, and must be an even number less than or equal to 46.
- **Routing Type.** 0.
- **Segments Left.** 8-bit unsigned integer, the number of route segments remaining, i.e., number of explicitly listed intermediate nodes still to be visited before reaching the final destination. Maximum legal value is 23.

- **Reserved.** 8-bit reserved field, this is initialized to zero for transmission and ignored on reception.
- **Strict/Loose Bit Map.** 24-bit bit-map, numbered 0 to 23, left-to-right. It indicates for each segment of the route, whether or not the next destination address must be a neighbor of the preceding address: 1 means strict (must be a neighbor), 0 means loose (need not be a neighbor).
- **Address[1..n].** Vector of 128-bit addresses, numbered 1 to n, multicast addresses must not appear in a Routing header of Type 0, or in the IPv6 Destination Address field of a packet carrying a Routing header of Type 0. If bit number 0 of the Strict/Loose Bit Map has value 1, the Destination Address field of the IPv6 header in the original packet must identify a neighbor of the originating node. If bit number 0 has value 0, the originator may use any legal, non-multicast address as the initial destination address.

Bits numbered greater than n, where n is the number of addresses in the Routing header, must be set to 0 by the originator and ignored by receivers.

A Routing header is not examined or processed until it reaches the node identified in the Destination Address field of the IPv6 header. In that node, dispatching on the Next Header field of the immediately preceding header causes the Routing header module to be invoked, which, in the case of routing type 0, performs the following algorithm:

```
if Segments Left = 0
{
proceed to process the next header in the packet, whose type is
identified by the Next Header field in the Routing header
}
else if Hdr Ext Len is odd or greater than 46
{
send an ICMP Parameter Problem, Code 0, message to the Source Address,
pointing to the Hdr Ext Len field, and discard the packet
}
else
{
compute n, the number of addresses in the Routing header, by dividing
Hdr Ext Len by 2 if Segments Left is greater than n
{
send an ICMP Parameter Problem, Code 0, message to the source address,
pointing to the Segments Left field, and discard the packet
}
   else
{
decrement Segments Left by 1; compute i, the index of the next address
to be visited in the address vector, by subtracting Segments Left from
n if Address [i] or the IPv6 Destination Address is multicast
```

```
{
discard the packet
}
else
{
swap the IPv6 Destination Address and Address[i] if bit i of the
Strict/Loose Bit map has value 1 and the new Destination Address is
not the address of a neighbor of this node
{
send an ICMP Destination Unreachable—Not a Neighbor message to the
source address and discard the packet
}
else if the IPv6 hop limit is less than or equal to 1
{
send an ICMP Time Exceeded—Hop Limit Exceeded in Transit message to
the source address and discard the packet
}
else
{
decrement the Hop Limit by 1 and resubmit the packet to the IPv6 mod-
ule for transmission to the new destination
                             }
                 }
         }
}
```

Consider the case of a source node S sending a packet to destination node D, using a Routing header to cause the packet to be routed via intermediate nodes I1, I2, and I3. The values of the relevant IPv6 header and Routing header fields on each segment of the delivery path would be:

```
As the packet travels from S to I1:
Source Address = S                      Hdr Ext Len = 6
Destination Address = I1                Segments Left = 3
                                        Address[1] = I2
(if bit 0 of the Bit Map is 1,         Address[2] = I3
S and I1 must be neighbors;             Address[3] = D
this is checked by S)
As the packet travels from I1 to I2:
Source Address = S                      Hdr Ext Len = 6
Destination Address = I2                Segments Left = 2
                                        Address[1] = I1
(if bit 1 of the Bit Map is 1,         Address[2] = I3
I1 and I2 must be neighbors;            Address[3] = D
this is checked by I1)
As the packet travels from I2 to I3:
Source Address = S                      Hdr Ext Len = 6
Destination Address = I3                Segments Left = 1
                                        Address[1] = I1
(if bit 2 of the Bit Map is 1,         Address[2] = I2
I2 and I3 must be neighbors;            Address[3] = D
```

```
        this is checked by I2)
        As the packet travels from I3 to D:
        Source Address = S                          Hdr Ext Len = 6
        Destination Address = D                     Segments Left = 0
                                                    Address[1] = I1
        (if bit 3 of the Bit Map is 1,              Address[2] = I2
        I3 and D must be neighbors;                 Address[3] = I3
        this is checked by I3)
```

IPv6 Fragment Header

The Fragment header is used by an IPv6 source to send packets larger than would fit in the path MTU to their destinations. (Note: unlike IPv4, fragmentation in IPv6 is performed only by source nodes, not by routers along a packet's delivery path.) The Fragment header is identified by a Next Header value of 44 in the immediately preceding header, and has the following format:

```
+-+-+-+-+-+-+-+-+-+-+-+-+-+-+-+-+-+-+-+-+-+-+-+-+-+-+-+-+-+-+-+-+
| Next Header   |   Reserved    |      Fragment Offset    |Res|M|
+-+-+-+-+-+-+-+-+-+-+-+-+-+-+-+-+-+-+-+-+-+-+-+-+-+-+-+-+-+-+-+-+
|                         Identification                        |
+-+-+-+-+-+-+-+-+-+-+-+-+-+-+-+-+-+-+-+-+-+-+-+-+-+-+-+-+-+-+-+-+
```

- **Next Header.** 8-bit selector; it identifies the initial header type of the fragmentable part of the original packet and uses the same values as the IPv4 Protocol field.
- **Reserved.** 8-bit reserved field; it is initialized to zero for transmission and ignored on reception.
- **Fragment Offset.** 13-bit unsigned integer; the offset, in 8-octet units, of the data following this header, relative to the start of the fragmentable part of the original packet.
- **Res.** 2-bit reserved field; it is initialized to zero for transmission and ignored on reception.
- **M flag.** 1 = more fragments; 0 = last fragment
- **Identification 32 bits.** See description below.

In order to send a packet that is too large to fit in the MTU of the path to its destination, a source node may divide the packet into fragments and send each fragment as a separate packet, to be reassembled at the receiver. For every packet that is to be fragmented, the source node generates an Identification value. The identification must be different from that of any other fragmented packet sent recently* with the same source address and destination address. If a Routing header is present, the destination address of concern is that of the final destination.

The initial, unfragmented packet is referred to as the *original packet*, and it is considered to consist of two parts:

original packet:

```
+------------------+----------------------//-------------------+
|  Unfragmentable  |                Fragmentable               |
|       Part       |                    Part                   |
+------------------+----------------------//-------------------+
```

The unfragmentable part consists of the IPv6 header plus any extension headers that must be processed by nodes en route to the destination, that is, all headers up to and including the Routing header if present, or the Hop-by-Hop Options header if present, or no extension headers.

The fragmentable part consists of the rest of the packet, that is, any extension headers that need be processed only by the final destination node(s), plus the upper-layer header and data.

The fragmentable part of the original packet is divided into fragments, each, except possibly the last ("rightmost") one, being an integer multiple of 8 octets long. The fragments are transmitted in separate "fragment packets" as illustrated:

original packet:

```
+------------------+--------------+--------------+--//--+--------+
|  Unfragmentable  |    first     |    second    |      |  last  |
|       Part       |   fragment   |   fragment   | .... |fragment|
+------------------+--------------+--------------+--//--+--------+
```

fragment packets:

```
+------------------+--------+-------------+
|  Unfragmentable  |Fragment|    first    |
|       Part       | Header |   fragment  |
+------------------+--------+-------------+

+------------------+--------+-------------+
|  Unfragmentable  |Fragment|    second   |
|       Part       | Header |   fragment  |
+------------------+--------+-------------+
```

o

---

* Recently means within the maximum likely lifetime of a packet, including transit time from source to destination and time spent awaiting reassembly with other fragments of the same packet. However, it is not required that a source node know the maximum packet lifetime. Rather, it is assumed that the requirement can be met by maintaining the Identification value as a simple, 32-bit, "wrap-around" counter, incremented each time a packet must be fragmented. It is an implementation choice whether to maintain a single counter for the node or multiple counters, e.g., one for each of the node's possible source addresses, or one for each active (source address, destination address) combination.

```
                                o
                                o
        +------------------+--------+----------+
        |  Unfragmentable  |Fragment|  last    |
        |       Part       | Header | fragment |
        +------------------+--------+----------+
```

Each fragment packet is composed of:

1. The unfragmentable part of the original packet, with the payload length of the original IPv6 header changed to contain the length of this fragment packet only (excluding the length of the IPv6 header itself), and the Next Header field of the last header of the Unfragmentable Part changed to 44.

2. A Fragment header containing: the Next Header value that identifies the first header of the fragmentable part of the original packet. A fragment offset containing the offset of the fragment, in 8-octet units, relative to the start of the fragmentable part of the original packet. The fragment offset of the first ("leftmost") fragment is 0. There is an M Flag value of 0 if the fragment is the last rightmost one, or an M flag value of 1. The Identification value generated is for the original packet.

3. The fragment itself. The lengths of the fragments must be chosen such that the resulting fragment packets fit within the MTU of the path to the packets' destination(s).

At the destination, fragment packets are reassembled into their original, unfragmented form, as illustrated:

reassembled original packet:

```
        +------------------+-----------------------//--------------------+
        |  Unfragmentable  |                   Fragmentable              |
        |       Part       |                       Part                  |
        +------------------+-----------------------//--------------------+
```

The following rules govern reassembly:

An original packet is reassembled only from fragment packets that have the same source address, destination address, and fragment identification.

The unfragmentable part of the reassembled packet consists of all headers up to, but not including, the Fragment header of the first fragment packet (that is, the packet whose fragment offset is zero), with the following two changes:

The Next Header field of the last header of the unfragmentable part is obtained from the Next Header field of the first fragment's Fragment header.

The payload length of the reassembled packet is computed from the length of the unfragmentable part and the length and offset of the last fragment. For example, a formula for computing the payload length of the reassembled original packet is:

$$PL.orig = PL.first - FL.first - 8 + (8 * FO.last) + FL.last$$

where:

PL.orig = Payload length field of reassembled packet

PL.first = Payload length field of first fragment packet

FL.first = Length of fragment following fragment header of first fragment packet

FO.last = Fragment Offset field of Fragment header of last fragment packet

FL.last = Length of fragment following Fragment header of last fragment packet.

The fragmentable part of the reassembled packet is constructed from the fragments following the Fragment headers in each of the fragment packets. The length of each fragment is computed by subtracting from the packet's payload length the length of the headers between the IPv6 header and the fragment itself; its relative position in the fragmentable part is computed from its Fragment Offset value.

The Fragment header is not present in the final, reassembled packet. The following error conditions may arise when reassembling fragmented packets:

If insufficient fragments are received to complete reassembly of a packet within 60 seconds of the reception of the first-arriving fragment of that packet, reassembly of that packet must be abandoned and all the fragments that have been received for that packet must be discarded. If the first fragment (i.e., the one with a fragment offset of zero) has been received, an ICMP Time Exceeded—Fragment Reassembly Time Exceeded message should be sent to the source of that fragment.

If the length of a fragment, as derived from the fragment packet's Payload Length field, is not a multiple of 8 octets and the M flag of that fragment is 1, then that fragment must be discarded and an ICMP Parameter Problem, Code 0, message should be sent to the source of the fragment, pointing to the Payload Length field of the fragment packet.

If the length and offset of a fragment are such that the payload length of the packet reassembled from that fragment would exceed 65,535 octets, then that fragment must be discarded and an ICMP Parameter Problem, Code 0, message should be sent to the source of the fragment, pointing to the Fragment Offset field of the fragment packet.

The following conditions are not expected to occur, but are not considered errors if they do:

The number and content of the headers preceding the Fragment header of different fragments of the same original packet may differ. Whatever headers are present and precede the Fragment header in each fragment packet are processed when the packets arrive, prior to queuing the fragments for reassembly. Only those headers in the Offset Zero fragment packet are retained in the reassembled packet.

The Next Header values in the Fragment headers of different fragments of the same original packet may differ. Only the value from the Offset Zero fragment packet is used for reassembly.

IPv6 Destination Options Header

The Destination Options header is used to carry optional information that needs be examined only by a packet's destination node(s). The Destination Options header is identified by a Next Header value of 60 in the immediately preceding header, and has the following format:

```
+-+-+-+-+-+-+-+-+-+-+-+-+-+-+-+-+-+-+-+-+-+-+-+-+-+-+-+-+-+-+-+-+
| Next Header | Hdr Ext Len |                                 |
+-+-+-+-+-+-+-+-+-+-+-+-+-+-+-+                                 +
|                                                              |
.                                                              .
.                          Options                             .
.                                                              .
|                                                              |
+-+-+-+-+-+-+-+-+-+-+-+-+-+-+-+-+-+-+-+-+-+-+-+-+-+-+-+-+-+-+-+-+
```

- **Next Header.** 8-bit selector; it identifies the type of header immediately following the Destination Options header and uses the same values as the IPv4 protocol field.
- **Hdr Ext Len.** 8-bit unsigned integer; the length of the Destination Options header in 8-octet units, not including the first 8 octets
- **Options.** Variable-length field, of length such that the complete Destination Options header is an integer multiple of 8 octets long; it contains one or more TLV-encoded options.

The only destination options defined are the Pad1 and PadN options.

Note that there are two possible ways to encode optional destination information in an IPv6 packet: either as an option in the Destination Options header, or as a separate extension header. The Fragment header and the Authentication header are examples of the latter approach. Which approach to use depends on what action is desired of a destination node that does not understand the optional information.

If the desired action is for the destination node to discard the packet and, only if the packet's destination address is not a multicast address, send an ICMP Unrecognized Type message to the packet's source address, then the information may be encoded either as a separate header or as an option in the Destination Options header whose option type has the value 11 in its highest-order two bits. The choice may depend on such factors as which takes fewer octets, or which yields better alignment or more efficient parsing.

If any other action is desired, the information must be encoded as an option in the Destination Options header whose option type has the value 00, 01, or 10 in its highest-order two bits, specifying the desired action.

IPv6 No Next Header

The value 59 in the Next Header field of an IPv6 header or any extension header indicates that there is nothing following that header. If the Payload Length field of the IPv6 header indicates the presence of octets past the end of a header whose Next Header field contains 59 octets, those octets must be ignored, and passed on unchanged if the packet is forwarded.

IPv6 Packet Size Considerations

IPv6 requires that every link in the internet have an MTU of 576 octets or greater. On any link that cannot convey a 576-octet packet in one piece, link-specific fragmentation and reassembly must be provided at a layer below IPv6. From each link to which a node is directly attached, the node must be able to accept packets as large as that link's MTU. Links that have a configurable MTU (for example, PPP links must be configured to have an MTU of at least 576 octets) it is recommended that a larger MTU be configured, to accommodate possible encapsulations (i.e., tunneling) without incurring fragmentation.

It is strongly recommended that IPv6 nodes implement Path MTU Discovery, in order to discover and take advantage of paths with MTU greater than 576 octets. However, a minimal IPv6 implementation (e.g., in a boot ROM) may simply restrict itself to sending packets no larger than 576 octets, and omit implementation of Path MTU Discovery.

In order to send a packet larger than a path's MTU, a node may use the IPv6 Fragment header to fragment the packet at the source and have it reassembled at the destination(s). However, the use of such fragmentation is discouraged in any application that is able to adjust its packets to fit the measured path MTU (i.e., down to 576 octets).

A node must be able to accept a fragmented packet that, after reassembly, is as large as 1500 octets, including the IPv6 header. A node is permitted to accept fragmented packets that reassemble to more than 1500 octets. However, a node must not send fragments that reassemble to a size greater than 1500 octets unless it has explicit knowledge that the destination(s) can reassemble a packet of that size.

In response to an IPv6 packet that is sent to an IPv4 destination (i.e., a packet that undergoes translation from IPv6 to IPv4), the originating IPv6 node may receive an ICMP Packet Too Big message reporting a Next-Hop MTU less than 576. In that case, the IPv6 node is not required to reduce the size of subsequent packets to less than 576, but must include a Fragment header in those packets so that the IPv6-to-IPv4 translating router can obtain a suitable Identification value to use in resulting IPv4 fragments. Note that this means the payload may have to be reduced to 528 octets (576 minus 40 for the IPv6 header and 8 for the Fragment header), and smaller still if additional extension headers are used.

The Path MTU Discovery must be performed even in cases where a host "thinks" a destination is attached to the same link as itself.

Unlike with IPv4, it is unnecessary in IPv6 to set a "Don't Fragment" flag in the packet header in order to perform Path MTU Discovery; that is an implicit attribute of every IPv6 packet. Also, those parts of the RFC 1191 procedures that involve use of a table of MTU "plateaus" do not apply to IPv6, because the IPv6 version of the Datagram Too Big message always identifies the exact MTU to be used.

IPv6 Flow Labels

The 24-bit Flow Label field in the IPv6 header may be used by a source to label those packets for which it requests special handling

by the IPv6 routers, such as non-default quality of service or
real-time service. This aspect of IPv6 is, at the time of writing, still
experimental and subject to change as the requirements for flow support in the Internet become clearer. Hosts or routers that do not support the functions of the Flow Label field are required to set the field
to zero when originating a packet, pass the field on unchanged when
forwarding a packet, and ignore the field when receiving a packet.

A flow is a sequence of packets sent from a particular source to a
particular (unicast or multicast) destination for which the source
desires special handling by the intervening routers. The nature of
that special handling might be conveyed to the routers by a control
protocol, such as a resource reservation protocol, or by information
within the flow's packets themselves, e.g., in a hop-by-hop option.

The details of such control protocols or options are beyond the
scope of this discussion.

There may be multiple active flows from a source to a destination,
as well as traffic that is not associated with any flow. A flow is
uniquely identified by the combination of a source address and a
non-zero flow label. Packets that do not belong to a flow carry a flow
label of zero.

A flow label is assigned to a flow by the flow's source node. New
flow labels must be chosen (pseudo-)randomly and uniformly from
the range 1 to FFFFFF hex. The purpose of the random allocation is to
make any set of bits within the Flow Label field suitable for use as a
hash key by routers, for looking up the state associated with the flow.

All packets belonging to the same flow must be sent with the same
source address, destination address, priority, and flow label. If any of
those packets includes a Hop-by-Hop Options header, then they all
must be originated with the same Hop-by-Hop Options header contents (excluding the Next Header field of the Hop-by-Hop Options
header). If any of those packets includes a Routing header, then they
all must be originated with the same contents in all extension headers
up to and including the Routing header (excluding the Next Header
field in the Routing header). The routers or destinations are permitted,
but not required, to verify that these conditions are satisfied. If a violation is detected, it should be reported to the source by an ICMP
Parameter Problem message, Code 0, pointing to the high-order octet
of the Flow Label field (i.e., offset 1 within the IPv6 packet).

Routers are free to "opportunistically" set up flow-handling state
for any flow, even when no explicit flow establishment information
has been provided to them via a control protocol, a hop-by-hop

option, or other means. For example, upon receiving a packet from a particular source with an unknown, non-zero flow label, a router may process its IPv6 header and any necessary extension headers as if the flow label were zero. That processing would include determining the next-hop interface, and possibly other actions, such as updating a hop-by-hop option, advancing the pointer and addresses in a Routing header, or deciding on how to queue the packet based on its Priority field. The router may then choose to "remember" the results of those processing steps and cache that information, using the source address plus the flow label as the cache key. Subsequent packets with the same source address and flow label may then be handled by referring to the cached information rather than examining all those fields that, according to the requirements of the previous paragraph, can be assumed unchanged from the first packet seen in the flow.

A cached flow-handling state that is set up opportunistically, as discussed in the preceding paragraph, must be discarded no more than six seconds after it is established, regardless of whether or not packets of the same flow continue to arrive. If another packet with the same source address and flow label arrives after the cached state has been discarded, the packet undergoes full, normal processing (as if its flow label were zero), which may result in the re-creation of cached flow state for that flow.

The lifetime of the flow-handling state that is set up explicitly, for example by a control protocol or a hop-by-hop option, must be specified as part of the specification of the explicit set-up mechanism; it may exceed six seconds. A source must not re-use a flow label for a new flow within the lifetime of any flow-handling state that might have been established for the prior use of that flow label. Since a flow-handling state with a lifetime of six seconds may be established opportunistically for any flow, the minimum interval between the last packet of one flow and the first packet of a new flow using the same flow label is six seconds. Flow labels used for explicitly-set-up flows with longer flow-state lifetimes must remain unused for those longer lifetimes before being re-used for new flows.

When a node stops and restarts as a result of a *crash*, it must be careful not to use a flow label that it might have used for an earlier flow whose lifetime may not have expired yet. This may be accomplished by recording flow label usage on stable storage so that it can be remembered across crashes, or by refraining from using any flow labels until the maximum lifetime of any possible previously established flows has expired (at least six seconds; more if explicit flow set-up mechanisms with longer lifetimes might have been used). If the minimum time for rebooting the node is known (often more than six seconds), that time can be deducted from the necessary waiting period before starting to allocate flow labels.

There is no requirement that all, or even most, packets belong to flows, i.e., carry non-zero flow labels. This observation is placed here to remind protocol designers and implementors not to assume otherwise. For example, it would be unwise to design a router whose performance would be adequate only if most packets belonged to flows, or to design a header compression scheme that only worked on packets that belonged to flows.

IPv6 Packet Priority

The 4-bit Priority field in the IPv6 header enables a source to identify the desired delivery priority of its packets, relative to other packets from the same source. The Priority values are divided into two ranges: Values 0 through 7 are used to specify the priority of traffic for which the source is providing congestion control, i.e., traffic that "backs off" in response to congestion, such as TCP traffic. Values 8 through 15 are used to specify the priority of traffic that does not back off in response to congestion, e.g., "real-time" packets being sent at a constant rate.

For congestion-controlled traffic, the following Priority values are recommended for particular application categories:

0	Uncharacterized traffic
1	"Filler" traffic (e.g., netnews)
2	Unattended data transfer (e.g., email)
3	(Reserved)
4	Attended bulk transfer (e.g., FTP, NFS)
5	(Reserved)
6	Interactive traffic (e.g., telnet, X)
7	Internet control traffic (e.g., routing protocols, SNMP).

For non-congestion-controlled traffic, the lowest priority value (8) should be used for those packets that the sender is most willing to have discarded under conditions of congestion (e.g., high-fidelity video traffic), and the highest value (15) should be used for those packets that the sender is least willing to have discarded (low-fidelity audio traffic). There is no relative ordering implied between the congestion-controlled priorities and the non-congestion-controlled priorities.

IPv6 and Upper-Layer Protocols

Upper-Layer Checksums

Any transport or other upper-layer protocol that includes the addresses from the IP header in its checksum computation must be modified for use over IPv6, to include the 128-bit IPv6 addresses instead of 32-bit IPv4 addresses. In particular, the following illustration shows the TCP and UDP "pseudo-header" for IPv6:

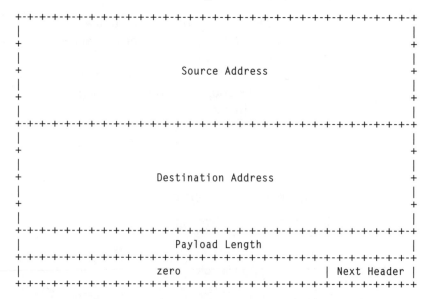

- If the packet contains a Routing header, the destination address used in the pseudo-header is that of the final destination. At the originating node, that address will be in the last element of the Routing header; at the recipient(s), that address will be in the Destination Address field of the IPv6 header.
- The Next Header value in the pseudo-header identifies the upper-layer protocol (6 for TCP or 17 for UDP). It will differ from the Next Header value in the IPv6 header if there are extension headers between the IPv6 header and the upper-layer header.

- The payload length used in the pseudo-header is the length of the upper-layer packet, including the upper-layer header. It will be less than the payload length in the IPv6 header (or in the Jumbo Payload option) if there are extension headers between the IPv6 header and the upper-layer header.
- Unlike in IPv4, when UDP packets are originated by an IPv6 node, the UDP checksum is not optional. That is, whenever originating a UDP packet, an IPv6 node must compute a UDP checksum over the packet and the pseudo-header, and, if that computation yields a result of zero, it must be changed to hex FFFF for placement in the UDP header. IPv6 receivers must discard UDP packets containing zero checksums, and should log the error.

The IPv6 version includes the above pseudo-header in its checksum computation; this is a change from the IPv4 version of ICMP, which does not include a pseudo-header in its checksum. The reason for the change is to protect ICMP from misdelivery or corruption of those fields of the IPv6 header on which it depends; unlike IPv4, these are not covered by an internet-layer checksum. The Next Header field in the pseudo-header for ICMP contains the value 58, which identifies the IPv6 version of ICMP.

Maximum Packet Lifetime

Unlike IPv4, IPv6 nodes are not required to enforce maximum packet lifetime. That is the reason the IPv4 Time to Live field was renamed "Hop Limit" in IPv6. In practice, very few, if any, IPv4 implementations conform to the requirement that they limit packet lifetime, so this is not a change in practice. Any upper-layer protocol that relies on the internet layer (whether IPv4 or IPv6) to limit packet lifetime ought to be upgraded to provide its own mechanisms for detecting and discarding obsolete packets.

Maximum Upper-Layer Payload Size

When computing the maximum payload size available for upper-layer data, an upper-layer protocol must take into account the larger size of the IPv6 header relative to the IPv4 header. For example, in IPv4, TCP's MSS option is computed as the maximum packet size (a default value or a value learned through Path MTU Discovery) minus 40 octets (20 octets for the minimum-length IPv4 header and

20 octets for the minimum-length TCP header). When using TCP over IPv6, the MSS must be computed as the maximum packet size minus 60 octets, because the minimum-length IPv6 header (i.e., an IPv6 header with no extension headers) is 20 octets longer than a minimum-length IPv4 header.

Formatting Guidelines for Options

This gives some advice on how to lay out the fields when designing new options to be used in the Hop-by-Hop Options header or the Destination Options header. These guidelines are based on the following assumptions:

- One desirable feature is that any multi-octet fields within the Option Data area of an option be aligned on their natural boundaries, i.e., fields of width n octets should be placed at an integer multiple of n octets from the start of the Hop-by-Hop or Destination Options header, where n = 1, 2, 4, or 8.
- Another desirable feature is that the Hop-by-Hop or Destination Options header take up as little space as possible, subject to the requirement that the header be an integer multiple of 8 octets long.
- It may be assumed that, when either of the option-bearing headers is present, it carries a very small number of options, usually only one.

These assumptions suggest the following approach to laying out the fields of an option: order the fields from smallest to largest, with no interior padding, then derive the alignment requirement for the entire option based on the alignment requirement of the largest field (up to a maximum alignment of 8 octets). This approach is illustrated in the following examples:

If an option X required two data fields, one of length 8 octets and one of length 4 octets, it would be laid out as follows:

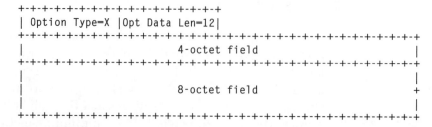

```
+-+-+-+-+-+-+-+-+-+-+-+-+-+-+-+-+
| Option Type=X |Opt Data Len=12|
+-+-+-+-+-+-+-+-+-+-+-+-+-+-+-+-+-+-+-+-+-+-+-+-+-+-+-+-+-+-+-+-+
|                         4-octet field                         |
+-+-+-+-+-+-+-+-+-+-+-+-+-+-+-+-+-+-+-+-+-+-+-+-+-+-+-+-+-+-+-+-+
|                                                               |
|                         8-octet field                         +
|                                                               |
+-+-+-+-+-+-+-+-+-+-+-+-+-+-+-+-+-+-+-+-+-+-+-+-+-+-+-+-+-+-+-+-+
```

Its alignment requirement is 8n+2, to ensure that the 8-octet field starts at a multiple-of-8 offset from the start of the enclosing header. A complete Hop-by-Hop or Destination Options header containing this one option would look as follows:

```
+-+-+-+-+-+-+-+-+-+-+-+-+-+-+-+-+-+-+-+-+-+-+-+-+-+-+-+-+-+-+-+-+
| Next Header  | Hdr Ext Len=1 | Option Type=X |Opt Data Len=12|
+-+-+-+-+-+-+-+-+-+-+-+-+-+-+-+-+-+-+-+-+-+-+-+-+-+-+-+-+-+-+-+-+
|                         4-octet field                        |
+-+-+-+-+-+-+-+-+-+-+-+-+-+-+-+-+-+-+-+-+-+-+-+-+-+-+-+-+-+-+-+-+
|                                                              |
+                         8-octet field                        +
|                                                              |
+-+-+-+-+-+-+-+-+-+-+-+-+-+-+-+-+-+-+-+-+-+-+-+-+-+-+-+-+-+-+-+-+
```

If an option Y required three data fields, one of length 4 octets, one of length 2 octets, and one of length 1 octet, it would be laid out as follows:

```
+-+-+-+-+-+-+-+-+
| Option Type=Y |
+-+-+-+-+-+-+-+-+-+-+-+-+-+-+-+-+-+-+-+-+-+-+-+-+-+-+-+-+-+-+-+-+
|Opt Data Len=7 | 1-octet field |        2-octet field         |
+-+-+-+-+-+-+-+-+-+-+-+-+-+-+-+-+-+-+-+-+-+-+-+-+-+-+-+-+-+-+-+-+
|                         4-octet field                        |
+-+-+-+-+-+-+-+-+-+-+-+-+-+-+-+-+-+-+-+-+-+-+-+-+-+-+-+-+-+-+-+-+
```

Its alignment requirement is 4n+3, to ensure that the 4-octet field starts at a multiple-of-4 offset from the start of the enclosing header. A complete Hop-by-Hop or Destination Options header containing this one option would look as follows:

```
+-+-+-+-+-+-+-+-+-+-+-+-+-+-+-+-+-+-+-+-+-+-+-+-+-+-+-+-+-+-+-+-+
| Next Header  | Hdr Ext Len=1 | Pad1 Option=0 | Option Type=Y |
+-+-+-+-+-+-+-+-+-+-+-+-+-+-+-+-+-+-+-+-+-+-+-+-+-+-+-+-+-+-+-+-+
|Opt Data Len=7 | 1-octet field |        2-octet field         |
+-+-+-+-+-+-+-+-+-+-+-+-+-+-+-+-+-+-+-+-+-+-+-+-+-+-+-+-+-+-+-+-+
|                         4-octet field                        |
+-+-+-+-+-+-+-+-+-+-+-+-+-+-+-+-+-+-+-+-+-+-+-+-+-+-+-+-+-+-+-+-+
| PadN Option=1 |Opt Data Len=2 |       0       |       0       |
+-+-+-+-+-+-+-+-+-+-+-+-+-+-+-+-+-+-+-+-+-+-+-+-+-+-+-+-+-+-+-+-+
```

A Hop-by-Hop or Destination Options header containing both options X and Y from Examples 1 and 2 would have one of the two following formats, depending on which option appeared first:

```
+-+-+-+-+-+-+-+-+-+-+-+-+-+-+-+-+-+-+-+-+-+-+-+-+-+-+-+-+-+-+-+-+
| Next Header   | Hdr Ext Len=3 | Option Type=X |Opt Data Len=12|
+-+-+-+-+-+-+-+-+-+-+-+-+-+-+-+-+-+-+-+-+-+-+-+-+-+-+-+-+-+-+-+-+
|                         4-octet field                         |
+-+-+-+-+-+-+-+-+-+-+-+-+-+-+-+-+-+-+-+-+-+-+-+-+-+-+-+-+-+-+-+-+
|                                                               |
+                         8-octet field                         +
|                                                               |
+-+-+-+-+-+-+-+-+-+-+-+-+-+-+-+-+-+-+-+-+-+-+-+-+-+-+-+-+-+-+-+-+
| PadN Option=1 |Opt Data Len=1 |       0       | Option Type=Y |
+-+-+-+-+-+-+-+-+-+-+-+-+-+-+-+-+-+-+-+-+-+-+-+-+-+-+-+-+-+-+-+-+
|Opt Data Len=7 | 1-octet field |        2-octet field          |
+-+-+-+-+-+-+-+-+-+-+-+-+-+-+-+-+-+-+-+-+-+-+-+-+-+-+-+-+-+-+-+-+
|                         4-octet field                         |
+-+-+-+-+-+-+-+-+-+-+-+-+-+-+-+-+-+-+-+-+-+-+-+-+-+-+-+-+-+-+-+-+
| PadN Option=1 |Opt Data Len=2 |       0       |       0       |
+-+-+-+-+-+-+-+-+-+-+-+-+-+-+-+-+-+-+-+-+-+-+-+-+-+-+-+-+-+-+-+-+
+-+-+-+-+-+-+-+-+-+-+-+-+-+-+-+-+-+-+-+-+-+-+-+-+-+-+-+-+-+-+-+-+
| Next Header   | Hdr Ext Len=3 | Pad1 Option=0 | Option Type=Y |
+-+-+-+-+-+-+-+-+-+-+-+-+-+-+-+-+-+-+-+-+-+-+-+-+-+-+-+-+-+-+-+-+
|Opt Data Len=7 | 1-octet field |        2-octet field          |
+-+-+-+-+-+-+-+-+-+-+-+-+-+-+-+-+-+-+-+-+-+-+-+-+-+-+-+-+-+-+-+-+
|                         4-octet field                         |
+-+-+-+-+-+-+-+-+-+-+-+-+-+-+-+-+-+-+-+-+-+-+-+-+-+-+-+-+-+-+-+-+
| PadN Option=1 |Opt Data Len=4 |       0       |       0       |
+-+-+-+-+-+-+-+-+-+-+-+-+-+-+-+-+-+-+-+-+-+-+-+-+-+-+-+-+-+-+-+-+
|       0       |       0       | Option Type=X |Opt Data Len=12|
+-+-+-+-+-+-+-+-+-+-+-+-+-+-+-+-+-+-+-+-+-+-+-+-+-+-+-+-+-+-+-+-+
|                         4-octet field                         |
+-+-+-+-+-+-+-+-+-+-+-+-+-+-+-+-+-+-+-+-+-+-+-+-+-+-+-+-+-+-+-+-+
|                                                               |
+                         8-octet field                         +
|                                                               |
+-+-+-+-+-+-+-+-+-+-+-+-+-+-+-+-+-+-+-+-+-+-+-+-+-+-+-+-+-+-+-+-+
```

IPv6 Address Architecture

IPv6 is more robust than its predecessor. The ability to accommodate many more entities in the addressing scheme is but one of the advantages it has over IPv4.

This section defines the addressing architecture of the IPv6 protocol. It includes the addressing model, text representations of IPv6 addresses, definition of IPv6 unicast addresses, anycast addresses, and multicast addresses. IPv6 addresses are 128-bit, and come in three types:

- **Unicast.** An identifier for a single interface. A packet sent to a unicast address is delivered to the interface identified by that address.

- **Anycast.** An identifier for a set of interfaces (typically belonging to different nodes). A packet sent to an anycast address is delivered to one of the interfaces identified by that address (the "nearest" one, according to the routing protocols' measure of distance).
- **Multicast.** An identifier for a set of interfaces (typically belonging to different nodes). A packet sent to a multicast address is delivered to all interfaces identified by that address.

There are no broadcast addresses in IPv6. This type of address is superseded by a multicast address. Here address fields are given a specific name, for example *subscriber*. When this name is used with the *ID* for identifier after the name subscriber, it refers to the contents of that field. When it is used with the term prefix it refers to all of the address up to and including this field.

In IPv6, all zeros and ones are legal values for any field unless specifically excluded. Prefixes may contain zero-valued fields or end in zeros.

IPv6 Addressing

IPv6 addresses of all types are assigned to interfaces, *not nodes*. Since each interface belongs to a single node, any of that node's interfaces' unicast addresses may be used as an identifier for the node.

An IPv6 unicast address refers to a single interface, which may be assigned multiple IPv6 addresses of any type (unicast, anycast, multicast). The two exceptions to this model are:

- A single address may be assigned to multiple physical interfaces if the implementation treats the multiple physical interfaces as one interface when presenting it to the internet layer.
- Routers may have unnumbered interfaces on point-to-point links to eliminate the necessity manually to configure and advertise the addresses.

Addresses are not required for point-to-point interfaces on routers if those interfaces are not to be used as the origins or destinations of any IPv6 datagrams.

IPv6 continues the IPv4 subnet model associated with one link. Multiple subnets may be assigned to that link. There are three conventional forms for representing IPv6 addresses as text strings:

1. The preferred form is x:x:x:x:x:x:x:x, where the xs are the hexadecimal values of the eight 16-bit pieces of the address. Examples:

   ```
   FEDC:BA98:7654:3210:FEDC:BA98:7654:3210
   1080:0:0:0:8:800:200C:417A
   ```

2. Due to the method of allocating certain styles of IPv6 addresses, it is common for addresses to contain long strings of zero bits. In order to make writing addresses containing zero bits easier, a special syntax is available to compress the zeros. The use of :: indicates multiple groups of 16-bits of zeros. The :: can only appear once in an address and can also be used to compress the leading and/or trailing zeros in an address.

   Consider the following addresses:

   ```
   1080:0:0:0:8:800:200C:417A      a unicast address
   FF01:0:0:0:0:0:0:43             a multicast address
   0:0:0:0:0:0:0:1                 a loopback address
   0:0:0:0:0:0:0:0                 unspecified addresses
   ```

   These may be represented as:

   ```
   1080::8:800:200C:417A           a unicast address
   FF01::43                        a multicast address
   ::1                             a loopback address
   ::                              unspecified addresses.
   ```

3. An alternative form that is sometimes more convenient when dealing with a mixed environment of IPv4 and IPv6 nodes is x:x:x:x:x:x:d.d.d.d, where the xs are the hexadecimal values of the six high-order 16-bit pieces of the address, and the ds are the decimal values of the four low-order 8-bit pieces of the address (standard IPv4 representation). Two examples are:

   ```
   0:0:0:0:0:0:13.1.68.3 and 0:0:0:0:0:0:FFFF:129.144.52.38.
   ```

   In compressed form these appear are:

   ```
   ::13.1.68.3 and ::FFFF:129.144.52.38.
   ```

Address Type Representation

The specific type of an IPv6 address is indicated by the address' leading bits. The variable-length field comprising these bits is called the Format Prefix (FP). The initial allocation of the prefixes is as follows:

Allocation Space	Prefix (binary)	Fraction of Address Space
Reserved	0000 0000	1/256
Unassigned	0000 0001	1/256
Reserved for NSAP Allocation	0000 001	1/128
Reserved for IPX Allocation	0000 010	1/128
Unassigned	0000 011	1/128
Unassigned	0000 1	1/32
Unassigned	0001	1/16
Unassigned	001	1/8
Provider-Based Unicast Address	010	1/8
Unassigned	011	1/8
Reserved for Geographically Based Unicast Addresses	100	1/8
Unassigned	101	1/8
Unassigned	110	1/8
Unassigned	1110	1/16
Unassigned	1111 0	1/32
Unassigned	1111 10	1/64
Unassigned	1111 110	1/128
Unassigned	1111 1110 0	1/512
Link Local Use Addresses	1111 1110 10	1/1024
Site Local Use Addresses	1111 1110 11	1/1024
Multicast Addresses	1111 1111	1/256

The unspecified address, the loopback address, and the IPv6 addresses with embedded IPv4 addresses are assigned out of the 0000 0000 format prefix space. This allocation supports the direct provider addresses allocation, local use addresses, and multicast addresses. Space is reserved for NSAP addresses, IPX addresses, and geographic addresses. The remainder of the address space is unassigned for future expansion of existing use or for new uses. Fifteen percent of the address space is initially allocated. The remaining 85% is reserved for future use.

Unicast addresses are distinguished from multicast addresses by the value of the high-order octet of the addresses: a value of FF (11111111) identifies an address as a multicast address; any other value identifies an address as a unicast address. Anycast addresses are taken from the unicast address space and are not syntactically distinguishable from unicast addresses.

Unicast Addresses

The IPv6 unicast address is contiguous bit-wise maskable, similar to IPv4 addresses under CIDR. There are several forms of unicast address assignment in IPv6, including the global provider-based unicast address, the geographic-based unicast address, the NSAP address, the IPX hierarchical address, the site-local-use address, the link-local-use address, and the IPv4-capable host address. Additional address types can be defined in the future.

IPv6 nodes may have considerable or little knowledge of the internal structure of the IPv6 address, depending on what the host does. A host is not necessarily a computer in the sense that a user works on it, it could be any valid network device. At a minimum, a node may consider that unicast addresses (including its own) have no internal structure.

```
|                     128 bits                    |
+-------------------------------------------------+
|                   node address                  |
+-------------------------------------------------+
```

A slightly sophisticated (but still rather simple) host may also be aware of subnet prefix(es) for the link(s) it is attached to and different addresses can have different n values.

```
|     n bits     |       128-n bits       |
+----------------+------------------------+
|    subnet prefix                |    interface ID    |
+---------------------------------+--------------------+
```

More sophisticated hosts may be aware of other hierarchical boundaries in the unicast address. Though a very simple router may have no knowledge of the internal structure of IPv6 unicast addresses, routers will more generally have knowledge of one or more of the hierarchical boundaries for the operation of routing protocols. The known boundaries will differ from router to router, depending on what positions the router holds in the routing hierarchy.

The example below is a unicast address format which will likely be common on LANs and other environments where IEEE 802 MAC addresses are available.

```
|     n bits    |    80-n bits    |     48 bits    |
+---------------+-----------------+----------------+
|   subscriber prefix  |   subnet ID   |   Interface ID   |
+----------------------+---------------+------------------+
```

Where the 48-bit interface ID is an IEEE-802 MAC address.

The use of IEEE 802 MAC addresses as interface IDs is expected to be very common in environments where nodes have IEEE 802 MAC addresses. In other environments, where IEEE 802 MAC addresses are not available, other types of link-layer addresses, such as E.164 addresses, can be used for the interface ID.

The inclusion of a unique global interface identifier, such as an IEEE MAC address, makes possible a very simple form of autoconfiguration of addresses. A node may discover a subnet ID by listening to Router Advertisement messages sent by a router on its attached link(s), and then fabricating an IPv6 address for itself by using its IEEE MAC address as the interface ID on that subnet.

Another unicast address format example arises when a site or organization requires additional layers of internal hierarchy. In this example the subnet ID is divided into an area ID and a subnet ID.

```
|    s bits     |    n bits    |    m bits    |  128-s-n-m bits  |
+---------------+--------------+--------------+------------------+
| subscriber prefix | area ID  | subnet ID  | interface ID      |
+---------------+--------------+--------------+------------------+
```

This technique can be continued to allow a site or organization to add additional layers of internal hierarchy. It may be desirable to use an interface ID smaller than a 48-bit IEEE 802 MAC address to allow more space for the additional layers of internal hierarchy. These could be interface IDs administratively created by the site or organization.

The address 0:0:0:0:0:0:0:0 is called the unspecified address. It must never be assigned to any node. It indicates the absence of an address. It is used in the Source Address field of any IPv6 datagrams sent by an initializing host before it has learned its own address.

The unspecified address must not be used as the destination address of IPv6 datagrams or in IPv6 routing headers.

The unicast address 0:0:0:0:0:0:0:1 is called a loopback address. It may be used by a node to send an IPv6 datagram to itself, but may never be assigned to any interface.

The loopback address must not be used as the source address in IPv6 datagrams sent outside a single node. An IPv6 datagram with a destination address of loopback must never be sent outside a single node.

IPv6 Addresses and IPv4 Addresses

The IPv6 transition mechanisms include a technique for hosts and routers dynamically to tunnel IPv6 packets over IPv4 routing infra-

structure. IPv6 nodes that use this technique are assigned special
IPv6 unicast addresses carrying an IPv4 address in the low-order 32
bits. This type of address whose format is noted below, is termed an
IPv4-compatible IPv6 address.

```
|     80 bits    |    16   |   32 bits     |
+---------------+-------------------------+
|0000......0000|00.....00|IPv4 address   |
+---------------+--------+---------------+
```

A second type of IPv6 address holding an embedded IPv4 address is
used to represent the addresses of IPv4-only nodes (those that do not
support IPv6) as IPv6 addresses. This type of address is represented
below and can be termed an IPv4-mapped IPv6 address.

```
|     80 bits    |    16   |   32 bits     |
+---------------+-------------------------+
|0000......0000|FFFF     | IPv4 address  |
+---------------+--------+---------------+
```

NSAP Addresses

The mapping of NSAP address into IPv6 addresses is represented
below.

```
|   7    |    121 bits    |
+--------+---------------+
|0000001| to be defined  |
+--------+---------------+
```

IPX Addresses

This mapping of IPX address into IPv6 addresses is represented
below.

```
|   7    |    121 bits    |
+--------+---------------+
| 0000010 | to be defined |
+--------+---------------+
```

Global Unicast Addresses

The initial assignment plan for these unicast addresses is similar to that
for assignment of IPv4 addresses under the CIDR scheme. The IPv6
global provider-based unicast address format is represented below.

```
| 3 | n bits | m bits | o bits | 125-n-m-o bits |
+---+--------+--------+--------+----------------+
|010|registry ID|provider ID|subscriber ID|intra-subscriber |
+---+-----------+----------+------------+----------------+
```

The high-order bit part of the address is allocated to registries, which assign portions of the address space to providers, which assign portions of the address space to subscribers, and so forth.

The registry ID identifies the registry assigning the provider portion of the address. The term "registry prefix" refers to the high-order part of the address up to and including the registry ID.

The provider ID identifies a specific provider assigning the subscriber portion of the address. The term "provider prefix" refers to the high-order part of the address up to and including the provider ID.

The subscriber ID distinguishes among multiple subscribers attached to the provider identified by the provider ID. The term "subscriber prefix" refers to the high-order part of the address up to and including the subscriber ID.

The intrasubscriber portion of the address is defined by an individual subscriber and is organized according to the subscriber's local internet topology. It is likely that many subscribers will choose to divide the intrasubscriber portion of the address into a subnet ID and an interface ID. In this case the subnet ID identifies a specific physical link and the interface ID identifies a single interface on that subnet.

IPv6 Unicast Addresses

The two types of local-use unicast addresses defined are link-local and site-local. The link-local address is for use on a single link and the site-local address is for use in a single site. The format of link-local addresses is represented below.

```
| 10 |  bits  |  n bits  |   118-n bits   |
+----+--------+----------------------------+
| 1111111010 | 0        | interface ID   |
+----+--------+----------------------------+
```

Link-local addresses are designed to be used for addressing on a single link for purposes such as autoaddress configuration, neighbor discovery, or when no routers are present. Routers are not permitted to forward any packets with link-local source addresses.

The format of site-local addresses is represented below.

```
| 10 | bits |  n bits | m bits |   118-n-m bits    |
+----+------+---------+--------------------------------+
|1111111011 |    0    | subnet ID | interface ID |
+----------+---------+-----------+-------------+
```

Site-local addresses may be used for sites or organizations not (yet) connected to the global Internet. These do not need to request or "steal" an address prefix from the global Internet address space; IPv6 site-local addresses can be used instead. When the organization connects to the global Internet, it can then form global addresses by replacing the site-local prefix with a subscriber prefix. Routers *must not* forward any packets with site-local source addresses outside the site.

Anycast Addresses

An IPv6 anycast address is assigned to more than one interface (typically belonging to different nodes), with the property that a packet sent to an anycast address is routed to the *nearest* interface having that address, according to the routing protocols' measure of distance.

Anycast addresses are allocated from the unicast address space, using any of the defined unicast address formats. Thus, anycast addresses are syntactically indistinguishable from unicast addresses. When a unicast address is assigned to more than one interface (becoming an anycast address) the nodes to which the address is assigned must be explicitly configured to know that it is an anycast address.

For any assigned anycast address, there is a longest-address prefix P that identifies the topological region in which all interfaces belonging to that anycast address reside. Within the region identified by P, each member of the anycast set must be advertised as a separate entry in the routing system (referred to as a *host route*); outside the region identified by P, the anycast address may be aggregated into the routing advertisement for prefix P.

Note that in the worst case, the prefix P of an anycast set may be the null prefix, i.e., the members of the set may have no topological locality. In that case, the anycast address must be advertised as a separate routing entry throughout the entire internet; this presents a severe scaling limit on how many such "global" anycast sets may be supported. Therefore, it is expected that support for global anycast sets may be unavailable or very restricted.

One expected use of anycast addresses is to identify the set of routers belonging to an internet service provider. Such addresses could be used as intermediate addresses in an IPv6 Routing header, to cause a packet to be delivered via a particular provider or sequence of providers. Other possible uses are to identify the set of routers attached to a particular subnet, or the set of routers providing entry into a particular routing domain.

There is little experience with widespread, arbitrary use of internet anycast addresses, and known complications and hazards exist when they are used in their full generality [ANYCST]. Until more experience has been gained and solutions agreed upon for those problems, the following restrictions are imposed on IPv6 anycast addresses:

- An anycast address *must not* be used as the source address of an IPv6 packet.
- An anycast address *must not* be assigned to an IPv6 host, that is, it may be assigned to an IPv6 router only.

The Subnet-Router anycast address is predefined; it's format is represented below.

```
|     n bits     |   128-n bits   |
+----------------+----------------+
|  subnet prefix | 00000000000000 |
+----------------+----------------+
```

The subnet prefix in an anycast address is the prefix which identifies a specific link. This anycast address is syntactically the same as a unicast address for an interface on the link whose interface identifier is set to zero.

Packets sent to the Subnet-Router anycast address will be delivered to one router on the subnet. All routers are required to support the Subnet-Router anycast addresses for the subnets with which they have interfaces.

The subnet-router anycast address is intended to be used for applications when a node needs to communicate with one of a set of routers on a remote subnet as when a mobile host needs to communicate with one of the mobile agents on its "home" subnet.

Multicast Addresses

An IPv6 multicast address is an identifier for a group of nodes. A node may belong to any number of multicast groups. The format of multicast addresses is represented below.

```
| 8 | 4 | 4 |            112 bits              |
+---+---+---+-------------------------------+
|11111111|flgs|scop|        group ID          |
+---+---+---+-------------------------------+
```

11111111 at the start of the address identifies the address as being a multicast address.

```
                              +-+-+-+-+
    flags is a set of 4 flags: |0|0|0|T|

                              +-+-+-+-+
```

The high-order 3 flags are reserved, and must be initialized to 0.

T = 0	This indicates a permanently-assigned multicast address, assigned by the global internet numbering authority.
T = 1	This indicates a non-permanently-assigned (transient) multicast address.

Scope is a 4-bit multicast scope value used to limit the scope of the multicast group; its values are:

0	Reserved	8	Organization-local scope
1	Node-local scope	9	(Unassigned)
2	Link-local scope	A	(Unassigned)
3	(Unassigned)	B	(Unassigned)
4	(Unassigned)	C	(Unassigned)
5	Site-local scope	D	(Unassigned)
6	(Unassigned)	E	Global scope
7	(Unassigned)	F	Reserved

Group ID identifies the multicast group, either permanent or transient, within the given scope. The "meaning" of a permanently-assigned multicast address is independent of the scope value. For example, if the NTP servers group is assigned a permanent multicast address with a group ID of 43 (hex), then:

FF01:0:0:0:0:0:0:43	Means all NTP servers on the same node as the sender.
FF02:0:0:0:0:0:0:43	Means all NTP servers on the same link as the sender.

continued on next page

| FF05:0:0:0:0:0:0:43 | Means all NTP servers at the same site as the sender. |
| FF0E:0:0:0:0:0:0:43 | Means all NTP servers in the internet. |

Non-permanently-assigned multicast addresses are meaningful only within a given scope. For example, a group identified by the non-permanent, site-local multicast address FF15:0:0:0:0:0:0:43 at one site bears no relationship to a group using the same address at a different site, nor to a non-permanent group using the same group ID with different scope, nor to a permanent group with the same group ID.

Multicast addresses must not be used as source addresses in IPv6 datagrams or appear in any routing header.

Predefined Multicast Addresses

The following well-known multicast addresses are predefined:

Reserved Multicast Addresses	
FF00:0:0:0:0:0:0:0	FF08:0:0:0:0:0:0:0
FF01:0:0:0:0:0:0:0	FF09:0:0:0:0:0:0:0
FF02:0:0:0:0:0:0:0	FF0A:0:0:0:0:0:0:0
FF03:0:0:0:0:0:0:0	FF0B:0:0:0:0:0:0:0
FF04:0:0:0:0:0:0:0	FF0C:0:0:0:0:0:0:0
FF05:0:0:0:0:0:0:0	FF0D:0:0:0:0:0:0:0
FF06:0:0:0:0:0:0:0	FF0E:0:0:0:0:0:0:0
FF07:0:0:0:0:0:0:0	FF0F:0:0:0:0:0:0:0

The above multicast addresses are reserved and shall never be assigned to any multicast group.

All Nodes Addresses	
FF01:0:0:0:0:0:0:1	FF02:0:0:0:0:0:0:1

The above multicast addresses identify the group of all IPv6 nodes, within scope 1 (node-local) or 2 (link-local).

All Routers Addresses
FF01:0:0:0:0:0:0:2   FF02:0:0:0:0:0:0:2

The above multicast addresses identify the group of all IPv6 routers, within scope 1 (node-local) or 2 (link-local).

DHCP Server/Relay-Agent
FF02:0:0:0:0:0:0:C

The above multicast address identifies the group of all IPv6 DHCP servers and relay agents within scope 2 (link-local).

Solicited-Node Address
FF02:0:0:0:0:1:XXXX:XXXX

The above multicast address is computed as a function of a node's unicast and anycast addresses. The solicited-node multicast address is formed by taking the low-order 32 bits of the address (unicast or anycast) and appending those bits to the 96-bit prefix FF02:0:0:0:0:1 resulting in a multicast address in the range FF02:0:0:0:0:1:0000:0000 to FF02:0:0:0:0:1:FFFF:FFFF.

For example, the solicited node multicast address corresponding to the IPv6 address 4037::01:800:200E:8C6C is FF02::1:200E:8C6C. IPv6 addresses that differ only in the high-order bits, e.g., due to multiple high-order prefixes associated with different providers, will map to the same solicited-node address thereby reducing the number of multicast addresses a node must join.

A node is required to compute and support a Solicited-Node multicast address for every unicast and anycast address it is assigned.

Node Address Requirement

A host is required to recognize the following addresses as identifying itself:

- Its link-local address for each interface
- Assigned unicast addresses
- The loopback address

- The All-nodes multicast address
- The solicited-node multicast address for each of its assigned unicast and anycast addresses
- Multicast Addresses of all other groups to which the host belongs.

A router is required to recognize the following addresses as identifying itself:

- Its link-local address for each interface
- Assigned unicast addresses
- The loopback address
- The subnet-router anycast addresses for the links with which it has interfaces
- All other anycast addresses with which the router has been configured
- The all-nodes multicast address
- The all-router multicast address
- A solicited-node multicast address for each of its assigned unicast and anycast addresses
- Multicast Addresses of all other groups to which the router belongs.

The only address prefixes that should be predefined in an implementation are the:

- Unspecified address
- Loopback address
- Multicast prefix (FF)
- Local-use prefixes (link-local and site-local)
- Predefined multicast addresses
- IPv4-compatible prefixes.

Implementations should assume all other addresses are unicast unless specifically configured (e.g., anycast addresses).

Internet Control Message Protocol (ICMP)

ICMP works with IP and is located at layer three with IP. Since IP is connectionless-oriented it has no way to relay messages or errors to the originating host. ICMP performs these functions on behalf of IP and sends status and error messages to the sending host.

ICMP Message Structure

ICMP utilizes IP to carry the ICMP data within it through a network. Just because ICMP uses IP as a vehicle does not make IP reliable, it means that IP carries the ICMP message.

The structure of an ICMP message is shown in Figure 11.4.

FIGURE 11.4
ICMP Message
Format

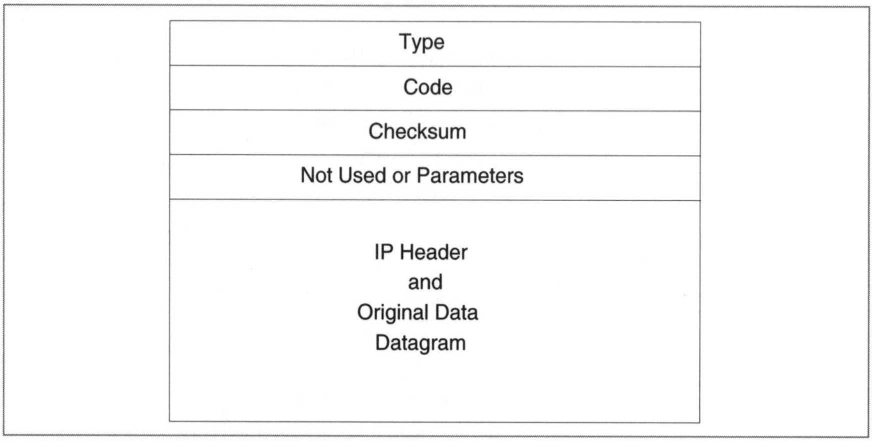

Type
Code
Checksum
Not Used or Parameters
IP Header and Original Data Datagram

The first part of the ICMP message is the Type field. This field has a numeric value reflecting its meaning and format. The numeric values and their meanings that can appear in this type of field are shown in Figure 11.5.

FIGURE 11.5
ICMP Messages
Types and
Meanings

Type	Meaning of Message
0	Echo Reply
3	Destination Unreachable
4	Source Quench
5	Redirect
8	Echo Request
11	Time Exceeded for a Datagram
12	Parameter Problem on a Datagram
13	Timestamp Request
14	Timestamp Reply
17	Address Mask Request
18	Address Mask Reply

The next field in the ICMP message is the Code field, which also has an assigned numeric value. These numeric values have an associated meaning as shown in Figure 11.6.

FIGURE 11.6
ICMP Codes and
Meanings

0	Network Unreachable
1	Host Unreachable
2	Protocol Unreachable
3	Port Unreachable
4	Fragmentation Needed
5	Source Route Failed
6	Destination Network Unknown
7	Destination Host Unknown
8	Source Host Isolated
9	Administrative Restrictions to Destination Network. Communication Prohibited
10	Communication with Destination Host Prohibited by Administration
11	Network Unreachable for Service Type
12	Host Unreachable for Service Type

The Checksum is computed from the ICMP message starting with the ICMP type.

The next field is the IP Header and Data Datagram.

ICMP is the source for many messages on a user's display. If a user attempts a remote logon and the host is not reachable, then the message *host unreachable* will appear on the screen. This message comes from ICMP.

ICMP detects errors, reports problems, and generates messages as well. For IP to be implemented, ICMP must be used because of the design of IP.

Address Resolution Protocol (ARP)

ARP is located at layer three along with IP and ICMP. ARP maps IP addresses to the underlying hardware address, dynamically binding these addresses.

Since TCP/IP works at layer three and above, it must have a mechanism to function with interface boards. When TCP/IP is implemented, this is done in software. Each host participating on a TCP/IP network must have TCP/IP and a unique IP address. The IP address is considered a software address since it is implemented at layer three in software.

Because any one of many data link protocols could be used, IP requires a way to correlate the IP address and the data link address. Data link addresses are generally considered hardware addresses. For example, if TCP/IP is implemented with Ethernet a 48-bit Ethernet address must be mapped to the 32-bit IP address. If token ring is used, a 12-digit hexadecimal address is the hardware address. Neither of these data-link protocol addresses matches the 32-bit IP address of TCP/IP. This is the reason for ARP.

ARP Theory of Operation

ARP can be explained using Ethernet for a data link. Assume five hosts reside on an Ethernet network. Assume a user on host A wants to connect to host E. Host A uses ARP to broadcast a packet that includes A's IP, Ethernet address and host E's IP address. All five hosts on the network "hear" the ARP broadcast for host E. However, only host E recognizes its IP address inside the ARP request. Figure 11.7 depicts this.

FIGURE 11.7
ARP Request

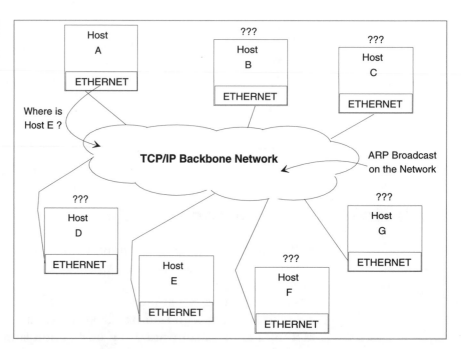

When host E recognizes its hardware address, it replies to host A
with its IP address. Figure 11.8 is an example of this process.

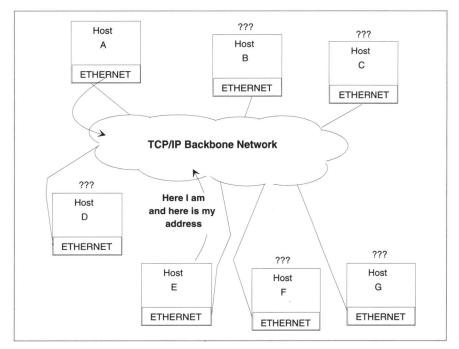

It is obvious that all hosts shown in Figure 11.7 must examine the
ARP request. This is expensive in terms of network use. To avoid this
constant barrage an ARP cache is maintained. This is a list of network hosts' physical and IP addresses which curbs the number of
ARP packets on the network.

When a host receives an ARP reply, that host keeps the IP address
of the other host in the ARP table. Then, when a host wants to communicate with another host on the network it first examines its ARP
cache for the IP address. If the desired IP address is found there is no
need to perform an ARP broadcast. The communication occurs via
hardware communication: for example, Ethernet boards communicating with one another.

ARP Message Format

Figure 11.9 is an example of ARP message format.

FIGURE 11.9
ARP Message
Format

| Physical Layer Header |
| Hardware Type |
| Protocol Type |
| Hardware Address Length |
| Protocol Address Length |
| Operation Code |
| Sender Hardware Address |
| Sender Protocol Address |
| Target Hardware Address |
| Target Protocol Address |

The fields in the ARP packet and their meaning include:

- **Hardware Type.** Indicates the hardware interface type
- **Protocol Type.** Specifies the upper-level protocol address the originator sent
- **Hardware Address Length.** Specifies the length of the bytes in the packet
- **Protocol Address Length.** Specifies the length in bytes of the high level protocol
- **Operation Code.** Specifies one of the following: ARP request, ARP response, RARP request or RARP response
- **Sender Hardware Address.** If known, it is supplied by the sender
- **Sender Protocol Address.** Like the hardware address, it is sent if known
- **Target Hardware Address.** Destination address
- **Target Protocol Address.** Contains the IP address of the destination host.

Since ARP functions at the lowest layers within a network, the ARP request itself must be encapsulated within the hardware protocol frame because it is the frame that physically moves through the network at this level. Conceptually, the frame carrying the ARP message appears as in Figure 11.10.

FIGURE 11.10
ARP Frame and
ARP Message

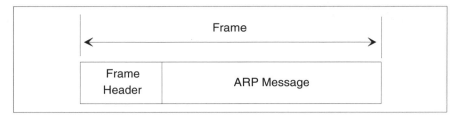

ARP's dynamic address translation provides a robust method for obtaining an unknown address. The efficiency of ARP is in the use of the caching mechanism.

Reverse Address Resolution Protocol (RARP)

RARP is the reverse of ARP and it is used commonly where diskless workstations are implemented. When a diskless workstation boots, it knows its hardware address, which is in the interface card connecting the workstation to the network. However, the workstation does not know its IP address.

RARP Request and Server Operation

Devices using RARP require that a RARP server be present on the network to answer RARP requests. The question RARP requests ask, "what is my IP address?" is broadcast on the network and a designated RARP server replies by examining the physical address received in the RARP packet, comparing it against the tables of IP addresses, and sending the response back to the requesting host. Figure 11.11 is an example of a RARP broadcast.

Figure 11.11 shows the RARP request going to all hosts on the network. It also shows a RARP server. Notice in Figure 11.12 the RARP server answers the RARP request.

For RARP to be used in a network a RARP server must exist. In most implementations with RARP multiple RARP servers are used. One is designated as a primary server and another as a secondary server.

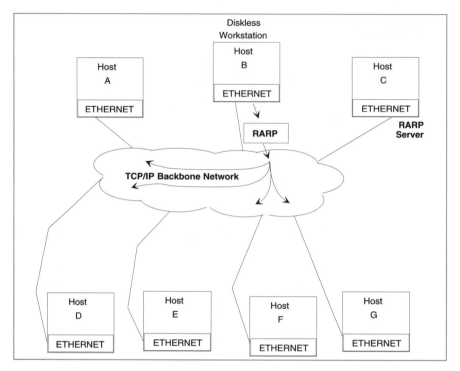

FIGURE 11.11
RARP Broadcast

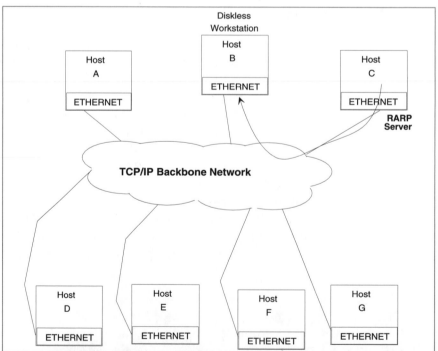

FIGURE 11.12
RARP Response

Router Protocols

This section focuses on Interior Gateway Protocols and is defined as routing in an autonomous system. An autonomous system is a collection of routers controlled by one administrative authority and using a common interior gateway protocol. Two popular routing protocols in this category are Router Information Protocol (RIP) and Open Shortest Path First (OSPF).

These protocols are used by network devices such as routers, hosts, and others normally implemented in TCP/IP software. These protocols *can* be implemented by firmware.

RIP

RIP has its origins in Xerox's network systems protocol. It was at one time included in the software distribution of TCP/IP with Berkeley UNIX. RIP is an example of a de facto protocol and was implemented before a standard RFC existed. It was part of TCP/IP, it worked, and it was needed; it therefore became popular. RFC 1058 bought RIP into a formal standard.

Consider Figure 11.13, an example of the RIP message format.

FIGURE 11.13
RIP Message
Format

Command
Version
Zero
Address Family Identfier
Zero
IP Address
Zero
Zero
Distance to Net A

A description of each field in the RIP message format follows:

- **Command.** This specifies a operation that could be a request or response.
- **Version.** This identifies the protocol version.
- **Zero.** This is a blank field.
- **Address Family Identifier.** This is used to identify the protocol family under which the message should be interpreted.

- **Zero.** This is a blank field.
- **IP Address.** The IP address usually has a default route attached to it.
- **Zero.** This is a blank field.
- **Zero.** This is a blank field.
- **Distance to Net _n_.** This is a value indicating the distance to the target network.

RIP messages are either conveying or requesting routing information. RIP is based on broadcast technology. Periodically a router (or designated device) broadcasts the entire RIP routing table throughout the network, LAN or otherwise. This aspect alone has become a problem in some environments because of the lack of efficiency.

In addition to broadcasts and updates from that process, RIP also gets updates due to changes in the network configuration. These updates are referred to as responses.

Another characteristic of RIP is that it relies on other devices (adjacent nodes) for routing information for targets more than one hop away. RIP also calculates its distances by cost per hop. One hop is defined as a metric. The maximum hops RIP can make along one path is fifteen.

RIP maintains a table with entries, the one broadcast throughout the network. Information contained in each entry in this table includes:

- The destination IP address
- The number of hops required to reach the destination
- The IP address for the next router in the path
- Any indication of whether the route has recently changed
- Timers along the route.

Many vendors support RIP. In certain environments it may be a good _gateway_ protocol to use. Many vendors also support OSPF.

Open Shortest Path First (OSPF)

The philosophy of OSPF differs from that of RIP. It was recommended as a standard in 1990 and by 1991 version 2 OSPF was available. Tenets OSPF maintains include:

- Type of service routing is noted
- Capability of defining virtual networks
- Route distribution is offered
- Broadcasts are minimized

- A method for trusted routers is supported.

Other tenets support OSPF and, depending upon the vendor, a variety of them may be implemented.

OSPF Advertisements

OSPF advertisements are ways for routers to inform other routers about paths. Four distinct types of advertisements include:

- **Autonomous.** This has information on routes in other autonomous systems.
- **Network.** This contains a list of routers connected to the network.
- **Routers.** This contains information about given router interfaces in certain areas.
- **Summary.** This maintains route information outside a given area.

These advertisements enable a more focused approach to spreading information throughout a network. Besides the advertisements, OSPF uses a number of messages for communication, including hello, database description, link state request, link state update, and link state acknowledgment.

Two of these are presented and explained in detail to provide insight on the operation of OSPF. Additional information about OSPF can be found in RFCs 1245–1247.

OSPF Header Analysis

The OSPF packet header appears as in Figure 11.14.

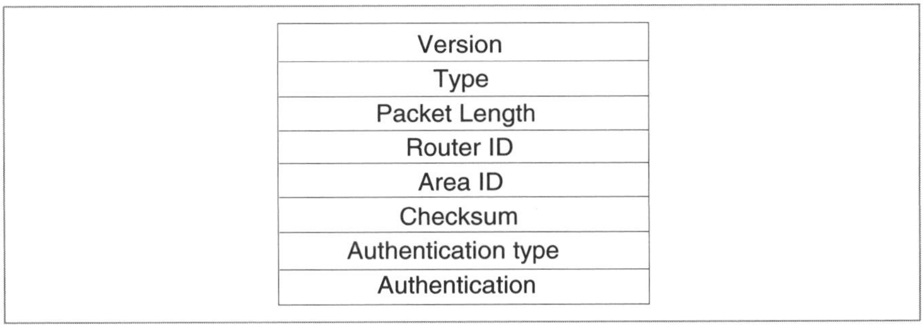

FIGURE 11.14
OSPF Packet
Header

Version
Type
Packet Length
Router ID
Area ID
Checksum
Authentication type
Authentication

OSPF header fields include:

- **Version.** This indicates the protocol version.

- **Type.** This indicates messages as one of the following: hello, database description, link status, link status update, or link status acknowledgment.
- **Message Length.** This indicates the length of the field including the OSPF header.
- **Source Gateway IP Address.** This provides the sender's address.
- **Area ID.** This identifies the area from which the packet was transmitted.
- **Checksum.** The checksum is performed on the entire packet.
- **Authentication Type.** This identifies the authentication type to be used.
- **Authentication.** This includes a value from the authentication type.

The Hello packet includes messages that are periodically sent on each link to establish whether a destination can be reached. It appears as Figure 11.15.

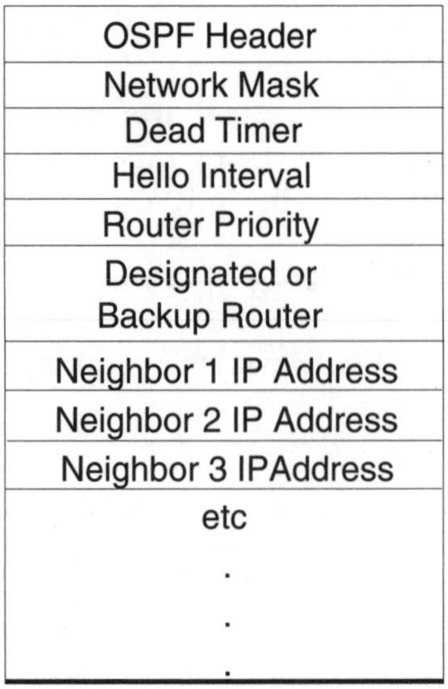

FIGURE 11.15
Hello Packet
Format

The fields in the Hello packet include:

- **OSPF Header.** This is required.
- **Network Mask.** This contains the network mask for the network where the message originated.
- **Dead Timer.** This is a value, in seconds, that indicates a neighbor is dead if no response is received.

- **Hello Interval.** This has a value, in seconds, reflecting the amount of time before a router sends another Hello packet.
- **Router Priority.** This is used if a designated router is a backup.
- **Designated or Backup Router.** This identifies the backup router.
- **Neighbor Router ID.** This field, and subsequent ones, indicate the IDs of routers which have recently received Hello packets within the network.

The Database Description packet message includes an OSPF header and fields of information about messages received. The fields can be broken into smaller units. There is also indication if information is missing. The packet also includes information about the type of link and its ID. A checksum is provided to ensure that corruption has not occurred.

The Link state packet header includes an OSPF header and fields that provide information such as: router, network, link station type, and other information.

The essence of OSPF is that it reduces traffic overhead in the network because it performs individual updates rather than broadcasts than permeate the entire network. OSPF also provides an ability for authentication. Another strength of OSPF is that it can exchange subnet masks as well as subnet addresses.

Transmission Control Protocol (TCP)

TCP is a connection-oriented, end-to-end reliable protocol designed to fit into a layered hierarchy of protocols which support multinetwork applications. The TCP provides for reliable inter-process communication between pairs of processes in host computers attached to distinct but interconnected computer communication networks. Very few assumptions are made about the reliability of the communication protocols below the TCP layer. TCP assumes it can obtain a simple, potentially unreliable datagram service from the lower-level protocols. In principle, the TCP should be able to operate above a wide spectrum of communication systems ranging from hard-wired connections to packet-switched or circuit-switched networks.

TCP interfaces on one side to user or application processes and on the other side to a lower-level protocol such as IP. The interface between an application process and TCP consists of a set of calls much like the calls an operating system provides to an application process for manipulating files. There are calls to open and close connections and to send and receive data on established connections. It is also expected that the TCP can synchronously communicate with application programs. Although considerable freedom is permitted to TCP implementors to design interfaces appropriate to a particular operating system environment, a minimum functionality is required at the TCP/user interface for any valid implementation.

The interface between TCP and lower-level protocols is essentially unspecified except that it is assumed there is a mechanism so that the two levels can synchronously pass information to each other. Typically, the lower-level protocol is expected to specify this interface. TCP is designed to work in a general environment of interconnected networks.

TCP Operation

As noted above, the primary purpose of the TCP is to provide reliable, securable logical circuit or connection service between pairs of processes. To provide this service on top of a less reliable internet communication system requires facilities in the following areas: basic data transfer, reliability, flow control, multiplexing, connections, and precedence and security.

Basic Data Transfer

TCP is able to transfer a continuous stream of octets in each direction between its users by packaging some number of octets into segments for transmission through the internet system. In general, TCP decides when to block and forward data at its own convenience.

Sometimes users need to be sure that all the data they have submitted to TCP has been transmitted. For this purpose a push function is defined. To ensure that data submitted to TCP are actually transmitted, the sending user indicates that data should be pushed through to the receiving user. A push causes prompt forwarding and delivery of data up to that point by the TCPs to the receiver. The exact push point might not be visible to the receiving user and the push function does not supply a record boundary marker.

Reliability

TCP must recover from data damaged, lost, duplicated, or delivered out of order by the internet communication system. This is achieved by assigning a sequence number to each octet transmitted, and requiring a positive acknowledgment (ACK) from the receiving TCP. If the ACK is not received within a timeout interval, the data is retransmitted. At the receiver, the sequence numbers are used correctly to order segments that may be received out of order and to eliminate duplicates. Damage is handled by adding a checksum to each segment transmitted, checking it at the receiver, and discarding damaged segments.

As long as the TCPs continue to function properly and the internet system does not become completely partitioned, no transmission errors will affect the correct delivery of data. TCP recovers from internet communication system errors.

Flow Control

TCP provides a means for the receiver to govern the amount of data sent by the sender. This is achieved by returning a "window" with every ACK indicating a range of acceptable sequence numbers beyond the last segment successfully received. The window indicates an allowed number of octets that the sender may transmit before receiving further permission.

Multiplexing

To allow for many processes within a single host to use TCP communication facilities simultaneously, the TCP provides a set of addresses or ports within each host. Concatenated with the network and host addresses from the internet communication layer, this forms a socket. A pair of sockets uniquely identifies each connection. That is, a socket may be simultaneously used in multiple connections. The binding of ports to processes is handled independently by each host. However, it proves useful to attach frequently used processes (a *logger* or timesharing service) to fixed sockets which are made known to the public. These services can then be accessed through the known addresses. Establishing and learning the port addresses of other processes may involve more dynamic mechanisms.

Connections

The reliability and flow control mechanisms described above require that TCPs initialize and maintain certain status information for each data stream. The combination of this information, including sockets, sequence numbers, and window sizes, is called a *connection*.

Each connection is uniquely specified by a pair of sockets identifying its two sides.

When two processes wish to communicate, their TCPs must first establish a connection (initialize the status information on each side). When their communication is complete, the connection is terminated or closed to free the resources for other uses. Since connections must be established between unreliable hosts and over the unreliable internet communication system, a handshake mechanism with clock-based sequence numbers is used to avoid erroneous initialization of connections.

Precedence and Security

The users of TCP may indicate the security and precedence of their communication. Provision is made for default values to be used when these features are not needed.

TCP and the Host Environment

TCP is assumed to be a module in an operating system or a part of the protocol suite running on a given host. The users access the TCP much as they would access the file system. TCP may call on other operating system functions, for example, to manage data structures. The actual interface to the network is assumed to be controlled by a device driver module. The TCP does not call on the network device driver directly, but rather calls on the internet datagram protocol module which may in turn call on the device driver.

The mechanisms of TCP do not preclude implementation of the TCP in a front-end processor. However, in such an implementation, a host-to-front-end protocol must provide the functionality to support the type of TCP-user interface described.

Interfaces and TCP

The TCP/user interface provides for calls made by the user on the TCP to OPEN or CLOSE a connection, to SEND or RECEIVE data, or to obtain STATUS about a connection. These calls are like other calls from user programs on the operating system, for example, the calls to open, read from, and close a file.

The TCP/internet interface provides calls to send and receive datagrams addressed to TCP modules in hosts anywhere in the internet system. These calls have parameters for passing the address, type of service, precedence, security, and other control information.

TCP Reliability

A stream of data sent on a TCP connection is delivered reliably and in order at the destination. Transmission is made reliable via the use of sequence numbers and acknowledgments. Each octet of data is assigned a sequence number. The sequence number of the first octet of data in a segment is transmitted with that segment and is called the segment sequence number. Segments also carry an acknowledgment number which is the sequence number of the next expected data octet of transmissions in the reverse direction. When the TCP transmits a segment containing data, it puts a copy on a retransmission queue and starts a timer; when the acknowledgment for that data is received, the segment is deleted from the queue. If the acknowledgment is not received before the timer runs out, the segment is retransmitted.

An acknowledgment by TCP does not guarantee that the data have been delivered to the end user; it does mean that the receiving TCP has taken the responsibility to do so. To govern the flow of data between TCPs, a flow control mechanism is employed. The receiving TCP reports a "window" to the sending TCP. This window specifies the number of octets, starting with the acknowledgment number, that the receiving TCP is currently prepared to receive.

TCP Connection Establishment/Clearing

To identify the separate data streams that a TCP may handle, the TCP provides a port identifier. Since port identifiers are selected independently by each TCP they might not be unique. To provide for unique addresses within each TCP, we concatenate an internet address identifying the TCP with a port identifier to create a *socket* which is unique throughout all networks connected together.

A connection is fully specified by the pair of sockets at the ends. A *local socket* may participate in many connections to different foreign sockets. A connection can be used to carry data in both directions; it is full duplex.

TCPs are free to associate ports with processes however they choose. However, several basic concepts are necessary in any implementation. There must be well-known sockets which the TCP associates only with the appropriate processes by some means. We envision that processes may *own* ports, and that processes can initiate connections only on the ports they own. (Ways to implement ownership are a local issue, but it would be possible to have a Request Port user command, or a method of uniquely allocating a group of ports to a given process, by associating the high order bits of a port name with a given process.)

A connection is specified in the OPEN call by the local port and foreign socket arguments. In return, the TCP supplies a (short) local connection name by which the user refers to the connection in subsequent calls. There are several things that must be remembered about a connection. To store this information we imagine that there is a data structure called a Transmission Control Block (TCB). One implementation strategy would have the local connection name be a pointer to the TCB for this connection. The OPEN call also specifies whether the connection establishment is to be actively pursued, or to be passively waited for.

A passive OPEN request means that the process wants to accept incoming connection requests rather than attempting to initiate a connection. Often the process requesting a passive OPEN will accept a connection request from any caller. In this case a foreign socket of all zeros is used to denote an unspecified socket. Unspecified foreign sockets are allowed only on passive OPENs. A service process that wished to provide services for unknown other processes would issue a passive OPEN request with an unspecified foreign socket. Then a connection could be made with any process that requested a connection to this local socket. It would help if this local socket were known to be associated with this service.

Well-known sockets are a convenient mechanism for a priori associating a socket address with a standard service. For instance, the Telnet-Server process is permanently assigned to a particular socket, and other sockets are reserved for File Transfer, Remote Job Entry, Text Generator, Echoer, and Sink processes. A socket address might be reserved for access to a Look-Up service which would return the specific socket at which a newly created service would be provided. The concept of a well-known socket is part of the TCP specification, but the assignment of sockets to services is outside this specification.

Processes can issue passive OPENs and wait for matching active OPENs from other processes and be informed by the TCP when connections have been established. Two processes which issue active OPENs to each other at the same time will be correctly connected. This flexibility is critical for the support of distributed computing in which components act synchronously with respect to each other.

There are two principal cases for matching the sockets in the local passive OPENs and an foreign active OPENs. In the first case, the local passive OPENs have fully specified the foreign socket. In this case, the match must be exact. In the second case, the local passive OPENs have left the foreign socket unspecified. In this case, any foreign socket is acceptable as long as the local sockets match. Other possibilities include partially restricted matches.

If there are several pending passive OPENs (recorded in TCBs) with the same local socket, an foreign active OPEN will be matched to a TCB with the specific foreign socket in the foreign active OPEN, if such a TCB exists, before selecting a TCB with an unspecified foreign socket. The procedures to establish connections use the synchronize (SYN) control flag and involve an exchange of three messages. This exchange has been termed a three-way handshake.

A connection is initiated by the rendezvous of an arriving segment containing a SYN and a waiting TCB entry each created by a user OPEN command. The matching of local and foreign sockets determines when a connection has been initiated. The connection becomes *established* when sequence numbers have been synchronized in both directions. The clearing of a connection also involves the exchange of segments, in this case carrying the FIN control flag.

TCP and Data Communication

The data that flow on a connection may be thought of as a stream of octets. The sending user indicates in each SEND call whether the data in that call (and any preceding calls) should be immediately pushed through to the receiving user by the setting of the PUSH flag.

A sending TCP is allowed to collect data from the sending user and to send that data in segments at its own convenience, until the push function is signaled, then it must send all unsent data. When a receiving TCP sees the PUSH flag, it must not wait for more data from the sending TCP before passing the data to the receiving process.

There is no necessary relationship between push functions and segment boundaries. The data in any particular segment may be the result of a single SEND call, in whole or part, or of multiple SEND calls.

The purpose of the Push function and PUSH flag is to push data through from the sending user to the receiving user. It does not provide a record service. There is a coupling between the Push function and the use of buffers of data that cross the TCP/user interface. Each time a PUSH flag is associated with data placed into the receiving user's buffer, the buffer is returned to the user for processing even if the buffer is not filled. If data arrive that fill the user's buffer before a PUSH is seen, the data are passed to the user in buffer size units. TCP also provides a means to communicate to the receiver of data that at some point further along in the data stream than the receiver is currently reading, there are urgent data. TCP does not attempt to define what the user specifically does upon being notified of pending urgent data, but the general notion is that the receiving process will take action to process the urgent data quickly.

TCP Precedence and Security

The TCP makes use of the internet protocol type of service field and security option to provide precedence and security on a per-connection basis to TCP users. Not all TCP modules will necessarily function in a multilevel secure environment; some may be limited to unclassified use only, and others may operate at only one security level and compartment. Consequently, some TCP implementations and services to users may be limited to a subset of the multilevel secure case.

TCP modules which operate in a multilevel secure environment must properly mark outgoing segments with the security, compartment, and precedence. Such TCP modules must also provide to their users or higher-level protocols such as Telnet or THP an interface to allow them to specify the desired security level, compartment, and precedence of connections.

TCP Segment (Header) Format

TCP segments are sent as internet datagrams. The Internet Protocol header carries several information fields, including the source and destination host addresses. A TCP header follows the IP header, supplying information specific to the TCP protocol. This division allows for the existence of host-level protocols other than TCP.

TCP Segment Format is shown in Figure 11.16.

Source Port
Destination Port
Sequence Number
Acknowledgement Number
Data Offset
Reserved
Urgent
Acknowledgement
Push
Reset
Synchronizer
Finished
Window
Checksum
Urgent Pointer
Options
Padding
Data

- **Source Port.** 16 bits; the source port number
- **Destination Port.** 16 bits; the destination port number
- **Sequence Number.** 32 bits; the sequence number of the first data octet in this segment (except when SYN is present). If SYN is present the sequence number is the initial sequence number (ISN) and the first data octet is ISN+1.
- **Acknowledgment Number.** 32 bits; if the ACK control bit is set, this field contains the value of the next sequence number the sender of the segment is expecting to receive. Once a connection is established this is always sent.
- **Data Offset.** 4 bits; the number of 32-bit words in the TCP Header. This indicates where the data begin. The TCP header (even one including options) is an integral number 32 bits long.
- **Reserved.** 6 bits; reserved for future use; must be zero
- **Control Bits.** 6 bits (from left to right):
  - URG. Urgent Pointer field significant

- ACK: Acknowledgment field significant
- PSH: Push function
- RST: Reset the connection
- SYN: Synchronize sequence numbers
- FIN: No more data from sender

- **Window.** 16 bits; the number of data octets beginning with the one indicated in the acknowledgment field which the sender of this segment is willing to accept

- **Checksum.** 16 bits; the checksum field is the 16 bit ones complement of the ones complement sum of all 16-bit words in the header and text. If a segment contains an odd number of header and text octets to be checksummed, the last octet is padded on the right with zeros to form a 16-bit word for checksum purposes. The pad is not transmitted as part of the segment. While computing the checksum, the checksum field itself is replaced with zeros.

  The checksum also covers a 96-bit pseudo-header conceptually prefixed to the TCP header. This pseudo-header contains the source address, the destination address, the protocol, and TCP length. This gives the TCP protection against misrouted segments. This information is carried in the Internet Protocol and is transferred across the TCP/Network interface in the arguments or results of calls by the TCP on the IP.

```
+--------+--------+--------+--------+
|           Source Address          |
+--------+--------+--------+--------+
|         Destination Address       |
+--------+--------+--------+--------+
|  zero  |  PTCL  |    TCP Length   |
+--------+--------+--------+--------+
```

The TCP Length is the TCP header length plus the data length in octets (this is not an explicitly transmitted quantity, but is computed), and it does not count the 12 octets of the pseudo-header.

- **Urgent Pointer.** 16 bits; this field communicates the current value of the urgent pointer as a positive offset from the sequence number in this segment. The urgent pointer points to the sequence number of the octet following the urgent data. This field can only be interpreted in segments with the URG control bit set.

- **Options.** Variable; options may occupy space at the end of the TCP header and are a multiple of 8 bits in length. All options are included in the checksum. An option may begin on any octet boundary. There are two cases for the format of an option: Case 1 is a single octet of option-kind; Case 2 is an octet of option-kind, an octet of option-length, and the actual option-data octets. The option-length counts the two octets of option-kind and option-length as well as the option-data octets.

The list of options may be shorter than the data offset field might imply. The content of the header beyond the End-of-Option option must be header padding (i.e., zero). A TCP must implement all options.

Defined options include (kind indicated in octal):

Kind	Length	Meaning
0	—	End of option list
1	—	No-Operation
2	4	Maximum Segment Size

Specific Option Definitions:

```
End of Option List
    +--------+
    |00000000|
    +--------+
     Kind=0
```

This option code indicates the end of the option list. This might not coincide with the end of the TCP header according to the Data Offset field. This is used at the end of all options, not the end of each option, and need only be used if the end of the options would not otherwise coincide with the end of the TCP header.

```
No-Operation
    +--------+
    |00000001|
    +--------+
     Kind=1
```

This option code may be used between options, for example, to align the beginning of a subsequent option on a word boundary. There is no guarantee that senders will use this option, so receivers must be prepared to process options even if they do not begin on a word boundary.

```
Maximum Segment Size
  +--------+--------+---------+--------+
  |00000010|00000100|  max seg size  |
  +--------+--------+---------+--------+
   Kind=2  Length=4
```

- **Maximum Segment Size Option Data.** 16 bits; if this option is present, then it communicates the maximum receive segment size at the TCP which sends this segment. This field must only be sent in the initial connection request (i.e., in segments with the SYN control bit set). If this option is not used, any segment size is allowed.
- **Padding.** Variable; the TCP header padding is used to ensure that the TCP header ends and data begins on a 32-bit boundary. The padding is composed of zeros.

TCP Terminology

It is important to understand some detailed terminology. Consider the following information. The maintenance of a TCP connection requires the remembering of several variables. We conceive of these variables as being stored in a connection record called a Transmission Control Block or TCB. Among the variables stored in the TCB are the local and remote socket numbers, the security and precedence of the connection, pointers to the user's send and receive buffers, pointers to the retransmit queue and to the current segment. In addition several variables relating to the send and receive sequence numbers are stored in the TCB.

Send Sequence Variables	
SND.UNA	Send unacknowledged
SND.NXT	Send next
SND.WND	Send window
SND.UP	Send urgent pointer
SND.WL1	Segment sequence number used for last window update
SND.WL2	Segment acknowledgment number used for last window update
ISS	Initial send sequence number

Receive Sequence Variables	
RCV.NXT	Receive next
RCV.WND	Receive window
RCV.UP	Receive urgent pointer
IRS	Initial receive sequence number

Consider the following to relate some of these variables to sequence space.

```
Send Sequence Space
            1            2            3            4
    ----------|----------|----------|----------
          SND.UNA    SND.NXT    SND.UNA
                                +SND.WND
```

1—old sequence numbers which have been acknowledged
2—sequence numbers of unacknowledged data
3—sequence numbers allowed for new data transmission
4—future sequence numbers which are not yet allowed

```
Receive Sequence Space
              1            2            3
      ----------|----------|----------
            RCV.NXT     RCV.NXT
                        +RCV.WND
```

1—old sequence numbers which have been acknowledged
2—sequence numbers allowed for new reception
3—future sequence numbers which are not yet allowed

There are also some variables used frequently in the discussion that take their values from the fields of the current segment

Current Segment Variables	
SEG.SEQ	Segment sequence number
SEG.ACK	Segment acknowledgment number
SEG.LEN	Segment length
SEG.WND	Segment window
SEG.UP	Segment urgent pointer
SEG.PRC	Segment precedence value

A connection progresses through a series of state during its lifetime. The state are:

```
LISTEN
SYN-SENT
SYN-RECEIVED
ESTABLISHED
FIN-WAIT-1
FIN-WAIT-2
CLOSE-WAIT
CLOSING
LAST-ACK
TIME-WAIT
```

The fictional state CLOSED.

CLOSED is fictional because it represents the state when there is no TCB, and therefore, no connection. Briefly the meanings of the state are: LISTEN represents waiting for a connection request from any remote TCP and port. SYN-SENT represents waiting for a matching connection request after having sent a connection request. SYN-RECEIVED represents waiting for a confirming connection request acknowledgment after having both received and sent a connection request. ESTABLISHED represents an open connection; data received can be delivered to the user. This is the normal state for the data transfer phase of the connection.

FIN-WAIT-1 represents waiting for a connection termination request from the remote TCP, or an acknowledgment of the connection termination request previously sent. FIN-WAIT-2 represents waiting for a connection termination request from the remote TCP. CLOSE-WAIT represents waiting for a connection termination request from the local user.

CLOSING represents waiting for a connection termination request acknowledgment from the remote TCP.

LAST-ACK represents waiting for an acknowledgment of the connection termination request previously sent to the remote TCP (which includes an acknowledgment of its connection termination request).

TIME-WAIT represents waiting for enough time to pass to be sure the remote TCP received the acknowledgment of its connection termination request. CLOSED represents no connection state at all.

A TCP connection progresses from one state to another in response to events. The events are the user calls, OPEN, SEND, RECEIVE, CLOSE, ABORT, and STATUS; the incoming segments, particularly those containing the SYN, ACK, RST and FIN flags; and timeouts.

The example at the top of page 734 illustrates only state changes, together with the causing events and resulting actions, but addresses neither error conditions nor actions which are not connected with state changes. More detail is offered with respect to the reaction of the TCP to events forthwith.

TCP Sequence Numbers

A fundamental notion in the design is that every octet of data sent over a TCP connection has a sequence number. Since every octet is sequenced, each of them can be acknowledged. The acknowledgment mechanism employed is cumulative so that an acknowledgment of sequence number X indicates that all octets up to but not including X have been received. This mechanism allows for straightforward duplicate detection in the presence of retransmission. Numbering of octets within a segment is such that the first data octet immediately following the header has the lowest number, and the following octets are numbered consecutively.

It is essential to remember that the actual sequence number space is finite, though very large. This space ranges from 0 to $2^{**}32 - 1$. Since the space is finite, all arithmetic dealing with sequence numbers must be performed by modulo $2^{**}32$. This unsigned arithmetic preserves the relationship of sequence numbers as they cycle from $2^{**}32 - 1$ to 0 again. There are subtleties to computer module arithmetic, so great care should be taken in programming the comparison of such values.

The typical sequence number comparisons which the TCP must perform include:

1. Determining that an acknowledgment refers to some sequence number sent but not yet acknowledged
2. Determining that all sequence numbers occupied by a segment have been acknowledged (to remove the segment from a retransmission queue)
3. Determining that an incoming segment contains sequence numbers which are expected (i.e., that the segment "overlaps" the receive window).

In response to sending data the TCP will receive acknowledgments. The following comparisons are needed to process the acknowledgments.

SND.UNA	Oldest unacknowledged sequence number
SND.NXT	Next sequence number to be sent
SEG.ACK	Acknowledgment from the receiving TCP (next sequence number expected by the receiving TCP)
SEG.SEQ	First sequence number of a segment
SEG.LEN	The number of octets occupied by the data in the segment (counting SYN and FIN)
SEG.SEQ+SEG.LEN-1	Last sequence number of a segment.

A new acknowledgment (called an "acceptable ACK"), is one for which the inequality below holds:

```
SND.UNA < SEG.ACK =< SND.NXT
```

A segment on the retransmission queue is fully acknowledged if the sum of its sequence number and length is less than or equal to the acknowledgment value in the incoming segment.

When data are received the following comparisons are needed:

RCV.NXT	Next sequence number expected on an incoming segment; this is the left or lower edge of the receive window
RCV.NXT+RCV.WND-1	Last sequence number expected on an incoming segment; this is the right or upper edge of the receive window
SEG.SEQ	First sequence number occupied by the incoming segment
SEG.SEQ+SEG.LEN-1	Last sequence number occupied by the incoming segment.

A segment is judged to occupy a portion of a valid receive sequence space if

```
RCV.NXT =< SEG.SEQ < RCV.NXT+RCV.WND
```

or

```
RCV.NXT =< SEG.SEQ+SEG.LEN-1 < RCV.NXT+RCV.WND.
```

The first part of this test checks to see if the beginning of the segment falls in the window, the second part checks to see if the end of the segment falls in the window; if the segment passes either part of the test it contains data in the window.

Actually, it is a little more complicated than this. Because there are zero windows and zero length segments, we have four cases for the acceptability of an incoming segment:

Segment Length	Receive Window	Test
0	0	SEG.SEQ = RCV.NXT
0	>0	RCV.NXT =< SEG.SEQ < RCV.NXT+RCV.WND
>0	0	not acceptable
>0	>0	RCV.NXT =< SEG.SEQ < RCV.NXT+RCV.WND or RCV.NXT =< SEG.SEQ+SEG.LEN-1 < RCV.NXT+RCV.WND

When the receive window is zero no segments should be acceptable except ACK segments. Thus, it is be possible for a TCP to maintain a zero receive window while transmitting data and receiving ACKs. However, even when the receive window is zero, a TCP must process the RST and URG fields of all incoming segments.

We have taken advantage of the numbering scheme to protect certain control information as well. This is achieved by implicitly including some control flags in the sequence space so they can be retransmitted and acknowledged without confusion (i.e., one and only one copy of the control will be acted upon). Control information is not physically carried in the segment data space. Consequently, we must adopt rules for implicitly assigning sequence numbers to control. The SYN and FIN are the only controls requiring this protection, and these controls are used only at connection opening and closing. For sequence number purposes, the SYN is considered to occur before the first actual data octet of the segment in which it occurs, while the FIN is considered to occur after the last actual data octet in a segment in which it occurs. The segment length (SEG.LEN) includes both data and sequence space occupying controls. When a SYN is present then SEG.SEQ is the sequence number of the SYN.

Initial Sequence Number Selection

The protocol places no restriction on a particular connection being used over and over again. A connection is defined by a pair of sockets. New instances of a connection will be referred to as incarnations of the connection. The question to be answered is how the TCP identifies duplicate segments from previous incarnations of the connection. The problem apparent if the connection is being opened and closed in quick succession, or if the connection breaks with loss of memory and is then reestablished.

To avoid confusion we must prevent segments from one incarnation of a connection from being used while the same sequence numbers may still be present in the network from an earlier incarnation. We want to assure this, even if a TCP crashes and loses all knowledge of the sequence numbers it has been using. When new connections are created, an initial sequence number (ISN) generator is employed which selects a new 32-bit ISN. The generator is bound to a (possibly fictitious) 32-bit clock whose low-order bit is incremented roughly every 4 microseconds. Thus, the ISN cycles approximately every 4.55 hours. Since we assume that segments will stay in the network no more than the Maximum Segment Lifetime (MSL) and that the MSL is less than 4.55 hours we can reasonably assume that ISNs will be unique.

For each connection there is a send sequence number and a receive sequence number. The initial send sequence number (ISS) is chosen by the data-sending TCP, and the initial receive sequence number (IRS) is learned during the connection-establishing procedure. For a connection to be established or initialized, the two TCPs must synchronize on each other's initial sequence numbers. This is done in an exchange of connection establishing segments carrying a control bit called SYN (for synchronize) and the initial sequence numbers. As a shorthand, segments carrying the SYN bit are also called SYNs. Hence, the solution requires a suitable mechanism for picking an initial sequence number and a slightly involved handshake to exchange the ISNs.

The synchronization requires each side to send its own initial sequence number and to receive a confirmation of it in acknowledgment from the other side. Each side must also receive the other side's initial sequence number and send a confirming acknowledgment.

1. A --> B   SYN my sequence number is X
2. A <-- B   ACK your sequence number is X
3. A <-- B   SYN my sequence number is Y
4. A --> B   ACK your sequence number is Y

Steps 2 and 3 can be combined in a single message; this is called the three-way (or three-message) handshake. A three-way handshake is necessary because sequence numbers are not tied to a global clock in the network, and TCPs may have different mechanisms for picking the ISNs. The receiver of the first SYN has no way of knowing whether the segment was an old delayed one or not, unless it remembers the last sequence number used on the connection (which is not always possible); it must ask the sender to verify this SYN. The three-way handshake and a clock-driven scheme are advantages in a TCP network.

Knowing When to Keep Quiet

To be sure that a TCP does not create a segment that carries a sequence number which may be duplicated by an old segment remaining in the network, the TCP must keep quiet for an MSL before assigning any sequence numbers upon starting up or recovering from a crash in which memory of sequence numbers in use was lost. For this specification the MSL is taken to be 2 minutes. This is an engineering choice, and may be changed if experience indicates it is desirable to do so. Note that if a TCP is reinitialized in some sense, yet retains its memory of sequence numbers in use, then it need not wait at all; it must only be sure to use sequence numbers larger than those recently used.

TCP Quiet Time Concept

This specification provides that hosts which "crash" without retaining any knowledge of the last sequence numbers transmitted on each active (i.e., not closed) connection shall delay emitting any TCP segments for at least the agreed MSL in the internet system of which the host is a part. In the paragraphs below, an explanation for this specification is given. TCP implementors may violate the "quiet time" restriction, but only at the risk of causing some old data to be accepted as new or new data rejected as old duplicated by some receivers in the internet system.

TCPs consume sequence number space each time a segment is formed and entered into the network output queue at a source host. The duplicate detection and sequencing algorithm in the TCP protocol relies on the unique binding of segment data to sequence space to the extent that sequence numbers will not cycle through all $2**32$ values before the segment data bound to those sequence numbers have been delivered and acknowledged by the receiver and all duplicate copies of the segments have "drained" from the internet. Without such an assumption, two distinct TCP segments could conceivably be assigned the same or overlapping sequence numbers, causing confusion at the receiver as to which data is new and which is old. Remember that each segment is bound to as many consecutive sequence numbers as there are octets of data in the segment.

Under normal conditions, TCPs keep track of the next sequence number to emit and the oldest awaiting acknowledgment so as to avoid mistakenly reusing a sequence number before its first use has been acknowledged. This alone does not guarantee that old duplicate data are drained from the net, so the sequence space has been made very large to reduce the probability that a wandering duplicate will cause trouble upon arrival. At 2 megabits/sec. it takes 4.5 hours to use up 2**32 octets of sequence space. Since the maximum segment lifetime in the net is not likely to exceed a few tens of seconds, this is deemed ample protection for foreseeable nets, even if data rates escalate to 10s of megabits/sec. At 100 megabits/sec, the cycle time is 5.4 minutes, which may be a little short, but still within reason.

The basic duplicate-detection and sequencing algorithm in TCP can be defeated, however, if a source TCP does not have any memory of the sequence numbers it last used on a given connection. For example, if the TCP were to start all connections with sequence number 0, then upon crashing and restarting, a TCP might re-form an earlier connection (possibly after half-open connection resolution) and emit packets with sequence numbers identical to or overlapping with packets still in the network which were emitted on an earlier incarnation of the same connection. In the absence of knowledge about the sequence numbers used on a particular connection, the TCP specification recommends that the source delay for MSL seconds before emitting segments on the connection, to allow time for segments from the earlier connection incarnation to drain from the system.

Even hosts which can remember the time of day and used it to select initial sequence number values are not immune from this problem (even if time of day is used to select an initial sequence number for each new connection incarnation).

Suppose a connection is opened starting with sequence number S. Suppose that this connection is not used much and that eventually the initial sequence number function (ISN(t)) takes on a value equal to the sequence number, say S1, of the last segment sent by this TCP on a particular connection. Now suppose, at this instant, the host crashes, recovers, and establishes a new incarnation of the connection. The initial sequence number chosen is S1 = ISN(t)—the last used sequence number on old incarnation of connection. If the recovery occurs quickly enough, any old duplicates in the net bearing sequence numbers in the neighborhood of S1 may arrive and be treated as new packets by the receiver of the new incarnation of the connection.

The problem is that the recovering host may not know for how long it crashed or whether there still are old duplicates in the system from earlier connection incarnations.

One way to deal with this problem is to deliberately delay emitting segments for one MSL after recovery from a crash—this is the *quiet time* specification. Hosts which prefer to avoid waiting are willing to risk possible confusion of old and new packets at a given destination may choose not to wait for the *quiet time*. Implementors may provide TCP users with the ability to select on a connection-by-connection basis whether to wait after a crash, or may informally implement the quiet time for all connections.

Obviously, even where a user elects to wait, this is not necessary after the host has been up for at least MSL seconds. To summarize: every segment emitted occupies one or more sequence numbers in the sequence space; the numbers occupied by a segment are *busy* or *in use* until MSL seconds have passed; upon crashing a block of space-time is occupied by the octets of the last emitted segment; if a new connection is started too soon and uses any of the sequence numbers in the space-time footprint of the last segment of the previous connection incarnation, there is a potential sequence number overlap area which could cause confusion at the receiver.

Establishing a TCP Connection

The *three-way handshake*, the procedure used to establish a connection, is normally initiated by one TCP and responded to by another TCP. The procedure also works if two TCPs simultaneously initiate the procedure. When simultaneous attempts occur, each TCP receives a SYN segment which carries no acknowledgment after it has sent a SYN. Of course, the arrival of an old duplicate SYN segment can potentially make it appear to the recipient that a simultaneous connection initiation is in progress. Proper use of reset segments can remove ambiguity in these cases. Although examples do not show connection synchronization using data-carrying segments, this is perfectly legitimate, so long as the receiving TCP does not deliver the data to the user until it is clear the data are valid; this means the data must be buffered at the receiver until the connection reaches the Established state. The three-way handshake reduces the possibility of false connections. It is the implementation of a tradeoff between memory and messages to provide information for this checking.

The simplest three-way handshake was explained previously. This should be interpreted in the following way.

Each line is numbered for reference purposes. Right arrows (—>) indicate departure of a TCP segment from TCP A to TCP B, or arrival of a segment at B from A. Left arrows (<—), indicate the reverse. Ellipsis (...) indicates a segment still in the network (delayed). An "XXX" indicates a segment which is lost or rejected. Comments appear in parentheses. TCP state represent the state after the departure or arrival of the segment (whose contents are shown in the center of each line). Segment contents are shown in abbreviated form, with sequence number, control flags, and ACK field. Other fields such as window, addresses, lengths, and text have been left out in the interest of clarity.

TCP A		TCP B
1	CLOSED	LISTEN
2	SYN-SENT --> <SEQ=100><CTL=SYN> -->	SYN-RECEIVED
3	ESTABLISHED <-<SEQ=300><ACK=101> <CTL=SYN,ACK><-	SYN-RECEIVED
4	ESTABLISHED -><SEQ=101><ACK=301> <CTL=ACK>-->	ESTABLISHED
5	ESTABLISHED-><SEQ=101><ACK=301> <CTL=ACK><DATA>->	ESTABLISHED

In line 2 above, TCP A begins by sending a SYN segment indicating that it will use sequence numbers starting with sequence number 100. In line 3, TCP B sends a SYN and acknowledges the SYN it received from TCP A. Note that the acknowledgment field indicates TCP B is now expecting to hear sequence 101, acknowledging the SYN which occupied sequence 100. At line 4, TCP A responds with an empty segment containing an ACK for TCP B's SYN; and in line 5, TCP A sends some data. Note that the sequence number of the segment in line 5 is the same as in line 4 because the ACK does not occupy sequence number space (if it did, we would wind up ACKing ACKs).

Simultaneous initiation is only slightly more complex. Each TCP cycles from CLOSED to SYN-SENT to SYN-RECEIVED to ESTABLISHED.

TCP A		TCP B
1	CLOSED	CLOSED
2	SYN-SENT--> <SEQ=100><CTL=SYN>	...
3	SYN-RECEIVED <-<SEQ=300><CTL=SYN><-	SYN-SENT
4	... <SEQ=100><CTL=SYN>->	SYN-RECEIVED
5	SYN-RECEIVED ->\<SEQ=100><ACK=301> <CTL=SYN,ACK>	...
6	ESTABLISHED <-<SEQ=300><ACK=101> <CTL=SYN,ACK><-	SYN-RECEIVED
7	... <SEQ=101><ACK=301><CTL=ACK> -->	ESTABLISHED

The principal reason for the three-way handshake is to prevent old duplicate connection initiations from causing confusion. To deal with this, a special control message, RST (reset), has been devised. If the receiving TCP is in a non-synchronized state (i.e., SYN-SENT, SYN-RECEIVED), it returns to LISTEN on receiving an acceptable reset. If the TCP is in one of the synchronized state (ESTABLISHED, FIN-WAIT-1, FIN-WAIT-2, CLOSE-WAIT, CLOSING, LAST-ACK, TIME-WAIT), it aborts the connection and informs its user.

Consider half-open connections shown below.

TCP A		TCP B
1	CLOSED	LISTEN
2	SYN-SENT->\<SEQ=100><CTL=SYN>	...
3	(duplicate) ... <SEQ=90><CTL=SYN>-->	SYN-RECEIVED
4	SYN-SENT <-<SEQ=300><ACK=91> <CTL=SYN,ACK><-	SYN-RECEIVED
5	SYN-SENT->\<SEQ=91><CTL=RST>->	LISTEN
6	... <SEQ=100><CTL=SYN>->	SYN-RECEIVED
7	SYN-SENT<-<SEQ=400><ACK=101> <CTL=SYN,ACK><-	SYN-RECEIVED
8	ESTABLISHED->\<SEQ=101><ACK=401> <CTL=ACK>->	ESTABLISHED

At line 3, an old duplicate SYN arrives at TCP B. TCP B cannot tell that this is an old duplicate, so it responds normally (line 4). TCP A detects that the ACK field is incorrect and returns an RST with its SEQ field selected to make the segment believable. TCP B, on receiving the RST, returns to the LISTEN state.

When the original SYN finally arrives at line 6, the synchronization proceeds normally. If the SYN at line 6 had arrived before the RST, a more complex exchange might have occurred with RSTs sent in both directions.

Half-Open Connections and Other Anomalies

An established connection is said to be *half-open* if one of the TCPs has closed or aborted the connection at its end without the knowledge of the other, or if the two ends of the connection have become desynchronized owing to a crash that resulted in loss of memory. Such connections will automatically become reset if an attempt is made to send data in either direction. However, half-open connections are expected to be unusual, and the recovery procedure is mildly involved.

If at site A the connection no longer exists, then an attempt by the user at site B to send any data on it will result in the site B TCP receiving a reset control message. Such a message indicates to the site B TCP that something is wrong, and it is expected to abort the connection.

Assume that user processes A and B are communicating with one another when a crash occurs causing loss of memory to A's TCP. Depending on the operating system supporting A's TCP, it is likely that some error-recovery mechanism exists. When the TCP is up again, A is likely to start again from the beginning or from a recovery point. As a result, A will probably try to OPEN the connection again or try to SEND on the connection it believes open. In the latter case, it receives the error message "connection not open" from the local (A's) TCP. In an attempt to establish the connection, A's TCP will send a segment containing SYN.

After TCP A crashes, the user attempts to reopen the connection. TCP B, in the meantime, thinks the connection is open. Consider the following.

TCP A		TCP B
1	(CRASH)	(send 300,receive 100)
2	CLOSED	ESTABLISHED
3	SYN-SENT-><SEQ=400><CTL=SYN>->	(??)
4	(!!)<-<SEQ=300><ACK=100><CTL=ACK><-	ESTABLISHED
5	SYN-SENT-><SEQ=100><CTL=RST>->	(Abort!!)
6	SYN-SENT	CLOSED
7	SYN-SENT-><SEQ=400><CTL=SYN>	-->

When the SYN arrives at line 3, TCP B, being in a synchronized state, and the incoming segment outside the window, responds with an acknowledgment indicating what sequence it next expects to hear (ACK 100). TCP A sees that this segment does not acknowledge anything it sent and, being unsynchronized, sends an RST because it has detected a half-open connection. TCP B aborts at line 5. TCP A will continue to try to establish the connection; the problem is now reduced to the basic three-way handshake.

An interesting alternative case occurs when TCP A crashes and TCP B tries to send data on what it thinks is a synchronized connection. This is illustrated in the example below. The data arriving at TCP A from TCP B (line 2) are unacceptable because no such connection exists, so TCP A sends an RST. The RST is acceptable so TCP B processes it and aborts the connection.

	TCP A	TCP B
1	(CRASH)	(end 300, receive 100)
2	(??) <-<SEQ=300><ACK=100><DATA=10> <CTL=ACK><-	ESTABLISHED
3	-><SEQ=100><CTL=RST>->	(ABORT!!)

The illustration below shows TCPs A and B with passive connections waiting for SYN. An old duplicate arriving at TCP B (line 2) stirs B into action. A SYN-ACK is returned (line 3) and causes TCP A to generate a RST (the ACK in line 3 is not acceptable). TCP B accepts the reset and returns to its passive LISTEN state.

	TCP A	TCP B
1	LISTEN	LISTEN
2	...<SEQ=Z><CTL=SYN>->	SYN-RECEIVED
3	(??)<-<SEQ=X><ACK=Z+1><CTL=SYN,ACK><-	SYN-RECEIVED
4	-><SEQ=Z+1><CTL=RST>->	(return to LISTEN!)
5	LISTEN	LISTEN

Old duplicate SYN initiates a reset on two passive sockets for by the following rules for RST generation and processing.

Reset Generation

As a general rule, RST must be sent whenever a segment arrives which apparently is not intended for the current connection. A reset must not be sent if it is not clear that this is the case. There are three groups of states:

1. If the connection does not exist (CLOSED) then a reset is sent in response to any incoming segment except another reset. In particular, SYNs addressed to a nonexistent connection are rejected by this means. If the incoming segment has an ACK field, the reset takes its sequence number from the ACK field of the segment, otherwise the reset has sequence number zero and the ACK field is set to the sum of the sequence number and segment length of the incoming segment. The connection remains in the CLOSED state.

2. If the connection is in any non-synchronized state (LISTEN, SYN-SENT, SYN-RECEIVED), and the incoming segment acknowledges something not yet sent (the segment carries an unacceptable ACK), or if an incoming segment has a security level or compartment which does not exactly match the level and compartment requested for the connection, a reset is sent.

   If our SYN has not been acknowledged and the precedence level of the incoming segment is higher than the precedence level requested, then either raise the local precedence level (if allowed to by the user and the system) or send a reset; or if the precedence level of the incoming segment is lower than the precedence level requested, then continue as if the precedence matched exactly (if the remote TCP cannot raise the precedence level to match ours this will be detected in the next segment it sends, and the connection will be terminated then). If our SYN has been acknowledged (perhaps in this incoming segment) the precedence level of the incoming segment must match the local precedence level exactly; if it does not a reset must be sent.

   If the incoming segment has an ACK field, the reset takes its sequence number from the ACK field of the segment, otherwise the reset has sequence number zero and the ACK field is set to the sum of the sequence number and segment length of the incoming segment. The connection remains in the same state.

3. If the connection is in a synchronized state (ESTABLISHED, FIN-WAIT-1, FIN-WAIT-2, CLOSE-WAIT, CLOSING, LAST-ACK, TIME-WAIT), any unacceptable segment (out of window sequence number or unacceptable acknowledgment number) must elicit

only an empty acknowledgment segment containing the current send-sequence number and an acknowledgment indicating the next sequence number expected to be received, and the connection remains in the same state.

If an incoming segment has a security level, or compartment, or precedence which does not exactly match the level, and compartment, and precedence requested for the connection, a reset is sent and connection goes to the CLOSED state. The reset takes its sequence number from the ACK field of the incoming segment.

TCP Reset Processing

In all states except SYN-SENT, all RST segments are validated by checking their SEQ fields. A reset is valid if its sequence number is in the window. In the SYN-SENT state (an RST received in response to an initial SYN), the RST is acceptable if the ACK field acknowledges the SYN.

The receiver of an RST first validates it, then changes state. If the receiver was in the LISTEN state, it ignores it. If the receiver was in SYN-RECEIVED state and had previously been in the LISTEN state, then the receiver returns to the LISTEN state, otherwise the receiver aborts the connection and goes to the CLOSED state. If the receiver was in any other state, it aborts the connection, advises the user, and goes to the CLOSED state.

Closing a TCP Connection

CLOSE is an operation meaning "I have no more data to send." The notion of closing a full-duplex connection is subject to ambiguous interpretation, since it may not be obvious how to treat the receiving side of the connection. We have chosen to treat CLOSE in a simplex fashion. The user who CLOSEs may continue to RECEIVE until he is told that the other side has CLOSED also. Thus, a program could initiate several SENDs followed by a CLOSE, and then continue to RECEIVE until signaled that a RECEIVE failed because the other side has CLOSED. We assume that the TCP will signal a user, even if no RECEIVEs are outstanding, that the other side has closed, so the user can terminate his side gracefully. A TCP will reliably deliver all buffers SENT before the connection was CLOSED so a user who expects no data in return need only wait to hear the connection was CLOSED successfully to know that all his data were received at the destination TCP. Users must keep reading connections they close for sending until the TCP says no more data.

Essentially three cases exist:

1. The user initiates by telling the TCP to CLOSE the connection
2. The remote TCP initiates by sending a FIN control signal
3. Both users CLOSE simultaneously.

Case # 1: Local user initiates the close

In this case, a FIN segment can be constructed and placed on the outgoing segment queue. No further SENDs from the user will be accepted by the TCP, and it enters the FIN-WAIT-1 state. RECEIVEs are allowed in this state. All segments preceding and including FIN will be retransmitted until acknowledged. When the other TCP has both acknowledged the FIN and sent a FIN of its own, the first TCP can ACK this FIN. Note that a TCP receiving a FIN will ACK but not send its own FIN until its user has CLOSED the connection also.

Case 2: TCP receives a FIN from the network

If an unsolicited FIN arrives from the network, the receiving TCP can ACK it and tell the user that the connection is closing. The user will respond with a CLOSE, upon which the TCP can send a FIN to the other TCP after sending any remaining data. The TCP then waits until its own FIN is acknowledged whereupon it deletes the connection. If an ACK is not forthcoming, after the user timeout the connection is aborted and the user is told.

Case 3: Both users close simultaneously

A simultaneous CLOSE by users at both ends of a connection causes FIN segments to be exchanged. When all segments preceding the FINs have been processed and acknowledged, each TCP can ACK the FIN it has received. Both will, upon receiving these ACKs, delete the connection.

TCP A	TCP B
1 ESTABLISHED	ESTABLISHED
2 Close FIN-WAIT-1-><SEQ=100><ACK=300><CTL=FIN,ACK>->	CLOSE-WAIT
3 FIN-WAIT-2<-<SEQ=300><ACK=101><CTL=ACK><-	CLOSE-WAIT
4 Close TIME-WAIT<-<SEQ=300><ACK=101><CTL=FIN,ACK><-	LAST-ACK

```
5  TIME-WAIT-><SEQ=101><ACK=301>
   <CTL=ACK>->                                                CLOSED
6  2 MSL                                                       CLOSED
```

TCP A	**TCP B**
1 ESTABLISHED	ESTABLISHED
2 Close	Close
FIN-WAIT-1-><SEQ=100><ACK=300> <CTL=FIN,ACK>...FIN-WAIT-1	
<--<SEQ=300><ACK=100><CTL=FIN,ACK><- <SEQ=100><ACK=300><CTL=FIN,ACK>->	...
3 CLOSING-><SEQ=101><ACK=301><CTL=ACK>...	CLOSING
<-- <SEQ=301><ACK=101><CTL=ACK>	<--
... <SEQ=101><ACK=301><CTL=ACK>	-->
4 TIME-WAIT	TIME-WAIT
2 MSL	2 MSL
CLOSED	CLOSED

Precedence and Security

The intent is that connection be allowed only between ports operating with exactly the same security and compartment values and at the higher of the precedence levels requested by the two ports. The precedence and security parameters used in TCP are exactly those defined in the Internet Protocol (IP). The term *security/compartment* is intended to indicate the security parameters used in IP including security, compartment, user group, and handling restriction. A connection attempt with mismatched security/compartment values or a lower precedence value must be rejected by sending a reset. Rejecting a connection due to too low a precedence only occurs after an acknowledgment of the SYN has been received. TCP modules which operate only at the default value of precedence will still have to check the precedence of incoming segments and possibly raise the precedence level they use on the connection.

The security parameters may be used even in a non-secure environment (the values would indicate unclassified data), thus hosts in non-secure environments must be prepared to receive the security parameters, though they need not send them.

TCP and Data Communication

Once the connection is established data are communicated by the exchange of segments. Because segments may be lost due to errors (checksum test failure), or network congestion, TCP uses retransmission (after a timeout) to ensure delivery of every segment. Duplicate segments may arrive due to network or TCP retransmission. As discussed in the section on sequence numbers the TCP performs certain tests on the sequence and acknowledgment numbers in the segments to verify their acceptability.

The sender of data keeps track of the next sequence number to use in the variable SND.NXT. The receiver of data keeps track of the next sequence number to expect in the variable RCV.NXT. The sender of data keeps track of the oldest unacknowledged sequence number in the variable SND.UNA. If the data flow is momentarily idle and all data sent have been acknowledged then the three variables will be equal. When the sender creates a segment and transmits it the sender advances SND.NXT. When the receiver accepts a segment it advances RCV.NXT and sends an acknowledgment. When the data sender receives an acknowledgment it advances SND.UNA. The extent to which the values of these variables differ is a measure of the delay in the communication. The amount by which the variables are advanced is the length of the data in the segment. Note that once in the ESTABLISHED state all segments must carry current acknowledgment information. The CLOSE user call implies a push function, as does the FIN control flag in an incoming segment.

TCP Retransmission Timeout

Because of the variability of the networks that compose an internetwork system and the wide range of uses of TCP connections the retransmission timeout must be dynamically determined. One procedure for determining a retransmission time out is given here as an illustration.

An Example Retransmission Timeout Procedure is to measure the elapsed time between sending a data octet with a particular sequence number and receiving an acknowledgment that covers that sequence number (segments sent do not have to match segments received). This measured elapsed time is the Round Trip Time (RTT). Next compute a Smoothed Round Trip Time (SRTT) as:

```
SRTT = ( ALPHA * SRTT ) + ((1-ALPHA) * RTT)
```

and based on this, compute the retransmission timeout (RTO) as:

```
RTO = min[UBOUND,max[LBOUND,(BETA*SRTT)]]
```

where UBOUND is an upper bound on the timeout (e.g., 1 minute), LBOUND is a lower bound on the timeout (e.g., 1 second), ALPHA is a smoothing factor (e.g., .8 to .9), and BETA is a delay variance factor (e.g., 1.3 to 2.0).

TCP Communication of Urgent Information

The objective of the TCP urgent mechanism is to allow the sending user to stimulate the receiving user to accept some urgent data and to permit the receiving TCP to indicate to the receiving user when all the currently known urgent data has been received by the user. This mechanism permits a point in the data stream to be designated as the end of urgent information. Whenever this point is in advance of the receive sequence number (RCV.NXT) at the receiving TCP, that TCP must tell the user to go into "urgent mode;" when the receive sequence number catches up to the urgent pointer, the TCP must tell user to go into "normal mode." If the urgent pointer is updated while the user is in "urgent mode," the update will be invisible to the user.

The method employs a urgent field which is carried in all segments transmitted. The URG control flag indicates that the urgent field is meaningful and must be added to the segment sequence number to yield the urgent pointer. The absence of this flag indicates that there are no urgent data outstanding.

To send an urgent indication the user must also send at least one data octet. If the sending user also indicates a push, timely delivery of the urgent information to the destination process is enhanced.

Managing the Window

The window sent in each segment indicates the range of sequence numbers the sender of the window (the data receiver) is currently prepared to accept. There is an assumption that this is related to the currently available data buffer space available for this connection.

Indicating a large window encourages transmissions. If more data arrive than can be accepted, they will be discarded. This will result in excessive retransmissions, adding unnecessarily to the load on the network and the TCPs. Indicating a small window may restrict the transmission of data to the point of introducing a round-trip delay between each new segment transmitted.

The mechanisms provided allow a TCP to advertise a large window and subsequently to advertise a much smaller window without having accepted that much data. This *shrinking the window*, is strongly discouraged. The robustness principle dictates that TCPs will not shrink the window themselves, but will be prepared for such behavior on the part of other TCPs.

The sending TCP must be prepared to accept from the user and send at least one octet of new data even if the send window is zero. The sending TCP must regularly retransmit to the receiving TCP even when the window is zero. Two minutes is recommended for the retransmission interval when the window is zero. This retransmission is essential to guarantee that when either TCP has a zero window the reopening of the window will be reliably reported to the other.

When the receiving TCP has a zero window and a segment arrives it must still send an acknowledgment showing its next expected sequence number and current window (zero).

The sending TCP packages the data to be transmitted into segments which fit the current window, and may repackage segments on the retransmission queue. Such repackaging is not required, but may be helpful.

In a connection with a one-way data flow, the window information will be carried in acknowledgment segments that all have the same sequence number so there will be no way to reorder them if they arrive out of order. This is not a serious problem, but it will allow the window information to be on occasion temporarily based on old reports from the data receiver. A refinement to avoid this problem is to act on the window information from segments that carry the highest acknowledgment number (that is segments with acknowledgment number equal or greater than the highest previously received).

Window management procedure has significant influence on the communication performance. The following comments are suggestions.

- Allocating a small window causes data to be transmitted in many small segments when better performance is achieved using fewer large segments.
- Another suggestion for avoiding small windows is for the receiver to defer updating a window until the additional allocation is at

least X percent of the maximum allocation possible for the connection (where X might be 20 to 40).
- Another suggestion is for the sender to avoid sending small segments by waiting until the window is large enough before sending data. If the user signals a push function then the data must be sent even if it is a small segment.

Acknowledgments should not be delayed or unnecessary retransmissions will result. One strategy would be to send an acknowledgment when a small segment arrives (without updating the window information), and then to send another acknowledgment with new window information when the window is larger. The segment sent to probe a zero window may also begin a breakup of transmitted data into smaller and smaller segments. If a segment containing a single data octet sent to probe a zero window is accepted, it consumes one octet of the window now available. If the sending TCP simply sends as much as it can whenever the window is nonzero, the transmitted data will be broken into alternating big and small segments. As time goes on, occasional pauses in the receiver making window allocation available will result in breaking the big segments into a small and a not quite so big pair. And after a while the data transmission will be in mostly small segments.

TCP implementations need actively to attempt to combine small window allocations into larger windows, since the mechanisms for managing the window tend to lead to many small windows in the simplest-minded implementations.

Two TCP interfaces are of concern: the user/TCP interface and the TCP/lower-level interface.

User/TCP Interface

The following functional description of user commands to the TCP is, at best, fictional, since every operating system will have different facilities. Consequently, you should be aware that different TCP implementations may have different user interfaces. However, all TCPs must provide a certain minimum set of services to guarantee that they can support the same protocol hierarchy.

TCP User Commands

The following sections functionally characterize a user/TCP interface. The notation used is similar to most procedure or function calls in high-level languages, but this usage is not meant to rule out trap-type service calls (e.g., SVCs, UUOs, EMTs).

User commands described below specify the basic functions the TCP must perform to support interprocess communication. Individual implementations must define their own exact format, and may provide combinations or subsets of the basic functions in single calls. In particular, some implementations may wish to automatically OPEN a connection on the first SEND or RECEIVE issued by the user for a given connection.

In providing interprocess communication facilities, the TCP must not only accept commands, but must also return information to the processes it serves. The latter consists of:

- General information about a connection (e.g., interrupts, remote close, binding of unspecified foreign socket)
- Replies to specific user commands indicating success or various types of failure.

Open Format

```
OPEN (local port, foreign socket, active/passive [, timeout] [,
precedence] [, security/compartment] [, options]) -> local
connection name
```

We assume that the local TCP is aware of the identity of the processes it serves and will check the authority of the process to use the connection specified. Depending upon the implementation of the TCP, the local network and TCP identifiers for the source address will either be supplied by the TCP or by the lower-level protocol (e.g., IP). These considerations are the result of concern about security, to the extent that no TCP be able to masquerade as another one, and so on. Similarly, no process can masquerade as another without the collusion of the TCP.

If the active/passive flag is set to passive, then this is a call to LISTEN for an incoming connection. A passive open may have either a fully specified foreign socket to wait for a particular connection or an unspecified foreign socket to wait for any call. A fully specified passive call can be made active by the subsequent execution of a SEND.

A transmission control block (TCB) is created and partially filled in with data from the OPEN command parameters. On an active OPEN command, the TCP will begin the procedure to synchronize (i.e., establish) the connection at once. The timeout, if present, permits the caller to set up a timeout for all data submitted to TCP. If data are not successfully delivered to the destination within the timeout period, the TCP will abort the connection. The present global default is five minutes.

The TCP or some component of the operating system will verify the user's authority to open a connection with the specified precedence or security/compartment. The absence of precedence or security/compartment specification in the OPEN call indicates the default values must be used.

TCP will accept incoming requests as matching only if the security/compartment information is exactly the same and only if the precedence is equal to or higher than the precedence requested in the OPEN call.

The precedence for the connection is the higher of the values requested in the OPEN call and received from the incoming request, and fixed at that value for the life of the connection. Implementers may want to give the user control of this precedence negotiation. For example, the user might be allowed to specify that the precedence must be exactly matched, or that any attempt to raise the precedence be confirmed by the user.

A local connection name will be returned to the user by the TCP. The local connection name can then be used as a short hand term for the connection defined by the <local socket, foreign socket> pair.

Send Format

```
SEND (local connection name, buffer address, byte count, PUSH flag,
URGENT flag [,timeout])
```

This call causes the data contained in the indicated user buffer to be sent on the indicated connection. If the connection has not been opened, the SEND is considered an error. Some implementations may allow users to SEND first; in which case, an automatic OPEN would be done. If the calling process is not authorized to use this connection, an error is returned.

If the PUSH flag is set, the data must be transmitted promptly to the receiver, and the PUSH bit will be set in the last TCP segment created from the buffer. If the PUSH flag is not set, the data may be combined with data from subsequent SENDs for transmission efficiency.

If the URGENT flag is set, segments sent to the destination TCP will have the urgent pointer set. The receiving TCP will signal the urgent condition to the receiving process if the urgent pointer indicates that data preceding the urgent pointer has not been consumed by the receiving process. The purpose of urgent is to stimulate the receiver to process the urgent data and to indicate to the receiver when all the currently known urgent data has been received. The number of times the sending user's TCP signals urgent will not necessarily be equal to the number of times the receiving user will be notified of the presence of urgent data.

If no foreign socket was specified in the OPEN, but the connection is established (e.g., because a LISTENing connection has become specific due to a foreign segment arriving for the local socket), then the designated buffer is sent to the implied foreign socket. Users who make use of OPEN with an unspecified foreign socket can make use of SEND without ever explicitly knowing the foreign socket address.

However, if a SEND is attempted before the foreign socket becomes specified, an error will be returned. Users can use the STATUS call to determine the status of the connection. In some implementations the TCP may notify the user when an unspecified socket is bound.

If a timeout is specified, the current user timeout for this connection is changed to the new one. In the simplest implementation, SEND would not return control to the sending process until either the transmission was complete or the timeout had been exceeded. However, this simple method is both subject to deadlocks (for example, both sides of the connection might try to do SENDs before doing any RECEIVEs) and offers poor performance, so it is not recommended. A more sophisticated implementation would return immediately to allow the process to run concurrently with network I/O, and, furthermore, to allow multiple SENDs to be in progress.

Multiple SENDs are served in first-come, first-served order, so the TCP will queue those it cannot service immediately.

We have implicitly assumed an asynchronous user interface in which a SEND later elicits some kind of SIGNAL or pseudo-interrupt from the serving TCP. An alternative is to return a response immediately. For instance, SENDs might return immediate local acknowledgment, even if the segment sent had not been acknowledged by the distant TCP. We could optimistically assume eventual success. If we are wrong, the connection will close anyway due to the timeout. In implementations of this kind (synchronous), there will still be some asynchronous signals, but these will deal with the connection itself, and not with specific segments or buffers.

In order for the process to distinguish among error or success indications for different SENDs, it might be appropriate for the buffer address to be returned along with the coded response to the SEND request. TCP-to-user signals are discussed below, indicating the information which should be returned to the calling process.

Receive Format

```
RECEIVE (local connection name, buffer address, byte count) -> byte
count, urgent flag, push flag
```

This command allocates a receiving buffer associated with the specified connection. If no OPEN precedes this command or the calling process is not authorized to use this connection, an error is returned. In the simplest implementation, control would not return to the calling program until either the buffer was filled, or some error occurred, but this scheme is highly subject to deadlocks. A more sophisticated implementation would permit several RECEIVEs to be outstanding at once. These would be filled as segments arrive. This strategy permits increased throughput at the cost of a more elaborate scheme (possibly asynchronous) to notify the calling program that a PUSH has been seen or a buffer filled.

If enough data arrive to fill the buffer before a PUSH is seen, the PUSH flag will not be set in the response to the RECEIVE. The buffer will be filled with as much data as it can hold. If a PUSH is seen before the buffer is filled the buffer will be returned partially filled and PUSH indicated. If there are urgent data the user will have been informed as soon as it arrived via a TCP-to-user signal. The receiving user should thus be in "urgent mode." If the URGENT flag is on, additional urgent data remains. If the URGENT flag is off, this call to RECEIVE has returned all the urgent data, and the user may now leave "urgent mode." Note that data following the urgent pointer (non-urgent data) cannot be delivered to the user in the same buffer with preceding urgent data unless the boundary is clearly marked for the user.

To distinguish among several outstanding RECEIVEs and to take care of the case that a buffer is not completely filled, the return code is accompanied by both a buffer pointer and a byte count indicating the actual length of the data received.

Alternative implementations of RECEIVE might have the TCP allocate buffer storage, or the TCP might share a ring buffer with the user.

Close Format

```
CLOSE (local connection name)
```

This command causes the connection specified to be closed. If the connection is not open or the calling process is not authorized to use this connection, an error is returned. Closing connections is intended to be a graceful operation in the sense that outstanding SENDs will be transmitted (and retransmitted), as flow control permits, until all have been serviced. Thus, it should be acceptable to make several SEND calls, followed by a CLOSE, and expect all the data to be sent to the destination. It should also be clear that users should continue to RECEIVE on CLOSING connections, since the other side may be trying to transmit the last of its data. Thus, CLOSE means "I have no more to send" but does not mean "I will not receive any more." It may happen (if the user-level protocol is not well thought out) that the closing side is unable to get rid of all its data before timing out. In this event, CLOSE turns into ABORT, and the closing TCP gives up.

The user may CLOSE the connection at any time on his own initiative, or in response to various prompts from the TCP (e.g., remote close executed, transmission timeout exceeded, destination inaccessible). Because closing a connection requires communication with the foreign TCP, connections may remain in the closing state for a short time. Attempts to reopen the connection before the TCP replies to the CLOSE command will result in error responses. Close also implies push function.

Status Format

```
STATUS (local connection name) -> status data
```

This is an implementation-dependent user command and could be excluded without adverse effect. Information returned would typically come from the TCB associated with the connection.

This command returns a data block containing the following information:

- Local socket
- Foreign socket
- Local connection name
- Receive window
- Send window
- Connection state
- Number of buffers awaiting acknowledgment
- Number of buffers pending receipt
- Urgent state
- Precedence
- Security/compartment
- Transmission timeout.

Depending on the state of the connection, or on the implementation itself, some of this information may not be available or meaningful. If the calling process is not authorized to use this connection, an error is returned. This prevents unauthorized processes from gaining information about a connection.

Abort Format

`ABORT (local connection name)`

This command causes all pending `SEND`s and `RECEIVE`s to be aborted, the TCB to be removed, and a special `RESET` message to be sent to the TCP on the other side of the connection. Depending on the implementation, users may receive abort indications for each outstanding `SEND` or `RECEIVE`, or may simply receive an `ABORT` acknowledgment.

TCP-to-User Messages

It is assumed that the operating system environment provides a means for the TCP synchronously to signal the user program. When the TCP does signal a user program, certain information is passed to the user. Often in the specification the information will be an error message. In other cases there will be information relating to the completion of processing a `SEND` or `RECEIVE` or other user call. The following information is provided:

Local Connection Name	Always
Response String	Always
Buffer Address	Send & Receive
Byte count (counts bytes received)	Receive
Push flag	Receive
Urgent flag	Receive

TCP/Lower-Level Interface

The TCP calls on a lower-level protocol module actually to send and receive information over a network. One case is that of the ARPA internetwork system where the lower-level module is the IP. If the lower-level protocol is IP it provides arguments for a type of service

and for a time to live. TCP uses the following settings for these parameters:

- Type of Service = Precedence: routine, Delay: normal, Through-
  put: normal, Reliability: normal; or 00000000.
- Time to Live = one minute, or 00111100.
- The assumed maximum segment lifetime is two minutes.

Here we explicitly ask that a segment be destroyed if it cannot be
delivered by the internet system within one minute. If the lower level
is IP (or other protocol that provides this feature) and source routing
is used, the interface must allow the route information to be communicated. This is especially important so that the source and destination addresses used in the TCP checksum be the originating source
and ultimate destination. It is also important to preserve the return
route to answer connection requests.

Any lower-level protocol will have to provide the source address,
destination address, and protocol fields, and some way to determine
the "TCP length," both to provide the functional equivalent service of
IP and to be used in the TCP checksum.

TCP Event Processing

The processing depicted in this section is an example of one possible
implementation. Other implementations may have slightly different
processing sequences. The activity of the TCP can be characterized as
responding to events. The events that occur can be cast into three categories: user calls, arriving segments, and timeouts. TCP does the
processing in response to each of the events. In many cases the processing required depends on the state of the connection.

Events that occur:

User Calls:
OPEN
SEND
RECEIVE
CLOSE
ABORT
STATUS
Arriving Segments:
SEGMENT ARRIVES
Timeouts:
USER TIMEOUT
RETRANSMISSION TIMEOUT

TIME-WAIT TIMEOUT

The model of the TCP/user interface is that user commands receive an immediate return and possibly a delayed response via an event or pseudo interrupt. In the following descriptions, the term *signal* means cause a delayed response. Error responses are given as character strings. For example, user commands referencing connections that do not exist receive *error: connection not open.*

Please note in the following that all arithmetic on sequence numbers, acknowledgment numbers, windows, et cetera, is modulo $2**32$ the size of the sequence number space. Also note that "=<" means less than or equal to (modulo $2**32$).

A natural way to think about processing incoming segments is to imagine that they are first tested for proper sequence number (i.e., that their contents lie in the range of the expected *receive window* in the sequence number space) and then that they are generally queued and processed in sequence number order.

When a segment overlaps other already received segments we reconstruct the segment to contain just the new data, and adjust the header fields to be consistent.

Note that if no state change is mentioned the TCP stays in the same state.

OPEN Call

CLOSED STATE (i.e., TCB does not exist)

Create a new TCB to hold connection state information. Fill in local socket identifier, foreign socket, precedence, security/compartment, and user timeout information. Note that some parts of the foreign socket may be unspecified in a passive OPEN and are to be filled in by the parameters of the incoming SYN segment. Verify the security and precedence requested are allowed for this user, if not, return error: precedence not allowed or error: security/compartment not allowed. If passive enter the LISTEN state and return. If active and the foreign socket is unspecified, return error: foreign socket unspecified; if active and the foreign socket is specified, issue a SYN segment. An ISS number is selected. A SYN segment of the form <SEQ=ISS><CTL=SYN> is sent. Set SND.UNA to ISS, SND.NXT to ISS+1, enter SYN-SENT state, and return.

If the caller does not have access to the local socket specified, return error: connection illegal for this process. If there is no room to create a new connection, return error: insufficient resources.

LISTEN State

If active and the foreign socket is specified, then change the connection from passive to active, select an ISS. Send a SYN segment, set SND.UNA to ISS, SND.NXT to ISS+1. Enter SYN-SENT state. Data associated with SEND may be sent with SYN segment or queued for transmission after entering ESTABLISHED state. The urgent bit if requested in the command must be sent with the data segments sent as a result of this command. If there is no room to queue the request, respond with error: insufficient resources. If the foreign socket was not specified, then return error: foreign socket unspecified.

SYN-SENT state
SYN-RECEIVED state
ESTABLISHED state
FIN-WAIT-1 state
FIN-WAIT-2 state
CLOSE-WAIT state
CLOSING state
LAST-ACK state
TIME-WAIT state
Return error: connection already exists.

SEND Call

CLOSED state (i.e., TCB does not exist)

If the user does not have access to such a connection, then return error: connection illegal for this process. Otherwise, return error: connection does not exist.

LISTEN State

If the foreign socket is specified, then change the connection from passive to active, select an ISS. Send a SYN segment, set SND.UNA to ISS, SND.NXT to ISS+1. Enter SYN-SENT state. Data associated with SEND may be sent with SYN segment or queued for transmission after entering ESTABLISHED state. The urgent bit if requested in the command must be sent with the data segments sent as a result of this command. If there is no room to queue the request, respond with error: insufficient resources. If the foreign socket was not specified, then return error: foreign socket unspecified.

SYN-SENT state
SYN-RECEIVED state

Queue the data for transmission after entering ESTABLISHED state. If no space to queue, respond with error: insufficient resources.

ESTABLISHED state
CLOSE-WAIT state

Segmentize the buffer and send it with a piggybacked acknowledgment (acknowledgment value = RCV.NXT). If there is insufficient space to remember this buffer, return error: insufficient resource.

If the urgent flag is set, then SND.UP <- SND.NXT-1 and set the urgent pointer in the outgoing segments.

FIN-WAIT-1 state
FIN-WAIT-2 state
CLOSING state
LAST-ACK state
TIME-WAIT state
Return error: connection closing and do not service the request.

RECEIVE Call

CLOSED state (i.e., TCB does not exist)

If the user does not have access to such a connection, return error: connection illegal for this process. Otherwise return error: connection does not exist.

LISTEN state
SYN-SENT state
SYN-RECEIVED state

Queue for processing after entering ESTABLISHED state. If there is no room to queue this request, respond with error: insufficient resources.

ESTABLISHED state
FIN-WAIT-1 state
FIN-WAIT-2 state

If insufficient incoming segments are queued to satisfy the request, queue the request. If there is no queue space to remember the RECEIVE, respond with `error: insufficient resources`.

Reassemble queued incoming segments into receive buffer and return to user. Mark "push seen" (PUSH) if this is the case. If `RCV.UP` is in advance of the data currently being passed to the user notify the user of the presence of urgent data.

When the TCP takes responsibility for delivering data to the user that fact must be communicated to the sender via an acknowledgment. The formation of such an acknowledgment is described below in the discussion of processing an incoming segment.

CLOSE-WAIT State

Since the remote side has already sent `FIN`, RECEIVEs must be satisfied by text already on hand, but not yet delivered to the user. If no text is awaiting delivery, the RECEIVE will get an `error: connection closing` response. Otherwise, any remaining text can be used to satisfy the RECEIVE.

> `CLOSING` state
> `LAST-ACK` state
> `TIME-WAIT` state
> Return `error: connection closing`.

CLOSE Call

`CLOSED` state (i.e., TCB does not exist)

If the user does not have access to such a connection, return `error: connection illegal for this process`. Otherwise, return `error: connection does not exist`.

LISTEN State

Any outstanding RECEIVEs are returned with `error: closing` responses. Delete TCB, enter `CLOSED` state, and return.

SYN-SENT State

Delete the TCB and return `error: closing` responses to any queued SENDs or RECEIVEs.

SYN-RECEIVED State

If no SENDs have been issued and there are no pending data to send, then form a FIN segment and send it, and enter FIN-WAIT-1 state; otherwise queue for processing after entering ESTABLISHED state.

ESTABLISHED State

Queue this until all preceding SENDs have been segmentized, then form a FIN segment and send it. In any case, enter FIN-WAIT-1 state.

> FIN-WAIT-1 state
> FIN-WAIT-2 state

Strictly speaking, this is an error and should receive an error: connection closing response. An OK response would be acceptable, too, as long as a second FIN is not emitted (the first FIN may be retransmitted though).

CLOSE-WAIT State

Queue this request until all preceding SENDs have been segmentized; then send a FIN segment and enter CLOSING state.

> CLOSING state
> LAST-ACK state
> TIME-WAIT state
> Respond with error: connection closing.

ABORT Call

CLOSED state (i.e., TCB does not exist)

If the user should not have access to such a connection, return error: connection illegal for this process. Otherwise return error: connection does not exist.

LISTEN State

Any outstanding RECEIVEs should be returned with error: connection reset responses. Delete TCB, enter CLOSED state, and return.

SYN-SENT State

All queued SENDs and RECEIVEs should be given connection reset notification, delete the TCB, enter CLOSED state, and return.

SYN-RECEIVED state
ESTABLISHED state
FIN-WAIT-1 state
FIN-WAIT-2 state
CLOSE-WAIT state
Send a reset segment: <SEQ=SND.NXT><CTL=RST>

All queued SENDs and RECEIVEs should be given connection reset notification; all segments queued for transmission (except for the RST formed above) or retransmission should be flushed, delete the TCB, enter CLOSED state, and return.

CLOSING state
LAST-ACK state
TIME-WAIT state

Respond with OK and delete the TCB, enter CLOSED state, and return.

STATUS Call

CLOSED state (i.e., TCB does not exist)

If the user should not have access to such a connection, return error: connection illegal for this process. Otherwise return error: connection does not exist.

LISTEN State

Return state = LISTEN, and the TCB pointer.

SYN-SENT State

Return state = SYN-SENT, and the TCB pointer.

SYN-RECEIVED State

Return state = SYN-RECEIVED, and the TCB pointer.

ESTABLISHED State

Return state = ESTABLISHED, and the TCB pointer.

FIN-WAIT-1 State

Return state = FIN-WAIT-1, and the TCB pointer.

FIN-WAIT-2 State

Return state = FIN-WAIT-2, and the TCB pointer.

CLOSE-WAIT State

Return `state` = `CLOSE-WAIT`, and the TCB pointer.

CLOSING State

Return `state` = `CLOSING`, and the TCB pointer.

LAST-ACK State

Return `state` = `LAST-ACK`, and the TCB pointer.

TIME-WAIT State

Return `state` = `TIME-WAIT`, and the TCB pointer.

Segment Arrives

If the state is `CLOSED` (i.e., TCB does not exist) then all data in the incoming segment are discarded. An incoming segment containing an `RST` is discarded. An incoming segment not containing an `RST` causes an `RST` to be sent in response. The acknowledgment and sequence field values are selected to make the reset sequence acceptable to the TCP that sent the offending segment.

If the `ACK` bit is off, sequence number zero is used:

`<SEQ=0><ACK=SEG.SEQ+SEG.LEN><CTL=RST,ACK>.`

If the `ACK` bit is on:

`<SEQ=SEG.ACK><CTL=RST>.`

Return.

If the state is `LISTEN` then first check for an `RST`. An incoming `RST` should be ignored. Return. Check for an `ACK`. Any acknowledgment is bad if it arrives on a connection still in the `LISTEN` state. An acceptable reset segment should be formed for any arriving `ACK`-bearing segment. The `RST` should be formatted as follows:

`<SEQ=SEG.ACK><CTL=RST>`

Return. Check for a `SYN`. If the `SYN` bit is set, check the security. If the security/compartment on the incoming segment does not exactly match the security/compartment in the TCB then send a reset and return.

ARRIVES

```
<SEQ=SEG.ACK><CTL=RST>
```

If the SEG.PRC is greater than the TCB.PRC then if allowed by the user and the system set TCB.PRC<-SEG.PRC, if not allowed send a reset and return.

```
<SEQ=SEG.ACK><CTL=RST>
```

If the SEG.PRC is less than the TCB.PRC then continue. Set RCV.NXT to SEG.SEQ+1, IRS is set to SEG.SEQ and any other control or text should be queued for processing later. ISS should be selected and a SYN segment sent of the form:

```
<SEQ=ISS><ACK=RCV.NXT><CTL=SYN,ACK>
```

SND.NXT is set to ISS+1 and SND.UNA to ISS. The connection state should be changed to SYN-RECEIVED. Note that any other incoming control or data (combined with SYN) will be processed in the SYN-RECEIVED state, but processing of SYN and ACK should not be repeated. If the listen was not fully specified (i.e., the foreign socket was not fully specified), then the unspecified fields should be filled in now.

Any other control or text-bearing segment (not containing SYN) must have an ACK and thus would be discarded by the ACK processing. An incoming RST segment could not be valid, since it could not have been sent in response to anything sent by this incarnation of the connection. You are unlikely to get here, but if you do, drop the segment, and return. If the state is SYN-SENT then first check the ACK bit if the ACK bit is set, if SEG.ACK =< ISS or SEG.ACK > SND.NXT, send a reset (unless the RST bit is set, if so drop the segment and return) <SEQ=SEG.ACK><CTL=RST> and discard the segment. Return. If SND.UNA =< SEG.ACK =< SND.NXT then the ACK is acceptable. Check the RST bit.

SEGMENT ARRIVES

If the RST bit is set, and if the ACK was acceptable then signal the user error: connection reset, drop the segment, enter CLOSED state, delete TCB, and return. Otherwise (no ACK) drop the segment and return. Check the security and precedence. If the security/compartment in the segment does not exactly match the security/compartment in the TCB, send a reset. If there is an ACK

```
<SEQ=SEG.ACK><CTL=RST>
```

otherwise

```
<SEQ=0><ACK=SEG.SEQ+SEG.LEN><CTL=RST,ACK>.
```

If there is an ACK, the precedence in the segment must match the precedence in the TCB, if not, send a reset `<SEQ=SEG.ACK><CTL=RST>`.

If there is no ACK and if the precedence in the segment is higher than the precedence in the TCB then if allowed by the user and the system, raise the precedence in the TCB to that in the segment: if not allowed to raise the precedence then send a reset.

```
<SEQ=0><ACK=SEG.SEQ+SEG.LEN><CTL=RST,ACK>
```

If the precedence in the segment is lower than the precedence in the TCB continue. If a reset was sent, discard the segment and return. Check the SYN bit. This step should be reached only if the ACK is OK, or there is no ACK, and if the segment did not contain an RST. If the SYN bit is on and the security/compartment and precedence SEGMENT ARRIVES are acceptable then, RCV.NXT is set to SEG.SEQ+1, IRS is set to SEG.SEQ. SND.UNA should be advanced to equal SEG.ACK (if there is an ACK), and any segments on the retransmission queue which are thereby acknowledged should be removed. If SND.UNA > ISS (our SYN has been ACKed), change the connection state to ESTABLISHED, form an ACK segment

```
<SEQ=SND.NXT><ACK=RCV.NXT><CTL=ACK>
```

and send it. Data or controls which were queued for transmission may be included. If there are other controls or text in the segment then continue processing at the step below where the URG bit is checked, otherwise return.

Otherwise enter SYN-RECEIVED, form a SYN,ACK segment `<SEQ=ISS><ACK=RCV.NXT><CTL=SYN,ACK>` and send it. If there are other controls or text in the segment, queue them for processing after the ESTABLISHED state has been reached, return. If neither of the SYN or RST bits is set then drop the segment and return. Otherwise, first check sequence number

```
SYN-RECEIVED state
ESTABLISHED state
FIN-WAIT-1 state
FIN-WAIT-2 state
CLOSE-WAIT state
```

```
CLOSING state
LAST-ACK state
TIME-WAIT state.
```

Segments are processed in sequence. Initial tests on arrival are used to discard old duplicates, but further processing is done in SEG.SEQ order. If a segment's contents straddle the boundary between old and new, only the new parts should be processed.

There are four cases for the acceptability test for an incoming segment:

Segment Length	Receive Window	Test
0	0	SEG.SEQ = RCV.NXT
0	>0	RCV.NXT =< SEG.SEQ < RCV.NXT+RCV.WND
>0	0	not acceptable
>0	>0	RCV.NXT =< SEG.SEQ < RCV.NXT+RCV.WND or RCV.NXT =< SEG.SEQ+SEG.LEN-1 < RCV.NXT+RCV.WND

If the RCV.WND is zero, no segments will be acceptable, but special allowance should be made to accept valid ACKs, URGs and RSTs. If an incoming segment is not acceptable, an acknowledgment should be sent in reply (unless the RST bit is set, if so drop the segment and return): <SEQ=SND.NXT><ACK=RCV.NXT><CTL=ACK>.

After sending the acknowledgment, drop the unacceptable segment and return.

In the following it is assumed that the segment is the idealized segment that begins at RCV.NXT and does not exceed the window. One could tailor actual segments to fit this assumption by trimming off any portions that lie outside the window (including SYN and FIN), and only processing further if the segment then begins at RCV.NXT. Segments with higher beginning sequence numbers may be held for later processing. Check the RST bit, SYN-RECEIVED state. If the RST bit is set and if this connection was initiated with a passive OPEN (i.e., came from the LISTEN state), then return this connection to LISTEN state and return. The user need not be informed. If this connection was initiated with an active OPEN (i.e., came from SYN-SENT state) then the connection was refused; signal the user connection refused. In either case, all segments on the retransmission queue should be removed. And in the active `OPEN` case, enter the `CLOSED` state and delete the TCB, and return.

```
ESTABLISHED
FIN-WAIT-1
FIN-WAIT-2
CLOSE-WAIT
```

If the `RST` bit is set then, any outstanding `RECEIVE`s and `SEND`s should receive RST responses. All segment queues should be flushed. Users should also receive an unsolicited general `connection reset` signal. Enter the `CLOSED` state, delete the TCB, and return.

```
CLOSING state
LAST-ACK state
TIME-WAIT
```

If the `RST` bit is set then, enter the `CLOSED` state, delete the TCB, and return.

SEGMENT ARRIVES

Check security and precedence.

SYN-RECEIVED

If the security/compartment and precedence in the segment do not exactly match the security/compartment and precedence in the TCB then send a reset, and return.

ESTABLISHED State

If the security/compartment and precedence in the segment do not exactly match the security/compartment and precedence in the TCB then send an `RST`, any outstanding `RECEIVE`s and `SEND`s should receive reset responses. All segment queues should be flushed. Users should also receive an unsolicited general `connection reset` signal. Enter the `CLOSED` state, delete the TCB, and return. This check is placed following the sequence check to prevent a segment from an old connection between these ports with a different security or precedence from causing an abort of the current connection.

Check the `SYN` bit,

```
SYN-RECEIVED
ESTABLISHED state
FIN-WAIT state-1
```

    FIN-WAIT state-2
    CLOSE-WAIT state
    CLOSING state
    LAST-ACK state
    TIME-WAIT state

If the SYN is in the window it is an error, send an RST, any outstanding RECEIVEs and SENDs should receive RST responses, all segment queues should be flushed, the user should also receive an unsolicited general connection reset signal, enter the CLOSED state, delete the TCB, and return.

If the SYN is not in the window this step would not be reached and an ACK would have been sent in the first step (sequence number check). Check the ACK field; if the ACK bit is off drop the segment; and return if the ACK bit is on SYN-RECEIVED state.

If SND.UNA =< SEG.ACK =< SND.NXT then enter ESTABLISHED state and continue processing. If the segment acknowledgment is not acceptable, form a reset segment, <SEQ=SEG.ACK><CTL=RST> and send it.

ESTABLISHED State

If SND.UNA < SEG.ACK =< SND.NXT then, set SND.UNA <- SEG.ACK. Any segments on the retransmission queue which are thereby entirely acknowledged are removed. Users should receive positive acknowledgments for buffers which have been SENT and fully acknowledged (i.e., SEND buffer should be returned with OK response). If the ACK is a duplicate (SEG.ACK < SND.UNA), it can be ignored. If the ACK acknowledges something not yet sent (SEG.ACK > SND.NXT) then send an ACK, drop the segment, and return.

If SND.UNA < SEG.ACK =< SND.NXT, the send window should be updated. If (SND.WL1 < SEG.SEQ or (SND.WL1 = SEG.SEQ and SND.WL2 =< SEG.ACK)), set SND.WND <- SEG.WND, set SND.WL1 <- SEG.SEQ, and set SND.WL2 <- SEG.ACK. SND.WND is an offset from SND.UNA, SND.WL1 records the sequence number of the last segment used to update SND.WND, and SND.WL2 records the acknowledgment number of the last segment used to update SND.WND. The check here prevents using old segments to update the window.

FIN-WAIT-1 State

In addition to the processing for the ESTABLISHED state, if our FIN is now acknowledged then enter FIN-WAIT-2 and continue processing in that state.

FIN-WAIT-2 State

In addition to the processing for the ESTABLISHED state, if the retransmission queue is empty, the user's CLOSE can be acknowledged (OK) but do not delete the TCB.

CLOSE-WAIT State

Do the same processing as for the ESTABLISHED state.

CLOSING State

In addition to the processing for the ESTABLISHED state, if the ACK acknowledges our FIN then enter the TIME-WAIT state, otherwise ignore the segment.

LAST-ACK State

The only thing that can arrive in this state is an acknowledgment of our FIN. If our FIN is now acknowledged, delete the TCB, enter the CLOSED state, and return.

TIME-WAIT State

The only thing that can arrive in this state is a retransmission of the remote FIN. Acknowledge it, and restart the 2 MSL timeout. Check the URG bit,

    ESTABLISHED state
    FIN-WAIT-1 state
    FIN-WAIT-2 state.

If the URG bit is set, RCV.UP <- max(RCV.UP,SEG.UP), and signal the user that the remote side has urgent data if the urgent pointer (RCV.UP) is in advance of the data consumed. If the user has already been signaled (or is still in the "urgent mode") for this continuous sequence of urgent data, do not signal the user again.

    CLOSE-WAIT state
    CLOSING state
    LAST-ACK state
    TIME-WAIT

This should not occur, since a FIN has been received from the remote side. Ignore the URG. Process the segment text,

    ESTABLISHED state

FIN-WAIT-1 state
FIN-WAIT-2 state

Once in the ESTABLISHED state, it is possible to deliver segment text to user RECEIVE buffers. Text from segments can be moved into buffers until either the buffer is full or the segment is empty. If the segment empties and carries a PUSH flag, then the user is informed, when the buffer is returned, that a PUSH has been received.

When the TCP takes responsibility for delivering the data to the user it must also acknowledge the receipt of the data.

Once the TCP takes responsibility for the data it advances RCV.NXT over the data accepted, and adjusts RCV.WND as appropriate to the current buffer availability. The total of RCV.NXT and RCV.WND should not be reduced.

Send an acknowledgment of the form:

<SEQ=SND.NXT><ACK=RCV.NXT><CTL=ACK>

This acknowledgment should be piggybacked on a segment being transmitted, if possible without incurring undue delay.

CLOSE-WAIT state
CLOSING state
LAST-ACK state
TIME-WAIT state

This should not occur, since a FIN has been received from the remote side. Ignore the segment text. Check the FIN bit. Do not process the FIN if the state is CLOSED, LISTEN or SYN-SENT since the SEG.SEQ cannot be validated; drop the segment and return.

If the FIN bit is set, signal the user connection closing and return any pending RECEIVEs with same message, advance RCV.NXT over the FIN, and send an acknowledgment for the FIN. Note that FIN implies PUSH for any segment text not yet delivered to the user.

SYN-RECEIVED state
ESTABLISHED state
Enter the CLOSE-WAIT state.

FIN-WAIT-1 State

If our FIN has been ACKed (perhaps in this segment), then enter TIME-WAIT, start the time-wait timer, turn off the other timers; otherwise enter the CLOSING state.

FIN-WAIT-2 State

Enter the TIME-WAIT state. Start the time-wait timer, turn off the other timers.

CLOSE-WAIT State

Remain in the CLOSE-WAIT state.

CLOSING State

Remain in the CLOSING state.

LAST-ACK State

Remain in the LAST-ACK state.

TIME-WAIT State

Remain in the TIME-WAIT state. Restart the 2 MSL time-wait timeout and return.

User Timeout

For any state if the user timeout expires, flush all queues, signal the user error: connection aborted due to user timeout in general and for any outstanding calls, delete the TCB, enter the CLOSED state and return.

Retransmission Timeout

For any state if the retransmission timeout expires on a segment in the retransmission queue, send the segment at the front of the retransmission queue again, reinitialize the retransmission timer, and return.

TIME-WAIT Timeout

If the time-wait timeout expires on a connection delete the TCB, enter the CLOSED state and return.

User Datagram Protocol (UDP)

UDP resides at transport layer four. In many ways it is the opposite of TCP; connectionless-oriented and unreliable. It does little more than provide a transport-layer protocol for applications that reside above it.

UDP Header Analysis

The extent of information about UDP is brief compared to that for TCP. An example of the UDP datagram is shown in Figure 11.17.

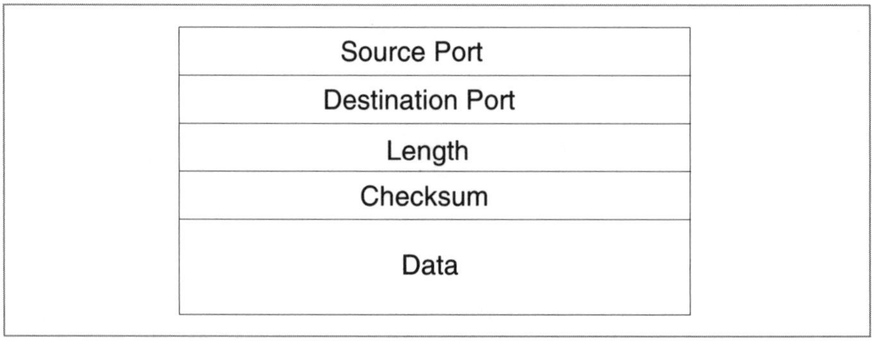

FIGURE 11.17
UDP Datagram

Source Port
Destination Port
Length
Checksum
Data

The components in the UDP datagram include:

- **Source Port.** The value in this field identifies the origin port. Ports are associated with either TCP or UDP and are addressable end points.
- **Destination Port.** This identifies the recipient port for the data.
- **Length.** The value in this field indicates the length of the data sent, including the header.
- **Checksum.** This algorithm computes the pseudo-IP header. the UDP header, and the data.
- **Data.** The data field is the data passed from applications using UDP.

UDP Applications

UDP is a useful protocol. Situations do exist where the need for a custom application meets the need. When this is the case, UDP is a good transport protocol to accomplish this task. Because UCP is unreliable and does not perform retransmissions and other services that TCP offers, the custom applications must perform these functions.

Because of UDP's nature this leaves work for application programmers, but these necessary operations can be achieved via the application; they merely requires more work by the creator of the application.

Messages sent to UDP from applications get forwarded to IP for transmission. Some applications that reside on the UDP protocol pass messages directly to IP and ICMP for transmission.

Summary

This chapter presented important topics in TCP/IP. The following chapter provides information that is also pertinent for designing and implementing network blueprints.

CHAPTER 12

TCP/IP Blueprints: Part 2

TCP/IP Addressing

Addressing in TCP/IP consists of a variety of factors that work together to make TCP/IP a functioning upper-layer network protocol. These factors include:

- IPv4 addressing
- Address classifications
- Ports
- Well-known ports
- Port manipulation
- Sockets
- Hardware addresses.

Each factor is presented with discussion of how they inter-relate.

IPv4 Addressing

Because IPv4 is still a significant presence in the marketplace, information on this topic is presented here. IPv4 uses a 32-bit addressing scheme which is usually implemented in software; in some network devices it is implemented in firmware and/or non-volatile RAM.

Each host participating in a TCP/IP network is identified with a 32-bit IP address different from the host's hardware address.

The IP addressing scheme structure appears as in Figure 12.1.

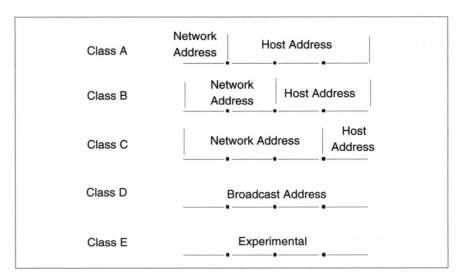

FIGURE 12.1
IP Address
Scheme

Figure 12.1 shows five classes of IP addresses. The IP addressing scheme is dotted decimal notation. The class of address indicate how many bits are used for a network address and how many for a host address. Before examining these in detail we should consider how these addresses are assigned.

As Figure 12.1 shows, multiple classes of addresses exist. Let us examine why. The two possible implementations of TCP/IP networks are the Internet and internets.

The Internet is a worldwide network with thousands of entities connecting to it. An agency responsible for maintaining Internet addresses assigns IP addresses to entities connecting to the Internet; an entity itself has no influence in the matter. On the other hand, if a TCP/IP network is implemented in a corporation, for example, then the IP addressing scheme is left up to the implementers responsible for that corporate network. In other words, it is "locally" administered.

With local implementation it is best for someone to understand the many ramifications of selecting an IP addressing scheme.

Address Classifications

In Figure 12.1 five classes of addresses were shown. The following explains their numerical meaning and how this affects hosts implemented with IP addresses.

ADDRESS CLASS	ASSIGNED NUMBERS
A	0–127
B	128–191
C	192–223
D	224–239
E	240–255

Class A addresses have fewer bits allocated to the network portion (one byte) and more bits (three bytes) dedicated to host addressing. More hosts than networks can be implemented.

Class B addressing allocates an equal number of bits for network addressing (two bytes) and host addressing (two bytes). This class is popular in locally-administered implementations.

Class C addressing allocates more bits (three bytes) to the network portion and fewer bits (one byte) to the host portion.

Class D is generally used as a broadcast address. The numerical value in each of the four bytes is 255.255.255.255.

Class E networks are for experimental purposes. No class E networks have been implemented.

Implementing an internet uses these addresses in conjunction with aliases. For example, an address assigned to a host usually has a name associated with it. If a host has a class B address such as 137.1.0.99, its alias might be RISC. This alias and internet address reside in a file on UNIX systems called /etc/hosts; another file related to this is the /etc/networks file. These two UNIX files are normal in the configuration. Later sections in this chapter discuss TCP/IP configuration in a UNIX environment.

Ports

Ports are the addressable endpoints at TCP and UDP. This is partially how applications atop TCP and UDP are addressed.

Well-Known Ports

TCP and UDP have popular applications using them as transport protocols. Without some standardization of ports and relationships to applications, chaos could exist. As a result TCP and UDP have applications that are assigned to well-known ports. This is a standardization to which most adhere, but flexibility does exist.

Port Manipulation

Port numbers can be but usually are not changed. The reason for this capability is that port manipulation can alleviate some addressing conflicts.

TCP and UDP applications can have their ports changed. Some port numbers are available for development of custom applications. During the explanation of UDP the concept of custom applications was presented. In these, being able to use a "free" port number would be required.

The disadvantage of changing a port number is that if the application using that port is popular there could be user problems in the network.

Sockets

A socket is the combination of an IP address and the port number appended to its end. Sockets are used in programming and are not normally of any concern for general users. However, in some instances it is important to understand the socket concept.

Hardware Address

TCP/IP operates at layers three and above in a network, therefore an interface of some type is needed for a TCP/IP host to participate in a network. The lower-layer protocol varies. If it is Ethernet, a 48-bit addressing scheme is used. If token ring, a 12-digit hexadecimal address is used; each lower-layer protocol has its own addressing scheme.

Understanding the addressing scheme is important, especially for those who troubleshoot or design networks and for implementers who have to make the scheme work.

Synthesis

Network size, purpose, and other site-specific parameters should be considered when selecting IP address classes and in other issues presented here. Understanding technical implications in the beginning, can save time and money in the long run.

Popular TCP Applications

Popular applications using TCP as a transport-layer protocol include:

- X window system
- Telnet
- File Transfer Protocol (FTP)
- Simple Mail Transfer Protocol (SMTP)
- Domain Name System (DNS).

X Window System

X is a distributed windowing system. At MIT in the early 1980s developers were looking for a way to develop applications in a distributed computed environment. At the time this was cutting-edge technology. They realized that a distributed windowing system would meet their needs very well.

Researchers at Stanford who had performed similar work were working along the same lines but had dubbed the system W for windowing. Those at MIT renamed it X because that was the next letter in the alphabet and the name stuck.

By the late 1980s X commanded a considerable market share specifically in UNIX-based environments. One of the factors in its growth was its hardware and software independence. X is a dominant user interface in the UNIX environment and has spread into MS-DOS and VMS environments as well.

X is asynchronous and based on a client/server model. It can manipulate two-dimensional graphics on a bitmapped display. Before examining some of the operational aspects of X, consider the layer of X and its relationship to the TCP/IP protocol suite, as shown in Figure 12.2.

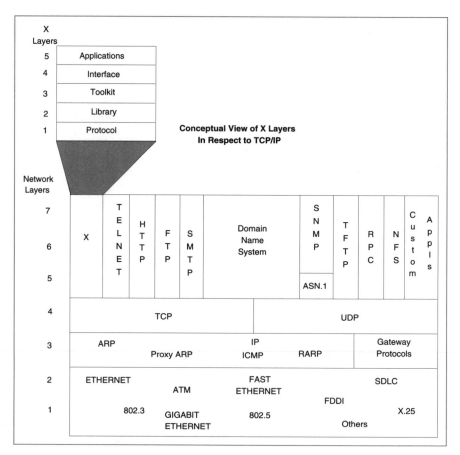

Figure 12.2 shows the TCP/IP protocol suite, but the focus is on X. The protocol suite helps us understand the relationship of X with TCP/IP. X is not a transport-layer protocol, but uses TCP for a transport protocol.

X can be evaluated two ways: from a TCP/IP perspective it comprises layers 5, 6, and 7; X itself has five layers. X's layer names and functions include:

- **Protocol.** This is the lowest layer in X and hooks into TCP. Here reside the actual X protocol components.
- **Library.** The X library consists of a collection of C language routines based upon the X protocol. X library routines perform functions such as responding to the pressing of a mouse button.
- **Toolkit.** The X toolkit is a higher level of programming tools. Support provided from this layer includes functions in programming related to scroll bars and menus.
- **Interface.** The interface is what a user sees. Examples of an interface include: Sun's OpenLook, HP's OpenView, OSF's Motif, and NeXT's interface.
- **Applications.** X applications can be defined as client applications that use X and conform to X programming standards that interact with the X server.

X Theory of Operation

X clients and X servers do not function as do other clients and servers in the TCP/IP environment. Normally a client *intiates* something and servers *serve* or *answer* the requests of clients. In X the concept is skewed.

A display manager exists in the X environment and its basic function is starting and keeping the X server operating. The X display manager (Xdm) itself can be started manually or automatically. In respect to X, the display manager is a client application.

An X display server (Xds) is a go-between for hardware components (such as a keyboard or mouse) and client applications. The Xds catches entered data and directs them to the appropriate X client application.

The correlation of Xdm and Xds can be understood by considering the following scenario. Two windows are active on a physical display. Each functions as a client application. With this in mind it the idea of directing data to the appropriate X client application takes on a different meaning. This architectural arrangement is required to maintain order because multiple windows may be on the display.

In summary, the X display manager and server control the operations on the display, which is what a user sees. Most entities in an X environment function as X client applications. Examples are the Xclock, an Xterm emulator, or even a TN3270 emulation software package used to access a 3270 data stream in an SNA environment.

Telnet

Telnet is a TCP application that provides the ability to perform remote logons to adjacent hosts. Telnet consists of client and server. The majority of TCP/IP software implementations have Telnet, simply because it is part of the protocol suite. As previously stated, *clients* initiate something (in this case a remote logon) and *servers* serve requests of clients. Figure 12.3 illustrates the TCP/IP protocol suite with Telnet highlighted, showing its client and server.

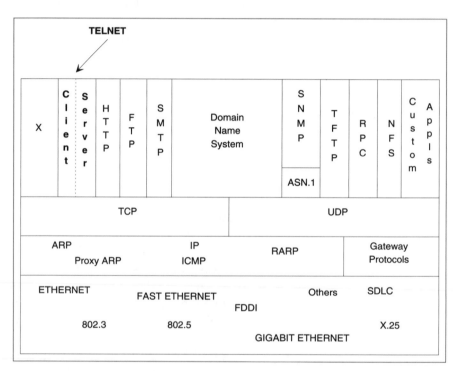

This example of Telnet is the same on practically all TCP/IP host implementations if the protocol suite has been developed according to the RFCs. Exceptions do apply. For example, TCP/IP on a DOS-based PC cannot implement a Telnet server because of the architectural constraints of the PC; the PC cannot truly multi-tast, and other nuances also apply. On some network devices this implementation cannot work; on most host implementations such as UNIX, VMS, MVS, VM, VSE, and some other operating systems the Telnet client and server will function.

Figure 12.4 is an example of Telnet client and server interaction on different hosts.

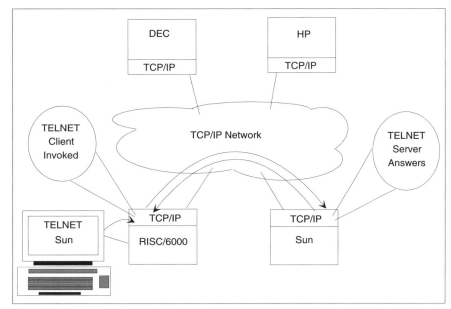

FIGURE 12.4
Telnet
Client/Server
Operation

This shows a RISC/6000 user invoking a Telnet client native to that machine because it is in the TCP/IP protocol suite. The RISC/6000 user wants to logon to the Sun host. The Sun host has Telnet in its TCP/IP protocol suite; consequently, the Telnet server answers the client's request and a logical connection is established between the RISC/6000 and the Sun host. To the RISC/6000 user, they "appear" to be physically connected to the Sun.

This functionality of Telnet works is supported by the majority of major vendors.

File Transfer Protcol (FTP)

FTP is a file transfer application that uses TCP for a transport protocol. FTP has a client and server like Telnet; they work the same way. The difference is that Telnet enables remote logons whereas FTP permits file transfers.

FTP does not actually transfer a file from one host to another—it copies it. The original file still exists and a copy has been put on a different machine. Figure 12.5 depicts this scenario.

FIGURE 12.5
FTP Client/Server
Operation

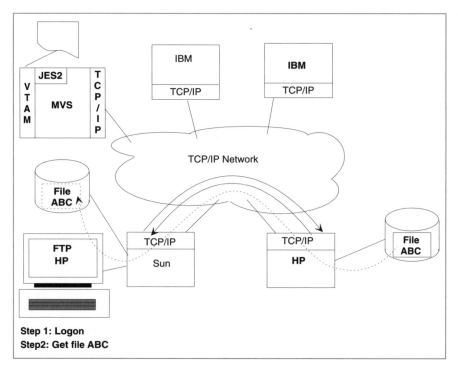

Here a user on a Sun host is performing two steps. First the Sun user executes FTP HP and a logon is established. The user issues the FTP command GET and designates the filename as FILEABC. The dotted line shows the file is copied from the HP disk to the Sun's disk.

Figure 12.5 also shows a Dell PC, Digital Equipment, and MVS host. The same operation can be performed on either of these as well. An FTP can be performed on a PC but a Telnet cannot because FTP uses two ports to function; it merely requests a file transfer—this does not require multi-tasking on behalf of the host. The DEC host can perform any of the TCP/IP functions, as can the Sun or HP host.

An interesting twist to this scenario is shown in Figure 12.5, where a DEC user can Telnet to the HP, then from the HP execute an FTP against the IBM and move a file *to* or *from* the IBM. This type of networking scenario is powerful.

In Figure 12.5 we see that an HP user could execute an FTP against the MVS host, PUT the FILEABC into the MVS JES2 subsystem and have it print on the printer attached to the MVS printer.

These are only a *few* examples to convey some simple operations.

Simple Mail Transfer Protocol (SMTP)

SMTP is another TCP application; it does not have a client and server, but the functionality is similar. SMTP uses a "user agent" and a "message transfer agent." Figure 12.6 shows a simple example of how SMTP operates.

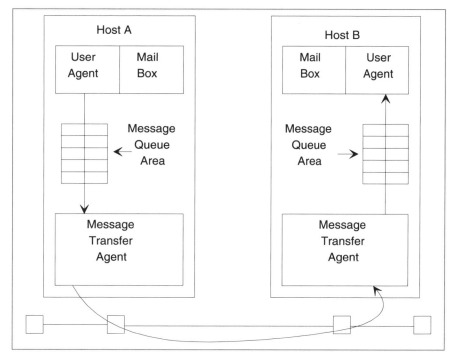

Sending mail is accomplished by invoking a user agent which in turn causes an editor to appear on the user's display. After the mail message is created and sent from the user agent it is transferred to the message transfer agent. The message transfer agent is responsible for establishing communication with the message transfer agent on the destination host. Once this is accomplished the sending message transfer agent sends the message to the receiving message transfer agent, then it stores it in the appropriate queue for the user. The recipient of the mail only needs to invoke the user agent on that machine to read the mail.

Domain Name System (DNS)

In the beginning, the Internet used *hosts* files to keep track of hosts on the Internet. This meant when new hosts were added to the Internet all participating hosts had to have their hosts files updated. As the Internet grew this task of updating became insurmountable. The Domain Name System (DNS) developed from the need for a replacement. The foundation of DNS was built around a distributed database architecture.

DNS Structure

DNS is a hierarchical structure that conceptually appears as an upside-down tree. The root is at the top and the layers below. Figure 12.7 is an example of how DNS is implemented on the Internet.

FIGURE 12.7
DNS Structure

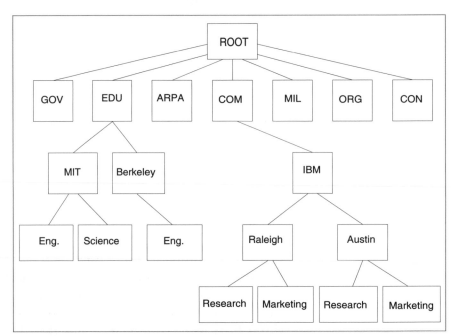

The legend for the DNS structure in Figure 12.7 is:

- **ROOT.** The root server contains information about itself and the top level domains immediately beneath it.
- **GOV.** This refers to government entitie`s.
- **EDU.** This refers to any educational institutions.
- **ARPA.** This refers to any ARPANET (Internet) host ID.

- **COM.** This refers to any commercial organizations.
- **MIL.** This refers to military organizations.
- **ORG.** This serves as a miscellaneous category for those not formally covered.
- **CON.** This refers to counties conforming to ISO standards.

Figure 12.7 shows the Internet implementation of DNS. Three examples aid in understanding the structure. Notice IBM is under COM (which is commercial), beneath IBM are Raleigh and Austin, and beneath each of them are research and marketing. The other examples are MIT and Berkeley. The example with MIT shows beneath it two *zones*, engineering and science. The Berkeley example has one layer beneath it, engineering.

At a local level, as in a corporation, most sites follow the naming scheme and structure because it is consistent and if a connection is ever made to the Internet, restructuring of DNS is not necessary.

DNS Components

Understanding DNS requires knowledge of the components that make it functional. These include:

- **Domain.** The last part in a domain name is considered the domain. For example eng.mit.edu; edu is the domain.
- **Domain Name.** This is defined by the DNS as being the sequence of names and domain. A domain name could be eng.mit.edu.
- **Label.** The DNS identifies each part of a domain name as a label. Our example eng.mit.edu has three labels.
- **Name Server.** This program operates on a host translating names to addresses by mapping domain names to IP addresses. Name server may be also used to refer to a dedicated processor running name server software.
- **Name Resolver.** This is software that functions as a client its interaction with a name server. This is sometimes referred to as the client.
- **Name Cache.** This is used by the name resolver to store frequently used information.
- **Zone.** This is a contiguous part of a domain.

Theory of Operation

Figure 12.8 shows a TCP/IP network with five hosts.

FIGURE 12.8
Conceptual View
of DNS

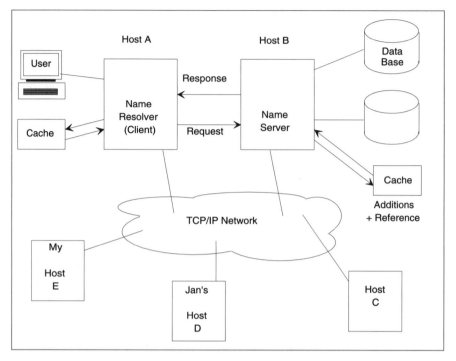

Of these five hosts, host B has been designated as the name server. It has a database with a list of aliases and IP addresses of participating hosts in the network. When the user on host A wants to communicate with host C the name resolver checks its local cache; if no match is found then the name resolver (client) sends a request (also known as a query) to the name server.

The name server in turn checks its cache for a match. If no match is found, then the name server checks its database. Though not shown in this figure, if the name server were unable to locate the name in its cache or database it would forward the request to another name server then return the response back to host A.

In an internet environment that implements DNS, there are some givens. A name resolver is required; a name server and usually a foreign name server are part of the network.

Implementation with UDP

The DNS provides service for TCP and UDP; this is why the figures have shown DNS residing above part of TCP and part of UDP. It serves the same purpose for both transport-layer protocols.

Obtaining Additional Information

Additional information should be consulted on this issue if DNS is implemented. The following RFCs are a good beginning point: 882, 883, 920, 973, 974, 1034, 1123, 1032, 1033, 1034, and 1035.

Popular UDP Applications

Popular UDP applications include:

- Simple Network Management Protocol (SNMP)
- Trivial File Transfer Protocol (TFTP)
- Network File System (NFS)
- Remote Procedure Call (RPC)
- Custom applications
- PING and Finger.

Simple Network Management Protocol (SNMP)

SNMP is considered the de facto standard for managing TCP/IP networks as of this writing. SNMP uses agents and application managers (or simply managers). A user agent can reside on any node that supports SNMP, and each agent maintains status information about the node on which it operates. These nodes, which may be hosts, gateways, routers, or other types of network devices are called *network elements* in SNMP parlance. This term is merely a generic reference to a node.

Normally, multiple elements exist in a TCP/IP network and each has its own agent. Typically, one node is designated as a network management node. Some refer to this node as the network manager. This host (network management node) has an application that communicates with each network element to obtain the status of a given element. The network management node and the element communicate via different message types. Some of these messages are:

- **GET Request.** This type of request is used by the network manager to communicate with an element to request a variable or list about that particular network element.
- **GET Response.** This is a reply to a GET request, SET request, or GET NEXT request.

- **GET NEXT Request.** This request is used sequentially to read information about an element.
- **SET Request.** This request enables variable values to be set in an element.
- **TRAP.** This type of a message is designed to report information such as:
  - Link status
  - Whether or not a neighbor responds
  - Whether or not a message is received
  - Status of the element.

Information stored on elements is maintained in a Management Information Base (MIB), which is a database containing information about a particular element; each element has an MIB. MIB includes:

- Statistical information regarding segments transferred to and from the manager application
- A community name
- An interface type
- Other element-specific information.

MIB information structure is defined by the Structure of Management Information (SMI), a language used to define a data structure and methods for identifying an element for the manager application. This information identifies object variables in the MIB. Object descriptions defined by SMI include:

- **Access.** Object access control is maintained via this description.
- **Definition.** This provides a textual description of an object.
- **Names.** This term is also synonymous with object identifiers and refers to a sequence of integers.
- **Object Descriptor.** This is a text name ascribed to the object.
- **Object Identifier.** This is a numeric ID to identify the object.
- **Status.** This describes the level of object support for status.

SNMP implementations use ASN.1 for defining data structures in network elements. Because this language is based on a data type definition it can be used to define practically any element on a network.

SNMP itself is event-oriented. An event is generated when a change occurs to an object. SNMP operation is such that approximately every 10–15 minutes the manager application communicates with each network element regarding MIB data.

Additional information can be obtained from RFCs 1155, 1156, and 1157.

Trivial File Transfer Protocol (TFTP)

TFTP is an application that uses UDP as a transport mechanism. The program itself is simpler than its counterpart FTP, which uses TCP as a transport mechanism. TFTP is small enough in size so that it can be part of ROM on diskless workstations.

TFTP maximum packet size is 512 bytes. Because of this and the nature of operation, TFTP is popular with network devices such as routers and bridges. If implemented it is normally used upon initial device boot.

TFTP uses no security provision or authentication; it does have basic timing and retransmission capabilities. Its five basic types of protocol data units (PDUs) are: acknowledgment, data, error, read request, and write request.

These PDUs are used by TFTP during file transfer. With the first packet TFTP establishes a session with the target TFTP program. It then requests a file transfer between the two. Next it identifies a file name and whether or not a file will be read or written.

These five PDUs comprise the operational ability of TFTP. It is straightforward and not as complex as FTP. Additional information can be obtained from RFCs 783 and 1068.

Remote Procedure Call (RPC)

RPC is a protocol that can operate over TCP or UDP as a transport mechanism. Applications use RPC to call a routine, executing like a client and making a call against a server on a remote host. This type of application programming is a high-level peer relationship between an application and an RPC server. These applications are portable to the extent that RPC is implemented.

Within RPC is the eXternal Data Representation (XDR) protocol. XDR data description language can be used to define datatypes when heterogeneous hosts are integrated. Having the capability to overcome the inherent characteristics of different architectures makes RPC and XDR a robust solution for distributed-application communication. This language permits parameter requests to be made against a file of an unlike type. XDR allows data type definition in the form of parameters, and transmission of these encoded parameters.

XDR provides data transparency by way of encoding (or encapsulating) data at the application layer so lower layers and hardware do not have to perform any conversions. A powerful aspect of XDR is automatic data conversion performed via declaration statements and the XDR compiler. The XDR compiler generates required XDR calls, making the operation less manual by nature. Figure 12.9 is an example of this type of implementation.

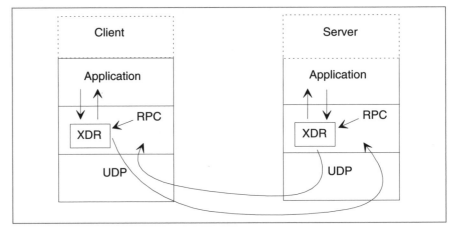

RPC implements a "port mapper." This starts upon RPC server initialization. When RPC services start, the operating system assigns a port number to each service. These services inform the port mapper of the port number, its program number, and other information required by the port mapper for it to be able to match a service with a requester.

Client applications issue service requests to a port mapper. The port mapper in turn identifies the requested service and returns the appropriate parameters to the requesting client application. The port mapper is similar in function to a manager's is knowing what services are available and their specific addressable locations.

The port mapper can be used in a broadcast scenario. A requesting RPC call can broadcast a call to all hosts on a network. Applicable port mappers report back to the information sought by the client, hence the term Remote Procedure Call (RPC).

Additional information on RPC and related components can be found in RFCs 1057 and 1014.

Network File System (NFS)

NFS is a product of Sun Microsystems that permits users to execute files without knowing the location of these files, which may be local or remote in respect to the user. Users can create, read, or remove a directory. Files themselves can be written to or deleted. NFS provides a distributed file system that permits a user to capitalize on access capabilities beyond the local file system.

NFS uses RPC to make possible execution of a routine on a remote server. Conceptually, NFS, RPC, and UDP (which it typically uses) appear as Figure 12.10 shows.

FIGURE 12.10
Conceptual View
of NFS, RPC,
and UDP

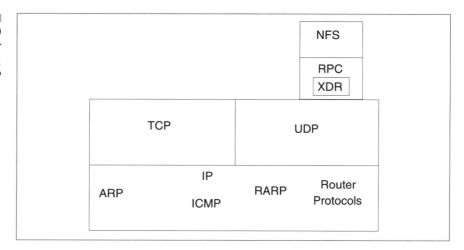

The idea behind NFS is to have one copy of it on a server that all users on a network can access. The consequence is that software (and updates) can be installed on one server and not on multiple hosts in a networked environment. NFS is based on a client/server model. With NFS a single NFS server can serve the requests of many clients.

NFS origins are in UNIX, where it is implemented in a hierarchical (tree) structure. However, NFS can operate with IBM's VM and MVS operating systems and with Digital Equipment's VMS operating system.

NFS uses a *mount* protocol; this identifies a file system and remote host to a local user's file system. NFS mount is known by the port mapper of RPC, and is thus capable of being known by requesting client applications.

NFS also uses the NFS protocol; it performs file transfers among systems. NFS uses port number 2049 in many cases, though this is not yet a well-known port number. The best approach to NFS is to use the NFS port number with the port mapper.

In a sense an NFS server operates with little information identified to it. A loose analogy to NFS operation is UDP. UDP assumes a custom application (or other entity operating on top of it) will perform requirements such as retransmissions (if required) and procedures that would otherwise be performed by a connection-oriented transport protocol such as TCP. NFS assumes required services are implemented in other protocols.

From a user perspective NFS is transparent. Typical user commands are entered, then passed to the NFS server and in most cases a user does not know the physical location of a file in a networked environment.

Additional information about the NFS and related components can be obtained from RFCs 1094, 1014 and 1057.

Custom Applications

Custom applications can be written and use UDP as a transport mechanism. One scenario might be when two hosts need peer-program communication through a network. Writing a custom application using UDP can achieve this task as Figure 12.11 shows.

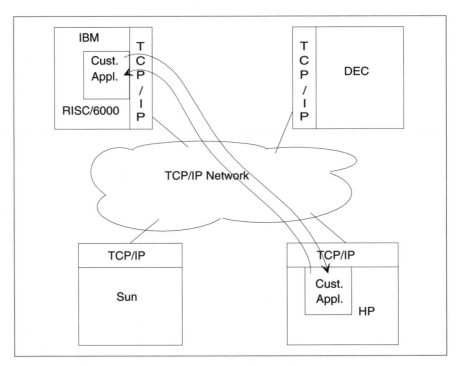

FIGURE 12.11
Custom
Applications
Using UDP

PING and Finger

Packet Internet Groper (PING) is a protocol that uses UDP as a transport mechanism to achieve its function. It is used to send messages to a host and wait for that host to respond to the messages (if the target host is *alive*). PING uses ICMP echo and echo reply messages.

PING is a helpful tool on TCP/IP networks that is used to determine if a device can be addressed. It is used in a network to determine if a network itself can be addressed. A PING can also be issued against a remote host *name*. This is for name verification and is generally used by individuals who troubleshoot TCP/IP networks.

Finger is a command issued against a host which will cause the target host to return information about users logged onto that host. Information retrievable via Finger includes: user name, user interface, and the job name the user is running.

More on Finger can be found in RFC 1288.

HyperText Transfer Protocol (HTTP)

HTTP is an application-level protocol for distributed, collaborative, hypermedia information systems. It has been in use by the World Wide Web global information initiative since 1990. The first version of HTTP, referred to as HTTP/0.9, was a simple protocol for raw data transfer across the Internet. HTTP/1.0 improved the protocol by allowing messages to be in the format of MIME-like messages, containing metainformation about the data transferred and modifiers on the request/response semantics. However, HTTP/1.0 does not sufficiently take into consideration the effects of hierarchical proxies, caching, the need for persistent connections, and virtual hosts. The proliferation of incompletely-implemented applications calling themselves "HTTP 1.0" has necessitated a protocol version change in order for two communicating applications to determine each other's true capabilities.

Explanations presented here about HTTP refer to *HTTP 1.1*. This protocol is more stringent than HTTP/1.0 in order to ensure reliable implementation of its features. Practical information systems require more functionality than simple retrieval, including search, front-end update, and annotation. HTTP allows an open-ended set of methods that indicates the purpose of a request. It builds on the discipline of reference provided by the Uniform Resource Identifier (URI), as a location (URL) or name (URN) for indicating the resource to which a method is to be applied. Messages are passed in a format similar to that used by Internet mail as defined by the Multipurpose Internet Mail Extensions (MIME).

HTTP is also used as a generic protocol for communication between user agents and proxies/gateways to other Internet systems, including those supported by SMTP, NNTP, FTP, Gopher, and WAIS protocols. In this way, HTTP allows basic hypermedia access to resources available from diverse applications.

Terminology

Terms to referring to the roles played by participants in, and objects of, the HTTP communication include:

- **Connection.** A transport layer virtual circuit established between two programs for the purpose of communication
- **Message.** The basic unit of HTTP communication, consisting of a structured sequence of octets matching the syntax and transmitted via the connection.
- **Request.** An HTTP request message
- **Response.** An HTTP response message
- **Resource.** A network data object or service that can be identified by a URI. Resources may be available in multiple representations (e.g. multiple languages, data formats, size, resolutions) or vary in other ways.
- **Entity.** The information transferred as the payload of a request or response; an entity consists of metainformation (entity-header fields) and content (an entity-body).
- **Representation.** An entity included with a response that is subject to content negotiation; there may exist multiple representations associated with a particular response status.
- **Content Negotiation.** The mechanism for selecting the appropriate representation when servicing a request. The representation of entities in any response can be negotiated (including error responses).
- **Variant.** A resource may have one, or more than one, representation(s) associated with it at any given instant. Each of these representations is termed a *variant*. Use of the term variant does not necessarily imply that the resource is subject to content negotiation.
- **Client.** A program that establishes connections for the purpose of sending requests.

- **User Agent.** The client which initiates a request; these are often browsers, editors, spiders (web-traversing robots), or other end user tools.
- **Server.** An application program that accepts connections in order to service requests by sending back responses; any given program may be capable of being both a client and a server; our use of these terms refers only to the role being performed by the program for a particular connection, rather than to the program's capabilities in general. Likewise, any server may act as an origin server, proxy, gateway, or tunnel, switching behavior based on the nature of each request.
- **Origin Server.** The server on which a given resource resides or is to be created
- **Proxy.** An intermediary program which acts as both a server and a client for the purpose of making requests on behalf of other clients. Requests are serviced internally or by passing them on, with possible translation, to other servers. A proxy must implement both the client and server requirements of this specification.
- **Gateway.** A server which acts as an intermediary for some other server. Unlike a proxy, a gateway receives requests as if it were the origin server for the requested resource; the requesting client may not be aware that it is communicating with a gateway.
- **Tunnel.** An intermediary program acting as a blind relay between two connections. Once active, a tunnel is not considered a party to the HTTP communication, though the tunnel may have been initiated by an HTTP request. The tunnel ceases to exist when both ends of the relayed connections are closed.
- **Cache.** A program's local store of response messages and the subsystem that controls its message storage, retrieval, and deletion. A cache stores cacheable responses in order to reduce the response time and network bandwidth consumption on future, equivalent requests. Any client or server may include a cache, though a cache cannot be used by a server acting as a tunnel.
- **Cacheable.** A response is cacheable if a cache is allowed to store a copy of the response message for use in answering subsequent requests. Even if a resource is cacheable, there may be additional constraints on whether a cache can use the cached copy for a particular request.
- **Firsthand.** A response is firsthand if it comes directly and without unnecessary delay from the origin server, perhaps via one or more proxies. A response is also firsthand if its validity has just been checked directly with the origin server.

- **Explicit Expiration Time.** The time at which the origin server intends that an entity should no longer be returned by a cache without further validation.
- **Heuristic Expiration Time.** An expiration time assigned by a cache when no explicit expiration time is available.
- **Age.** The age of a response is the time since it was sent by, or successfully validated with, the origin server.
- **Freshness Lifetime.** The length of time between the generation of a response and its expiration time.
- **Fresh.** A response is fresh if its age has not yet exceeded its freshness lifetime.
- **Stale.** A response is stale if its age has passed its freshness lifetime.
- **Semantically Transparent.** A cache behaves in a semantically transparent manner, with respect to a particular response, when its use affects neither the requesting client nor the origin server, except to improve performance. When a cache is semantically transparent, the client receives exactly the same response (except for hop-by-hop headers) that it would have received had its request been handled directly by the origin server.
- **Validator.** A protocol element (e.g., an entity tag or a last-modified time) that is used to find out whether a cache entry is an equivalent copy of an entity.

Overall Operation

HTTP is a request/response protocol. A client sends a request to the server in the form of a request method, URI, and protocol version, followed by a MIME-like message containing request modifiers, client information, and possible body content, over a connection with a server. The server responds with a status line, including the message's protocol version and a success or error code, followed by a MIME-like message containing server information, entity metainformation, and possible entity-body content.

Most HTTP communication is initiated by a user agent and consists of a request to be applied to a resource on some origin server. In the simplest case, this may be accomplished via a single connection (v) between the user agent (UA) and the origin server (O).

```
request chain ----------------------->
UA -------------------v------------------- O
<---------------------- response chain
```

A more-complicated situation occurs when one or more intermediaries are present in the request/response chain. There are three common forms of intermediary: proxy, gateway, and tunnel. A proxy is a forwarding agent, receiving requests for a URI in its absolute form, rewriting all or part of the message, and forwarding the reformatted request toward the server identified by the URI. A gateway is a receiving agent, acting as a layer above some other server(s) and, if necessary, translating the requests to the underlying server's protocol. A tunnel acts as a relay point between two connections without changing the messages; tunnels are used when the communication needs to pass through an intermediary (such as a firewall) even when the intermediary cannot understand the contents of the messages.

```
request chain ------------------------------------------>
UA -----v----- A -----v----- B -----v----- C -----v----- O
<-------------------------------------- response chain
```

The figure above shows three intermediaries (A, B, and C) between the user agent and origin server. A request or response message that travels the whole chain will pass through four separate connections. This distinction is important because some HTTP communication options may apply only to the connection with the nearest, non-tunnel neighbor, only to the end-points of the chain, or to all connections along the chain. Although the diagram is linear, each participant may be engaged in multiple, simultaneous communications. For example, B may be receiving requests from many clients other than A, and/or forwarding requests to servers other than C, at the same time that it is handling A's request.

Any party to the communication not acting as a tunnel may employ an internal cache for handling requests. The effect of a cache is that the request/response chain is shortened if one of the participants along the chain has a cached response applicable to that request. The following illustrates the resulting chain if B has a cached copy of an earlier response from O (via C) for a request which has not been cached by UA or A.

```
request chain ---------->
UA -----v----- A -----v----- B - - - - - - C - - - - - - O
<--------- response chain
```

Not all responses are usefully cacheable, and some requests may contain modifiers which place special requirements on cache behavior. In fact, there are a wide variety of architectures and configurations of caches and proxies currently being experimented with or deployed across the World Wide Web; these systems include national hierarchies of proxy caches to save transoceanic bandwidth, systems that broadcast or multicast cache entries, organizations that distribute subsets of cached data via CD-ROM, and so on. HTTP systems are used in corporate intranets over high-bandwidth links, and for access via PDAs with low-power radio links and intermittent connectivity. The goal of HTTP 1.1 is to support the wide diversity of configurations already deployed while introducing protocol constructs that meet the needs of those who build Web applications that require high reliability and, failing that, at least reliable indications of failure.

HTTP communication usually takes place over TCP/IP connections. The default port is TCP 80, but other ports can be used. This does not preclude HTTP from being implemented on top of any other protocol on the Internet, or on other networks. HTTP only presumes a reliable transport; any protocol that provides such guarantees can be used; the mapping of the HTTP 1.1 request and response structures onto the transport data units of the protocol in question is outside the scope of this discussion.

In HTTP 1.0, most implementations used a new connection for each request/response exchange. In HTTP 1.1, a connection may be used for one or more request/response exchanges, although connections may be closed for a variety of reasons.

Protocol Parameters

HTTP uses a <major>.<minor> numbering scheme to indicate versions of the protocol. The protocol versioning policy is intended to allow the sender to indicate the format of a message and its capacity for understanding further HTTP communication, rather than to show the features obtained via that communication. No change is made to the version number for the addition of message components which do not affect communication behavior or which only add to extensible field values.

The <minor> number is incremented when the changes made to the protocol add features which do not change the general message parsing algorithm, but which may add to the message semantics and imply additional capabilities of the sender. The <major> number is incremented when the format of a message within the protocol is changed.

The version of an HTTP message is indicated by an HTTP-Version field in the first line of the message.

```
HTTP-Version   =   "HTTP"    "/"    1*DIGIT "."    1*DIGIT
```

Major and minor numbers must be treated as separate integers and each may be incremented higher than a single digit. Thus, HTTP 2.4 is a lower version than HTTP 2.13, which in turn is lower than HTTP 12.3. Leading zeros must be ignored by recipients and must not be sent.

Applications sending Request or Response messages, as defined here, must include a version of HTTP 1.1. Use of this version number indicates that the sending application is at least conditionally compliant with this specification. The HTTP version of an application is the highest HTTP version for which the application is at least conditionally compliant.

Proxy and gateway applications must be careful when forwarding messages in protocol versions different from that of the application. Since the protocol version indicates the protocol capability of the sender, a proxy/gateway must never send a message with a version indicator greater than its actual version; if a higher version request is received, the proxy/gateway must either downgrade the request version, respond with an error, or switch to tunnel behavior. Requests with a version lower than that of the proxy/gateway's version may be upgraded before being forwarded; the proxy/gateway's response to that request must be in the same major version as the request.

Converting between versions of HTTP may involve modification of header fields required or forbidden by the versions involved.

Uniform Resource Identifiers (URIs)

URIs have been known by many names: WWW addresses, Universal Document Identifiers, Universal Resource Identifiers , and finally the combination of Uniform Resource Locators (URL) and Names (URN). As far as HTTP is concerned, URIs are simply formatted strings which identify—via name, location, or any other characteristic—a resource.

General Syntax

URIs in HTTP can be represented in absolute form or relative to some known base URI, depending upon the context of their use. The two forms are differentiated by the fact that absolute URIs always begin with a scheme name followed by a colon.

```
URI         = (absoluteURI | relativeURI) [ "#" fragment ]
absoluteURI = scheme ":" *( uchar | reserved )
relativeURI = net_path | abs_path | rel_path
```

```
net_path      = "//" net_loc [ abs_path ]
abs_path      = "/" rel_path
rel_path      = [ path ] [ ";" params ] [ "?" query ]
path          = fsegment *( "/" segment )
fsegment      = 1*pchar
segment       = *pchar
params        = param *( ";" param )
param         = *( pchar | "/" )
scheme        = 1*( ALPHA | DIGIT | "+" | "-" | "." )
net_loc       = *( pchar | ";" | "?" )
query         = *( uchar | reserved )
fragment      = *( uchar | reserved )
pchar         = uchar | ":" | "@" | "&" | "=" | "+"
uchar         = unreserved | escape
unreserved    = ALPHA | DIGIT | safe | extra | national
escape        = "%" HEX HEX
reserved      = ";" | "/" | "?" | ":" | "@" | "&" | "=" | "+"
extra         = "!" | "*" | "'" | "(" | ")" | ","
safe          = "$" | "-" | "_" | "."
unsafe        = CTL | SP | <"> | "#" | "%" | "<" | ">"
national      = <any OCTET excluding ALPHA, DIGIT, reserved,
                extra, safe, and unsafe>
```

The HTTP protocol does not place any a priori limit on the length of
a URI. Servers must be able to handle the URI of any resource they
serve, and should be able to handle URIs of unbounded length if they
provide GET-based forms that could generate such URIs. A server
should return 414 (Request-URI too long) status if a URI is longer
than the server can handle. Servers should be cautious about depending on URI lengths above 255 bytes, because some older client or
proxy implementations may not properly support these lengths.

HTTP URL

The "http" scheme is used to locate network resources via the HTTP
protocol. This section defines the scheme-specific syntax and semantics for http URLs.

```
http_URL  =    "http:" "//" host [ ":" port ] [ abs_path ]
```

Host = A legal Internet host domain name or IP address (in
       dotted-decimal form).
Port = *DIGIT

If the port is empty or not given, port 80 is assumed. The semantics
are that the identified resource is located at the server listening for
TCP connections on that port of that host, and the Request-URI for

the resource is `abs_path`. The use of IP addresses in URL's should be avoided whenever possible (see RFC 1900 [24]). If the `abs_path` is not present in the URL, it must be given as "/" when used as a Request-URI for a resource.

URI Comparison

When comparing two URIs to decide if they match or not, a client should use a case-sensitive octet-by-octet comparison of the entire URIs, with these exceptions:

* A port that is empty or not given is equivalent to the default port for that URI
* Comparisons of host names must be case-insensitive
* Comparisons of scheme names must be case-insensitive
* An empty `abs_path` is equivalent to an `abs_path` of "/".

Characters other than those in the "reserved" and "unsafe" sets are equivalent to their ""%" HEX HEX" encodings.

For example, the following three URIs are equivalent:

* http://abc.com:80/~smith/home.html
* http://ABC.com/%7Esmith/home.html
* http://ABC.com:/%7esmith/home.html.

Character Sets

HTTP uses the same definition of the term "character set" as that described for MIME: a method used with one or more tables to convert a sequence of octets into a sequence of characters. Note that unconditional conversion in the other direction is not required, in that not all characters may be available in a given character set and a character set may provide more than one sequence of octets to represent a particular character. This definition is intended to allow various kinds of character encodings, from simple single-table mappings such as US-ASCII to complex table-switching methods such as those that use ISO 2022's techniques. However, the definition associated with a MIME character set name must fully specify the mapping to be performed from octets to characters. In particular, use of external profiling information to determine the exact mapping is not permitted. This use of the term "character set" is more commonly referred to as a "character encoding." However, since HTTP and MIME share the same registry, it is important that the terminology also be shared.

HTTP character sets are identified by case-insensitive tokens. The complete set of tokens is defined by the IANA Character Set registry.

```
charset = token
```

Although HTTP allows an arbitrary token to be used as a charset value, any token that has a predefined value within the IANA Character Set registry must represent the character set defined by that registry. Applications should limit their use of character sets to those defined by the IANA registry.

Content Codings

Content coding values indicate an encoding transformation that has been or can be applied to an entity. Content codings are primarily used to allow a document to be compressed or otherwise usefully transformed without losing the identity of its underlying media type and without loss of information. Frequently, the entity is stored in coded form, transmitted directly, and only decoded by the recipient.

```
content-coding  = token
```

All content-coding values are case-insensitive. HTTP/1.1 uses content-coding values in the Accept-Encoding and Content-Encoding header fields. Although the value describes the content-coding, what is more important is that it indicates what decoding mechanism will be required to remove the encoding.

The IANA acts as a registry for content-coding value tokens. Initially, the registry contains the following tokens:

- **gzip.** An encoding format produced by the file compression program "gzip" (GNU zip). This format is a Lempel-Ziv coding (LZ77) with a 32 bit CRC.
- **Compress.** The encoding format produced by the common UNIX file compression program "compress". This format is an adaptive Lempel-Ziv-Welch coding (LZW).

Be aware that the use of program names for the identification of encoding formats is not desirable and should be discouraged for future encodings. Their use here is representative of historical practice, not good design. For compatibility with previous implementations of HTTP, applications should consider "x-gzip" and "x-compress" to be equivalent to "gzip" and "compress" respectively.

New content-coding value tokens should be registered; to allow interoperability between clients and servers, specifications of the content coding algorithms needed to implement a new value should be publicly available and adequate for independent implementation, and conform to the purpose of content coding.

HTTP Message Types

HTTP messages consist of requests from client to server and responses from server to client.

```
HTTP-message    =    Request | Response; HTTP/1.1 messages
```

Request and Response messages use the generic message format for transferring entities (the payload of the message). Both types of message consist of a start-line, one or more header fields (also known as "headers"), an empty line (i.e., a line with nothing preceding the CRLF) indicating the end of the header fields, and an optional message-body.

```
generic-message = start-line
*message-header
CRLF
[ message-body ]
start-line      =    Request-Line | Status-Line
```

In the interest of robustness, servers should ignore any empty line(s) received where a Request-Line is expected. In other words, if the server is reading the protocol stream at the beginning of a message and receives a CRLF first, it should ignore the CRLF.

HTTP Message Headers

HTTP header fields, which include general-header, request-header, response-header, and entity-header fields follow the same generic format. Each header field consists of a name followed by a colon (":") and the field value. Field names are case-insensitive. The field value may be preceded by any amount of LWS, though a single SP is preferred. Header fields can be extended over multiple lines by preceding each extra line with at least one SP or HT. Applications should follow "common form" when generating HTTP constructs, since there might exist some implementations that fail to accept anything beyond the common forms.

```
message-header = field-name ":" [ field-value ] CRLF
field-name     = token
field-value    = *( field-content | LWS )
field-content  = <the OCTETs making up the field-value and consisting
of either *TEXT or combinations of token, specials, and quoted-string>
```

The order in which header fields with differing field names are received is not significant. However, it is good practice to send general-header fields first, followed by request-header or response-header fields, ending with the entity-header fields.

Multiple message-header fields with the same field-name may be present in a message if, and only if, the entire field-value for that header field is defined as a comma-separated list. It must be possible to combine the multiple header fields into one "field-name: field-value" pair, without changing the semantics of the message, by appending each subsequent field-value to the first, each separated by a comma. The order in which header fields with the same field-name are received is therefore significant to the interpretation of the combined field value, and thus a proxy must not change the order of these field values when a message is forwarded.

HTTP Message-Body

The message body (if any) of an HTTP message is used to carry the entity-body associated with the request or response. The message-body differs from the entity-body only when a transfer coding has been applied, as indicated by the Transfer-Encoding header field.

```
message-body = entity-body
| entity-body encoded as per Transfer-Encoding>
```

Transfer-Encoding must be used to indicate any transfer codings applied by an application to ensure safe and proper transfer of the message. Transfer-Encoding is a property of the message, not of the entity, and thus can be added or removed by any application along the request/response chain.

The rules for when a message-body is allowed in a message differ for requests and responses. The presence of a message-body in a request is signaled by the inclusion of a Content-Length or Transfer-Encoding header field in the request's message-headers. A message-body may be included in a request only when the request method allows an entity-body.

For response messages, whether or not a message-body is included with a message is dependent on both the request method and the response status code. All responses to the HEAD request method must not include a message-body, even though the presence of entity-header fields might lead one to believe they do. All 1xx(informational), 204 (no content), and 304 (not modified) responses must not include a message-body. All other responses do include a message-body, although it may be of zero length.

HTTP Message Length

When a message-body is included with a message, the length of that body is determined by one of the following (in order of precedence):

1. Any response message which must not include a message-body (such as the 1xx, 204, and 304 responses and any response to a HEAD request) is always terminated by the first empty line after the header fields, regardless of the entity-header fields present in the message.
2. If a Transfer-Encoding header field is present and indicates that the "chunked" transfer coding has been applied, then the length is defined by the chunked encoding.
3. If a Content-Length header field is present, its value in bytes represents the length of the message-body.
4. If the message uses the media type "multipart/byteranges", which is self-delimiting, then that defines the length. This media type must not be used unless the sender knows that the recipient can parse it; the presence in a request of a Range header with multiple byte-range specifiers implies that the client can parse multipart/byteranges responses.
5. By the server closing the connection. (Closing the connection cannot be used to indicate the end of a request body, since that would leave no possibility for the server to send back a response.)

For compatibility with HTTP 1.0 applications, HTTP 1.1 requests containing a message-body must include a valid Content-Length header field unless the server is known to be HTTP 1.1-compliant. If a request contains a message-body and a Content-Length is not given, the server should respond with 400 (bad request) if it cannot determine the length of the message, or with 411 (length required) if it wishes to insist on receiving a valid Content-Length.

All HTTP/1.1 applications that receive entities must accept the "chunked" transfer coding (section 3.6), thus allowing this mechanism to be used for messages when the message length cannot be determined in advance.

Messages must not include both a Content-Length header field and the "chunked" transfer coding. If both are received, the Content-Length must be ignored.

When a Content-Length is given in a message where a message-body is allowed, its field value must exactly match the number of octets in the message-body. HTTP 1.1 user agents must notify the user when an invalid length is received and detected.

General Header Fields

There are a few header fields which have general applicability for both request and response messages, but do not apply to the entity being transferred. These header fields apply only to the message being transmitted.

The general-header Cache-Control has the following parts:

- Connection
- Date
- Pragma
- Transfer-Encoding
- Upgrade
- Via.

General-header field names can be extended reliably only in combination with a change in the protocol version. However, new or experimental header fields may be given the semantics of general header fields if all parties in the communication recognize them to be general-header fields. Unrecognized header fields are treated as entity-header fields.

HTTP Request

A request message from a client to a server includes, within the first line of that message, the method to be applied to the resource, the identifier of the resource, and the protocol version in use.

```
Request    =    Request-Line
               *(general-header
```

```
| request-header
| entity-header )
CRLF
[ message-body ]
```

HTTP Request-Line

The Request-Line begins with a method token, followed by the Request-URI and the protocol version, and ending with CRLF. The elements are separated by SP characters. No CR or LF are allowed except in the final CRLF sequence.

```
Request-Line = Method SP Request-URI SP HTTP-Version CRLF
```

Method

The Method token indicates the method to be performed on the resource identified by the Request-URI. The method is case-sensitive.

The method OPTIONS has the following subdivisions:

- GET
- HEAD
- POST
- PUT
- DELETE
- TRACE
- Extension-method
- Extension-method = token

The list of methods allowed by a resource can be specified in an Allow header field. The return code of the response always notifies the client whether a method is currently allowed on a resource, since the set of allowed methods can change dynamically.

Servers should return the status code 405 (Method Not Allowed) if the method is known by the server but not allowed for the requested resource, and 501 (Not Implemented) if the method is unrecognized or not implemented by the server. The list of methods known by a server can be listed in a Public response-header field.

The methods GET and HEAD must be supported by all general-purpose servers. All other methods are optional; however, if the above methods are implemented, they must be implemented with the same semantics.

HTTP Request-URI

The Request-URI is a Uniform Resource Identifier that identifies the resource upon which to apply the request.

```
Request-URI  = "*" | absoluteURI | abs_path
```

The three options for Request-URI are dependent on the nature of the request. The asterisk "*" means that the request does not apply to a particular resource, but to the server itself, and is only allowed when the method used does not necessarily apply to a resource. One example would be

```
OPTIONS * HTTP 1.1
```

The absolute URI form is required when the request is being made to a proxy. The proxy is requested to forward the request or service it from a valid cache, and return the response. Note that the proxy may forward the request on to another proxy or directly to the server specified by the absoluteURI. In order to avoid request loops, a proxy must be able to recognize all of its server names, including any aliases, local variations, and the numeric IP address. An example Request-Line would be:

```
GET http://www.w3.org/pub/WWW/TheProject.html HTTP/1.1
```

To allow for transition to absolute URIs in all requests in future versions of HTTP, all HTTP 1.1 servers must accept the absolute URI form in requests, even though HTTP/1.1 clients will only generate them in requests to proxies.

The most common form of Request-URI is that used to identify a resource on an origin server or gateway. In this case the absolute path of the URI must be transmitted as the Request-URI, and the network location of the URI (net_loc) must be transmitted in a Host header field. For example, a client wishing to retrieve the resource above directly from the origin server would create a TCP connection to port 80 of the host www.w3.org and send the lines:

```
GET /pub/WWW/TheProject.html HTTP/1.1
Host: www.w3.org
```

followed by the remainder of the Request. Remember, the absolute path cannot be empty; if none is present in the original URI, it must be given as "/" (the server root).

If a proxy receives a request without any path in the Request-URI and the method specified is capable of supporting the asterisk form of request, then the last proxy on the request chain must forward the request with "*" as the final Request-URI. For example, the request

```
OPTIONS http://www.ics.uci.edu:8001 HTTP/1.1
```

would be forwarded by the proxy as

```
OPTIONS * HTTP/1.1
Host: www.ics.uci.edu:8001
```

after connecting to port 8001 of host `www.ics.uci.edu`. The origin server must decode the Request-URI in order to properly interpret the request. Servers should respond to invalid Request-URIs with an appropriate status code.

In requests that they forward, proxies must not rewrite the `abs_path` part of a Request-URI in any way except as noted above to replace a null `abs_path` with "*", no matter what the proxy does in its internal implementation. The "no rewrite" rule prevents the proxy from changing the meaning of the request when the origin server is improperly using a non-reserved URL character for a reserved purpose. Implementers should be aware that some pre-HTTP 1.1 proxies have been known to rewrite the Request-URI.

The Resource Identified by a Request

HTTP 1.1 origin servers should be aware that the exact resource identified by an Internet request is determined by examining both the Request-URI and the Host header field.

An origin server that does not allow resources to differ by the requested host may ignore the Host header field value. An origin server that does differentiate resources based on the host requested (sometimes referred to as virtual hosts or vanity hostnames) must use the following rules for determining the requested resource on an HTTP 1.1 request:

1. If Request-URI is an absolute URI, the host is part of the Request-URI. Any Host header field value in the request must be ignored.

2. If the Request-URI is not an absolute URI, and the request includes a Host header field, the host is determined by the Host header field value.

3. If the host as determined by rule 1 or 2 is not a valid host on the server, the response must be a 400 (Bad Request) error message.

Recipients of an HTTP 1.0 request that lacks a Host header field may attempt to use heuristics (e.g., examination of the URI path for something unique to a particular host) in order to determine what exact resource is being requested.

Request-Header Fields

The request-header fields allow the client to pass additional information about the request, and about the client itself, to the server. These fields act as request modifiers, with semantics equivalent to the parameters on a programming language method invocation.

In the request-header Accept there are the following fields:

- Accept-Charset
- Accept-Encoding
- Accept-Language
- Authorization
- From
- Host
- If-Modified-Since
- If-Match
- If-None-Match
- If-Range
- If-Unmodified-Since
- Max-Forwards
- Proxy-Authorization
- Range
- Referer
- User-Agent.

Request-header field names can be extended reliably only in combination with a change in the protocol version. However, new or experimental header fields may be given the semantics of request-header fields if all parties in the communication recognize them to be request-header fields. Unrecognized header fields are treated as entity-header fields.

HTTP Response

After receiving and interpreting a request message, a server responds with an HTTP response message.

The response Status-Line is made up of:

- *(general-header
- response-header
- entity-header)
- CRLF
- [message-body].

HTTP Status-Line

The first line of a Response message is the Status-Line, consisting of the protocol version followed by a numeric status code and its associated textual phrase, with each element separated by SP characters. No CR or LF is allowed except in the final CRLF sequence.

```
Status-Line = HTTP-Version SP Status-Code SP Reason-Phrase CRLF
```

HTTP Status-Code and Reason-Phrase

The Status-Code element is a 3-digit integer result code of the attempt to understand and satisfy the request. The Reason-Phrase is intended to give a short textual description of the Status-Code. The Status-Code is intended for use by automata and the Reason-Phrase is intended for the human user. The client is not required to examine or display the Reason-Phrase.

The first digit of the Status-Code defines the class of response. The last two digits do not have any categorization role. There are 5 values for the first digit:

- **1xx: Informational.** Request received, continuing process
- **2xx: Success.** The action was successfully received, understood, and accepted
- **3xx: Redirection.** Further action must be taken in order to complete the request
- **4xx: Client Error.** The request contains bad syntax or cannot be fulfilled
- **5xx: Server Error.** The server failed to fulfill an apparently valid request.

The individual values of the numeric status codes defined for HTTP 1.1, and an example set of corresponding Reason-Phrases, are presented below. The Reason-Phrases listed here are only recommended—they may be replaced by local equivalents without affecting the protocol.

Status-Code =   100; Continue
                    101; Switching Protocols
                    200; OK
                    201; Created
                    202; Accepted
                    203; Non-Authoritative Information
                    204; No Content
                    205; Reset Content
                    206; Partial Content
                    300; Multiple Choices
                    301; Moved Permanently
                    302; Moved Temporarily
                    303; See Other
                    304; Not Modified
                    305; Use Proxy
                    400; Bad Request
                    401; Unauthorized
                    402; Payment Required
                    403; Forbidden
                    404; Not Found
                    405; Method Not Allowed
                    406; Not Acceptable
                    407; Proxy Authentication Required
                    408; Request Time-out
                    409; Conflict
                    410; Gone
                    411; Length Required
                    412; Precondition Failed
                    413; Request Entity Too Large
                    414; Request-URI Too Large
                    415; Unsupported Media Type

continued on next page

```
500; Internal Server Error
501; Not Implemented
502; Bad Gateway
503; Service Unavailable
504; Gateway Time-out
505; HTTP Version not supported
extension-code
Extension-code = 3DIGIT
Reason-Phrase = *<TEXT, excluding CR, LF>
```

HTTP status codes are extensible. HTTP applications are not required to understand the meaning of all registered status codes, though such understanding is obviously desirable. However, applications must understand the class of any status code, as indicated by the first digit, and treat any unrecognized response as being equivalent to the x00 status code of that class, with the exception that an unrecognized response must not be cached. For example, if an unrecognized status code of 431 is received by the client, it can safely assume that there was something wrong with its request and treat the response as if it had received a 400 status code. In such cases, user agents should present to the user the entity returned with the response, since that entity is likely to include human-readable information which will explain the unusual status.

HTTP Response-Header Fields

The Response-Header fields allow the server to pass additional information about the response which cannot be placed in the Status-Line. These fields give information about the server and about further access to the resource identified by the Request-URI.

Response-Header fields include:

- Age
- Location
- Proxy-Authenticate
- Public
- Retry-After
- Server
- Vary

- Warning
- WWW-Authenticate.

Response-Header field names can be extended reliably only in combination with a change in the protocol version. However, new or experimental header fields may be given the semantics of Response-Header fields if all parties in the communication recognize them to be Response-Header fields. Unrecognized header fields are treated as entity-header fields.

Entity

Request and Response messages may transfer an entity if not otherwise restricted by the request method or response status code. An entity consists of entity-header fields and an entity-body, although some responses will only include the entity headers.

In this section, both sender and recipient refer to either the client or the server, depending on who sends and who receives the entity.

Entity-Header Fields

Entity-header fields define optional metainformation about the entity-body or, if no body is present, about the resource identified by the request.

Entity headers include:

- Allow
- Content-Base
- Content-Encoding
- Content-Language
- Content-Length
- Content-Location
- Content-MD5
- Content-Range
- Content-Type
- ETag
- Expires
- Last-Modified
- Extension-header (message-header).

The extension-header mechanism allows additional entity-header fields to be defined without changing the protocol, but these fields cannot be assumed to be recognizable by the recipient. Unrecognized header fields should be ignored by the recipient and forwarded by proxies.

Entity-Body

The entity-body (if any) sent with an HTTP request or response is in a format and encoding defined by the entity-header fields.

```
entity-body   =   *octet
```

An entity-body is only present in a message when a message-body is present. The entity-body is obtained from the message-body by decoding any transfer-encoding that may have been applied to ensure safe and proper transfer of the message.

Type

When an entity-body is included with a message, the data type of that body is determined via the header-fields Content-Type and Content-Encoding. These define a two-layer, ordered encoding model:

```
entity-body := Content-Encoding( Content-Type( data ) )
```

Content-Type specifies the media type of the underlying data. Content-Encoding may be used to indicate any additional content codings applied to the data, usually for the purpose of data compression, that are a property of the requested resource. There is no default encoding.

Any HTTP 1.1 message containing an entity-body should include a Content-Type header field defining the media type of that body. If, and only if, the media type is not given by a Content-Type field, the recipient may attempt to guess the media type via inspection of its content and/or the name extension(s) of the URL used to identify the resource. If the media type remains unknown, the recipient should treat it as type "application/octet-stream".

Length

The length of an entity-body is the length of the message-body after any transfer codings have been removed.

HTTP Connections

Prior to persistent connections, a separate TCP connection was established to fetch each URL, increasing the load on HTTP servers and causing congestion on the Internet. The use of inline images and other associated data often requires a client to make multiple requests of the same server in a short amount of time. HTTP connections should be viewed in the light of TCP operation and the entire network wherein it is implemented.

Persistent HTTP connections have a number of advantages:

- By opening and closing fewer TCP connections, CPU time is saved, and memory used for TCP protocol control blocks is also saved.
- HTTP requests and responses can be pipelined on a connection. Pipelining allows a client to make multiple requests without waiting for each response, allowing a single TCP connection to be used much more efficiently, with much lower elapsed time.
- Network congestion is reduced by decreasing the number of packets caused by TCP opens, and by allowing TCP sufficient time to determine the congestion state of the network.
- HTTP can evolve more gracefully; since errors can be reported without the penalty of closing the TCP connection. Clients using future versions of HTTP might optimistically try a new feature; if communicating with an older server, they should retry with old semantics after an error is reported.

HTTP implementations should implement persistent connections.

HTTP Connection Operation

A significant difference between HTTP/1.1 and earlier versions of HTTP is that persistent connections are the default behavior of any HTTP connection. That is, unless otherwise indicated, the client may assume that the server will maintain a persistent connection.

Persistent connections provide a mechanism by which a client and a server can signal the close of a TCP connection. This signaling takes place using the Connection header field. Once a close has been signaled, the client must not send any more requests on that connection.

Negotiation

An HTTP 1.1 server may assume that an HTTP/1.1 client intends to maintain a persistent connection unless a Connection header including the connection-token close was sent in the request. If the server chooses to close the connection immediately after sending the response, it should send a Connection header including the connection-token close.

An HTTP 1.1 client may expect a connection to remain open, but would decide to keep it open based on whether the response from a server contains a Connection header with the connection-token close. In case the client does not want to maintain a connection for more than that request, it should send a Connection header including the connection-token close.

If either the client or the server sends the close token in the Connection header, that request becomes the last one for the connection.

Clients and servers should not assume that a persistent connection is maintained for HTTP versions less than 1.1 unless that is explicitly signaled. In order to remain persistent, all messages on the connection must have a self-defined message length.

Pipelining

A client supporting persistent connections may "pipeline" its requests (i.e., send multiple requests without waiting for each response). A server must send its responses to those requests in the same order that the requests were received.

Clients who assume persistent connections and pipeline immediately after connection establishment should be prepared to retry their connection if the first pipelined attempt fails. A client doing such a retry must not pipeline before knowing the connection is persistent. Clients must also be prepared to resend their requests if the server closes the connection before sending all of the corresponding responses.

Proxy Servers

The proxy server must signal persistent connections separately for its clients and the origin servers (or other proxy servers) that it connects to. Each persistent connection applies to only one transport link.

A proxy server must not establish a persistent connection with an HTTP 1.0 client.

Considerations

Servers will usually have some time-out value beyond which they will no longer maintain an inactive connection. Proxy servers might make this a higher value since it is likely that the client will be making more connections through the same server. The use of persistent connections places no requirements on the length of this time-out for either the client or the server.

A client or server wishing to time-out should issue a graceful close on the transport connection. Clients and servers should both constantly watch for the other side of the transport close, and respond to it as appropriate. A client or server not detecting the other side's close promptly could cause unnecessary resource drain on the network.

A client, server, or proxy may close the transport connection at any time. For example, a client may have started to send a new request at the same time that the server has decided to close the "idle" connection. From the server's point of view, the connection is being closed while it is idle, but from the client's point of view, a request is in progress.

This means that clients, servers, and proxies must be able to recover from asynchronous close events. Client software should reopen the transport connection and retransmit the aborted request without user interaction so long as the request method is idempotent; other methods must not be automatically retried, although user agents may offer a human operator the choice of retrying the request.

However, this automatic retry should not be repeated if the second request fails. Servers should always respond to at least one request per connection, if at all possible. Servers should not close a connection in the middle of transmitting a response, unless a network or client failure is suspected.

Clients using persistent connections should limit the number of simultaneous connections they maintain to a given server. A single-user client should maintain at most two connections with any server or proxy. A proxy should use up to 2*N connections to another server or proxy, where N is the number of simultaneously active users. These guidelines are intended to improve HTTP response times and avoid congestion of the Internet or other networks.

Message Transmission Requirements

General requirements:

- HTTP 1.1 servers should maintain persistent connections and use TCP's flow-control mechanisms to resolve temporary overloads, rather than terminating connections with the expectation that clients will retry. The latter technique can exacerbate network congestion.
- An HTTP/1.1 (or later) client sending a message-body should monitor the network connection for an error status while transmitting the request. A client who sees an error status should immediately cease transmitting the body. If the body is being sent using "chunked" encoding, a zero-length chunk and empty footer may be used to mark prematurely the end of the message. If the body was preceded by a Content-Length header, the client must close the connection.
- An HTTP 1.1 (or later) client must be prepared to accept a 100 (Continue) status followed by a regular response.
- An HTTP/1.1 (or later) server that receives a request from an HTTP 1.0 (or earlier) client must not transmit the 100 (Continue) response; it should either wait for the request to be completed normally (thus avoiding an interrupted request) or close the connection prematurely.

Upon receiving a method subject to these requirements from an HTTP 1.1 (or later) client, an HTTP 1.1 (or later) server must either respond with 100 (Continue) status and continue to read from the input stream, or respond with an error status. If it responds with an error status, it may close the transport (TCP) connection or it may continue to read and discard the rest of the request. It must not perform the requested method if it returns an error status.

Clients should remember the version number of at least the most recently used server; if an HTTP 1.1 client has seen an HTTP 1.1 or later response from the server, and sees the connection close before receiving any status from the server, the client should retry the request without user interaction so long as the request method is idempotent; other methods must not be automatically retried, although user agents may offer a human operator the choice of retrying the request.. If the client does retry the request, the client must first send the request header fields, and then must wait for the server to respond with either a 100 (Continue) response, in which case the client should continue, or with an error status.

If an HTTP 1.1 client has not seen an HTTP/1.1 or later response from the server, it should assume that the server implements HTTP 1.0 or older and will not use the 100 (Continue) response. If in this case the client sees the connection close before receiving any status from the server, the client should retry the request. If the client does retry the request to this HTTP 1.0 server, it should use the following "binary exponential backoff" algorithm to be assured of obtaining a reliable response:

1. Initiate a new connection to the server
2. Transmit the request-headers
3. Initialize a variable R to the estimated round-trip time to the server (e.g., based on the time it took to establish the connection), or to a constant value of 5 seconds if the round-trip time is not available.
4. Compute $T = R * (2**N)$, where N is the number of previous retries of this request.
5. Wait either for an error response from the server, or for T seconds (whichever comes first).
6. If no error response is received, after T seconds transmit the body of the request.
7. If the client sees that the connection is closed prematurely, repeat from step 1 until the request is accepted, an error response is received, or the user becomes impatient and terminates the retry process.

No matter what the server version, if an error status is received, the client must not continue and must close the connection if it has not completed sending the message.

An HTTP 1.1 (or later) client seeing the connection close after receiving a 100 (Continue) but before receiving any other status should retry the request, and need not wait for the 100 (Continue) response (but may do so if this simplifies the implementation).

Method Definitions

The set of common methods for HTTP/1.1 is defined below. Although this set can be expanded, additional methods cannot be assumed to share the same semantics for separately extended clients and servers.

The host request-header field must accompany all HTTP 1.1 requests.

Safe Methods

Implementers should be aware that the software represents the users in interactions over the Internet, and should be careful to make the users aware of any actions which may have an unexpected significance to themselves or others.

In particular, the convention has been established that the GET and HEAD methods should never have the significance of taking an action other than retrieval. These methods should be considered "safe." This allows user agents to represent other methods, such as POST, PUT, and DELETE, in a special way, so that the user is made aware of the fact that a possibly unsafe action is being requested.

Naturally, it is not possible to ensure that the server does not generate side-effects as a result of performing a GET request; in fact, some dynamic resources consider that a feature. The important distinction here is that the user did not request the side-effects, so therefore cannot be held accountable for them.

Idempotent Methods

Methods may also have the property of "idempotence" in that (aside from error or expiration issues) the side-effects of N > 0 identical requests is the same as for a single request. The methods GET, HEAD, PUT, and DELETE share this property.

Options

The Options method represents a request for information about the communication options available on the request/response chain identified by the Request-URI. This method allows the client to determine the options and/or requirements associated with a resource, or the capabilities of a server, without implying a resource action or initiating a resource retrieval.

Unless the server's response is an error, the response must not include entity information other than what can be considered as communication options (e.g., Allow is appropriate, but Content-Type is not). Responses to this method are not cacheable.

If the Request-URI is an asterisk ("*"), the Options request is intended to apply to the server as a whole. A 200 response should include any header fields which indicate optional features implemented by the server (e.g., Public), as well as any extensions not defined by this specification, and any applicable general or response-header fields.

If the Request-URI is not an asterisk, the Options request applies only to the options that are available when communicating with that resource. A 200 response should include any header fields which indicate optional features implemented by the server and applicable to that resource (e.g., Allow), including any extensions not defined by this specification, in addition to any applicable general or response-header fields. If the Options request passes through a proxy, the proxy must edit the response to exclude those options which apply to a proxy's capabilities and which are known to be unavailable through that proxy.

GET

The GET method means retrieve whatever information (in the form of an entity) is identified by the Request-URI. If the Request-URI refers to a data-producing process, it is the produced data which shall be returned as the entity in the response and not the source text of the process, unless that text happens to be the output of the process.

The semantics of the GET method change to a "conditional GET" if the request message includes an If-Modified-Since, If-Unmodified-Since, If-Match, If-None-Match, or If-Range header field. A conditional GET method requests that the entity be transferred only under the circumstances described by the conditional header field(s). The conditional GET method is intended to reduce unnecessary network usage by allowing cached entities to be refreshed without requiring multiple requests or transferring data already held by the client.

The semantics of the GET method change to a "partial GET" if the request message includes a Range header field. The partial GET method is intended to reduce unnecessary network usage by allowing partially-retrieved entities to be completed without transferring data already held by the client.

HEAD

The HEAD method is identical to GET except that the server must not return a message-body in the response. The meta-information contained in the HTTP headers in response to a HEAD request should be identical to the information sent in response to a GET request. This method can be used for obtaining metainformation about the entity implied by the request without transferring the entity-body itself.

This method is often used for testing hypertext links for validity, accessibility, and recent modification.

The response to a HEAD request may be cacheable in the sense that the information contained in the response may be used to update a previously cached entity from that resource. If the new field values indicate that the cached entity differs from the current entity (as would be indicated by a change in Content-Length, Content-MD5, ETag or Last-Modified), then the cache must treat the cache entry as stale.

POST

The POST method is used to request that the destination server accept the entity enclosed in the request as a new subordinate of the resource identified by the Request-URI in the Request-Line. POST is designed to allow a uniform method to cover the following functions:

- Annotation of existing resources
- Posting a message to a bulletin board, newsgroup, mailing list, or similar group of articles
- Providing a block of data, such as the result of submitting a form, to a data-handling process
- Extending a database through an append operation.

The actual function performed by the POST method is determined by the server and is usually dependent on the Request-URI. The posted entity is subordinate to that URI in the same way that a file is subordinate to a directory containing it, a news article is subordinate to a newsgroup to which it is posted, or a record is subordinate to a database.

The action performed by the POST method might not result in a resource that can be identified by a URI. In this case, either 200 (OK) or 204 (No Content) is the appropriate response status, depending on whether or not the response includes an entity that describes the result.

If a resource has been created on the origin server, the response should be 201 (Created) and contain an entity which describes the status of the request and refers to the new resource, and a Location header.

Responses to this method are not cacheable, unless the response includes appropriate Cache-Control or Expires header fields. However, the 303 (See Other) response can be used to direct the user agent to retrieve a cacheable resource.

PUT

The PUT method requests that the enclosed entity be stored under the supplied Request-URI. If the Request-URI refers to an already existing resource, the enclosed entity should be considered as a modified version of the one residing on the origin server. If the Request-URI does not point to an existing resource, and that URI is capable of being defined as a new resource by the requesting user agent, the origin server can create the resource with that URI. If a new resource is created, the origin server must inform the user agent via the 201 (Created) response. If an existing resource is modified, either the 200 (OK) or 204 (No Content) response codes should be sent to indicate successful completion of the request. If the resource could not be created or modified with the Request-URI, an appropriate error response should be given that reflects the nature of the problem. The recipient of the entity must not ignore any Content-* (e.g. Content-Range) headers that it does not understand or implement and must return a 501 (Not Implemented) response in such cases.

If the request passes through a cache and the Request-URI identifies one or more currently cached entities, those entries should be treated as stale. Responses to this method are not cacheable.

The fundamental difference between the POST and PUT requests is reflected in the different meaning of the Request-URI. The URI in a POST request identifies the resource that will handle the enclosed entity. That resource may be a data-accepting process, a gateway to some other protocol, or a separate entity that accepts annotations. In contrast, the URI in a PUT request identifies the entity enclosed with the request—the user agent knows what URI is intended and the server must not attempt to apply the request to some other resource. If the server desires that the request be applied to a different URI, it must send a 301 (Moved Permanently) response; the user agent may then make its own decision regarding whether or not to redirect the request.

A single resource may be identified by many different URIs. For example, an article may have a URI for identifying "the current version" which is separate from the URI identifying each particular version. In this case, a PUT request on a general URI may result in several other URIs being defined by the origin server. HTTP 1.1 does not define how a PUT method affects the state of an origin server.

DELETE

The DELETE method requests that the origin server delete the resource identified by the Request-URI. This method may be overridden by human intervention (or other means) on the origin server. The client cannot be guaranteed that the operation has been carried out, even if the status code returned from the origin server indicates that the action has been completed successfully. However, the server should not indicate success unless, at the time the response is given, it intends to delete the resource or move it to an inaccessible location.

A successful response should be 200 (OK) if the response includes an entity describing the status, 202 (Accepted) if the action has not yet been enacted, or 204 (No Content) if the response is OK but does not include an entity.

If the request passes through a cache and the Request-URI identifies one or more currently cached entities, those entries should be treated as stale. Responses to this method are not cacheable.

TRACE

The TRACE method is used to invoke a remote, application-layer loop-back of the request message. The final recipient of the request should reflect the message received back to the client as the entity-body of a 200 (OK) response. The final recipient is either the origin server or the first proxy or gateway to receive a Max-Forwards value of zero (0) in the request. A TRACE request must not include an entity.

TRACE allows the client to see what is being received at the other end of the request chain and use that data for testing or diagnostic information. The value of the Via header field is of particular interest, since it acts as a trace of the request chain.

Use of the Max-Forwards header field allows the client to limit the length of the request chain, which is useful for testing a chain of proxies forwarding messages in an infinite loop. If successful, the response should contain the entire request message in the entity-body, with a Content-Type of "message/http". Responses to this method must not be cached.

Status Code Definitions

Each status code is described below, including a description of which method(s) it can follow and any metainformation required in the response.

Informational 1xx

This class of status code indicates a provisional response, consisting only of the Status-Line and optional headers, and is terminated by an empty line. Since HTTP 1.0 did not define any 1xx status codes, servers must not send a 1xx response to an HTTP 1.0 client except under experimental conditions.

100 Continue

The client may continue with its request. This interim response is used to inform the client that the initial part of the request has been received and has not yet been rejected by the server. The client should continue by sending the remainder of the request or, if the request has already been completed, ignore this response. The server must send a final response after the request has been completed.

101 Switching Protocols

The server understands and is willing to comply with the client's request, via the Upgrade message-header field, for a change in the application protocol being used on this connection. The server will switch protocols to those defined by the response's Upgrade header field immediately after the empty line which terminates the 101 response.

The protocol should only be switched when it is advantageous to do so. For example, switching to a newer version of HTTP is advantageous over older versions, and switching to a real-time, synchronous protocol may be advantageous when delivering resources that use such features.

Successful 2xx

This class of status code indicates that the client's request was successfully received, understood, and accepted.

200 OK

The request has succeeded. The information returned with the response is dependent on the method used in the request, for example:

- GET. An entity corresponding to the requested resource is sent in the response

- HEAD. The entity-header fields corresponding to the requested resource are sent in the response without any message-body
- POST. An entity describing or containing the result of the action
- TRACE. An entity containing the request message as received by the end server.

201 Created

The request has been fulfilled and resulted in a new resource being created. The newly created resource can be referenced by the URI(s) returned in the entity of the response, with the most specific URL for the resource given by a Location header field. The origin server must create the resource before returning the 201 status code. If the action cannot be carried out immediately, the server should respond with 202 (Accepted) response instead.

202 Accepted

The request has been accepted for processing, but the processing has not been completed. The request may or may not eventually be acted upon, as it may be disallowed when processing actually takes place. There is no facility for re-sending a status code from an asynchronous operation such as this.

The 202 response is intentionally noncommittal. Its purpose is to allow a server to accept a request for some other process (perhaps a batch-oriented process that is only run once per day) without requiring that the user agent's connection to the server persist until the process is completed. The entity returned with this response should include an indication of the request's current status and either a pointer to a status monitor or some estimate of when the user can expect the request to be fulfilled.

203 Non-Authoritative Information

The returned metainformation in the entity-header is not the definitive set as available from the origin server, but is gathered from a local or a third-party copy. The set presented may be a subset or superset of the original version. For example, including local annotation information about the resource may result in a superset of the metainformation known by the origin server. Use of this response code is not required and is only appropriate when the response would otherwise be 200 (OK).

204 No Content

The server has fulfilled the request but there is no new information to send back. A client who is a user agent, should not change the document view from that which caused the request to be sent. This response is primarily intended to allow input for actions to take place without causing a change to the user agent's active document view. The response may include new metainformation in the form of entity-headers, which should apply to the document currently in the user agent's active view.

The 204 response must not include a message-body, and thus is always terminated by the first empty line after the header fields.

205 Reset Content

The server has fulfilled the request and the user agent should reset the document view which caused the request to be sent. This response is primarily intended to allow input for actions to take place via user input, followed by a clearing of the form in which the input is given so that the user can easily initiate another input action. The response must not include an entity.

206 Partial Content

The server has fulfilled the partial GET request for the resource. The request must have included a Range header field indicating the desired range. The response must include either a Content-Range header field indicating the range included with this response, or a multipart/byteranges Content-Type including Content-Range fields for each part. If multipart/byteranges are not used, the Content-Length header field in the response must match the actual number of octets transmitted in the message-body. A cache that does not support the Range and Content-Range headers must not cache 206 (Partial) responses.

Redirection 3xx

This class of status code indicates that further action needs to be taken by the user agent in order to fulfill the request. The action required may be carried out by the user agent without interaction with the user if and only if the method used in the second request is GET or HEAD. A user agent should not automatically redirect a request more than five times, since such redirections usually indicate an infinite loop.

300 Multiple Choices

The requested resource corresponds to any one of a set of representations, each with its own specific location, and agent-driven negotiation information (section 12) is being provided so that the user (or user agent) can select a preferred representation and redirect its request to that location.

Unless it was a HEAD request, the response should include an entity containing a list of resource characteristics and location(s) from which the user or user agent can choose the one most appropriate. The entity format is specified by the media type given in the Content-Type header field. Depending upon the format and the capabilities of the user agent, selection of the most appropriate choice may be performed automatically. However, this specification does not define any standard for such automatic selection.

If the server has a preferred choice of representation, it should include the specific URL for that representation in the Location field; user agents may use the Location-field value for automatic redirection. This response is cacheable unless indicated otherwise.

301 Moved Permanently

The requested resource has been assigned a new permanent URI and any future references to this resource should be done using one of the returned URIs. Clients with link editing capabilities should automatically re-link references to the Request-URI to one or more of the new references returned by the server, where possible. This response is cacheable unless indicated otherwise. If the new URI is a location, its URL should be given by the location field in the response. Unless the request method was HEAD, the entity of the response should contain a short hypertext note with a hyperlink to the new URI(s).

If the 301 status code is received in response to a request other than GET or HEAD, the user agent must not automatically redirect the request unless it can be confirmed by the user, since this might change the conditions under which the request was issued. When automatically redirecting a POST request after receiving a 301 status code, some existing HTTP/1.0 user agents will erroneously change it into a GET request.

302 Moved Temporarily

The requested resource resides temporarily under a different URI. Since the redirection may be altered on occasion, the client should continue to use the Request-URI for future requests. This response is only cacheable if indicated by a Cache-Control or Expires header field.

If the new URI is a location, its URL should be given by the Location field in the response. Unless the request method was HEAD, the entity of the response should contain a short hypertext note with a hyperlink to the new URI(s).

If the 302 status code is received in response to a request other than GET or HEAD, the user agent must not automatically redirect the request unless it can be confirmed by the user, since this might change the conditions under which the request was issued.

When automatically redirecting a POST request after receiving a 302 status code, some existing HTTP/1.0 user agents will erroneously change it into a GET request.

303 See Other

The response to the request can be found under a different URI and should be retrieved using a GET method on that resource. This method exists primarily to allow the output of a POST-activated script to redirect the user agent to a selected resource. The new URI is not a substitute reference for the originally requested resource. The 303 response is not cacheable, but the response to the second (redirected) request may be cacheable.

If the new URI is a location, its URL should be given by the Location field in the response. Unless the request method was HEAD, the entity of the response should contain a short hypertext note with a hyperlink to the new URI(s).

304 Not Modified

If the client has performed a conditional GET request and access is allowed, but the document has not been modified, the server should respond with this status code. The response must not contain a message-body. The response must include the following header fields:

- **Date**
- **ETag and/or Content-Location.** If the header would have been sent in a 200 response to the same request
- **Expires, Cache-Control, and/or Vary**. If the field-value might differ from that sent in any previous response for the same variant.

If the conditional GET used a strong cache validator, the response should not include other entity-headers. Otherwise (if, i.e., the conditional GET used a weak validator), the response must not include other entity-headers; this prevents inconsistencies between cached entity-bodies and updated headers.

If a 304 response indicates an entity not currently cached, then the cache must disregard the response and repeat the request without the conditional.

If a cache uses a received 304 response to update a cache entry, the cache must update the entry to reflect any new field values given in the response.

The 304 response must not include a message-body, and thus is always terminated by the first empty line after the header fields.

305 Use Proxy

The requested resource must be accessed through the proxy given by the Location field. The Location field gives the URL of the proxy. The recipient is expected to repeat the request via the proxy.

Client Error 4xx

The 4xx class of status code is intended for cases in which the client seems to have erred. Except when responding to a HEAD request, the server should include an entity containing an explanation of the error situation, and whether it is a temporary or permanent condition. These status codes are applicable to any request method. User agents should display any included entity to the user.

If the client is sending data, a server implementation using TCP should be careful to ensure that the client acknowledges receipt of the packet(s) containing the response, before the server closes the input connection. If the client continues sending data to the server after the close, the server's TCP stack will send a reset packet to the client, which may erase the client's unacknowledged input buffers before they can be read and interpreted by the HTTP application.

400 Bad Request

The request could not be understood by the server due to malformed syntax. The client should not repeat the request without modifications.

401 Unauthorized

The request requires user authentication. The response must include a WWW-Authenticate header field containing a challenge applicable to the requested resource. The client may repeat the request with a suitable Authorization header field. If the request already included Authorization credentials, then the 401 response indicates that authorization has been refused for those credentials. If the 401 response contains the same challenge as the prior response, and the user agent has already attempted authentication at least once, then the user should be presented the entity that was given in the response, since that entity may include relevant diagnostic information.

402 Payment Required

This code is reserved for future use.

403 Forbidden

The server understood the request, but is refusing to fulfill it. Authorization will not help and the request should not be repeated. If the request method was not HEAD and the server wishes to make public why the request has not been fulfilled, it should describe the reason for the refusal in the entity. This status code is commonly used when the server does not wish to reveal exactly why the request has been refused, or when no other response is applicable.

404 Not Found

The server has not found anything matching the Request-URI. No indication is given of whether the condition is temporary or permanent. If the server does not wish to make this information available to the client, the status code 403 (Forbidden) can be used instead. The 410 (Gone) status code should be used if the server knows, through some internally configurable mechanism, that an old resource is permanently unavailable and has no forwarding address.

405 Method Not Allowed

The method specified in the Request-Line is not allowed for the resource identified by the Request-URI. The response must include an Allow header containing a list of valid methods for the requested resource.

406 Not Acceptable

The resource identified by the request is only capable of generating response entities which have content characteristics not acceptable according to the accept headers sent in the request. Unless it was a HEAD request, the response should include an entity containing a list of available entity characteristics and location(s) from which the user or user agent can choose the one most appropriate. The entity format is specified by the media type given in the Content-Type header field. Depending upon the format and the capabilities of the user agent, selection of the most appropriate choice may be performed automatically. However, this specification does not define any standard for such automatic selection.

HTTP 1.1 servers are allowed to return responses which are not acceptable according to the accept headers sent in the request. In some cases, this may even be preferable to sending a 406 response. User agents are encouraged to inspect the headers of an incoming response to determine if it is acceptable. If the response could be unacceptable, a user agent should temporarily stop receipt of more data and query the user for a decision on further actions.

407 Proxy Authentication Required

This code is similar to 401 (Unauthorized), but indicates that the client must first authenticate itself with the proxy. The proxy must return a Proxy-Authenticate header field containing a challenge applicable to the proxy for the requested resource. The client may repeat the request with a suitable Proxy-Authorization header field.

408 Request Timeout

The client did not produce a request within the time that the server was prepared to wait. The client may repeat the request without modifications at any later time.

409 Conflict

The request could not be completed due to a conflict with the current state of the resource. This code is only allowed in situations where it is expected that the user might be able to resolve the conflict and resubmit the request. The response body should include enough information for the user to recognize the source of the conflict. Ideally, the response entity would include enough information for the user or user agent to fix the problem; however, that may not be possible and is not required.

Conflicts are most likely to occur in response to a PUT request. If versioning is being used and the entity being PUT includes changes to a resource which conflict with those made by an earlier (third-party) request, the server may use the 409 response to indicate that it can't complete the request. In this case, the response entity should contain a list of the differences between the two versions in a format defined by the response Content-Type.

410 Gone

The requested resource is no longer available at the server and no forwarding address is known. This condition should be considered permanent. Clients with link editing capabilities should delete references to the Request-URI after user approval. If the server does not know, or has no facility to determine, whether or not the condition is permanent, the status code 404 (Not Found) should be used instead. This response is cacheable unless indicated otherwise.

The 410 response is primarily intended to assist the task of web maintenance by notifying the recipient that the resource is intentionally unavailable and that the server owners desire that remote links to that resource be removed. Such an event is common for limited-time, promotional services and for resources belonging to individuals no longer working at the server's site. It is not necessary to mark all permanently unavailable resources as "gone" or to keep the mark for any length of time—that is left to the discretion of the server owner.

411 Length Required

The server refuses to accept the request without a defined Content-Length. The client may repeat the request if it adds a valid Content-Length header field containing the length of the message-body in the request message.

412 Precondition Failed

The precondition given in one or more of the request-header fields evaluated to false when it was tested on the server. This response code allows the client to place preconditions on the current resource metainformation (header field data) and thus prevent the requested method from being applied to a resource other than the one intended.

413 Request Entity Too Large

The server is refusing to process a request because the request entity is larger than the server is willing or able to process. The server may close the connection to prevent the client from continuing the request.

If the condition is temporary, the server should include a Retry-After header field to indicate that it is temporary and after what time the client may try again.

414 Request-URI Too Long

The server is refusing to service the request because the Request-URI is longer than the server is willing to interpret. This rare condition is only likely to occur when a client has improperly converted a POST request to a GET request with long query information, when the client has descended into a URL "black hole" of redirection (e.g., a redirected URL prefix that points to a suffix of itself), or when the server is under attack by a client attempting to exploit security holes present in some servers using fixed-length buffers for reading or manipulating the Request-URI.

415 Unsupported Media Type

The server is refusing to service the request because the entity of the request is in a format not supported by the requested resource for the requested method.

Server Error 5xx

Response status codes beginning with the digit "5" indicate cases in which the server is aware that it has erred or is incapable of performing the request. Except when responding to a HEAD request, the server should include an entity containing an explanation of the error situation, and whether it is a temporary or permanent condition. User agents should display any included entity to the user. These response codes are applicable to any request method.

500 Internal Server Error

The server encountered an unexpected condition which prevented it from fulfilling the request.

501 Not Implemented

The server does not support the functionality required to fulfill the request. This is the appropriate response when the server does not recognize the request method and is not capable of supporting it for any resource.

502 Bad Gateway

The server, while acting as a gateway or proxy, received an invalid response from the upstream server it accessed in attempting to fulfill the request.

503 Service Unavailable

The server is currently unable to handle the request due to a temporary overloading or maintenance of the server. The implication is that
this is a temporary condition which will be alleviated after some
delay. If known, the length of the delay may be indicated in a
Retry-After header. If no Retry-After is given, the client should handle the response as it would for a 500 response.

The existence of the 503 status code does not imply that a server
must use it when becoming overloaded. Some servers may wish to
simply refuse the connection.

504 Gateway Timeout

The server, while acting as a gateway or proxy, did not receive a timely response from the upstream server it accessed in attempting to
complete the request.

505 HTTP Version Not Supported

The server does not support, or refuses to support, the HTTP protocol
version that was used in the request message. The server is indicating
that it is unable or unwilling to complete the request using the same
major version as the client other than with this error message. The
response should contain an entity describing why that version is not
supported and what other protocols are supported by that server.

Access Authentication

HTTP provides a simple challenge-response authentication mechanism which may be used by a server to challenge a client request and
by a client to provide authentication information. It uses an extensible, case-insensitive token to identify the authentication scheme, followed by a comma-separated list of attribute-value pairs which carry
the parameters necessary for achieving authentication via that
scheme.

```
auth-scheme    = token
auth-param     = token "=" quoted-string
```

The 401 (Unauthorized) response message is used by an origin server
to challenge the authorization of a user agent. This response must
include a WWW-Authenticate header field containing at least one
challenge applicable to the requested resource.

```
challenge      = auth-scheme 1*SP realm *( "," auth-param )
realm          = "realm" "=" realm-value
realm-value    = quoted-string
```

The realm attribute (case-insensitive) is required for all authentication schemes which issue a challenge. The realm value (case-sensitive), in combination with the canonical root URL of the server being accessed, defines the protection space. These realms allow the protected resources on a server to be partitioned into a set of protection spaces, each with its own authentication scheme and/or authorization database. The realm value is a string, generally assigned by the origin server, which may have additional semantics specific to the authentication scheme.

A user agent that wishes to authenticate itself with a server—usually, but not necessarily, after receiving a 401 or 411 response—may do so by including an Authorization header field with the request. The Authorization field value consists of credentials containing the authentication information of the user agent for the realm of the resource being requested.

```
credentials    = basic-credentials
               | auth-scheme #auth-param
```

The domain over which credentials can be automatically applied by a user agent is determined by the protection space. If a prior request has been authorized, the same credentials may be reused for all other requests within that protection space for a period of time determined by the authentication scheme, parameters, and/or user preference. Unless otherwise defined by the authentication scheme, a single protection space cannot extend outside the scope of its server.

If the server does not wish to accept the credentials sent with a request, it should return a 401 (Unauthorized) response. The response must include a WWW-Authenticate header field containing the (possibly new) challenge applicable to the requested resource and an entity explaining the refusal.

The HTTP protocol does not restrict applications to this simple challenge-response mechanism for access authentication. Additional mechanisms may be used, such as encryption at the transport level or via message encapsulation, and with additional header fields specifying authentication information. However, these additional mechanisms are not defined by this specification.

Proxies must be completely transparent regarding user agent authentication. That is, they must forward the WWW-Authenticate and Authorization headers untouched. HTTP 1.1 allows a client to pass authentication information to and from a proxy via the Proxy-Authenticate and Proxy-Authorization headers.

Basic Authentication Scheme

The "basic" authentication scheme is based on the model that the user agent must authenticate itself with a user-ID and a password for each realm. The realm value should be considered an opaque string which can only be compared for equality with other realms on that server. The server will service the request only if it can validate the user-ID and password for the protection space of the Request-URI. There are no optional authentication parameters.

Upon receipt of an unauthorized request for a URI within the protection space, the server may respond with a challenge like the following:

```
WWW-Authenticate: Basic realm="WallyWorld"
```

where "WallyWorld" is the string assigned by the server to identify the protection space of the Request-URI.

To receive authorization, the client sends the user-ID and password, separated by a single colon (":") character, within a base 64 encoded string in the credentials.

```
basic-credentials  = "Basic" SP basic-cookie
basic-cookie       = <base64 [7] encoding of user-pass, except not
                     limited to 76 char/line>
user-pass          = userid ":" password
userid             = *<TEXT excluding ":">
password           = *TEXT
```

User-IDs might be case sensitive.

If the user agent wishes to send the user-ID "Aladdin" and password "open sesame," it would use the following header field:

```
Authorization: Basic QWxhZGRpbjpvcGVuIHNlc2FtZQ==
```

Content Negotiation

Most HTTP responses include an entity which contains information for interpretation by a human user. Naturally, it is desirable to supply the user with the "best available" entity corresponding to the request. Unfortunately for servers and caches, not all users have the same preferences for what is "best," and not all user agents are equally capable of rendering all entity types. For that reason, HTTP has provisions for several mechanisms for "content negotiation"—the process of selecting the best representation for a given response when there are multiple representations available. This is not called "format negotiation" because the alternate representations may be of the same media type, but use different capabilities of that type, be in different languages, etc.

Any response containing an entity-body may be subject to negotiation, including error responses.

There are two kinds of content negotiation which are possible in HTTP: server-driven and agent-driven. These are both orthogonal and thus may be used separately or in combination. One method of combination, referred to as transparent negotiation, occurs when a cache uses the agent-driven negotiation information provided by the origin server in order to provide server-driven negotiation for subsequent requests.

Server-driven Negotiation

If the selection of the best representation for a response is made by an algorithm located at the server, it is called server-driven negotiation. Selection is based on the available representations of the response (the dimensions over which it can vary; e.g. language, content-coding, etc.) and the contents of particular header fields in the request message or on other information pertaining to the request (such as the network address of the client).

Server-driven negotiation is advantageous when the algorithm for selecting from among the available representations is difficult to describe to the user agent, or when the server desires to send its "best guess" to the client along with the first response (hoping to avoid the round-trip delay of a subsequent request if the "best guess" is good enough for the user). In order to improve the server's guess, the user agent may include request header fields (Accept, Accept-Language, Accept-Encoding, etc.) which describe its preferences for such a response.

Server-driven negotiation has disadvantages:

1. It is impossible for the server to accurately determine what might be "best" for any given user, since that would require complete knowledge of both the capabilities of the user agent and the intended use for the response (e.g., does the user want to view it on screen or print it on paper?).

2. Having the user agent describe its capabilities in every request can be both very inefficient (given that only a small percentage of

responses have multiple representations) and a potential violation of the user's privacy.

3. It complicates the implementation of an origin server and the
algorithms for generating responses to a request.

4. It may limit a public cache's ability to use the same response for
multiple user's requests.

HTTP 1.1 includes the following request-header fields for enabling
server-driven negotiation through description of user agent capabilities and user preferences: Accept, Accept-Charset, Accept-Encoding,
Accept-Language, and User-Agent. However, an origin server is not
limited to these dimensions and may vary the response based on any
aspect of the request, including information outside the request-header fields or within extension header fields not defined by this specification.

HTTP 1.1 origin servers must include an appropriate Vary header
field in any cacheable response based on server-driven negotiation.
The Vary header field describes the dimensions over which the
response might vary (i.e. the dimensions over which the origin server
picks its "best guess" response from multiple representations).

HTTP 1.1 public caches must recognize the Vary header field
when it is included in a response.

Agent-driven Negotiation

With agent-driven negotiation, selection of the best representation for
a response is performed by the user agent after receiving an initial
response from the origin server. Selection is based on a list of the
available representations of the response included within the header
fields or entity-body of the initial response, with each representation
identified by its own URI. Selection from among the representations
may be performed automatically (if the user agent is capable of doing
so) or manually, by the user selecting from a generated (possibly
hypertext) menu.

Agent-driven negotiation is advantageous when the response would
vary over commonly-used dimensions (such as type, language, or
encoding), when the origin server is unable to determine a user agent's
capabilities from examining the request, and generally when public
caches are used to distribute server load and reduce network usage.

Agent-driven negotiation suffers from the disadvantage of needing
a second request to obtain the best alternate representation. This second request is only efficient when caching is used. In addition, this

specification does not define any mechanism for supporting automatic selection, though it also does not prevent any such mechanism from being developed as an extension and used within HTTP 1.1.

HTTP 1.1 defines the 300 (Multiple Choices) and 406 (Not Acceptable) status codes for enabling agent-driven negotiation when the server is unwilling or unable to provide a varying response using server-driven negotiation.

Transparent Negotiation

Transparent negotiation is a combination of both server-driven and agent-driven negotiation. When a cache is supplied with a form of the list of available representations of the response (as in agent-driven negotiation) and the dimensions of variance are completely understood by the cache, then the cache becomes capable of performing server-driven negotiation on behalf of the origin server for subsequent requests on that resource.

Transparent negotiation has the advantage of distributing the negotiation work that would otherwise be required of the origin server and also removing the second request delay of agent-driven negotiation when the cache is able to correctly guess the right response.

This specification does not define any mechanism for transparent negotiation, though it also does not prevent any such mechanism from being developed as an extension and used within HTTP 1.1. An HTTP 1.1 cache performing transparent negotiation must include a Vary header field in the response (defining the dimensions of its variance) if it is cacheable to ensure correct interoperation with all HTTP 1.1 clients. The agent-driven negotiation information supplied by the origin server should be included with the transparently negotiated response.

Caching in HTTP

HTTP is typically used for distributed information systems, where performance can be improved by the use of response caches. The HTTP 1.1 protocol includes a number of elements intended to make caching work as well as possible. Because these elements are inextricable from other aspects of the protocol, and because they interact with each other, it is useful to describe the basic caching design of HTTP separately from the detailed descriptions of methods, headers, response codes, etc.

Caching would be useless if it did not significantly improve performance. The goal of caching in HTTP 1.1 is to eliminate the need to send requests in many cases, and to eliminate the need to send full responses in many other cases. The former reduces the number of network round-trips required for many operations; we use an "expiration" mechanism for this purpose. The latter reduces network bandwidth requirements; we use a "validation" mechanism for this purpose.

Requirements for performance, availability, and disconnected operation require us to be able to relax the goal of semantic transparency. The HTTP/1.1 protocol allows origin servers, caches, and clients explicitly to reduce transparency when necessary. However, because non-transparent operation may confuse non-expert users, and may be incompatible with certain server applications (such as those for ordering merchandise), the protocol requires that transparency be relaxed only by an explicit protocol-level request when relaxed by client, origin server or only with an explicit warning to the end user when relaxed by cache or client.

Therefore, the HTTP/1.1 protocol provides these important elements:

1. Protocol features that provide full semantic transparency when this is required by all parties
2. Protocol features that allow an origin server or user agent explicitly to request and control non-transparent operation
3. Protocol features that allow a cache to attach warnings to responses that do not preserve the requested approximation of semantic transparency.

A basic principle is that it must be possible for the clients to detect any potential relaxation of semantic transparency. The server, cache, or client implementer may be faced with design decisions not explicitly discussed here. If a decision may affect semantic transparency, the implementer ought to err on the side of maintaining transparency unless a careful and complete analysis shows significant benefits in breaking transparency.

Header Field Definitions

This section defines the syntax and semantics of all standard HTTP 1.1 header fields. For entity-header fields, both sender and recipient refer to either the client or the server, depending on who sends and who receives the entity.

Accept

The Accept request-header field can be used to specify certain media types which are acceptable for the response. Accept headers can be used to indicate that the request is specifically limited to a small set of desired types, as in the case of a request for an in-line image.

```
accept      =    "Accept" ":"
                 #( media-range [ accept-params ] )
media-range    = ( "*/*"
                 | (type "/" "*")
                 | (type "/" subtype)
                 ) *(";" parameter)
accept-params = ";" "q" "=" qvalue *(accept-extension)
accept-extension = ";" token [ "=" (token | quoted-string) ]
```

The asterisk "*" character is used to group media types into ranges, with "*/*" indicating all media types and "type/*" indicating all sub-types of that type. The media-range may include media type parameters that are applicable to that range.

Each media-range may be followed by one or more accept-params, beginning with the "q" parameter for indicating a relative quality factor. The first "q" parameter (if any) separates the media-range parameter(s) from the accept-params. Quality factors allow the user or user agent to indicate the relative degree of preference for that media-range, using the qvalue scale from 0 to 1. The default value is q=1. The use of the "q" parameter name to separate media type parameters from Accept extension parameters is due to historical practice. Although this prevents any media type parameter named "q" from being used with a media range, such an event is believed to be unlikely given the lack of any "q" parameters in the IANA media type registry and the rare usage of any media type parameters in Accept. Future media types should be discouraged from registering any parameter named "q".

The example

```
Accept: audio/*; q=0.2, audio/basic
```

should be interpreted as "I prefer audio/basic, but send me any audio type if it is the best available after an 80% mark-down in quality." If no Accept header field is present, then it is assumed that the client accepts all media types. If an Accept header field is present, and if the server cannot send a response which is acceptable according to the combined Accept field value, then the server should send a 406 (Not Acceptable) response.

A more elaborate example is

```
Accept:   text/plain; q=0.5, text/html,
          text/x-dvi; q=0.8, text/x-c
```

Verbally, this would be interpreted as "text/html and text/x-c are the preferred media types, but if they do not exist, then send the text/x-dvi entity, and if that does not exist, send the text/plain entity."

Media ranges can be overridden by more specific media ranges or specific media types. If more than one media range applies to a given type, the most specific reference has precedence. For example:

Accept: text/*, text/html, text/html;level=1, */* has the following precedence:

1. text/html;level=1
2. text/html
3. text/*
4. */*

The media-type quality factor associated with a given type is determined by finding the media range with the highest precedence which matches that type. For example,

```
Accept:   text/*;q=0.3, text/html;q=0.7, text/html;level=1,
          text/html;level=2;q=0.4, */*;q=0.5
```

would cause the following values to be associated:

```
text/html;level=1   = 1
text/html           = 0.7
text/plain          = 0.3
image/jpeg          = 0.5
text/html;level=2   = 0.4
text/html;level=3   = 0.7
```

A user agent may be provided with a default set of quality values for certain media ranges. However, unless the user agent is a closed system which cannot interact with other rendering agents, this default set should be configurable by the user.

Accept-Charset

The Accept-Charset request-header field can be used to indicate what character sets are acceptable for the response. This field allows clients capable of understanding more comprehensive or special-purpose character sets to signal that capability to a server which is capable of representing documents in those character sets. The

ISO-8859-1 character set can be assumed to be acceptable to all user agents.

```
Accept-Charset = "Accept-Charset" ":"
                 1#( charset [ ";" "q" "=" qvalue ] )
```

Each charset may be given an associated quality value which represents the user's preference for that charset. The default value is q=1. An example is:

```
Accept-Charset: iso-8859-5, unicode-1-1;q=0.8
```

If no Accept-Charset header is present, the default is that any character set is acceptable. If an Accept-Charset header is present, and if the server cannot send a response which is acceptable according to the Accept-Charset header, then the server should send an error response with the 406 (Not Acceptable) status code, though the sending of an unacceptable response is also allowed.

Accept-Encoding

The Accept-Encoding request-header field is similar to Accept, but restricts the content-coding values which are acceptable in the response.

```
Accept-Encoding = "Accept-Encoding" ":"
#( content-coding )
```

An example of its use is

```
Accept-Encoding: compress, gzip
```

If no Accept-Encoding header is present in a request, the server may assume that the client will accept any content coding. If an Accept-Encoding header is present, and if the server cannot send a response which is acceptable according to the Accept-Encoding header, then the server should send an error response with the 406 (Not Acceptable) status code. An empty Accept-Encoding value indicates none are acceptable.

Accept-Language

The Accept-Language request-header field is similar to Accept, but restricts the set of natural languages that are preferred as a response to the request.

```
Accept-Language = "Accept-Language" ":"
1#( language-range [ ";" "q" "=" qvalue ] )
language-range = ( ( 1*8ALPHA *( "-" 1*8ALPHA ) ) | "*" )
```

Each language-range may be given an associated quality value which represents an estimate of the user's preference for the languages specified by that range. The quality value defaults to "q=1". For example:

```
Accept-Language: da, en-gb;q=0.8, en;q=0.7
```

would mean: "I prefer Danish, but will accept British English and other types of English." A language-range matches a language-tag if it exactly equals the tag, or if it exactly equals a prefix of the tag such that the first tag character following the prefix is "-". The special range "*", if present in the Accept-Language field, matches every tag not matched by any other range present in the Accept-Language field. This use of a prefix matching rule does not imply that language tags are assigned to languages in such a way that it is always true that if a user understands a language with a certain tag, then this user will also understand all languages with tags for which this tag is a prefix. The prefix rule simply allows the use of prefix tags if this is the case.

The language quality factor assigned to a language-tag by the Accept-Language field is the quality value of the longest language-range in the field that matches the language-tag. If no language-range in the field matches the tag, the language quality factor assigned is 0. If no Accept-Language header is present in the request, the server should assume that all languages are equally acceptable. If an Accept-Language header is present, then all languages which are assigned a quality factor greater than 0 are acceptable.

It may be contrary to the privacy expectations of the user to send an Accept-Language header with the complete linguistic preferences of the user in every request. As intelligibility is highly dependent on the individual user, it is recommended that client applications make the choice of linguistic preference available to the user. If the choice is not made available, then the Accept-Language header field must not be given in the request.

Accept-Ranges

The Accept-Ranges response-header field allows the server to indicate its acceptance of range requests for a resource:

```
Accept-Ranges    = "Accept-Ranges" ":" acceptable-ranges
acceptable-ranges = 1#range-unit | "none"
```

Origin servers that accept byte-range requests may send

```
Accept-Ranges: bytes
```

but are not required to do so. Clients may generate byte-range requests without having received this header for the resource involved.

Servers that do not accept any kind of range request for a resource may send

```
Accept-Ranges: none
```

to advise the client not to attempt a range request.

Age

The Age response-header field conveys the sender's estimate of the amount of time since the response (or its revalidation) was generated at the origin server. A cached response is "fresh" if its age does not exceed its freshness lifetime.

```
Age = "Age" ":" age-value
age-value = delta-seconds
```

Age values are non-negative decimal integers, representing time in seconds. If a cache receives a value larger than the largest positive integer it can represent, or if any of its age calculations overflows, it must transmit an Age header with a value of 2147483648. HTTP 1.1 caches must send an Age header in every response. Caches should use an arithmetic type of at least 31 bits of range.

Allow

The Allow entity-header field lists the set of methods supported by the resource identified by the Request-URI. The purpose of this field is strictly to inform the recipient of valid methods associated with the resource. An Allow header field must be present in a 405 (Method Not Allowed) response.

```
Allow=    "Allow" ":" 1#method
```

Example of use:

```
Allow: GET, HEAD, PUT
```

This field cannot prevent a client from trying other methods. However, the indications given by the Allow header field value should be followed. The actual set of allowed methods is defined by the origin server at the time of each request.

The Allow header field may be provided with a PUT request to recommend the methods to be supported by the new or modified resource. The server is not required to support these methods and should include an Allow header in the response giving the actual supported methods.

A proxy must not modify the Allow header field even if it does not understand all the methods specified, since the user agent may have other means of communicating with the origin server. The Allow header field does not indicate what methods are implemented at the server level. Servers may use the Public response-header field to describe what methods are implemented on the server as a whole.

Authorization

A user agent wishing to authenticate itself with a server—usually, but not necessarily, after receiving a 401 response—may do so by including an Authorization request-header field with the request. The Authorization field value consists of credentials containing the authentication information of the user agent for the realm of the resource being requested.

```
Authorization = "Authorization" ":" credentials
```

If a request is authenticated and a realm specified, the same credentials should be valid for all other requests within this realm.

When a shared cache receives a request containing an Authorization field, it must not return the corresponding response as a reply to any other request, unless one of the following specific exceptions holds:

1. If the response includes the "proxy-revalidate" Cache-Control directive, the cache may use that response in replying to a subsequent request, but a proxy cache must first revalidate it with the origin server, using the request-headers from the new request to allow the origin server to authenticate the new request.
2. If the response includes the "must-revalidate" Cache-Control directive, the cache may use that response in replying to a subsequent request, but all caches must first revalidate it with the ori-

gin server, using the request-headers from the new request to allow the origin server to authenticate the new request.

3. If the response includes the "public" Cache-Control directive, it may be returned in reply to any subsequent request.

Cache-Control

The Cache-Control general-header field is used to specify directives that must be obeyed by all caching mechanisms along the request/response chain. The directives specify behavior intended to prevent caches from adversely interfering with the request or response. These directives typically override the default caching algorithms. Cache directives are unidirectional in that the presence of a directive in a request does not imply that the same directive should be given in the response.

HTTP 1.0 caches may not implement Cache-Control and may only implement Pragma: no-cache. Cache directives must be passed through by a proxy or gateway application, regardless of their significance to that application, since the directives may be applicable to all recipients along the request/response chain. It is not possible to specify a cache-directive for a specific cache.

```
Cache-Control        = "Cache-Control" ":" 1#cache-directive
cache-directive= cache-request-directive
                     | cache-response-directive
cache-request-directive =
    "no-cache" [ "=" <"> 1#field-name <"> ]
                     | "no-store"
                     | "max-age" "=" delta-seconds
                     | "max-stale" [ "=" delta-seconds ]
                     | "min-fresh" "=" delta-seconds
                     | "only-if-cached"
                     | cache-extension
cache-response-directive
                  = "public"
                     | "private" [ "=" <"> 1#field-name <"> ]
                     | "no-cache" [ "=" <"> 1#field-name <"> ]
                     | "no-store"
                     | "no-transform"
                     | "must-revalidate"
                     | "proxy-revalidate"
                     | "max-age" "=" delta-seconds
                     | cache-extension
cache-extension = token [ "=" ( token | quoted-string ) ]
```

When a directive appears without any 1#field-name parameter, the directive applies to the entire request or response. When such a directive appears with a 1#field-name parameter, it applies only to the named field or fields, and not to the rest of the request or response. This mechanism supports extensibility; implementations of future versions of the HTTP protocol may apply these directives to header fields not defined in HTTP/1.1.

The cache-control directives can be broken down into these general categories:

- **Restrictions on what is cacheable.** These may only be imposed by the origin server
- **Restrictions on what may be stored by a cache.** These may be imposed by either the origin server or the user agent
- **Modifications of the basic expiration mechanism.** These may be imposed by either the origin server or the user agent
- **Controls over cache revalidation and reload.** These may only be imposed by a user agent.
- **Control over transformation of entities.** Extensions to the caching system.

What is Cacheable

By default, a response is cacheable if the requirements of the request method, request header fields, and the response status indicate that it is cacheable. The following Cache-Control response directives allow an origin server to override the default cachability of a response:

- **Public.** Indicates that the response is cacheable by any cache, even if it would normally be non-cacheable or cacheable only within a non-shared cache.
- **Private.** Indicates that all or part of the response message is intended for a single user and must not be cached by a shared cache. This allows an origin server to state that the specified parts of the response are intended for only one user and are not a valid response for requests by other users. A private (non-shared) cache may cache the response. Usage of the word private only controls where the response may be cached, and cannot ensure the privacy of the message content.
- **No-cache.** Indicates that all or part of the response message must not be cached anywhere. This allows an origin server to prevent caching even by caches that have been configured to return stale responses to client requests. Most HTTP 1.0 caches will not recognize or obey this directive.

What May be Stored by Caches

The purpose of the no-store directive is to prevent the inadvertent release or retention of sensitive information (for example, on backup tapes). The no-store directive applies to the entire message, and may be sent either in a response or in a request. If sent in a request, a cache must not store any part of either this request or any response to it. If sent in a response, a cache must not store any part of either this response or the request that elicited it. This directive applies to both non-shared and shared caches. "Must not store" in this context means that the cache must not intentionally store the information in non-volatile storage, and must make a best-effort attempt to remove the information from volatile storage as promptly as possible after forwarding it.

Even when this directive is associated with a response, users may explicitly store such a response outside of the caching system (e.g., with a "Save As" dialog). History buffers may store such responses as part of their normal operation.

The purpose of this directive is to meet the stated requirements of certain users and service authors who are concerned about accidental releases of information via unanticipated accesses to cache data structures. While the use of this directive may improve privacy in some cases, we caution that it is not in any way a reliable or sufficient mechanism for ensuring privacy. In particular, malicious or compromised caches may not recognize or obey this directive; and communications networks may be vulnerable to eavesdropping.

Modifications of the Basic Expiration Mechanism

The expiration time of an entity may be specified by the origin server using the Expires header. Alternatively, it may be specified using the max-age directive in a response. If a response includes both an Expires header and a max-age directive, the max-age directive overrides the Expires header, even if the Expires header is more restrictive. This rule allows an origin server to provide, for a given response, a longer expiration time to an HTTP 1.1 (or later) cache than to an HTTP 1.0 cache. This may be useful if certain HTTP 1.0 caches improperly calculate ages or expiration times, perhaps due to desynchronized clocks. Older caches, not compliant with this specification, do not implement any Cache-Control directives. An origin server wishing to use a Cache-Control directive that restricts, but does not prevent, caching by an HTTP 1.1-compliant cache may exploit the requirement that the max-age directive overrides the

Expires header, and the fact that non-HTTP 1.1-compliant caches do not observe the max-age directive.

Other directives allow an user agent to modify the basic expiration mechanism. These directives may be specified on a request:

- **max-age.** Indicates that the client is willing to accept a response whose age is no greater than the specified time in seconds. Unless a max-stale directive is also included, the client is not willing to accept a stale response.
- **min-fresh.** Indicates that the client is willing to accept a response whose freshness lifetime is no less than its current age plus the specified time in seconds. That is, the client wants a response that will still be fresh for at least the specified number of seconds.
- **max-stale.** Indicates that the client is willing to accept a response that has exceeded its expiration time. If max-stale is assigned a value, then the client is willing to accept a response that has exceeded its expiration time by no more than the specified number of seconds. If no value is assigned to max-stale, then the client is willing to accept a stale response of any age.

    If a cache returns a stale response, either because of a max-stale directive on a request, or because the cache is configured to override the expiration time of a response, the cache must attach a Warning header to the stale response, using Warning 10 (Response is stale).

Cache Revalidation and Reload Controls

Sometimes an user agent may want or need to insist that a cache revalidate its cache entry with the origin server (and not just with the next cache along the path to the origin server), or to reload its cache entry from the origin server. End-to-end revalidation may be necessary if either the cache or the origin server has overestimated the expiration time of the cached response. End-to-end reload may be necessary if the cache entry has become corrupted for some reason. End-to-end revalidation may be requested either when the client does not have its own local cached copy, in which case we call it "unspecified end-to-end revalidation", or when the client does have a local cached copy, in which case we call it "specific end-to-end revalidation."

The client can specify these three kinds of action using Cache-Control request directives:

- **End-to-end reload.** The request includes a no-cache Cache-Control directive or, for compatibility with HTTP/1.0 clients, Pragma:

no-cache. No field names may be included with the no-cache directive in a request. The server must not use a cached copy when responding to such a request.

- **Specific end-to-end revalidation.** The request includes a max-age=0 Cache-Control directive, which forces each cache along the path to the origin server to revalidate its own entry, if any, with the next cache or server. The initial request includes a cache-validating conditional with the client's current validator.
- **Unspecified End-to-End Revalidation.** The request includes max-age=0 Cache-Control directive, which forces each cache along the path to the origin server to revalidate its own entry, if any, with the next cache or server. The initial request does not include a cache-validating conditional; the first cache along the path (if any) that holds a cache entry for this resource includes a cache-validating conditional with its current validator.

When an intermediate cache is forced, by means of a max-age=0 directive, to revalidate its own cache entry, and the client has supplied its own validator in the request, the supplied validator may differ from the validator currently stored with the cache entry. In this case, the cache may use either validator in making its own request without affecting semantic transparency.

However, the choice of validator may affect performance. The best approach is for the intermediate cache to use its own validator when making its request. If the server replies with 304 (Not Modified), then the cache should return its now validated copy to the client with a 200 (OK) response. If the server replies with a new entity and cache validator, however, the intermediate cache should compare the returned validator with the one provided in the client's request, using the strong comparison function. If the client's validator is equal to the origin server's, then the intermediate cache simply returns 304 (Not Modified). Otherwise, it returns the new entity with a 200 (OK) response.

If a request includes the no-cache directive, it should not include min-fresh, max-stale, or max-age. In some cases, such as times of extremely poor network connectivity, a client may want a cache to return only those responses that it currently has stored, and not to reload or revalidate with the origin server. To do this, the client may include the only-if-cached directive in a request. If it receives this directive, a cache should either respond using a cached entry that is consistent with the other constraints of the request, or respond with a 504 (Gateway Timeout) status. However, if a group of caches is being operated as a unified system with good internal connectivity, such a request may be forwarded within that group of caches.

Because a cache may be configured to ignore a server's specified expiration time, and because a client request may include a max-stale directive (which has a similar effect), the protocol also includes a mechanism for the origin server to require revalidation of a cache entry on any subsequent use. When the must-revalidate directive is present in a response received by a cache, that cache must not use the entry after it becomes stale to respond to a subsequent request without first revalidating it with the origin server. That is, the cache must do an end-to-end revalidation every time, if, based solely on the origin server's Expires or max-age value, the cached response is stale.)

The must-revalidate directive is necessary to support reliable operation for certain protocol features. In all circumstances an HTTP1.1 cache must obey the must-revalidate directive; in particular, if the cache cannot reach the origin server for any reason, it must generate a 504 (Gateway Timeout) response.

Servers should send the must-revalidate directive if, and only if, failure to revalidate a request on the entity could result in incorrect operation, such as a silently unexecuted financial transaction. Recipients must not take any automated action that violates this directive, and must not automatically provide an unvalidated copy of the entity if revalidation fails.

Although this is not recommended, user agents operating under severe connectivity constraints may violate this directive but, if so, must explicitly warn the user that an unvalidated response has been provided. The warning must be provided on each unvalidated access, and should require explicit user confirmation.

The proxy-revalidate directive has the same meaning as the must-revalidate directive, except that it does not apply to non-shared user agent caches. It can be used on a response to an authenticated request to permit the user's cache to store and later return the response without needing to revalidate it (since it has already been authenticated once by that user), while still requiring proxies that service many users to revalidate each time (in order to make sure that each user has been authenticated). Note that such authenticated responses also need the public cache control directive in order to allow them to be cached at all.

No-Transform Directive

Implementers of intermediate caches (proxies) have found it useful to convert the media type of certain entity bodies. A proxy might, for example, convert between image formats in order to save cache space or to reduce the amount of traffic on a slow link. HTTP has to date been silent on these transformations.

Serious operational problems have already occurred, however, when these transformations have been applied to entity-bodies intended for certain kinds of applications. For example, applications for medical imaging, scientific data analysis and those using end-to-end authentication, all depend on receiving an entity-body that is bit-for-bit identical to the original entity-body.

Cache-Control Extensions

The Cache-Control header field can be extended through the use of one or more cache-extension tokens, each with an optional assigned value. Informational extensions (those which do not require a change in cache behavior) may be added without changing the semantics of other directives. Behavioral extensions are designed to work by acting as modifiers to the existing base of cache directives. Both the new directive and the standard directive are supplied, such that applications which do not understand the new directive will default to the behavior specified by the standard directive, and those that understand the new directive will recognize it as modifying the requirements associated with the standard directive. In this way, extensions to the Cache-Control directives can be made without requiring changes to the base protocol.

This extension mechanism depends on an HTTP cache obeying all of the cache-control directives defined for its native HTTP-version, obeying certain extensions, and ignoring all directives that it does not understand.

For example, consider a hypothetical new response directive called community which acts as a modifier to the private directive. We define this new directive to mean that, in addition to any non-shared cache, any cache which is shared only by members of the community named within its value may cache the response. An origin server wishing to allow the "UCI" community to use an otherwise private response in their shared cache(s) may do so by including:

```
Cache-Control: private, community="UCI"
```

A cache seeing this header field will act correctly even if the cache does not understand the community cache-extension, since it will also see and understand the private directive and thus default to the safe behavior. Unrecognized cache-directives must be ignored; it is assumed that any cache-directive likely to be unrecognized by an HTTP 1.1 cache will be combined with standard directives (or the response's default cachability) such that the cache behavior will remain minimally correct even if the cache does not understand the extension(s).

Connection

The Connection general-header field allows the sender to specify options that are desired for that particular connection and must not be communicated by proxies over further connections.

The Connection header has the following grammar:

```
Connection-header = "Connection" ":" 1#(connection-token)
connection-token = token
```

HTTP 1.1 proxies must parse the Connection-header field before a message is forwarded and, for each connection-token in this field, remove any header field(s) from the message with the same name as the connection-token. Connection options are signaled by the presence of a connection-token in the Connection-header field, not by any corresponding additional header field(s), since the additional header field may not be sent if there are no parameters associated with that connection option. HTTP 1.1 defines the close connection option for the sender to signal that the connection will be closed after completion of the response. For example: `Connection: close`.

In either the request- or the response-header fields indicates that the connection should not be considered "persistent" after the current request/response is complete.

HTTP 1.1 applications that do not support persistent connections must include the close connection option in every message.

Content-Base

The Content-Base entity-header field may be used to specify the base URI for resolving relative URLs within the entity. This header field is described as Base in RFC 1808, which is expected to be revised.

```
Content-Base    = "Content-Base" ":" absoluteURI
```

If no Content-Base field is present, the base URI of an entity is defined either by its Content-Location (if that Content-Location URI is an absolute URI) or the URI used to initiate the request, in that order of precedence. Note, however, that the base URI of the contents within the entity-body may be redefined within that entity-body.

Content-Encoding

The Content-Encoding entity-header field is used as a modifier to the media-type. When present, its value indicates what additional content codings have been applied to the entity-body, and thus what decoding mechanisms must be applied in order to obtain the media-type referenced by the Content-Type header field. Content-Encoding is primarily used to allow a document to be compressed without losing the identity of its underlying media type.

```
Content-Encoding = "Content-Encoding" ":" 1#content-coding
```

The Content-Encoding is a characteristic of the entity identified by the Request-URI. Typically, the entity-body is stored with this encoding and is only decoded before rendering or analogous usage.

If multiple encodings have been applied to an entity, the content codings must be listed in the order in which they were applied.

Additional information about the encoding parameters may be provided by other entity-header fields not defined by this specification.

Content-Language

The Content-Language entity-header field describes the natural language(s) of the intended audience for the enclosed entity. This may not be equivalent to all the languages used within the entity-body.

```
Content-Language = "Content-Language" ":" 1#language-tag
```

The primary purpose of Content-Language is to allow a user to identify and differentiate entities according to the user's own preferred language. Thus, if the body content is intended only for a Danish-literate audience, the appropriate field is

```
Content-Language: da
```

If no Content-Language is specified, the default is that the content is intended for all language audiences. This may mean that the sender does not consider it to be specific to any natural language, or that the sender does not know for which language it is intended.

Multiple languages may be listed for content that is intended for multiple audiences. For example, a rendition of the "Treaty of Wait-angi," presented simultaneously in the original Maori and English versions, would call for

```
Content-Language: mi, en
```

However, just because multiple languages are present within an entity does not mean that it is intended for multiple linguistic audiences. An example would be a beginner's language primer, such as "A First Lesson in Latin," which is clearly intended to be used by an English-literate audience. In this case, the Content-Language should only include en.

Content-Language may be applied to any media type—it is not limited to textual documents.

Content-Length

The Content-Length entity-header field indicates the size of the message-body, in decimal number of octets, sent to the recipient or, in the case of the HEAD method, the size of the entity-body that would have been sent had the request been a GET.

```
Content-Length  = "Content-Length" ":" 1*DIGIT
```

An example is:

```
Content-Length: 3495
```

Applications should use this field to indicate the size of the message-body to be transferred, regardless of the media type of the entity. It must be possible for the recipient reliably to determine the end of HTTP 1.1 requests containing an entity-body, e.g., because the request has a valid Content-Length field, uses Transfer-Encoding: chunked or a multipart body.

Any Content-Length greater than or equal to zero is a valid value. The meaning of this field is significantly different from the corresponding definition in MIME, where it is an optional field used within the "message/external-body" content-type. In HTTP, it should be sent whenever the message's length can be determined prior to being transferred.

Content-Location

The Content-Location entity-header field may be used to supply the resource location for the entity enclosed in the message. In the case where a resource has multiple entities associated with it, and those entities actually have separate locations by which they might be individually accessed, the server should provide a Content-Location for the particular variant which is returned. In addition, a server should provide a Content-Location for the resource corresponding to the response entity.

```
Content-Location = "Content-Location" ":"
                   ( absoluteURI | relativeURI )
```

If no Content-Base header field is present, the value of Content-Location also defines the base URL for the entity.

The Content-Location value is not a replacement for the original requested URI; it is only a statement of the location of the resource corresponding to this particular entity at the time of the request. Future requests may use the Content-Location URI if the desire is to identify the source of that particular entity.

A cache cannot assume that an entity with a Content-Location different from the URI used to retrieve it can be used to respond to later requests on that Content-Location URI. However, the Content-Location can be used to differentiate between multiple entities retrieved from a single requested resource.

If the Content-Location is a relative URI, the URI is interpreted relative to any Content-Base URI provided in the response. If no Content-Base is provided, the relative URI is interpreted relative to the Request-URI.

Content-MD5

The Content-MD5 entity-header field, as defined in RFC 1864 is an MD5 digest of the entity-body for the purpose of providing an end-to-end message integrity check (MIC) of the entity-body. MIC is good for detecting accidental modification of the entity-body in transit, but is not proof against malicious attacks.

```
Content-MD5  = "Content-MD5" ":" md5-digest
md5-digest   = <base64 of 128 bit MD5 digest (RFC 1864)>
```

The Content-MD5 header field may be generated by an origin server to function as an integrity check of the entity-body. Only origin servers may generate the Content-MD5 header field; proxies and gateways must not generate it, as this would defeat its value as an end-to-end integrity check. Any recipient of the entity-body, including gateways and proxies, may check that the digest value in this header field matches that of the entity-body as received.

The MD5 digest is computed based on the content of the entity-body, including any Content-Encoding that has been applied, but not including any Transfer-Encoding that may have been applied to the message-body. If the message is received with a Transfer-Encoding, that encoding must be removed prior to checking the Content-MD5 value against the received entity.

This has the result that the digest is computed on the octets of the entity-body exactly as, and in the order that, they would be sent if no Transfer-Encoding were being applied.

HTTP extends RFC 1864 to permit the digest to be computed for MIME composite media-types (e.g., multipart/* and message/rfc822), but this does not change how the digest is computed as defined in the preceding paragraph. Several consequences of this exist. The entity-body for composite types may contain many body-parts, each with its own MIME and HTTP headers (including Content-MD5, Content-Transfer-Encoding, and Content-Encoding headers). If a body-part has a Content-Transfer-Encoding or Content-Encoding header, it is assumed that the content of the body-part has had the encoding applied, and the body-part is included in the Content-MD5 digest as is—i.e., after the application. The Transfer-Encoding header field is not allowed within body-parts.

While the definition of Content-MD5 is exactly the same for HTTP as in RFC 1864 for MIME entity-bodies, there are several ways in which the application of Content-MD5 to HTTP entity-bodies differs from its application to MIME entity-bodies. One is that HTTP, unlike MIME, does not use Content-Transfer-Encoding, and does use Transfer-Encoding and Content-Encoding. Another is that HTTP uses binary content types more frequently than MIME does, so it is worth noting that, in such cases, the byte order used to compute the digest is the transmission byte order defined for the type. Lastly, HTTP allows transmission of text types with any of several line break conventions and not just the canonical form using CRLF. Conversion of all line breaks to CRLF should not be done before computing or checking the digest: the line break convention used in the text actually transmitted should be left unaltered when computing the digest.

Content-Range

The Content-Range entity-header is sent with a partial entity-body to specify where in the full entity-body the partial body should be inserted. It also indicates the total size of the full entity-body. When a server returns a partial response to a client, it must describe both the extent of the range covered by the response, and the length of the entire entity-body.

```
Content-Range = "Content-Range" ":" content-range-spec
content-range-spec  = byte-content-range-spec
byte-content-range-spec = bytes-unit SP first-byte-pos "-"
                          last-byte-pos "/" entity-length
entity-length           = 1*DIGIT
```

Unlike byte-ranges-specifier values, a byte-content-range-spec may only specify one range, and must contain absolute byte positions for both the first and last byte of the range.

A byte-content-range-spec whose last-byte-pos value is less than its first-byte-pos value, or whose entity-length value is less than or equal to its last-byte-pos value, is invalid. The recipient of an invalid byte-content-range-spec must ignore it and any content transferred along with it. Examples of byte-content-range-spec values, assuming that the entity contains a total of 1234 bytes are:

- The first 500 bytes: bytes 0-499/1234
- The second 500 bytes: bytes 500-999/1234
- All except for the first 500 bytes: bytes 500-1233/1234
- The last 500 bytes: bytes 734-1233/1234.

When an HTTP message includes the content of a single range (for example, a response to a request for a single range, or to a request for a set of ranges that overlap without any holes), this content is transmitted with a Content-Range header, and a Content-Length header showing the number of bytes actually transferred. For example:

```
HTTP 1.1 206 Partial content
Date: Wed, 15 Nov 1995 06:25:24 GMT
Last-modified: Wed, 15 Nov 1995 04:58:08 GMT
Content-Range: bytes 21010-47021/47022
Content-Length: 26012
Content-Type: image/gif
```

When an HTTP message includes the content of multiple ranges (for example, a response to a request for multiple non-overlapping ranges), these are transmitted as a multipart MIME message. The multipart MIME content-type used for this purpose is defined in this specification to be "multipart/byteranges".

A client that cannot decode a MIME multipart/byteranges message should not ask for multiple byte-ranges in a single request. When a client requests multiple byte-ranges in one request, the server should return them in the order that they appeared in the request.

If the server ignores a byte-range-spec because it is invalid, the server should treat the request as if the invalid Range header field did not exist. (Normally, this means return a 200 response containing the full entity). The reason is that the only time a client will make such an invalid request is when the entity is smaller than the entity retrieved by a prior request.

Content-Type

The Content-Type entity-header field indicates the media type of the entity-body sent to the recipient or, in the case of the HEAD method, the media type that would have been sent had the request been a GET.

```
Content-Type  = "Content-Type" ":" media-type
```

Media type field examples are:

```
Content-Type: text/html; charset=ISO-8859-4.
```

Date

The Date general-header field represents the date and time at which the message was originated, having the same semantics as orig-date in RFC 822.

```
Date = "Date" ":" HTTP-date
```

An example is:

```
Date: Tue, 15 Nov 1994 08:12:31 GMT
```

If a message is received via direct connection with the user agent (in the case of requests) or the origin server (in the case of responses), then the date can be assumed to be the current date at the receiving end. However, since the date—as it is believed by the origin—is important for evaluating cached responses, origin servers must include a Date header field in all responses. Clients should only send a Date header field in messages that include an entity-body, as in the case of the PUT and POST requests, and even then it is optional. A received message which does not have a Date header field should be assigned one by the recipient if the message will be cached by that recipient or gatewayed via a protocol which requires a Date. In theory, the date should represent the moment just before the entity is generated. In practice, the date can be generated at any time during the message origination without affecting its semantic value. The format of the Date is an absolute date and time must be sent in RFC1123 [8]-date format.

ETag

The ETag entity-header field defines the entity tag for the associated entity. The entity tag may be used for comparison with other entities from the same resource.

```
ETag = "ETag" ":" entity-tag
```

Examples:

```
ETag: "xyzzy"
ETag: W/"xyzzy"
ETag: ""
```

Expires

The Expires entity-header field gives the date/time after which the response should be considered stale. A stale cache entry may not normally be returned by a cache (either a proxy cache or an user agent cache) unless it is first validated with the origin server (or with an intermediate cache that has a fresh copy of the entity). The presence of an Expires field does not imply that the original resource will change or cease to exist at, before, or after that time.

The format is an absolute date and time as defined by HTTP-date must be in RFC 1123-date format:

```
Expires = "Expires" ":" HTTP-date
```

An example of its use is:

```
Expires: Thu, 01 Dec 1999 16:00:00 GMT
```

If a response includes a Cache-Control field with the max-age directive, that directive overrides the Expires field. HTTP 1.1 clients and caches must treat other invalid date formats, especially including the value 0, as in the past (i.e., "already expired").

To mark a response as "already expired," an origin server should use an Expires date that is equal to the Date header value. To mark a response as "never expires," an origin server should use an Expires date approximately one year from the time the response is sent. HTTP1.1 servers should not send Expires dates more than one year in the future.

The presence of an Expires header field with a date value of some time in the future on an response that otherwise would by default be non-cacheable indicates that the response is cacheable, unless indicated otherwise by a Cache-Control header field.

From

The From request-header field, if given, should contain an Internet e-mail address for the human user who controls the requesting user agent. The address should be machine-usable, as defined by mailbox in RFC 822 (updated by RFC 1123):

```
From  = "From" ":" mailbox
```

An example is:

```
From: webmaster@w3.org
```

This header field may be used for logging purposes and as a means for identifying the source of invalid or unwanted requests. It should not be used as an insecure form of access protection. The interpretation of this field is that the request is being performed on behalf of the person given, who accepts responsibility for the method performed. In particular, robot agents should include this header so that the person responsible for running the robot can be contacted if problems occur on the receiving end.

The Internet e-mail address in this field may be separate from the Internet host which issued the request. For example, when a request is passed through a proxy the original issuer's address should be used. The client should not send the From header field without the user's approval, as it may conflict with the user's privacy interests or their site's security policy. It is strongly recommended that the user be able to disable, enable, and modify the value of this field at any time prior to a request.

Host

The Host request-header field specifies the Internet host and port number of the resource being requested, as obtained from the original URL given by the user or referring resource. The Host field value must represent the network location of the origin server or gateway given by the original URL. This allows the origin server or gateway to differentiate between internally-ambiguous URLs, such as the root "/" URL of a server for multiple host names on a single IP address.

```
Host = "Host" ":" host [ ":" port ]
```

A "host" without any trailing port information implies the default port for the service requested (e.g., "80" for an HTTP URL). For example, a request on the origin server for <http://www.w3.org/pub/WWW/> must include:

```
GET /pub/WWW/ HTTP 1.1
Host: www.w3.org
```

A client must include a Host header field in all HTTP 1.1 request messages on the Internet (i.e., on any message corresponding to a request for a URL which includes an Internet host address for the service being requested). If the Host field is not already present, an HTTP 1.1 proxy must add a Host field to the request message prior to forwarding it on the Internet. All Internet-based HTTP 1.1 servers must respond with a 400 status code to any HTTP 1.1 request message which lacks a Host header field.

If-Modified-Since

The If-Modified-Since request-header field is used with the GET method to make it conditional: if the requested variant has not been modified since the time specified in this field, an entity will not be returned from the server; instead, a 304 (not modified) response will be returned without any message-body.

```
If-Modified-Since = "If-Modified-Since" ":" HTTP-date
```

An example of the field is:

```
If-Modified-Since: Sat, 29 Oct 1999 19:43:31 GMT
```

A GET method with an If-Modified-Since header and no Range header requests that the identified entity be transferred only if it has been modified since the date given by the If-Modified-Since header. The algorithm for determining this includes the following cases:

1. If the request would normally result in anything other than a 200 (OK) status, or if the passed If-Modified-Since date is invalid, the response is exactly the same as for a normal GET. A date which is later than the server's current time is invalid.
2. If the variant has been modified since the If-Modified-Since date, the response is exactly the same as for a normal GET.
3. If the variant has not been modified since a valid If-Modified-Since date, the server must return a 304 (Not Modified) response.

The purpose of this feature is to allow efficient updates of cached information with a minimum amount of transaction overhead. Remember that the Range request-header field modifies the meaning of If-Modified-Since. Remember that If-Modified-Since times are interpreted by the server, whose clock may not be synchronized with the client's. Also, if a client uses an arbitrary date in the If-Modified-Since header instead of a date taken from the Last-Modified header for the same request, the client should be aware of the fact that this date is interpreted in the server's understanding of time. The client should consider unsynchronized clocks and rounding problems due to the different encodings of time between the client and server. This includes the possibility of race conditions if the document has changed between the time it was first requested and the If-Modified-Since date of a subsequent request, and the possibility of clock-skew-related problems if the If-Modified-Since date is derived from the client's clock without correction to the server's clock. Corrections for different time bases between client and server are at best approximate due to network latency.

If-Match

The If-Match request-header field is used with a method to make it conditional. A client with one or more entities previously obtained from the resource can verify that one of those entities is current by including a list of their associated entity tags in the If-Match header field. The purpose of this feature is to allow efficient updates of cached information with a minimum amount of transaction overhead. It is also used, on updating requests, to prevent inadvertent modification of the wrong version of a resource. As a special case, the value "*" matches any current entity of the resource.

```
If-Match = "If-Match" ":" ( "*" | 1#entity-tag )
```

If any of the entity-tags match the entity-tag of the entity that would have been returned in the response to a similar GET request (without the If-Match header) on that resource, or if "*" is given and any current entity exists for that resource, then the server may perform the requested method as if the If-Match header field did not exist.

A server must use the strong comparison function to compare the entity-tags in If-Match. If none of the entity-tags matches, or if "*" is given and no current entity exists, the server must not perform the requested method, and must return a 412 (Precondition Failed) response. This behavior is most useful when the client wants to prevent an updating method, such as PUT, from modifying a resource that has changed since the client last retrieved it. If the request would, without the If-Match header field, result in anything other than a 2xx status, then the If-Match header must be ignored.

The meaning of "If-Match: *" is that the method should be performed if the representation selected by the origin server (or by a cache, possibly using the Vary mechanism) exists, and must not be performed if the representation does not exist. A request intended to update a resource (e.g., a PUT) may include an If-Match header field to signal that the request method must not be applied if the entity corresponding to the If-Match value (a single entity tag) is no longer a representation of that resource. This allows users to indicate that they do not wish the request to be successful if the resource has been changed without their knowledge. Consider these examples:

```
If-Match: "xyzzy"
If-Match: "xyzzy", "r2d2xxxx", "c3piozzzz"
If-Match: *
```

If-None-Match

The If-None-Match request-header field is used with a method to make it conditional. A client that has one or more entities previously obtained from the resource can verify that none of those entities is current by including a list of their associated entity tags in the If-None-Match header field. The purpose of this feature is to allow efficient updates of cached information with a minimum amount of transaction overhead. It is also used, on updating requests, to prevent inadvertent modification of a resource which was not known to exist.

As a special case, the value "*" matches any current entity of the resource.

```
If-None-Match = "If-None-Match" ":" ( "*" | 1#entity-tag )
```

If any of the entity-tags match the entity-tag of the entity that would have been returned in the response to a similar GET request (without the If-None-Match header) on that resource, or if "*" is given and any current entity exists for that resource, then the server must not perform the requested method. Instead, if the request method was GET or HEAD, the server should respond with a 304 (Not Modified) response, including the cache-related entity-header fields (particularly ETag) of one of the entities that matched. For all other request methods, the server must respond with a status of 412 (Precondition Failed).

The weak comparison function can only be used with GET or HEAD requests. If none of the entity-tags matches, or if "*" is given and no current entity exists, then the server may perform the requested method as if the If-None-Match header field did not exist. If the request would, without the If-None-Match header field, result in anything other than a 2xx status, then the If-None-Match header must be ignored.

The meaning of "If-None-Match: *" is that the method must not be performed if the representation selected by the origin server (or by a cache, possibly using the Vary mechanism) exists, and should be performed if the representation does not exist. This feature may be useful in preventing races between PUT operations.

Examples are:

```
If-None-Match: "xyzzy"
If-None-Match: W/"xyzzy"
If-None-Match: "xyzzy", "r2d2xxxx", "c3piozzzz"
If-None-Match: W/"xyzzy", W/"r2d2xxxx", W/"c3piozzzz"
If-None-Match: *
```

If-Range

If a client has a partial copy of an entity in its cache, and wishes to have an up-to-date copy of the entire entity in its cache, it could use the Range request-header with a conditional GET (using either or both of If-Unmodified-Since and If-Match.) However, if the condition fails because the entity has been modified, the client would then have to make a second request to obtain the entire current entity-body.

The If-Range header allows a client to short-circuit the second request. Informally, its meaning is "if the entity is unchanged, send me the part(s) that I am missing; otherwise, send me the entire new entity."

```
If-Range = "If-Range" ":" ( entity-tag | HTTP-date )
```

If the client has no entity-tag for an entity, but does have a Last-Modified date, it may use that date in a If-Range header. (The server can distinguish between a valid HTTP-date and any form of entity-tag by examining no more than two characters.) The If-Range header should only be used together with a Range header, and must be ignored if the request does not include a Range header, or if the server does not support the sub-range operation.

If the entity-tag given in the If-Range header matches the current entity-tag for the entity, then the server should provide the specified sub-range of the entity using a 206 (Partial Content) response. If the entity-tag does not match, then the server should return the entire entity using a 200 (OK) response.

If-Unmodified-Since

The If-Unmodified-Since request-header field is used with a method to make it conditional. If the requested resource has not been modified since the time specified in this field, the server should perform the requested operation as if the If-Unmodified-Since header were not present.

If the requested variant has been modified since the specified time, the server must not perform the requested operation, and must return a 412 (Precondition Failed).

```
If-Unmodified-Since = "If-Unmodified-Since" ":" HTTP-date
```

An example of the field is:

```
If-Unmodified-Since: Sat, 29 Oct 1999 19:43:31 GMT
```

If the request normally (i.e., without the If-Unmodified-Since header) would result in anything other than a 2xx status, the If-Unmodified-Since header should be ignored. If the specified date is invalid, the header is ignored.

Last-Modified

The Last-Modified entity-header field indicates the date and time at which the origin server believes the variant was last modified.

```
Last-Modified = "Last-Modified" ":" HTTP-date
```

An example of its use is

```
Last-Modified: Tue, 15 Nov 1999 12:45:26 GMT
```

The exact meaning of this header field depends on the implementation of the origin server and the nature of the original resource. For files, it may be just the file system last-modified time. For entities with dynamically included parts, it may be the most recent of the set of last-modify times for its component parts. For database gateways, it may be the last-update time stamp of the record. For virtual objects, it may be the last time the internal state changed.

An origin server must not send a Last-Modified date which is later than the server's time of message origination. In such cases, where the resource's last modification would indicate some time in the future, the server must replace that date with the message origination date.

An origin server should obtain the Last-Modified value of the entity as close as possible to the time that it generates the Date value of its response. This allows a recipient to make an accurate assessment of the entity's modification time, especially if the entity changes near the time that the response is generated. HTTP 1.1 servers should send Last-Modified whenever feasible.

Location

The Location response-header field is used to redirect the recipient to a location other than the Request-URI for completion of the request or identification of a new resource. For 201 (Created) responses, the Location is that of the new resource created by the request. For 3xx responses, the location should indicate the server's preferred URL for automatic redirection to the resource. The field value consists of a single absolute URL.

```
Location = "Location" ":" absoluteURI
```

One example is:

```
Location: http://www.w3.org/pub/WWW/People.html
```

Remember, the Content-Location header field differs from Location in that the Content-Location identifies the original location of the entity enclosed in the request. It is therefore possible for a response to contain header fields for both Location and Content-Location.

Max-Forwards

The Max-Forwards request-header field may be used with the TRACE method to limit the number of proxies or gateways that can forward the request to the next inbound server. This can be useful when the client is attempting to trace a request chain which appears to be failing or looping in mid-chain.

```
Max-Forwards  = "Max-Forwards" ":" 1*DIGIT
```

The Max-Forwards value is a decimal integer indicating the remaining number of times this request message may be forwarded.

Each proxy or gateway recipient of a TRACE request containing a Max-Forwards header field should check and update its value prior to forwarding the request. If the received value is zero, the recipient should not forward the request; instead, it should respond as the final recipient with a 200 (OK) response containing the received request message as the response entity-body. If the received Max-Forwards value is greater than zero, then the forwarded message should contain an updated Max-Forwards field with a value decreased by one.

The Max-Forwards header field should be ignored for all other methods defined by this specification and for any extension methods for which it is not explicitly referred to as part of that method definition.

Pragma

The Pragma general-header field is used to include implementation-specific directives that may apply to any recipient along the request/response chain. All Pragma-directives specify optional behavior from the viewpoint of the protocol; however, some systems may require that behavior be consistent with the directives.

```
Pragma = "Pragma" ":" 1#pragma-directive
Pragma directive = "no-cache" | extension-pragma
extension-pragma = token [ "=" ( token | quoted-string ) ]
```

When the No-cache directive is present in a request message, an application should forward the request toward the origin server even if it has a cached copy of what is being requested. This Pragma-directive has the same semantics as the No-cache cache-directive and is defined here for backwards compatibility with HTTP 1.0. Clients should include both header fields when a No-cache request is sent to a server not known to be HTTP/1.1 compliant.

Pragma directives must be passed through by a proxy or gateway application, regardless of their significance to that application, since the directives may be applicable to all recipients along the request/response chain. It is not possible to specify a pragma for a specific recipient; however, any Pragma-directive not relevant to a recipient should be ignored by that recipient.

HTTP 1.1 clients should not send the Pragma request-header. HTTP 1.1 caches should treat "Pragma: no-cache" as if the client had sent "Cache-Control: no-cache". No new Pragma-directives will be defined in HTTP.

Proxy-Authenticate

The Proxy-Authenticate response-header field must be included as part of a 407 (Proxy Authentication Required) response. The field value consists of a challenge that indicates the authentication scheme and parameters applicable to the proxy for this Request-URI.

```
Proxy-Authenticate = "Proxy-Authenticate" ":" challenge
```

Unlike WWW-Authenticate, the Proxy-Authenticate header field applies only to the current connection and should not be passed on to downstream clients. However, an intermediate proxy may need to obtain its own credentials by requesting them from the downstream client, which in some circumstances will appear as if the proxy is forwarding the Proxy-Authenticate header field.

Proxy-Authorization

The Proxy-Authorization request-header field allows the client to identify itself (or its user) to a proxy which requires authentication. The Proxy-Authorization field value consists of credentials containing the authentication information of the user agent for the proxy and/or realm of the resource being requested.

```
Proxy-Authorization = "Proxy-Authorization" ":" credentials
```

Unlike Authorization, the Proxy-Authorization header field applies only to the next outbound proxy that demanded authentication using the Proxy-Authenticate field. When multiple proxies are used in a chain, the Proxy-Authorization header field is consumed by the first outbound proxy that was expecting to receive credentials. A proxy may relay the credentials from the client request to the next proxy if that is the mechanism by which the proxies cooperatively authenticate a given request.

Public

The Public response-header field lists the set of methods supported by the server. The purpose of this field is strictly to inform the recipient of the capabilities of the server regarding unusual methods. The methods listed may or may not be applicable to the Request-URI; the Allow header field may be used to indicate methods allowed for a particular URI.

```
Public = "Public" ":" 1#method
```

Example of use:

```
Public: OPTIONS, MGET, MHEAD, GET, HEAD
```

This header field applies only to the server directly connected to the client (i.e., the nearest neighbor in a chain of connections). If the response passes through a proxy, the proxy must either remove the Public header field or replace it with one applicable to its own capabilities.

Byte Ranges

Since all HTTP entities are represented in HTTP messages as sequences of bytes, the concept of a byte range is meaningful for any HTTP entity. (However, not all clients and servers need to support byte-range operations.)

Byte-range specifications in HTTP apply to the sequence of bytes in the entity-body (not necessarily the same as the message-body).

A byte-range operation may specify a single range of bytes, or a set of ranges within a single entity.

```
ranges-specifier = byte-ranges-specifier
byte-ranges-specifier = bytes-unit "=" byte-range-set
byte-range-set = 1#(byte-range-spec|suffix-byte-range-spec)
byte-range-spec = first-byte-pos "-" [last-byte-pos]
first-byte-pos = 1*DIGIT
last-byte-pos = 1*DIGIT
```

The first-byte-pos value in a byte-range-spec gives the byte-offset of the first byte in a range. The last-byte-pos value gives the byte-offset of the last byte in the range; that is, the byte positions specified are inclusive. Byte offsets start at zero. If the last-byte-pos value is present, it must be greater than or equal to the first-byte-pos in that byte-range-spec, or the byte-range-spec is invalid. The recipient of an invalid byte-range-spec must ignore it.

If the last-byte-pos value is absent, or if the value is greater than or equal to the current length of the entity-body, last-byte-pos is taken to be equal to one less than the current length of the entity-body in bytes.

By its choice of last-byte-pos, a client can limit the number of bytes retrieved without knowing the size of the entity.

```
suffix-byte-range-spec = "-" suffix-length
suffix-length = 1*DIGIT
```

A suffix-byte-range-spec is used to specify the suffix of the entity-body, of a length given by the suffix-length value. (That is, this form specifies the last N bytes of an entity-body.) If the entity is shorter than the specified suffix-length, the entire entity-body is used.

Examples of byte-ranges-specifier values (assuming an entity-body of length 10000):

- The first 500 bytes (byte offsets 0-499, inclusive): bytes=0-499
- The second 500 bytes (byte offsets 500-999, inclusive): bytes=500-999
- The final 500 bytes (byte offsets 9500-9999, inclusive): bytes=-500 or bytes=9500
- The first and last bytes only (bytes 0 and 9999): bytes=0-0,-1
- Several legal but not canonical specifications of the second 500 bytes (byte offsets 500-999, inclusive): bytes=500-600,601-999; bytes=500-700,601-999

Range Retrieval Requests

HTTP retrieval requests using conditional or unconditional GET methods may request one or more sub-ranges of the entity, instead of the entire entity, using the Range request header, which applies to the entity returned as the result of the request:

```
Range = "Range" ":" ranges-specifier
```

A server may ignore the Range header. However, HTTP/1.1 origin servers and intermediate caches should support byte ranges when possible, since Range supports efficient recovery from partially failed transfers, and supports efficient partial retrieval of large entities.

If the server supports the Range header and the specified range or ranges are appropriate for the entity:

- The presence of a Range header in an unconditional GET modifies what is returned if the GET is otherwise successful. In other words, the response carries a status code of 206 (Partial Content) instead of 200 (OK).
- The presence of a Range header in a conditional GET (a request using one or both of If-Modified-Since and If-None-Match, or one or both of If-Unmodified-Since and If-Match) modifies what is returned if the GET is otherwise successful and the condition is true. It does not affect the 304 (Not Modified) response returned if the conditional is false.

In some cases, it may be more appropriate to use the If-Range header in addition to the Range header. If a proxy that supports ranges receives a Range request, forwards the request to an inbound server, and receives an entire entity in reply, it should only return the requested range to its client. It should store the entire received response in its cache, if that is consistent with its cache allocation policies.

Referer

The Referer request-header field allows the client to specify, for the server's benefit, the address (URI) of the resource from which the Request-URI was obtained (the "referrer", although the header field is misspelled.) The Referer request header allows a server to generate lists of back-links to resources for interest, logging, optimized caching, etc. It also allows obsolete or mistyped links to be traced for maintenance. The Referer field must not be sent if the Request-URI was obtained from a source that does not have its own URI, such as input from the user keyboard.

```
Referer = "Referer" ":" ( absoluteURI | relativeURI )
```

Example:

```
Referer: http://www.w3.org/hypertext/DataSources/Overview.html
```

If the field value is a partial URI, it should be interpreted relative to the Request-URI. The URI must not include a fragment. Because the

source of a link may be private information or may reveal an otherwise private information source, it is strongly recommended that the
user be able to select whether or not the Referer field is sent. For
example, a browser client could have a toggle switch for browsing
openly/anonymously, which would respectively enable/disable the
sending of Referer and From information.

Retry-After

The Retry-After response-header field can be used with a 503 (Service Unavailable) response to indicate how long the service is expected to be unavailable to the requesting client. The value of this field
can be either an HTTP-date or an integer number of seconds (in decimal) after the time of the response.

```
Retry-After = "Retry-After" ":" (HTTP-date | delta-seconds)
```

Two examples of its use include:

```
Retry-After: Fri, 31 Dec 1999 23:59:59 GMT
Retry-After: 120
```

In the latter example, the delay is 2 minutes.

Server

The Server response-header field contains information about the software used by the origin server to handle the request. The field can
contain multiple product tokens and comments identifying the server
and any significant subproducts. The product tokens are listed in
order of their significance for identifying the application.

```
Server = "Server" ":" 1*( product | comment )
```

Example:

```
Server: CERN/3.0 libwww/2.17
```

If the response is being forwarded through a proxy, the proxy application must not modify the Server response-header. Instead, it should
include a Via field. Revealing the specific software version of the
server may allow the server machine to become more vulnerable to
attacks against software that is known to contain security holes. Server implementers are encouraged to make this field a configurable
option.

Transfer-Encoding

The Transfer-Encoding general-header field indicates what (if any) type of transformation has been applied to the message body in order to safely transfer it between the sender and the recipient. This differs from the Content-Encoding field in that the transfer coding is a property of the message, not of the entity.

```
Transfer-Encoding = "Transfer-Encoding" ":" 1# transfer-coding
```

An example of transfer codings is: Transfer-Encoding: chunked. Older HTTP 1.0 applications do not understand the Transfer-Encoding header.

Upgrade

The Upgrade general-header allows the client to specify what additional communication protocols it supports and would like to use if the server finds it appropriate to switch protocols. The server must use the Upgrade header field within a 101 (Switching Protocols) response to indicate which protocol(s) are being switched.

```
Upgrade = "Upgrade" ":" 1#product
```

Example:

```
Upgrade: HTTP 2.0, HTTP 1.3, IRC/6.9, RTA/x11
```

The Upgrade header field is intended to provide a simple mechanism for transition from HTTP 1.1 to some other, incompatible protocol. It does so by allowing the client to advertise its desire to use another protocol, such as a later version of HTTP with a higher major version number, even though the current request has been made using HTTP 1.1. This eases the difficult transition between incompatible protocols by allowing the client to initiate a request in the more commonly supported protocol while indicating to the server that it would like to use a "better" protocol if available (where "better" is determined by the server, possibly according to the nature of the method and/or resource being requested).

The Upgrade header field only applies to switching application-layer protocols upon the existing transport-layer connection. Upgrade cannot be used to insist on a protocol change; its acceptance and use by the server is optional. The capabilities and nature of the application-layer communication after the protocol change is entirely dependent upon the new protocol chosen, although the first action after changing the protocol must be a response to the initial HTTP request containing the Upgrade header field.

The Upgrade header field only applies to the immediate connection. Therefore, the upgrade keyword must be supplied within a Connection header field whenever Upgrade is present in an HTTP 1.1 message. The Upgrade header field cannot be used to indicate a switch to a protocol on a different connection. For that purpose, it is more appropriate to use a 301, 302, 303, or 305 redirection response. This specification only defines the protocol name "HTTP" for use by the family of Hypertext Transfer Protocols. Any token can be used as a protocol name; however, it will only be useful if both the client and server associate the name with the same protocol.

User-Agent

The User-Agent request-header field contains information about the user agent originating the request. This is for statistical purposes, the tracing of protocol violations, and automated recognition of user agents for the sake of tailoring responses to avoid particular user agent limitations. User agents should include this field with requests. The field can contain multiple product tokens and comments identifying the agent and any subproducts which form a significant part of the user agent. By convention, the product tokens are listed in order of their significance for identifying the application.

```
User-Agent = "User-Agent" ":" 1*( product | comment )
```

For example:

```
User-Agent: CERN-LineMode/2.15 libwww/2.17b3
```

Vary

The Vary response-header field is used by a server to signal that the response entity was selected from the available representations of the response using server-driven negotiation. Field-names listed in Vary headers are those of request-headers. The Vary field value indicates either that the given set of header fields encompasses the dimensions over which the representation might vary, or that the dimensions of variance are unspecified ("*") and thus may vary over any aspect of future requests.

```
Vary = "Vary" ":" ( "*" | 1#field-name )
```

An HTTP 1.1 server must include an appropriate Vary header field with any cacheable response that is subject to server-driven negotiation. Doing so allows a cache to properly interpret future requests on that resource and informs the user agent about the presence of negotiation on that resource. A server should include an appropriate Vary header field with a non-cacheable response that is subject to server-driven negotiation, since this might provide the user agent with useful information about the dimensions over which the response might vary. The set of header fields named by the Vary field value is known as the "selecting" request-headers.

When the cache receives a subsequent request whose Request-URI specifies one or more cache entries including a Vary header, the cache must not use such a cache entry to construct a response to the new request unless all of the headers named in the cached Vary header are present in the new request, and all of the stored selecting request headers from the previous request match the corresponding headers in the new request.

The selecting request headers from two requests are defined to match if and only if the selecting request headers in the first request can be transformed to the selecting request headers in the second request by adding or removing linear whitespace (LWS) at places where this is allowed by the corresponding BNF, and/or combining multiple message-header fields with the same field name.

A Vary field value of "*" signals that unspecified parameters, possibly other than the contents of request-header fields (e.g., the network address of the client), play a role in the selection of the response representation. Subsequent requests on that resource can only be properly interpreted by the origin server, and thus a cache must forward a (possibly conditional) request even when it has a fresh response cached for the resource.

A Vary field value consisting of a list of field names signals that the representation selected for the response is based on a selection algorithm which considers only the listed request-header field values in selecting the most appropriate representation. A cache may assume that the same selection will be made for future requests with the same values for the listed field names, for the duration of time in which the response is fresh.

The field names given are not limited to the set of standard request-header fields defined by this specification. Field names are case-insensitive.

Via

The Via general-header field must be used by gateways and proxies to indicate the intermediate protocols and recipients between the user agent and the server on requests, and between the origin server and the client on responses. It is analogous to the "Received" field of RFC 822 and is intended to be used for tracking message forwards, avoiding request loops, and identifying the protocol capabilities of all senders along the request/response chain.

```
Via = "Via" ":" 1#(received-protocol received-by [comment ])
received-protocol   =  [ protocol-name "/" ] protocol-version
protocol-name       =  token
protocol-version    =  token
received-by         =  ( host [ ":" port ] ) | pseudonym
pseudonym           =  token
```

The received-protocol indicates the protocol version of the message received by the server or client along each segment of the request/response chain. The received-protocol version is appended to the Via field value when the message is forwarded so that information about the protocol capabilities of upstream applications remains visible to all recipients.

The protocol name is optional if, and only if, it would be "HTTP". The received-by field is normally the host and optional port number of a recipient server or client that subsequently forwarded the message. However, if the real host is considered to be sensitive information, it may be replaced by a pseudonym. If the port is not given, it may be assumed to be the default port of the received-protocol.

Multiple Via field values represent each proxy or gateway that has forwarded the message. Each recipient must append its information such that the end result is ordered according to the sequence of forwarding applications.

Comments may be used in the Via header field to identify the software of the recipient proxy or gateway, analogous to the User-Agent and Server header fields. However, all comments in the Via field are optional and may be removed by any recipient prior to forwarding the message.

For example, a request message could be sent from an HTTP 1.0 user agent to an internal proxy code-named fred, which uses HTTP 1.1 to forward the request to a public proxy at nowhere.com, which completes the request by forwarding it to the origin server at www.ics.uci.edu. The request received by www.ics.uci.edu would then have the following:

Via header field:

```
Via: 1.0 fred, 1.1 nowhere.com (Apache/1.1)
```

Proxies and gateways used as a portal through a network firewall should not, by default, forward the names and ports of hosts within the firewall region. This information should only be propagated if explicitly enabled. If not enabled, the received-by host of any host behind the firewall should be replaced by an appropriate pseudonym for that host.

For organizations that have strong privacy requirements for hiding internal structures, a proxy may combine an ordered subsequence of Via header field entries with identical received-protocol values into a single such entry. For example:

```
Via: 1.0 hewey, 1.1 dewey, 1.1 loui, 1.0 screwy
```

could be collapsed to

```
Via: 1.0 jake, 1.1 joe, 1.0 john
```

Applications should not combine multiple entries unless they are all under the same organizational control and the hosts have already been replaced by pseudonyms. Applications must not combine entries which have different received-protocol values.

Warning

The Warning response-header field is used to carry additional information about the status of a response which may not be reflected by the response status code. This information is typically, though not exclusively, used to warn about a possible lack of semantic transparency from caching operations.

Warning headers are sent with responses using:

```
Warning = "Warning" ":" 1#warning-value
warning-value = warn-code SP warn-agent SP warn-text
warn-code  = 2DIGIT
warn-agent = ( host [ ":" port ] ) | pseudonym
             ; the name or pseudonym of the server adding
             ; the Warning header, for use in debugging
             warn-text = quoted-string
```

A response may carry more than one Warning header.

The warn-text should be in a natural language and character set that is most likely to be intelligible to the human user receiving the response. This decision may be based on any available knowledge, such as the location of the cache or user, the Accept-Language field in a request, the Content-Language field in a response, etc. The default language is English and the default character set is ISO-8859-1. Any server or cache may add Warning headers to a response. New Warning headers should be added after any existing Warning headers. A cache must not delete any Warning header that it received with a response. However, if a cache successfully validates a cache entry, it should remove any Warning headers previously attached to that entry except as specified for specific Warning codes. It must then add any Warning headers received in the validating response. In other words, Warning headers are those that would be attached to the most recent relevant response.

When multiple Warning headers are attached to a response, the user agent should display as many of them as possible, in the order that they appear in the response. If it is not possible to display all of the warnings, the user agent should follow these heuristics:

- Warnings that appear early in the response take priority over those appearing later in the response.
- Warnings in the user's preferred character set take priority over warnings in other character sets but with identical warn-codes and warn-agents.

Systems that generate multiple Warning headers should order them with this user agent behavior in mind.

This is a list of the currently-defined warn-codes, each with a recommended warn-text in English, and a description of its meaning.

- **10 Response is stale.** Must be included whenever the returned response is stale; a cache may add this warning to any response, but may never remove it until the response is known to be fresh.
- **11 Revalidation failed.** Must be included if a cache returns a stale response because an attempt to revalidate the response failed, due to an inability to reach the server; a cache may add this warning to any response, but may never remove it until the response is successfully revalidated.
- **12 Disconnected operation.** Should be included if the cache is intentionally disconnected from the rest of the network for a period of time
- **13 Heuristic expiration.** Must be included if the cache heuristically chose a freshness lifetime greater than 24 hours and the response's age is greater than 24 hours

- **14 Transformation applied.** Must be added by an intermediate cache or proxy if it applies any transformation changing the content-coding (as specified in the Content-Encoding header) or media-type (as specified in the Content-Type header) of the response, unless this Warning code already appears in the response; must not be deleted from a response even after revalidation.
- **99 Miscellaneous warning.** The warning text may include arbitrary information to be presented to a human user, or logged. A system receiving this warning must not take any automated action.

WWW-Authenticate

The WWW-Authenticate response-header field must be included in 401 (Unauthorized) response messages. The field value consists of at least one challenge that indicates the authentication scheme(s) and parameters applicable to the Request-URI.

```
WWW-Authenticate = "WWW-Authenticate" ":" 1#challenge
```

User agents must take special care in parsing the WWW-Authenticate field value if it contains more than one challenge, or if more than one WWW-Authenticate header field is provided, since the contents of a challenge may itself contain a comma-separated list of authentication parameters.

TCP/IP Blueprint #1

The first blueprint for TCP/IP is in Figure 12.12.

This figure shows a simple network with computers (which may be a combination of workstations and a server or two) or merely individual workstations connected for the purpose of mail exchange among users. This blueprint is the simplest of all because the following are minimum ingredients:

- Network hub
- Computers (including related software)
- Network interface cards (nics)
- Cables from the nic to the hub.

For the most part these components comprise the network. Actual configuration of it will determine what functions can be performed in it.

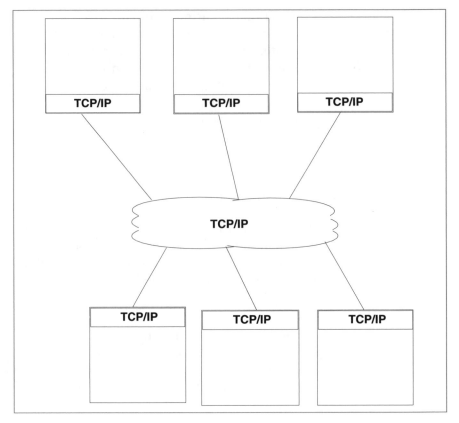

FIGURE 12.12
Blueprint #1

TCP/IP Blueprint #2

A second TCP/IP blueprint is illustrated in Figure 12.13.

This figure shows a network printer attached to a host as well as other computers networked liked blueprint 1. This is a good blueprint for a workgroup network such as a documentation department. The size of the network can be scaled. Most of the work in such an implementation could involve file exchange ability, mail, and sharing a printer. This blueprint presents the most options for the least cost and is not difficult to implement.

This particular blueprint could also be implemented for a workgroup such as customer support. The actual number of users is not important; the functions that individual user and the group need to perform should be the determining factor. For example, this blueprint could be sized to accommodate dozens or hundreds of users if the appropriate equipment is selected and implemented to sustain such loads.

FIGURE 12.13
Blueprint #2

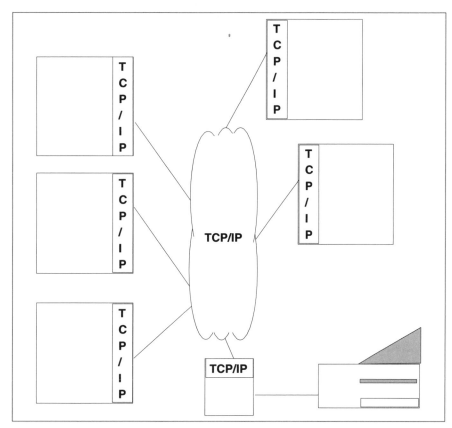

As the illustration shows, the printer is attached to a computer and the computer is attached to the network. In this case the computer is the print server. The printer could be attached directly to the network; one advantage to this scenario is being able to manage large numbers of print jobs at a single instance. Another is the ability to maintain a log of print jobs, users, time, departments, etc.

TCP/IP Blueprint #3

A third TCP/IP blueprint is illustrated in Figure 12.14.

This figure shows a network attached to a network as well as other computers connected to the network. This blueprint is ideal for basically any form of workgroup. The size of the network can be scaled. This type of network can be implemented in many different user scenarios. It would be an ideal small- to medium-size office network, providing shared print services.

FIGURE 12.14
Blueprint #3

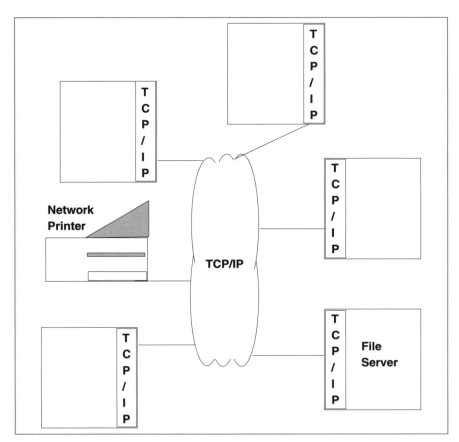

This blueprint presupposes that the network printer is substantial enough to handle network print jobs. Remember in your planning phase to size the network printer for this type of TCP/IP blueprint.

Another presupposition is that all participating computers in the network are configured and can interoperate with the network printer. This point should also be addressed in the planning phase of networks.

Another presupposition in blueprint 3 is that each of the computers on the network is basically self contained. This means no application server, file server, or other comparative server is used by parties in the network.

Figure 12.14 can be implemented in any size. This blueprint will work for five users or five hundred; it will even work with five thousand—assuming those planning and implementing the network can cope with numbers of that size.

Blueprint 3 is a powerful beginning point for many network environments because it can be used as a the basis for building.

TCP/IP Blueprint #4

This blueprint is similar to blueprint 3.

FIGURE 12.15
Blueprint #4

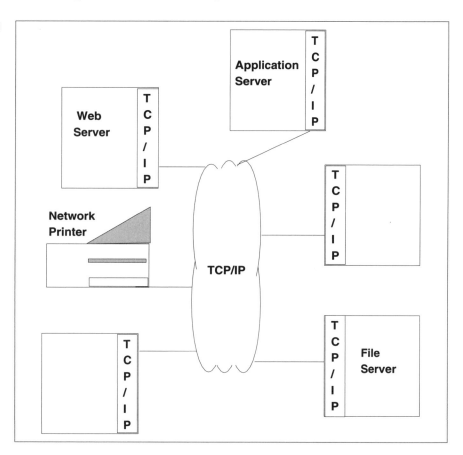

Figure 12.15 blueprint shows a network printer, users connected to the network, a Web server, application server, and file server. This blueprint is the follow-up to the #2. The Web server could serve one or more of the following purposes:

- Intranet server

- Internet server
- Departmental/regional server.

This type of network blueprint lends itself to flexibility in terms of TCP/IP network implementation. A well-designed Web server could serve all three purposes listed above. This presupposes certain levels of security as well as machine size and connectivity to other networks. Given these conditions, the Web server in this case could easily become a multihomed host where a single repository of data is shared throughout an enterprise as well as the Internet.

TCP/IP Blueprint #5

Blueprint 5 is a step to more complex TCP/IP network design.

Figure 12.16 shows four networks. The illustration shows accounting, marketing, and a sales departments. These departmental networks are connected to a TCP/IP backbone network with multiple routers and servers attached.

Consider the TCP/IP network to which the departments are attached. A corporate Web server, two corporate file servers, and corporate mail server are connected to the network. Three routers are attached to the main corporate network backbone. Each router is dedicated and serves a single departmental network.

This type of blueprint has numerous advantages. It has four distinct networks. It enables maximum throughput through routers, provides an ability to perform maintenance functions by disabling any given network from the entire network complex, and enables security control to through architectural design. Other advantages exist.

Use of three routers in this configuration enables traffic load balancing to and from each department and puts less stress on each individual router, assuming the routers can be configured in multiple ways and are large enough to handle network loads. Since three routers exist in the same geographic location, initial planning can create a powerful backup and maintenance ability.

This blueprint with multiple routers enables maintenance and a level of redundancy if the following conditions are met. Other conditions may be required depending upon the location and implementation. Consider these conditions for the routers:

1. All the routers in this blueprint are the same or very closely compatible.

FIGURE 12.16
Blueprint #5

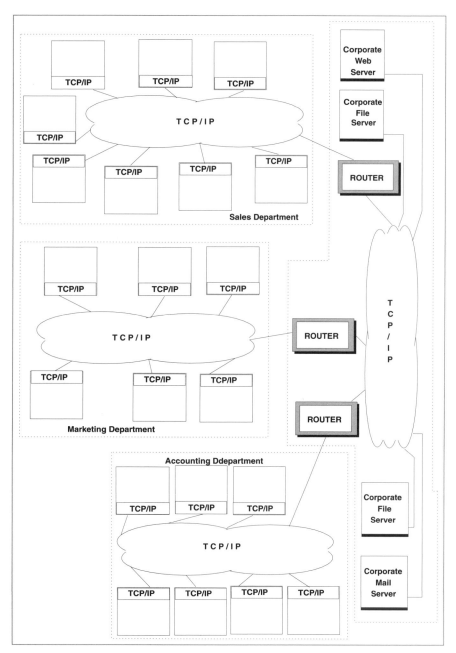

2. Each router is capable of handling enough traffic for each department.

3. Each router is physically capable of accommodating each network simultaneously.

4. Each router has a logical program load for all networks.

5. Personnel understand how to make a switch for one router to accommodate all networks.

With these conditions met and others required for any given site, it is entirely possible for this blueprint to provide a level of redundancy and ease of certain maintenance in the network.

This blueprint also shows a corporate Web server. Each department shown can access it. Even though this blueprint does not show the Web server as a multihomed host, it very well could be. A multihomed host is a host that is known on two or more networks. This type of host implementation is well-suited to designing security in a network. In a network where a multihomed host is used the following formula illustrates its functionality of the network.

$$
\begin{array}{c}
X = Y \\
\underline{Y = Z} \\
X = Z
\end{array}
$$

This formula, also known as a hypothetical syllogism in symbolic logic, serves as a powerful tool in computers and networks alike. It is the foundation and basis on which the vast majority of, if not all, Application Program Interfaces (APIs) are built. It is also a great foundation on which to build hardware and software in networks to implement security beyond software applications.

Notice the corporate file servers are located on the backbone network in blueprint 5. Actual implementation of these file servers can take on many variations. Both file servers could be accessed by all network users in the corporate network. On the other hand, either file server could be restricted to use by any given department. These file servers could serve as redundant file servers, each for the other.

The mail server in this corporate blueprint is the repository for all mail users in this network environment. With mail functions isolated to a single server, loads for such traffic are reduced to the backbone itself and not to multiple network hosts. Another powerful feature of this type of blueprint is the ability to convert the implementation of the mail server to an isolated network with interaction with outside users (even the Internet) and minimal exposure to the corporate network infrastructure.

In summary, this network blueprint is a powerful, flexible blueprint for larger environments. It can be expanded and sized according to network requirements. Assuming those who purchase hardware and software for this type of network understand the individual pieces, the flexibility of this blueprint can be exploited to its maximum potential.

TCP/IP Blueprint #6

Figure 12.17 illustrates blueprint 6.

FIGURE 12.17
Blueprint #6

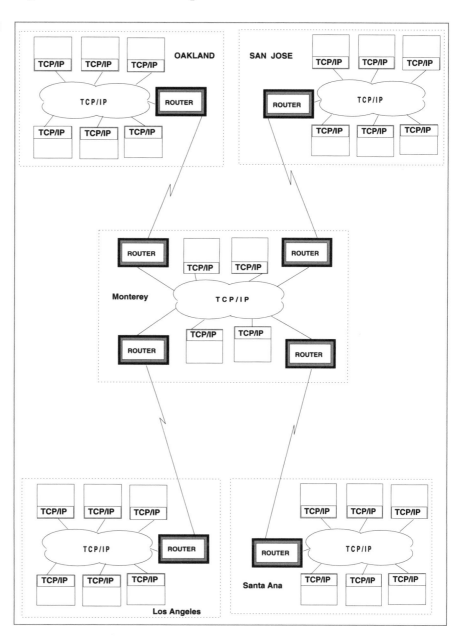

Five independent networks are shown. The Monterey location is the network hub where four networks connect. This is a generic network implementation, but it is the power behind this type of blueprint.

The Monterey location is the central or corporate office and the other locations are satellite offices. In this example, each satellite office is linked to the main office. One function that can be achieved through this type blueprint is centralized mail. Four TCP/IP hosts are on the network in the Monterey location. These hosts could be mail, application, program, and Intranet server. Consequently, a central location for critical information can be easily maintained and updated. A distributed environment like this requires some degree of centralization for basic corporate functions.

Now think of these four independent locations and networks, as four distributed departments in the same company. The Oakland location could be the order entry department for a corporate toll-free number where those desiring to purchase products can call, speak with a representative, have the order placed, and the purchase transaction completed.

The San Jose location could be where orders are received, filled, and shipped. It would obviously need some method for receiving orders that have been placed, but not necessarily in the same location.

The Los Angeles location could be the corporate marketing group. Their efforts are typical for marketing; they need access to corporate location for e-mail, repositories for data files, and interaction with other corporate departments. The marketing efforts include communication with the research and development group, sales group, and other corporate functions that comprise a complete corporate structure.

The Santa Ana location appears the same as the other locations, and it is from a logical network blueprint design. However, this location could be the support group for all corporate products. If this is the case, two conclusions can be made: this location has numerous technically oriented staff and there is a well of information in the form of data repositories. This location needs to have access to information reflecting orders placed, paid for, and shipped; information from the marketing group about forthcoming products; and information from corporate headquarters that could affect any employee or corporate policy influencing or working with support scenarios.

This blueprint is typical of many modern corporations worldwide. It is not unusual to have entire departments located in different cities. The important thing to remember is that business operates around information; making information readily available and distributed appropriately is key to corporate life. Networks are the infra-structure that carries the lifeblood of corporations, information. This blueprint can easily fit into companies of all sizes, and entities of all sorts can benefit from this design.

TCP/IP Blueprint #7

Blueprint 7 is a migration to a more complex implementation.

FIGURE 12.18
Blueprint #7

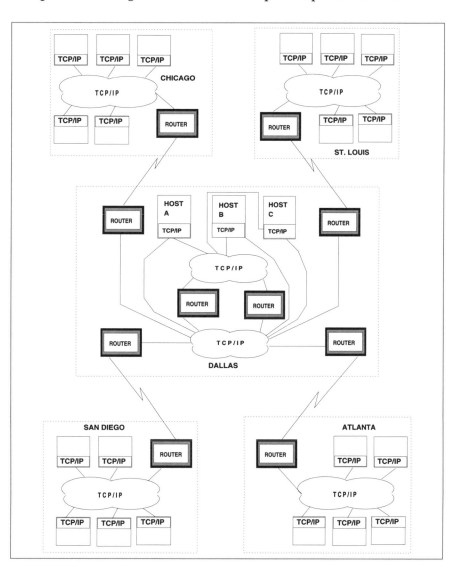

Figure 12.18 shows five distinct geographic locations, each with a network. The Dallas central office consists of the following:

- Two TCP/IP networks
- Three TCP/IP hosts
- Two routers connecting the two networks
- Four routers to accommodate remote access.

The two networks in the Dallas location provide numerous advantages. Implemented appropriately, redundancy is inherent in this design. One network could fail completely and the other network would automatically take over. For some installations this one feature alone is of paramount importance.

These two networks also provide a strong backbone for growth after implementation. They do not appear to be overloaded, and if the right technology is implemented, the number of hosts that could be added to these networks could be multiplied tenfold or more. These backbone networks could also accommodate more routers or other network devices such as gateways and other network-related equipment.

Three TCP/IP hosts in this blueprint could serve three single purposes/functions or any combination thereof. The actual host size and configuration will determine to a significant degree the functionality of a host in the network. In this example one of these hosts could be a dedicated application server, another a file server, and the third a data repository for moving files in batches at varying intervals. Notice also that these hosts are connected to both TCP/IP networks. Because of this multihomed configuration, maximized throughput is achieved in the backbone network.

The two routers connecting the two networks in the Dallas location provide load balancing and a degree of redundancy. Notice that one of the networks has all the routers connected to it: the routers connecting the other network in the Dallas location and the routers used to connect the networks in other locations.

Notice the four routers in the Dallas location. All the routers used to connect networks in other locations connect to a single network. This has advantages and disadvantages. Advantages of the router configuration shown include a method to throttle the throughput in the network and an ability to measure the data flow through the backbone, thus providing a reasonable avenue for network load measurements. This type of configuration also provides a unique ability to isolate inbound and outbound traffic, thus giving a reference point for tracking network traffic.

A disadvantage to this configuration is that all remote location operation is contingent on the backbone segment where the routers attach. This is not necessarily a bad way design, but one should certainly be aware of it. This is the weakest point of the entire network. This illustration was purposely designed to show how easy it is to configure what looks like a solid network design, yet have a flaw at the core.

The blueprint is both flawed and not-flawed depending upon the environment where this blueprint design is placed. Some implementations would benefit from this type of network. On the other hand, some implementations would operate with a certain degree of risk. The important issue here is to understand the risk and ask: "Can this level of risk be tolerated in a worst-case scenario?" The risk in this blueprint can be removed by connecting all the routers to both backbone networks in the Dallas location.

The remote offices each have a network. The Chicago, St. Louis, San Diego, and Atlanta offices are duplicates with regard to network design. The advantage of this design is the ability to manage all remote locations with a standard method of network management. This type of network design also makes support and software distribution easier.

TCP/IP Blueprint #8

This is a good blueprint to implement for growing networks and multiple locations where continuity is required.

Figure 12.19 shows two locations, one in Denver and the other in Boulder. The Denver location consists of Sites A and B. These sites are relatively close together. Notice only one router is in the Denver location. Site A has three hosts like Site B. Site A has a router used for Site A and B to connect to the Boulder location.

The Denver scenario is a good way to implement a design that can be added to. For example, Sites C, D, E, and so on could be added and connected to the router as in Site B in the example. This growth ability is appealing to many network designers. However, be aware that too much growth can outstrip the design and require a more robust network design.

The Boulder location shows four sites, different from the two sites in the Denver location. Each site in the Boulder location has a router, and some routers have multiple connections to sustain high throughput. Site D in the Boulder location has two routers, one not connected to anything but its *home* network. This is a standby router to be used in case of failure in the router that connects Site D to Site A.

FIGURE 12.19
Blueprint #8

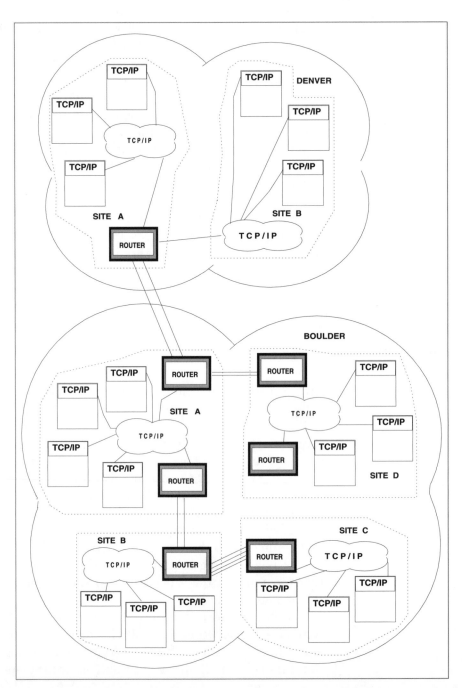

Blueprint 8 could be duplicated numerous times then connected together via routers. In fact, some entities today have networks based around this basic blueprint approach.

Summary

Two chapters have been devoted to TCP/IP because of its complexity. Reference information was provided before the TCP/IP blueprints were discussed. The information here is intended to be a guide, with principles to use in TCP/IP network design.

Many books on TCP/IP are available should your endeavors in TCP/IP require additional information.

ATM Technology and Blueprints

ATM has not been on the market for long, but credit is due to Bell Lab researchers for work in this area long before it came to the forefront of media attention in the late 1980s–1990s. The driving force behind the development of ATM was a need for a fast switching technology that supported data, voice, video, and multimedia. At the time of this writing (1998), ATM is a technology that can be implemented in a variety of environments supporting data, multimedia, voice, and even hybrid networks. Information fundamental to understanding ATM is presented here. Aspects of ATM technology are still emerging and standards are changing. Blueprints for possible ATM implementations are also discussed.

A Perspective on ATM

Asychonous Transfer Mode (ATM) is a cell-switching technology using a 53-byte cell and consisting of a header with routing and other network-related information and an information field for data, images, voice, and/or video. A major thrust behind ATM is its capability to support multimedia and integrate these services along with data over a single type of transmission method. Heretofore this was attainable but awkward, and hindered by timing problems and other significant issues.

ATM can be implemented at the enterprise level (privately), in public networks, and/or both. Realization of ATM throughout a dispersed network environment is twofold: it is implemented at the local level, as in a given organization or corporation; it is also implemented at the public level (by a service provider). ATM usage capabilities can be customized to meet a given environment's needs; it is application-transparent so that integration of multimedia and data does not cause problems.

As of this writing ATM is not new, but neither is it seasoned with regard to implementations. Trade magazines, forums, and other technical communications predict ATM will dominate LANs, WANs, and public service providers in the not too distant future. ATM growth has been quick over the past 2–3 years. Many vendors are in some phase of support for ATM. Some have ATM products to offer today while others are beginning to create ATM products. The technology itself is being defined and this will continue to happen for some time.

Fundamental ATM Concepts

Before examining ATM in greater detail consider the following core/fundamental concepts of ATM.

- **Adaptation.** In certain parts of networks, frames of data are divided into cells. This occurs at lower layers in networks whether the data is outbound or inbound. Data streams that are continuous, such as video and voice, and assembled, pose an interesting technical challenge for ATM because of the conversion of data frames into cells. In the sending part of the network, frames of video or voice, for example, are divided into cells, then transported to the destination network. The receiving part of the network takes these cells and reconstructs them into data frames to make them usable to the end user. This function is called adaptation and operates at a higher level in a network (technology) than the transport (movement) of cells.

- **Cells.** A cell is a 48 data-byte and 5-byte header that all data, voice, video, images, etc. are stored in for transport through ATM devices and networks.

- **Congestion Control.** This is a form of management in ATM networks. When links or nodes in ATM networks become congested, ATM cells are discarded until the congestion is stopped. ATM cells carry priorities; lower-priority cells can be marked as first to be discarded in a congestion situation. When cells are discarded during congestion, endpoints within ATM networks are not notified. The recovery, and hence the detection, of cell loss is the reasonability of the adaptation function or higher-layer protocols in the network.

- **Error Control.** ATM switching networks check cell headers and discard those with errors. ATM adaptation functions are external to the ATM switching network; normally in data traffic the adaptation layer checks for layers; if they are found the entire frame is discarded. ATM networks do not perform retransmission in an attempt to recover from errors that result in loss. Retransmission of any type of traffic in ATM networks is contingent on the end-user devices and the type of traffic moved throughout the network.

- **Flow Control.** In the inception and early phase of ATM design, flow control was not included as part of the internal function of ATM. Today different guidelines and implementations exist on this topic.

- **Hardware-Based Switching.** Techniques are built into hardware to provide very high-speed switching, which may be employed at individual nodes.

- **Routing.** Moving data from one place to another in an ATM network is achieved by way of virtual channels. A series of virtual channels comprises ATM networks and enables routing. A cell header contains routing information for that cell. Any given group of cells traversing a network uses the same virtual channel; the cells are received at the destination location in the same order in which they were received through the ATM network.

ATM Layer Structure

Many network protocols are compared and contrasted with the OSI model. ATM does not fit the structure of the OSI model except in the physical layer.

Figure 13.1 depicts ATM structure in light of a layered approach.

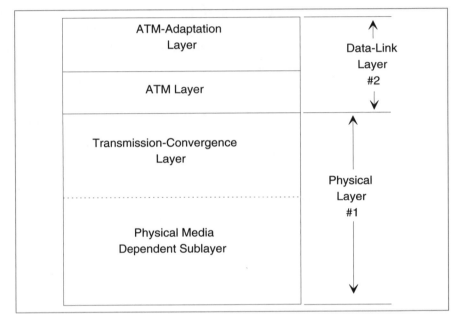

ATM Layers Defined

The physical layer of the ATM model can be divided into two sublayers: the Physical Media Dependent (PMD) sublayer and the transmission convergence sublayer. The PMD performs two primary functions: bit timing and line coding. The function of the transmission convergence sublayer is contingent on the interface used beneath it. Interfaces supported include: SONET at 155.52 Mb/sec, DS3 at 44.736 Mb/sec, multimode fiber at 100 Mb/sec, and "pure cells" at 155 Mb/sec.

Functions at the transmission convergence sublayer are contingent on the interface used. Functions at this sublayer include: performing Header Error Correction (HEC) which covers the entire cell header (this includes generation and verification); multiplexing, frame generation and recovery, and mapping of the ATM cells onto DS3 facilities, if used, by the PLCP. In addition, PLCP framing and delineation is performed if DS3 is used. Other functions are performed relate to the interface in use.

ATM layer functions include switching, multiplexing, routing, and congestion management. Above the ATM layer is the ATM Adaptation Layer (AAL). Here different categories of functions are identifiable. Figure 13.2 shows the components at the physical media-dependent sublayer with interfaces supported; the transmission convergence sublayer, the ATM layer functional components, and the ATM Adaptation Layer (AAL).

FIGURE 13.2
ATM Adaptation
Components and
ATM Layer

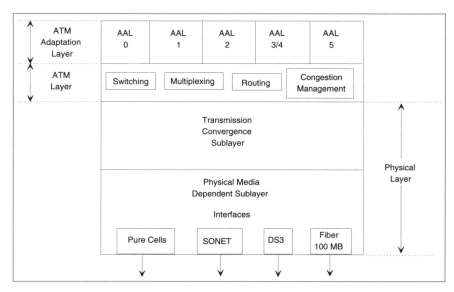

Figure 13.2 shows functions that occur at the ATM layer and categories of functions that occur at the AAL. Details of AAL functions are explained below.

The ATM layer also defines two virtual connections: a Virtual Channel Connection (VCC) between two ATM VCC endpoints which may be either point-to-point or point-to-multipoint, and multiple virtual channel connections carried through Virtual Path Connection (VPC) endpoints. This connection will be either point-to-point or point-to-multipoint.

This layer also translates the Virtual Path Indicators (VPIs) and the Virtual Channel Indicators (VCIs). It is responsible for cell multiplexing and demultiplexing.

The AAL is responsible for mapping data from higher layers within a network into and out of cell fields. It operates on end-to-end functions.

The connection-oriented or connectionless conversion protocol incorporates broadband data service and includes the B-ISDN standard. This B-ISDN support includes interactive service: conversational (such as video, voice, and sounds) as well as document messaging (for electronic mail and multimedia). It also specifies the way text, data, sound, pictures, and video are transmitted and received.

ATM Adaptation Layer (AAL) Functions

The AAL layer is that protocol layer which maps upper-layer protocols onto ATM. Devices that use this layer terminate signals. This layer provides functional support for traffic (signals) that comes from upper-layer protocols. Categories of functions are: AAL types 0, 1, 2, 3/4, and 5.

AAL Type 0

AAL type 0 is considered a place holder when Customer Premises Equipment (CPE) performs required functions. It is a passthrough capability for cell-oriented service. Figure 13.3 is a detailed view at the AAL.

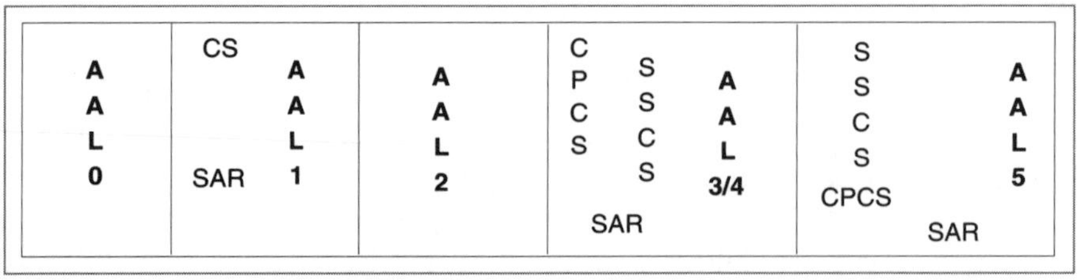

FIGURE 13.3
Conceptual View
of Functions at
the ATM
Adaptation Layer

AAL Type 1

AAL type 1 functions provide constant bit-rate services and is also known as unstructured circuit transport between points. This type of function is connection-oriented. The **CS** component in AAL 1 in Figure 13.3 is called the *convergence sublayer*. It modulates differences that may occur in the physical interfaces. The **SAR** function performs segmentation and reassembly on data moving through AAL 1.

AAL Type 2

This specifies support for isochronous service with varying bit rates. A user of this function is compressed or packetized video.

AAL Type 3/4

The type 3/4 function supports LAN traffic and a variable bit rate. Connection-oriented and connectionless-oriented connections are supported. The **SSCS** is the Service Specific Convergence Sublayer. One of its functions is data translation; it also maps upper-layer services to the ATM layer. **CPCS** is the Common Part Convergence Sublayer, it works in conjunction with switched multimegabit data service. **SAR** is the component that performs segmentation and reassembly.

AAL Type 5

Type 5 is designed for variable bit-rate services and is similar to type 3/4; it differs in being easier to implement. Most ATM LAN devices support this type.

ATM Cell Structure

The components of an ATM cell, as it appears at the User Network Interface (UNI), are shown in Figure 13.4.

FIGURE 13.4
ATM Cell
Structure
at the UNI

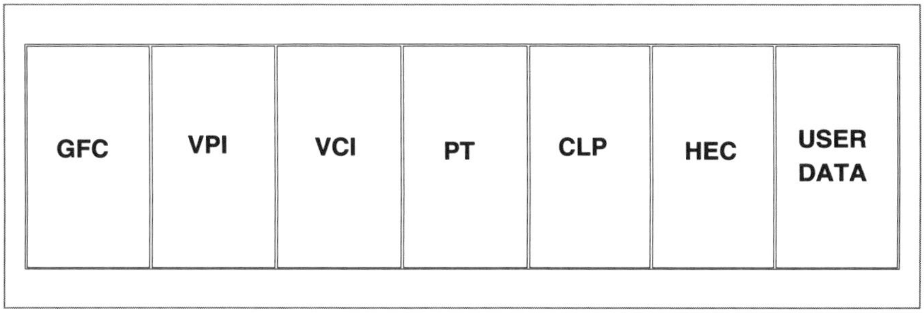

| GFC | VPI | VCI | PT | CLP | HEC | USER DATA |

The cell structure contains 5 bytes of header information and 48 bytes of user information.

ATM Cell Components

The Generic Flow Control (GFC) controls data traffic locally and can be used to customize a local implementation. The bit value in this field is not moved from end to end. Once the cell is into the network ATM switches overwrite the fields.

The next two fields are the virtual path identifier and the virtual channel identifier bits. Information stored in these fields performs routing functions. The number of bits here varies because the bits used for virtual channel identifiers for user-to-user virtual paths are negotiated with users of the virtual paths. These two fields constitute the way nodes communicate.

The Payload Type (PT) tells whether the data carried is user data or management-related information. The field is also used to indicate network congestion.

The Cell Loss Priority (CLP) is used explicitly to indicate the cell priority: whether or not the cell is a candidate for discarding if network congestion occurs.

The Header Error Control field is used by the physical layer used to detect errors in the header and correct bit errors therein.

The user data field contains the user data from upper layers in the network. It is a 48 byte field that does not have error checking performed on it.

The other cell type, the Network Node Interface (NNI), is similar to Figure 13.4, though a difference is indicated in the header portion of the cell.

ATM Interface Types

Two types of nodes are recognized. The User Network Interface (UNI) can be divided into two groups: private and public.

Private

Private UNIs are typically used to connect an ATM user with an ATM switch when both are considered local and part of the site. The switch itself may be referred to as private and considered Customer Premises Equipment (CPE). CPE is that ATM equipment located on a customer site and not in the public arena. An ATM user may be a device such as a router or workstation. The ATM switch is a private ATM switch; it is what connects the "private" user to the "public" interface.

Public

The public UNI is the interface connecting an ATM user to an ATM switch in the domain of the public service provider. Figure 13.5 depicts these concepts.

FIGURE 13.5
Conceptual View
of the User
Network Interface

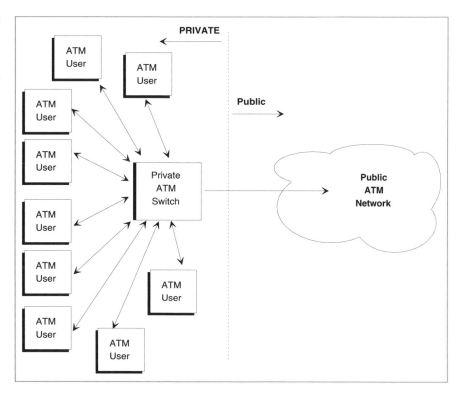

Figure 13.5 shows private customer premise equipment and the public ATM switch. The ATM switches (both private and public) use the same functionality at the physical layer, though different media may be implemented.

The network node interface refers to the ATM switches in the public service provider network that communicate with one another to achieve routing and end-to-end service. Figure 13.6 is an example of this concept.

FIGURE 13.6
Public ATM
Network

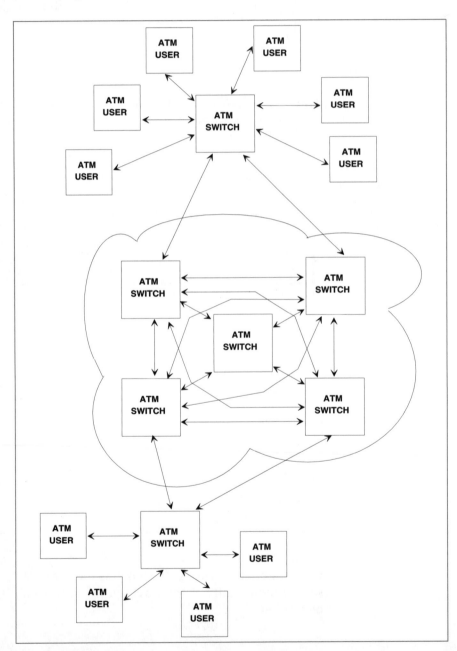

Figure 13.6 shows the network nodes implemented in a public ATM network, ATM users, an ATM switch, and implicitly the boundaries between the public ATM network and the private ATM switch.

ATM Transmission Concepts

The three concepts used with ATM include: transmission path, virtual path, and virtual circuit.

Transmission Path

Transmission paths physical connections between ATM-supported devices. These paths may be have different characteristics, but nevertheless exist. The physical transmission path between entities indicates the virtual concepts and the usage to which the paths are mapped.

Virtual Path

The idea of a virtual path is derived from the existence of a physical transmission path on which the virtual path can be mapped. Figure 13.7 is an example of this concept.

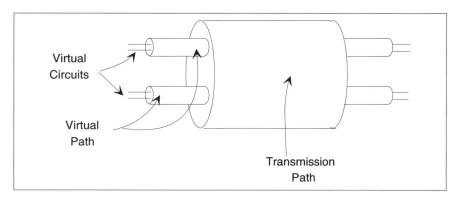

FIGURE 13.7
Conceptual View of Paths and Circuits

Virtual Circuit

The virtual circuit or virtual channel is mapped to both a virtual path and a transmission (physical) path.

The concepts of transmission path, virtual path, and virtual circuit are implemented at the physical layer in the ATM model. This is another method of multiplexing. This structure is part of the intricate nature of the ATM physical layer and contributes to the robust nature of ATM.

Implementation

Because ATM's support is versatile and it can accommodate high speeds, multiple possibilities for how and where it is implemented exist. Four such possibilities are: local router and ATM backbone, ATM-based LANs, ATM backbone nodes, and ATM LANs and ATM Backbone.

Local Router and ATM Backbone

This implementation uses routers that support ATM in a local geographical area. A LAN exists with other lower-layer protocols and network devices; a router with an ATM interface is used to connect the LAN into the ATM backbone that serves a much larger geographical area. Figure 13.8 portrays this idea.

Figure 13.8 illustrates a router with an ATM interface in a local implementation along with devices directly or indirectly attached to it. It also indicates the local router with an ATM interface connected to an ATM backbone to which other sites connect. The ATM backbone consists of ATM devices. This is a simple example.

ATM Backbone LANs

The LANs are built around ATM equipment. Figure 13.9 is an illustration of this idea.

Three ATM-based LANs are shown, along with the network connected via the router to an ATM interface. Two local implementations are shown; one has two ATM-based LANs. Each local implementation accesses the ATM network backbone which consists of all ATM equipment.

ATM Backbone Nodes

ATM backbone nodes are typically implemented in public environments. Many ATM nodes working together constitute an ATM backbone. Figure 13.10 shows multiple ATM nodes creating a WAN backbone.

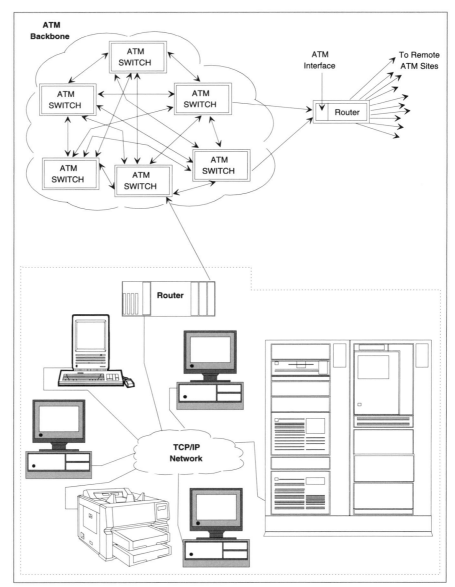

FIGURE 13.8
Local ATM
Hub-Router and
ATM Backbone

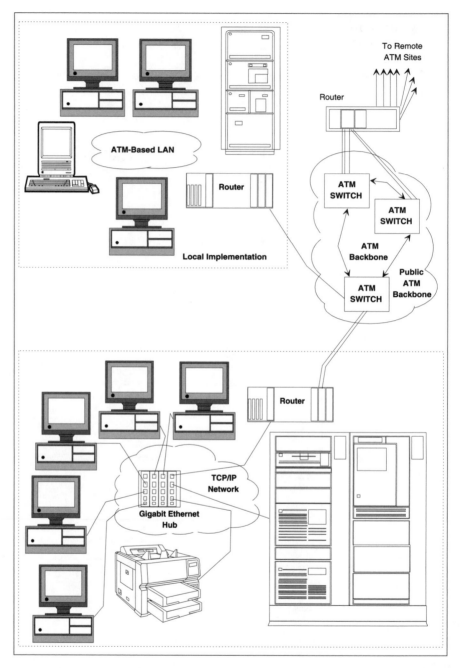

FIGURE 13.9
Local Gigabit
Ethernet LAN and
Local ATM LAN
Connected to a
Public ATM
Switch

FIGURE 13.10
Conceptual View
of an ATM
Backbone

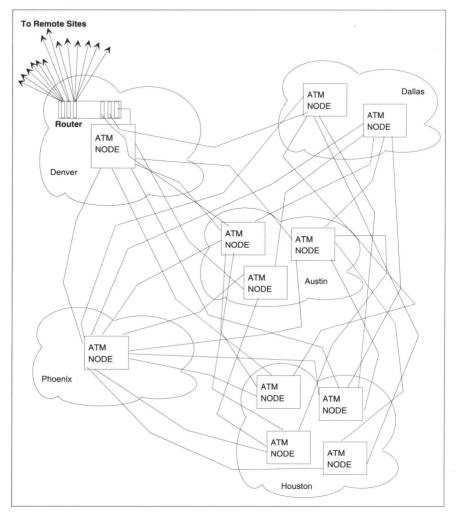

Figure 13.10 includes a network attached to the ATM node in Salt Lake City. The Salt Lake City network enters the ATM network via a router. A similar scenario could be repeated in other sites shown in Figure 13.10.

ATM LANs and ATM Backbone

The notion of ATM LANs and an ATM backbone is a complete ATM implementation. Figure 13.11 depicts this.

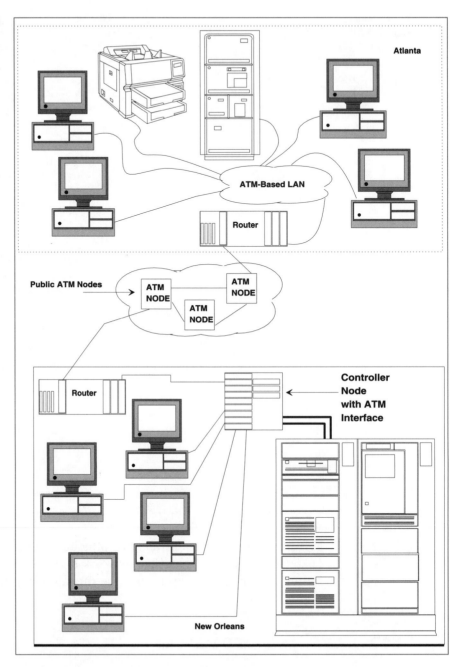

Here ATM nodes comprise the backbone of the ATM network and the focal point of the networks in Boise and Syracuse. There is maximum use of ATM locally and in a WAN sense.

Variations of the last four figures are possible. These are representative of likely implementations. Other *hybrid* ways of implementing ATM are possible and depend heavily on the site.

Physical-Layer Architecture

In the discussion of ATM layer structure, Figure 13.2 illustrated details of interfaces supported by the physical media-dependent sublayer. These include: SONET, DS3, and Fiber 100 Mb.

SONET

Synchronous Optical Network (SONET) is one of the supported interfaces indicated by Figure 13.2. Its data rate transfer can accommodate speed up to 155.52 Mb/sec. SONET frame structure can easily accommodate ATM by mapping ATM cells, aligned by row, correlating to every SONET byte structure. Figure 13.12 is an example of how SONET, ATM, and other technology can merge.

Here an ATM device connects into a SONET interface. In turn, an ATM LAN is attached to the ATM device. This implementation utilizes speeds through the SONET interface.

DS3

DS3 can be used as an interface to carry ATM cells. Its data rate is 44.7 Mb/sec. If it is used, a Physical Layer Convergence Protocol (PLCP) must be defined; then ATM cells are mapped to the DS3 PLCP frame. Figure 13.13 shows an example of this.

Fiber 100 Mb

This interface supports up to 100 Mb/sec. The physical link is between the equipment at a given site and a private ATM switch. This specification calls for the current FDDI implementation. Figure 13.14 shows an example.

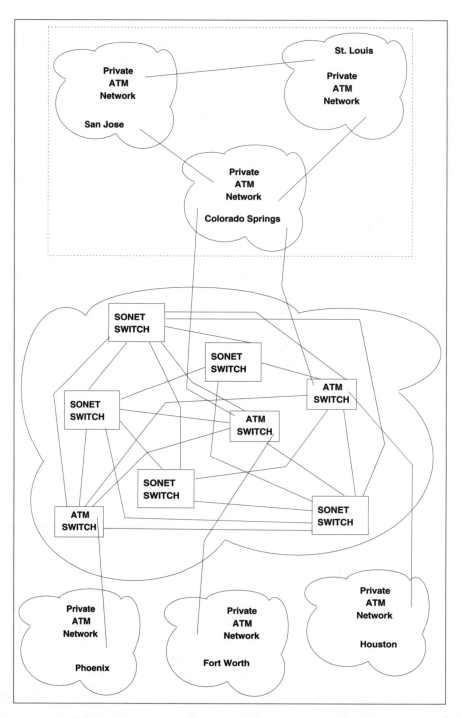

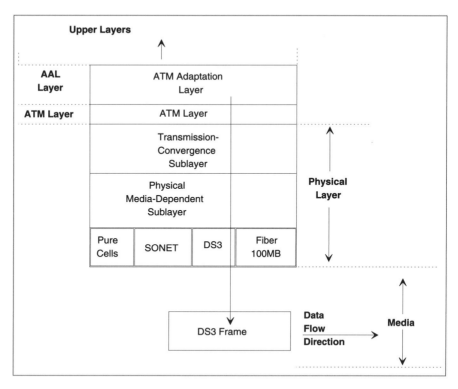

FIGURE 13.13
Perspective of
DS3 and ATM

Other interfaces are supported in the ATM environment, but these are good illustrations of how ATM works with other protocols.

Reasons for ATM Use

Reasons for using ATM technology in a LAN and/or WAN environment include: bandwith, isochronous traffic support, capacity per person per use, and expandability.

Bandwith

One reason for using ATM is the high bandwidth it offers. High bandwith capacity is the speed at which ATM operates. Figure 13.2 showed physical level implementations of ATM. In this figure 100 Mbps fiber, DS3, and SONET are possible physical implementations. The capacity of each of these is much higher than the capacities of other types of physical layer implementations.

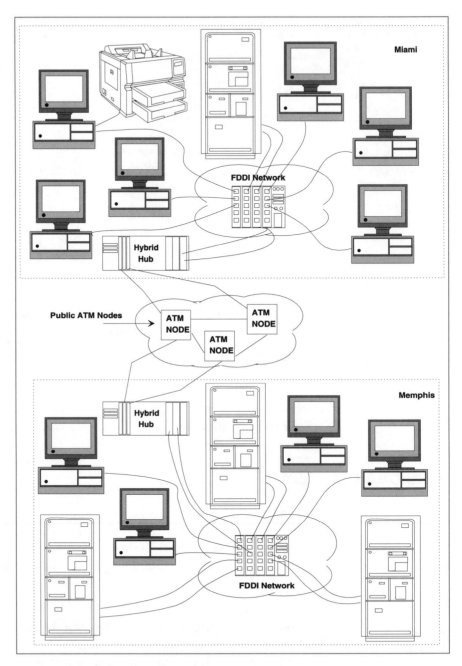

FIGURE 13.14
ATM and FDDI
Implementation

Isochronous Traffic Support

ATM is a strong contender for multimedia, voice, data, and video networks, technologies requiring timing-dependent transfer methods. ATM can accommodate all these various forms of user applications. Any given network could be a combination of data and voice, or any variation, and ATM is sufficient to carry the payload.

Timing-dependent transfer is becoming more and more of a concern. Many applications once segmented fairly obviously as data, voice, video, or multimedia are becoming blurred. Today a simple word processor can include an array of information presentation beyond text only. About 15 years ago word processors were evaluated on their ability to move blocks of text (cut and paste) and other things considered rudimentary today. Today many word processors have the ability not only to import graphics but to manipulate them. Some can even accommodate multimedia presentations.

Capacity Per-Person Per-Use

Another reason for the use of ATM is its ability to accommodate a wide variety of implementations. For example, an ATM backbone could be the right fit for a company where heavy video and multimedia traffic occurs. In this type of environment, some users probably need only minimal network support, for example, printing and e-mail.

For these people the use of ATM is overkill. However, users in a network with heavy video traffic might consume large capacities of bandwidth, utilization of the network can be measured on a per-person per-use basis. It might initially seem too expensive to implement ATM for a complete enterprise-wide network, but analysis from a deferent perspective could easily tell another story. For example, 70% of the network might need ATM to function adequately; the remaining 30% might not approach this requirement. If ATM is implemented enterprise-wide, all users benefit. Hence, accommodating all users averages the price per-person per-use down rather than up. The net effect is a well-designed ATM network implementation yielding room to grow and accommodating immediate needs as well.

Expandability

Another reason for ATM use is the expandability it provides. If designed appropriately, ATM can be scaled upward to accommodate the growth needs of any organization.

ATM Terminology

ATM has a highly specialized vocabulary. Terms presented here serve as a specific ATM reference source.

- **AAL Connection.** The establishment of an association between AAL (ATM Adaptation Layer) or higher entities
- **ATM.** A fast packet-switched, cell-based method of moving voice, data, video, and other data and telecommunication-oriented information from one location to another. The ATM cell is 53 bytes long with 5 bytes of header information and 48 bytes of user information.
- **ATM Layer Link.** A connection between two ATM layers
- **ATM Link.** A virtual path or a virtual circuit (channel) connection
- **ATM Peer-to-Peer Connection.** A virtual channel connection or a virtual path connection.
- **ATM Traffic Descriptor.** A list of generic traffic parameters; these can be used to obtain traffic characteristics of a given ATM connection
- **Cell.** An ATM protocol data unit.
- **Connection Admission Control.** The method used to determine if an ATM link request can be accepted; it is based upon the origin's and destination's attributes
- **Connection Endpoint.** A layer connection SAP termination
- **Connection Endpoint Identifier.** A characteristic of an endpoint used to identify a Service Access Point (SAP)
- **End System.** The place where an ATM connection is terminated
- **Header.** That control information which precedes the user information in an ATM cell
- **Fairness.** The meeting of all specified quality-of-service requirements through control of active connections across an ATM link
- **Metasignalling.** A way of managing virtual circuits and different types of signals
- **Network Node Interface.** The ATM interface as it relates to the network node

- **Segment.** An ATM link, or group of links, that comprise an ATM connection
- **Service Access Point (SAP).** An addressable endpoint at a given layer within a network
- **Sublayer.** The logical division of a layer
- **Switched Connection.** A connection established via a signaling method
- **Symmetric Connection.** A connection where both directions have the same bandwidth
- **Virtual Channel (or circuit).** That which an ATM cell can traverse
- **Virtual Path.** The logical association of virtual circuits
- **Virtual Path Connection.** A one-way joining of virtual path links
- **Virtual Path Link.** The connection between points where a virtual path identifier is assigned
- **Virtual Path Terminator.** The system which processes the virtual circuits (channels) after they are demultiplexed.

ATM Blueprint #1

Multiple ways to implement ATM technology exist. Figure 13.15 is one example.

Here we see two physical locations implementing ATM with an ATM WAN backbone used to connect them. The New York location has multiple users connected to both an FDDI hub and a host. The host itself has an attached printer and is connected to a hybrid hub. The hub is attached to an ATM concentrator which in turn, is connected to the ATM interface.

The Chicago location has three major hosts connected to an ATM concentrator. This location is primarily a data network with large data repositories. This particular blueprint is based on an ATM backbone in the public carrier network as well as in the respective locations.

This is a basic implementation for ATM. One aspect not shown is the requirement for ATM interface boards in those devices connected to ATM devices such as a concentrator or hub.

Notice also that this blueprint shows a variety of other technologies in addition to ATM. In the New York location an FDDI hub is installed and used to connect personal computers and a host system. An installed hybrid hub could support other lower-layer technologies in addition to ATM and FDDI.

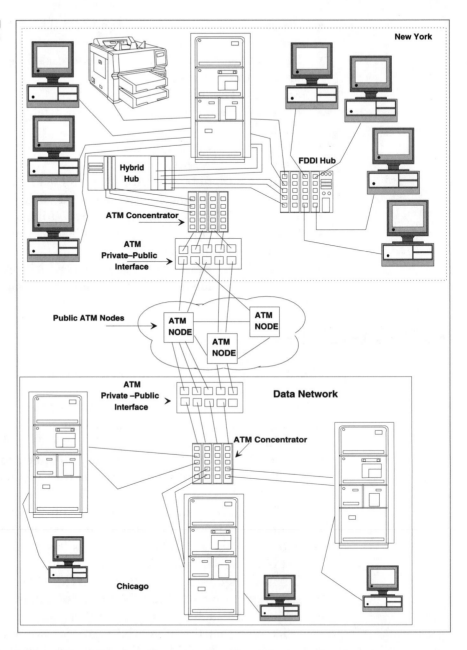

This blueprint would fit well where the need exists for data to be available in real time. ATM can accommodate high speeds over great distances and is also a good technology for building an infrastructure inside a company or other entity.

ATM Blueprint #2

ATM blueprint 2 is more complex than its predecessor.

FIGURE 13.16
ATM Blueprint #2

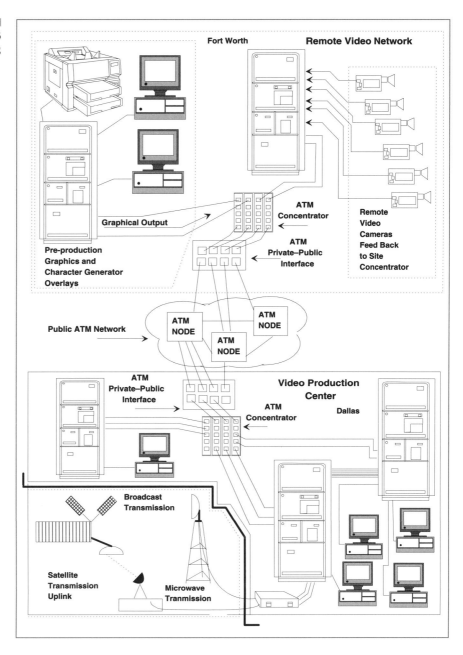

Figure 13.16 shows two locations: one in Fort Worth and the other in Dallas; these are connected via an ATM backbone network.

The Fort Worth location has a pre-production graphics group and remote video cameras that send live feeds back to the host connected to the ATM concentrator. The pre-production group has a host where graphics are stored and character generator overlays are produced. It requires large amounts of disk storage. The files stored in the systems in use are generally large because of their graphical nature. Because large amounts of storage are required factors other than pure speed of data transfer from one location to another need to be considered. Speed of data transfer on CD's, disk drives, tape drives, and other methods of storage are important as is processor speed. Bus width and other factors need to be considered when designing a network or implementing a blueprint similar to this. The remote video network has different concerns even though it is a part of the same Fort Worth office.

The remote video network has the same need for large amounts of storage. However, it requires large amounts of bandwidth between the intake source (to move images from the cameras) and to the system in which they are stored. In some instances the intake (video cameras) directs input to a specialized device that feeds it directly to production. Either use of images from the cameras requires large capacities for throughput.

The Dallas location in Figure 13.16 shows an ATM interface and ATM concentrator. Other hosts and computers are also connected in the network. The Dallas location in this example is the broadcast location for the production and requires maximum throughput internally and externally.

ATM Blueprint #3

ATM blueprint 3 is shown in Figure 13.17.

Here we see a video production group, a graphical group, multiple workstations, remote users, various storage devices, and printers.

This blueprint provides a foundation based on various ATM devices that can be expanded when the need arises. Look at the video production center shown: both hosts are connected to an ATM concentrator. Plans are to add six more hosts and three additional ATM concentrators. If this happens, these concentrators could work in parallel to connect this part of the blueprint to the data center.

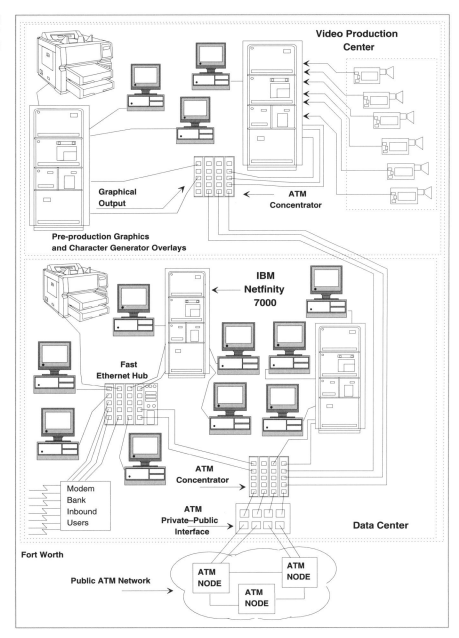

FIGURE 13.17
ATM Blueprint #3

We also see the ability of the data and video production centers to be a public ATM network as at the bottom of the illustration. This could enable remote ATM connections in different geographic locations.

Another advantage of this blueprint is its ability to split the location with the ATM concentrators and let each of them feed a public

ATM network connection, thus providing a fair degree of redundancy and serviceability.

Additional Information

Additional ATM information can be obtained from the following CCITT specifications: I.113, I.121, I.150, I.211, I.311, I.321, I.327, I.361, I.362, I.363, I.413, I.432, I.610, G.707, G.708 and G.709.

Summary

ATM is a cell-based, fast-packet switching technology which can be implemented privately or publicly. It has gained considerable attention since its entry into the technical arena in the late 1980s. Many public-service providers are opting for ATM installations.

ATM conceptual structure does not correlate one-for-one with the OSI model. ATM layers begin with a physical layer which has two sublayers: the Physical Media Dependent Sublayer, and above it the Transmission Convergence Sublayer. Next is the ATM layer which includes the four functions discussed above. The ATM Adaptation Layer is above the ATM layer. Part of the ATM layer and the ATM Adaptation Layer make up layer two. The ATM Adaptation Layer includes five types of functions.

ATM cells are unique because they are small and can handle voice, data, video, and other multimedia information. The ATM adaptation-layer protocols are an interface between ATM and upper-layer protocols.

ATM utilizes a transmission path, virtual path, and virtual call as part of its implementation and method of passing information. Virtual paths and virtual calls are mapped to a transmission path.

The CCITT lists ATM specifications, some are directly and some indirectly related.

Blueprints provided above show some principles to use in the design phase of an ATM network. Each blueprint has many variations and can be up-sized, with different components scaled to meet the needs of different sites.

CHAPTER 14

Frame Relay Technology and Blueprints

Frame relay provides real-time communication between end users by serving as an interface into public and/or private networks. Frame relay networks pass frames from origin to destination without intermediate nodes performing packet assembly/disassembly. Frame relay is also considered a protocol. A frame relay control protocol is also defined, explaining how users make service requests in the network.

Frame relay is designed to support data in bursts and provide high speeds. It is *not* a store-and-forward-based technology, but a bidirectional conversational method of communication. Most frame relay standards are concentrated at layers one and two, though standards do define the mechanism for upper-layer protocols to "hook" into frame relay.

For example, this means that frame relay operates between users, between origin and destination *networks*. Figure 14.1 best conveys this concept.

The hypothetical scenario in Figure 14.1 shows three sites using frame relay as an interface into a dispersed frame relay network. Frame relay also connects multiple geographically different networks. Here each location implements frame relay.

The frame relay network in Figure 14.1 is using TCP/IP for an upper-layer protocol. The Netware protocol is used as well as SNA, Windows NT, and TCP/IP. Each physical location uses frame relay for an interface into what is considered a frame relay network.

Frame relay has been defined by at least three bodies: ANSI, CCITT, and the Local Management Interface (LMI) group. ANSI has a list of specifications; these standards generally have the ISDN name within them. The CCITT has its list of CCITT recommendations and two groups of standards that relate to frame relay: the I and Q groups. The LMI standards were generated by Cisco Systems, Digital Equipment Corporation, Northern Telecom, Inc., and StrataCom, Inc., four vendors who collectively created standards that parallel ANSI and the CCITT. Later in this chapter we will discuss what information comes from which source and how to obtain additional information.

The remainder of the chapter explains frame relay's principles, frame structure, virtual circuits, and access devices, with consumer tips, and a list of reference material.

Principles of Frame Relay

Frame relay operates upon multiple principles; those included in this section are: virtual links, permanent virtual connections, the data-link connection identifier, and others.

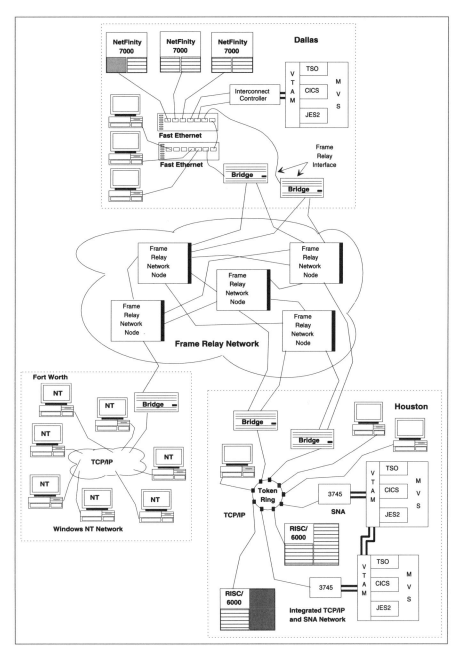

The Virtual Link

A basic frame relay principle is a *virtual connection* which may vary according to the time it exists. Practically, the connection is permanent because it *remains* as long as necessary. Figure 14.2 shows a basic frame relay example.

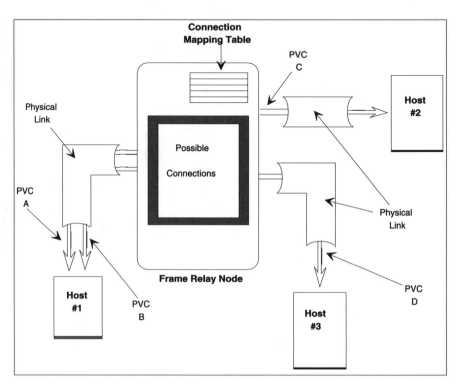

FIGURE 14.2
Enhanced View of a Frame Relay Node

Here three hosts are connected to a frame relay node, with physical links connecting each host to the node, memory inside the frame relay device, and a connection-mapping table within the frame relay node. Host 1's physical link supports two permanent virtual connections (PVCs). Hosts 2 and 3's physical links support one PVC each.

The connection-mapping table is at the heart of frame relay operations within the frame relay node shown. The connections are dynamic, based upon requests from the incoming data stream. The connection-mapping table is responsible for matching the request of a source to the destination; this constitutes a route, in frame relay parlance a virtual connection.

Figure 14.3 is similar to Figure 14.2, but shows the frames and a highlighted view of the mapping table.

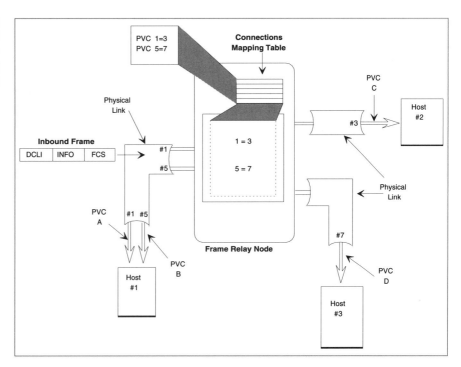

FIGURE 14.3
Highlighted View
of the Mapping
Table

Notice PVC A 1 and PVC B 5 originate at host 1. Figure 14.3 also shows these PVC's connecting to PVC C 3 and PVC D 7, respectively. In other words, mapping between A 1 and C 3 and B 5 and D 7 is performed inside the frame relay node.

Data Link Connection Identifier (DCLI)

The inbound frame from host 1 via PVC A 1 contains a DCLI, the local address in frame relay that is relevant in reference to the particular link. It identifies the frame and its type. This means that the same DCLI value could be used at both ends of the frame relay network where each host connects via a particular link. Differentiating the DCLIs are the physical link the frame traverses and the host. More than one identifying factor is used for frame identification.

In the connection-mapping table each entry includes the node ID, link ID, and DCLI.

Frame Relay Costs

Aside from the cost of hardware and software required to implement a frame relay connection, additional fees include: the Commitment Information Rate (CIR), the bandwidth available from one end to another; the port access rate, for access into the frame relay network; and a network access charge that reflects the costs of the line connecting a given site to the access point in the frame relay network.

Understanding these aspects of frame relay is important. If data are transmitted in bursts one must know what the burst data rate is; the normal or average throughput required on a daily basis must also be known.

Frame Relay Frame Components

Frame relay frame components are shown in Figure 14.4. Maximum frame size is 8,250 bytes, and the minimum is generally considered 262 bytes.

FIGURE 14.4
CCITT I.441
Frame Relay
Frame Format

Flag	Address Field	Control	Information	FCS	Flag

Figure 14.4 is based upon the CCITT I.441 recommendation. Variations of this structure are primarily those with different methods of implementing addressing. Frame relay uses the same standards as those of ISDN.

The flag field indicates the beginning of the frame.

The address field typically consists of the components in Figure 14.5.

FIGURE 14.5
Highlighted
View of the
Address Field

DLCI	CR	EAB	DLCI	FN	BN	DE	EAB

In Figure 14.5 a **DLCI** field identifies a logical channel connection in a physical channel or port, thus identifying a pre-determined destination (it identifies the connection). The **CR** field contains a bit indicating a command response. The **EAB** field contains a bit set at either 1 or 0. The field indicates extended addressing. The **FN** field is sometimes referred to as the Forward Explicit Congestion Notification (FECN). The bit in this field indicates whether or not congestion was encountered during the transfer from origin to destination. The **BN** field indicates that congestion was encountered on the return path. The **DE** field indicates discard eligibility: whether or not the frame can be disposed of during transfer if congestion is encountered. A bit setting of 1 means discard eligibility, whereas a bit setting of 0 indicates a higher setting for the frame and that it should not be discarded.

Virtual Circuits

Different frame types of virtual circuits have been defined for use with frame relay. In a sense these circuits represent different definable services; they include:

- Switched Virtual Circuit (SVC)
- Permanent Virtual Circuit (PVC)
- Multicast Virtual Circuit (MVC).

Switched Virtual Circuit (SVC)

This type of circuit is similar to telephone usage. When the circuit is needed, a request is made. When the circuit is not needed the circuit is not used. Information is passed from origin to destination to set up the call and to end it. Information provided in the call setup phase includes: bandwidth allocation parameters, quality of service parameters, and virtual channel identifiers.

Permanent Virtual Circuit (PVC)

This type of connection is considered point-to-point. It could be thought of as a leased line since it is dedicated. This circuit is used for long periods of time; commands are still used to set up the call and to end it. The difference between PVC and SVC is duration.

Multicast Virtual Circuit (MVC)

MVCs are best described as connections between groups of users, through which individual users can use SVC and PVC connections. Technically, this type of connection is considered permanent. It is generally considered a Local Management Interface (LMI) extension.

Access Devices

Devices that can be used as connections into a frame relay environment include the following items.

Switches

Frame relay networks can be accessed via different types of devices. Switches similar to those accommodating X.25 provide an access method. However, these switches are typically implemented in the sense of creating a backbone. Figure 14.6 is an example of this type of device implemented in three environments.

Figure 14.6 shows a network backbone made up of multiple locations.

Network Device

A more focused view of Denver is represented by Figure 14.7.

Here a network device (specifically a bridge) connecting a token ring and Ethernet network into the frame relay environment. It also depicts the lines to Dallas, Denver, and Detroit.

FRAD

A Frame Relay Access Device (FRAD) is a particular piece of equipment that typically connotes capabilities including packet assembly/disassembly and speeds of DS0, T1, or fractional T1. Most FRADs can handle multiple protocols and focus network traffic into a centralized managed facility such as Figure 14.8 shows.

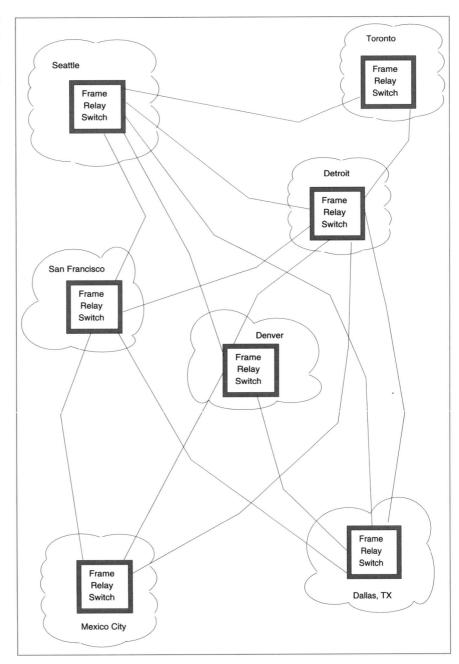

FIGURE 14.6
Conceptual View
of a Frame Relay
Network

FIGURE 14.7
Highlighted
View of Denver
Equipment

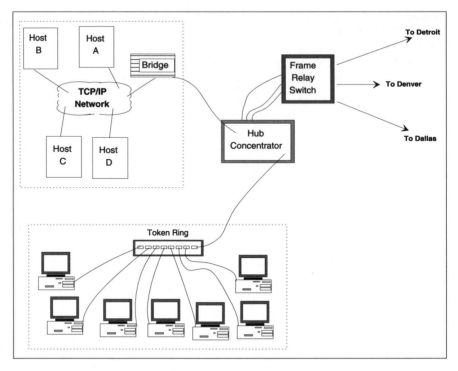

FIGURE 14.8
Highlighted View
of a FRAD

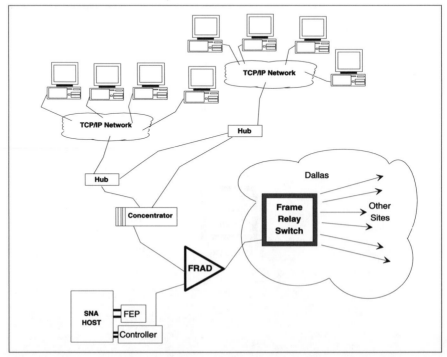

FRADs can be the best component to concentrate multiple devices into a single unit. Vendors such as Wellfleet and Cisco Systems provide such devices.

Other devices may be used in connecting a variety of resources into a frame relay network. Vendors who offer frame relay support as an additional function IBM, whose Network Control Program (NCP) operates on a Front End Controller (FEP).

Frame Relay with TCP/IP and SNA

Frame relay is a lower-layer network protocol. Protocols that operate above it can be integrated into it. TCP/IP can use frame relay as its data link-oriented protocol. Consider Figure 14.9.

FIGURE 14.9
Frame Relay
Format with
TCP/IP

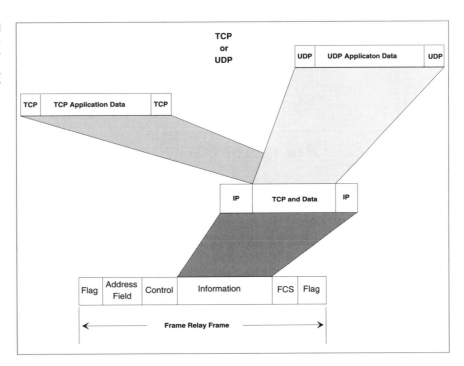

This figure shows the frame relay frame format and a conceptual view of how TCP and UDP operate with it. Notice TCP and UDP are shown as either/or, because TCP/IP applications operate on top of TCP or UDP. Telnet, HTTP and FTP are all TCP applications. TFTP, RPC, and others use UDP for a transport-layer protocol.

Figure 14.10 illustrates frame relay and SNA.

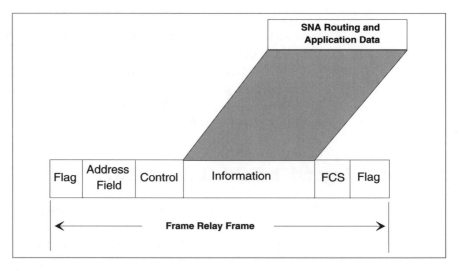

FIGURE 14.10
Frame Relay
Format with SNA

Here we see where an SNA frame would fit into a frame relay frame. Included in this illustration are implied SNA applications such as CICS, TSO, DB/2, and others. Frame relay is not a native SNA protocol, but is now supported by IBM and hence compatible with native SNA.

Frame Relay Blueprint #1

Frame relay can be a complex technology to implement. Understanding the concepts of how it operates in different implementations makes it easier to plan and design for network operation. Consider Figure 14.11.

This shows three network segments connected to a backbone segment. An internal token ring network backbone is on the customer premises; the internal network is connected to a frame relay network connecting it to multiple remote sites.

Frame Relay Blueprint #2

A more complex implementation of frame relay is shown in Figure 14.12.

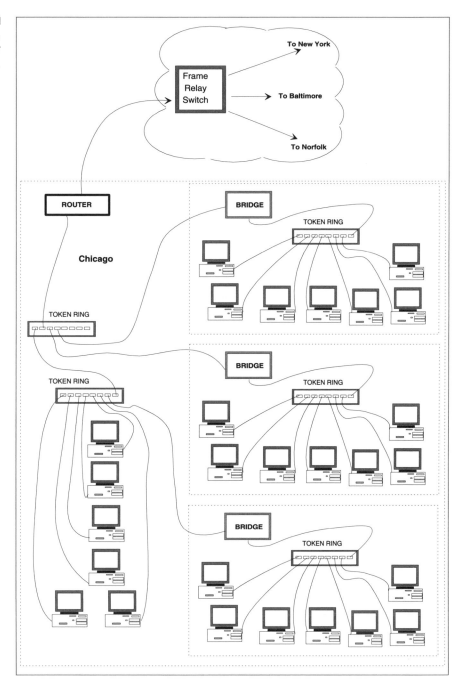

FIGURE 14.11
Frame Relay
Blueprint #1

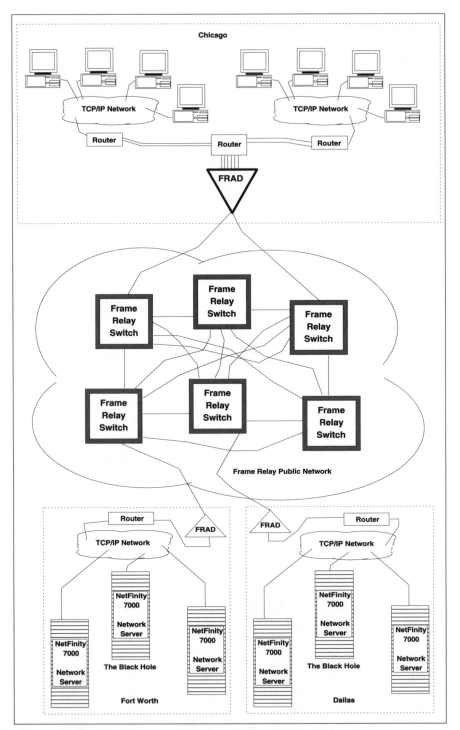

FIGURE 14.12
Frame Relay
Blueprint #2

This illustration shows three sites in different geographic locations connected by a frame relay network. This blueprint reflects an idea in implementation that is common in many locations today. Multiple servers are located in two locations and there is a concentration of workstations in a third location. Any variation of this could be a valid implementation. Cost versus performance is one benefit this blueprint provides.

Frame Relay Blueprint #3

Consider Figure 14.13. Notice there is a *private* frame relay network. This type of blueprint is viable in many situations where a need exists to distribute information to a large number of users in a single location. An example of this type private frame relay implementation could be a university campus-type setting.

Blueprint 3 has marketing, data bank, pre-sales support, and product support departments. Such an internal network is robust enough to sustain large amounts of data traffic and a high number of users. This blueprint is well-suited for a private (closed) network. A benefit is that the blueprint lends itself easily to incorporation into a public frame relay network, and thus connection to other locations.

Consumer Tips

My work with and research on frame relay has generated questions that the consumer purchasing frame relay equipment should ask and general important tips.

1. Frame relay standards are still being defined and variously implemented by vendors.
2. When considering a frame relay device ascertain what it specifically does.
3. Determine if a frame relay device has DCLI support, header-bits support, FCS, FECN, BECN, and DE bits within the frame. Also determine if congestion control is performed to standards and if so, which one(s)? Determine if multiple protocols are supported.
4. Find out in what way a given device supports FECN, BECN, and DE bits. How do they function in respect to congestion management? For example, one may say DE is supported, but what does this mean? Does it mean the bit is read or it can be set? The latter is important.

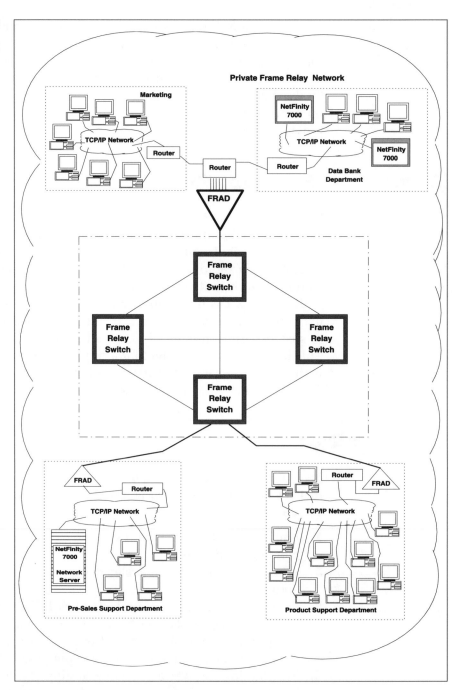

FIGURE 14.13
Frame Relay
Blueprint #3

5. Is link management supported, and if so, what type?
6. Does the device support transparent mode?
7. Is the device switch oriented or primarily a device used to provide access into a frame relay network?

Additional Information

Sources of considerably more detail are divided by category:

ANSI

T1.601	Basic Access Interface
T1.602	ISDN Data Link layer Signaling Specifications
T1S1	/90-75 Frame Relay Bearer Service, Architectural Framework Description
T1S1	/90-214 Core Aspects of Frame Protocol for Use with Frame Relay Bearer Service
T1S1	/90-213 Signaling Specification for Frame Relay Bearer Service
T1.606	ISDN Architectural Framework
T1.607	Digital Subscriber Signaling Service
T1.617	Standards Concerning Customer Interface
T1.618	Standards Concerning Customer Interface
T1S1	/90-051R2 Carrier to Customer Interface

CCITT

I.122	Q.920	1.320	X.25
I.233	Q.921	1.320	X.31
I.130	Q.922	1.430	X.134
I.441	Q.930	1.431	X.213
I.450	Q.931	1.462	X.300
I.451			

Summary

An explanation of frame relay principles included the concept of virtual links, the data link connection identifier, and the associated costs of frame relay beyond those of supporting hardware and software. Frame relay frame components were presented and the fields that comprise a frame briefly explained.

The concept of virtual circuits was explained. The Switched Virtual Circuit (SVC) is similar to a telephone, a Permanent Virtual Circuit (PVC) is similar to a leased-line arrangement, and in a Multicast Virtual Circuit (MVC) a group of users can be reached through one multicast.

Access devices used in frame relay networks were discussed. The basic function of a switch, network related devices, and frame relay access devices were explained. Different implementations may use one or more of these devices.

A list of consumer tips was included for the consumer who is new to frame relay. A list of reference sources was included in section for those who desire more in-depth knowledge of this topic.

Network
Blueprint
Acronyms

10Base-T	Technical name for Ethernet implemented on twisted wire
3270	Reference to a 3270 Data Stream Supporting Entity
3770	Reference to Remote Job Entry
370/XA	370/ eXtended Architecture
5250	Reference to a 5250 Data Stream Supporting Entity
576	The minimum datagram size all hosts including routers, must accommodate
AAA	Autonomous Administrative Area
AAI	Administration Authority Identifier
AAL	ATM Adaptation Layer
AARP	AppleTalk Address Resolution Protocol
ABOM	A-bis Operations and Maintenance
ACB	Application Control Block
ACB	Access Method Control Block
ACCS	Automated Calling Card Service
ACD	Automatic Call Distribution
ACDF	Access Control Decision Function
ACE	Access Control List Entry
ACF	Access Control Field
ACF	Advanced Communications Function
ACIA	Access Control Inner Areas
ACID	Atomicity, Consistency, Isolation, and Durability
ACK	Positive Acknowledgment
ACL	Access Control List
ACP	Ancillary Control Process
ACS	Access Control Store
ACSA	Access Control Specific Area
ACSE	Association Control Service Element
ACSP	Access Control Specific Point
ACTLU	Activate Logical Unit
ACTPU	Activate Physical Unit
ACU	Auto Calling Unit
AD	Addendum Document to an OSI Standard
ADF	Adapter Description File

ADMD	Administrative Management Domain
ADP	Adapter Control Block
ADP	AppleTalk Data Stream Protocol
ADPCM	Adaptive Differential Pulse Code Modulation
ADSP	AppleTalk Data Stream Protocol
AE	Application Entity
AEI	Application Entity Invocation
AEP	AppleTalk Echo Protocol
AET	Application Entity Title
AF	Auxiliary Facility
AFI	Authority and Format Identifier
AFP	AppleTalk Filing Protocol
AI	Artifical Intelligence
AIFF	Audio Interchange File Format
AIX	Advanced Interactive Executive
ALS	Application Layer Structure
ALU	Application Layer User
AMI	Alternating Mark Inversion
ANI	Automatic Number Identification
ANS	American National Standard
ANSI	American National Standards Institute
AP	Application Process
AP	Argument Pointer
APB	Alpha Primary Bootstrap
APD	Avalanche Photodiode
APDU	Application Protocol Data Unit
API	Application Program Interface; Application Programming Interface
APIC	Advanced Programming Interrupt Controller
APLI	ACSE/Presentation Library Interface
APP	Applications Portability Profile
APPC	Advanced Peer-to-Peer Communications
APPC	Advanced Program-to-Program Communications
APPL	Application Program
APPN	Advanced Peer-to-Peer Networking

APT	Application Process Title
ARP	Address Resolution Protocol
ARPA	Advanced Research Projects Agency
ARQ	Automatic Repeat Request
ARS	Automatic Route Selection
AS/400	Application System/400
ASC	Accredited Standard Committee
ASCII	American Standard Code for Information Interchange
ASDC	Abstract Service Definition Convention
ASE	Application Service Element
ASN	Abstract Syntax Notation
ASN.1	Abstract Syntax Notation One
ASO	Application Service Object
ASP	Abstract Service Primitive; AppleTalk Session Protocol
AST	Asynchronous System Trap
ASTLVL	Asynchronous System Trap Level
ASTSR	Asynchronous System Trap Summary Register
ATM	Asynchronous Transfer Mode; Abstract Text Method
ATP	AppleTalk Transaction Protocol
ATS	Abstract Test Suite
AU	Access Unit
AVA	Attribute Value Assertion
B-ISDN	Broadband ISDN
B8ZS	Bipolar 8-Zeros Substitution
BACM	Basic Access Control Model
BAR	Base Address Register
BAS	Basic Activity Subset
BASIC	Beginners All-purpose Instruction Code
BB	Begin Bracket
BBS	Bulletin Board System
BC	Begin Chain
BCC	Block Check Character
BCS	Basic Combined Subset
BCVT	Basic Class Virtual Terminal

Bellcore	Bell Communications Research, Inc.
BER	Box Event Records
BER	Bit Error Rate
BF	Boundary Function
BGP	Border Gateway Protocol
BIB	Backward Indicator Bit
BIS	Bracket Initiation Stopped
BISUP	Broadband ISUP
BITS	Building Integrated Timing Systems
BITNET	Because It's Time Network
BIU	Basic Information Unit
BMS	Basic Mapping Support
BMU	Basic Measurement Unit
BNN	Boundary Network Node
BOC	Bell Operating Company
BOM	Beginning-of-Message
bps	Bits Per Second
BRI	Basic Rate Interface
BSC	Binary Synchronous Communications
BSS	Basic Synchronization Subset; Base Station Subsystem
BSSMAP	Base Station Subsystem Mobile Application Part
BTAM	Basic Telecommunications Access Method
BTU	Basic Transmission Unit
CA	Channel Adapter, Certification Authority, Channel Attachment
CAD	Computer-aided design
CAE	Common Applications Environment
CAF	Channel Auxiliary Facility
CAI	Computer-Assisted Instruction
CASE	Common Application Service Elements
CATV	Community Antenna Television
CBD	Changeback Declaration
CBEMA	Computer & Business Equipment Manufacturers Association
CCA	Conceptual Communication Area
CCAF	Call Control Agent Function

CCAF+	Call Control Agent Function Plus
CCB	Connection Control Block; Channel Control Block
CCIRN	Coordinating Committee for Intercontinental Research Networking
CCIS	Common Channel Interoffice Signaling
CCITT	Consultative Committee for International Telephone & Telegraph
CCO	Context Control Object
CCR	Commitment, Concurrency, and Recovery
CCS	Common Communications Support ; Common Channel Signaling
CCU	Central Control Unit; Communications Control Unit
CCW	Channel Command Word (SNA)
CD	Countdown Counter
CD	Committee Draft
CDF	Configuration Dataflow
CDI	Change Direction Indicator
CDRM	Cross Domain Resource Manager (SNA)
CDRSC	Cross-Domain Resource (SNA)
CDS	Conceptual Data Storage
CDS	Conceptual Data Store
CEBI	Conditional End Bracket Indicator
CEI	Connection Endpoint Identifier
CEN/ELEC	Comite' Europien de Normalization Electrotechnique
CEP	Connection-endpoint
CEPT	Conference of European Postal and Telecommunications Administrations
CESID	Caller Emergency Service Identification
CF	Control Function
CGM	Computer Graphics Metafile
CHILL	CCITT High-Level Language
CICS	Customer Information Control System
CID	Communication Xdentifier; Connection identifier
CIDR	Classless Inter-Domain Routing
CIGOS	Canadian Interest Group on Open Systems
CIM	Computer Integrated Manufacturing
CIS	Card Information Structure

CLI	Connectionless Internetworking
CLIST	Command List
CLNP	Connectionless Network Protocol
CLNS	Connectionless Network Service
CLSDST	Close Destination
CLTP	Connectionless Transport Protocol
CLTS	Connectionless Transport Service
CMC	Communications Management Configurations
CMIP	Common Management Information Protocol
CMIS	Common Management Information Service
CMISE	Common Management Information Service Element
CMOL	CMIP Over Logical Link Control
CMOT	CMIP Over TCP/IP
CMS	Conversational Monitor System
CMT	Connection Management
CN	Composite Node
CNM	Communication Network Management
CNMA	Communication Network for Manufacturing Applications
CNMI	Communication Network Management Interface
CNN	Composite Network Node
CNOS	Change Number of Sessions
CNT	Communications Name Table
CO	Central Office
COCF	Connection-Oriented Convergence Function
CODEC	Coder/Decoder
COI	Connection-Oriented Internetworking
COM	Continuation-of-Message DMPDU
CONF	Confirm
CONS	Connection-Oriented Network Service
CORBA	Common Object-Oriented Request Broker Architecture
COS	Class of Service; Corporation for Open Systems
COTP	Connection-Oriented Transport Protocol
COTS	Connection-Oriented Transport Service
CP	Control Point

CP	Control Program
CPCB	Control Program Control Block; Control Point Control Block
CPE	Customer Premises Equipment
CPH	Call Party Handling
CPF	Control Program Facility
CPI	Common Programming Interface
CPI-C	Common Programming Interface with C Language
CPMS	Control Point Management Services
CPU	Central Processing Unit
CRACF	Call-Related Radio Access Control Function
CRC	Cyclical Redundancy Check
CRST	Cluster-Route-Set-Test
CRT	Cathode Ray Tube
CRV	Call Reference Value
CSm	Call Segment Model
CS-MUX	Circuit Switching Multiplexer
CSA	Common Service Area; Common Storage Area
CSA/LIMIT	Common Service Area buffer use limit
CSMA/CA	Carrier Sense Multiple Access with Collision Avoidance
CSMA/CD	Carrier Sense Multiple Access with Collision Detection
CSP	Communications Scanner Processor
CSN	Card Select Number Register
CSNET	Computer+Science Network
CSS	Control, Signaling, and Status Store
CSU	Channel Service Unit
CTC	Channel-to-Channel
CTCA	Channel-to-Channel Adapter
CTCP	Communication and Transport Control Program
CTS	Clear-to-Send
CUA	Channel Unit Address; Common User Access
CURACF	Call Unrelated Service Function
CUT	Control Unit Terminal
CVS	Connection View State
CVT	Communications Vector Table

DACD	Directory Access Control Domain
DAD	Draft Addendum
DAF	Distributed Architecture Framework; Framework for Distributed Applications; Destination Address Field
DAP	Directory Access Protocol
DAS	Dual Attachment Station; Dynamically Assigned Sockets
DAT	Dynamic Address Translation
dB	Decibels
DBCS	Double-Byte Character Set
DC	Data Chaining
DCA	Document Content Architecture
DCC	Data Country Code
DCE	Data Communications Equipment; Distributed Computing Environment; Data Circuit-Terminating Equipment
DCS	Defined Context Set
DCSS	Discontiguous Shared Segment
DDCMP	Digital Data Communication Message Protocol
DDIM	Device Driver Initialization Model
DDM	Distributed Data Management
DDN	Data Defense Network
DDP	Datagram Delivery Protocol
DDS	Digital Data Service
DES	Data Encryption Standard
DFC	Data Flow Control
DECNET	Digital Equipment's Network Architecture
DFI	DSP Format Identifier
DFT	Distributed Function Terminal
DHCP	Dynamic Host Configuration Protocol
DH	DMPDU Header
DIA	Document Interchange Architecture
DIB	Directory Information Base
DIS	Draft International Standard
DISP	Draft International Standardized Profile
DISP	Directory Information Shadowing Protocol

DIT	Directory Information Tree
DIU	Distribution Interchange Unit
DL	Distribution List
DLC	Data Link Control; Data Link Connection
DLCEP	Data Link Connection Endpoint
DLCI	Data Link Connection Identifier
DLPDU	Data Link Protocol Data Unit
DLS	Data Link Service
DLSAP	Data Link Service Access Point
DLSDU	Data Link Service Data Unit
DLU	Dependent Logical Unit; Destination Logical Unit
DMA	Direct Memory Access
DMD	Directory Management Domain
DMI	Digital Multiplexed Interface; Definition of Management Information; Desktop Management Interface
DMO	Domain Management Organization
DMPDU	Derived MAC Protocol Data Unit
DMTF	Desktop Management Task Force
DMUX	Double Multiplexer
DN	Distinguished Name
DNS	Domain Name System
DNHR	Dynamic Nonhierarchical Routing
DoD	U.S. Department of Defense
DOP	Directory Operational Binding Management Protocol
DOS	Disk Operating System
DP	Draft Proposal
DPG	Dedicated Packet Group
DPI	Dots Per Inch
DQDB	Distributed Queue Dual Bus
DR	Definite Response
DRDS	Dynamic Reconfiguration Data Set (s)
DS	Directory Service; Desired State
DS3	Telephony classification of leased-line speed
DS-n	Digital Signaling Level n

DSA	Directory Service Agent
DSAP	Destination Service Access Point
DSD	Data Structure Definition
DSE	DSA Specific Entries; Data Switching Exchange
DSL	Digital Subscriber Line
DSP	Directory Service Protocol
DSP	Domain Specific Part
DSS 1	Digital Subscriber Signaling System No. 1
DSTINIT	Data Services Task Initialization
DSU	Digital Services Unit
DSUN	Distribution Services Unit Name
DT	DMPDU Trailer
DTE	Data Terminal Equipment
DTMF	Dual-Tone Multifrequency
DTR	Data Terminal Ready
DU	Data Unit
DUP	Data User Port
DUA	Directory User Agent
DVMRP	Distance Vector Multicast Routing Protocol
E.164	An ATM address format specified by the ITU-TS
E-mail	Electronic Mail
EAS	Extended Area Service
EB	End Bracket
EBCDIC	Extended Binary-Coded Decimal Interchange Code
EACK	Extended Acknowledgment
EARN	European Academic Research
ECA	Event Detection Point
ECC	Enhanced Error Checking and Correction
ECH	Echo Canceller with Hybrid
ECMA	European Computer Manufacturers' Association
ECO	Echo Control Object
ECSA	Exchange Carriers Standards Association
EDI	Electronic Data Interchange
EDIFACT	EDI For Administration, Commerce and Transport

EDIM	EDI Message
EDIME	EDI Messaging Environment
EDIMS	EDI Messaging System
EDI-MS	EDI Message Store
EDIN	EDI Notification
EDI-UA	EDI-User Agent
EEI	External Environment Interface
EGP	Exterior Gateway Protocol
EIA	Electronic Industries Association
EISA	Extended Industry Standard Architecture
EIT	Encoded Information type
EN	End Node
ENA	Extended Network Addressing
ENV	European Pre-standards
EOM	End-of-Message DMPDU
EOT	End of Transmission
EP	Emulation Program
ER	Explicit Route; Exception Response
EREP	Environmental Recording, Editing and Printing
ERP	Error Recovery Procedures
ES	End System
ESA	Enterprise Systems Architecture; Enhanced Subarea Addressing
ESCON	Enterprise System Connectivity
ESF	Extended Superframe Format
ESH	End System Hello
ES-IS	End System Intermediate System
ESS	Electronic Switching System
ESTELLE	Extended State Transition Language
ETB	End-of-Text Block
ETR	Early Token Release
ETX	End of Text
EUnet	European UNIX network
EUUG	European UNIX Users' Group
EWOS	European Workshop on Open Systems

EXLST	Exit List
FA	Framework Advisory
FADU	File Access Data Unit
FARNET	Federation of American Research Networks
FAS	Frame Alignment Sequence
FAT	File Allocation Table
FC	Frame Control Field
FCC	Federal Communications Commission
FCS	Frame Check Sequence
FDCO	Field Definition Control Object
FDDI	Fiber Distributed Data Interface
FDDI-FO	FDDI Follow-On
FDM	Frequency Division Multiplexing
FDR	Field Definition Record
FDT	Formal Description Technique
FDX	Full Duplex
FEC	Field Entry Condition
FEE	Field Entry Event
FEI	Field Entry Instruction
FEICO	Field Entry Instruction Control Object
FEIR	Field Entry Instruction Record
FEP	Front End Processor
FEPCO	Field Entry Pilot Control Object
FEPR	Field Entry Pilot Record
FER	Field Entry Reaction
FFOL	FDDI Follow-on LAN
FH	Frame Handler
FID	Format Identification
FIFO	First In/First Out
FIPS	Federal Information Processing Standard
FISU	Fill In Signal Unit
FM	Function Management
FMH	Function Management Header
FOD	Office Document Format

FOR	Forward Transfer
FNC	Federal Networking Council
FRICC	Federal Research Internet Coordinating Committee
FR	Family of Requirement
FRFH	Frame Relay Frame Handler
FRMR	Frame Reject
FRSE	Framd-Relay Switching Equipment
FRTE	Frame-Relay Terminal Equipment
FS	Frame Status Field
FSG	SGML Interchange Format
FSM	Finite State Machine
FTAM	File Transfer and Access Management
FTP	File Transfer Protocol in TCP/IP
FYI	For Your Information
FX	Foreign Exchange Service
GB	Gigabits
GBps	Gigabits Per Second
GCS	Group Control System
GDDM	Graphical Data Display Manager
GDMO	Guidelines for the Definition of Managed Objects
GDS	Generalized Data Stream
GFI	General Format Indicator
GFP	Global Functional Plane
GGP	Gateway-to-Gateway Protocol
GMT	Greenwich Mean time
GPS	Global Positioning System
GOSIP	Government OSI Protocol
GSA	General Services Administration
GTF	Generalized Trace Facility
GWNCP	Gateway NCP
GWSSCP	Gateway SSCP
HAL	Hardware Abstraction Layer
H-MUX	Hybrid Multiplexer
HCL	Hardware Compatibility List

HCS	Header Check Sequence
HDB3	High-Density Bipolar - 3 zeros
HDLC	High Level Data Link Control
HDX	Half Duplex
HI-SAP	Hybrid Isochronous-MAC Service Access Point
HLR	Home Location Register
HMP	Host Monitoring Protocol
HOB	Head of Bus
HP-SAP	Hybrid packet-MAC Service Access Point
HPO	High Performance Option
HRC	Hybrid Ring Control
HSLN	High-Speed Local Network
HTML	Hypertext Markup Language
HTTP	Hypertext Transfer Protocol
Hz	Hertz (cycles per second)
I/O	Input/Output
IAB	Internet Architecture Board
IANA	Internet Assigned Number Authority
IADCS	Inter-Activity Defined Context Set
IAN	Integrated Analog Network
IAP	Inner Administrative Point
IBM	International Business Machines Corporation
IC	Interexchange Carrier
ICA	Integrated Communication Adapter
ICD	International Code Designator
ICF	Isochronous Convergence Function
ICI	Interface Control Information
ICMP	Internet Control Message Protocol
ICV	Integrity Check Value
ID	Identifier; Identification
IDI	Initial Domain Identifier
IDN	Integrated Digital Network
IDN	Interface Definition Notation
IDP	Initial Domain Part

IDP	Internetwork Datagram Packet
IDU	Interface Data Unit
IEC	Interexchange Carrier
IEC	International Electrotechnical Commission
IEEE	Institute of Electrical and Electronic Engineers
IEN	Internet Engineering Notes
IESG	Internet Engineering Steering Group
IETF	Internet Engineering Task Force
IF	Information Flow
IGP	Interior Gateway Protocol
IGMP	Internet Group Management Protocol
IGRP	Internet Gateway Routing Protocol
ILD	Injection Laser Diode
ILU	Independent Logical Unit
IMAC	Isochronous Media Access Control
IMIL	International Managed Information Library
IML	Initial Microcode Load
IMPDU	Initial MAC Protocol Data Unit
IMS	Information Management System
IMS/VS	Information Management Systems/Virtual Storage
IN	Intelligent Network
IND	Indication
INN	Intermediate Network Node
INT	Internal Trace Table
INTAP	Interoperability Technology Association for Information Processing
IOC	Input/Output Control
IOCP	Input/Output Control Program
IONL	Internal Organization of Network Layer
IOPD	Input/Output Problem Determination
IP	Internet Protocol
IPng	IP Next Generation
IPv4	IP version 4
IPv6	IP version 6
IPC	Interprocess Communication

IPCS	Interactive Problem Control System
IPDS	Intelligent Printer Data Stream
IPI	Initial Protocol Identifier
IPICS	ISP Implementation Conformance Statement
IPL	Initial Program Load (er)
IPM	Interpersonal Message
IPM-UA	Interpersonal Messaging User Agent
IPMS	Interpersonal Messaging System
IPN	Interpersonal Notification
IPR	Isolated Pacing Response
IPX	Internetwork Packet Exchange
IR	Internet Router
IRN	Intermediate Routing Node
IRQ	Interrupt Request Lines
IRTF	Internet Research Task Force
IS	International Standard
ISA	Industry Standard Architecture
ISAM	Index-Sequential Access Method
ISC	Inter System Communications in CICS
ISCF	Inter Systems Control Facility
ISDN	Integrated Services Digital Network
ISH	Intermediate System Hello
IS-IS	Intermediate System-to-Intermediate System
ISO	International Standards Organization
ISODE	ISO Development Environment
ISP	International Standard Profile
ISPBX	Integrated Services Private Branch Exchange
ISPF	Interactive System Productivity Facility
ISPSN	Initial Synchronization Point Serial Number
ISR	Intermediate Session Routing
ISSI	Inter Switching System Interface
ISUP	ISDN User Part
IT	Information Technology
ITC	Independent Telephone Company

ITU	International Telecommunication Union
ITU-TS	International Telecommunication Union–Telecommunication Section
IUCV	Inter-User Communication Vehicle
IUT	Implementation Under Test
IVDT	Integrated Voice/Data Terminal
IWU	Interworking Unit
IXC	Interexchange Carrier
JCL	Job Control Language
JES	Job Entry Subsystem
JTC	Joint Technical Committee
JTM	Job Transfer and Manipulation
KA9Q	TCP/IP implementation for amateur radio
kb	Kilobits
kbps	Kilobits per second
kHz	Kilohertz
km	Kilometers
LAB	Latency Adjustment Buffer
LAB	Line Attachment Base
LAN	Local Area Network
LANSUP	LAN Adapter NDIS Support
LAP	Link Access Procedure
LAPB	Link Access Procedure Balanced
LAPD	Link Access Procedures on the D-channel
LAPS	LAN Adapter and Protocol Support
LATA	Local Access and Transport Area
LCF	Log Control Function
LCN	Logical Channel Number
LE	Local Exchange
LEC	Local Exchange Carrier
LED	Light-Emitting Diode
LEN	Low-Entry Networking
LI	Length Indicator
LIB	Line Interface Base
LIC	Line Interface Coupler

LIDB	Line Information Database
LIS	Logical IP Subnet
LLAP	LocalTalk Link Access Protocol
LL2	Link Level 2
LLC	Logical Link Control
LME	Layer Management Entity
LMI	Layer Management Interface
LOCKD	Lock Manager Daemon
LOTOS	Language of Temporal Ordering Specifications
LPD	Line Printer Daemon
LPDA	Link Problem Determination Application
LPR	Line Printer
LRC	Longitudinal Redundancy Check
LSE	Local System Environment
LSL	Link Support Layer
LSS	Low-Speed Scanner
LSSU	Link Status Signal Unit
LT	Local Termination
LU	Logical Unit
m	Meters
MAC	Media Access Control; Medium Access Control
MACE	Macintosh Audio Compression and Expansion
MACF	Multiple Association Control Function
MAN	Metropolitan Area Network
MAP	Manufacturing Automation Protocol
MAU	Media Access Unit
MAU	Multistation Access Unit
Mb	Megabits
MBA	MASSBUS Adapter
MBONE	Multicast Backbone
Mbps	Megabits Per Second
MBZ	Must be Zero
MCA	Microchannel Architecture
MCF	MAC Convergence Function

MCI	Microwave Communications, Inc.
MCP	MAC Convergence Protocol
MCR	Monitor Console Routine
MD	Management Domain
MFA	Management Functional Areas
MFJ	Modified Final Judgment
MFS	Message Formatting Services in IMS
MH	Message Handling Package
MHS	Message Handling Service; Message Handling System
MHz	Megahertz
MIB	Management Information Base
MIC	Media Interface Connector
MID	Message Identifier
MILNET	Military Network
MIM	Management Information Model
MIME	Multipurpose Internet Mail Extension
MIN	Mobile Identification Number; Multiple Interaction Negotiation
MIPS	Million Instructions Per Second
MIS	Management Information Systems
MIT	Managed Information Tree
MLID	Multiple Link Interface Driver
MMF	Multimode Fiber
MMI	Man-Machine Interface
MMS	Manufacturing Message Specification
MOSS	Maintenance and Operator Subsystem
MOTIS	Message Oriented Text Interchange System
MOT	Means of Testing
MPAF	Mid-Page Allocation Field
MPC	Multipath Channel
MRO	Multiregion Operation in CICS
ms	Millisecond
MS	Management Services; Message Store
MSC	Mobile Switching Center
MSCP	Mass Storage Control Protocol

MSG	Console Messages
MSN	Multiple Systems Networking
MSNF	Multiple Systems Networking Facility
MSS	MAN Switching System; Maximum Segment Size
MST	Multiplexed Slotted and Token Ring
MSU	Management Services Unit
MTA	Message Transfer Agent
MTACP	Magnetic Tape Ancillary Control Process
MTBF	Mean Time Between Failures
MTTD	Mean Time of Diagnosis
MTOR	Mean Time of Repair
MTP	Message Transfer Part
MTS	Message Transfer System
MTSE	Message Transfer Service Element
MTU	Maximum Transfer Unit
MVS	Multiple Virtual Systems; Multiple Virtual Storage
MVS/XA	Multiple Virtual Storage/Extended Architecture
MVS/370	Multiple Virtual Storage/370
NAK	Negative Acknowledgment in BSC
NAP	Network Access Provider
NAU	Network Addressable Unit
NBP	Name-Binding Protocol
NC	Network Connection; Numerical Controller
NCB	Node Control Block
NCCF	Network Communications Control Facility
NCEP	Network Connection Endpoint
NCP	Network Control Program; Network Core Protocol
NCS	Network Computing System
NCTE	Network Channel-Terminating Equipment
NDIS	Network Driver Interface Specification
NFS	Network File System
NIB	Node Identification Block; Node Initialization Block
NIC	Network Interface Card
NIF	Network Information File

NISDN	Narrow-band ISDN
NIS	Names Information Socket
NIST	National Institute of Standards and Technology
NIUF	North American ISDN Users' Forum
NJE	Network Job Entry
NLM	NetWare Loadable Module
NLDM	Network Logical Data Manager
nm	Nanometer
NM	Network Management
NMP	Network Management Process
NMVT	Network Management Vector Transport
NMS	Network Management Station
NN	Network Node
NNT	NetView-NewView Task
NOC	Network Operations Center
NPA	Numbering Plan Area
NPAI	Network Protocol Control Information
NPDA	Network Problem Determination Application
NPDU	Network Protocol Data Unit
NPM	Netview Performance Monitor
NPSI	NCP Packet Switching Interface
NRN	Non-receipt Notification
NRZ	Non Return-to-Zero
NRZI	Non Return-to-Zero Inverted
ns	Nanosecond
NS	Network Service
NSAP	Network Service Access Points
NSDU	Network Service Data Unit
NSF	National Science Foundation
NTFS	Windows NT File System
NTO	Network Terminal Option
NVLAP	National Voluntary Accreditation Program
OAF	Origination Address Field
OAM	Operations, Administration and Maintenance

OAM&P	Operations, Administration, Maintenance and Provisioning
OC-n	Optical Carrier level n
OC3	155 million bits per second over fiber
OCA	Open Communication Architectures
OCC	Other Common Carrier
ODA	Office Document Architecture
ODI	Open Data-Link Interface
ODIF	Office Document Interchange Format
ODINSUP	ODI NSIS Support
ODP	Open Distributed Processing
OIT	Object Identifier Tree
OIW	OSI Implementation Workshop
OLRT	Online Realtime
OLU	Originating Logical Unit
OM	Object Management
ONA	Open Network Architecture
ONC	Open Network Computing
OPNDST	Open Destination
O/R	Originator/Recipient
OS	Operating System
OS/400	Operating System/400 for the AS/400 Computer
OSE	Open Systems Environment
OSF	Open Software Foundation
OSI	Open Systems Interconnection
OSI/CS	OSI Communications Subsystem
OSIE	Open System Interconnection Environment
OSILL	Open Systems Interconnection Lower Layers
OSIUL	Open Systems Interconnection Upper Layers
OSPF	Open Shortest Path First
OSNS	Open Systems Network Services
P-MAC	Packet Switched Media Access Control
PA	Pre-Arbitrated
PABX	Private Automatic Branch Exchange
PAD	Packet Assembler Disassembler

PAF	Pre-Arbitrated Function
PAI	Protocol Address Information
PAM	Pass Along Message
PANS	Pretty Amazing New Stuff
PAP	Printer Access Protocol
PBX	Private Branch Exchange
PC	Path Control
PC	Personal Computer
PCCU	Physical Communications Control Unit
PCEP	Presentation Connection End-point
PCI	Protocol Control Information; Presentation Context Identifier; Peripheral Component Interconnect bus
PCM	Pulse Code Modulation
PCO	Points of Control and Observation
PCTR	Protocol Conformance Test Report
PDAD	Proposed Draft Addendum
PDAU	Physical Delivery Access Unit
PDC	Packet Data Channel
pDISP	Proposed Draft International Standard Profile
PDN	Public Data Network
PDU	Protocol Data Unit
PDV	Presentation Data Value
PELS	Picture Elements
PEM	Privacy Enhanced Mail
PEP	Partition Emulation Program
PETS	Parameterized Executable Test Suite
PH	Packet Handler or Packet Handling
PhC	Physical Layer Connection
PhCEP	Physical Connection Endpoint
PhL	Physical Layer
PhPDU	Physical Layer Protocol Data Unit
PhS	Physical Layer Service
Ph-SAP or PhSAP	Physical Layer Service Access Point
PhSDU	Physical Layer Service Data Unit

PHY	Physical Layer
PICS	Protocol Information Conformance Statement
PIN	Positive-Intrinsic Negative Photodiode
PING	Packet Internet Groper
PIP	Program Initialization Parameters
PIU	Path Information Unit
PIXIT	Protocol Implementation eXtra Information for Testing
PKCS	Public Key Cryptosystems
PLC	Programmable Logic Controller
PLCP	Physical Layer Convergence Protocol
PLMN	Public Land Mobile Network
PLP	Packet Layer Protocol
PLS	Primary Link Station; Physical Signaling
PLU	Primary Logical Unit
PM	Protocol Machine
PMD	Physical Layer Medium-Dependent
POI	Point of Initiation; Program Operator Interface
POP	Point of Presence
POSI	Promoting Conference for OSI
POSIX	Portable Operating System Interface
POTS	Plain Old Telephone Service
PPDU	Presentation Protocol Data Unit
PPO	Primary Program Operator
PPP	Point-to-Point Protocol
PPSDN	Public Packet Switched Data Network
PRI	Primary Rate Interface
PRMD	Private Management Domain
PS	Presentation Services
PSAP	Public Safety Answering Point
PSC	Public Service Commission
PSDN	Packet-Switched Data Network
PSN	Packet-Switched Network
PSPDN	Packet-Switched Public Data Network
PSTN	Public Switched Telephone Network

PTF	Program Temporary Fix
PTLXAU	Public Telex Access Unit
PTN	Public Telephone Network
PTT	Post, Telegraph and Telephone
PU	Physical Unit
PUC	Public Utility Commission
PUCP	Physical Unit Control Point
PUMS	Physical Unit Management Services
PUP	Parc Universal Packet
PUT	Program Update Tape
PVC	Private Virtual Circuit
PVN	Private Virtual Network
P 1	Protocol 1 (Message transfer protocol/MHS/X.400)
P 2	Protocol 2 (Interpersonal messaging MHS/X.400)
P 3	Protocol 3 (submission and delivery protocol/MHS/X.400)
P 5	Protocol 5 (Teletext access protocol)
P 7	Protocol 7 (Message store access protocol in X.400)
QA	Queued Arbitrated
QAF	Queued Arbitrated Function
QC	Quiesce Complete
QEC	Quiesce at End-of-Chain
QMF	Query Management Facility
QOS	Quality of Service
QPSX	Queued Packet and Synchronous Switch
QUIPU	X.500 Conformant Directory Services in ISODE
RAM	Random Access Memory
RARE	Reseaux Associes pour la Recherche Europeenne/ European Association of Research Networks
RARP	Reverse Address Resolution Protocol
RAS	Remote Access Service
RBOC	Regional Bell Operating Company
RD	Routing Domain
RD	Route Redirection
RDA	Relative Distinguished Names

RDA	Remote Database Access
RDI	Restricted Digital Information
RDN	Relative Distinguished Name
RDP	Reliable Datagram Protocol
RDT	Resource Definition Table
RECFMS	Record Formatted Maintenance Statistics
REJ	Reject
REQ	Request
RESP	Response
RESYNC	Resynchronization
RFC	Request For Change
RFP	Request for Proposal
RFQ	Request for Price Quotation
RH	Response Header; Request Header
RIB	Routing Information Base
RIF	Routing Information Field
RIM	Request Initialization Mode
RIP	Router Information Protocol
RIPE	Reseaux IP Europeens/ European continental TCP/IP network operated by EUnet
RISC	Reduced Instruction Set Computer
RJE	Remote Job Entry
RM	Reference Model
RMT	Ring Management
RN	Receipt Notification
RNAA	Request Network Address Assignment
RNR	Receiver Not Ready
ROSE	Remote Operations Service Element
RPC	Remote Procedure Call in OSF/DCE; Remote Procedure Call
RPL	Request Parameter List; Remote Program Load
RPOA	Recognized Private Operating Agency
RQ	Request Counter
RR	Receiver Ready
RS	Relay System

RSF	Remote Support Facility
RSP	Response
RTM	Response Time Monitor
RTMP	Routing Table Maintenance Protocol
RTO	Round Trip time-Out
RTR	Ready to Receive
RTS	Request to Send
RTSE	Reliable Transfer Service Element
RTT	Round Trip Time
RU	Request Unit; Response Unit
S/390	IBM's System/390 Hardware Architecture
s	Second
SA	Source Address field
SA	Subarea
SA	Sequenced Application
SAA	System Applications Architecture
SAA	Specific Administrative Areas
SABM	Set Asynchronous Mode Balanced
SACF	Single Association Control Function
SACK	Selective Acknowledgment
SAF	SACF Auxiliary Facility
SALI	Source Address Length Indicator
SAM	Security Accounts Manager
SAMBE	Set Asynchronous Mode Balanced Extended
SAO	Single Association Object
SAP	Service Access Point; Service Advertising Protocol
SAPI	Service Access Point Identifier
SAS	Single-Attachment Station
SAS	Statically Assigned Sockets
SASE	Specific Application Service Element
SATS	Selected Abstract Test Suite
SAW	Session Awareness Data
SBA	Set Buffer Address
SBI	Stop Bracket Initiation

SC	Session Connection; Subcommittee
SCC	Specialized Common Carrier
SCCP	Signaling Connection Control Part
SCEP	Session Connection Endpoint
SCP	Service Control Point
SCS	System Conformance Statement; SNA Character String
SCSI	Small Computer System Interface
SCTR	System Conformance Test Report
SDH	Synchronous Digital Hierarchy
SDIF	Standard Document Interchange Format
SDL	System Description Language
SDLC	Synchronous Data Link Control
SDN	Software Defined Network
SDSE	Shadowed DSA Entries
SDU	Service Data Unit
SE	Session Entity
SG	Study Group
SGFS	Special Group on Functional Standardization
SGML	Standard Generalized Markup Language
SIA	Stable Implementation Agreements
SID	Security ID
SIM	Set Initialization Mode
SIO	Start I/O
SIP	SMDS Interface Protocol
SLU	Secondary Logical Unit
SM	Session Manager
SMAE	Systems Management Application Entity
SMASE	Systems Management Application Service Element
SMB	Server Message Block
SMDR	Station Message Detail Recording
SMDS	Switched Multi Megabit Data Service
SMF	Single Mode Fiber; System Management Facility
SMFA	Systems Management Functional Area
SMI	Structure of the OSI Management Information Service

SMIB	Stored Message Information Base
SMP	System Modification Program
SMS	Service Management System; Storage Management Subsystem
SMT	Station Management Standard
SMTP	Simple Mail Transfer Protocol
SNA	Systems Network Architecture
SNAP	Subnetwork Attachment Point
SNAcF	Subnetwork Access Function
SNAcP	Subnetwork Access Protocol
SNADS	SNA Distribution Services
SNARE	Subnetwork Address Routing Entity
SNCP	Single Node Control Point
SNDCP	Subnetwork Dependent Convergence Protocol
SNI	Subscriber-Network Interface
SNI	SNA Network Interconnection; SNA Network Interface
SNICP	Subnetwork Independent Convergence Protocol
SNMP	Simple Network Management Protocol
SNPA	Subnetwork Point of Attachment
SNRM	Set Normal Response Mode
SOA	Start Of Authority
SONET	Synchronous Optical Network
SP	Signaling Point
SPAG	Standards Promotion and Applications Group
SPC	Signaling Point Code
SPDU	Session Protocol Data Unit
SPE	Synchronous Payload Envelope
SPF	Shortest Path First
SPI	Subsequent Protocol Identifier
SPM	FDDI to SONET Physical-Layer Mapping Standard
SPSN	Synchronization Point Serial Number
SQL	Structured Query Language
SRH	SNARE Request Hello
SS	Switching System; Session Service
SS6	Signaling System Number 6

SS7	Signaling System Number 7
SSA	Subschema Specific Area
SSAP	Source Service Access Point; Session Service Access Point
SSCP	System Services Control Point
SSDU	Session Service Data Unit
SSM	Single-Segment Message DMPDU
SSP	System Support Programs
ST	Sequenced Terminal
STA	Spanning Tree Algorithms
STD	Standard
STM	Synchronous Transfer Mode; Station Management
STM-n	Synchronous Transport Module level n
STP	Shielded Twisted Pair; Service Transaction Program in LU 6.2; Signal Transfer Point
STS-n	Synchronous Transport Signal level n
SUERM	Signal Unit Error Rate Monitor
SUT	System Under Test
SVA	Shared Virtual Area
SVC	Switched Virtual Circuit
SWS	Silly Window Syndrome
SYN	Synchronizing Segment; Synchronous Character in IBM's Bisync Protocol
SYNC	Synchronization
T3	A designation of telephony used over DS3 speed lines
T	Transport
TA	Terminal Adapter
TC	Technical Committee
TCP	Transmission Control Protocol
TAG	Technology Advisory Group
TAP	Trace Analysis Program
TC	Transport Connection or Technical Committee
TCAM	Telecommunications Access Method
TCB	Task Control Block
TCEP	Transport Connection Endpoint

TCM	Time-Compression Multiplexing
TCP	Transmission Control Protocol
TCP/IP	Transmission Control Protocol/Internet Protocol
TCT	Terminal Control Table in CICS
TDM	Time Division Multiplexing
TDMA	Time Division Multiple Access
TE	Terminal Equipment
Telnet	Remote Logon in TCP/IP
TEP	Transport End Point
TFTP	Trivial File Transfer Protocol
TG	Transmission Group
TH	Transmission Header
THT	Token Holding Timer
TIC	Token-Ring Interface Coupler
TINA	Telecommunications Inforamtion Network Architecture
TINA-C	Telecommunication Information Network Architecture Consortium
TI RPC	Transport Independent RPC
TLI	Transport Layer Interface
TLMAU	Telematic Access Unit
TLV	Type, Length and Value
TLXAU	Telex Access Unit
TMP	Text Management Protocol
TMS	Time Multiplexed Switching
TOP	Technical and Office Protocol
TOS	Type Of Service
TN3270	A version of Telnet that implements the IBM 3270 data stream
TP	Transaction Program; Transaction Processing; Transport Protocol
TPDU	Transport Protocol Data Unit
TP-PMD	Twisted Pair PMD
TPS	Two Processor Switch
TPSP	Transaction Processing Service Provider
TPSU	Transaction Processing Service User
TPSUI	TPSU Invocation
TP 0	TP class 0–simple

TP 1	TP class 1–basic error recovery
TP 2	TP class 2–multiplexing
TP 3	TP class 3–error recovery and multiplexing
TP 4	TP class 4–error detection and recovery
TR	Technical Report; Token Ring
TRA	Token Ring Adapter
TRPB	Truncated Reverse Path Broadcast
TRSS	Token Ring Subsystem
TRT	Token Rotation Timer
TS	Transaction Services; Transport Service
TSAP	Transport Service Access Point
TSC	Transmission Subsystem Controller
TSDU	Transport Service Data Unit
TSCF	Target System Control Facility
TSI	Time Slot Interchange
TSO	Time Sharing Option
TSR	Terminate-and-Stay-Resident Program
TSS	Transmission Subsystem
TTCN	Tree and Tabular Combined Notation
TTL	Time to Live
TTP	Timed Token Protocol; Transport Test Platform
TTRT	Target Token Rotation Time
TTY	Teletype
TUP	Telephone User Part
TVX	Valid Transmission Timer (FDDI)
TWX	Teletypewriter Exchange Service
UA	Unnumbered Acknowledgment; User Agent; Unsequenced Application
UART	Universal Asynchronous Receiver and Transmitter
UDI	Unrestricted Digital Information
UDP	User Datagram Protocol
UOW	Unit of Work
UPS	Uninterruptable Power Supply
URL	Universal Resource Locator

User-ASE	User Application Service Element
USS	Unformatted System Services
UT	Unsequenced Terminal
UTC	Coordinated Universal Time
UTP	Unshielded Twisted Pair
UUCP	UNIX-to-UNIX Copy Program
VAC	Value-Added Carrier
VAN	Value-Added Network
VAS	Value-Added Service
vBNS	A reference to the 155 Mps deployment of an Internet backbone to have been implemented in 1995
VCI	Virtual Channel Identifier (DQDB)
VDT	Video Display Terminal
VESA	Video Electronics Standards Association
VIT	VTAM Internal Trace
VLR	Visitor Location Register
VLSI	Very Large Scale Integration
VPI/VCI	Virtual Path Identifier and a Virtual Call Identifier
VM	Virtual Machine
VMD	Virtual Manufacturing Device
VM/ESA	Virtual Machine/Enterprise Systems Architecture
VM/SP	Virtual Machine System Product
VM/SPHPO	Virtual Machine System Product High Performance Option
VPN	Virtual Private Network
VR	Virtual Route
VRPWS	Virtual Route Pacing Window Size
VS	Virtual Storage
VSAM	Virtual Storage Access Method
VSE	Virtual Storage Extended
VSE/SEA	Virtual Storage Extended/Enterprise Systems Architecture
VT	Virtual Terminal
VTAM	Virtual Telecommunications Access Method
VTE	Virtual Terminal Environment
VTP	Virtual Terminal Protocol

VTPM	Virtual Terminal Protocol Machine
VTSE	Virtual Terminal Service Element
WACA	Write Access Connection Acceptor
WACI	Write Access Connection Initiator
WAN	Wide Area Network
WAVAR	Write Access Variable
WBC	Wideband Channel
WD	Working Document
WG	Working Group
WNM	Workgroup Node Manger
WP	Working Party
WWW	The World Wide Web
X	The X Window System
X.25	An ITU-TX standard; a transport-layer service
X.400	The ITU-TS protocol for electronic mail
XAPIA	X.400 API Association
XDR	External Data Representation
XDS	X/Open Directory Services API
XI	SNA X.25 Interface
XID	Exchange Identification
XNS	Xerox Network Standard
XTI	X/Open Transport Interface
XUDTS	Extended Unit data Service
ZIP	Zone Information Protocol
ZIS	Zone Information Socket

Network
Blueprint
Terminology

Abend   Abnormal end of task.

Abstract Syntax   The OSI language used to describe abstract entities or concepts in a
Notation One   machine.

Abstract Syntax   Machine-independent types and values, defined using an ASN.1.

ACB   In VTAM, access method control block; in NCP, adapter control
                          block.

ACB Name   The name of a micro instruction. A name is typically specified on the
                          VTAM APPL definition statement.

Accept   In a VTAM application program, this means to establish a session
                          with a logical unit in response to CINIT request.

Access   Specifies identifiers and access rights to granted or denied holders of
Control Entry   the identifiers, default protection for directories, or security alarms.

Access   A list defining the kinds of access granted or denied to users of an
Control List   object.

Access Method   A technique for moving data between main storage and input/output
                          devices; also a technique used in telecommunications.

Access Method   A control block that links an application program to VSAM or
Control Block   VTAM.
(ACB)

ACF/VTAM   Advanced Communications Function for the Virtual Telecommunica-
                          tions Access Method.

Acknowledgment   A positive response sent indicating successful reception of informa-
                          tion.

Acquire   In VTAM, to take over resources that were formerly controlled by an
                          access method in another domain.

Activate   To initialize a resource.

Active   The state of a resource when it has been activated and is operational.
Operational

Active   An application currently capable of being used by a user.
Application

Active Window   The terminal window where current operations are in the fore-
                          ground.

ACTLU   In SNA, a command used to start a session with a logical unit.

ACTPU   In SNA, a command used to start a session with a physical unit.

Adapter Control   In NCP, a control block that contains line control information and the
Block (ACB)   stets of I/O operations; a definition in an I/O database describing an
                          adapter or device controller and the I/O interconnect.

Adaptive Session-Level Pacing	Pacing in which session components exchange pacing windows that may vary in size during the course of a session.
Address	In data communication, a designated identifier.
Address Descriptor Record	Information that reflects the address of an Apple event.
Address Mask	A bit mask used to select bits from an IP address for subnet addressing.
Address Resolution	Conversion of an IP address into a corresponding physical address; such as Ethernet or token ring.
Address Resolution Protocol (ARP)	A TCP/IP protocol used to dynamically bind a high-level IP Address to low-level physical hardware addresses. ARP works across single physical networks and is limited to networks that support hardware broadcast.
Address Space	Addresses used as unique identification for network accessible units, sessions, adjacent link stations, and links in a node for each network in which the node participates.
Addressing	In data communication, the way in which a station selects the station to which it is to send data.
Adjacent Control Point	A control point directly connected to an APPN, LEN, or composite node.
Adjacent NCPs	Network control programs connected by subarea links with no intervening NCPs.
Adjacent Nodes	Two nodes connected by at least one path that connects no other node.
Adjacent SSCP-Table	A table identifying SSCPs with which VTAM can enter into a session.
Adjacent Subareas	Subareas connected by one or more links with no intervening subareas.
Advanced Communications Function (ACF)	A group of IBM-licensed programs.
Advanced Peer-to-Peer Network (APPN)	An upper-layer networking protocol based on peer technology. The fundamental difference between APPN and SNA is that with APPN, VTAM is not required for session establishment after initial download of parameters.
Advanced Peer-to-Peer Network (APPN) End Node	A node that can register its local LUs with its network node server. It can also have links to multiple nodes, but can have only one CP-CP session at a time with a network node CP-CP sessions can never be established between end nodes.

Advanced Peer-to-Peer Network (APPN) Interchange Node
This type of node can characteristically be described by its functions, which include controlling network resources, performing CDRM functions in subarea networks, and ability to own NCPs. This type of node appears to an APPN network to be an APPN type node , and it appears to a subarea network to be a subarea node. It can reside between an APPN network and a subarea network, thus providing integration of the two.

Advanced Peer-to-Peer Network (APPN) LEN Node
This type of node supports functions not supported by an END node, for example, ILU protocols but not CP-CP sessions.

Advanced Peer-to-Peer Network (APPN) Network Node
An APPN network node performs the followings functions:
• Distributed directory services
• Intermediate routing services in an APPN network
• Network services for specific end nodes
• Intermediate session routing
• Management service focal point.
   The APPN network node cooperates with other network nodes to maintain a network topology database, used to select optimal routes for LU-LU sessions based on requested classes of service. An APPN network node can also attach to a subarea network as a peripheral node, or to other end nodes.

Advanced Program-to-Program Communication (APPC)
A protocol architecture based on T2.1 utilizing LU6.2 to accomplish peer communications; many references to APPC are simply LU6.2. The basic meaning of APPC is communication between programs: i.e., transactions programs. This protocol permits communication between programs written in different languages.

Advanced Research Projects Agency (ARPA)
Formerly named DARPA, the government agency that funded ARPANET.

Alert
In SNA, a message sent to a management subsystem typically using the network management vector transport (NMVT) protocol.

Alertable
In DECnet architecture, a synchronous alert that delivers data to specific points.

Alertsafe
According to Digital Equipment documentation, a routine that can be called without risk of triggering an alert while asynchronous delivery of alerts is enabled.

Alias File
A file that contains a pointer to another file, directory, or volume.

Alias Name	A naming convention sometimes used to refer to a different name which means the same as the alias; it may refer to another name which may be used as a pointer.
Allocate	A LU6.2 verb that assigns a session to a conversation.
Allocation Class	According to Digital Equipment documentation, a unique number between 0 and 255 that the system manager assigns to a pair of hosts and to the dual-pathed devices the hosts make available to other nodes in a VMS cluster.
Alpha Primary Bootstrap	According to Digital Equipment documentation, the primary boot strap program that initializes an AXP system with OpenVMS AXP.
Alternate Route	A route not the primary method of moving data from point to another point.
Ampersand (&)	When used in the command of most UNIX operating systems, it places the task or tasks in background operation.
Ancillary Control Process	A process acting as an interface between software and an I/O driver.
APAR	Authorized Program Analysis Report.
Apple Event	According to Apple documentation, a high-level event that adheres to the Apple Event Interprocess Messaging protocol.
Apple Event Handler	According to Apple documentation, a defined function that extracts pertinent data from an Apple event.
Apple Event Interprocess Messaging Protocol	A standard defined by Apple Computer, Inc., for communication among applications. According to Apple documentation, high-level events that adhere to this protocol are called Apple events.
Apple Event Parameter	According to Apple documentation, a keyword specifying a descriptor record containing data which the target application of an Apple event must use.
Apple File Exchange	A program that permits file transfer between Apple computers and DOS-based computers.
AppleShare File Server	Software that permits users to perform tasks in AppleTalk networks.
AppleShare Print Server	A Macintosh computer and software that manage network printing.
AppleTalk Data Stream Protocol (ADSP)	An AppleTalk protocol that provides the capability for maintaining a connection-oriented session between entities on an internet.

AppleTalk Echo Protocol (AEP)	A response-oriented protocol whereby a response is sent when a packet is received.
AppleTalk Filing Protocol (AFP)	The protocol used between an application and a file server; AFP is a client of ASP.
AppleTalk Internet Router	Router software operating on an Apple computer supporting up to eight AppleTalk networks.
AppleTalk Phase 2	Introduced in June 1989, it extended the capability of AppleTalk Phase 1; for example, it supports token ring and provides more efficient routing techniques. It is included in System/7 software.
AppleTalk Session Protocol (ASP)	Used to establish and maintain logical connections between a workstation and a server.
AppleTalk Transaction Protocol (ATP)	Functions in many ways like a connection-oriented protocol. For example, it orients the packets into the order they need to be received; if any packets have been lost, automatic retransmission of a packet(s) is performed.
AppleTalk Transition	A message containing information indicating specific occurrences that relate to the AppleTalk Transition Queue.
AppleTalk Transition Queue	An operating system queue.
Application Layer	According to the ISO OSI model, this is layer seven; provides application services.
Application program	Software that provides functions needed by a user. A user may be defined as a human, API, a transaction program, or any other logical entity.
Application Program Interface (API)	An addressable point that serves to bring together two or more entities.
Application Program Major Node	According to IBM documentation, in VTAM, this is a group of application-program minor nodes.
Application Result Handler	A program designed to perform predefined functions of results generated from applications.
Application Server	A computer used solely to provide processing power for application programs.
Application Service Element (ASE)	A definition explaining the capabilities of an application entity.

Application Service Object	A subobject of an application entity; it may contain ASE elements or service objects as subobjects.
Application Transaction Program	The program built around LU6.2 protocols.
Apply	A System Modification Program (SMP) command, used in certain SNA environments, whereby programs and/or program fixes are added to system libraries.
APPN Intermediate Routing Network	An APPN network consisting of network nodes and their inter-connections.
Argument List	According to Digital Equipment, a vector of entries representing a procedure parameter list and possibly a function value.
Argument Pointer	According to Digital Equipment, general register 12 on VAX systems; by convention, AP contains the address of the base of the argument list for procedures initiated using CALL instructions.
Address Resolution Protocol (ARP)	A TCP/IP protocol that maps IP addresses to hardware addresses.
Advance Research Projects Agency (ARPA)	A participant in early development of TCP/IP.
ARPANET	Served as central backbone for the IN during the '70s and '80s.
ASCII (American Standard Code for Information Interchange)	A standard code using a character set based on binary digits (1s and 0s). This character set is the foundation for defining letters, numbers, and specialized control functions.
Assignment Statement	In Digital Command Language (DCL), the association of a symbol name with a character string or numeric value. In Digital Equipment implementations, symbols can define synonyms for system commands or can be used for variables in command procedures.
Asynchronous (ASYNC)	In data communication, transmission of data without a synchronous protocol.
Asynchronous System Trap	A method to identify a specific event via a software-simulated interrupt.
Asynchronous Transfer Mode (ATM)	A CCITT standard defining cell relay. This is where data of multiple types of services, (data, voice, and/or video), are moved in fixed-size cells throughout a network.

Association Control Service Element   Used to establish and terminate associations between applications.

Attenuation   A term used with fiber optics. This refers to the reduction of signal loss, measured in decibels.

Attribute   From a security perspective, an identifier or holder of an identifier. When used in a conversation concerning threads, it specifies detailed properties of the objects to be created.

Attributes Object   Describes details of the objects to be created.

Authentication   A process of establishing identity.

Authorized Path   In VTAM under MVS, a facility that enables an application program to specify that a data transfer or related operation be carried out in a privileged and more efficient manner.

Automatic Logon   In SNA, a process by which VTAM automatically creates a session-initiation request to establish a session between two logical units (LUs). The result of this request is the SNA BIND command from the Primary Logical Unit (PLU) to the Secondary Logical Unit (SLU). A LU-LU session is established if the BIND image is correct and other parameters are accurate.

Automatic Record Locking   According to Digital Equipment documentation, a capability provided Open VMS Record Management Services that allows a user to lock only one record in a specific shared file at any given time.

A/UX Toolbox   According to Apple documentation, a library that enables a program running under the A/UX operating system to call Macintosh User Interface Toolbox and operating system routines.

Background Process   A term used in most UNIX environments; a process not requiring total attention of the system for operation.

Backplane Interconnect   According to Digital Equipment documentation, VAX systems have an internal processor bus that allows I/O device controllers to communicate with main memory and the central processor. These I/O controllers may reside on the same bus as memory and the central processor, or may be on a separate bus.

Base Disk   In SNA, and specifically the VM operating system, the disk containing text decks and macroinstructions for VTAM, NetView, and VM/SNA console support (VSCS).

Base Priority   The priority a VM system assigns to a process when it is created. Normally, it comes from the authorization file.

Basic Logical Object	An object in a specific logical structure that has no subordinate.
Baud Rate	The number of times per second a signal can change on a transmission line.
Begin Bracket	In SNA, the value of the begin-bracket indicator in the request header (RH); it is the first request in the first chain of a bracket and its value denotes the start of a bracket.
Berkeley Broadcast	A non-standard IP broadcast address using all zeros in the host portion instead of all ones.
Best-effort Delivery	A description of network technologies that do not provide reliability at link levels.
Bezier Curve	A curve defined by three outline points. Two outline points on a curve serve as endpoints and one is not on the curve point. These determine degree of curvature.
Big Endian	A format for storage or transmission of binary data in which the most significant byte comes first.
Binary Synchronous Communication (BSC)	A telecommunication protocol using a standard set of transmission control characters and control character sequences.
BIND	In SNA, a request for session activation between logical units.
BIND Command	In SNA, the command used to start a session and define the characteristics thereof.
BIND Image	In SNA, session parameters used to establish and govern the session between logical units. In VTAM, the BIND image is located in the LOGMODE table in the form of entries—one entry per type of image required to define the LU.
BIND Pacing	In SNA, BIND pacing can be used to prevent a BIND standoff. It is a technique used by the Address Space Manager (ASM).
Bitmap	Generally speaking, an array of data bits used for graphic images.
Bitmap Device	A device that displays bitmaps.
Bitmap Font	A bitmap font is created from a matrix of dots.
BIU Segment	In SNA, data contained within a Path Information Unit (PIU), it consists of either a Request/Response Header (RH) followed by all or part of a Request/Response unit (RU), or only part of an RU.
Blocking AST	An AST that can be requested by a process using the lock management system services. A blocking AST is delivered to the requesting process when it is preventing another process from accessing a resource.

Boot Server   According to Digital Equipment documentation, the management center for a VMS cluster system and its major source provider. The boot server provides disk access and downline loads satellite nodes.

Bootstrap Block   That part of the index file on a system disk that contains a program which loads the operating system into memory.

Boundary Function   In SNA, protocol support for attached peripheral nodes.

Boundary Node (BN) A boundary node fundamentally performs the function of transforming network addresses to local addresses.

Bracket   In SNA, one or more chains of RUs and their responses that are exchanged between session partners.

Bracket Protocol   A data flow control protocol in which session partners exchange data via IBM's SNA bracket protocol.

Broadcast   In TCP/IP, a request for logical connection at layers one and two in the network. Broadcast technology is exemplified by Ethernet.

Broadcast Search   In APPN, the simultaneous search to all network nodes in the form of a request for some type of data.

Broadcast Storm   A situation in a network using broadcast technology where a considerable number of broadcasts are put on the medium at one time.

Browse   With regard to functions that can be performed on a entity, browse merely permits viewing.

Btrieve   According to Novell documentation, a complete indexed record management system designed for high-performance data handling.

Bucket   According to Digital Equipment documentation, a storage structure used for building and processing files. A bucket contains one or more records or record cells. Buckets are the unit of contiguous transfer between Open VMS Record Management Services buffers and the disk.

Buffer   A temporary storage area used to hold input or output data.

Bundle Bit   The finder uses information in a bundle bit (BNDL Resource) to associate icons with the file.

Button   Generally agreed to be that which is pressed on a mouse. Mice may have two or three buttons. Two-button mice are common in non-Xwindow environments. Three-button mice are common in Xwindow environments and can be used in non-Xwindow environments, depending on the mouse vendor.

Cache   A high-speed storage buffer.

Call   To invoke a program, routine, or subroutine.

Call-Connected Packet	A DTE packet transmission indicating DCE acceptance of the incoming call.
Call Progress Signal	Communication from the DCE to the calling DTE indicating status of a call.
Call Request Packet	In X.25 communications, a call supervision packet transmitted by a DTE to ask for a call establishment through the network.
Calling	The process of transmitting selection signals to establish a connection between data stations.
Cancel	To terminate.
Carrier	In data communication, a continuous frequency capable of being modulated.
Carrier Sense	A device (transceiver, interface board, or other entity) capable of detecting a constant frequency.
Carrier Sense Multiple Access with Collision Detection (CSMA/CD)	A protocol utilizing equipment capable of detecting a carrier permitting multiple access to a common medium. This protocol can also detect a collision, because this type of technology is broadcast-oriented.
Casual Connection	In SNA, this type of connection is made in subarea networks with PU T5 nodes attached via a boundary function using low-entry networking capabilities.
Catalog	In SNA, a list of pointers to libraries, files, or datasets.
CCITT	Comité Consultatif International Télégraphique et Téléphonique. The International Telegraph and Telephone Consultative Committee.
Central Directory Server	According to IBM documentation, an APPN network node that provides a repository for network resource locations.
Central Processing Unit (CPU)	The circuitry that executes instructions.
Channel	Generically speaking, a path over which data can move. In most IBM documentation, the word channel has a specific meaning: IBM supports two types of channels today—parallel and serial.
Channel Adapter	A device used to attach the communication controller to a host channel.
Channel-Attached	In SNA terminology, a serial or parallel data-link protocol. IBM has other data link protocols, such as SDLC, ESCON, token ring, etc.
Channel Link	A data link connection between two devices.
Character-coded	An SNA term used in VTAM meaning unformatted.

Chooser According to Apple documentation, an accessory that lets a user select shared devices, such as printers and file servers.

CI Only VMS Cluster Configuration According to Digital Equipment, a type of VMS cluster configuration in which the computer interconnect, or CI, device is used for most interprocessor communication. In these configurations, a node may be a VAX processor or a Hierarchical Storage Controller (HSC).

CINIT A request sent from an SSCP to a primary logical unit requesting that a BIND command be issued.

Circuit Switching Connectivity on demand between DTEs and DCEs.

Cladding The surrounding part of a cable that protects the core optical fibers; this part is between the fibers and the cable jacket.

Class of Service (COS) In SNA, explicit routes, virtual routes, and priority; used to provide a variety of services within the network.

Class of Service Database In APPN, a database maintained independently by each network node, and optionally by APPN end nodes.

Cleanup In SNA, refers to how sessions are terminated between LUs. Specifically, it is a network services request that causes a particular LU-LU session to be ended immediately.

Clear Indication Packet A call supervision packet that data circuit-terminating equipment (DCE) transmits to inform data terminal equipment (DTE) that a call has been cleared.

Clear Request Packet A call supervision packet transmitted by DTE to ask that a call be cleared.

Click To press and release a mouse button.

Client Connotes peer technology. Clients are programs used to initiate something. In TCP/IP clients can be found in Telnet and FTP. In the X windowing system, a client is typically a program that conforms to the X protocol and works in conjunction with a X server.

Client Application In Apple environments, an application using Apple Event Interprocess Messaging Protocol to request a service, for example, printing a list of files or spell-checking a list of words.

Clocking The use of clock pulses to control synchronization.

Closed User Group (CUG) A user group that can communicate with other users in the group, but not with users outside the group.

Cluster A network of computers in which only one computer has file-system disk drives attached to it.

Cluster Controller   In SNA, the precursor to the establishment controller. It is a device to which terminals and printers attach. IBM's 3174 cluster controllers appear as a PU2.0.

CMOT   The use of Common Management Information Services over TCP/IP; the implementation of the OSI network management specification over TCP/IP.

Collision   Two or more devices simultaneously perform a broadcast on the same medium. This term is used in Ethernet networks, and in networks where broadcast technology is implemented.

Collision Detector   A device that can determine when a simultaneous transmission attempt has been made.

Command   A request to execute an event; or, according to Digital Equipment, when this is used in reference to Digital Command Language (DCL) it means an instruction, generally an English word, entered by the user at a terminal or included in a command procedure.

Command Facility   A component of IBM's NetView program which is the base for command processors that can monitor, control, automate, and improve the operation of an SNA network.

Command-Line Prompt   Generally, a place on a terminal where commands can be entered. The direction of these commands is contingent on the system or software from which the command line is generated. According to Hewlett-Packard's documentation, it is that which appears on the screen immediately after login. Usually the command-line prompt is either a $ (for Bourne and Korn shells) or a % (for C shells), but it can be modified. A popular modification is to print the current working directory and the history stack number before the $ or %. Find the command-line prompt by pressing Return several times. Every time Return is pressed, the HP-UX operating systems prints the prompt.

Command List (CLIST)   In IBM's SNA, a list of commands and statements designed to perform a specific function for the user. A variety of CLISTs exist in NetView, TSO, and REXX, for example.

Common Management Information Protocol (CMIP)   The OSI protocol for systems management.

Common Management Information Service Element   The application service element responsible for relaying systems management information.

Common Parent   The lowest-level directory that appears in path names of multiple files or directories on the same volume.

Communication Adapter   Generally agreed to be a device (normally an interface) that provides a common point for the device and the data communication device being used.

Communication Control Unit   A communication device that controls transmission of data over lines in a network.

Communication Controller   A control unit whose operations are controlled by one or more programs stored and executed in the unit. In most instances it manages lines and routing data through a network.

Communication Identifier (CID)   A VTAM key for locating the control blocks that represent a session. This key is created during session establishment and deleted when the session ends.

Communication Line   Deprecated term for telecommunication line.

Communication Network Management (CNM)   According to IBM documentation, the term applies to SNA, and is the process of designing, installing, operating, and managing distribution of information and control among users of communication systems.

Communication Network Management Application Program   According to IBM documentation, a VTAM application that issues and receives formatted management services request units for PUs. NetView is an example of a CNM application program.

Communication Network Management Interface   A common point where applications can move data and commands to the access method. The data and commands are associated with communication system management.

Component   Generally speaking, hardware or software.

Composite LEN Node   A group of nodes made up of a single type 5 node and subordinate type 4 nodes. To a type 2.1 node, a composite LEN node appears as one LEN node. An example of a composite LEN node is NCP and VTAM.

Composite Network Node (CNN)   A group of nodes made up of a type 5 node and its subordinate type 4 nodes that appear as a single APPN network node to the APPN network.

Composite Node   In IBM networking, specifically SNA with VTAM, a type 5 node and its owned type 4 nodes that collectively appear as a single node to other APPN nodes in an APPN network.

Computer Interconnect (CI)	A fault-tolerant, dual-path bus, with a bandwidth of 70 Mb per second.
Concurrency Controls	Methods provided by Btrieve to resolve possible conflicts when two applications attempt to update or delete the same records at the same time.
Configuration	The manner in which the hardware and software of an information processing system are organized and interconnected.
Configuration Restart	In SNA, the VTAM recovery facility that can be used after a failure or deactivation of a major node, VTAM, or the host processor to restore the domain to its status at the time of the failure or deactivation.
Configuration Services	A type of network services in a control point. Configuration services activate, deactivate, and records the status of PUs, links, and link stations.
Congestion Loss	In Digital Equipment's DECnet, a condition in which data packets transmitted over a network are lost when the DECnet for Open VMS Routing layer is unable to buffer them.
Connected	To have a physical path from one point to another.
Connection	In data communications two types of connections exist: physical and logical. A physical connection is a tangible path between two or more points. A logical connection is a capability to communicate between two or more endpoints.
Connection Control Block	A data structure used by ADSP to store state information about the connection end.
Connection End	The combination of an AppleTalk socket and the ADSP information maintained by the socket client.
Connection Listening Socket	A socket that accepts ADSP requests to open connections and passes them on to a socket client.
Connection Network	A representation within an APPN network of a shared-access transport facility (SATF), such as a token ring, that allows nodes identifying their connectivity to the SATF by a common virtual routing node to communicate without having individually-defined connections to one another.
Connection Oriented Internetworking	A set of subnetworks connected physically so their nature is capable of connection-oriented network service.
Connection-Oriented Service	A service offered in some networks; it has three phases: connection establishment, data transfer, and connection release.

Connectivity	The notion of device communication interchange, even if such devices are diverse.
Connection Server	A program that accepts an open connection request passed to it by a connection listener and selects a socket to respond to the request.
Connectionless Internetworking	A set of subnetworks connected physically so that their nature is capable of providing connectionless network service.
Connectionless Network Protocol (CLNP)	A protocol that does not perform retransmissions, or error recovery at a transport layer.
Connectionless Service	A network service that delivers data or packets as separate pieces. An example of this type of service is TCP/IP's Internet Protocol.
Console Communication Services (CCS)	SNA environments that act as interfaces between the control program and the VSCS component of VTAM for VM.
Contention	In SNA, it has multiple meanings, depending upon the context. A session can be explained by the network-accessible units attempting to initiate the same action at the same time against each other; or contention in LU6.2: the attempt to allocate a session by two programs against each other, at the same time.
Context	Information on a process maintained by the process manager.
Context Dependence	When the glyph corresponding to a character can be modified depending on the preceding and following characters.
Continue–Any Mode	This specifies whether VTAM is to receive the data in terms of logical records or buffers.
Continue–Specific Mode	In VTAM, the state of a session or APPC conversation permitting its input to satisfy only `RECEIVE` requests issued in a specific mode.
Contour	A closed loop in a TrueType outline glyph, defined by a group of outline points.
Control Block	A storage area that holds control information.
Control Logical Unit (CLU)	A logical unit that resides in a Transaction Processing Facility (TPF) type 2.1 node. It is used to pass private protocol requests between the TPF type 2.1 node and the logon manager, which is a VTAM application program. Communication flow between the CLU and the logon manager enables a logical unit controlled by VTAM to establish a session with TPF.
Control Panel	A place that allows a user to set or "control" a feature of some sort.

Control Panels Folder	In Apple documentation, a directory located in the System Folder for storing control panels. This allows users to modify their work environment on their Apple or Macintosh computers.
Control Point (CP)	The component of a type 2.1 node that manages the resources of that node. In an APPN network node the CP can engage in CP-CP sessions with other APPN nodes.
Control Program	Normally this type of program performs system-oriented functions such as scheduling and supervising execution of programs of a computer system. In IBM's Account Interactive executive it is that part of the operating system which determines the order for performing basic functions.
Control Vector	A particular structure that is one of a general class of RU substructures basically characterized by a variable length and a one-byte key used as an identifier.
Controller	A device that coordinates and controls the operation of one or more input/output devices.
Controlling Application Program	According to IBM documentation, an application program with which a secondary logical unit (other than an application program) is automatically put in session whenever the secondary logical unit is available.
Controlling Logical Unit	Either an application program or a device-type LU.
Conversation	A logical connection between two transaction programs using an LU 6.2 session.
Conversational Monitor System (CMS)	An IBM Virtual Machine (VM) operating system facility that provides interactive time sharing, problem solving, and program development capabilities. CMS operates under control of the Control Program component of a VM system.
Converted Command	An intermediate form of a character-coded command produced by VTAM through use of an unformatted system services definition table. Converted commands' formats are fixed. The Unformatted System Services (USS) table must be constructed in a manner so that character-coded commands are converted into the predefined, converted command format.
Core Apple Event	According to Apple documentation, an event that nearly all applications can use to communicate.

Cost	According to Digital Equipment documentation, a numeric value assigned to a circuit that exists between two adjacent nodes. In the DECnet for Open VMS network, data packets are routed on paths with the lowest cost.
CP (Control Point or Control Program)	A control point is a part of T2.1 architecture. A control program in IBM terminology is software that runs on a VM host. The CP communicates with the hardware.
CP Capabilities	In IBM documentation, the level of network services provided by the control point (CP) in an APPN end node or network node. Control program capabilities are exchanged during the activation of CP-CP sessions between nodes.
CP-CP Session	A parallel session between two control points, using LU 6.2 protocols and a mode name of CPSVCMG; network services requests and replies are exchanged.
CP Name	The name of a control point, consisting of an ID qualifier identifying the network to which the CP's node belongs, and a unique name within the scope of that network ID identifying the CP. Each APPN or LEN end node has one CP name, assigned to it at system-definition time.
Cross-Domain	In SNA, refers to resources in a different domain. Domains, in SNA, have to have ownership.
Cross-Domain Keys	In SNA, a pair of cryptographic keys used by a System Services Control Point (SSCP) to encipher the session cryptography key that is sent to another SSCP.
Cross-Domain Link	A link connecting two subareas that are in different domains. A physical link connecting two domains.
Cross-Domain Resource (CDRSC)	In SNA, refers to a resource (typically software) that resides in another domain, under the control of a different VTAM.
Cross-Domain Resource Manager (CDRM)	In SNA, refers to the function in the SSCP which controls initiation and termination of cross-domain sessions.
Cross-Network LU-LU Session	In SNA, refers to a session between logical units (LUs) in different networks.
Cross-Network Session	A session whose path traverses more than one SNA network.
Cryptographic	In SNA terminology, pertains to transformation of data to conceal its meaning.

Cryptographic Session	In SNA, an LU-LU session in which a Function Management Data (FMD) request may be enciphered before it is transmitted, and deciphered after it is received.
CUA	In SNA, particularly in VTAM, refers to the channel unit address.
Currency	The previous, current, and next position of a record in a file. There are two types of currency; logical and physical. According to Zac, money.
Customer Information Control System (CICS)	An IBM software program that supports real-time transactions between remote users and custom written transactions. It includes facilities for building, using, and maintaining databases.
Cut Buffer	A memory area that holds text which has been deleted from a file.
Cycle	A complete oscillation of a wave.
CWALL	An NCP threshold of buffer availability, below which the NCP will accept only high-priority Path Information Units (PIUs).
DARPA	Defense Advanced Research Projects Agency formerly called ARPA, the government agency that funded research and experimentation with the ARPANET.
DASD (Direct Access Storage Device)	IBM's terminology for a disk drive in mainframe environments.
Data Channel	An IBM synonym for input/output channel.
Data Circuit	A pair of associated transmit and receive channels providing a means for two-way data communication.
Data Circuit-Terminating Equipment (DCE)	In a data station, equipment that provides signal conversion and coding between the data terminal equipment (DTE) and the line.
Data Communication	Transfer of data among functional units by means of data transmission according to a protocol. The transmission, reception, and validation of data.
Data Encryption Standard (DES)	In computer security, refers to the National Institute of Standards and Technology (NIST) Data Encryption Standard, adopted by the US government as Federal Information Processing Standard (FIPS) Publication 46, which allows only hardware implementations of the data encryption algorithm.
Data Flow Control (DFC)	In SNA, a request or response unit (RU) category used for requests and responses exchanged between the data flow control layer in one half-session and the data flow control layer in the session partner.

Data Host Node   An SNA term referring to a host dedicated to processing applications that does not control network resources, except for its channel-attached or communication adapter-attached devices.

Data Link   In SNA, synonym for link.

Data Link Control (DLC)   A set of rules used by nodes at layer two within a network. The data link is governed by data-link protocols such as Ethernet or token ring.

Data Link Control (DLC) Protocol   Rules used by two nodes at a data link layer to accomplish an orderly exchange of information in Ethernet, Channel, FDDI, or token ring.

Data Link Layer   Layer two of the OSI Reference Model; it synchronizes transmission and handles error correction for a data link.

Data Link Level   The conceptual level of control logic between high-level logic and a data-link protocol that maintains control of the data link.

Data Network   An arrangement of data circuits and switching facilities for establishing connections between data terminal equipment; a term commonly found in X.25 network implementations.

Data Packet   In X.25, refers to a packet used for the transmission of user data on a virtual circuit at the DTE/DCE interface.

Data Server   According to common definition in Apple documentation, an application that acts like an interface between a database extension on a Macintosh computer and a data source, which can be on the Macintosh or on a remote host computer. It can be a database server program that can provide an interface to a variety of different databases, or it can be the data source itself, such as a Macintosh application.

Data Set   A way data, programs, and other representations of information are stored in IBM's MVS operating system environment.

Data Stream   In SNA, multiple data streams are identified; generally, a continuous stream of data elements being transmitted, in character or binary-digit form, using a defined format.

Data Switching Exchange (DSE)   Equipment at a single location that provides functions such as circuit, message, and packet switching.

Data Terminal Equipment (DTE)   That part of a data station which constitutes a data source, data link, or both.

Data Types   In SNA, particularly NetView, alerts, events, and statistics.

Data Unit   In the OSI environment, the smallest unit of a file content meaningful to an FTAM file action.

Database   A collection of data with a given structure.

Datagram Delivery Protocol   In AppleTalk networks, a protocol that provides socket-to-socket delivery of data packets.

DCE Clear Confirmation Packet	A call supervision packet that a DCE transmits to confirm that a call has been cleared.
DDname	Data Definition Name.
Deactivate	A term frequently used in SNA environments: to take a resource out of service.
Deallocate	A term used in APPC: an LU6.2 application program interface (API) terminates a conversation and makes the session free for a future conversation.
Decipher	To convert enciphered data in order to restore the original data.
Decrypt	In computer security, to decipher or decode. Synonym for decipher.
De Facto Standard	A standard which is the result of technology that has been developed and used, and has achieved some level of popularity.
Default SSCP List	In VTAM, a list of SSCPs to which a session request can be routed when a cross-domain resource manager is not specified.
Defense Data Network (DDN)	Used loosely to refer to MILNET, ARPANET, and the TCP/IP protocols they use. More specifically, it is MILNET and associated parts of the Internet that connects military installations.
Defined Context Set	A set of presentation contexts negotiated between peer presentation entities.
Definite Response (DR)	According to IBM documentation, a protocol used in SNA that requests the receiver of a request to return a response unconditionally, whether positive or negative, to that request chain.
Definition Statement	In IBM's VTAM program, an element of the network. In IBM's NCP, a type of instruction that defines a resource.
Delta Disk	In SNA, the virtual disk in a VM operating system that contains Program Temporary Fixes (PTFs) installed but not yet merged.
De Jure Standard	A standard set by a body or official consensus.
Descent Line	An imaginary line usually marking the furthest distance below the base line of the descenders of glyphs in a particular font.
Descriptor	A data buffer parameter passed for an extended get or extended step operation.
Descriptor Type	An identifier for the type of data referred to by the handle in a descriptor record.
Desktop Folder	In Apple environments, a directory located at the root level of each volume. It is used by the Finder for storing information about the icons that appear on the desktop area of the screen. The Folder itself is invisible to the user, but contains what the user sees on screen.

Destination Logical Unit (DLU)   The logical unit to which data are to be sent.

DEV   Device Address Field.

Device   When the term is used in networking scenarios, it is typically used generically. It could be a modem, host, terminal, or other entity.

Dial-in   In most SNA environments, the notion of inbound traffic towards the host.

Dial-out   In most networking environments, the notion of outbound capabilities to access resources elsewhere.

Digital Command Language   According to Digital Equipment documentation, a command interpreter in the operating system that provides a means of communication between the user and the operating system.

Digital Data Communication Message Protocol (DDCMP)   According to Digital Equipment documentation, the link-level protocol DEC uses in their network products. DDCMP operates over serial lines, delimits frames by a special character, and includes checksums at the link level. It was relevant to TCP/IP because the original NSFNET used DDCMP over its backbone lines.

Digital Network Architecture   According to Digital Equipment, a set of protocols governing the format, control, and sequencing of message-exchange for all Digital network implementations. The protocols are layered and define rules for data exchange from the physical-link level up through the user-interface level. DNA controls all data that travel throughout a Digital network. It also defines standard network management and network generation procedures.

Digital Storage Architecture (DSA)   According to Digital Equipment documentation, the specifications from Digital governing the design of and interface to mass storage products. DSA defines the functions to be performed by host computers, controllers, and drives, and specifies how they interact to manage mass storage.

Digital Storage Systems Interconnect   A data bus that uses the system communication architecture protocols for direct host-to-storage communications. The DSSI cable can extend to 6 meters and has a peak bandwidth of 4 MB.

Direct Access Storage Device (DASD)   A device in which access time is effectively independent of the location of the data.

Direct Activation   According to IBM documentation, the activation of a resource as a result of an activation command specifically naming the resource.

Direct Deactivation	According to IBM documentation, the deactivation of a resource as a result of a deactivation command specifically naming the resource.
Directed Broadcast Address	In TCP/IP-based environments, an IP address that specifies all hosts on a particular network. A single copy of a directed broadcast is routed to the specified network where it is broadcast to all machines on that network.
Directed Locate Search	A search request sent to a specific destination node known to contain a resource, such as a logical unit, to verify the continued presence of the resource at the destination node and to obtain the node's connectivity information for route calculation.
Directed Search	Synonym for directed locate search.
Directory	Depending upon the environment, this term is used in different ways. In UNIX, a directory is a listing of files and the files themselves. This definition is generally the case in most environments. In IBM's VM/SP environment, a control program (CP) disk file that defines each virtual machine's normal configuration: the user ID, password, normal and maximum allowable virtual storage, CP command privilege classes allowed, dispatching priority, logical editing symbols to be used, account number, and CP options desired. In APPN, this is a database that lists names of resources and records the CP name of the node where each resource is located. Another definition of a directory is the subdivision of a volume, available in the hierarchical file system. A directory can contain files and other directories.
Directory Access Protocol	The protocol used between a directory user agent and a directory system agent.
Directory Entry	An object in the directory information base to model information. It can be an object entry or an alias entry.
Directory Information Base	A set of directory entries; it contains objects to which the directory provides access and which includes all the pieces of information which can be read or manipulated using the directory operations.
Directory Information Shadowing Protocol	A protocol used for shadowing between two directory service agents in the directory services standard.
Directory Information Tree	A tree structure of the directory information base.
Directory Name	Names for directory entries in the directory information base.

Directory Operational Binding Management Protocol	A protocol used by directory service agents to activate showing agreement. This allows directory service agents to establish, modify, and terminate operational bindings.
Directory Service (DS)	According to its use in OSI environments, an application service element that translates the symbolic names used by application processes into the complete network addresses used or a control point component of an APPN node that maintains knowledge of the location of networks resources.
Directory Service Agent	An application entity that offers the directory services.
Directory Service Protocol	The protocol used between two directory system agents.
Directory User Agent	An application entity that provides the Directory services.
Disable	In a loose sense similar to deactivate.
Disabled	Pertains to a state of a processing unit that prevents the occurrence of certain types of interruptions.
Discarded Packet	A piece of data, called a packet, that is intentionally destroyed.
Disconnection	Termination of a physical connection.
Discontiguous Shared Segment (DCSS)	According to IBM documentation, an area of virtual storage outside the address range of a virtual machine. It can contain read-only data or re-entrant code. It connects discontiguous segments to a virtual machine's address space so programs can be fetched.
Discretionary Controls	Security controls applied at the user's option.
Distributed Computing Environment (DCE)	An Open Software Foundation (OSF) set of standards for distributed computing. DCE is also distributed computing in the general sense of the term.
Disjoint Network	According to IBM documentation, a network of two or more subnetworks with the same network identifier that are indirectly connected, for example, through SNA network interconnection.
Disjoint SSCP	According to IBM documentation, an SSCP that does not have a direct session with other SSCPs in its network-ID subnetwork.
Disk Cache	A part of RAM that acts as an intermediate buffer when data is read from and written to file systems on secondary storage devices.

Display	Generally, refers to a terminal.
Display Server	As defined in X-Window System arenas, the software that controls the communication between client programs and the display, including the keyboard, mouse, and screen combination.
Distinguished Name	Name of a directory entry.
Distributed Directory Database	According to documentation related to IBM's APPN architecture, the complete listing of all resources in the network as maintained in individual directories scattered throughout an APPN network.
Distributed Network Directory	Synonym for distributed directory database.
Domain	That part of a computer network in which the data processing resources are under common control; or a part of the DNS naming hierarchy; syntactically, a domain name consists of a sequence of names separated by periods.
Domain Name Service (DNS)	In TCP/IP environments, a protocol for matching object names and network addresses. It was designed to replace the need to update host files of participating entities throughout a network.
Domain Name System (DNS)	The online distributed database system used to map human-readable machine names into IP addresses. DNS servers throughout the connected Internet implement a hierarchical name space that allows sites freedom in assigning machine names and addresses. DNS also supports separate mappings between mail destinations and IP addresses.
Domain Operator	According to IBM documentation, a person or program controlling operation of resources controlled by one SSCP.
Domain Search	In the context of APPN networking, a search initiated by a network node to all of its client APPN end nodes when a search request is received by a network node and that network node does not have any entry in its database for the requested resource.
Dotted Decimal Notation	A phase typical in TCP/IP network conversations, specifically refers to the addressing scheme of the Internet Protocol (IP). It is the representation of a 32-bit address consisting of four 8-bit numbers written in base 10 with periods separating them.
Double-Byte Character Set (DBCS)	A set of characters in which each is represented by 2 bytes. Languages like Japanese, Chinese, and Korean use this method to represent characters.

Downline System Load	According to Digital Equipment documentation, a DECnet for Open VMS function that permits an unattended target node to receive an operating system file image or terminal server image from another node.
DR	In SNA, dynamic reconfiguration or definite response.
Drag	In Apple and X window environments it is to press and hold down a mouse button while moving the mouse on the desktop. Typically, dragging is used with menu selecting, moving, and resizing operations.
Drain	Refers to APPC; to honor pending allocation requests before deactivating a session with a partner logical unit.
Drop Cable	In the IBM cabling system, a cable that runs from a faceplate to the distribution panel in a wiring closet. In TCP/IP networking environments where thicknet cable and transceivers are used, it is that cable between the devices' network interface card and the transceiver.
Drop Folder	In Apple environments, a type of folder (holding place) that serves as a private mailbox for individuals. Once someone places a file in a drop folder, only the owner of the drop folder can retrieve it. According to Apple documentation, users can create drop folders by setting the appropriate AppleShare or Macintosh file sharing access privileges.
DSECT	Dummy Control Section.
DSname	Data Set Name.
DSRLST (Direct Search List)	In SNA, a message unit that contains a search request sent throughout subarea networks to obtain information about a network resource such as its name, routing information, and status information.
DTE/DCE Interface	The physical interface and link access procedures between data terminal equipment (DTE) and data circuit-terminating equipment (DCE).
Dump	A term used frequently in SNA environments. Typically it means to obtain the contents of some aspect of memory. Specifically, it means to record, at a particular instant, the contents of all or part of one storage device in another storage device. It has also been defined as the contents of memory used for debugging. A core dump means extracting the contents of main memory. A VTAM dump is used loosely to refer to reading data areas in IBM's VTAM program offering.
Duplex	Pertaining to communication in which data can be sent and received at the same time.

DVT	Destination Vector Table.
Dynamic	In a generic sense, it means to do something on the fly. A more specific explanation is, to perform an operation that does not require a predetermined or fixed time.
Dynamic Node ID Assignment	According to Apple documentation, the AppleTalk addressing scheme that assigns node IDs dynamically, rather than associating a permanent address with each node. Dynamic node ID assignment facilitates addition and removal of nodes from the network by preventing conflicts between old node IDs and new node IDs.
Dynamic Path Update	A generic reference meaning the process of changing network path parameters for sending information without regenerating complete configuration tables.
Dynamic Reconfiguration Data Set (DRDS)	According to IBM documentation, a term used in VTAM. It refers to a data set used for storing definition data that can be applied to a generated communication controller configuration at the operator's request, or can be used to accomplish dynamic reconfiguration of NCP, local SNA, and packet major nodes. This type of reconfiguration data set can be used dynamically to add PUs and LUs, delete PUs and LUs, and move PUs. It is activated with the VARY DREDS operator command.
Dynamic Window	A window that may change its title or reposition any of the objects within its content area.
EBCDIC (Extended Binary-Coded Decimal Interchange Code)	IBM's basic character set used to represent data within the SNA environment. It consists of 8-bit coded characters.
Echo	In data communication, a reflected signal on a communications channel.
Electronic Data Interchange (EDI)	A set of standard data formats for electronic information exchange.
Element	This term has meanings in different networking environments; in SNA, it is the particular resource within a subarea that is identified by an element address.
Element Address	According to IBM documentation, a value in the element address field of the network address identifying a specific resource within a subarea.
Electromagnetic Interference (EMI)	A type of noise that is the result of currents induced in electric conductors.

**Emulation
Program (EP)**
A program that simulates the functions of another program. A generic example could be a 3270 terminal emulation program. Other possibilities also exist.

EN
In IBM's APPN architecture manuals, an APPN End node.

Enable
To make functional; in a loose sense, to activate.

Enabled
The state of being capable of performing work.

Encapsulate
Generally agreed upon in the internetworking community as surrounding one protocol with another protocol for the purpose of passing the foreign protocol through the native environment.

Encipher
According to IBM documentation, to scramble data or to convert it to a secret code that masks the meaning of the data to any unauthorized recipient. In VTAM, to convert clear data into enciphered data.

Encrypt
Synonym for encipher.

Encryption
The process of transforming data into an unintelligible form.

End Bracket
A term specifically used in SNA: the value of the end bracket indicator in the request header of the first request of the last chain of the bracket. The value denotes the end of the bracket.

END Node
In APPN, a node that can receive packets addressed to it and send packets to other nodes. It cannot route packets from other nodes.

**END Node
Domain**
That area defined by an end node control point, attached links, and its local LUs.

End-user
Defined by IBM documentation as either a program or a human.

**End-user
Verification**
LU6.2 identification check of end-users by means of identifiers and passwords on the attached Function Management Headers (FMHs).

Entry Mask
According to Digital Equipment documentation on VAX systems, a word whose bits represent the registers to be saved when a procedure is called with a CALLS or CALLG instruction, and restored when the procedure executes a RET instruction.

Entry Point
According to IBM documentation, a type 2.0, 2.1, 4, or 5 node that provides distributed network management support. It sends network management data about itself and the resources it controls to a focal point for centralized processing, and it receives and executes focal-point initiated commands to manage and control its resources.

ES-IS Routing
An Open Systems term used to refer a routing exchange protocol that provides an automated means for ISs and ESs on a subnetwork dynamically to determine the existence of each other. It also means to permit an IS to inform an ES of a potentially better route toward a destination.

Ethernet	A data link-level protocol. Version 2.0 was defined by Digital Equipment Corporation, Intel Corporation, and the Xerox Corporation in 1982. It specified a data rate of 10Mb/sec, a maximum station distance of 2.8 km, a maximum stations number of 1024, a shielded coaxial cable using baseband signaling, functionality of CSMA/CD, and a best-effort delivery system.
Ethernet Meltdown	A term used where Ethernet protocol is used as the data link layer protocol in a network. It is an event that causes saturation or near saturation on an Ethernet data link. This scenario usually results from illegal or misrouted packets and lasts a short time.
EtherTalk	A term used in Apple and Ethernet environments; it is software that enables AppleTalk protocols to run over industry standard Ethernet technology.
Event	A predefined occurrence in a given network. In SNA (NetView), it is a record indicating irregularities of operation in physical elements of a network.
Event Class	In Apple documentation, an attribute that identifies a group of related Apple events. The event class appears in the message field of the Apple event's event record. In conjunction with the event ID attribute, the event class specifies what action an Apple event performs.
Event ID	In Apple documentation, an attribute that identifies a particular Apple event within a group of related Apple events. In conjunction with the event class attribute, the event ID specifies what action an Apple event performs.
Exception	An abnormal condition when compared to what has been predefined as a normal condition.
Exception Response (ER)	In IBM documentation, a protocol requested in the response-requested field of a Request Header that directs the receiver to return a response only if the request is unacceptable as received or cannot be processed.
Exception Service Routine	In Digital Equipment documentation, a routine by which VAX and AXP hardware initially pass control to service an exception. An exception service routine passes control to a general exception dispatcher that attempts to locate a condition handler further to service the exception.
Exchange Identification (XID)	In SNA, a specific type of basic link unit that used to convey node and link characteristics between adjacent nodes. In the SNA network, XIDs are exchanged between link stations before and during link activation to establish and negotiate link and node characteristics, and after link activation to communicate changes in these characteristics.

EXEC
In IBM documentation, in a VM operating system, a user-written command file that contains CMS commands, other user-written commands, and execution-control statements, such as branches.

Executable Image
An image that can be run in a process. When run, an executable image is read from a file for execution in a process.

Executive
A generic name for the collection of procedures included in the operating system software that provides the operating system's basic control and monitoring functions.

Executive Mode
In Digital Equipment documentation, the second-most-privileged processor access mode. The Open VMS Record Management Services and many of the operating system's system service procedures execute in executive mode.

Exit
To execute an instruction within a portion of a program in order to terminate the execution of that portion.

Exit List (EXLST)
In IBM documentation, in VTAM, a control block that contains the addresses of routines that receive control when specified events occur during execution.

Exit Program
Synonym for exit routine.

Exit Routine
One of two types of routines: installation exit routes or User exit routes.

Expedited Flow
According to IBM's documentation, a data flow designated in the transmission header used to carry network control, session control, and various data flow control request/response units. Expedited flow is separate from the normal flow which carries primarily end-user data.

Explicit Route (ER)
In IBM documentation, in SNA, a series of one or more transmission groups that connect two subarea nodes. It is identified by an origin subarea address, a destination subarea address, an explicit route number, and a reverse explicit route number.

Explicit Route Length
The number of transmission groups in an explicit route.

EXT
External Trace File.

Extended Architecture (XA)
In IBM documentation, an extension to System/370 architecture. It takes advantage of changing the addressability of the hardware architecture.

Extended Attribute Block
In Digital Equipment documentation, an Open VMS Record Management Services user data structure that contains additional file attributes beyond those expressed in the file access block, such as boundary types and file protection information.

Extended Binary-Coded Decimal Interchange Code (EBCDIC)	IBM's coded character set of 256 8-bit characters and control functions.
Extended Network Addressing	In IBM's traditional subarea networking this is the addressing system that splits addresses into an 8-bit subarea and a 15-bit element portion. The subarea portion of the address is used to address host processors or communication controllers. The element portion is used to permit processors or controllers to address resources.
Extended Recovery Facility (XRF)	In SNA, a facility that provides an alternate subsystem to take over sessions from the failing subsystem.
Extended Subarea Addressing	In IBM documentation, a network addressing system used in a network with more than 255 subareas.
Fan Out Box	In LAN circles this refers to a device that functions like a hub. It provides the capability for multiple connections to make a central connection.
Fiber Distributed Data Interface (FDDI)	An IEEE 802-compatible physical and data link control standard for a 100-Mbps fiber ring or an American National Standards Institute (ANSI) standard for a 100-megabit-per-second LAN using optical fibers. A data-link protocol compatible to the IEEE 802 specification.
FDM (Frequency Division Multiplexing)	A technique that provides for division of frequency bandwidth into smaller sub-bands to provide each user exclusive use of a sub-band.
Field-Formatted	In SNA, this pertains to requests or responses encoded into fields, each having a specified format such as binary codes, bit-significant flags, and symbolic names.
File Definition Language	In Digital Equipment documentation, a special-purpose language used to write specifications for data files. The specifications are written in text files called FDL files; they are then used by Open VMS Record Management Services utilities and library routines to create the actual data files.
File Filter Function	In Apple documentation, a function supplied by application for determining which files the user can open through a standard file dialog box.
File Header	In Digital Equipment documentation, a block in the index file describing a file on a Files–11 disk structure. The file header contains information needed by the file system to find and use the file. Some of this information is displayed when the DCL command DIRECTORY is entered. There is at least one file header for every file on the disk.

File ID	In the Apple environment, an unchanging number assigned by the file manager to identify a file on a volume. When it establishes a file ID, the file manager records the file name and parent directory ID of the file.
File Identifier	In Digital Equipment documentation, a 6-byte value used uniquely to identify a file on a Files-11 disk volume. The file number, file sequence number, and relative volume number are contained in the file identifier.
File Organization	In Digital Equipment networks, the particular file structure used as the physical arrangement of the data comprising a file on mass storage media. The Open VMS Record Management Services file organizations are sequential, relative, and indexed.
Files-11	A Digital Equipment term used to refer to the name of the structure used by the RSX-111, IAS, and Open VMS operating systems.
Files-11 Ancillary Control Process	A Digital Equipment term referring to the interface process that is the files manager for the Files-11 on-disk structure.
Files-11 On-Disk Structure Level 1	In Digital Equipment documentation, the original Files-11 structure used by IAS, RSX-11M, and RSX-11S for disk volumes. VAX systems support structure level 1 to ensure compatibility among systems AXP systems do not support structure level 1.
Files-11 On-Disk Structure Level 2	Digital Equipment reference to the second-generation disk file structure supported by The operating system. The Files-11 data structure prepares a volume to receive and store data in a way recognized by the operating system.
File System Specification Record	In Apple environments, a record that identifies a stored file or directory by volume reference number, parent directory ID, and name. The file system specification record is the file identification convention adopted by system software version 7.0.
File Server	A generic term used to refer to a computer whose primary task is to control the storage and retrieval of data from hard disks. Any number of other computers can be linked to the file server in order to use it to access data. This means that less storage space is required on the individual computer.
File Access Data Unit	A subtree of the hierarchical access structure, it is used to specify a location on a file structure.
File Attributes	Terminology with origins in OSI to refer to the properties of a file that do not depend on an FTAM dialogue.
File Directory	The OSI equivalent of a directory in a file system.

File Transfer, Access and Management	An OSI application protocol standard which allows remote files to be transferred, accessed and managed.
File Translator	A generic term referring to a utility program that converts a file from one computer format to another, such as from Macintosh to DOS. Apple File Exchange is a file translator that is supplied with Macintosh system software.
Filter	A device or program that separates data, signals, or material in accordance with specified criteria.
Flow Control	In SNA, the process of managing data rate transfer between components within the network. This same concept also refers to other networking environments.
Focal Point	In IBM documentation, in NetView, the focal point domain is the central host domain. It is the central control point for any management services element containing control of the network management data.
Font Size	The size of the glyphs in a font in points, measured from the baseline of one line of text to the baseline of the next line of single-spaced text.
Font Style	How a font (character or number) is represented.
Foreground Process	In the X-window system, a process that has the terminal window's attention. This is in contrast to a background process.
Foreground Process	A process currently interacting with the user.
Formatted System Services	A term used in IBM's SNA, specifically VTAM. It is a portion of VTAM that provides certain system services as a result of receiving a field-formatted command, such as an initiate or terminate command.
Fragment	A term used in TCP/IP network environments. One of the pieces that results when an IP router divides an IP datagram into smaller pieces for transmission across a network. Fragments use the same format as datagrams. Fields in the IP header declare whether a datagram is a fragment, and if so, the offset of the fragment in the original datagram. IP software at the receiving end must reassemble fragments into complete datagrams.
Frame	One definition generally agreed upon: a packet as it is transmitted across a serial line. The term's origin comes from character-oriented protocols; in OSI environments, a data structure pertaining to a particular area of data. It also consists of slots that can accept values of specific attributes.

Frame Relay	A protocol defined by the CCITT and ANSI that identifies how data frames are switched in higher speeds than X.25, but in packet mode.
Frame-Relay Frame Handler (FRFH)	A router function using the address field in a frame-relay frame.
Frame-Relay Switching Equipment (FRSE)	A device capable of relaying frames to the next device in a frame-relay network en route to a frame-relay terminal equipment destination.
Frame-Relay Switching Equipment Subport Set	In Frame Relay technology, the set of primary and optional substitute subports within an FRSE that are used for a given segment set.
Frame-Relay Switching Equipment Support	An agreed-upon set of NCP frame-relay functions that include the frame-relay frame handler functions, defined by ANSI Standards T1.617 and T1.618.
Frame-Relay Terminal Equipment (FRTE)	In frame-relay technology based networks, a device capable of connecting to a frame-relay network. An FRTE adds a frame header when sending data to the frame-relay network and removes the frame header when receiving data from the frame-relay network.
Frequency	The rate of signal oscillation, expressed in hertz.
Frequency Division Multiplexing (FDM)	A method of multiplexing data on a carrier channel based upon frequency.
FTAM	A term from the OSI networking protocols; it manipulates file transfer, access, and management.
FTP (File Transfer Protocol)	In TCP/IP-based networks, a program that runs as a TCP application. It does not move a file from one place to another, but copies a source file to a destination file. Consequently, two files exist unless one is deleted. FTP consists of client and server. The FTP client is used to invoke the FTP program; the server is used to serve the request of the client. In normal implementations, FTP uses ports 20 and 21.
Full Duplex (FDX)	Synonym for duplex.
Full-Screen Mode	The contents of an entire terminal screen can be displayed at once.

Function Management Header (FMH)	In IBM documentation, one or more headers, optionally present in the leading request units of an RU chain, that allow one LU to select a transaction program or device as the session partner. It also permits other control functions, such as changing the destination or the characteristics of the data during the session, and transmits between session partners status or user information about the destination.
Gateway	In internetworking terminology, it performs protocol conversion between dissimilar protocols. This may be upper-layer protocol conversion only, or may include lower-layer protocol conversion; this depends upon the vendor offering and the implementation. For example, TCP/IP to SNA gateways, DECnet to SNA gateways, and AppleTalk to TCP/IP gateways exist. In SNA, IBM uses the term in multiple ways. It is the combination of machines and programs that provides address translation, name translation, and SSCP rerouting between independent SNA networks. In SNA, a gateway consists of one "gateway" NCP and at least one "gateway" VTAM.
Gateway-Capable Host	In IBM documentation, a host node that has a defined Net ID and SSCP Name but does not perform gateway control functions.
Gateway NCP	In IBM documentation, an NCP that performs address translation permitting cross-network session traffic. In this sense the gateway NCP connects two or more independent SNA networks.
Gateway VTAM	In IBM documentation, an SSCP capable of cross-network session initiation, termination, takedown, and session outage notification.
Generalized Trace Facility (GTF)	In SNA, an optional program that records significant system events, such as supervisor calls and start I/O operations, for the purpose of problem determination.
Generation	In SNA, the process of assembling and link editing definition statements so that resources can be identified to all the necessary programs in a network. This is the origin of the term Gen.
Generation definition	In IBM documentation, the definition statement of a resource used in generating a program.
Generic Unbind	Synonym for session deactivation request.
Global	Affecting the entire file, the entire system, or the entire image, depending on context.
Global Symbol	A symbol defined in a module of a program potentially available for reference by another module. The linker resolves (matches references with definitions) global symbols.

Global Symbol Table	In a library, an index of defined global symbols used to access the modules defining the global symbols. The linker also puts global symbol tables into an image.
Glyph	A distinct visual representation of a character that a display device, such as a monitor or printer, can display.
Gold Key	In Digital Equipment documentation, the upper left key on VT100 series terminal keypads; it enables alternate keypad functions.
GOSIP (Government Open Systems Interconnect Profile)	A Federal Information Processing Standard that specifies a well-defined set of OSI protocols for government communications systems procurement. GOSIP was intended to eliminate the use of TCP/IP protocols on government internets, but clarifications have specified that government agencies can continue to use TCP/IP.
Government OSI Profiles	Functional standards used by the government agencies in their procurement of open system equipment and software.
Graphical Data Display Manager (GDDM)	In IBM documentation, used in the NetView Performance Monitor (NPM), in conjunction with the Presentation Graphics Feature (PGF) to generate online graphs in the NPM graphic subsystem.
Gray Region	Typically used in X-window or Apple environments. A gray region defines the desktop, or the display area of all active devices, excluding the menu bar on the main screen and the rounded corners on the outermost screens. It is the area in which windows can be moved.
Group	Generically defined as a set of users in a system.
Group Control System (GCS)	A VM component that provides multiprogramming and shared memory support.
Guest	Used in the Apple environment to mean a user who is logged on to an AppleShare file server without a registered user name and password. A guest cannot own a directory or folder.
Half-Duplex (HD, HDX)	Transmission in only one direction at a time.
Half-Duplex Operation	Data-link transmission where data can be in both directions one way at a time.
Half-Duplex Transmission	Data transmission in either direction, one direction at a time.
Half-Open Connection	A connection scenario when one end connection is established, but the other is unreachable or has disposed of its connection information.

Half-Session	In IBM documentation, a session-layer component consisting of the data-flow control and transmission control components. These comprise one end of a session.
Hardcopy	Generally a printout.
Hardware Address	Also called a hard address. In Ethernet networks, this is the 48-bit address assigned to the Ethernet network interface card. In token ring is the 12-digit hex address assigned to the network interface card.
Hardware Monitor	In SNA, a component of NetView. It is called the network problem determination application and is used to identify network problems, in hardware, software, and microcode.
Header	Control information that precedes user data in a frame or datagram that passes through networks. Specifically, this portion of a message contains control information.
Hertz	The number of cycles per second.
Heartbeat	Technically, signal quality error (SQE). It is a voltage in a receiver that can be sent to a controller (interface board) to inform the controller that collision detection is functional.
Help Balloon	A term typically used in Apple environments; a rounded-type window containing explanatory information for the user.
Help Panel	Also called a help menu; a display of information concerning a particular topic requested.
Hierarchical Routing	From a TCP/IP perspective, this type of routing is based on a hierarchical addressing scheme. Most TCP/IP routing is based on a two-level hierarchy in which an IP address is divided into a network portion until the datagram reaches a gateway that can deliver it directly. The concept of subnets introduces additional levels of hierarchical routing.
Hierarchy	In SNA, this type of networking is considered traditional. Traditional SNA networking requires VTAM for session establishment. The networking term can be contrasted with peer networking, which does not require an intervening component for session establishment.
High Performance Option (HPO)	In IBM documentation, an extension to VM/SP. The fundamental purpose of HPO is to provide performance and operation enhancements for large system environments.

Home Directory   Generally, this concept exists in all hosts. It is the place where a user originates there operations in any system. For example, in UNIX the `.profile` file contains the beginning place for a user. This `.profile` is customized for users and the beginning place, or home base can differ. In Digital Equipment's VMS environment, the same is true but different terms are used. So it is with IBM's MVS, VM, and VSE operating systems.

Hop   In APPN, a portion of a route that has no intermediate nodes. It consists only of a single transmission group connecting adjacent nodes. Another definition is: the moving of a packet through a router.

Hop Count   A measure of distance between two points in the Internet. Each hop count corresponds to one router separating a source from a destination (for example, a hop count of 3 indicates that three routers separate a source from a destination). The term is generally used in TCP/IP networks where the basic definition is a measure of distance between two points in an internet. A hop count of n means that n routers separate the source and destination.

Host Master Key   In SNA, deprecated term for master cryptography key.

Host Node   In Digital Equipment's DECnet for Open VMS network, a node that provides services for another node. For the VAX Packetnet System interface, a node that accesses a packet switching data network by means of an X.25 multihost connector node. It is also referred to as the node that makes a device available to other nodes in a VMS cluster configuration. A host node can be either a processor that adds the device to the mass storage control protocol server database or a hierarchical storage controller server. In IBM documentation, it is defined as a processor.

Host Processor   A processor that controls all or part of a user application network. Normally, the data communication access method resides on this host.

Hpterm   In Hewlett-Packard documentation, a type of terminal window, sometimes called a "terminal emulator program" that emulates HP2622 terminals, complete with softkeys. In the HP-UX environment, the hpterm window is the default window for the X environment.

IAB (Internet Architecture Board)   A group related to TCP/IP protocol. People who set policy and review standards for TCP/IP and the Internet. The IAB was reorganized in 1989; technically-oriented individuals moved to research and engineering subgroups. See also IRTF and IETF.

ICMP (Internet Control Message Protocol)	Specific to the TCP/IP protocol suite; an integral part of the Internet Protocol. It handles error and control messages. Routers and hosts use ICMP to send reports of problems about datagrams back to the original source that sent the datagram. ICMP also includes an echo request/reply used to test whether a destination is reachable and responding.
Icon	A small, graphic representation of an object on the root window. Icons are found in Apple hosts as well as on the X-window system.
Icon Family	In the Apple family of products, the set of icons that represent an object, such as an application or document, on the desktop.
Idle State	A state in which the Macintosh portable computer slows from its normal 16-MHz clock speed to a 1-MHz clock speed. The power manager puts the Macintosh portable in the idle state when the system has been in active for 15 seconds.
IETF (Internet Engineering Task Force)	A group of people concerned with short- and medium-term problems with TCP/IP and the connected Internet. IETF is divided into six areas which are further divided into working groups.
Image	Procedures and data bound together by the linker to form a program executed by the process. There are three types of images: executable, sharable, and system.
Image Mode	The default screen mode using multiple image planes for a single screen. The number of image planes determines the variety of colors available to the screen.
Image Name	The name of the file in which an image is stored.
Image Planes	The primary display planes on a device that supports two sets of planes. The other set of display planes is known as the overlay planes. These two sets of planes are treated as two separate screens in stacked mode and one screen in combined mode.
Image Privileges	The privileges assigned to an image when it is installed.
Inactive	This term has a variety of meanings depending upon context or environment. It is generally agreed that something is not operational and may pertain to a node or device not connected or not available for connection to another node or device. In IBM's AIX operating system, it pertains to a window that does not have an input focus. In SNA, particularly VTAM, the state of a resource, a major or minor node not activated or for which the VARY INACT command has been issued.
Incoming Call Packet	A call-supervision packet transmitted by a data circuit-terminating equipment to inform a called data terminal equipment that another DTE has requested a call.

Independent Logical Unit (ILU)	In SNA, a type of LU that does not require VTAM for session establishment after the initial download of parameters.
Index	A structure that permits retrieval of records in an indexed file by key value.
Indexed File Organization	A Digital Equipment type of file organization in which a file contains records and a primary key index used to process the records sequentially by index or randomly by index.
Indexed Sequential File	In Digital Equipment documentation, a record file in which each record has one or more data keys embedded in it. Records in the file are individually accessible by specifying a key associated with the record.
Index File	In Digital Equipment documentation, the file on Files-11 volume that contains the access information for all files on the volume and enables the operating system to identify and access the volume.
Index File Bitmap	In Digital Equipment documentation, a table in the index file of a Files-11 volume that indicates which file headers are in use.
Index Path	In NetWare documentation, a logical ordering of records in a Btrieve file based on the values of an index. An index path for each index in a file exists. A file may have up to 24 separate index paths.
Indirect activation	In IBM documentation, in VTAM, the activation of a lower-level resource of the resource hierarchy as a result of SCOPE or ISTATUS specifications related to an activation command naming a higher-level resource.
Indirect deactivation	In IBM documentation, in VTAM, the deactivation of a lower-lever reserve of the resource hierarchy as a result of a deactivation command naming a higher-level resource.
Information (I) Format	A format used for information transfer.
Information (I) Frame	A frame in I format used for numbered information transfer.
Information Management System/Virtual Storage (IMS/VS)	A software subsystem offering of IBM, it is a database/data communication system that can manage complex databases and networks.
Information/ Management	A feature of the Information/System that provides interactive systems management applications for problem, change, and configuration management.

Inhibited	According to IBM, a logical unit that has indicated to its system services control point that it is temporarily not ready to establish LU-LU sessions. An initiate request for a session with an inhibited LU will be rejected by the SSCP. The LU can separately indicate whether this applies to its ability to act as a primary logical unit or a secondary logical unit.
Initial Program Load (IPL)	An IBM term, referring to the initialization procedure that causes an operating system to commence operation. The process by which a configuration image is loaded into storage at the beginning of a work day or after a system malfunction. The process of loading system programs and preparing a system to run jobs.
INITIATE	In SNA, a network services request sent from a logical unit to a system services control point requesting that an LU-LU session be established.
Initiating LU (ILU)	In SNA, the LU that first requests a session setup. The ILU may be one of the LUs that will participate in the session, or it may be a third-party LU. If it is one of the session participants, the ILU is also called the origin LU.
Initiator	In OSI, a file service user that requests an FTAM establishment.
Inoperative	The condition of a resource that has been active, but is no longer so. The resource may have failed, received an INOP request, or be suspended while a reactivate command is being processed.
Input/Output Channel	In a data processing system, a functional unit that handles transfer of data between internal and peripheral equipment. In a computing system, a functional unit, controlled by a processor, that handles transfer of data between processor storage and local peripheral devices. In IBM terminology, a specific type of path, either parallel or serial.
Installation exit	The means (or way by which) an IBM software product may be modified by a customer's system programmers to change or extend the functions of the IBM software product. Such modifications consist of exit routines written to replace one or more existing modules of an IBM software product, or to add one or more modules or subroutines to an IBM software product, for the purpose of modifying or extending the functions of the product.
Installation Exit Routine	A routine written by a user to take control at an installation exit of an IBM software product.
Installation-wide Exit	Synonym for installation exit.

Integrated Communication Adapter (ICA)	A communication adapter that is an integral part of the host processor.
Integrity Control	In Novell documentation, the method used to ensure the completeness of files. Specifically, Btrieve uses pre-imaging and NetWare's Transaction Tracking System to guarantee integrity.
Intensive Mode Recording (IMR)	An NCP function that forces recording of temporary errors for a specified resource.
Interapplication Communication (IAC)	In Apple terminology, a collection of features, provided by the edition manager, Apple event manager, event manager, and PPC toolbox, that help applications work together.
Internet	A collection of networks, routers, gateways and other networking devices that use the TCP/IP protocol suite and function as a single, cooperative virtual network. The Internet provides universal connectivity and three levels of network services: unreliable, connectionless-packet delivery; reliable, full-duplex stream delivery; and application-level services like electronic mail that build on the first two.
Internet Address	According to Apple documentation, an AppleTalk address that includes the socket number, node ID, and network number. According to TCP/IP documentation, the 32-bit address assigned to the host. It is a software address that on internets is locally managed, but on the Internet is dictated to the user (entity desiring access to the Internet).
Internet Packet Exchange (IPX)	A Novell protocol that operates at layer three, according to the OSI model. It is used in the NetWare protocols and is similar to IP in TCP/IP.
Interpersonal Message	According to OSI-related documents, as a message type used for human-to-human communication in MHS.
Interpersonal Messaging System	According to multiple explanations in the OSI community, an MHS system supporting the communication of interpersonal messages.
InterPoll	In Apple documentation, software from Apple that helps administrators monitor the network and diagnose the sources of problems.
Inter-user Communication Vehicle (IUCV)	In IBM documentation, it is a VM facility for passing data between virtual machines and VM components.
Interactive Problem Control System (IPCS)	In IBM documentation, a component of VM that permits online problem management, interactive problem diagnosis, online debugging for disk-resident CP abend dumps, problem tracking, and problem reporting.

Interactive System Productivity Facility (ISPF)	An IBM-licensed program that serves as a full-screen editor and dialogue manager. Used for writing application programs, it provides a means of generating standard screen panels and interactive dialogues between the application programmer and terminal user.
Interchange Node	A new type of node supported by VTAM beginning in Version 4.1. It acts as both as an APPN network node and a subarea type 5 node to transform APPN protocols to subarea protocols and vice versa.
Interconnected Networks	According to IBM, SNA networks connected by gateway NCPs.
Interface	A shared boundary between two functional units, defined by functional, signal, or other characteristics, as appropriate. The concept includes the specification of the connection of two devices having different functions. Hardware, software, or both, that links systems, programs, or devices.
Intermediate Node	A node at the end of more than one branch.
Intermediate Routing Node (IRN)	A node containing an intermediate routing function.
Intermediate Session Routing (ISR)	An APPN term for a type of routing function within an APPN network node that provides session-level flow control and outage reporting for all sessions that pass through the node whose end points are elsewhere.
Intermediate SSCP	In SNA, an SSCP along a session initiation path that owns neither of the LUs involved in a cross-network LU-LU session.
International Organization for Standardization (ISO)	An organization of national standards bodies from various countries established to promote development of standards to facilitate international exchange of goods and services, and develop cooperation in intellectual, scientific, technological, and economic activity.
Internet Protocol (IP)	A protocol used to route data from its source to its destination. The TCP/IP standard protocol that defines the IP datagram as the unit of information passed across an internet and provides the basis for connectionless, best-effort packet delivery service. IP includes the ICMP control and error message protocol as an integral part. The entire protocol suite is often referred to as TCP/IP because TCP and IP are the two fundamental protocols.
Interpret Table	In IBM's VTAM, an installation-defined correlation list that translates an argument into a string of eight characters. This table can translate logon data into the name of an application program for which the logon is intended.

IP Address

The 32-bit dotted decimal address assigned to hosts that want to participate in a TCP/IP internet or the Internet. IP addresses are software addresses. An IP address consists of a network portion and a host portion. The partition makes routing efficient.

IP Datagram

A term used with TCP/IP networks; a basic unit of information passed across a TCP/IP internet. An IP datagram is to an internet as a hardware packet is to a physical network. It contains a source and destination address along with data.

IRSG (Internet Research Steering Group)

A committee consisting of the IRTF research group chairpersons plus the IRTF chairperson, who direct and coordinate research related to TCP/IP and the connected Internet.

IRTF (Internet Research Task Force)

A group of people working on research problems related to TCP/IP and the connected Internet.

ISDN (Integrated Services Digital Network)

A set of standards being developed within ANSI, ISO, and CCITT for the delivery of various services over digital networks.

IS-IS Routing

Routing between ISs within a routing domain.

Isode

In the ISO environment, a set of public domain software subroutines that provide an interface between the GOSIP-specified session layer (ISO) and the DoD-specified transport layer (TCP/IP). Allows the development of applications that will execute over both OSI and TCP/IP protocol stacks as a migration path from TCP/IP networks to GOSIP networks.

Istatus

In IBM documentation, in VTAM and NCP, a definition specification method for indication the initial status of resources.

Job

A way by which an accounting unit is assigned to a process and its subprocesses, if any, and all subprocesses that they create. Jobs are classified as batch and interactive. For example, the job controller creates an interactive job to handle a user's requests when the user logs into the system, and it creates a batch job when the symbiont manager passes a command input file to it.

Job Controller

The system process that establishes a job's process context, starts a process running the `LOGIN` image for the job, maintains the accounting record for the job, manages symbionts, and terminates a process and its subprocesses.

Job Control Language

A language in IBM's MVS operating system environment used to identify a job to an operating system and to describe the job's requirements.

Job Information Block	A data structure associated with a job that contains the quotas pooled by all processes in the job.
Katakana	A character set of symbols used in one of the two common Japanese phonetic alphabets, primarily to write foreign words phonetically.
Keyboard Binding	In an X-window environment, an association of a special key press with a window manager function. For example, pressing the special keys Shift Esc displays the system menu of the active window.
Keyboard Resources	In Apple documentation, a category of files stored in a resource file by the resource manager and used by the Macintosh script management system, including the international utilities package.
Keyboard Script	The script for keyboard input. It determines the character input method and the keyboard mapping: what character codes are produced when a sequence of keys is pressed.
Keyword	In Apple documentation, a four-character code used uniquely to identify the descriptor record for either an attribute or a parameter in an Apple event. In Apple Event Manager functions, constants are typically used to represent the four-character codes. In programming languages, a lexical unit that, in certain contexts, characterizes some language constructs. In some contexts, IF characterizes an if-statement. A keyword normally has the form of an identifier. One of the predefined words of an artificial language. A significant and informative word in a title or document that describes the content of that document. A name or symbol that identifies a parameter.
Keyword Operand	A term used in the IBM environment, particularly with JCL. It is an operand that consists of a keyword followed by one or more values (such as DSNAME=HELLO).
Keyword Parameter	A parameter that consists of a keyword followed by one or more values.
LAP Manager	In Apple documentation, a set of operating system utilities that provide a standard interface between the AppleTalk protocols and the various link access protocols, such as LocalTalk (LLAP), EtherTalk (ELAP), and TokenTalk (TLAP).
Least-Weight Route	In IBM documentation, in APPN, the one route calculated by topology and routing services to have the lowest total weight after TRS compares the node characteristics and TG characteristics of each intermediate node and intermediate TG of each possible route for the class of service requested, and computes the total combined weight for nodes and TGs in each route. After a least-weight route is calculated between two given nodes, the result may be stored to prevent repetition of this calculation in future route selections.

LEN Connection   A link over which LEN protocols are used.

LEN Node   A term used in APPN. In IBM documentation, a node that supports independent LU protocols but does not support CP-CP sessions. It may be a peripheral node attached to a boundary node in a subarea network, an end node attached to an APPN network node in an APPN network, or a peer-connected node directly attached to another LEN node or APPN end node.

Level 1 Router   In Digital Equipment documentation, a DECnet for Open VMS node that can send and receive packets, and route packets from one node to another node within a single area.

Level 2 Router   In Digital Equipment documentation, a DECnet for Open VMS node that can send and receive packets, and route packets from one node to another within its own area and between areas.

Lexical Function   In Digital Equipment documentation, a command language construct that the Digital Command Language command interpreter evaluates and substitutes before it parses a command string.

Librarian   According to Digital Equipment, a program that allows the user to create, update, modify, list, and maintain object library, help library, text library, and assembler macro library files.

Limited Resource   In IBM documentation, a connection facility that causes a session traversing it to be terminated if no session activity is detected for a specified period of time.

Limited-Resource Session   In IBM documentation, a session that traverses a limited-resource link. This session is terminated if no session activity is detected for a specified period of time.

Line   The portion of a data circuit external to data circuit-terminating equipment that connects the DCE to a data switching exchange that connects a DCE to one or more other DCEs, or that connects a DSE to another DSE.

Line Control   Synonym for data-link control protocol.

Line Control Discipline   Synonym for link protocol.

Line Discipline   Synonym for link protocol.

Line Group   One or more telecommunication lines of the same type that can be activated and deactivated as a unit.

Line Speed   The number of binary digits that can be sent over a telecommunication line in one second, expressed in bits per second (bps).

Line Switching   Synonym for circuit switching.

Link The combination of the link connection (the transmission medium) and two link stations, one at each end of the link connection.

Link Access Protocol (LAP) In Digital Equipment documentation, a set of procedures used for link control on a packet switching data network. X.25 defines two sets of procedures. LAP is the data terminal equipment/data circuit-terminating equipment interface is defined as operating in two-way simultaneous asynchronous response mode with the DTE and DCE containing a primary and secondary function. LAPB is the DTE/DCE interface defined as operating in two-way asynchronous balanced mode.

Link Access Protocol In Apple documentation, an AppleTalk protocol that controls the access of a node to the network hardware. A link access protocol makes it possible for many nodes to share the same communications hardware.

Link-Attached Pertaining to devices that are connected to a controlling unit by a data link.

Link Connection The physical equipment providing two-way communication between one link station and one or more other link stations; for example, a telecommunication line and data circuit-terminating equipment.

Link-Connection Segment A part of the configuration located between two resources listed consecutively in the service point command service query link-configuration request list.

Link Level The physical connection between two nodes and/or the protocols used to govern that connection.

Link Problem Determination Aid (LPDA) In IBM documentation, a series of procedures used to test the status of and to control DCEs, the communication line, and the remote device interface. These procedures, or a subset of them, are implemented by host programs (such as NetView and VTAM), communication controller programs (such as NCP), and IBM LPDA DCEs.

Link Protocol Rules for sending and receiving data over a medium.

Link Services Layer (LSL) Routes packets between LAN boards with their MLIDs and protocol stacks. The LSL maintains LAN board, protocol stack, and packet buffer information.

Link Station In IBM documentation, the hardware and software components within a node representing a connection to an adjacent node over a specific link. In VTAM, a named resource within an APPN or a subarea node that represents the connection to another APPN or subarea node attached by an APPN or a subarea link. In the resource hierarchy in a subarea network, the link station is subordinate to the subarea link.

Little Endian	A storage format or transmission of binary data in which the least-significant byte comes first.
LLC (Logical Link Control)	In OSI documentation, a sublayer in the data link layer of the OSI model. The LLC provides the basis for an unacknowledged connectionless service or connection-oriented service on the local area network.
Local	Pertaining to a device accessed directly without use of a telecommunication line.
Local Access	The ability to execute a program on the computer to which you are attached.
Local Address	In IBM documentation, in SNA, an address used in a peripheral node in place of a network address and transformed to or from a network address by the boundary function in a subarea node.
Local Area Network (LAN)	A collection of computers and other related devices connected together on the premises within a limited geographical area.
Local Area Transport	In Digital Equipment documentation, a communications protocol that the operating system uses within a local area network to communicate with terminal servers.
Local Area VAX Cluster System	In Digital Equipment documentation, a type of VAX cluster configuration in which cluster communication is carried out over the Ethernet by software that emulates certain computer interconnect, or CI, port functions. A VAX cluster node can be a VAX or Micro VAX processor; hierarchical storage controllers (HSCs) are not used.
Local Client	A term in an X window environment referring to a program running on the local computer, the same system that is running the X server.
Local Directory Database	In IBM documentation, a set of LUs in a network known at a particular node. The resources included are all those in the node's domain as well as any cache entries.
Local Management Interface (LMI)	A set of operational procedures and messages as well as DLCI 1023 are defined in Frame-Relay Specification with Extensions, a document based on proposed T1S1 standards, which are copyrighted by Digital Equipment Corporation, Northern Telecom, Inc., and StrataCom, Inc. In this context, the term LMI is a deprecated term for link integrity verification tests (LIVT). Current meaning: any frame-relay management interface procedures, such as DLCI 1023 or DLCI 0.
Local Non-SNA Major Node	In IBM documentation, in VTAM, a major node whose minor nodes are channel-attached non-SNA terminals.
Local SNA Major Node	In IBM documentation, in VTAM, a major node whose minor nodes are channel-attached peripheral nodes.

Local Symbol
In Digital Equipment documentation, a symbol meaningful only to the module that defines it. Symbols not identified to a language processor as global symbols are considered local symbols. A language processor resolves local symbols. They are not known to the linker and cannot be made available to another object module. They can, however, be passed through the linker to the symbolic debugger.

LocalTalk
In Apple documentation, a type of AppleTalk network that is inexpensive and easy to set up. LocalTalk is commonly used to connect small- to medium-sized workgroups.

Local Topology Database
In IBM documentation, a database in an APPN NN or LEN node containing an entry for each transmission group having at least one end node for an endpoint. In an APPN end node, the database has one entry for each TG connecting to the node. In a network node, the database has an entry for each TG connecting the network node to an end node. ach entry describes the current characteristics of the TG it represents. A network node has both a local and a network topology database while an end node has only a local topology database.

Locate Mode
In Digital Equipment documentation, an Open VMS Record Management Services record access technique in which a program accesses records in a Open VMS RMS I/O buffer area to reduce overhead.

Location Name
An identifier for the network location of the computer on which a port resides. The PPC toolbox provides the location name. It contains an object string, a type string, and a zone. An application can specify an alias for its location name by modifying its type string.

Log Off
To request that a session be terminated.

Log On
In SNA products, to initiate a session between an application program and a logical unit.

Logical Channel
In packet mode operation, a sending channel and a receiving channel that are used to send and receive data over a data link at the same time.

Logical Channel Identifier
A bit string in the header of a packet that associates the packet with a specific switched virtual circuit or permanent virtual circuit.

Logical Link Control (LLC) Protocol
In a LAN, the protocol that governs the exchange of transmission frames between data stations independently of how the transmission medium is shared.

Logical Name
In Digital Equipment documentation, a user specified name for any portion or all of a file specification. For example, the logical name INPUT can be assigned to a terminal device from which a program reads data entered by a user. Logical name assignments are maintained in logical name tables for each process, each group, and the

system. Logical names can be assigned translation attributes, such as terminal and concealed.

Logical Name Table
In Digital Equipment documentation, a table that contains a set of logical names and their equivalent names for a particular process, a particular group, or the system.

Logical Record
A group of related fields treated as a unit.

Logical Unit (LU)
An addressable endpoint.

Logical Unit 6.2
Those protocols and that type of LU which support advanced program-to-program communication.

Login Directory
The default directory to which a user is assigned upon logon into a system.

Logoff
In IBM documentation, in VTAM, an unformatted session-termination request. In general to terminate interaction with a system; actually, entering a command of some sort to close the connection.

Logon
In IBM documentation, in VTAM, an unformatted session-initiation request for a session between two logical units. In general, to sign on or get to the point where work can be done.

Logon Manager
A VTAM application program that provides logon services for the Transaction Processing Facility.

Logon Mode
In IBM documentation, in VTAM, a subset of session parameters specified in a logon mode table for communication with a logical unit.

Logon Mode Table
In IBM documentation, in VTAM, a set of sentries for one or more logon modes. Each logon mode is identified by a logon mode name.

Low-Entry Networking (LEN)
In IBM documentation, a capability in nodes allowing them directly to attach to one another using peer-to-peer protocols and to support multiple and parallel sessions between logical units. LEN does not provide all of the capabilities of APPN; it does not provide CP-CP session support.

Low-Entry Networking (LEN) End Node
In IBM documentation, an end node that provides all SNA end-user services, can attach directly to other nodes using peer protocols, and derives network services implicitly from an adjacent network node when attached to an APPN network without a session between its local CP and another CP.

Low-Entry Networking (LEN) Node
In IBM documentation, a node that supports independent LU protocols but does not support CP-CP sessions.

LU Group	In IBM documentation, in the NetView Performance Monitor, a file containing a list of related or unrelated logical units. The LU group is used to help simplify data collection and analysis.
LU-LU Session	A logical connection between two logical units in an SNA network that provides communication between two end-users.
LU-Mode Pair	In IBM documentation, in the VTAM implementation of the LU 6.2 architecture, the coupling of an LU name entry and a mode name entry; this coupling allows a pool of sessions with the same characteristics to be established.
LU Type	In IBM documentation, the classification of an LU in terms of SNA protocols and options it supports for a given session.
LU Type 6.2 (LU6.2)	In IBM documentation, a type of Logical Unit that supports general communication between programs in a distributed processing environment. LU6.2 is characterized by a peer relationship between transaction programs and efficient utilization of a session for multiple transactions.
LU6.2 Session	A logical connection utilizing LU6.2 protocols.
Macroinstruction	In IBM documentation, an instruction in a source language that is to be replaced by a defined sequence of instructions in the same source language and may also specify values for parameters in the replaced instructions.
Main Screen	The screen on which a menu bar appears.
Maintain System History Program (MSHP)	In IBM documentation, a program used for automating and controlling various installation, tailoring, and service activities for a VSE system.
Maintenance and Operator Subsystem (MOSS)	In IBM documentation, a subsystem of an IBM communication controller, such as 3725 or 3720, that contains a processor and operates independently of the rest of the controller. It loads and supervises the controller, runs problem determination procedures, and assists in maintaining both hardware and software.
Major Node	In IBM documentation, in VTAM, a set of resources that can be activated and deactivated as a group.
Management Information Base	A collection of managed objects; a term used with the concept of SNMP-based network management.
Management Information Tree	A tree structure of the management information base.

Management Services (MS)	In IBM documentation, one of the types of network services in control points and physical units. Management services provided to assist in the management of SNA networks include problem management, performance and accounting management, configuration management, and change management.
MASSBUS Adapter	In Digital Equipment documentation, an interface device between the backplane interconnect and the MASSBUS device.
Mass Storage Control Protocol	In Digital Equipment documentation, the software protocol used to communicate I/O commands between a VAX processor and DSA-compliant devices on the system.
Master File Directory (MFD)	In Digital Equipment documentation, the file directory on a disk volume that contains the names of all user file directories on a disk, including its own.
Matte	A term used in window-based environments; it is the border located inside the window between the client area and the frame and used to create a three-dimensional effect for the frame and window.
Media Access Control	According to OSI nomenclature, a sublayer in the data-link layer which controls access to the physical medium of a network.
Medium	A physical carrier of electrons or photons. The medium may be hard, as in a type of cable, or soft in the sense of microwave.
Medium Access Control (MAC)	A protocol that comprises the lower part of the second layer in the OSI model.
Medium Access Control Protocol	The protocol that governs access to the transmission medium to enable the exchange of data between nodes.
Medium Access Control Sublayer	The MAC sublayer supports topology-dependent functions and uses services of the physical layer to provide services to the logical link control sublayer.
Menu	A list of selections from which to make a choice.
Merge Disk	In IBM documentation, a virtual disk in the VM operating system that contains program temporary fixes after the VMFMERGE EXEC is invoked.
Message	A generic reference to meaningful data passed from one end user to another. The end user may be human or a program.
Message	In OSI documentation, a structured set of data that is sent from a user agent to one or more recipient user agents.
Message Block	In Apple documentation, a byte stream that an open application uses. It is used to send data to and receive data from another open application. The PPC toolbox delivers message blocks to an application in the same sequence in which they were sent.

Message Store	A term used in a TCP/IP environment; it refers to an entity acting as an intermediary between an user agent and its local message transfer agent.
Message Transfer Agent	In TCP/IP, a sub-part of the electronic mail component known as Simple Mail Transfer Protocol. It is an object in the Message Transfer System. MTAs use a store-and-forward method to relay messages from originator to recipient. They interact with user agents when a message is submitted, and upon delivery.
Message Unit	In IBM documentation, in SNA, the unit of data processed by any layer; for example, a basic information, path information, or request-response unit (RU).
MILNET	Originally this network was part of the ARPANET. In 1984 it was segmented for military installation usage.
Migration Data Host	In IBM documentation, a VTAM node support that acts as both an APPN end node and an SNA subarea node.
Minimize	To turn a window into an icon.
Minor Node	In IBM documentation, in VTAM, a uniquely defined resource within a major node.
MHS (Message Handling Service)	The service provided by the CCITT X.400 series of standards, consisting of a user agent to allow users to create and read electronic mail, a message transfer agent to provide addressing, sending, and receiving services, and a reliable transfer agent to provide routing and delivery services.
Mixed Interconnect VMS Cluster System	In Digital Equipment documentation, any VMS cluster system that utilizes more than one interconnect for SCA traffic. Mixed interconnect VMS cluster systems provide maximum flexibility in combining CPUs, storage, and workstations into highly available configurations.
MMS (Manufacturing Messaging Service)	In OSI documentation, a messaging service between programmable devices.
Mode Name	In SNA, a name used by the initiator of a session to designate the characteristics desired for the session.
Modem (modulator/ demodulator)	A device that converts digital to analog signals and vice versa for the purpose of using computer devices in remote locations.
Monitor	Generally considered the same as a display. It can also mean to watch a task, program execution, or the like.

Monitor Console Routine In Digital Equipment documentation, the command interpreter in an RSX-11 system; also an optional command interpreter in the operating system.

Mounting a Volume In Digital Equipment documentation, the logical association of a volume with the physical unit on which it is loaded. Loading or placing a magnetic tape or disk pack on a drive and placing the drive on line.

Mount Verification In Digital Equipment documentation, a feature that suspends I/O to and from volumes while they are changing status. Mount verification also ensures that, following a suspension in disk I/O, the volume being accessed is the same one previously mounted.

Move Mode In Digital Equipment documentation, an Open VMS Record Management Services record I/O access technique in which a program accesses records in its own working storage area.

MTU Maximum Transfer Unit The largest amount of data that can be transferred across a given physical network. For LANs like the Ethernet, the MTU is determined by the network hardware. For long-haul networks that use aerial lines to interconnect packet switches, the MTU is determined by software.

Mutex A term used in Digital Equipment network environments; a semaphore is used to control exclusive access to a region of code that can share a data structure or other resource. The mutex semaphore ensures that only one process at a time has write access to the region of code.

Multicast A technique that allows copies of a single packet to be passed to a selected subset of all possible destinations. Some hardware supports multicast by allowing a network interface to belong to one or more multicast groups. Broadcast is a special form of multicast in which the subset of machines to receive a copy of a packet consists of the entire set. IP supports an internet multicast facility.

Multicast Address In Apple documentation, an Ethernet address for which the node accepts packets just as it does for its permanently assigned Ethernet hardware address. The low-order bit of the high-order byte is set to 1. Each node can have any number of multicast addresses, and any number of nodes can have the same multicast address. The purpose of a multicast address is to allow a group of Ethernet nodes to receive the same transmission simultaneously, in a fashion similar to the way the AppleTalk broadcast service operates.

Multicasting A directory service agent uses this mode to chain a request to many other directory service agents.

MultiFinder	In Apple documentation, prior to version 7.0 system software, a multitasking operating system for Macintosh computers that enables several applications to be open at the same time. In addition, processes (such as print spooling) can operate in the background so that users can perform one task while the computer performs another.
Multi-Homed Host	A TCP/IP host connected to two or more physical networks so that they have more than one address. They can serve as router-type devices.
Multilink Transmission Group	In IBM documentation, a transmission group containing two or more links.
Multimode	The transmission of multiple modes of light.
Multipath channel (MPC)	In IBM documentation, a channel protocol that uses multiple unidirectional subchannels for VTAM-to-VTAM bidirectional communication.
Multiple-Domain Network	In IBM documentation, a network with more than one system services control point in traditional subarea SNA. In APPN, an APPN network with more than one network node.
Multiple Link Interface Driver	In Novell documentation, this type driver accepts multiple protocol packets. When an MLID device driver receives a packet, the MLID does not interpret the packet; it copies identification information and passes the packet to the link support layer. MLIDs are supplied by Novell, the network board manufacturer, or a third-party supplier.
Multipoint line	A telecommunication line or circuit that connects two or more stations.
MVS/XA (Multiple Virtual Storage/Extended Architecture)	An IBM operating system.
Name-Binding Protocol (NBP)	In Apple documentation, the AppleTalk transport level protocol that translates a character string into a network address. It maintains a table that contains the internet address and name of each entity in the node that is visible to other entities on the internet (that is, each entity that has registered a name with NBP).
Name Block	In Digital Equipment documentation, an Open VMS Record Management Services user data structure that contains supplementary information used in parsing file specifications.

Name Resolution   The process of locating an entry by sequentially matching each relative distinguished name in a purported name to a vertex of the Directory Information Tree.

Name Translation   In IBM documentation, an SNA network interconnection. It includes the conversion of logical unit names, logon mode table names, and class-of-service names used in one network to equivalent names for use in another network.

Naming Context   In OSI networks, a substructure of the directory information tree. It starts at a vertex and extends downwards to leaf and/or non-leaf structures.

Naming Context Tree   In OSI documentation, a tree structure where each node represents a naming context.

NCCF (Network Communications Control Facility)   A part of IBM's NetView. It is the command that starts the NetView command facility. This command line in NetView allows various commands to be offered.

NCP Major Node   In IBM documentation, in VTAM, a set of minor nodes represent resources, such as lines and peripheral nodes, controlled by IBM's network control program.

NCP/EP Definition Facility (NDF)   In IBM documentation, a program that is part of system support programs. It is used to generate a partitioned emulation program load module or a load module for a network control program or for an emulation program.

Negative Response (NR)   In IBM documentation, a term used in SNA refer to a response indicating that a request did not arrive successfully or was not processed successfully by the receiver.

Negotiable BIND   In IBM documentation, a term in SNA referring to the ability to allow two half-sessions to negotiate the parameters of a session when the session is being activated.

NetBIOS   NetBIOS is the standard interface to networks used by IBM PCs and compatibles. With a TCP/IP network, NetBIOS refers to a set of guidelines that describe how to map NetBIOS operations into equivalent TCP/IP operations.

NetView Performance Monitor (NPM)   According to IBM, a program that collects, monitors, analyzes, and displays data relevant to the performance of VTAM.

NetView   According to IBM, a program used to monitor and manage a network and diagnose network problems.

NetWare Loadable Module (NLM)	According to Novell documentation, a program that is part of a file server memory with NetWare. An NLM can be loaded or unloaded while the file server is running, become part of the operating system, and access NetWare directly.
Network	A collection of computers and related devices connected in such a way that collectively they can be more productive than standalone equipment.
Network Address	In general, each participating entity on a network has an address so that it can be identified when exchanging data. In IBM documentation, in a subarea network, an address consists of subarea and element fields that identify a link, link station, PU, LU, or SSCP.
Network Address Translation	In IBM documentation, in an SNA network interconnection, the conversion of the network address assigned to an LU in one network into an address in an another network.
Network Architecture	The logical and physical structure of a computer network.
Network Connect Block	In Digital Equipment documentation, a user-generated data structure used in a nontransparent task to identify a remote task and optionally send user data in calls to request, accept, or reject a logical-link connection. For the VAX Packetnet System interface, a block that contains the information necessary to set up an X.25 virtual circuit or to accept or reject a request to set up an X.25 virtual circuit.
Network Control	In IBM documentation, in SNA, a request or response unit category used for requests and responses exchanged between PUs. The purpose is activating and deactivating explicit and virtual routes. The term is used to refer to send-load modules to adjust peripheral nodes.
Network Control Program	In Digital Equipment documentation, an interactive utility program that allows control and monitoring of a network. In IBM documentation, it is a program that controls the operation of a communication controller.
Network Layer	In OIS documentation, layer three. It is responsible for data transfer across the network, and functions independently of the network media and the topology.
Network Management Vector Transport (NMVT)	In IBM documentation, a protocol used for management services in an SNA network.

Network Name	In IBM documentation, in SNA, the symbolic identifier by which end-users refer to a network-accessible unit, a link, or a link station within a given network. In APPN networks, network names are also used for routing purposes. In a multi-domain network, the name of the APPL statement defining a VTAM application program. This network name must be unique across domains.
Network Node Server	In IBM documentation, an APPN network node that provides network services for its local LUs and client end nodes.
Network Number	In Apple documentation, a 16-bit number that provides a unique identifier for a network in an AppleTalk internet.
Network Operator	A person who performs a variety of functions on a network, some of them control functions.
Network-Qualified Name	A name that uniquely identifies a specific resource within a specific network. It consists of a network identifier and a resource name, each of which is a 1- to 8-byte symbol string.
Network Range	In Apple documentation, a unique range of contiguous network numbers used to identify each Ethernet and token ring networks on an AppleTalk internet.
Network Routing Facility (NRF)	In IBM documentation an IBM program that resides in an NCP. NRF provides a path for routing messages between terminals without going through the host processor.
Network Services	In IBM documentation, those services within network accessible unit that control network operation.
Network Services Header	In IBM documentation, in traditional SNA, a 3-byte field in a function management data request or response unit that flows in an SSCP-LU, SSCP-PU, or SSCP-SSCP session. This is used primarily to identify the network services category of the request unit.
Network Services Protocol	In Digital Equipment documentation, a formal set of conventions used in a DECnet for Open VMS network to perform network management and to exchange messages over logical links.
Network Terminal Option (NTO)	In IBM documentation, a program, used in conjunction with NCP, that allows some non-SNA devices to participate in sessions with SNA application programs in the host processor.
Network Topology Database	In an APPN network, in IBM documentation, the representation of the current connectivity between the network nodes within an APPN network. It includes entries for all network nodes and the transmission groups interconnecting them and entries for all virtual routing nodes to which network nodes are attached.

NFS (Network File System)	According to Sun microsystems, a protocol developed by Sun that uses IP to allow a set of cooperating computers to access each other's file systems as if they were local. NFS hides differences between local and remote files by placing them in the same name space. Originally designed for UNIX systems, it is now implemented on many other systems, including PC and Apple personal computers.
NLDM (Network Logical Data Manager)	In IBM documentation, a subset of NetView. NLDM is a command that starts the NetView sessions monitor. It also identifies various panels and functions as part of the session monitor.
No Response	In IBM documentation, in SNA, a protocol requested in the response-requested field of the request header. It directs the receiver of the request not to return any response, regardless of whether or not the request is received and processed successfully.
Node	Generally, a term used to refer to a computer or related device. In IBM's SNA, node types exist that reflect certain functions they can perform. In Digital Equipment documentation, an individual computer system in a network that can communicate with other computer systems in the network. A VAXBI interface—such as a central processor, controller, or memory subsystem—that occupies one of 16 logical locations on a VAXBI bus. A VAX processor or HSC that is recognized by system communications services software.
Node Initialization Block (NIB)	In IBM documentation, in VTAM, a control block associated with a particular node or session that contains information used by the application program. The information identifies the node or session and indicates how communication requests on a session are to be handled by VTAM.
Node Name	In IBM documentation, in VTAM, the symbolic name assigned to a specific major or minor node during network definition.
Node Number	A unique number used to identify each node on a network.
Node Type	In IBM documentation, a designation of a node according to the protocols it supports and the network-accessible units it can contain. Five types are defined: 1. 2.0, 2.1, 4, and 5. Within a subarea network, type 1, type 2.0, and type 2.1 nodes are peripheral nodes, while type 4 and type 5 nodes are subarea nodes.
Non-client	A program that is written to run on a terminal and must be fooled by a terminal emulation window into running in the window environment.
Non-command Image	In Digital Equipment documentation, a program not associated with a DCL command. To invoke a non-command image, use the file name containing the program as the parameter to the RUN command.

Nonprivileged	In Digital Equipment documentation, an account with no privilege other than TMPMBX and NETMBX and a user-identification code greater than the system parameter MAXSYSGROUP. In DECnet for Open VMS, this term means no privileges in addition to NETMBS, which is the minimal requirement for any network activity.
Normal Flow	In IBM documentation, in SNA, a data flow designated in the transmission header that is used primarily to carry end-user data. It refers to the rate at which requests flow. On normal flow, regulation can be achieved by session-level pacing. Normal and expedited flows move in both the primary-to-secondary and secondary-to-primary directions.
Normalize	A term used in windowing environments; to change an icon back into its original appearance. The opposite of iconify.
Notification	An indication that something in the network requires the operator's attention.
NOTIFY	In IBM documentation, a network services request sent by an SSCP to an LU. It is used to inform the LU of the status of a requested procedure.
NPDA (Network Problem Determination Application)	In IBM documentation, a part of NetView. It is also a command that starts the NetView hardware monitor. NPDA identifies various panels and functions as part of the hardware monitor.
NPDU (Network Protocol Data Unit)	In OSI terminology, refers to packet; a logical block of control symbols and data transmitted by the network layer protocol.
NSF (National Science Foundation)	A government agency that has enabled scientists to connect to networks comprising the Internet.
NSFNET (National Science Foundation NETwork)	A network that spans the USA.
Null Key	In Novell documentation, a key field that allows the value of the field to be a user-defined null character. For this type of key, Btrieve does not index a record if the record's key value matches the null value.
NVP (Network Voice Protocol)	A TCP/IP protocol for handling voice information.

Object	In Apple documentation, the first field in the name of an AppleTalk entity. The object is assigned by the entity itself and can be anything the user or application assigns. In Digital Equipment documentation, a passive repository of information to which the system controls access. Access to an object implies access to the information it contains. Examples of protected objects are files, volumes, global sections, and devices. A DECnet for OpenVMS process that receives a logical link request. It performs a specific network function or is a user defined image for a special purpose application. A VAX Packet-net System Interface management component that contains records to specify account information for incoming calls and a command procedure that is initiated when the incoming call arrives.
Object Class	In Digital Equipment documentation, on VAX systems, a set of protected objects with common characteristics. For example, all files belong to the FILE class whereas all devices belong to the DEVICE class.
Object Entry	In Open Systems networking, a directory entry which is the primary collection of information in the directory information base about an object in the real world, not an alias entry.
Object Identifier Based Name	A name based on the Object Identifier type.
Object Identifier Tree	In OSI terminology, a tree where edges are labeled with integers.
Object Identifier Type	In OSI and other environments that implement ASN.1, an ASN.1 type whose values are the path names of the nodes of the object-identifier tree.
Offline	A resource which is not available.
Online	A resource which is available.
Open Application Event	In Apple documentation, an Apple event that asks an application to perform the tasks—such as displaying untitled windows—associated with opening itself; one of the four required Apple events.
Open Datalink Interface	In Novell documentation, a set of specifications defining relationships between one or more protocol stacks, the LSL, and one or more MLIDs. These specifications allow multiple communication protocols such as IPX/SPX, TCP/IP, and AppleTalk to share the same driver and adapter.
Open Shortest Path First (OSPF)	A routing protocol based on the least cost for routing.

Operand	In SNA, an entity on which an operation is performed. That which is operated upon. An operand is usually identified by an address part of an instruction.
Optional Parameter	In Apple documentation, a supplemental parameter in an Apple event used to specify data the server application should use in addition to the data specified in the direct parameter.
Oscillation	The periodic movement between two values.
Other-Domain Resource	In IBM documentation, a representation for an LU that is owned by another domain and is referenced by a symbolic name, which can be qualified by a network identifier.
Owner	In Digital Equipment documentation, a user with the same user-identification code as the protected object. An owner always can access control to the object and can therefore modify the object's security profile. When the system processes an access request from an owner, it considers the access rights in the owner field of a protection code.
Pacing	In IBM's SNA, a technique by which a receiving component controls the rate of transmission of a sending component to prevent overrun or congestion.
Pacing Response	In IBM documentation, in SNA, an indicator that signifies the readiness of a receiving component to accept another pacing group. The indicator is carried in a response header for session-level pacing and in a transmission header for virtual-route pacing.
Pacing Window	In IBM documentation, the path information units that can be transmitted on a virtual route before a virtual-route pacing response is received indicating that the virtual-route receiver is ready to receive more PIUs on the route.
Packet	A generic term; a small unit of control information and data that is processed by the network protocol.
Packet Assembly/ Disassembly Facility (PAD)	A term used in packet switching technology. A device at a packet switching network permitting access from an asynchronous terminal. Terminals connect to a PAD, and a PAD puts the terminal's input data into packets, then takes the terminal's output data out of packets.
Page	A term used when virtual storage is being discussed. It refers to a fixed-length block that has a virtual address and is transferred as a unit between real storage and secondary storage.
Pagelet	In Digital Equipment documentation, a 512-byte unit of memory in an AXP environment. On AXP systems, certain DCL and utility commands, system services, and system routines accept as input or provide as output memory requirements and quotas in terms of pagelets.

Page Table Base Register	In Digital Equipment documentation, on AXP systems, the processor register or its equivalent, in a hardware-privileged, context block that contains the page frame number of the process first level page table.
Panel	In IBM documentation, an arrangement of information presented in a window.
Parallel Links	In IBM documentation, in SNA, two or more links between adjacent subarea nodes.
Parallel Sessions	In IBM documentation, two or more concurrently active sessions between the same two network accessible units using different pairs of network addresses or local-form session identifiers. Each session can have independent session parameters.
Parallel Transmission Groups	In IBM documentation, multiple transmission groups connecting two adjacent nodes.
Parameter	A generic term for a given constant value for a specified application, it may denote the application.
Parent Window	In windowing environments, a window that causes another window to appear. Specifically, it refers to windows that "own" other windows.
Partitioned Data Set (PDS)	In IBM documentation, a type of storage, divided into partitions, called members. Each member contains records that are the actual data stored.
Path	In a network, any route between two or more nodes.
Path Control (PC)	In IBM documentation, the function that routes message units between network-accessible units in the network and provides the paths between them. It is depicted in traditional SNA layers. PC converts the BIUs from transmission control (possibly segmenting them) into path information units and exchanges basic transmission units containing one or more PIUs with data link control.
Path Information Unit (PIU)	In IBM documentation, a message unit containing only a transmission header, or a TH followed by a basic information unit or a BIU segment.
Pending Active Session	In IBM documentation, in VTAM, the state of an LU-LU session recorded by the SSCP when it finds both LUs available and has sent a CINIT request to the primary logical unit of the requested session.
Performance Assist	In Digital Equipment documentation, the Open VMS Volume Shadowing uses controller performance assists to improve full copy and merge operation performance. There are two distinct types of performance assists: the full copy and minimerge.

Peripheral Host Node	In IBM documentation, a type of node defined in SNA terminology. It does not provide SSCP functions and is not aware of the network configuration. The peripheral host node does not provide subarea node services. It has boundary function provided by its adjacent subarea.
Peripheral Logical Unit (PLU)	A logical unit in a peripheral node found in SNA networks. It should not be confused with a primary logical unit, also known as a PLU.
Peripheral LU	Peripheral logical unit.
Peripheral Node	In IBM documentation, a node that uses local addresses for routing and is not affected by changes in network addresses. A peripheral node requires boundary-function assistance from an adjacent subarea node.
Peripheral Path Control	In IBM documentation, the function in a peripheral node that routes message units between units with local addresses and provides the paths between them.
Permanent Virtual Circuit	A term used in many different network environments. Generally, a permanent logical association between two DTEs, which is analogous to a leased line. Packets are routed directly by the network from one DTE to the other.
Personal Computer (PC)	A term becoming more vague with the passing of time. It basically refers to an individual's computer. It has its own processor, memory, storage, and display.
Phase	The place of a wave in an oscillation cycle.
Physical Connection	A link that makes transmission of data possible. Generally, a tangible link; it may support electron, photon, or other data-type representation transfer.
Physical Layer	A term used in OSI, the lowest layer defined by the OSI model. However, layer zero would be the lowest of layers in such a model, and represents the medium (hard or soft).
Physical Unit (PU)	In IBM documentation, a component (software or firmware) that manages and monitors specified resources associated with a node. The type of PU, indicated by number, is typically either 5, 4, 2.0, or 2.1. The type of PU dictates what supporting services are available.
Physical Unit Services	In IBM documentation, that component within a PU that provides configuration and maintenance services for SSCP-PU sessions.
PING Packet InterNet Groper	A program found in TCP/IP-based networks; used to test reachability of destinations by sending them an ICMP echo request and waiting for a reply.

Pixel	The smallest dot that can be drawn on the screen.
Point	A unit of measurement for type.
Point-to-Point Protocol (PPP)	A type of protocol used over asynchronous and synchronous connections for router-to-router or a host-to-network communications.
Polling	The process whereby data stations are invited, one at a time, to transmit on a multipoint or point-to-point connection.
Port	A term used in TCP/IP based networks, where two transport protocols exist: TCP and UDP. Applications that reside on top of these protocols have a port number assigned for addressing purposes. Generally, an addressable point.
Port Name	That which contains a name string, a type string, and a script code. A term used in Apple documentation.
Power Manager	In Apple documentation, firmware that provides an interface to the power management hardware in the Macintosh portable computer.
PPDU (Presentation Protocol Data Unit)	In OSI terminology, a term referring to logical blocks of control symbols and data transmitted at the presentation-layer protocol.
Presentation Layer	In the OSI terminology, layer six. Data representation occurs here. Syntax of data such as ASCII or EBCDIC is determined at this layer.
Primary Application Program	In IBM documentation, in VTAM, an application program acting as the primary end of an LU-LU session.
Primary End of a Session	In IBM documentation, the end of a session that uses primary protocols. The primary end establishes the session. For an LU-LU session, the primary end of the session is the primary logical unit.
PrimaryInit Record	In Apple documentation, a data structure in the declaration ROM of a NuBus card that contains initialization code. The slot manager executes the code in the PrimaryInit record when it first locates a declaration ROM during system startup.
Primary Logical Unit (PLU)	In IBM documentation, the logical unit that sends the BIND to activate a session with its partner LU.
Primary Key	In Digital Equipment documentation, the mandatory key within the data records of an indexed file; used by Open VMS Record Management Services to determine the placement of records within the file and to build the primary index.
PrintMonitor	In Apple documentation, a background print spooler included with the Macintosh MultiFinder.

Print Server   In networking, a term used in a general sense to convey that a com-
                           puter controls spooling and other printer operations.

Private Partition   In IBM documentation, in VSE, an allocated amount of memory for
                           the execution of a specific program or application program. Storage
                           in a private partition is not addressable by programs running in other
                           virtual address spaces.

Privilege   In Digital Equipment documentation, protecting the use of certain
                           system functions that can affect system resources and integrity. Sys-
                           tem managers grant privileges according to users' needs and deny
                           them as a means of restricting access to the system.

Process   Depending on the context, an open application or an open desk
                           accessory.

Processor   That component which interprets and executes instructions.

Processor Status   In Digital Equipment documentation, on VAX systems, a privileged
                           processor register, known as the processor status longword, consist-
                           ing of a word of privileged processor status and the processor status
                           word itself. The privileged processor status information includes the
                           current interrupt priority level, the previous access mode, the current
                           access mode, the interrupt stack bit, the trace trap pending bit, and
                           the compatibility mode bit.

Processor   In Digital Equipment VAX systems, the low-order word of the
Status Word   processor status longword. Processor status information includes the
                           condition codes (carry, overflow, 0, negative), the arithmetic trap
                           enable bits (integer overflow, decimal overflow, floating underflow),
                           and the trace enable bit.

Product-Set   In IBM documentation, a technique for identifying the hardware and
Identification   software products that implement a network component.
(PSID)

PROFILE EXEC   In IBM documentation, in VM, a special EXEC procedure with a file
                           name of PROFILE. The procedure is normally executed immediately
                           after CMS is loaded into a virtual machine. It contains CP and CMS
                           commands that are to be issued at the start of every terminal session.

Program Operator   A term used in SNA. In IBM documentation, a VTAM application
                           program authorized to issue VTAM operator commands and receive
                           VTAM operator awareness messages.

Program   In IBM documentation, a temporary solution or bypass of a problem
Temporary Fix   diagnosed by IBM in a current unaltered release of the program.
(PTF)

Protocol   An agreed-upon way of doing something.

Protocol Data Unit	A general term to refer to that which is exchanged between peer-layer entities.
PU-PU Flow	In IBM documentation, in SNA, the exchange between physical units of network control requests and responses.
Proxy ARP	In TCP/IP networks, a technique in which one machine answers ARP requests intended for another by supplying its own physical address.
Pulse Dispersion	The spreading of pulses as they traverse an optical fiber.
Queued Session	In IBM documentation, in VTAM, this pertains to a requested LU-LU session that cannot be started because one of the LUs is not available. If the session-initiation request specifies queuing, the system services control points record the request and later continue with the session-establishment procedure when both LUs become available.
Quit Application Event	In Apple documentation, an Apple event that requests that an application perform the tasks—such as releasing memory, asking the user to save documents, and so on—associated with quitting; one of the four required Apple events. The Finder sends this event to an application immediately after sending it a Print Documents event or if the user chooses Restart or Shut Down from the Finder's special menu.
RACF (Resource Access Control Facility)	An IBM security program package.
RARP (Reverse Address Resolution Protocol)	A TCP/IP protocol for mapping Ethernet addresses to IP addresses. It is used by diskless workstations that do not know their IP address. In essence it asks, "Who am I?" Normally, a response occurs and is cached in the host.
Read-Only Memory (ROM)	Memory in which stored data cannot be modified except under special conditions.
Real Resource	In VTAM, a resource identified by its real name and its real network identifier.
Receive Pacing	In IBM documentation, the pacing of message units being received by a component.
Record Access Block (RAB)	In Digital Equipment documentation, an Open VMS Record Management Services user control block allocated at either assembly or run time to communicate with RMS. The control block describes the records in a particular file and associates with a file access block to form a record access stream. A RAB defines the characteristics needed to perform record related operations, such as update, delete, or get.

Record Management Services (RMS)	In Digital Equipment documentation, a set of operating system procedures called by programs to process files and records within files. RMS allows programs to issue GET and PUT requests at the record level as well as to read and write blocks. RMS is an integral part of the system software; its procedures run in executive mode.
Region Code	In Apple documentation, a number used to indicate a particular localized version of Macintosh system software.
Relative Path	The path through a volume's (disk's) hierarchy from one file or directory to another.
Release	A distribution of a new product or new function and APAR fixes for an existing product. Normally, programming support for the prior release is discontinued after some specified period of time following availability of a new release.
Remote Client	A term used in X-window environments: an X program running on a remote system, but the output of the program can be viewed locally.
Remote Operations Service Element	A term used in Open Networking environments; an application service element that provides the basis for remote requests.
Request Header (RH)	In IBM documentation, control information that precedes a Request Unit.
Request Parameter List (RPL)	In IBM documentation, a VTAM control block that contains the parameters necessary for processing a request for data transfer, for establishing or terminating a session, or for some other operation.
Request Unit (RU)	In IBM documentation, a message unit that contains control information, end-user data, or both.
Request/Response Header (RH)	In IBM documentation, control information associated with a particular RU. The RH precedes an RU and specifies the type of RU (request or response unit).
Request/Response Unit (RU)	A generic term for a request or response unit.
Required Apple Event	In Apple documentation, one of four core Apple events that the Finder sends to applications: Open Documents, Open Application, Print Documents, and Quit Application.
Reset	Generally, a change to the original state of operation.
Resource	Generally, main storage, secondary storage, input/output devices, the processing unit, files, and control or processing programs, or anything else that can be used by a user directly or indirectly.

Resource Access Control Facility (RACF)	In IBM documentation, an IBM program that provides for access control by identifying and verifying the users of the system, by authorizing access to protected resources, by logging the detected unauthorized attempts to enter the system, and by logging the detected accesses to protected resources.
Resource Definition Table (RDT)	In IBM documentation, a VTAM table that describes characteristics of each node available to VTAM and associates each node with a network address. This is a main VTAM network configuration table.
Resource Hierarchy	In IBM documentation, a VTAM relationship among network resources in which some resources are subordinate to others as a result of their position in the network structure and architecture; for example the logical units of a peripheral physical unit are subordinate to the PU, which, in turn, is subordinate to the link attaching it to its subarea node.
Resource Registration	In IBM documentation, the process of identifying names of resources, such as LUs, to a network node server or a central directory server.
Resource Takeover	In IBM documentation, a VTAM action initiated by a network operator to transfer control of resources from one domain to another without breaking the connections or disrupting existing LU-LU sessions on the connection.
Resource Types	In IBM documentation, with reference to NetView, a concept describing the organization of panels. Resource types are central processing unit, channel, control unit, and I/O device for one category; and communication controller, adapter, link, cluster controller, and terminal for another category. Resource types are combined with data types and display types to describe display organization.
Response	A reply to some occurrence, or the lack thereof.
Response Header (RH)	In IBM documentation, a header, optionally followed by a response unit, that indicates whether the response is positive or negative, it may contain a pacing response.
Response Time	In IBM documentation, used with NetView, the elapsed time between the end of an inquiry or demand on a computer system and the beginning of the response; for example, the length of time between an indication of the end of an inquiry and the display of the first character of the response at a user terminal.
Response Unit (RU)	In IBM documentation, a message unit that acknowledges a request unit. It may contain prefix information received in a request unit.
Restoring	A term used in window-based environments; it is the changing of minimized or maximized window back to its regular size.

Restructured Extended Executor (REXX)	In IBM documentation, a general-purpose, procedural language for end-user personal programming, designed for ease of use by both casual users and computer professionals. It is also useful for application macros.
Result Handler	A routine that the data access manager calls to convert a data item to a character string.
Return Code	A code used to identify the action or lack thereof of a program execution.
RFC (Request For Comments)	Proposed and accepted TCP/IP standards.
RLOGIN (Remote LOGIN)	A logon service provided by Berkeley 4BSD UNIX systems that allows users of one machine to connect to other UNIX systems.
RMS–11	In Digital Equipment documentation, a set of routines linked with compatibility mode programs; they provide similar functional capabilities to Open VMS Record Management Services. The file organizations and record formats use by RMS–11 are very similar to those of RMS.
Root Men	That menu which could be called the main menu. That menu from which other menus originate.
Root Window	In the X-windowing environment, this is what is presented on the screen once the X graphical user interface is visible to the user. It is the window on which other windows are based.
Route Selection Services (RSS)	In IBM documentation, a subcomponent of the topology and routing services component that determines the preferred route between a specified pair of nodes for a given class of service.
Routing	The moving of data through paths in a network.
Routing Information Base	A collection of output from route calculations.
Routing Table Maintenance Protocol	In Apple documentation, a protocol used by routers on an AppleTalk internet to determine how to forward a data packet to the network number to which it is addressed.
RTMP Stub	In Apple documentation, the portion of the routing table maintenance protocol contained in an AppleTalk node other than a router. DDP uses the RTMP stub to determine the network number of the network cable to which the node is connected and to determine the network number and node ID on one router on that network cable.
RTT (Round Trip Time)	A measure of delay between two hosts.

RU Chain	In IBM documentation, an SNA set of related request/response units that are consecutively transmitted on a particular normal or expedited data flow.
RUN Disk	In IBM documentation, a virtual disk that contains the VTAM, NetView, and VM/SNA console support load libraries, program temporary fixes, and user-written modifications from the Zap disk.
SACK (Selective ACKnowledgment)	A term used in TCP/IP, an acknowledgment mechanism used with sliding window protocols. This permits a receiver to acknowledge packets received out of order within the current sliding window.
Same-Domain	In IBM documentation this pertains to communication between entities in the same SNA domain.
Satellite Node	In Digital Equipment documentation, a processor that is part of a local area VMS cluster system. A satellite node is booted remotely from the system disk of the boot server in this type of system.
Screen	In SAA basic common user access architecture, the physical surface of a display device upon which information is shown to a user.
Screen Dump	A screen capture capable of being routed to a file.
Secondary End of a Session	In IBM documentation, the end of a session that uses secondary protocols. For an LU-LU session, the secondary end of the session is the secondary logical unit.
SecondaryInit Record	In Apple documentation, a data structure in the declaration ROM of a NuBus card that contains initialization code. The slot manager executes the code in the SecondaryInit record after RAM patches to the operating system have been loaded from disk during system startup.
Secondary Logical Unit (SLU)	In IBM documentation, the LU that contains the secondary half-session for a particular LU-LU session. An LU may contain secondary and primary half-sessions for different active LU-LU sessions.
Segment	In IBM documentation, with reference to a token-ring network, a section of cable between components or devices. A segment may consist of a single patch cable, several patch cables that are connected, or a combination of building cable and patch cables that are connected. In TCP/IP this is the unit of transfer sent from TCP on one machine to TCP on another.
Segmentation	In IBM documentation, a process by which path control divides basic information units into smaller units, called BIU segments, to accommodate smaller buffer sizes in adjacent nodes. Both segmentation and segment assembly are optional path control features. The support for either or both is indicated in the BIND request and response.

Semaphore	In Digital Equipment documentation, in a DECnet for Open VMS network, a common data structure used to control the exchange of signals between concurrent processes.
Send Pacing	In IBM documentation, the pacing of message units (in SNA) that a component is sending.
Sequential Access Mode	In Digital Equipment documentation, the retrieval or storage of records where a program reads or writes records one after the other in the order in which they appear, starting and ending at any arbitrary point in the file.
Sequential File Organization	In Digital Equipment documentation, a file organization in which records appear in the order in which they were originally written. The records can be fixed-length or variable-length. Sequential file organization permits sequential record access and random access by the record's file address. Sequential file organization with fixed length records also permits random access by relative record number.
Server	An entity that serves the request of a client. This may be in the context of TCP/IP applications with clients and servers, or it could refer to a print or file server.
Service Access Point (SAP)	A logical addressable point.
Service Primitive	Part of a service element. Four types exist: confirm, indication, request, and response.
Session	A logical connection between two addressable end points.
Session Activation Request	In IBM documentation, a request in SNA that activates a session between two network accessible units and specifies session parameters that control various protocols during session activity; for example, BIND and ACTPU.
Session Awareness (SAW) Data	In IBM documentation, data collected by the NetView program about a session that includes the session type, the names of session partners, and information about the session activation status. It is collected for LU-LU, SSCP-LU, SSCP-PU, and SSCP-SSCP sessions and for non-SNA terminals not supported by NTO. It can be displayed in various forms, such as most-recent sessions lists.
Session Connector	In IBM documentation, a session-layer component in an APPN network node or in a subarea node boundary or gateway function that connects two stages of a session. Session connectors swap addresses from one address space to another for session-level intermediate routing; segment session message units as needed; and (except for gateway function session connectors) adaptively pace the session traffic in each direction.

Session Control (SC)	In IBM documentation, one of the following: One of the components of transmission control. Session control is used to purge data flowing in a session after an unrecoverable error occurs, to resynchronize the data flow after such an error, and to perform cryptographic verification. A request unit category used for requests and responses exchanged between the session control components of a session and for session activation and deactivation requests and responses.
Session Control Block (SCB)	In IBM documentation, in NPM, control blocks in common storage area for session collection.
Session Data	In IBM documentation, data about a session, collected by the NetView program consisting of session awareness, session trace, and session response time data.
Session Deactivation Request	In IBM documentation, a term used in SNA to refer to a request that deactivates a session between two network accessible units; for example, UNBIND and DACTPU.
Session-Establishment Request	In IBM documentation, in VTAM, a request to an LU to establish a session. For the primary logical unit of the requested session, the session-establishment request is the CINIT sent from the system services control point to the PLU. For the secondary logical unit of the requested session, the session-establishment request is the BIND sent from the PLU to the SLU.
Session ID	In IBM documentation, a number that uniquely identifies a session.
7.0-Compatible	In Apple documentation, refers to an application that runs without problems in system software version 7.0.
7.0-Dependent	In Apple documentation, refers to an application that requires the existence of features present only in system software version 7.0.
7.0-Friendly	In Apple documentation, refers to an application that is 7.0-compatible and takes advantage of some of the special features of system software version 7.0, but is still able to perform all its principal functions when operating in version 6.0.
Session Initiation Request	In IBM documentation, an initiate or logon request from a logical unit to a system services control point that an LU-LU session be activated.
Session Layer	In the OSI reference model, this is layer five. It coordinates the dialogue between two communicating application processes.
Session-Level LU-LU Verification	In IBM documentation, an LU 6.2 security service used to verify the identity of each logical unit when a session is established.

Session-Level Pacing	In IBM documentation, a flow control technique that permits a receiving half-session or session connector to control the data transfer rate (the rate at which it receives request units) on the normal flow. It is used to prevent overloading a receiver with unprocessed requests when the sender can generate requests faster than the receiver can process them.
Session Limit	In IBM documentation, refers to the maximum number concurrently active LU-LU sessions that a specific LU can support.
Session Manager (SM)	Typically a third-party product that permits a user on one terminal to logon to multiple applications concurrently.
Session Monitor	In IBM documentation, a component of NetView that collects and correlates session-related data and provides online access to this information.
Session Parameters	In IBM documentation, the parameters that specify or constrain the protocols (such as bracket protocol and pacing) for a session between two network-accessible units.
Session Partner	In IBM documentation, in SNA, one of the two network accessible units having an active session.
Session Path	In IBM documentation, the half-sessions delimiting a given session and their interconnection (including any intermediate session connectors).
Session Services	In IBM documentation, one of the types of network services in the control point and the logical unit. These services provide facilities for an LU or a network operator to request that a control point aid with initiating or terminating sessions between LUs. Assistance with session termination is needed only by SSCP-dependent LUs.
Session Stage	In IBM documentation, that portion of a session path consisting of two session-layer components that are logically adjacent and their interconnection. An example is the paired session-layer components in adjacent type 2.1 nodes and their interconnection over the link between them.
Shadow Resource	In IBM documentation, an alternate representation of a network resource that is retained as a definition for possible future use.
Shareable Image	In Digital Equipment documentation, an image that has all of its internal references resolved, but must be linked with one or more object modules to produce an executable image. A shareable image cannot be executed. A shareable image file can be used to contain a library of routines.

Shared-Access Transport Facility (SATF)	A transmission facility, such as a multipoint link connection or a token ring network, where multiple pairs of nodes can form concurrently active links.
Shared Image	In Digital Equipment documentation, an image that is installed so that multiple users in a system can share the memory pages where the image is loaded.
Shared Partition	In IBM documentation, in VSE, a partition allocated for a program such as VSE/POWER that provides services for and communicates with programs in other partitions of the system's virtual address spaces. Storage in a shared partition is addressable by programs running concurrently in other partitions.
Sibling Networks	In Novell documentation, two or more co-equal networks branching off the same node in an internetwork. Workstations on these networks that use NetWare Btrieve must have access to a file server loaded with BSERVER.
Sift-Down Effect	In IBM documentation, the copying of a value from a higher-level resource to a lower-level resource. The sift-down effect applies to many of the keywords and operands in NCP and VTAM definition statements. If an operand is coded on a macroinstruction or generation statement for a higher-level resource, it need not be coded for lower-level resources for which the same value is desired. The value "sifts down," that is, becomes the default for all lower-level resources.
Silly-Window Syndrome	In TCP/IP based networks, a scenario in which a receiver keeps indicating a small "window" and a sender continues to send small segments to it.
Single-Byte Character Set (SBCS)	In IBM documentation, a character set in which each character is represented by a one-byte code.
Single Console Image Facility (SCIF)	In IBM documentation, a VM facility that allows multiple consoles to be controlled from a single virtual machine console.
Single-Domain Network	In IBM documentation, a network with one SSCP.
Single Mode	A type fiber optic cable containing just one mode.
Sleep State	In Apple documentation, a low-power consumption state of the Macintosh Portable computer. In the sleep state, the power manager and the various device drivers shut off power or remove clocks from the computer's various subsystems, including the CPU, RAM, ROM, and I/O ports.

Sliding Window   A scenario in which a protocol permits the transmitting station to sending a stream of bytes before an acknowledgment arrives.

SLIP (Serial Line IP)   A protocol to run IP over serial lines, such as using telephone lines.

SMTP (Simple Mail Transfer Protocol)   A TCP/IP application that provides electronic mail support. The SMTP protocol specifies how two mail systems interact and the format of control messages.

SNA Network   A collection of IBM hardware and software put together to form a collective greater than the parts. The components comprising the network conform to the SNA format and protocol specifications defined by IBM.

SNA Network Interconnection (SNI)   According to IBM, the connection of two or more independent SNA networks to allow communication between logical units in those networks. The individual SNA networks retain their independence.

SNMP (Simple Network Monitoring Protocol)   A de facto industry standard-protocol used to manage TCP/IP networks.

Socket   A concept from Berkeley 4BSD UNIX that allows an application program to access the TCP/IP protocols. Or in TCP/IP networks, the internet address of the host and the port number it uses. A TCP/IP application is identified by its socket.

Solicited Message   In IBM documentation, a response from VTAM to a command entered by a program operator.

Source Route   A route determined by the source. TCP/IP implements source routing by using an option field in an IP datagram.

Specific Mode   In IBM documentation, in VTAM, the following: the form of a RECEIVE request that obtains input from one specific session. The form of an accept request that completes the establishment of a session by accepting a specific queued CINIT request.

SSCP-Dependent LU   An LU requiring assistance from an SSCP to establish a LU-LU session.

SSCP ID   In IBM documentation, in SNA, a number that uniquely identifies an SSCP. The SSCP ID is used in session activation requests sent to physical units and other SSCPs.

SSCP-Independent LU   In IBM documentation, an LU that can activate an LU-LU session (that is, send a BIND request) without assistance from an SSCP. It does not have an SSCP-LU session. Currently, only an LU 6.2 can be an independent LU.

SSCP-LU Session	In IBM documentation, in SNA, a session between the SSCP and a logical unit. The session enables the LU to request the SSCP to help initiate LU-LU sessions.
SSCP-PU Session	In IBM documentation, in SNA, a session between an SSCP and a PU. SSCP-PU sessions allow SSCPs to send requests to and receive status information from individual nodes in order to control the network configuration.
SSCP Rerouting	In IBM documentation, an SNA network interconnection. A technique used by the gateway system services control point to send session-initiation RUs, by way of a series of SSCP-SSCP sessions, from one SSCP to another, until the owning SSCP is reached.
SSCP-SSCP Session	In IBM documentation, a session between the SSCP in one domain and the SSCP in another domain. This type of session is used to initiate and terminate cross-domain LU-LU sessions.
Stack	An area of memory in the application partition that is used to store temporary variables.
Start-Stop (SS) Transmission	Asynchronous transmission whereby each signal that represents a character is preceded by a start signal and is followed by a stop signal.
Station	An input or output point.
Statistic	Significant data about a defined resource.
Status	Generally speaking, a condition or state of a resource. In Digital Equipment documentation, a display type for the network control program commands SHOW and LIST. Status refers to dynamic information about a component that is kept in the volatile or the permanent database.
Status monitor	In IBM documentation, a component of the NetView program that collects and summarizes information on the status of resources defined in a VTAM domain.
Stream	In IBM's SNA, a structed protocol. For example, a 3270 data stream, a GDS data stream, or LU6.2 data stream. In Digital Equipment documentation, an access window to a file associated with a record-control block, supporting record operation requests. Generally, it is a full-duplex connection between a user's task and a device.
Subarea	In IBM documentation, a portion of the SNA network consisting of a subarea node, attached peripheral nodes, and associated resources.
Subarea Address	In IBM documentation, a value in the subarea field of a network address that identifies a particular subarea.

**Subarea Host
  Node**   In IBM documentation, a node that provides both subarea function
and an application program interface (API) for running application
programs. It provides SSCP functions and subarea node services, and
is aware of the network configuration.

Subarea Link   In IBM documentation, a link that connects two subarea nodes.

Subarea LU   In IBM documentation, a logical unit that resides in a subarea node.

Subarea Network   In IBM documentation, interconnected subareas, their directly
attached peripheral nodes, and the transmission groups that connect
them.

**Subarea Node
  (SN)**   In IBM documentation, a node that uses network addresses for
routing and maintains routing tables that reflect the configuration of
the network. Subarea nodes can provide gateway function to connect
multiple subarea networks, intermediate routing functions, and
boundary function to support peripheral nodes. Type 4 and type 5
nodes are subarea nodes.

**Subarea Path
  Control**   In IBM documentation, the function in a subarea node that routes
message units between network accessible units and provides the
paths between them.

Subdirectory   In Digital Equipment documentation, a directory file, cataloged in a
higher level directory, that lists additional files belonging to the
owner of the directory.

Subsystem   A secondary or subordinate software system.

Summary   In Digital Equipment documentation, the default display type for the
network control program commands SHOW and LIST. A summary
includes the most useful information for a component, selected from
the status and characteristics information.

Supervisor   In IBM documentation, that part of a control program that coordinates the use of resources and maintains the flow of processing unit
operations.

**Supervisor Call
  (SVC)**   In IBM documentation, a request that serves as the interface into
operating system functions, such as allocating storage. The SVC protects the operating system from inappropriate user entry. All operating system requests must be handled by SVCs.

**Switched
  Connection**   A data-link connection that functions like a dial telephone.

Switched Line   A line whose connection is established by dialing.

**Switched Major
  Node**   In IBM documentation, in VTAM, a major node whose minor nodes
are physical units and logical units attached by switched SDLC links.

Switched Network A network that establishes connections by a dialing function.

Switched Network Backup In IBM documentation, an optional facility that allows a user to specify, for certain types of physical units, a switched line to be used as an alternate path if the primary line becomes unavailable or unusable.

Switched Virtual Circuit A temporary logical association between two DTEs connected to a packet-switching data network.

Symbiont In Digital Equipment documentation, a process that transfers record-oriented data to or from a device. For example, an input symbiont transfers data from card readers to disks. An output symbiont transfers data from disks to line printers.

Symbiont Manager In Digital Equipment documentation, the function that maintains spool queues and dynamically creates symbiont processes to perform the necessary I/O operations.

Symbol In Digital Equipment documentation, an entity that ,when defined, will represent a particular function or entity (for example, a command string, directory name, or file name) in a particular context.

Symbol Table In Digital Equipment documentation, that portion of an executable image that contains the definition of global symbols used by the debugger for images linked with the DEBUG qualifier. A table in which the digital command language places local symbols. DCL maintains a local symbol table for each command level.

Synchronous Backplane Interconnect In Digital Equipment documentation, that part of the hardware that interconnects the VAX processor, memory controllers, MASSBUS adapters, and the UNIBUS adapter.

Synchronization Point In IBM documentation, an intermediate or end point during processing of a transaction at which an update or modification to one or more of the transaction's protected resources is logically complete and error-free.

Sync Point Services (SPS) In IBM documentation, the component of the sync point manager that is responsible for coordinating the managers of protected resources during sync point processing. SPS coordinates two-phase commit protocols, resync protocols, and logging.

System Communications Services In Digital Equipment documentation, a protocol responsible for the formation and breaking of intersystem process connections and for flow control of message traffic over those connections. System services such as the VMS cluster connection manager and the mass storage control protocol disk server communicate with this protocol.

System Control Block	In Digital Equipment documentation, on VAX systems, the data structure in system space that contains all the interrupt and exception vectors known to the system.
System Definition	In IBM documentation, the process, completed before a system is put into use, by which desired functions and operations of the system are selected from various available options.
System Disk	In Digital Equipment documentation, the disk that contains the operating system. In a VMS cluster environment, a system disk is set up so that most of the files can be shared by several processors. In addition, each processor has its own directory on the system disk that contains its page, swap, and dump files.
System File	In Apple documentation, a file, located in the System Folder, that contains the basic system software plus some system resources, such as font and sound resources.
System Generation	Synonym for system definition.
System GETVIS Area	In IBM documentation, a storage space that is available for dynamic allocation to VSE's system control programs or other application programs.
System Image	In Digital Equipment documentation, the image read into memory from disk when the system is started up.
System Management Facility (SMF)	In IBM documentation, a feature of MVS that collects and records a variety of system and job-related information.
System Menu	In a windowing environment, particularly the X-window environment, the menu that displays when the system menu button on the window manager window frame is pressed. Every window has a system menu that enables you to control the size, shape, and position of the window.
System Modification Program (SMP)	In IBM documentation, a program used to install software changes on MVS systems.
System Services Control Point (SSCP)	In IBM documentation, a component within a subarea network for managing the configuration, coordinating network operator and problem determination requests, and providing directory services and other session services for end-users of the network. Multiple SSCPs, cooperating as peers with one another, can divide the network into domains of control, with each SSCP having a hierarchical control relationship to the physical and logical units within its own domain.

System Services Control Point (SSCP) Domain	In IBM documentation, the system services control point, the physical units, the logical units, the links, the link stations, and all the resources the SSCP has the ability to control by means of activation and deactivation requests.
System Support Programs (SSP)	In IBM documentation, an IBM-licensed program, made up of a collection of utilities and small programs, that supports the operation of the NCP.
Systems Network Architecture (SNA)	IBM's description of the logical structure, formats, protocols, and operational sequences for their network offering called SNA.
Takeover	In IBM documentation, the process by which the failing active subsystem is released from its extended recovery facility (XRF) sessions with terminal users and replaced by an alternate subsystem.
Task Specifier	In Digital Equipment documentation, information provided to DECnet that enables Open VMS software to complete a logical link connection to a remote task. This information includes the name of the remote node on which the target task runs and the name of the task itself.
TCP (Transmission Control Protocol)	The TCP/IP standard transport-level protocol that provides the reliable, full-duplex, stream service on which many application protocols depend. It is connection-oriented: before transmitting data, participants must establish a connection.
Telecommunications Access Method (TCAM)	In IBM documentation, the access method prior to VTAM.
Telnet	The TCP/IP standard protocol for remote terminal service.
Terminal	Generally, as a point of entry with a display and keyboard.
Terminal Access Facility (TAF)	In IBM documentation, in NetView, a facility that allows a network operator to control a number of subsystems. In a full-screen or operator control session, operators can control any combination of such subsystems simultaneously.
Terminal-Based Program	In the X-window environment, a program (non-client) written to be run on a terminal (not in a window). Terminal-based programs must be fooled by terminal-emulation clients to run on the X-window system.
Terminal Emulator	Generally refers to a program that performs some type of simulation; typically of a type of terminal.
Terminate	In IBM documentation, in SNA, a request unit that is sent by a logical unit to its system services control point to cause the SSCP to start a procedure to end one or more designated LU-LU sessions.

Terminal Server	A network device used to connect "dumb" terminals to a network medium. Consequently, these terminals have virtual terminal access to hosts and devices located on a network.
Terminal Type	The type of terminal attached to a computer. UNIX uses the terminal type to set the TERM environment variable so that it can communicate with the terminal correctly. In the SNA environment, the terminal type is required in order to know how to configure the system so it can function.
Term 0	In Hewlett-Packard documentation, a level 0 terminal is a reference standard that defines basic terminal functions.
TFTP (Trivial File Transfer Protocol)	A TCP/IP standard protocol for file transfer that uses UDP as a transport mechanism. TFTP depends only on UDP so it can be used on machines such as diskless workstations.
TG Weight	In IBM documentation, a quantitative measure of how well the values of a transmission group's characteristics satisfy the criteria specified by the class-of-service definition, as computed during route selection for a session.
Thread	In Digital Equipment documentation, a single, sequential flow of control within a program. It is the active execution of a designated routine, including any nested routine invocations. A single thread has a single point of execution within it. A thread can be executed in parallel with other threads.
Threshold	Generally, a percentage value set for a resource.
Tile	In the X-window environment, a rectangular area used to cover a surface with a pattern or visual texture.
Time Division Multiplexing (TDM)	A technique used to multiplex data on a channel by a time sharing of the channel.
Time Domain Reflectometer (TDR)	A device used to troubleshoot networks. It sends signals through a network medium to check for continuity.
Time Sharing Option Extensions (TSO/E)	In IBM, it is the base for all TSO enhancements.
Timeout	An event that occurs at the end of a predetermined period of time.
Title Bar	In the X-window environment, the rectangular area between the top of the window and the window frame. The title bar contains the title of the window object. For example, Xclock for clocks.

TN3270	A program that uses Telnet protocol but produces an EBCDIC 3270 data stream. The program is normally found as a TN3270 client application that provides access into a 3270-based environment.
Token	The symbol of authority passed successively from one data station to another to indicate the station temporarily in control of the transmission medium.
Token Ring	A network with a ring topology that passes tokens from one attaching device to another.
Token-ring Interface Coupler (TIC)	An interface board used to connect a device such as a 3720, 3725, or 3745 communication controller to a token-ring network.
Token-ring Network	A ring network that allows unidirectional data transmission between data stations by a token-passing procedure.
Topology and Routing Services (TRS)	In IBM documentation, an APPN control point component that manages the topology database, computes routes, and provides a route selection Control Vector that specifies the best route through the network for a given session based on its requested class of service.
Trace	A record of events captured and used to troubleshoot hardware and/or software.
Transaction	In Apple documentation, a sequence of Apple events sent back and forth between a client and a server application, beginning with the client's initial request for a service.
Transaction Processing Facility (TPF)	A software system designed to support real-time applications.
Transaction Program	According to IBM, a program that conforms to LU6.2 protocols.
Transceiver	A device that connects a host's cable from the interface board to the main cable of the network.
Trap	An event used in SNMP-managed networks to send data to the network manager. A trap is sent from an SNMP agent.
Trash Folder	In Apple documentation, a directory at the root level of a volume for storing files the user has moved to the Trash icon. After opening the Trash icon, the user sees the collection of all items moved to the Trash icon—that is, the union of appropriate Trash directories from all mounted volumes. A Macintosh set up to share files among users in a network environment maintains separate Trash subdirectories for remote users within its shared, network Trash directory. The Finder

for system software version 7.0 empties a Trash directory only when the user of that directory chooses the Empty Trash command.

Translated Code In Digital Equipment documentation, it is the native AXP object code in a translated image. Translated code includes: AXP code that reproduces the behavior of equivalent VAX code in the original image; calls to the translated image environment.

Translated Image In Digital Equipment documentation, it is an AXP executable or shareable image created by translating the object code of an VAX image. The translated image, functionally equivalent to the VAX image from which it was translated, includes both translated code and the original image.

Translated Image Environment (TIE) In Digital Equipment documentation, a native AXP shareable image that supports the execution of translated images. The TIE processes all interactions with the native AXP system and provides an environment similar to VAX for the translated image by managing VAX state; by emulating VAX features such as exception processing, AST delivery, and complex VAX instructions; and by interpreting untranslated VAX instructions.

Translation In Digital Equipment documentation, the process of converting a VAX binary image to an AXP image that runs with the assistance of the TIE on an AXP system. Translation is a static process which converts as much VAX code as possible to native Alpha AXP instructions. The TIE interprets any untranslated VAX code at run time.

Translation Table A table used to replace one or more characters with alternative characters.

Transmission Group (TG) According to IBM, a group of links between adjacent subarea nodes, appearing as a single logical link for routing of messages.

Transmission Header (TH) According to SNA, control information, optionally followed by a basic information unit, created and used by path control to route message units and to control their flow within the network.

Transmission Priority In IBM documentation, a rank assigned to a message unit that determines its precedence for selection by the path control component in each node along a route for forwarding to the next node in the route.

Transport Layer In the OSI model, the layer that provides a reliable end-to-dnd service to its users.

Transport Network In IBM documentation, the part of an SNA network that includes the data link-control and path-control layers.

TSO/E (Time Sharing Option Extensions) In IBM documentation, a program that provides enhancements to MVS/XA users.

TTL (Time To Live)
A technique used in best-effort delivery systems to avoid endlessly looping packets. For example, packets have a "time" associated with their lifetime.

Type
In Apple documentation, the second field in the name of an AppleTalk entity. The type is assigned by the entity itself and can be anything the user or application assigns.

Type 2.1 End Node
In IBM documentation, a type 2.1 node that provides full SNA end-user services, but no intermediate routing or network services to any other node; it is configured only as an endpoint in a network.

Type 2.1 Network
In IBM documentation, a collection of interconnected type 2.1 network nodes and type 2.1 end nodes. A type 2.1 network may consist of nodes of just one type, namely, all network nodes or all end nodes; a pair of directly attached end nodes is the simplest case of a type 2.1 network.

Type 2.1 Node
A node that conforms to IBM's type 2.1 architecture.

Type 5 Node
In IBM documentation, a node that can be any one of the following: an advanced peer-to-peer networking (APPN) end node; an advanced peer-to-peer networking (APPN) network node; an interchange node; a Low-entry networking (LEN) node, a migration data host, or a subarea node. It is also a node that traditionally has the SSCP.

UDP (User Datagram Protocol)
A TCP/IP standard protocol that is in contrast to TCP. UDP is connectionless and unreliable.

UNBIND
According to IBM, a request to deactivate a session between two logical units.

Unformatted
According to IBM, pertains to commands (such as `LOGON` or `LOGOFF`) entered by an end-user and sent by a logical unit in character form.

Unformatted System Services (USS)
In IBM documentation, in SNA, a system services control point (SSCP) facility that translates a character-coded request, such as a logon or logoff request, into a field-formatted request for processing by formatted system services; it translates field-formatted replies and responses into character-coded requests for processing by a logical unit.

Unit Control Block (UCB)
In Digital Equipment documentation, a structure in the I/O database that describes the characteristics of and current activity on a device unit. The unit control block also holds the fork block for its unit's device driver; the fork block is a critical part of a driver fork process. The UCB also provides a dynamic storage area for the driver.

Universal Symbol	In Digital Equipment documentation, a global symbol in a shareable image that can be used by modules as that shareable image. Universal symbols are typically a subset of all the global symbols in a shareable image. When creating a shareable image, the linker ensures that universal symbols remain available for reference after symbols have been resolved.
Unsolicited Message	In IBM documentation, a message from VTAM to a program operator that is unrelated to any command entered by the program operator.
Upline Dump	In Digital Equipment documentation, in DECnet for Open VMS, a function that allows an adjacent node to dump its memory to a file on a system.
User Exit	In IBM documentation, a point in an IBM-supplied program at which a user exit routine may be given control.
User Exit Routine	In IBM documentation, a user-written routine that receives control at predefined user exit points. User exit routines can be written in assembly or a high-level language.
User File Directory	In Digital Equipment documentation, a file that briefly catalogs a set of files stored on disk or tape. The directory includes the name, type, and version number of each file in the set. It also contains a unique number that identifies that file's actual location and points to a list of its file attributes.
User Privileges	In Digital Equipment documentation, those privileges granted to a user by the system manager.
UUCP (UNIX-to-UNIX Copy Program)	An application program that allows one UNIX system to copy files to or from another UNIX system.
VAXBI	In Digital Equipment documentation, the part of the VAX 8200, VAX 8250, VAX 8300, or VAX 8350 hardware that connects I/O adapters with memory controllers and the processor. In VAX 8530, VAX 8550, VAX 8700, or VAX 8800 systems, or VAX 6200 and VAX 6300 systems, the part of the hardware that connects I/O adapters with the bus that interfaces with the processor and memory.
VAX Cluster Configuration	In Digital Equipment documentation, a highly integrated organization of Open VMS systems that communicate over a high-speed communications path. VAX cluster configurations have all the functions of single-node systems, plus the ability to share CPU resources, queues, and disk storage. Like a single-node system, the VAX cluster configuration provides a single security and management environment. Member nodes can share the same operating environment or serve specialized needs.

VAX Environment Software Translator (VEST)	In Digital Equipment documentation, a software migration tool that translates VAX executable and shareable images into images that run on AXP systems. VEST is part of the DECmigrate tool set.
VAX Vector Instruction Emulation Facility (VVIEF)	In Digital Equipment documentation, a standard feature of the operating system that allows vectorized applications to be written and debugged in a VAX system in which vector processors are not available. VVIEF emulates the VAX vector processing environment, including the nonprivileged VAX vector instructions and the vector system services. Use of VVIEF is restricted to user mode code.
Vector	In Digital Equipment documentation, a storage location that contains the starting address of a procedure to be executed when a given interrupt or exception occurs.
Vector Present System	In Digital Equipment documentation, a VAX system that in its hardware implementation complies with the VAX vector architecture and incorporates one or more optional vector processors.
Virtual Disk	In IBM documentation, in VM, a physical disk storage device, or a logical subdivision of a physical disk storage device, that has its own address, consecutive storage space for data, and index or description of stored data so that the data can be accessed.
Virtual Filestore	A concept in OSI that refers to the OSI abstraction of a collection of files, directories, and/or references.
Virtual Machine (VM)	In IBM documentation, in VM, a functional equivalent of a computing system. On the 370 Feature of VM, a virtual machine operates in System/370 mode. On the ESA feature of VM, a virtual machine operates in System/370, 370-XA, ESA/370, or ESA/390 mode. Each virtual machine is controlled by an operating system. VM controls the concurrent execution of multiple virtual machines on an actual processor complex.
Virtual Machine Group	In IBM documentation, in the group control system, two or more virtual machines associated with each other through the same named system.
Virtual Machine/ Enterprise Systems Architecture (VM/ESA)	In IBM documentation, an IBM program that manages the resources of a single computer so that multiple computing systems appear to exist. Each virtual machine is the functional equivalent of a real machine.

Virtual Machine/ Extended Architecture (VM/XA)	In IBM documentation, an operating system that facilitates conversion to MVS/XA by allowing several operating systems (a production system and one or more test systems) to run simultaneously on a single 370-XA processor.
Virtual Machine/ System Product (VM/SP)	According to IBM, a program that manages the resources of a single computer so that multiple computing systems appear to exist.
Virtual Machine/ System Product High Performance Option (VM/SP HPO)	In IBM documentation, a program that can be installed and executed in conjunction with VM/SP to extend the capabilities of VM/SP with programming enhancements, support for microcode assists, and additional functions.
Virtual Route (VR)	In IBM documentation, in SNA, either of the following: a logical connection between two subarea nodes that is physically realized as a particular explicit route, or a logical connection that is wholly contained within a subarea node for intranode sessions.
Virtual Route (VR) Pacing	In IBM documentation, in SNA, a flow-control technique used by the virtual route control component of path control at each end of a virtual route to control the rate at which path information units flow over the virtual route.
Virtual Routing Node	In IBM documentation, a representation of a node's connectivity to a connection network defined on a shared-access transport facility, such as a token ring.
Virtual Storage	In IBM documentation, storage space that may be regarded as addressable main storage by the user of a computer system in which virtual addresses are mapped into real addresses.
Virtual Storage Access Method (VSAM)	In IBM documentation, an access method of direct or sequential processing of fixed and variable-length records on direct access devices.
Virtual Storage Extended (VSE)	In IBM documentation, a program whose full name is the Virtual Storage Extended/Advanced Function. It is a software operating system controlling the execution of programs.
Virtual Telecommun- ication Access Method (VTAM)	In IBM documentation, a program that controls communication and the flow of data in an SNA network. It provides single- domain, multiple-domain, and interconnected network capability.
VM/SNA Console Support (VSCS)	In IBM documentation, a VTAM component for the VM environment that provides systems network architecture support. It allows SNA terminals to be virtual machine consoles.

VM/370 Control Program (CP)	In IBM documentation, the component of VM/370 that manages the resources of a single computer with the result that multiple computing systems appear to exist. Each virtual machine is the functional equivalent of an IBM System/370 computing system.
VSE/Advanced Functions	In IBM documentation, the basic operating system support needed for a VSE-controlled installation.
VMS Cluster Configuration	In Digital Equipment documentation, a highly integrated organization of Open VMS AXP systems, or a combination of AXP or VAX systems, that communicate over a high-speed communications path. VMS cluster configurations have all the functions of single-node systems, plus the ability to share CPU resources, queues, and disk storage. Like a single-node system, the VMS cluster configuration provides a single security and management environment. Member nodes can share the same operating environment or serve specialized needs.
VTAM Application Program	In IBM documentation, a program that has opened an access method control block to identify itself to VTAM and can therefore issue VTAM macroinstructions.
VTAM Common Network Services (VCNS)	In IBM documentation, VTAM's support for shared physical connectivity between systems network architecture networks and certain non-SNA networks.
VTAM Definition	In IBM documentation, the process of defining the user-application network to VTAM and modifying IBM-defined characteristics to suit the needs of the user.
VTAM Definition Library	In IBM documentation, the operating system files or data sets that contain the definition statements and start options filed during VTAM definition.
VTAM Internal Trace (VIT)	In IBM documentation, a trace used in VTAM to collect data on channel I/O, use of locks, and storage-management services.
VTAM Operator	In IBM documentation, a person or program authorized to issue VTAM operator commands.
VTAM Operator Command	In IBM documentation, a command used to monitor or control a VTAM domain.
Waveform	The representation of a disturbance as a function, as it occurs in time, and its relationship to space.
Wavelength	The distance an electromagnetic wave can travel in the amount of time it takes to oscillate through a complete cycle.
Well-Known Port	In TCP/IP, applications and programs that reside on top of TCP and UDP, respectively, have a designated port assigned to them, the well-known port.

Window	A term used with environments such as X windows. Generally used in contrast with line or full-screen mode.
Window-Based Program	A program written for use with a windowing system; for example, an X-window environment or the MS window environment. The opposite of a window-based program is a terminal-based program.
Window Decoration	In the X-window environment, the frame and window control buttons that surround windows managed by the window manager.
Window Manager	A program in the X-windowing system that controls size, placement, and operation of windows on the root window. The window manager includes the functional window frames that surround each window object as well as a menu for the root window.
Xenix	A version of UNIX that can run on a PC.
X.21	A CCITT standard defining logical link control and media access control in X.25 networks.
X.25	A CCITT standard for packet-switched network-layer services.
X.400	A CCITT and ISO combination of standards for providing electronic mail services.
X.500	A CCITT and ISO combination of standards for providing directory services.
X Application	An application program that conforms to X protocol standards.
X Library	A collection of C-language routines based on the X protocol.
X Protocol	A protocol that uses TCP as a transport mechanism. It supports asynchronous, event-driven distributed window environments; this can be across heterogeneous platforms.
X Terminal	A terminal and machine specifically designed to run a X server. In this type of environment, X clients are run on remote systems.
X Toolkit	A collection of high-level programs based on programming from the X library.
X-Window System	A software system developed at MIT whose original design intent was to provide distributed computing support for the development of programs. It supports two-dimensional bitmapped graphics.
Zap Disk	In IBM documentation, the virtual disk in the VM operating system that contains the user-written modifications to VTAM code.
Zone	In Digital Equipment documentation, a section of a fully configured VAXft fault-tolerant computing system that contains a minimum of a CPU module, memory module, I/O module, and associated devices. A VAXft system consists of two such zones with synchronized processor operations. If one zone fails, processing continues uninter-

rupted through automatic failover to the other zone. Or, in AppleTalk, a logical grouping of devices in an AppleTalk internet that makes it easier for users to locate network services. The network administrator defines zones during the router setup process. According to Apple documentation, a logical grouping of a subset of the nodes on the internet. The zone is the third field in the name of an AppleTalk entity.

Zone Information Protocol An AppleTalk protocol that maintains a zone information table in each router that lists the relationship between zone names and networks.

Zone Name In Apple documentation, a name defined for each zone in an AppleTalk internet. A LocalTalk network can have just one zone name. Ethernet and token ring networks can have multiple zone names, called a zone list.

Zone of Authority A term used with the domain name system to refer to the group of names for which a given name server is an authority.

Bibliography

Aspray, William, 1990, *John Von Neumann and The Origins of Modern Computing*, Cambridge, MA: MIT Press.

Bashe, Charles J., Johnson, Lyle R., Palmer, John H., and Pugh, Emerson W., 1986, *IBM's Early Computers*, Cambridge, MA: MIT Press.

Bohl, Marilyn, 1971, *Information Processing*, Third Edition, Chicago, NY: Science Research Associates, Inc.

Digital Equipment Corp., 1991, *DECnet Digital Network Architecture (Phase V): Network Routing Layer Functional Specification*, EK-DNA03-FS-001, Maynard, MA: Digital Equipment Corp.

Digital Equipment Corp., 1993, *OpenVMS Glossary* , AA-PV5UA-TK, Maynard, MA: Digital Equipment Corp.

Digital Equipment Corp., 1993, *OpenVMS DCL Dictionary: N-Z*, AA-PV5LA-TK, Maynard, MA: Digital Equipment Corp.

Digital Equipment Corp., 1993, *OpenVMS DCL Dictionary: A-M*, AA-PV5LA-TK, Maynard, MA: Digital Equipment Corp.

Digital Equipment Corp. 1993, *OpenVMS Software Overview*, AA-PVXHA-TE, Maynard, MA: Digital Equipment Corp.

Digital Equipment Corp., 1993, *DECnet/OSI for OpenVMS: Introduction and Planning*, AA-PNHTB-TE, Maynard, MA: Digital Equipment Corp.

Hewlett Packard Company, 1992, *Using HP-UX: Hp 9000 Workstations*, B2910-90001, Ft. Collins, CO: Hewlett Packard Company.

Hewlett Packard Company, 1991, *Using the X Window System*, B1171-90037,Ft. Collins, CO: Hewlett Packard Company.

Hewlett Packard Company, 1992, *HP OpenView SNMP Agent Administrator's Reference*, J2322-90002, Ft.Collins, CO: Hewlett Packard Company.

Hewlett Packard Company, 1992, *HP OpenView SNMP Management Platform Administrator's Reference*, J2313-90001, Ft. Collins, CO: Hewlett Packard Company.

Hewlett Packard Company, 1992, *HP OpenView Windows User's Guide*, J2316-90000, Ft. Collins, CO: Hewlett Packard Company.

IBM Corp., 1990, *IBM 3172 Interconnect Controller: Presentation Guide*, White Plains, NY: IBM Corp.

IBM Corp., 1993, *VTAM: Resource Definition Feference Version 4 Release 1 for MVS/ESA*, SC31-6427-00, Research Triangle Park, NC: IBM Corp.

IBM Corp., 1992, *IBM Networking Systems: Planning and Reference*, SC31-6191-00, Research Triangle Park, NC: IBM Corp.

IBM Corp., 1985, *IBM 3270 Information Display System: 3274 Control Unit Description and Programmer's Guide*, GA23-0061-2, Research Triangle Park, NC: IBM Corp.

IBM Corp., 1992, *TCP/IP Version 2 Release 2.1 for MVS: Planning and Customization*, SC31-6085-02, Research Triangle Park, NC: IBM Corp.

IBM Corp., 1990, *Enterprise Systems Architecture/390: Principles of Operation*, SA22-7201-00, Poughkeepsie, NY: IBM Corp.

IBM Corp., 1991, *3174 Establishment Controller: Functional Description*, GA23-0218-08, Research Triangle Park, NC: IBM Corp.

IBM Corp., 1983, *IBM System/370 Extended Architecture: Principles of Operation*, SA22-7085-0, Research Triangle Park, NC: IBM Corp.

IBM Corp., 1993, *NetView: Installation and Administration*, SC31-7084-00, Research Triangle Park, NC: IBM Corp.

IBM Corp., 1988, *IBM Enterprise Systems Architecture/370: Principles of Operation*, SA22-7200-0, Poughkeepsie, NY: IBM Corp.

IBM Corp., 1992, *Sockets Interface for CICS - Using TCP/IP Version 2 Release 2 for MVS: User's Guide*, GC31-7015-00, Research Triangle Park, NC: IBM Corp.

IBM Corp., 1993, *System Information Architecture: Formats*, GA27-3136, Research Triangle Park, NC: IBM Corp.

IBM Corp., 1991, *Systems Network Architecture: Type 2.1 Node Reference*, Version 1, SC20-3422-2, Research Triangle Park, NC: IBM Corp.

IBM Corp., 1991, *Enterprise Systems Architecture/390 ESCON I/O Interface: Physical Layer*, SA23-0394-00, Kingston, NY: IBM Corp.

IBM Corp., 1991, *Systems Network Architecture: Concepts and Products*, GC30-3072-4, Research Triangle Park, NC: IBM Corp.

IBM Corp., 1991, *Systems Network Architecture: Technical Overview*, GC30-3073-3, Research Triangle Park, NC: IBM Corp.

IBM Corp., 1990, *VM/ESA and Related Products: Overview*, GG24-3610-00, Poughkeepsie, NY: IBM Corp.

IBM Corp., 1992, *High Speed Networking Technology: An Introductory Survey*, GG24-3816-00, Raleigh, NC: IBM Corp.

IBM Corp., 1993, *System Network Architecture: Architecture Reference*, Version 2, SC30-3422-03, Research Triangle Park, NC: IBM Corp.

IBM Corp., 1993, *IBM Network Products Implementation Guide*, GG24-3649-01, Raleigh NC: IBM Corp.

IBM Corp., 1991, *Enterprise Systems Connection Manager*, GC23-0422-01, Kingston, NY: IBM Corp.

IBM Corp., 1987, *IBM System/370: Principles of Operation*, GA22-7000-10, Poughkeepsie, NY: IBM Corp.

IBM Corp., 1992, *Synchronous Data Link Control: Concepts* GA27-3093-04, Research Triangle Park, NC: IBM Corp.

IBM Corp., 1991, *Enterprise Systems Connection: ESCON I/O Interface*, SA22-7202-01, Poughkeepsie, NY: IBM Corp.

IBM Corp., 1992, *TCP/IP Version2 Release 2.1 for MVS: Offload of TCP/IP Processing*, SA31-7033-00, Research Triangle Park, NC: IBM Corp.

IBM Corp., 1991, *Enterprise Systems Connection*, GA23-0383-01, Kingston, NY: IBM Corp.

IBM Corp., 1992, *The IBM 6611 Network Processor*, GG24-3870-00, Raleigh, NC: IBM Corp.

IBM Corp., 1992, *VSE/ESA Version 1.3: An Introduction Presentation Foil Master*, GG24-4008-00, Raleigh, NC: IBM Corp.

IBM Corp., 1993, *IBM VSE/Interactive Computing and Control Facility: Primer*, SC33-6561-01, Charlotte, NC: IBM Corp.

IBM Corp., 1990, *IBM VSE/POWER: Networking*, SC33-6573-00, Mechanicsburg, PA: IBM Corp.

IBM Corp., 1991, *Virtual Machine/Enterprise System Architecture: General Information*, GC24-5550-02, Endicott, NY: IBM Corp.

IBM Corp., 1993, *Virtual Machine/Enterprise Systems Architecture*, SC24-5460-03, Endicott, NY: IBM Corp.

IBM Corp., 1990, *IBM VSE/ESA: System Control Statements*, SC33-6513-00, Mechanicsburg, PA: IBM Corp.

IBM Corp., 1994, *Lan Resource Extension and Services/VM: General Information*, GC24-5618-03, Endicott, NY: IBM Corp.

IBM Corp., 1989, *MVS/ESA Operatons: System Commands Reference Summary*, GX22-0013-1, Poughkeepsie, NY: IBM Corp.

IBM Corp., 1993, *The Host as a Data Server Using LANRES and Novell NetWare*, GG24-4069-00, Poughkeepsie, NY: IBM Corp.

IBM Corp., 1993, *MVS/ESA: System Commands*, GC28-1626-05, Poughkeepsie, NY: IBM Corp.

IBM Corp., 1992, *3172 Interconnect Controller: Planning Guide*, GA27-3867-05, Research Triangle Park, NC: IBM Corp.

IBM Corp., 1992, *3172 Interconnect Controller: Operator's Guide*, GA27-3970-00, Research Triangle Park, NC: IBM Corp.

IBM Corp., 1990, *Virtual Machine/Enterprise Systems Architecture*, GC24-5441, Endicott, NY: IBM Corp.

IBM Corp., 1993, *LAN File Services/ESA: VM Guide and Reference*, SH24-5264-00, Endicott, NY: IBM Corp.

IBM Corp., 1992, *VM/ESA : CMS Primer*, SC24-5458-02, Endicott, NY: IBM Corp.

IBM Corp., 1991, *NetView: NetView Graphic Monitor Facility Operation*, SC31-6099-1, Research Triangle Park, NC: IBM Corp.

IBM Corp., 1990, *MVS/ESA SP Version 4 Technical Presentation Guide*, GG24-3594-00, Poughkeepsie, NY: IBM Corp.

IBM Corp., 1986, *JES3 Introduction*, GC23-0039-2, Poughkeepsie, NY: IBM Corp.

IBM Corp., 1980, *IBM Virtual Machine Facility: Terminal User's Guide*, GC20-1810-9, Poughkeepsie, NY: IBM Corp.

IBM Corp., 1992, *MVS/ESA and Data in Memory: Performance Studies*, GG24-3698-00, Poughkeepsie, NY: IBM Corp.

IBM Corp., 1993, *VM/ESA: CMS Command Reference*, SC24-5461-03, Endicott, NY: IBM Corp.

IBM Corp., 1993, *VM/ESA: CP Command and Utility Reference*, SC24-5519-03, Endicott, NY: IBM Corp.

IBM Corp., 1992, *APPN Architecture and Product Implementations Tutorial*, GG24-3669-01, Research Triangle Park, NC: IBM Corp.

IBM Corp., 1988, *3270 Information Display System: Introduction*, GA27-2739-22, Research Triangle Park, NC: IBM Corp.

IBM Corp., 1994, *LAN Resource Extension and Services/MVS: General Information*, GC24-5625-03, Endicott, NY: IBM Corp.

IBM Corp., 1993, *LAN Resource Extension and Services/VM: Guide and Reference*, SC24-5622-01, Endicott, NY: IBM Corp.

IBM Corp., 1994, *LAN Resource Extension and Services/MVS: Guide and Reference*, SC24-5623-02, Endicott, NY: IBM Corp.

IBM Corp., 1991, *Dictionary of Computing*, SC20-1699-8, Poughkeepsie, NY: IBM Corp.

IBM Corp., 1992, *3270 Information Display System: Data Stream Programmer's Reference*, GA23-0059-07, Research Triangle Park, NC: IBM Corp.

IBM Corp., 1993, *MVS/ESA: JES2 Command Reference Summary*, GX22-0017-03, Poughkeepsie, NY: IBM Corp.

IBM Corp., 1991, *Installation Guidelines for the IBM Token-Ring Network Products*, GG24-3291-02, Research Triangle Park, NC: IBM Corp.

IBM Corp., 1993, *Lan file Services/ESA: MVS Guide and Reference*, SH24-5265-00, Endicott, NY: IBM Corp.

IBM Corp., 1990, *Enterprise System/9000 Models 120, 130, 150, and 170: Introducing the System*, GA24-4186-00, Endicott, NY: IBM Corp.

IBM Corp., 1993, *NetView: Command Quick Reference*, SX75-0090-00, Research Triangle Park, NC: IBM Corp.

IBM Corp., 1993, *VTAM: Operation*, SC31-6420-00, Research Triangle Park, NC: IBM Corp.

IBM Corp., 1992, *ES/9000 Multi-Image Processing Volume1: Presentation and Solutions Guidelines*, GG24-3920-00, Poughkeepsie, NY: IBM Corp.

IBM Corp., 1993, *MVS/ESA JES2 Commands*, GC23-0084-04, Poughkeepsie, NY: IBM Corp.

IBM Corp., 1992, *VM/ESA Release 2 Overview*, GG24-3860-00, Poughkeepsie, NY: IBM Corp.

IBM Corp., 1992, *MVS/ESA: General Information for MVS/ESA System Product Version 4*, GC28-1600-04, Poughkeepsie, NY: IBM Corp.

Nash, Stephen G., Editor, 1990, *A History of Scientific Computing*, New York, NY: ACM Press.

Pugh, Emerson W., Johnson, Lyle R., and Palmer, John H., *IBM's 360 and Early 370 Systems*, Cambridge, MA: MIT Press.

Pugh, Emerson W., 1984, *Memories That Shaped an Industry*, Cambridge, MA: MIT Press.

Umar, Amjad, 1993, *Distributed Computing: A Practical Synthesis*, Englewood Cliffs, New Jersey, Prentice-Hall, Inc.

Kessler, Gary C., 1990, *ISDN*, McGraw-Hill, Inc.

Hecht, Jeff, 1990, *Understanding Fiber Optics*, Carmel, In, Howard W. Sams & Company.

Dayton, Robert L., 1991, *Telecommunications: The Transmission of Information*, New York, NY, McGraw-Hill, Inc.

Blyth, W. John, Blyth, Mary M., 1990, *Telecommunications: Concepts, Development, and Management*, Mission Hills, CA, Glencoe/McGraw-Hill, Inc.

Campbell, Joe, 1984, *The RS-232 Solution*, Alameda, CA, SYBEX.

Kochan, Stephen G, Wood, Patrick H., 1984, *Exploring the UNIX System*, Indianapolis, IN, Hayden Books.

Comer, Douglas, 1988, *Internetworking With TCP/IP Principles, Protocols, and Architecture*, Englewood Cliffs, New Jersey, Prentice Hall.

Forney, James S., 1992, *DOS Beyond 640K 2nd Edition*, Windcrest/McGraw-Hill, Inc.

Forney, James S., 1989, *MS-DOS Beyond 640K Working with Extended and Expanded Memory*, Blue Ridge Summit, PA, Windcrest Books.

Ranade, Jay, Sackett, George C., 1989, *Introduction to SNA Networking Using VTAM/NCP*, New York, NY, McGraw-Hill, Inc.

Ashley, Ruth, Fernandez, Judi N., 1984, J*ob Control Language*, John Wiley & Sons, Inc.

Chorafas, Dimitris N., 1989, *Local Area Network Reference*, New York, NY, McGraw-Hill, Inc.

Edmunds, John J., 1992, *SAA/LU 6.2 Distributed Networks and Applications*, New York, NY, McGraw-Hill, Inc.

Comer, Douglas E., 1991, *Internetworking With TCP/IP Vol I: Principles, Protocols, and Architecture*, Englewood Cliffs, NJ, Prentice Hall.

Fortier, Paul J., 1989, *Handbook of LAN Technology*, New York, NY, Intertext Publications/Multiscience Press, Inc.

Feit, Sidnie, 1993, *TCP/IP Architecture, Protocols, and Implementation*, New York, NY, McGraw-Hill, Inc.

McClain, Gary R., 1991, *Open Systems Interconnection Handbook*, New York, NY, Intertext Publications/Multiscience Press.

Black, Uyless, 1992, *TCP/IP and Related Protocols*, New York, NY, McGraw-Hill, Inc.

Black, Uyless,1991, *The V Series Recommendations Protocols for Data Communications Over the Telephone Network*, New York, NY, McGraw-Hill, Inc.

Comer, Douglas E., and Stevens, David L., 1991, *Internetworking With TCP/IP Vol II: Design, Implementation, and Internals*, Englewood Cliffs, New Jersey, Prentice Hall.

Rose, Marshall T., 1991, *The Simple Book An Introduction to Management of TCP/IP - Based Internets,* Englewood Cliffs, New Jersey, Prentice Hall.

Jain, Bijendra N., and Agrawala, Ashok K., 1993, *Open Systems Interconnection*, New York, NY, McGraw-Hill, Inc.

Madron, Thomas W., 1988, *Local Area Networks The Next Generation*, New York, NY, John Wiley & Sons, Inc.

Schatt, Stan, 1990, *Understnding Local Area Networks, Second Edition*, Carmel, IN, Howard W. Sams & Company.

Killen, Michael, 1992, *SAA and UNIX IBM's Open Systems Strategy*, New York, NY, McGraw-Hill, Inc.

Tang, Adrian, and Scoggins, Sophia, 1992, *Open Networking with OSI*, Englewood Cliffs, New Jersey, Prentice-Hall, Inc.

Groff, James R., and Weinbert, Paul N., 1983, *Understanding UNIX A Conceptual Guide*, Carmel, IN, Que Corporation.

Rose Marshall T., 1990, *The Open Book A Practical Perspective on OSI*, Englewood Cliffs, New Jersey, Prentice Hall, Inc.

Campbell, Joe, 1987, *C Programmer's Guide to Serial Communications*, Carmel, IN, Howard W. Sams & Company.

Killen, Michael, 1992, *SAA Managing Distributed Data*, New York, NY, McGraw-Hill, Inc.

ZWass, Vladimir, 1981, *Introduction to Computer Science*, New York, NY, Barnes & Noble Books.

Bradbeer, Robin, De Bono, Peter, and Laurie, Peter, 1982, *The Beginner's Guide to Computers*, Addison-Wesley Publishing Company.

Bryant, David, 1971, *Physics*, Great Britain, Hodder and Stoughton Ltd.

Bach, Maurice J., 1986, *The Design of The UNIX Operating System*, Englewood Cliffs, New Jersey, Prentice-Hall, Inc.

Black, Uyless, 1991, *The X Series Recommendations Protocols for Data Communications Networks*, New York, NY, McGraw-Hill, Inc.

Seyer, Martin D., 1991, *RS-232 Made Easy: connecting Computers, Printers, Terminals, and Modems*, Englewood Cliffs, New Jersey, Prentice-Hall, Inc.

Meijer, Anton, 1987, *Systems Network Architecture a tutorial*, London, England, Pitman; New York, NY, John Wiley & Sons, Inc.

O'Dell, Peter, 1989, *The Computer Networking Book*, Chapel Hill, NC Ventana Press, Inc.

Brookshear, J. Glenn, 1988, *Computer Science An Overview*, Menlo Park, CA The Benjamin/Cummings Publishing Company, Inc.

White, Gene, 1992, *Internetworking and Addressing*,
New York, NY, McGraw-Hill, Inc.

Stallings, William, 1987, *Handbook of Computer-Communications Standards Volume 2*, New York, NY, Macmillan Publishing Company.

Stallings, William, 1987, *Handbook of Computer Communications Standards Volume 1*, New York, NY, Macmillan Publishing Company.

Stallings, William, 1988, *Handbook of Computer-Communications Standards Volume 3*, New York, NY, Macmillan Publishing Company.

Abbatiello, Judy and Sarch, Ray edited by, 1987, *Telec Communications & Data Communications Factbook*, New York, NY, Data Communications; Ramsey, NJ, CCMI/McGraw-Hill, Inc.

Naugle, Matthew G., 1991, *Local Area Networking*, New York, NY, McGraw-Hill, Inc.

Schlar, Serman K., 1990, *Inside X.25: A Manager's Guide*, New York, NY, McGraw-Hill, Inc.

Dern, Daniel P., 1994, *The Internet Guide for New Users*, New York, NY, McGraw-Hill, Inc.

Samson, Stephen L., 1990, *MVS Performance Management*, New York, NY, McGraw-Hill, Inc.

Graubart-Cervone, H. Frank, 1994, *VSE/ESA JCL Utilities, Power, and VSAM*, New York, NY, McGraw-Hill, Inc.

Merrow, Bill, 1993, *VSE/ESA Performance Management and Fine Tuning*, New York, NY, McGraw-Hill, Inc.

Savit, Jeffrey, 1993, *VM/CMS Cconcepts and Facilities*,
New York, NY, McGraw-Hill, Inc.

Merrow, Bill, 1994, *VSE/ESA Concepts and Facilities*, New York, NY, McGraw-Hill, Inc.

Stallings, William, 1989, *ISDN an Introduction*, New York, NY, Macmillan Publishing Company.

Stamper, David A., 1986, *Business Data Communications*, Menlo Park, CA, The Benjamin/Cummings Publishing Company, Inc.

Sidhu, Gursharan S., Andrews, Richard F. Oppenheimer, Alan B., 1990, *Inside AppleTalk, Second Edition*, Menlo Park, CA, Addison-Wesley Publishing Company.

Apple Computer, Inc., 1991, *Planning and Managing AppleTalk Networks*, Menlo Park, CA, Addison-Wesley Publishing Company.

Apple Computer, Inc., 1992, *Technical Introduction to the Macintosh Family Second Edition*, Menlo Park, CA, Addison-Wesley Publishing Company.

The ATM Forum, 1993, *ATM User-Network Interface Specification*, Englewood Cliffs, New Jersey, Prentice-Hall, Inc.

Kessler, Gary C., and Train, David A., 1992, *Metropolitan Area Networks Concepts, Standards, and Services*, New York, NY, McGraw-Hill, Inc.

Nemzow, Martin A. W., 1992, *The Ethernet Management Guide Keeping the Link Second Edition*, New York, NY, McGraw-Hill, Inc.

Berson, Alex, 1990, *APPC Introduction to LU6.2*, New York, NY, McGraw-Hill, Inc.

Parker, Sybil P., 1984, *McGraw-Hill Dictionary of Science and Engineering*, New York, NY, McGraw-Hill, Inc.

Gasman, Lawrence, 1994, *Broadband Networking*, New York, NY, Van Nostrand Reinhold.

Baggott, Jim, 1992, *The Meaning of Quantum Theory*, New York, NY, Oxford University Press Inc.

Black, Uyless, 1989, *Data Networks Concepts, Theory, and Practice*, Englewood Cliffs, New Jersey, Prentice-Hall, Inc.

Naugle, Matthew, 1994, *Network Protocol Handbook*, New York, NY, McGraw-Hill, Inc.

Spohn, Darren L., 1993, *Data Network Design*, New York, NY McGraw-Hill, Inc.

Martin, James, 1989, *Local Area Networks Architectures and Implementations*, Englewood Cliffs, New Jersey, Prentice-Hall, Inc.

Network
Blueprint
Trademarks

The following are trademarks of Digital Equipment Corporation:
ACMS, ALL-IN-1, Alpah AXP, AXP, Bookreader, CDA, CDD,
CDD/REpository, CI COHESION, DEC, DEC ACCESSWORKS, DEC
MAILworks, DEC GKS, DEC PHIGS, DEC Rdb for Open VMS, DEC
RTR, DEC VTX, DEC VUIT, DECalert, DECamds, DECdecision,
DECdesign, DECdtm, DECforms, DECmcc, DECmessageQ, DECnet,
DECNIS, DECperformance Solution, DECplan, DECprint, DECquery,
DECram, DECscheduler, DECserver, DECset, DECtalk, DEC term, DEC-
threads, DECtp, DECtrace, DECwindows, DECwrite, Digital, DNA,
EDT, eXcursion, HSC, Lat, LinkWorks, MSCP, OpenVMS, PATH-
WORKS, POLYCENTER, Reliable Transaction router, rtVAX, TMSCP,
Trellis, TURBOchannel, ULTRIX, VAX, VAX Ada, VAX APL, VAX
BASIC, VAX BLISS-32, VAX C, VAX COBOL, VAX DBMS, VAX
DIBOL, VAX DOCUMENT, VAX DATATRIEVE, VAX DSM, VAX FOR-
TRAN, VAX LISP, VAX MACRO, VAX Notes, VAX OPS5, VAX Pascal,
VAX RALLY, VAX RMS, VAX SCAN, VAX SQL, VAX TEAMDATA,
VAXcluster, VAXELN, VAXft, VAXmail, VAXshare, VAXsimPLUS,
VAXstation, VIDA, VMS, WPS, WPS-PLUS, XUI, the AXP logo, and
the DIGITAL logo.

Microsoft C is a registered trademark of the Microsoft Corporation

NFS is a registered trademark of Sun Microsystems, Incorporated

PC-NFS is a registered trademark of Sun Microsystems, Incorporated

Portmapper is a registered trademark of Sun Microsystems, Incorporated

Sun is a registerd trademark of Sun Microsystems, Incorporated

SunOS is a registered trademark of Sun Microsystems, Incorporated

UNIX is a registered trademark of UNIX System Laboratories, Inc.

Apollo is a registered trademark of Apollo Computer, Inc.

HYPERchannel is a registered trademark of Network Systems Corporation

NCS is a registered trademark of Apollo Computer, Inc.

Network Computing System is a registered trademark of Apollo Computer, Inc.

Network File System is a resigtered trademark of Sun Microsystems, Inc.

NFS is a registered trademark of Sun Microsystems, Inc.

Portmapper is a registered trademark of Sun Microsystems, Inc.

PostScript is a registered trademark of Adobe Systems, Inc.

Sun is a registered trademark of Sun Microsystems, Inc.

DEC is a registered trademark of Digital Equipment Corporation

DECNET is a registered trademark of Digital Equipment Corporation

LattisNet is a registered trademark of SynOptics Communications, Inc.

NAP is a registered trademark of Automated Network Management, Inc.

NETMAP is a registered trademark of SynOptics Communications, Inc.

UNIX is a registered trademark of UNIX System Laboratories, Inc.

OSF is a registered trademark of the Open Software Foundation, Inc.

OSF/Motif is a registered trademark of the Open Software foundation

AppleShare is a trademark of Apple Computer, Inc.

AppleTalk is a trademark of Apple Computer, Inc.

EtherCard PLUS is a trademark of Western Digital Corporation

Etherlink is a trademark of 3Com Corporation

LaserWriter is a trademark of Apple Computer, Inc.

Macintosh is a trademark of Apple Computer, Inc.

Madge is a trademark of Madge Networks Ltd.

Microsoft is a trademark of Microsoft Corporation

NetWare is a trademark of Novell, Inc.

Novell is a trademark of Novell, Inc.

PostScript is a trademark of Adobe Systems, Inc.

Windows is a trademark of Microsoft Corporation

Word for Windows is a trademark of Microsoft Corporation

80386, 80486, 80386SX 80486SX are trademarks of Intel Corporation

AppleTalk is a registered trademark of Apple Computer, Inc.

Internetwork Packet eXchange is a registered trademark of Novell, Inc.

IPX is a registered trademark of Novell, Inc.

MS-DOS is a registered trademark of Microsoft Corporation

NetWare is a registered trademark of Novell, Inc.

Novell is a registered trademark of Novell, Inc.

AppleTalk is a trademark of Apple Computer, Inc.

DEC is a trademrk of Digital Equipment Corporation

DECnet is a trademark of Digital Equipment corporation

Ethernet is a trademark of Xerox Corporation

IPX is a trademark of Novell, Inc.

NetWare is a trademark of Novell, Inc.

NFS is a trademark os Sun Microsystems, Inc.

Novell is a trademark of Novell, Inc.

Sun is a trademark of Sun Microsystems, Inc.

UNIX is a trademark of Unix System Laboratories, Inc.

Windows is a trademark of Microsoft, Inc.

X-Windows is a trademark of Massachusetts Institute of Technology

Xerox is a trademark of Xerox Corporation

Cisco is a registered trademark of Cisco Systems, Inc.

Intel is a registered trademark of Intel Corporation

Internetwork Packet Exchange (Novell Corporation)

IPX is a registered trademark of Novell Corporation

Microsoft Windows is a registered trademark of Microsoft Corporation

OSF (Open Software Foundation, Inc.)

XNS is a trademark of the Xerox Corporation

AIX is a trademark of International Business Machines Corporation.

AIXwindows is a trademark of International Business Machines Corporation.

DEC is a trademark of Digital Equipment Corporation.

VT100, VT220, and VT330 are trademarks of Digital Equipment Corporation.

HP is a trademark of Hewlett-Packard Company.

IBM is a registered trademark of International Business Machines Corporation.

PC-AT are trademarks of International Business Machines Corporation.

PS/2 are trademarks of International Business Machines Corporation.

POSIX is a trademark of the Institute of Electrical and Electronic Engineers

PostScript is a trademark of Adobe Systems Incorporated.

Proprinter is a trademark of International Business Machines Corporation.

RISC System/6000 is a trademark of International Business Machines Corporation.

RT is a trademark of International Business Machines Corporation.

SUN is a trademark of Sun Microsystems.

UNIX is licensed by and is a registered trademark of UNIX System Laboratories, Inc.

Apple, the Apple logo, AppleShare, AppleTalk, Apple IIGS, A/UX, HyperCard, ImageWrite, LaserWriter, Lisa, MacApp, Macintosh, Mac-Works, and SANE are registered trademarks of Apple Computer, Inc.

APDA, AppleColor, Apple Disktop Bus, Finder, KanjiTalk, MPW, MultiFinder, and Switcher are trademarks of Apple Computer, Inc.

MacDraw, MacPaint, and MacWrite are registered trademarks of Claris Corporation.

NuBus is a trademark of Texas Instruments.

UNIX is a registered trademark of AT&T Information Systems.

AS/400 is a registered trademark of IBM Corporation.

DB2 is a registered trademark of IBM Corporation.

DECnet is a registered trademark of Digital Equipment Corporation.

Ethernet is a registered trademark of Xerox Corporation.

HP is a registered trademark of Hewlett-Packard Company.

IMS, DB2, CICS is a registered trademark of International Business Corporation.

Information Warehouse is a registered trademark of IBM Corporation.

Kerberos is a registered trademark of the Massachusetts Institute of Technology.

Macintosh is a registered trademark of Apple Computers, Inc.

MVS, MVS/ESA, MVS/XA are registered trademarks of International Business Corporation.

Netview is a registered trademark of IBM Corporation.

Network File System is a registered trademark of Sun Microsystems, Inc.

NFS is a registered trademark of Sun Microsystems Inc.

OS/2 is a registered trademark of IBM Corporation.

RS6000 is a registered trademark of IBM Corporation.

SNA, VTAM, NCP, SDLC are registered trademarks of International Business Corporation.

VAX is a registered trademark of Digital Equipment Corporation.

X/Open is a registered trademark of X.Open Company Ltd.

XWindow is a registered trademark of the Massachusetts Institute of Technology.

The following are registered trademarks of the IBM Corporation:

ACF/VTAM
CICS
CICS/ESA
CICS/MVS

DATABASE 2
DB2
DFSMS
DFSMS.MVS
Enterprise System/3090
Enterprise System/4381
Enterprise System/9000
Enterprise Systems Architecture/370
Enterprise Systems Architecture/390
Enterprise Systems connection Architecture
ESCON
ESCON XDF
ES/3090
ES/4381
ES/9000
ESA/370
ESA/390
GDDM
Hardware Configuration Definition
Hiperspace
Hiperbatch
IBM
IBMLink
IMS/ESA
MVS/DFP
MVS/ESA
MVS/SP
MVS/XA
NetView
OS/2
OpenEdition
PR/SM
Presentation Manager
Processor Resource/Systems Manager
PSF
PS/2
RACF
Sysplex Timer
SystemView
System/370
VM/ESA

VM/XA
VTAM
3090

Index

About the Author

Ed Taylor is the founder of Information World Inc. He is a former network architect for IBM. He has authored *The Network Architecture Design Handbook, Multiplatform Network Management*, as well as *The McGraw-Hill Internetworking Handbook* and *TCP/IP Complete*.

Some of Mr. Taylor's consulting experience includes work for NEC, Orange County, CA, BASF, Chrysler, Hewlett-Packard, Dow Jones, Ore-Ida Foods, Mutual of New York (MONY), and IBM Education.